—THE—
Good Food
Guide® 1993

D0258579

THE
Good Food Guide® 1993

Edited by Tom Jaine

Published by Consumers' Association
and Hodder & Stoughton

Which? Books are commissioned and researched by
The Association for Consumer Research and published by
Consumers' Association,
2 Marylebone Road, London NW1 4DF and
Hodder & Stoughton,
47 Bedford Square, London WC1B 3DP

Cover photograph by John Parker
Cover design by Paul Saunders
Typographic design by Tim Higgins
Maps by Bartholomew, a division of
HarperCollins Publishers

British Library Cataloguing-in-Publication Data
A catalogue record for this book is available
from the British Library.

ISBN 0-340-56658-2

Photoset in Linotron Meridien Medium
by Tradespools Ltd, Frome, Somerset
Printed and bound in The Netherlands
by Rotatie Boekendruk B.V., Krommenie

Contents

Restaurants

A service to keep readers up to date

From December 1992 *The Good Food Guide* will offer a recorded telephone message giving details of restaurant sales, closures, chef changes and so on, since this edition was published. Telephone 071-224 4597 to hear the latest information.

To all readers

The Good Food Guide is your guide. It is independent, takes no free meals, inducements or advertising, and reflects the experience of thousands of consumers in restaurants throughout the land. Nor is it a self-appointed arbiter of hide-bound gastronomic taste. It reports on real experiences by real people in search of nourishment, pleasure or celebration.

As purchaser of this *Guide*, you are part of a huge network of correspondents, and you are a member of the Good Food Club. Please help other readers by recounting your own experiences to us.

There are forms at the back of this book; you can ask for more report forms from the *Guide* office; the address is FREEPOST, so you do not have to use a stamp. Every letter received is one more brick in the edifice of next year's *Guide*.

How to use this *Guide*

All the entries in this year's *Guide* have been rewritten between April and August 1992. The information on which they are based is from reports sent in by readers over the last year and confirmed by anonymous inspection. No entry is based on a single nomination. In every case readers and inspectors have been prepared to endorse the quality of the cooking, the dining-room and the value for money.

The rating system grades restaurants, on the basis of their cooking, from 1 to 5. This takes less account of elegance, ambience, service and value than it does of food and cooking. The marks take into account the perception of the *Guide* and its reporters, and signify the following:

1 **Competent cooking** Restaurants that achieve a satisfactory standard, endorsed by readers as worthy of the *Guide*.

2 **Good cooking** Restaurants that produce good food in most departments, though some inconsistencies may have been noted. They please most readers much of the time.

3 **Very good cooking** The kitchen achieves consistent quality, rarely disappointing in any department. Seldom faulted by *Guide* reporters.

4 **Excellent cooking** Restaurants with a high level of ambition and achievement. Generally, they delight.

5 **The best** These may excite debate, not as to whether the cooking is good, but whether it is better than their peers'.

* An asterisk next to a mark signifies that the *Guide* and its readers are of the opinion that the restaurant is a particularly fine example within its numeric classification.

The *Guide* office is reliant on proprietors for price information. Each year owners are asked to mark on a questionnaire the cost, for autumn of that year, of any set meals, and also the lowest and highest à la carte prices for each course. We then calculate the lowest and highest prices for a three-course meal per person, including the cost of coffee, service (if any) and half a bottle of house wine. The lowest price forms the first figure that you see in the cost line above an entry. In practice,

7

some people may have drinks before the meal and drink a more expensive wine; also, prices are likely to rise during the currency of the *Guide*. To reflect this, the second price in the cost line is the highest price we have calculated for a three-course meal (sometimes four or five courses if it is a set meal) inflated by 10 per cent to bring some realism to bear on the likely upper limit. In essence, the cost line shows the least and the most you are likely to pay, with most meals falling somewhere in between.

How to read a *Guide* entry

CANTERBURY Kent [1]   map 3 [2]

▲ *Mary's Kitchen* [3] ♈ ▮ [4] ✶ [5] £ [6] | NEW ENTRY | [7]

16 Elwood Avenue, Canterbury CT41 4RX [8]
CANTERBURY (0227) 7770666 [9]   COOKING 2* [11]
on B2068, 2m S of Canterbury [10]   COST £19–£24 [12]

(main text) [13]   CELLARMAN'S CHOICE [14]

CHEF: Mary Smith PROPRIETORS: Mary and David Smith [15] OPEN: Mon to Sat; 12 to 2, 7 to 9 [16] CLOSED: Aug [17] MEALS: alc. Set L £12, Set D £15. [18] Cover £1. Minimum £5 L. Unlicensed, but bring your own: corkage £1 [19] SERVICE: net prices, card slips closed [20] CARDS: Access, Amex, Diners, Visa [21] DETAILS: 72 seats. 4 tables outside. Private parties: 26 main room, 10 private room. [22] Car park. Vegetarian meals. [23] Healthy eating options. [24] Children's helpings. No children under 10. [25] Jacket and tie. [26] No-smoking in dining-room. [27] Wheelchair access (2 steps; also WC). [28] No music. [29] Air-conditioned ACCOMMODATION: 14 rooms, all with bath/shower. B&B £20 to £40. [30] Deposit: £50. [31] Rooms for disabled. [32] Children welcome. [33] Baby facilities. [34] Pets welcome. [35] Afternoon teas. [36] Garden. Swimming-pool. Sauna. Tennis. Air-conditioned. TV. Phone. Doors close at 11.30. Confirm by 6 (*The Which? Hotel Guide*) [37]

---

1 The town and county. The *Guide*'s main entries are divided into eight sections: London, England, Scotland, Wales, Isle of Man, Channel Islands, Northern Ireland and Republic of Ireland. In the London section, restaurants are listed alphabetically by name; in all other sections, they are listed under town. The maps (at the back of the book) can be used as a starting point to locate areas of interest; then look up the entries under the town name. The London maps locate restaurants by name.

2 The map number. The maps are at the end of the *Guide*.

3 The name of the restaurant. ▲ in front of the name denotes that it offers accommodation too.

4 ♈ denotes a wine list that is good, well above the ordinary. The symbol
   ▮ indicates a truly outstanding wine list.

5 ✹ indicates that smoking (cigarettes, pipes and cigars) is either banned altogether or that one dining-room is maintained for non-smokers. The symbol does not appear if a restaurant simply has a no-smoking area, although this facility will be mentioned in the details at the end of an entry. Establishments that do not allow smoking in a dining-room may allow it elsewhere on the premises, such as in the bar or lounge. If you are a smoker, it is always worth checking beforehand.

6 £ indicates that it is possible to have a three-course meal, including coffee, a half-bottle of house wine and service, at *any* time the restaurant is open (i.e. at dinner as well as at lunch, unless a place is only open for dinner), for £20 or less per person. Meals may often cost much more than this, but, by choosing carefully, £20 should be achievable.

7 If a restaurant is new to the *Guide* this year (did not appear as a main entry in the last edition) NEW ENTRY appears opposite its name.

8 The restaurant's address and post code.

9 The restaurant's telephone number, including its STD code.

10 Any special directions in case the restaurant is difficult to find.

11 The *Guide*'s mark, out of five, for cooking quality, ranging from 1 for competent cooking to 5 for the best. See page 7 or the inside front cover for a full explanation.

12 This is the price range for three-course meals (lunch and/or dinner), including coffee, wine and service, according to minimum and maximum prices provided by the proprietor. The first figure shows what is probably the least you would have to pay for a three-course meal (often at lunch only), while the second figure indicates a likely maximum amount. The second figure has been inflated by 10 per cent to reflect (i) that some readers will order extra drinks and some top-range dishes, and (ii) likely price rises that will come into play during the life of the *Guide*. Sometimes a single figure only appears when a restaurant offers set meals at a single price.

13 The text is based on reports sent in by readers during the last *Guide* year, confirmed by commissioned, anonymous inspections.

14 Some entries conclude with a CELLARMAN'S CHOICE. These are wines, usually more expensive than the house wine, that the restaurant assures us will be in stock during 1993, and recommends as suitable for the kind of food served.

15 The names of the chef(s) and owner(s), so that any change in management will be instantly detectable.

16 The days of the week the restaurant is open, and the times of first and last orders for meals. It is always advisable to book before going to a restaurant. If you book and then cannot go, please remember to telephone the restaurant to cancel.

17 Annual closures.

18 The types of meals that are available, with any variations for lunch (L) or dinner (D). The letters alc denote an à la carte menu. Set L and/or Set D denote set lunches and set dinners, and include the basic charge for those meals. Set meals consist usually of three courses, but can cover anything from two to six courses. Coffee is often included, wine very occasionally. Special menus, such as a cheaper bar menu or vegetarian menu, may be mentioned in this line. The meal information will be followed by details of any cover charge and minimum charge.

19 A restaurant is unlicensed but customers may bring their own alcoholic drinks on to the premises. Any corkage charge is indicated.

20 Net prices indicates that the prices given on a menu and on a bill are inclusive of VAT and service charge, and that this practice is clearly stated on menu and bill. Card slips closed indicates that the total on the slips of credit cards is closed when handed over for signature. When a fixed service charge is added to the bill the percentage is specified. When not inc is stated, service is at the discretion of the customer.

21 The credit cards accepted by the restaurant.

22 Not all restaurants will take private parties. The maximum number of people in a party is given for both main and private rooms.

23 This means a vegetarian dish should always be available. Many restaurants claim to cater for vegetarians but do not include suitable dishes on their menus as a matter of course. It is always advisable to explain, when booking, if you do not eat meat or fish.

24 Healthy eating options indicates that a restaurant marks on its menu, in words and/or using symbols, low-fat dishes or other healthy eating choices.

25 Some restaurants and hotels are not keen on children in the dining-room. Where it says children welcome or children's helpings, this indicates that they don't mind. Any limitations on age are specified.

26 Jackets and ties are compulsory in very few restaurants and this is specified; otherwise it is indicated if smart dress is preferred.

27 Any no-smoking arrangements as given to us by the restaurants. See also point 5.

28 Wheelchair access means that the proprietor has confirmed that the entrance is at least 80cm wide and passages at least 120cm across – The Royal Association for Disability and Rehabilitation (RADAR) recommendations. Where there are steps it will say so. If it says 'also WC', then the owner has told us that the toilet facilities are suitable for disabled people. The *Guide* relies on proprietors giving accurate information on wheelchair access. If you find the details in the *Guide* are inaccurate, please tell us. It is always important to ring first and inform the restaurant of any special requirements.

29 Dining-rooms where live and recorded music will never be played.
Where a restaurant has told us that music may be played we indicate this.

30 The price for rooms and breakfast as given to us by hotels. The first price
is for one person in a single room or single occupancy of a double, the
second is the upper price for two people in a double room or suite. When
a price is for dinner, bed and breakfast it is indicated as D,B&B.

31 The deposit required to secure accommodation. It may also be expressed
as a percentage.

32 There are rooms suitable for wheelchair users.

33 Children are welcome in the accommodation. Any age limitations are
specified.

34 At least some facilities, such as cots and high chairs, are available for those
guests with babies. It is important to inform the proprietors of any special
requirements.

35 Pets are welcome in the hotel.

36 Teas are served to non-residents.

37 (*The Which? Hotel Guide*) denotes that this establishment is also listed in the
1993 edition of our sister guide to over 1,000 hotels in Britain.

The top-rated restaurants

Mark 5 for cooking

London
Le Gavroche, W1
Tante Claire, SW3

England
Le Manoir aux Quat'Saisons,
    Great Milton
L'Ortolan, Shinfield

Scotland
Altnaharrie Inn, Ullapool

Mark 4 for cooking

London
Alastair Little, W1
L'Arlequin, SW8
Bibendum, SW3
Capital Hotel, SW3
Clarke's, W8
Connaught, W1
Harveys, SW17
Inn on the Park, Four Seasons, W1
Inter-Continental Hotel,
    Le Soufflé, W1
Le Meridien Hotel, Oak Room, W1

England
Adlard's, Norwich
Carved Angel, Dartmouth
Chester Grosvenor Hotel,
    Arkle, Chester
Croque-en-Bouche, Malvern Wells
Gidleigh Park, Chagford

Hambleton Hall, Hambleton
Lettonie, Bristol
Morels, Haslemere
Oakes, Stroud
Old Manor House, Romsey
Old Vicarage, Ridgeway
Le Poussin, Brockenhurst
Restaurant Nineteen, Bradford
Seafood Restaurant, Padstow
Sharrow Bay, Ullswater
Winteringham Fields, Winteringham

Scotland
Airds Hotel, Port Appin
Kinnaird, Dunkeld
Peat Inn, Peat Inn

Wales
Plas Bodegroes, Pwllheli
Walnut Tree Inn, Llandewi Skirrid

Restaurants with outstanding wine cellars
marked in the text with a ▮

London
Au Jardin des Gourmets, W1
Bibendum, SW3
Boyd's, W8
Clarke's, W8
Gilbert's, SW7
Leith's, W11
Mijanou, SW1
Odette's, NW1
192, W11
Pollyanna's, SW11
Le Pont de la Tour, SE1
RSJ, SE1

England
Adlard's, Norwich
Angel Inn, Hetton
Beetle & Wedge, Moulsford
Bell, Aston Clinton
Bridgefield House, Spark Bridge
Brookdale House, North Huish
Carved Angel, Dartmouth
Cobwebs, Leck
Corse Lawn House Hotel,
    Corse Lawn
Croque-en-Bouche,
    Malvern Wells
Crown, Southwold
Dundas Arms, Kintbury
Epworth Tap, Epworth
Fountain House, Dedham
Fox and Goose, Fressingfield
French Partridge, Horton
George, Stamford
Gidleigh Park, Chagford
Gravetye Manor, East Grinstead
Hambleton Hall, Hambleton
Hope End, Ledbury
Manor, Chadlington
Markwick's, Bristol
Normandie, Birtle
Old Beams, Waterhouses
Old Manor House, Romsey
Old Post Office, Clun

Old Vicarage, Ridgeway
Old Vicarage, Witherslack
Pool Court, Pool in Wharfedale
Porthole Eating House,
    Bowness-on-Windermere
Read's, Faversham
Redmond's, Cleeve Hill
Röser's, St Leonards
Seafood Restaurant, Padstow
Sir Charles Napier Inn, Chinnor
Sloans, Birmingham
Ston Easton Park, Ston Easton
Summer Lodge, Evershot
Le Talbooth, Dedham
Three Lions, Stuckton
Village Restaurant, Ramsbottom
White Moss House, Grasmere
White Horse Inn, Chilgrove
White House Hotel, Williton

Scotland
Airds Hotel, Port Appin
Ard-Na-Coille, Newtonmore
Braeval Old Mill, Aberfoyle
Cellar, Anstruther
Champany Inn, Linlithgow
The Cross, Kingussie
Knipoch Hotel, Oban
Peat Inn, Peat Inn
La Potinière, Gullane
Summer Isles Hotel, Achiltibuie
Ubiquitous Chip, Glasgow

Wales
Cemlyn, Harlech
Dolmelynllyn Hall, Dolgellau
Llangoed Hall, Llyswen
Meadowsweet Hotel, Llanrwst
Old Rectory, Llansanffraid
    Glan Conwy
Penhelig Arms Hotel, Aberdovey
Plas Bodegroes, Pwllheli
Walnut Tree Inn,
    Llandewi Skirrid

13

County restaurants of the year

Our indulgence. The aim of this award is not just to give first prize – to the highest-rated restaurant in any county – but to alert you to especial virtue and commitment. The award may go to a new place or an old favourite: all the places below have in common is that they are worth visiting on their own merits, and they have gingered up the scene in their area. More power to them. Not all counties get a gong.

England
Avon Hunt's, Bristol
Bedfordshire Paris House, Woburn
Buckinghamshire Bell, Aston Clinton
Cheshire Nunsmere Hall, Northwich
Cornwall Pig'n'Fish, St Ives
Cumbria Michael's Nook, Grasmere
Derbyshire Bridge End, Hayfield
Devon Pophams, Winkleigh
Dorset Stock Hill Country House Hotel, Gillingham
East Sussex Landgate Bistro, Rye
Essex Stour Bay Cafe, Manningtree
Gloucestershire Country Elephant, Painswick
Greater Manchester Normandie, Birtle
Hampshire Provence, Lymington
Hereford & Worcester Lygon Arms, Broadway
Kent Read's, Faversham
Lancashire September Brasserie, Blackpool
Leicestershire Hambleton Hall, Hambleton
Lincolnshire Jew's House, Lincoln
Norfolk Rococo, King's Lynn
Northumberland General Havelock Inn, Haydon Bridge
North Yorkshire Millers, Harrogate
Nottinghamshire Truffles, Nottingham
Oxfordshire Fish at Sutton Courtenay, Sutton Courtenay

Shropshire Hundred House Hotel, Norton
Somerset Castle Hotel, Taunton
Suffolk Scutchers Bistro, Long Melford
Surrey Morels, Haslemere
Tyne & Wear Fumi, Gateshead
Warwickshire Billesley Manor, Billesley
West Midlands Swallow Hotel, Sir Edward Elgar, Birmingham
West Sussex Angel Hotel, Midhurst
West Yorkshire Restaurant Nineteen, Bradford
Wiltshire Howard's House Hotel, Teffont Evias

Scotland
Dumfries & Galloway Riverside Inn, Canonbie
Fife Peat Inn, Peat Inn
Grampian Courtyard, Elrick
Highland Crannog, Fort William
Lothian Champany Inn, Linlithgow
Strathclyde One Devonshire Gardens, Glasgow

Wales
Clwyd Café Niçoise, Colwyn Bay
Dyfed Seguendo di Stagioni, Llanwrda
Gwynedd Chandler's, Trefriw
Powys Lake Hotel, Llangammarch Wells

The *Guide*'s longest-serving restaurants

The *Guide* has seen many restaurants come and go. Some, however, have stayed the course with tenacity. Congratulations to the Connaught on hitting the 40 years mark. (Qualification for this list is that the restaurant must be in each edition of the *Guide* subsequent to its first entry.)

Connaught, W1	40 years
Gay Hussar, W1	36 years
Porth Tocyn Hotel, Abersoch, Gwynedd	36 years
Gravetye Manor, East Grinstead, West Sussex	32 years
Sharrow Bay, Ullswater, Cumbria	32 years
Dundas Arms, Kintbury, Berkshire	30 years
French Partridge, Horton, Northamptonshire	28 years
Walnut Tree Inn, Llandewi Skirrid, Gwent	28 years
Butley-Orford Oysterage, Orford, Suffolk	26 years
Chez Moi, W11	24 years
Pool Court, Pool in Wharfedale, West Yorkshire	24 years
Rothay Manor, Ambleside, Cumbria	24 years
Sundial, Herstmonceux, East Sussex	24 years
Le Gavroche, W1	22 years
Summer Isles Hotel, Achiltibuie, Highland	22 years
Timothy's, Perth, Tayside	22 years

Introduction

Eating out should be fun, restaurants a playground. *The Good Food Guide* has not been in business for more than 40 years to dampen your spirits, only to direct them to the most enjoyable places.

The Good Food Guide is a digest of thousands of meals eaten through Britain by people like you and me. We all have prejudices. Our meat may be your poison. My function is to sift through these, to achieve a balanced picture. What emerges is a true record: real food has passed real lips in many social situations, making possible a true assessment of the skill of the cooks at their work and the ability of the servers at theirs.

The Good Food Guide is no spokesperson for 'the industry', it has no special corner to argue, not even that of self-appointed gourmet expert. On the contrary, it is *your* mouthpiece. Independent of any interest, it reflects your views, your meals, your problems.

The world of hotels and restaurants does not always like our intrusion. It says we are not able to judge, that assessment should only be by its peers. This is a pathetic fallacy. Everyone works hard in a restaurant. Chefs sweat, waiters run, cashiers' minds are scrambled by all that adding up, owners risk their livelihood. Their vision of life is blinkered by their very effort. Rapidly, they discover that everything would be hunky-dory if only there were no customers to give them problems. They resent criticism and dismiss quiet nights as the fault of the recession or caused by ignorance. But they have to accept that the customer is king, and the source of all income. The outside view, such as this guide's, is important.

How we work

This book is a list of recommendations. It is affirmative. It is not an assessment of every eating-place in the land, just those that have met with approval. Entries, therefore, are optimistic. A comparatively humble place deserves the same enthusiasm as the best and most plush. Unperceptive readers may then think we oversold some quayside bistro that does its best with honest materials. Entries have to be taken in some form of context: the mark we give for cooking, the price of a meal, the description of the locale and the style of the place. A chef deemed moderate in London might rule in Cleveland; it's a question of supply and demand.

The Good Food Guide is a post-box. At our office in London, we receive thousands of letters and reports about restaurants written by consumers everywhere, all of which are acknowledged and fed into our information system. We also scan the press and correspond with restaurateurs, to keep up with what's going on. Drawing on this information, we commission inspections of places that are in the *Guide*, or which might be candidates. The inspections serve to act as a control on the veracity of reports: if Aunt Sally has been put up to recommending nephew George's new business, we soon discover the truth; if support is due to misplaced enthusiasm, our inspectors describe it for us. Inspections also help chart the progress of existing businesses: how a new chef is working out; whether complaints of recent performance are justified.

Our initial reports, therefore, are from unseen correspondents. We can only guess their prejudices and preferences, though many have been faithful supporters for decades. Inspectors are super-consumers. We do not employ professionals, but we pay the expenses of men and women who have long been associated with our work. We know them and talk to them. In everyday life, they may be consultants, professors, journalists, authors, engineers, accountants, translators, shopworkers, farmers or musicians. But they also go to restaurants: for love, for work, and for fun. Many of them cook, and just a few have worked in the industry at one time or another.

This exercise in selective democracy needs constant input from readers. Letters and reports are our lifeblood. 'How can you have been so wrong about this restaurant?' someone writes after the new edition is published. My only reaction will be to wish that he or she had written before. We do not get financial backing from industry, such as drinks companies or telephone networks. We get support from you. You buy the book, you write us letters, we try our best to lead you to good restaurants.

Nor do we take free meals as we go round the restaurants described, nor accept advertisements, or allow restaurants to use the *Guide* for publicity purposes. *The Good Food Guide* is independent. In order to keep it so, I urge you to use the forms at the back of the book, to report on every meal you eat out, even if it be summarily.

What's new

Every year the *Guide* has something new to offer, perhaps another sign or symbol, perhaps another point about fair-dealing that seems to have escaped the notice of those who write the bills and needs special attention in the body of the *Guide*.

Last year we urged a more straightforward approach to tipping (when haven't we?) and noted those places which stated on the menu that service was included in a net charge, and who also *closed* the total-line on credit card slips so as not to gull you into paying a supplementary tip unawares. It is gratifying to note that a joint committee of industry and consumer interests has urged the government to cast regulations that might put this into practice. We would repeat that the ideal position for the consumer is that all charges in restaurants should be NET. Menus should state prices which are inclusive of service, so that what you see is what you pay. There is no touting for extra.

Last year we also listed those places that did not play music of any kind to accompany your meal. It is not that we hate all music, more that we wish this item of information to be as clear as possible so that people who do hate it can avoid it if they so wish. Or so that people who cannot possibly digest lobster thermidor without Johann Strauss belting out from a loudspeaker know where to look for it. The *Guide* is about choice, not prescription.

In line with this approach we have introduced a new symbol (✝✳) this year for those restaurants which have done something positive about smoking. The arguments on this subject will rage until the habit, or the smoker, dies. However, our post-bag would suggest a majority of people who frequent the restaurants in this book do not smoke, and do not wish to have their chateaubriand affected by other people's fumes. Many restaurants have introduced more effective means of ventilation or air-conditioning. Although this helps, it is only a partial solution. Other places have either banned smoking in dining-rooms altogether, or set aside whole rooms (or physically separated sections of a room) where smoking is not permitted. This is one step further than merely designating a no-smoking area, sited next to a group of 10 tables equipped with ashtrays. Where effective action has been taken (smoking either banned, or a dining-room set aside for non-smokers), this is indicated by the new sign.

Another new symbol (£) is for 'cost-consciousness'. Every place in this book is considered fair value. Were it not, it would not gain entry. That does not mean we deny ourselves the right to criticise its pricing, but some element of value must be there. A £60-a-head dinner could be excellent value, but not everyone wishes to spend that sort of money on eating out. We have therefore introduced a sign to show places where it is possible to eat well yet inexpensively (at dinner, as well as lunch), spending not more than £20 per person for a three-course meal, including coffee, wine and service.

The recession

The 1980s were spendthrift years. It seemed many could afford to eat in restaurants, expensive ones too, and worried not. Although food is an essential, good food can be deemed a luxury. Quality needs to be paid for. The devil-may-care attitude of consumer and producer alike meant that for a while cost was considered less important than quality. Creativity was given its head, but restaurateurs got greedy and the price of meals went through the roof.

We reap the consequences today. Economic uncertainty reduces the amount people are prepared to spend; restaurants see their income fall, their tables empty. Catering as a whole has seen a high number of bankruptcies. That many of the entries in this book have escaped total closure is a measure of the importance of quality in keeping a business alive. But everyone has felt the draught.

To draw in customers, many places have reviewed their costs and, more important, their profit margins. Restaurateurs have thought twice before charging silly money. Cheaper places have opened and done well; many restaurants offer more for the money. A new realism is abroad. This is good news. The tendency has marched in step with a shift in cooking style. There are not so many who are keen to experiment with the real luxuries, or to indulge in haute cuisine when they know too little. Pale imitations of Le Manoir aux Quat'Saisons are at a premium. Foie gras and truffles are not so liberally scattered.

These consequences have perhaps been more beneficial to London and the big cities than to the country. You need a large local population to keep a big restaurant busy, and restaurants need to be busy to keep their costs down. The recession has therefore been felt more in the provinces. This is especially true of the country-house hotel: the fastest-growing of all the new breeds of the 1980s. The country gentry gave up their large houses because income would not cover maintenance and improvement. The country-house hoteliers thought up a way of tapping into new-earned city wealth by offering fine living and a graceful style to people at weekends. When this evaporated, along with a reduction in international tourism, the hoteliers discovered just why the houses were lying vacant in the first place. They are very expensive to run. Saddled with high costs, and loans from the bank, proprietors have found it very difficult to reduce the bill to the customer.

The gap between town and country, between London and the provinces, has in some respects never been wider. Crucified by costs, many country houses have to charge too much for not enough. Not only are meal costs too high – and let's not think of the bedrooms – but the standard of cooking bears little relation to the bill. Good housewifely skills may be fine at home, but should we pay a premium for them when trapped miles away from civilisation unable to eat elsewhere?

Wine prices

No one wishes restaurants to run at a loss: it can't be done. Nor should they be thought means to a lifestyle beyond the possible. If you want to be rich, don't run a restaurant. But when a customer sees a humble bottle of Rhône wine at more than three times the cost of the self-same in the off-licence, he or she wonders whose school fees are being subsidised.

Wine prices cause argument. From the restaurant's point of view, a certain income must be generated. How it comes to them matters not a jot. So a bit more on wine means a little less on food – it can make a place seem cheaper, even if the total bill is the same. This may be an innocent deceit, but it does mean that the drinker supports the non-drinker. In a place that makes a flat percentage mark-up across the whole range, the couple who like a good bottle are contributing far more than their fair share to the profits.

Of course a cellar costs money. There is capital tied up; time and trouble are expended in choosing, ordering, fetching and storing. But it is not *that* much. It is not justification for a multiplier of three on cost price. And that overall percentage mechanism is not acceptable either. It would do much for customer relations if restaurateurs thought about applying fairer charges for food and wines together.

Tom Jaine

All the rage

Cooking does not stand still. New habits, new dishes, new countries are explored and find their way on to menus. Allied to this, there has been a power struggle behind the green door; a hand-to-hand between chef and waiter. Who is to be leader of the team?

As the chef comes out from behind his hot cupboard, to emerge a media star, having been given fair credit by this guide and others, so his or her ideas and prejudices have become more important in creating the character of a restaurant. This is grand, but we poor customers have had to work quite hard to keep up. We should eat this dish with chopsticks? Who says so? Ah! Chef thinks we should. All because chef went on holiday to Tokyo and thought he would put some tempura on the menu. Who is strong-willed enough to say he or she wants a fork, please?

The essential document for chef's self-respect is the menu. We may have had difficulty understanding French, but now we need Italian, Japanese, Spanish and a few other languages besides. We have had to shop daily in delicatessens to know the ins and outs of sausage-making and pasta terminology. And, above all, we have had to keep reading those recipe books. This is because a menu today can be as difficult to understand as it ever used to be, even though it is officially in English.

To help thread your way through the new menus, we have compiled a short glossary of words that seem to embody many current veins of fashion. If your favourite restaurant is still working in the rut of nouvelle cuisine, the words will not be very familiar and you will feel as silly as you used to when you were handed a four-page document and your partner asked, 'What *is* Potage Crécy?'

It will become obvious that the real reason for this list is that we have changed (even if only for a few years) our kitchen language from French to Italian. The tongue is here harbinger of the taste and inspiration.

AÏOLI   An oil emulsion (mayonnaise) made with lashings of garlic. As the Mediterranean became our heaven, so garlic was our ecstasy.

BEANS   Dried pulses are deployed to give balance and body to dishes. It is a clear sign that a chef likes 'granny food'. Flageolet beans are the small green haricot bean popular in France. Boston beans (haricots) are the small white beans used in cassoulet. Cannellini beans are fluffier and larger than Boston beans and used by Italians. Borlotti beans are also used by Italians, particularly in salads.

BRANDADE   This provençal recipe is an emulsification of pounded salt-cod, garlic, milk and oil. Sometimes it has potato as a softener. It is quite a popular dish, though not easy to make well; but often the word is used as a hook on which to hang some ingredient other than salt-cod as the heart of the purée.

BREAD   Perhaps the most popular ingredient of today's fashion. Who would have thought, when *The Good Food Guide* was teased in 1990 for showing too much interest in breads in restaurants, that this would be the case? The serious bread fancier will only eat French sourdough derivatives. The most significant player is the Paris baker Lionel Poilâne, but for the most part we use London-produced doughs. We have also taken on board the concept of novelty bread, with olives, sun-dried tomatoes, you name it. Sometimes the addition is so characterless and scanty – little flecks in the dough – that guessing its origins is a new parlour game for waiting customers. The appalling nature of many frozen French doughs is a sad development of our rejection of British bakery. The replacements are just as claggy, tasteless and horrid as the loaves we once railed against. Many places, especially in the country, make their own bread. In London, there are now enough good specialist bakers for this not to be necessary. It should be noted, with regret, that not every roll or loaf made by a restaurant is necessarily better than one bought-in.

BRUSCHETTA   At the head of dell'Ugo's menu (see entry, London) are listed 'Breads, Bruschetta, Crostini, Panini'. Bruschetta are grilled or toasted slices of country bread (French sourdough or Italian pane pugliese), with various toppings, often grilled vegetables, usually with buckets of olive oil. Sometimes it is an accompaniment, while a selection of items is more often a first course.

CARPACCIO   This was originally very thin slices of raw beef with a dressing of oil and some shaved Parmesan, or a mustardy dressing (at the inventor's, the Cipriani in Venice). The meaning has been extended to include any thinly sliced raw protein, for example, tuna, or even thin slices of fruit.

CHARGRILL   Grilling is the cooking method of the moment: meats, fish, vegetables, anything. The salamander grill is gas or electric heat applied from above the food; it is out of favour. The charcoal grill is the barbecue we know and love but is expensive to run, smoky and troublesome. It uses semi-permanent lava rocks, instead of charcoal, heated by a gas flame. Charcoal still gives the best flavour of carbon but butane may contaminate foods where the grill-chef uses artificial aids to lighting.

CHICKPEA   Another pulse that has some popularity, even though it can be difficult to make tender and toothsome. Hummus is made with it in the Middle East, but here it will come as a salad ingredient, or perhaps spiced up as a side dish. In America, chickpeas are called garbanzo beans.

CIABATTA   The most prevalent of the new-wave Italian loaves: 'slipper bread'. It has a soft crust, a rather cakey crumb and is made with more or less olive oil.

CONFIT   The French would preserve joints of ducks and geese by slow-cooking them before putting in jars immersed in their rendered fat. For some reason, this has become tremendously popular in Britain, though the joints (usually legs) are rarely preserved, merely very slowly cooked with fat. They are succulent and sticky (or dry and stringy). Duck is the most common meat used. The method appeals to chefs because they need to use up legs after they have produced so many breasts. They misuse the word 'confit' simply to mean slow-cooked, possibly potted, anything.

CORIANDER   The rank yet addictive taste of green coriander may have come to us through Middle Eastern, Indian and south-east Asian cookery, or, more likely, it was imported via the Californian influence. (It is called cilantro in the US.) Because coriander is so unlike basil, tarragon and chervil – the master herbs of Franco-Italian cooking – it is used to give a different edge and bite to dishes. Dried coriander seed, much milder and quite different, is no substitute.

CROSTINI   Italian for croûtons, i.e. small pieces, not large. It is fried (not grilled) bread, sometimes served with toppings – for example, liver.

FOCACCIA   Italian hearth bread – an antecedent of pizza. The dough is thicker than for pizza, and it usually contains much olive oil. It should be savoured for its dough rather than its topping, which may be no more than crystals of salt or a few olives. The British interpretation of it is often more liberal.

LENTILS   The standard-bearer, with mashed potato, of the minor movement called 'cuisine grand-mère'. Lentils crop up frequently, rarely in sufficient quantity, but just as some cosmetic touch. The Indian yellow, brown or red lentil (dal) usually cooks to a purée. It does not have the cachet, or the nutty flavour, of the green Puy lentil from France or the brown lentil from Italy.

MASCARPONE   An Italian unripened cheese made from fresh cream, used in sweet dishes, especially tiramisù.

MILLE-FEUILLE   The French were the first to take mille-feuille – layers of the lightest puff pastry – and change it into any old club sandwich, sometimes sweet, sometimes savoury, with the layers made of apple, celeriac, thin biscuit, filo, anything. All you can tell from seeing the word on the menu is that something will arrive as a tottering pile.

MOZZARELLA   A mild cheese made from buffalo milk, a staple of pizzas, focaccia, salads with tomato and olives, and many other simple dishes. When made in Scotland or Denmark, from cow's milk, it is almost entirely without character.

MUSHROOMS   Once, it seemed as if only Poles and East Europeans who had settled in Britain after the war picked our wild mushrooms. Then everyone caught the bug, led by the French and Italians who had, of course, been picking mushrooms for centuries. There are more cultivated wild mushrooms on the menus of Britain than any other sort. They are the most common flavour in country-house dining-rooms, and have managed to bridge the gap between nouvelle cuisine and new-wave Italian. The arrival of brown-caps in our markets has improved the flavour of cultivated mushrooms. Oyster mushrooms are the principal variety of cultivated 'wild' mushroom. They may be available, but they don't have nearly the flavour or the appeal of the classic wild varieties. Shiitake from the Far East are also used to give variety to mushroom dishes. Ceps (porcini) are always available dried and get used a lot for giving real taste to otherwise characterless mushroom dishes. Morels are also used dried, and never have the succulence of the fresh – they are a much-abused luxury. Chanterelles and girolles are two good varieties that deserve their popularity. Other sorts are mostly served in mixtures (trompettes de mort, and so on). The problem with wild mushrooms is the attraction of chefs to the dried varieties, which means they are not often cooked properly and the result can be soggy and lacking in flavour.

OLIVE OIL   The most important ingredient in current cookery. Butter lost out, though it is still used extensively; cream definitely seemed banished (again, there is much secret use, but we don't like to admit it). Oil was good for you – all those wrinkled Mediterranean peasants without heart attacks were proof. It comes up everywhere, usually as cold-pressed virgin or extra virgin. Various things can be steeped in it to impart flavour, hence lemon oil, truffle oil and pimento oil. These are novelty ingredients. The essential is the olive.

PANCETTA   Italian bacon. It is salted and spiced and often sold in tight rolls. Its flavour is important for real Italian recipes. Salt pork or green bacon are no substitute, but bacon can be tried if pancetta is unavailable.

PASTA   Who would have thought we would become a nation of spaghetti-eaters? Pasta of some sort, often home-made or bought semi-fresh from specialists, figures on almost every menu. The names of the various shapes are legion, and set to catch you out. Gone are the days when it was just spaghetti, tagliatelle, lasagne or cannelloni. Watch for tortellini, linguine, pappardelle, penne or rigatone.

PESTO   A cold mixture of basil, pine-kernels, hard cheese such as pecorino, tomato and olive oil. Add garlic, or use walnuts for variations. As basil became the herb of all time in the '80s, so pesto became the relish. It is pistou in France. Liberties are taken with pesto, and it has become a generic name for a cold purée made in similar fashion, but with other flavourings such as coriander or parsley.

PIZZA   We all love pizza. In fancy places pizzas may occur as pizzette – little ones. Not many of us have a proper oven to cook them in, but only really horrid places pile them high with unsuitable toppings. The pizza also comes to us through restaurants that have been influenced by California and other parts of America.

POLENTA   Cornmeal, as used in northern Italy. It has benefited from the popularity of Italian food and of starchy foods in general. It may be cooked in liquid then moulded into cakes before frying or grilling, or it can be served as a moist lump, on its own, mixed with herbs or spices (saffron), or with flavourings (wild mushrooms).

POTATOES   These are important in the current scheme of things. Mash crops up everywhere – perhaps given an haute cuisine kick-start by Robuchon, but now re-absorbed into English tradition. The big question is: is it made with dairy products or with olive oil? Watch that it is not made gluey by a machine instead of elbow grease. Potato pancakes are another popular form, this time coming from French maestro Georges Blanc. Rösti, dauphinois, and so on, are old friends and still in favour, even if rarely perfectly executed. The super-trendy varieties are Pink Fir Apple (new potatoes all the year round and salads) and Ratte (French salad potatoes).

PROSCIUTTO   Italian air-dried ham. Parma ham was what everyone used to use (coppa if you wanted to economise), but San Daniele is now more in favour. There are a number of British rivals – from Cumbria and from Dorset – which redress the balance, especially in Lake District restaurants.

RAVIOLI   Some clever-clogs put it in the singular – raviolo; literally correct, but it leaves you wondering. Ravioli are the familiar pasta, now stuffed with any number of mousses, forcemeats and mixtures. An 'open ravioli' is a single layer of pasta, not a parcel. Sometimes the pasta is replaced by a vegetable, such as sheets of celeriac, when 'ravioli' applies to the form alone. Tortelloni (tortelli are a larger version) are a variation on ravioli for wrapping up foods with pasta.

RICE   Another beneficiary of our love for bulk, as well as our discovery of the perfection of things Italian. Risotto will be on most menus in the course of a year. One of the developments of the '80s was the discovery of different varieties, of potatoes, lettuce and so on, and that customer and chef alike wanted to use the right one, and tell everybody what he or she was doing. It's part of the revolution in writing that went hand in hand with changes at the stove-top. Hence risottos had to be made from arborio rice, and curries had to come with basmati. There's more to rice than 'quick-cook'.

ROCKET   The mildly mustardy salading with long thin leaves that is used as a salad leaf or a variant on wilted spinach. Its great quality is that it is not too bitter, as were many leaves of the last 'salad revolution', especially radicchio, now out of fashion. Also called arugla (US), roquette (French), rucola (Italian).

SALSA   Italy, California and Mexico have contributed to the growth of salsas. They are cold, raw relishes – but not chutneys – which use olive oil as a vehicle. They contain chopped vegetable (tomato, onion or pimento) and herb or flavouring (chilli in Mexican-inspired salsas). There are no smooth salsas. Salsa verde, green sauce with bags of chopped herbs, is the oldest and most famous, but salsas take myriad forms. As they are usually semi-solid, they do not serve the same function as a sauce. To that extent their closest parallel in the British tradition is chutney.

SASHIMI   Not many British chefs offer sushi – the Japanese vinegar rice and raw fish rolls – but sashimi, i.e. thin slices of raw fish, and its derivatives have gained their place. (Tataki is raw fish that has been briefly seared before slicing.) The Japanese leave their sashimi as it is; the European tradition, influenced by the great '70s dish ceviche, is often to marinate it briefly, or dress it as you would do the beef in carpaccio.

SAUCE VIERGE   This is a sauce made largely from virgin olive oil. It may be given flavour by steeping or heating an ingredient in the oil to extract its essence.

SESAME   Both seeds and the strong oil have found popularity. They impart a certain oriental blush to recipes. There is light oil used for stir-frying and cooking, and the dark oil made from toasted seeds that tastes stronger and is added at the end of the cooking process as a seasoning.

SOY   A large dose of Worcestershire Sauce would be thought vulgar, but soy is thought politically correct by many chefs. Its strong, salty taste is often used to give pep to light vinaigrette sauces.

STIR-FRY   Chinese cookery has had a mixed influence on British restaurant fare, even if we do all eat Chinese at the drop of a hat. Stir-frying has been accepted as a valid cooking method, especially for vegetables – less fatty than our own sauté pans, fresher in taste and finish.

TAPÉNADE   Very trendy, this is a mix of black olives, capers and sometimes anchovies. It crops up as a form of relish, and chefs are fond of putting it with fish to lend zip.

TEMPURA   Japanese cookery has influenced presentation, but is less evident in actual cooking and ingredients, except in the work of certain chefs – for instance, Alastair Little and Anton Mosimann. Tempura, the frying of small pieces of meat, fish or vegetables in a very light batter, is one exception. It seems to make acceptable battered foods, which otherwise have the image of British fried fish and ill-health.

VINAIGRETTE   When butter and cream sauces lost medical favour, and brown demi-glace reductions became boring, oil emulsions became the sauce-maker's delight. They were less heavy, they were different. Their drawback is that they are often insipid, and there is rarely very much of them. They are identified on menus as vinaigrettes, but don't taste like French dressing.

ZAMPONE   An Italian sausage which is, in fact, stuffed pig's trotter, often sold pre-cooked, reheated and served with lentils.

Tourism and the seasonal restaurant

Ken Goody, chef and proprietor of the Cemlyn restaurant in Harlech on the west Welsh coast, describes the peculiar problems of running a restaurant in a tourist area that relies on seasonal trade.

March 1992: we are closed and waiting for a late Easter on the Celtic fringe. We have been closed (apart from New Year's Eve) since last October. 'Not open yet Ken?' asks an occasional visitor, almost indignantly. I tell him I'm about to leave for a holiday in Italy and, aghast, he turns on his heels. A decade here has taught us a little, and off to Italy I go.

A few days later: Lucca, enchanting, is alight with magnolias and we visit a much recommended, new, aspiring restaurant on the city walls – all elegance and quiet charm. We are the only diners. There are seasons here too and we feel for the owners; but I think how right I was to come away.

At home by the sea with a tiny permanent population we have a very short season and our problems are acute. It all starts with Easter, whenever it comes, and not before. We have a busy 10 days and then, apart from the May Day and Spring Bank Holiday weekends, we scratch for business until July and August. It fades away through September and the curtain comes down firmly in October.

Most seasonal restaurants have an eclectic clientele. Our tourist visitors include a relatively small number of foreign visitors – a very volatile factor from year to year, at the mercy of fashion, wars, terrorism and the exchange rate. Most visitors are UK residents passing through on a touring holiday, or walking, or climbing, or here for a few days' golf. The beach holiday has declined in importance, but with a fine stretch of beach like ours there are, not surprisingly, families who come (and return with dogged loyalty) to enjoy it, mainly in the July and August school holidays. Some tourists bring or rent caravans, hire cottages or camp. The rest are taken up by a variety of hotels and bed and breakfasts. Their eating requirements vary dramatically both in content and volume. Second-home owners and golfers form the hard core of our business. These are very important because they keep us precariously in business in the quieter times. They in turn have rather different expectations of us.

There is little local tradition of eating out among the full-time residents, certainly not one of any sophistication, and although there is a growing number of retired incomers, most cannot afford to eat out regularly. Without letting bedrooms to provide captive diners our task is, therefore, to attract and provide for this very mixed bag of potential customers and to do so over a very short period of time.

Cafés and fast-food outlets absorb much of the business in our area. We must somehow provide for the not too affluent but discerning, the hungry golfers, climbers and walkers and give a nod in the direction of the not too discerning but affluent who descend from time to time from a plethora of country-house hotels. (Some do prove to be genuine refugees!) In addition, we want to provide something practical and of interest for the 'locals' – both the indigenous Welsh and incomers either here on business or retired. An impossible task – but one we attempt.

Our food must not be too expensive – price is crucial – yet quality and pleasant ambience are demanded. People must have goodly portions without pretentiousness. Nouvelle cuisine passed us by and I cherish the story of a party of our regular customers who went to a temple of the art for Sunday lunch and felt it necessary to stop for a 'top up' at a Little Chef on the way home! Fresh food, freshly cooked, is required and we must be prepared to cope with five on a June Friday and forty-five the following evening. Menu planning and thoughtful purchasing never were more important.

Finding the raw materials in this relative isolation is a challenge in itself. It has got easier over the years with the general rise in food standards but a lot still has to come from centres over a hundred miles away. Much of our produce comes from Manchester and Liverpool on delivery runs that are seasonal and volatile. Ten years ago a decent lettuce was hard to come by, but now we have growers nearby producing organically grown fruit and vegetables and even specialist produce like superb baby cauliflowers. After years of cajoling and pleading, I can now buy locally produced free-range pork, chicken and eggs and good Welsh beef and lamb, specially hung for me. Welsh cheeses, butter and cream are delivered where once I had to drive for miles to collect. A young local fisherman goes out daily for crab and lobster and rings in on his mobile telephone to report the progress of the catch and to obtain an order; another brings fresh prawns and scallops.

This is all very welcome, but I am a customer for only half the year and the suppliers too have to face the precarious nature of the seasonal tourist business – one of them is reduced to selling firewood in winter.

Not only must we find supplies, but we also need staff – and staff for half the year and sometimes only for days at a time. Of course the student population can be a help at peak times but for much of the year we must have local, congenial and willing souls who will come (and go) at short notice. After years of struggling with a very high turnover of helpers we have a loyal little band of housewives and young men with daytime jobs who know and care for our regulars and who welcome new customers with a genuine smile. However, I remain puzzled as to why, in an area of high unemployment, it should be so difficult to find part-time evening workers. Admittedly youngsters must often find work away but it has proved difficult to coax older married women to work one or two evenings a week.

In the more isolated areas of Wales and Scotland, and probably elsewhere in the UK, tourism does not really provide a year-round living. Having opened for business for the season with staff and raw materials arduously gathered in, what can the tourist restaurant do to attract customers? We endeavour to offer good food at keen prices; we try to look pretty and we post attractive menus outside. We attempt to win recommendations from the bed and breakfast owners and the local shops. Also, the various guides to eating out are much more important to us, I believe, than to restaurants in urban areas. We have a village information office staffed by local women who by repute are at least candid. The story goes that some years ago the eccentric owner of a frankly eccentric hotel (now no more), feeling he was not getting any referrals from this office, went in one day posing as a visitor and asked about his own hotel. 'Don't go there, it's awful and the owner is crackers!' he was told. Clearly, local opinion is important as is gossip amongst residents and visitors. A kind American once told me my cooking was 'assertive without being aggressive'. I hate to think how that might have emerged later in Welsh!

Local attitudes to tourism vary. Shopkeepers rely on a busy summer to enable them to keep open through the winter, but a goodly number of residents would prefer to be without the visitors. (I was branded a 'Philistine' for suggesting the construction of a chair-lift from the beach to the castle square.) The attitude of the local authority, therefore, is inevitably ambivalent and Harlech has been unable to tackle its chronic parking problem for this reason. A far cry, sadly, from Sainte Maxime on the French Riviera where there is an enormous central car park reserved in season 'for tourist visitors only' and free of charge when last I saw it. The French seem to have got the chicken and egg the right way round but the lucrative coach trade has passed Harlech by.

The *hotel* restaurant in a tourist area is in a slightly more flexible position than the seasonal restaurant without rooms. If a hotel can struggle through the winter by staying open on 'bargain breaks' and the like and thereby be able to give year-round employment, it may qualify for a Development Agency grant. Tourist Board grants are available to seasonal hotels but the Board seems obsessed with bedrooms and bathrooms rather as one of the motoring organisations appears to be fixated by full-length mirrors. The Welsh Tourist Board appears to have no policy on restaurants, which is surprising in an area where it is promoting camping sites and bed and breakfasts.

In our part of Wales a few valiant hotels and restaurants struggle to remain open all year, if only for part of the week, but 'bucking the system' can prove more expensive than an early spring holiday in Italy. I suspect we are here because initially we really thought we could break out of the seasonal constraints of tourism, yet having failed we stayed on because we love the wonderful countryside and find some winter leisure to be a compensation indeed for the absence of year-round financial rewards.

A tip is not a tip, it's a service charge

Tipping is a vexed question, not least because people use different words for a single concept and misunderstandings abound. This is an idiot's guide to every sort of extra payment – whether it's called tip, gratuity or service.

There are four ways in which extra payments for service may be referred to on a bill or menu.

(1)   *The menu states that prices include service and VAT.*
(2)   *There is a percentage surcharge on the bill called 'Service'.*
(3)   *There is a percentage charge called 'Optional gratuity' or 'Optional service charge' on the bill.*
(4)   *There is a note on the menu and bill that a service charge is not included in the total and that gratuities are at the discretion of the customer. This will often be expressed as 'Service is not included'.*

All these are tips. People may try to distinguish between 'service' and 'gratuity' but there is no difference.

(1)   *The menu states that prices include service and VAT.*

It is a legal requirement that prices on a menu should include VAT (Price Marking [Food and Drink on Premises] Order 1979). This Order does not extend to other surcharges such as service, although many restaurants have chosen to incorporate all such extras within their stated prices. This tendency was encouraged by a Code of Practice issued in 1988 by the Department of Trade and Industry under the Consumer Protection Act 1987. The Code has proved inadequate, as it only requires that prices are all-inclusive 'where practicable'.

For the consumer, inclusive pricing makes everything much easier but, even here, there are rubs and wrinkles that can catch you out. 'Is service included?' 'Yes, but tips are not' is a common exchange in otherwise admirable restaurants. 'The service charge is used to pay the staff wages' is another explanation offered by employers. Nonsense. If a restaurant states 'Service is included', there is no need for the customer to leave a further tip or free-will offering for the staff. The service charge is the tip.

If the restaurant charges £10 for a steak (VAT and service included) there is no way that the customer can discover how much of that £10 goes to the staff. An element ($^7\!/_{47}$ × £10) will be passed on to Customs & Excise as VAT, but we will never be told if the restaurant owner puts another portion in a box labelled 'staff'. To that extent, the wording may be inaccurate. The £10 does not 'incorporate a service charge', it merely indicates that, as far as the owner is concerned, the service element of a bill has been looked after.

In consequence, the customer does not need to worry where the tips are going to end up. The employer and the staff have made a contract between themselves and one must hope it is a fair contract.

Another consequence of inclusive service is that there is no 'Service' figure which the customer may withhold if he or she claims the restaurant failed to do its job properly, although you can refuse to pay all or part of a bill if you are unhappy with any element of the meal, including service.

(2)   *There is a percentage surcharge on the bill called 'Service'.*

The Code of Practice issued in 1988 allowed some extra charges where it was 'impracticable' to incorporate them in a net price. Service is one of these – or certainly has been taken to be. The bill for your steak can therefore read:

Steak	£10.00
Service charge at 10 per cent	£ 1.00
Total	£11.00

A VAT element will be payable by the restaurant on the total ($^7\!/_{47}$ × £11). (No VAT is due on cheque, credit card and cash – i.e. all discretionary – tips, nor on 'optional' service charges.) You, the customer, may refuse to pay service if it was non-existent or unsatisfactory, but otherwise you are obliged to meet the bill in full. The restaurant must prominently display the existence of a percentage service charge on both menus and bills.

What happens to this 'Service'? At first, it goes to the proprietor, along with all other receipts. It belongs to him and he is under no legal obligation to pass it on. Often, however, it will be distributed to the staff – normally the waiting staff, not those in the kitchen – in proportions that may depend on time worked, seniority, and so on.

When it is passed to the staff, it comes as part of their wages. It will have income tax deducted, as well as National Insurance contributions where appropriate. The employer has to match any NI contributions from his own revenue, so this method of levying a service charge is expensive to the employer. The percentage surcharge may be seen as a way of paying waiters according to performance: the more trade, the bigger the wage. If you ask the waiting staff what happens to the service you have just paid, they may well answer that it is used for their wages. Did it not exist, they would have to survive on a very low basic shift payment. But it is still a tip by any reasonable definition.

(3) *There is a percentage surcharge called 'Optional gratuity' or 'Optional service charge' on the bill.*

This form of levy has declined. It was strongly discountenanced in the Code of Practice on Misleading Prices and most restaurateurs took the criticism to heart. The reasons for its existence were almost entirely fiscal.

If the proprietor could maintain that the service charge was truly 'optional', it became a free-will gift. It then did not carry VAT – so long as it was distributed to the staff.

It may say 'optional', but the options to the customer are in effect no greater than the normal form of percentage addition for service. You have to pay it, unless you can dispute the standard of service received, and so long as the charge was indicated on menus and bills beforehand.

(4) *There is a note on the menu and bill that a service charge is not included in the total and that gratuities are at the discretion of the customer. This will often be expressed as 'Service is not included'.*

In cases like this the restaurant is leaving the tipping to the customer. The moral pressure encouraging you to leave a tip is strong. 'Service not included' implies that you will do right by your waiter. However, the restaurant can bring no sanctions to bear if you choose not to leave a tip – beyond a snarl at the door as you leave.

Money will be left to the waiting staff in two forms, either as cash, or as a top-up to a cheque or credit card (if the card voucher is left open). In the first case, the cash belongs legally (depending on any contract) to the waiter who receives it. In the second, the money is the property of the restaurant. Both parties (waiter and proprietor) will probably donate the money to a 'tronc' (originally meaning 'poor box') before it is shared out among the waiting staff as a whole. In fast-food places and cafés, it is possible that cash tips will be retained by the individual who received them.

In strict circumstances, the tronc has a designated 'master' (i.e. one of the staff) who undertakes distribution and is responsible for paying income tax (PAYE), on behalf of the tronc members, on the sums involved. There is no National Insurance or VAT liability.

In less strict circumstances, there is no tronc or tronc master and each employee is responsible for declaring his or her earnings to the Inland Revenue. The money that comes through the employer (i.e. top-ups in cheque or credit card payments) forms part of the tax liability dealt with each week in PAYE.

The proportions given of tips levied in this manner, i.e. not as a fixed percentage, to each person will depend on the custom of the house. Often the head waiter will take a larger share than any other person; sometimes the (working) owner will cut himself or herself into the share-out.

Waiters and waitresses often complain that their chosen vocation is ill-paid. However, it is worth noting that revenue from tips can be very great. In a restaurant that imposes a percentage levy, 10–15 per cent of the session's takings will be distributed to the staff. Let's say that each waiter is responsible for 10–15 customers at every session. In a restaurant where the bill is £30 per person, that is an extra payment of between £30 and £67. In a restaurant that imposes no surcharge, but displays net prices and even closes card slips, there will still be a certain amount of tipping. Experience shows that this may be about 2.5 per cent of the turnover. Restaurants that leave it up to the client may see a level of between 8 and 10 per cent in most instances, though large parties are notoriously mean. This is one reason why many places reserve the right to impose a surcharge on bills of parties of six and over.

In some countries attempts have been made to clear up the service question. Particularly in Europe there are various regulations that impose inclusive pricing on restaurants and discourage all forms of solicitation. Visitors to France will have noted 'Les prix sont nets' on menus in posh places.

In Britain, the Code of Practice issued in 1988 that encouraged restaurants to display inclusive prices has had little effect, beyond a reduction in the number of places that operate the 'optional service charge' system. The Code did suggest that restaurants that failed to adopt the approved mode of price display might find the courts less willing to hear their pleas if the matter was ever the subject of legal action. In fact, in a case during the summer of 1992, a restaurateur was acquitted of any attempt to mislead even though he had ignored the Code.

More recently, Consumers' Association has been joined by the Restaurateurs' Association of Great Britain, Trading Standards Officers, the Office of Fair Trading and others in a concerted move to end the addition of a percentage levy for service on restaurant bills and ensure the adoption of an all-inclusive price. There is a DTI Monitoring Committee on the Code of Practice on Misleading Price Indications that has received submissions and reports on this topic, all urging government action.

Any moves to enforce inclusive pricing ignore the problem of tipping, which will not go away simply because the service charge is banned. *The Good Food Guide* has held a position on this subject for some years now and it would be wise to repeat it. We do not wish to stop free-will gifts by individuals if they are really keen to hand them out. We would, however, like to see an end to moral or informal pressure on people to pay a tip as an inevitable part of eating out. Prices should be net, credit card slips closed, staff paid properly and there should be no more notes on the bill saying 'service not included'.

A sobering thought for a catering industry that is more or less stuck in depression is that one sector – pubs, fast-food and 'cheap' restaurants – is growing apace. No one tips in pubs, not many in hamburger bars. Is there a moral?

London

L'Accento £

NEW ENTRY map 11

16 Garway Road, W2 4NH
071-243 2201

COOKING 1
COST £18–£29

'The best thing about this restaurant is the décor, which consists of bare walls and no pictures' was the first report to come through of a new Italian place just off Westbourne Grove that seemed to specialise in home-cooking at affordable prices. It has a certain specialism in noise – when full it's deafening – and characterful staff: 'the waiter was "out-to-lunch"' was a reaction. 'It doesn't help if the waitress, when asked about the all-Italian wine list, answers with a lofty, "Well, they mean nothing to me, I've been used to working with French wines."' People are flocking here for cheerful cooking of fresh pasta (macaroni with cheese and eggs, tagliolini with artichokes and ham), gnocchi, risotto nero, Ligurian fish stew, poached breast of chicken with salsa verde, tiramisù and various custards. There is a set-price menu as well as a short *carte*. People often find it excellent; but some discover that the angles are somewhat rough. It's a pity when something out of the ordinary is done like tongue with salsa rossa to find that the tender meat is not flavourful, the salsa is too strong for its job, the mange-tout are overcooked, and the sauté potatoes are past their best. The wine list will not require an overdraft and is weighted towards Piedmont. House Sicilian is £7.50.

CHEF: Andrea Beltrami PROPRIETORS: Giovanni Tomaselli and Andrea Beltrami OPEN: Mon to Sat, exc Sat L; 12 to 2.30, 6 to 11.15 MEALS: alc. Set L and D £10.50 SERVICE: 10%, card slips closed CARDS: Access, Visa DETAILS: 50 seats. 4 tables outside. Private parties: 12 main room. Vegetarian meals. Children's helpings. Wheelchair access (1 step). Music

Adams Café £

map 10

77 Askew Road, W12 9AH
081-743 0572

COOKING 1
COST £11–£16

'Quite a remarkable place,' comments a local reporter who recently discovered this night-time café/restaurant dealing in Tunisian dishes. 'Bare surroundings are transformed by one or two additions such as the silver-lurex cloth to cover the hot counter. But it works, and works well.' Four versions of couscous are the centrepieces, but the kitchen also delivers grilled red mullet, skewered merguez sausages and gargoulette (a Tunisian lamb casserole with a thick, spicy sauce tinged with mint). To start there are salads, substantial soups and briks – fans of filo pastry with various fillings. Portions are gargantuan, and few people find room for Tunisian pastries, although a sorbet might be appropriate. The truth of this is reinforced by the scale of the appetisers: a meal in themselves on good nights. The place is unlicensed, but there is mint tea and Turkish coffee and you can bring your own wine. During the day, it is undiluted British café fare.

CHEF: Abdel Boukraa   PROPRIETORS: Abdel and Frances Boukraa   OPEN: Mon to Sat, D only; 7.30 to 10.30   CLOSED: bank hols   MEALS: alc. Cover 95p. Unlicensed, but bring your own: no corkage   SERVICE: not inc   DETAILS: 36 seats. Private parties: 36 main room. Vegetarian meals. Children welcome. Wheelchair access. Music

Alastair Little

map 14

49 Frith Street, W1V 5TE
071-734 5183

COOKING 4
COST £27–£64

The bare little room with a series of strip lights hanging from the ceiling – giving remarkably even illumination – has lost the colour lent by bold canvasses. Their replacements don't help the image of prison canteen much promoted by the restaurant's detractors. Time never stands still and its knocks and buffets are beginning to show – bare, yes; gaunt, not so hot. Food, just like decoration, is ephemeral and fashionable. Alastair Little's signal contribution to London's eating out is less unique than it was. 'We all change as we get older,' sympathised one reader. 'He must soon question where he goes from here.' Every meal, every day, there is a new (or modified) menu. There are more first than main courses, with a handful of desserts; the *carte* offers freshness and immediacy, and often long hours of work masked by curt descriptions. 'The charring technique is used on rump of lamb, the size of a fist, which is marinated in rosemary, thyme and olive oil for three days, before being seared in fierce heat so that the surface is almost black. Before serving, the meat is rested for 15 minutes to allow the juices to settle evenly, and for the texture to soften almost to melting point.' This may be offered as 'Rump of lamb with flageolets'. The fundamental honesty of purpose is the restaurant's major attraction. The result is many dishes of intense flavour – not least the various forms of chicken breast with wild mushrooms or morels. It may also be its downfall. Too often the flavours are not felt to be deep enough, complex enough, or even competent enough on days of failure. 'I had a salad of tomato, mozzarella, olives, basil and olive oil. This was actually pretty, a rare achievement here. A pile of excellent plum tomatoes had slices of mozzarella on top, surmounted by a single basil leaf – what parsimony – and about eight olives were disposed round the perimeter, with a dribble of oil. This was very satisfying and refreshing, but obviously a hell of a mark-up.' This visitor must have had a penchant for tomato and olives as his next course was grilled tuna, seared on the outside but translucent in the centre, with a tomato sauce and tapénade. As a side dish, he took a gratin of Swiss chard stalks and blue cheese. When this style is on song, it's tone is perfect; when, as too often this year, it shows a cracked note or two, the simplicity is condemned as clumsiness, the prices held to be much too strong. Little-watchers have sensed a retreat from things Japanese, and a greater espousal of warm, winter dishes of légumes and upstanding stocks – Italian bean soups, for instance. They have also claimed improvement in desserts: chocolate brownies, pear frangipane tart with fine puff pastry (though sometimes noted as burnt), crèmes brûlées of light texture (like mousses to critics), or a savarin with rhubarb. Service is lovely, if you like informality and a normal approach to life. The wine list changes a lot and is very short – not many more than a dozen of each colour. This causes imbalance, one spring list having but a Beaujolais from Burgundy and no clarets. The New World is more favoured and some uncommon items are to be found. House wine is £11.

CHEFS: Alastair Little and Juliet Peston PROPRIETORS: Mercedes Andre-Vega, Kirsten Pedersen and Alastair Little OPEN: Mon to Sat, exc Sat L; 12 to 3, 6 to 11.30 CLOSED: bank hols MEALS: alc. Set L £18 SERVICE: not inc CARDS: Access, Amex, Visa DETAILS: 40 seats. Vegetarian meals. Children's helpings. Wheelchair access (2 steps). No music

Alba

map 11

107 Whitecross Street, EC1Y 8JH
071-588 1798

COOKING 1*
COST £23–£33

Alba is concealed inside a fine Georgian house in what is by day a busy market street, by night a quiet backwater – a useful place for Barbican-bound concertgoers. The decoration has none of the overblown about it, nor, in general, does the cooking. A constant framework to the menu means that old favourites (for Alba customers), such as panzerotti alle noci (pasta filled with ricotta and spinach, with a walnut and cream sauce), trout fillets with hazelnuts and anchovy, and swordfish with pink peppercorns, are supplemented by changing lists of pasta, salads, veal dishes, and lots of white truffles and porcini when in season. A winter evening meal that kicked off with Tuscan bean soup kept up the menu's rib-sticking nature with hare in red wine – it would have been better hotter – and finished with a sensational chocolate mousse from the trolley of puds. Espresso was good, bread was poor and the cost was not exactly low. On that night, the reporter regretted the smoking behind (not in front of) the bar and at the waiters' main station. The wine list is short, Italian and worth browsing through. Growers are not always given, there is quite a lot of Pio Cesare from Piedmont, and the list is longer on Piedmont than Tuscany. There are only three half-bottles: the Italians expect you to drink deeply. House wines are £7.50.

CHEF: Armando Liboi PROPRIETOR: Rudi Venerandi OPEN: Mon to Fri; 12 to 3, 6 to 11 MEALS: alc. Cover 90p SERVICE: 10%, card slips closed CARDS: Access, Amex, Visa DETAILS: 45 seats. Private parties: 70 main room. Vegetarian meals. Children's helpings. Wheelchair access (1 step). Music

'While we were waiting to be served an elderly lady with an injured foot struggled upstairs with a stick, only to be told that she was supposed to order drinks and meals downstairs. It was only because her husband refused to let her struggle downstairs that she was allowed to remain. The following morning we were inadvertently locked in our room, and had to call to a passer-by for assistance. There was no apology and we were made to feel it was our fault.' On staying in Devon

Al Bustan

NEW ENTRY map 12

27 Motcomb Street, SW1X 8JU
071-235 8277

COOKING 1
COST £28–£41

This location in deepest Belgravia means that Al Bustan is not cheap. Tables are too closely packed, but otherwise this Lebanese restaurant is stylishly put together, with an army of staff. The menu offers a fairly typical selection of Lebanese and Middle Eastern dishes, with a lengthy selection of hot and cold meze. Sawdat djaj (fried chicken livers with pomegranate molasses) is an unusual but highly recommended example. Main courses include a short selection of raw lamb dishes. Baby chicken, chargrilled and served with a special sauce (a fresh-tasting garlic purée), and kibbeh besayniyeh (minced lamb with crushed wheat, spices, pine-nuts and onions) have both been enjoyed. The £2 cover charge pays for the plate of fresh vegetables at the start of the meal. The short, mainly French wine list (just a few Lebanese labels) is notable for its high prices; there is little under £20. House wine is £15.

PROPRIETORS: Mr and Mrs N. Atalla OPEN: all week; noon to 11 (10 Sun) CLOSED: 26 Dec, 1 Jan MEALS: alc. Cover £2 SERVICE: not inc CARDS: Access, Amex, Diners, Visa
DETAILS: 65 seats. 10 tables outside. Private parties: 65 main room. Vegetarian meals. Children welcome. Wheelchair access (3 steps). Music. Air-conditioned

Al Hamra

map 13

31–33 Shepherd Market, W1Y 7RJ
071-493 1954 and 6934

COOKING 2
COST £29–£47

At the heart of the village enclave of Shepherd Market is Al Hamra, long established and generally rated as one of the better Lebanese eating-places in London. The dining-room, with windows on three sides and mirrors on the fourth, creates a feeling of space, enhanced by real plants used as table dividers. It is classy without being too formal. The cover charge of £2.50 seems 'outrageous' to some visitors, but it pays for olives and raw vegetables left on the table. Most reports favour the impressive range of almost 40 hot and cold meze: hummus ('a very highly refined version'), moutabal (grilled aubergine purée) and ful moukala (fried broad beans with garlic, fresh coriander and olive oil) have been praised. Main courses rely heavily on the chargrill, and are based around formidable quantities of animal protein, which can make for dry, tedious eating. As an accompaniment, steamed rice generously spiced with mace has been good. Meals are good value, although there is a suggestion that service is not as good as it was. To drink there are mint tea, Turkish coffee, Iyran yoghurt, plus arak. The wine list is minimal. House wine is £11.

CHEF: Hassan Mardani PROPRIETORS: R. Nabulsi and H. Fansa OPEN: all week; noon to midnight CLOSED: 25 Dec and 1 Jan MEALS: alc. Set L £18 to £22, Set D £20 to £25. Cover £2.50. Minimum £15 SERVICE: not inc CARDS: Access, Amex, Diners, Visa
DETAILS: 73 seats. 4 tables outside. Private parties: 80 main room. Vegetarian meals. Children's helpings. Wheelchair access. Music

The Good Food Guide *is a registered trade mark of Consumers' Association Ltd.*

Al San Vincenzo

NEW ENTRY   map 11

30 Connaught Street, W2 2AF
071-262 9623

COOKING 1
COST £29–£42

The Borgonzolos finally completed their move from Cheam to this gently
pleasant area at the south end of Edgware Road. They are installed in a plain
but potentially sympathetic room, warmed up by the colour of chair coverings
and with an enjoyable view on to the street outside. The menu conceived by
Signor Borgonzolo is always exciting in its evocation of real provincial Italian
cooking. Calf's liver with onions marinated in balsamic and rosemary, black
tagliatelle with prawns and a lemon and cream sauce, rack of lamb with a sauce
of peas, mint and pecorino, and sweetbreads with pancetta and porcini are all
worth trying. At the moment dishes nearly work, but not quite. Faults crop up
in many: either the balance is wrong (too many walnuts, too much oil, not
enough broth) or materials are not quite right (a dish of sweetbreads spoiled by
the oil). The family is eager, and one wants the place to succeed. In a way, what
is needed is a greater sense of fun and a lightness of touch in the kitchen. The
Italian aperitifs are well worth exploring, as are the wines, and the grappe are
essential after-meal drinking. House wines from Sardinia are £9.

CHEF: Vincenzo Borgonzolo   PROPRIETORS: Mr and Mrs Vincenzo Borgonzolo   OPEN:
Mon to Sat, exc Sat L; 12 to 2, 7 to 10.30   CLOSED: 2 weeks Christmas   MEALS: alc
SERVICE: not inc   CARDS: Access, Visa   DETAILS: 38 seats. Private parties: 6 main room, 10
private room. Children welcome. No music

L'Altro

NEW ENTRY   map 11

210 Kensington Park Road, W11 1NR
071-792 1066 and 1077

COOKING 3
COST £22–£51

L'Altro is at the northern end of Kensington Park Road, near Ladbroke Grove
tube station. It is 'the other' of Cibo (see entry, London) but cooks only, or
nearly exclusively, fish, in such a way that most carnivores will be happy. The
place is operatic (and draughty of a winter's night) to say the least, the room
likened to a stage set with its street lights, false windows and murals – 'as if
Giotto had been practising in a reformatory'. The food, however, is expressive
in the best possible way, and generous with it: not one, but two red mullet,
perhaps stuffed with prosciutto. Prices are not low, but lunch is a definite
bargain. Diners are encouraged when they order linguine with lobster to find
the lobster is whole, in the shell, and the dish is not just starch and sauce.
Others are encouraged when they find squid dealt with in some different
fashion than usual – for instance, with broad beans and roasted red pepper –
or courgette flowers filled not with mushroom and chicken mousse, but with
mozzarella and anchovies. Just as Cibo opened some eyes to the possibilities of
Italy, so this place will broaden our minds on fish. It's a pity the place isn't
more comfortable. The wine list has an educational slant, with long notes for its
bottles. House wines are £8.90.

If a restaurant is new to the Guide *this year (did not appear as a main entry in the last
edition)* NEW ENTRY *appears opposite its name.*

CHEF/PROPRIETOR: Gino Taddei   OPEN: all week, exc Sun D; 12 (12.30 Sun) to 2.30 (3.30 Sat and Sun), 7 to 11 (11.30 Fri and Sat)   MEALS: alc. Set L £10.50   SERVICE: not inc, card slips closed   CARDS: Access, Amex, Diners, Visa   DETAILS: 40 seats. 2 tables outside. Private parties: 40 main room. Vegetarian meals. Children's helpings. Wheelchair access (1 step; also WC). Music. Air-conditioned. Fax: 071-602 1371

Anna's Place £

map 11

90 Mildmay Park, N1 4PR
071-249 9379

COOKING 2
COST £20–£28

You know what you'll get at Anna's Place. First off, it's Anna or her daughter; they recite the menu, make sure everything is to your liking and see you to the door at the end of the evening. This attention makes a neighbourhood restaurant. The menu shows few signs of major change: eat the gravlax, the marinated herrings, the lax pudding or the biff Strindberg and think yourself bathed in the aurora, even on Mildmay Park. Press through to the garden on a hot night and take monkfish with red peppercorns, swordfish with a tomato and anchovy topping and dream of the Mediterranean. Finish with Swedish apple cake and sink beneath the weight. The experience remains fair value, which may reconcile you to any faults. The short wine list is reliable and cheap; house wine is £6.75.

CHEFS: Richard Allen and René Christensen   PROPRIETORS: Anna Hegarty and Mark Stocks   OPEN: Tue to Sat; 12.15 to 2.15, 7.15 to 10.45   CLOSED: 2 weeks Christmas and Easter, 4 weeks Aug   MEALS: alc   SERVICE: 10%   DETAILS: 52 seats. 5 tables outside. Private parties: 12 main room. Vegetarian meals. Children's helpings. Wheelchair access. Music

Argyll

NEW ENTRY   map 11

316 King's Road, SW3 5UH
071-352 0025

COOKING 2
COST £26–£41

A cool little King's Road property painted entirely in white, and furnished with generously sized tables and an assortment of high-class dining-room chairs. It has nice touches like the domestic feel to the stripped-wood floor and the chunky second-hand plated candlesticks, and generally seems full of savvy. The venture is on the one hand that of Christian Arden (who was a partner in the late-lamented Sutherlands) and on the other that of Anand Sastry, a young chef who was last seen at Woolley Grange in Bradford-on-Avon (see entry). His cooking sometimes seems the last dying breath of nouvelle cuisine. After two courses, you desperately need a third. This has a lot to do with spare arrangement, and nothing to do with the trend to *nouvelle paysannerie*, which a glance at the menu may lead you to think it represents. The menu can be very unbalanced. In the summer, three of the six first courses were poultry-based, and of seven main dishes two were poultry, two offal and two fish, and one was vegetarian. Sauces are pleasantly light. A first course composed of a courgette flower stuffed with wild mushrooms and served with a little tomato and some broad beans in a light, sweet tomato-flavoured chicken-stock sauce was impeccable. The finish to a dish of goose liver with chickpeas, beans and lentils was less satisfactory, while the sweetness of the sauce with tough chunks of lamb and fine pieces of sweetbread was going too strong on a single note of sugar. Service can be toffee-nosed. The wine list is not cheap (house French is £11.50), but the choice is fashionable.

CHEF: Anand Sastry   PROPRIETORS: Christian Arden, John Keating and Anand Sastry   OPEN: all week, exc Mon L and Sun D; 12 to 2.30, 7 to 10.45   MEALS: alc. Set L £12 to £15.75   SERVICE: not inc   CARDS: Access, Amex, Visa   DETAILS: 60 seats. Private parties: 10 main room. Vegetarian meals. Children's helpings. No pipes in dining-room. Wheelchair access. No music. Air-conditioned. Fax: 071-352 1652

L'Arlequin

map 10

123 Queenstown Road, SW8 3RH   COOKING 4
071-622 0555   COST £28–£60

Whereas Queenstown Road seemed to be developing as a culinary *quartier*, L'Arlequin now appears a lone ambassador of haute cuisine on the south side of the river, albeit only a 'bus ride from Victoria'. It is hoped this affects neither morale nor performance, though for the first time for many years notes of reservation have crept into reports. The restaurant is relaxing: gentle greens, sufficient upholstery and space, an even pace of service – each gives its bit to calm and pleasure. The cooking, too, has tranquillity and assurance enough to tame potentially strident tastes, as in a cabbage stuffed with venison with a tomato sauce that was 'understated but adequate', which in hands less refined than Christian Delteil's would have been a paean to granny's cooking. The same comment was made about the saucing of some grilled scallops; no barrier was placed to enjoying the scallops themselves, yet the sauce gave variety and point. This skill combined with reticence makes Delteil's braises – for example, pot au feu of squab or daube of beef à l'ancienne – an excellent choice (if only to see how the stew can be civilised). He is equally at home with luxury materials cooked exactly: praise abounds for his foie gras. As he takes pleasure in transforming otherwise workaday dishes (try the lyonnais sausage in a brioche), so he has taken to working with spices, especially with fish. Once more, the tastes are hints, not statements, in combinations such as scallops or lobster with ginger, or turbot with spices. That he can make strong flavours work for him is apparent in noisettes of lamb with tapénade coating, or mallard with green peppercorn sauce – 'an excellent foil for this rather strong duck'. Vegetables, provided with each main course, often receive special mention, be it potato and celeriac purée or a galette of potatoes on a bed of spinach. Cheeses are well kept; dessert is often foregone for the large helping of petits fours, this year given more approval. But a gratin of apples with almonds was singled out for the fine taste of the apples themselves, as well as their split-second timing to retain bite, yet not be hard. Lunch remains very fair value. The wine list is not the restaurant's strongest point. The range is too narrow, the sources are not the most exciting, and prices are fairly high.

CHEF: Christian Delteil   PROPRIETORS: Mr and Mrs Christian Delteil   OPEN: Mon to Fri; 12.30 to 2, 7.30 to 10.30   CLOSED: 1 week Christmas   MEALS: alc. Set L £20.50, Set D £40   SERVICE: net prices, card slips closed   CARDS: Access, Amex, Diners, Visa   DETAILS: 45 seats. Vegetarian meals with prior notice. Children's helpings on request. Smart dress preferred D. No pipes in dining-room. Wheelchair access (also WC). No music. Air-conditioned. Fax: 071-498 7015

Les Associés map 10

172 Park Road, N8 8LY   COOKING 1*
081-348 8944   COST £25–£43

'In a part of London saturated with satay and teeming with tandoori it is a pleasure to find a real French restaurant' was a response to the discovery of this one . The associates are actual Frenchmen, the menu and wine list fit the bill too, and the atmosphere preserves that special Gallic fug, even if the tobacco is blonde, not black. A touch of French is manna to Crouch Enders on a Saturday night when the throng may decimate the service. 'One of the Associés waits,' said a wag. 'One might add that one waits and waits and waits.' The compensation, for this man, was in the food. Superior bistro fare is cooked creatively or soundly enough to provoke endorsement of fish soup, scallops in orange butter sauce, lamb in puff pastry, salmon with spinach, fillet of beef with morel and port sauce, chocolate mousse and nougat glace. Perhaps ventilation should be installed, to dilute cigars in full flight. The wine list is prosaically French. House wines are £9.60.

CHEF: Gilles Charvet   PROPRIETORS: Gilles Charvet, Dominique Chéhere and Didier Bertran   OPEN: Tue to Sat, exc L Tue and Sat; 12.30 to 2, 7.30 to 10   CLOSED: 10 days Christmas, 10 days Easter, Aug   MEALS: alc. Set L £15.95   SERVICE: not inc, card slips closed   CARDS: Access, Visa   DETAILS: 36 seats. Car park. Vegetarian meals. Children's helpings. Wheelchair access. Music

Au Jardin des Gourmets 🍾 map 14

5 Greek Street, W1V 5LA   COOKING 2
071-437 1816   COST £24–£46

Better-heeled Soho society has dallied here for years and more recently better cooking has justified the habit. Private parties in the Ludovic Kennedy room are a fixture. Less familiar faces have suffered staff insouciance, but Gallic chivalry is more widely encountered. Daniel Crow's tenure has begun favourably and kitchen discipline appears to have improved. Fish is a forte: steamed brill is with virgin olive oil and tarragon; fillet of pike with white wine, cream and mustard; salmon is in red wine. A light touch is applied in most directions including desserts. The set-price menus at lunch and dinner continue to offer fair value. The selection of wines is definitive; few lists are collated with the same care. Burgundies make the running; some bottles are bargains. Two of the finest and least-known champagnes are represented: Bruno Paillard and Gosset. House wine is £7.25. CELLARMAN'S CHOICE: Bourgogne Chardonnay 1988, Dom. Coche-Dury, £18.50; Bourgogne Rouge 1987, Dom. Michel Lafarge, £16.25.

CHEF: Daniel Crow   PROPRIETORS: Au Jardin des Gourmets Ltd   OPEN: Mon to Sat, exc Sat L; 12.30 to 2.30, 6.15 to 11.15 (11.30 Sat)   MEALS: alc. Set L and D £17.50 to £20.50 SERVICE: 15%, card slips closed   CARDS: Access, Amex, Diners, Visa   DETAILS: 150 seats. Private parties: 12, 18 and 50 private rooms. Vegetarian meals. Children's helpings. No-smoking area. Wheelchair access. Music. Air-conditioned. Fax: 071-437 0043

🍾 *denotes an outstanding wine cellar;* 🍷 *denotes a good wine list, worth travelling for.*

L'Aventure

NEW ENTRY   map 11

3 Blenheim Terrace, NW8 0EH
071-624 6232

COOKING 1*
COST £25–£35

Blenheim Terrace has overtones of *Passport to Pimlico* – a cul-de-sac of handsome London houses, a full kit of trees and, save for all the parked cars, the world might pass beyond the junction and no one would be the wiser. Some of the greenery hangs over the deep terrace of this neighbourhood spot – ideal for summer eating – where Catherine Parisot has long ruled. Inside is still a bit rustic, with bare brick walls, tiled floor and bentwood furniture. The countryside of the mind, however, is France, with a daily menu of straight-down-the-middle bourgeois stuff. Confit of duck with lentils, scallops florentine, chicken livers *en salade*, carré of lamb, bream with fennel, and chicken with chanterelles are examples from a summer's eve. Standards are very fair, and the restaurant is humanised by its clientele, by its owner and by her dog. The wine list is short and French and does the job nicely, with a dozen clarets to add interest. House wines are £10.50.

CHEF: Christian Brèteché   PROPRIETORS: Catherine Parisot and Chris Mitas   OPEN: all week, exc Sat L; 12.30 to 2.30, 7.30 to 11 (10 Sun)   MEALS: Set L £17.50, Set D £23.50   SERVICE: not inc   CARDS: Access, Amex, Visa   DETAILS: 38 seats. 6 tables outside. Private parties: 40 main room. Vegetarian meals with prior notice. Children's helpings. No cigars before 11. Music

Bahn Thai

map 14

21A Frith Street, W1V 5TS
071-437 8504

COOKING 2
COST £22–£33

The recent redecoration may do away with the grumbles about darkness and cramped surroundings on the ground floor, even if some character is lost, just as the provision of a new room will give more space for private junkets, Thai-style. Philip Harris was the harbinger of the 'Thai revolution' and he has not yet laid up his arms. Bahn Thai still delivers some of the more arcane dishes in the capital (try those involving dried shrimps, 'sashimi' prawns or Thai blue swimming crabs) and still imports materials direct from the Far East. The menu is usefully annotated (it gives marks for spiciness) and covers a wide range of Thai dishes, with perhaps less emphasis on northern casserole dishes than some. However, lots of recommendations come for the soups, the chargrilled meats and the green curries, which do not stint on Thai vegetables, even if the meat content can be rather slim. There was a feeling during last year that standards were under fire. This is not so now. The wine list may be among the most intelligent selections for oriental food. House wines are £7.75. The list and the menu both show Mr Harris' tremendous urge to instruct and enlighten. This is laudable; it's a pity that sometimes his staff are not endowed with the same sense of mission.

'Small lumps of bread had been scattered beneath a cedar tree and a large rat made insistent forays for food despite our presence some six feet away. The waitress, when taxed about it, answered with a Gallic shrug.'   On eating in Berkshire

---

CHEF: Penn Squires   PROPRIETORS: Bahn Thai plc   OPEN: all week; 12 to 2.45 (2.30 Sun), 6 to 11.15 (6.30 to 10.30 Sun)   CLOSED: some bank hols, some days Christmas and Easter   MEALS: alc. Cover 75p D   SERVICE: 12.5%, card slips closed   CARDS: Access, Amex, Visa   DETAILS: 100 seats. Private parties: 25 main room, 12, 20, 35 and 50 private rooms. Vegetarian meals. Children welcome. No cigars/pipes in dining-room. Wheelchair access (also WC). Music. Air-conditioned. Fax: 071-439 0340

Bedlington Café £   map 10

24 Fauconberg Road, W4 3JY   COOKING 1*
081-994 1965   COST £10–£21

'Lots of people in not a lot of space,' observes a reporter, but the atmosphere is tremendous and the cooking fully justifies the crowds. By day it is a café, pure and simple. At night it offers 'Thai cooking executed with verve and brio with the delicacy of flavours being retained,' according to one visitor. It reminded others, who had just returned from Thailand, of the genuine taste of village cooking. Flavours are full-frontal, vivid and aromatic: tom yam koong soup bursts with coriander and chilli heat; fried fish with chilli is 'sweet and hot'. 'Green' beef curry with baby aubergines, and chicken with sweet basil, have also been excellent. Cheques are not accepted. The place is unlicensed, but there is an off-licence on the corner and you can bring your own. Topsy-Tasty, 5 Station Parade, Burlington Lane, W4 3HD, Tel: 081-995 3407, is larger, runs along similar lines, but is not so exciting even if there is more space.

CHEF: Mrs P. Priyanu   PROPRIETORS: Mr and Mrs Priyanu   OPEN: all week, exc Sun L; 12 to 2, 6.30 to 9.30   MEALS: alc. Unlicensed, but bring your own: corkage 50p   SERVICE: not inc   DETAILS: 30 seats. Private parties: 30 main room. Vegetarian meals. Children's helpings. No-smoking area. Wheelchair access (1 step). No music

Belgo £   <u>**NEW ENTRY**</u>   map 11

72 Chalk Farm Road, NW1 8AN   COOKING 2
071-267 0718   COST £16–£40

Belgo is a Belgian food factory. At least, it looks like a factory and serves authentic Belgian food. The servers are dressed like monks, but Belgo isn't a monastery. The architecture is wildly modern (the extraction system might be Sir Richard Rogers encounters a hardware store, the legs of the chairs and tables are all made from axe-handles, and the lavatories are built from glass bricks). This is a fun place, with willing and enthusiastic service and a mission to bring inexpensive Belgian style to the streets of London. The star of the show is mussels and chips, and the drink to drink is beer, but the food can be greasy, so order with care unless you are extra-hungry. Lobsters are live and not overpriced. Beers include Trappist and fruit, and the blond wheat beer is recommended. The 15 per cent service charge is called 'optional' and is too high; though perhaps that's why the service is so keen.

✱ indicates that smoking is either banned altogether or that a dining-room is maintained for non-smokers. The symbol does not apply to restaurants that simply have no-smoking areas.

CHEF: Robert Gutteridge   PROPRIETORS: André Plisnier, Denis Blais and Richard Koch
OPEN: all week; 12 to 3, 6 to 11.30 (all day Sat and Sun)   MEALS: alc. Set L and D £8.75 to
£25   SERVICE: 15%, card slips closed   CARDS: Access, Amex, Visa   DETAILS: 75 seats.
Private parties: 10 main room. Vegetarian meals. Children welcome. Wheelchair access
(2 steps; also WC). No music. Fax: 071-284 2179

Bertorelli's £   NEW ENTRY   map 14

44A Floral Street, WC2E 9DA   COOKING 1
071-836 3969 and 1868   COST £20–£39

This revamped Covent Garden stalwart scores because of its location and
because it is possible to eat one or two light dishes in addition to full meals. On
the ground floor is the coolly decorated restaurant; downstairs is the café/wine
bar serving simpler fare. Maddalena Bonino cooked at 192 (see entry, London)
before moving here. Early reports suggest that she has the potential to deliver
some accomplished dishes, although flavours do not always dazzle the palate.
The short menu is Italian new-wave, along the lines of grilled tuna steak with
tomato and basil salsa, and roast maize-fed chicken with artichoke, sun-dried
tomato and spring onion salad. Reporters have been impressed by radicchio,
bresaola and pickled red onion salad ('a study in reds with only flecks of
shaved Parmesan for contrast'); grilled monkfish on leek and grilled sweet
potato salad with parsley and lemon oil; and duck breast ('satisfyingly pink
inside') with braised brown lentils. Deep-fried zucchini and lightly steamed
spinach with oil and lemon suggest a sure hand with vegetables. Desserts, such
as tiramisù, have been unconvincing. There is an interesting little list of
reasonably priced wines. House wine is £7.75.

CHEF: Maddalena Bonino   PROPRIETORS: Groupe Chez Gérard Ltd   OPEN: restaurant and
café Mon to Sat, exc Sat L restaurant; 12 to 3, 5.45 to 11.30   MEALS: alc. Cover £1.50
SERVICE: 12.5%, card slips closed   CARDS: Access, Amex, Diners, Visa   DETAILS:
restaurant 80 seats, café 40 seats. Private parties: 50 main room, Vegetarian meals.
Children's helpings. No-smoking area restaurant. Restaurant wheelchair access. No music
(restaurant), music (café). Air-conditioned

Bibendum ▮   map 12

Michelin House,
81 Fulham Road, SW3 6RD   COOKING 4*
071-581 5817   COST £36–£72

The partnership which owns this restaurant is astonishingly active. Sir Terence
Conran has opened the gastrodome at Le Pont de la Tour (see entry, London)
and is soon to reopen Quaglino's in Soho, while Paul Hamlyn has converted
the medieval Château de Bagnols in Beaujolais country into a luxurious hotel.
Meantime, Simon Hopkinson sticks to his last at the stoves of Bibendum. The
restaurant is on the first floor of the former Michelin building, reached by
passing the Oyster Bar that occupies more and more of the narthex of this
cathedral of modern living. The dining-room is effervescence and airy calm at
once; the quality of light is remarkable. Spacious tables, seats that wear
modesty covers which change colour with the season ('a riot of delphiniums in

the centre of the room' one June morning), and staff bustling about – it feels right. Avoid the bench of twos strung along one wall ('too close for either gossip or romance'). The world goes to Bibendum – 'three of us could dress up and the fourth wear jeans, no tie, no jacket and all feel right'. You do have to save up, however. 'It was our first wedding anniversary, financed by the sale of all my old *Oz* magazines, transferred into something rather nicer' is a measure of whether it might be worth it – it was for them. Now that so many restaurants in the capital make a virtue of simplicity, Simon Hopkinson's direct approach to fine cooking may seem less shocking than it used to be (except for the bottom line). There is no flim-flam here. The long *carte* (at lunch it is shorter, and at a set price) seems a repertory of all the things, rather than dishes, that you might want to eat. It is not total minimalism, art is employed to convert them, but that itself may draw on a hypothetical directory of the ideal way of doing things. Bibendum is almost a living museum of a certain style of life: *this* is how it should be done. Baltic herrings à la crème; deep-fried calf's brains, with sauce gribiche; smoked eel, potato pancake and horseradish; deep-fried lemon sole, tartare sauce; ox tongue with spinach dumplings; fillet steak au poivre; calf's sweetbreads, sherry vinegar and capers; grilled veal chop and wild mushrooms: these are items in a single menu that make the point. A meal taken by two people shopping on a winter's day could be an exemplar. On the table were olives. Them came bought-in baguette and good butter. To start, there were buffalo mozzarella, grilled focaccia, roasted tomato, with pepper and olive salad: 'you have to be addicted to olive oil'. For the next course, lightly roasted Arctic char, sweet and moist, was cooked with a mixture of olive oil, lemon, parsley, tiny crisp croûtons and capers: 'it was almost a perfect dish, and the fish was left to speak for itself'. The vegetables were mashed swede, roasted potatoes and French beans. At lunch, vegetables are included, at night you choose them. This was the least satisfactory aspect of the meal. Pear sorbet with poire William ('the texture was almost like cream, with a full intense flavour') was the final course. Coffee, which a visiting American thought the best in London, was served with chocolate truffles. The characteristics of this visit are often repeated: strong flavours, direct methods, good materials, a calm simplicity. It is clear that some people find the methods too direct to support the cost. Clear too that a mistake will be immediately apparent, and that over-boldness will cause distress. But for others, it is close to paradise. The dishes that have pleased would form a long list, but mention should be made of the tart of ceps, rabbit in a peppered sauce, and a raspberry tart. If you see them, order them. Service runs on well-greased lines. The house wines (from £8.50) are good, as is all on the list. The strengths are particularly in claret and burgundy, but the Italians, Australasians and Californians are very impressive, and even the French country wines are magisterial. The Oyster Bar gets more popular by the year. Not every meal has shown equal care, but the plateau of seafood is impressive (so it should be at £39 for two), the oysters are excellent, the Caesar salad is enjoyed, and so too are the crostinis. Comfortable it is not.

CHEFS: Simon Hopkinson and Matthew Harris   PROPRIETORS: Paul Hamlyn, Sir Terence Conran and Simon Hopkinson   OPEN: all week; 12.30 to 2.30 (3 Sat and Sun), 7 to 11.30   CLOSED: 26 Dec, Easter Mon   MEALS: alc D. Set L £24   SERVICE: 15%, card slips closed   CARDS: Access, Visa   DETAILS: 74 seats. Children's helpings. No pipes in dining-room. Wheelchair access. No music. Air-conditioned. Fax: 071-823 7925

Billboard Café £

map 11

222 Kilburn High Road, NW6 4JP
071-328 1374

COOKING 1
COST £17–£34

This converted warehouse deals in home-made pasta and robust Italian dishes.
The place is high on atmosphere, the mood is relaxed, and service can be
'brilliant'. Occasional live music is a bonus. Reports are less optimistic about
the food, suggesting 'useful' and 'value' over quality or verve. The menu,
which changes every few days, takes in bresaola, baked aubergines, spicy
Italian sausages with spinach, stuffed breast of chicken and fresh fish. Pesto
toasts – split torpedo-shaped rolls topped with mozzarella, pesto and roasted
peppers – have been enjoyable; the pasta is creditable, although accompanying
sauces and toppings can be 'low key'. There are also salads, cheeses and
various sweets including the 'wackiest' tiramisù ever encountered by one
knowledgeable reporter: it was 'a long, thin rectangle of not-bad crumbled
stuff tasting of booze and coffee, with a thin creamy layer on top, garnished
with red anonymous fruit and surrounded by half-moons of kiwi fruit – with
the skin on!' The short wine list is a blend of bottles from Italy and the New
World. House wine from Tuscany is £6.95.

CHEFS: Nasser Nateghi and Stelios B. Lambis PROPRIETOR: Stelios B. Lambis OPEN: all
week D, Sat and Sun L; 12 to 2.45, 6.30 to 12.45 CLOSED: bank hols MEALS: alc
SERVICE: 10%, card slips closed CARDS: Access, Visa DETAILS: 65 seats. Private parties:
65 main room. Vegetarian meals. Children's helpings. Wheelchair access. Music

Bistrot 190 £

map 12

189 Queen's Gate, SW7 5EU
071-581 5666

COOKING 1
COST £20–£32

Peripatetic Antony Worrall-Thompson leaves Chris Millar to fill the orders for
hybrid metropolitan peasant food which he made so fashionable. The menu is a
Mediterranean mêlée of robust flavours designed for impact. Roast peppers vie
with marinated chillies in the assault amid a great deal of olive oil and
balsamic vinegar. Although much cooking has been inexact, a civet of hare
with mushrooms and leeks was 'tender and well-hung', and duck livers with
rösti are reported as 'perfect'. Good ancillary ciabatta, olives and coffee help
redress the balance that comes from inattention. Portions can overwhelm and
so may the noise in a crowded dining-room, where service suffers under
pressure. There is no booking unless you are a member of the 190 Club, and a
wait in the adjoining bar pushes up the price of an evening. The wine list varies
according to the shipper of the month, but you can be sure it's up-to-the-
minute stuff. House wines are £8.95. As we go to press, there comes news that
the 190 Queensgate restaurant, in the basement of this building, is to change
course. No longer will it be the flagship of the Worrall-Thompson style –
complicated, many-layered, rich and inventive; instead, it is to bring to fish
cookery some of the fresh ideas that Antony Worrall-Thompson has already
expended on the art of the bistro: 'the first fish bistro in London' is the message.
Reports, please.

CHEFS: Antony Worrall-Thompson and Chris Millar   PROPRIETORS: 190 Queensgate plc
OPEN: all week; 7am to 12.30am (11.30 Sun)   CLOSED: 25 and 26 Dec   MEALS: alc
SERVICE: not inc   CARDS: Access, Amex, Diners, Visa   DETAILS: 45 seats. Private
parties: 45 main room, 25 private room. Vegetarian meals. Children welcome. Music.
Fax: 071-581 8172

Blue Elephant

map 10

4–6 Fulham Broadway, SW6 1AA
071-385 6595

COOKING 2
COST £30–£49

The décor is a talking point. Luxuriant displays of greenery, bridges, fountains, ponds and rushing water create an extraordinarily opulent atmosphere. 'Almost like being in Thailand,' notes a visitor, 'even down to the fierce air-conditioning.' The menu features many unusual dishes not widely available here. 'Jungle salad' of steamed vegetables, chicken and tuna with pungent sesame dressing, and laab phed (thinly sliced marinated duck breast stir-fried with herbs and potent spices) have been recommended. More familiar items include fish-cakes, satays, curries, stir-fried beef with chillies and baby aubergines, and deep-fried giant prawns rolled in sesame seeds served with sweet-and-sour sauce. The quality of the ingredients is high and dishes are flamboyantly adorned with extravagant garnishes of salad leaves and sculpted vegetables. Some reporters feel that prices are unjustifiably steep, that you are paying for the décor and the garnishes, not to mention the orchid presented to each lady on leaving. The practice of leaving credit card slips open when 15 per cent service has already been added continues unabated. House French is £8.95.

CHEF: Rungsan Mulijan   PROPRIETORS: Blue Elephant Ltd   OPEN: all week, exc Sat L;
12 to 2.30, 7 to 12.30 (10.30 Sun)   CLOSED: 25 and 26 Dec   MEALS: alc. Set L and D £25 to
£28. Cover £1.50 (alc only)   SERVICE: 15%   CARDS: Access, Amex, Diners, Visa
DETAILS: 230 seats. Private parties: 100 main room, 12, 16, 30, 40 and 50 private rooms.
Vegetarian meals. Children welcome. Smart dress preferred. Wheelchair access (2 steps;
also WC). Music. Air-conditioned. Fax: 071-386 7665

Blueprint Café

map 11

Design Museum,
Butlers Wharf, SE1 2YD
071-378 7031

COOKING 1*
COST £25–£38

The view across the river is one of the attractions of this restaurant above the Design Museum, and the understated Conran design is a talking point. Visitors respond to the mood of the place: 'We sat down at 1pm and didn't get up until 3.45pm – even from their uncomfortable chairs.' The kitchen operates without a freezer, ingredients are delivered fresh twice daily and the menu changes with each session, although some dishes are regular fixtures. The style is modern, with a fondness for Italy and California: vitello tonnato, roast cod with red pepper sauce, and lamb shank with lentils and Italian sausage, for example. In-vogue traditional British dishes such as black pudding and mash, fish and chips and sticky toffee pudding also get an airing. The cooking is often spot-on: witness a risotto milanese with stunning colour and wonderful fragrance. On other occasions it does not quite hit the mark: roasted goats' cheese was 'a bit too dry'; calf's liver with caramelised onions was 'a little overdone'. The atmosphere buzzes, although the service has been described as 'a bit Sloanish and unprofessional at times'. Wines are in tune with the modernity of the enterprise. House Italian is £9.50.

CHEFS: Rod Eggleston and Lucy Crabb PROPRIETOR: Sir Terence Conran OPEN: all week, exc Sun D; 12 to 3 (3.30 Sun), 7 to 11 MEALS: alc SERVICE: 12.5%, card slips closed CARDS: Access, Visa DETAILS: 120 seats. 8 tables outside. Private parties: 100 main room. Vegetarian meals. Children's helpings. No pipes in dining-room. Wheelchair access (also WC). No music

Bombay Brasserie
map 12

Courtfield Close,
Courtfield Road, SW7 4QH
071-370 4040 and 373 0971

COOKING 1
COST £20–£48

Brass planters displaying mature, exotic plants, a large comfortable bar, a well-appointed, discreetly lit restaurant, a stylish conservatory: the Bombay Brasserie is obviously not a run-of-the-mill curry house. But opinions remain divided about the merits of this fashionable, even opulent, Indian restaurant. This year's postbag has revealed a crop of complaints about basic inconsistencies, especially the value-for-money equation, given the high prices and small portions. The menu centres on the Bombay region and the Punjab, with a few specialities from other parts of the subcontinent. Shrimp masala, chicken korma Asafjahi (in a delicate almond and apricot sauce), Mangalorean chicken curry, and dum ka biriani (chicken and basmati rice cooked in a sealed pot) have been well reported; mint paratha and nan are good. Others have found dull lamb kebabs and poor Parsi chicken masala. Most reporters now find the service sporadic. The buffet lunch is perhaps better value. There are decent wines to be had, including Omar Khayyam méthode champenoise for Indian bubbles. House wine is £9.75.

CHEF: Udit Sarkhel PROPRIETORS: Taj International Hotels OPEN: all week; 12.30 to 3, 7.30 to 12 MEALS: alc. Set L £13.50. Minimum £20 D SERVICE: not inc CARDS: Access, Visa DETAILS: 175 seats. 25 tables outside. Vegetarian meals. Children's helpings. Music. Fax: 071-835 1669

Boyd's ▮
map 11

135 Kensington Church Street, W8 7LP
071-727 5452

COOKING 3
COST £19–£45

Boyd's is an 'airy restaurant, in keeping with Kensington', with simple green tables (no cloths), flowers and plants and a daytime feel to it even at night – but avoid sitting near the door to the loos, which lets in gobbets of cold air. Boyd Gilmour has taken the recession by the horns: wine prices decrease and there is a two-course lunch at under £10 to tempt people away from pub benches to proper service. That service can slip on busy nights; perhaps the place should stagger its bookings more carefully, but people do not question the food itself. This seems to embrace simplicity and clarity, without sacrificing variety and interesting flavour. Thus recommendations this year have included grilled scallops with rocket, watercress and a Chinese vinaigrette; ravioli of foie gras, wild mushrooms and smoked bacon with a Sauternes sauce that stopped short of sweetness and over-richness; plain cold asparagus; ceps on toasted brioche with a red wine sauce; roast grouse with redcurrant sauce; noisette of lamb with a mango chutney and curry 'marmalade'; pan-fried calf's liver and sweetbreads with potato and celeriac pancakes and foie gras sauce; and, finally, glorious chocolate marquise or bavarois of passion-fruit. Service is amiable and natural, yet intelligent. Wines are provided via a consultancy with Neville Blech of Mijanou in Ebury Street (see entry, London). The house selection (from £8.85), mostly available by the glass, provides good value as well as interesting drinking. What follows is a list as intelligently condensed and well presented as any; in a broad sweep that encompasses Cape Mentelle and Jean Léon Chardonnay in whites and Mascarello's Nebbiolo d'Alba and a neat group of petits châteaux for reds, all is of quality and everything priced fairly. There are good half-bottles. Four vintages of the eponymous Ch. Boyd-Cantenac round off the clarets in style. CELLARMAN'S CHOICE: Muscadet-sur-Lie 'Baron Noury' 1988, Dom. Douillard, £11.60; Châteauneuf-du-Pape, 'Clos des Papes' 1987, Avril, £21.

CHEF/PROPRIETOR: Boyd Gilmour   OPEN: Mon to Sat; 12.30 to 2.30, 7 to 11   CLOSED: 2 weeks Christmas   MEALS: alc. Set L £8.50 to £14.95   SERVICE: not inc   CARDS: Access, Amex, Visa   DETAILS: 40 seats. Private parties: 40 main room. Vegetarian meals. Children welcome. Music. Air-conditioned. Fax: 071-221 0615

Brackenbury £   NEW ENTRY   map 10

129–131 Brackenbury Road, W6 0BQ   COOKING 2
081-748 0107   COST £17–£26

The two rooms were once adjoining shops. They have been made Siamese twins by a join at the back, where there is a little bar and a view to a tree. The Brackenbury has been the toast of the town for most of the last year – booking is essential. Good food at very low prices, intelligent shopping, interesting recipes, no flim-flam and a wine list 'into which I could stick a pin and guarantee a decent bottle' are the ingredients of success. 'A large salad of smoky red peppers and tender strips of squid bathed in a delicious pepper-infused oil started the meal well; a simple concept, but how many times (elsewhere) have the peppers been slimy and squid like rubber? Confit of duck was crisp outside, gentle and succulent inside. It sat on a bed of braised cabbage, well soused in meat stock. I finished with prune and armagnac mousse, the prune in pieces large enough to give texture, the mousse with more than a dribble of brandy.' This account may be a paradigm: there is an ability here to cook standards, a willingness to experiment and range round fashion's hoard for recipes, and fair dealing when it comes to tastes and flavours. The menu changes at every meal, is as good on fish as on meat, and is short enough for there to be no makeweights. Pressure of business may mean untidy presentation and the occasional missed targets as to cooking time, but what the Brackenbury avoids is unpalatability through a desperate search for new combinations and a wish to shock. It is conservative in its modernity. From a short list of wines, most are offered by the glass as well as by the bottle. The choices are unfamiliar to those weaned on standard merchants' lists, and the prices are very fair. House wine is £8.20.

CHEF: Adam Robinson   PROPRIETORS: Adam and Katie Robinson   OPEN: all week, exc Mon and Sat L, and Sun D; 12.30 to 2.45, 7 to 10.45   CLOSED: Christmas, bank hols MEALS: alc   SERVICE: not inc   CARDS: Access, Amex, Visa   DETAILS: 50 seats. 5 tables outside. Private parties: 12 main room. Vegetarian meals. Children's helpings Sun L. No cigars/pipes in dining-room. Wheelchair access. No music

Brady's £

map 10

513 Old York Road, SW18 1TF   COOKING 1*
081-877 9599   COST £12–£21

'This is a fish and chip shop with tables,' observes a succinct reporter, 'but with no cloths or mats.' Luke and Amelia Brady's experience at The Black Lion, Long Melford, has stayed with them, and gives this restaurant the edge over most rival chippies. The secret is in exemplary supplies of fresh fish, accurate frying and a determined effort to keep prices low. Haddock and cod are now boned and skinned before cooking – otherwise, little else changes. The bestseller is still fish and chips, perhaps with mushy peas, but there are also plates of smoked salmon, potted shrimps, salmon fish-cakes and a range of grills that might include tuna, swordfish and sardines. Treacle tart is a regularly mentioned sweet. To drink there is good coffee, some interesting beers (including La Facon from Boulogne), plus a few cheap but pleasurable wines. House wine is from £6.40.

CHEFS/PROPRIETORS: Luke and Amelia Brady   OPEN: Mon to Sat, D only, and Sat L; 12.30 to 2.30, 7 to 11   CLOSED: Christmas and New Year   MEALS: alc   SERVICE: 10%   DETAILS: 40 seats. Children's helpings on request. Wheelchair access (1 step; also WC). Music

Brasserie du Marché aux Puces £

NEW ENTRY   map 11

349 Portobello Road, W10 5SA   COOKING 1
081-968 5828   COST £20–£31

Walking through the Spanish and Portuguese quarter at the top of Portobello Road on a windswept January night can be a bleak experience. At this juncture, the Brasserie does not inspire confidence of comfort, with its dimmish lights and acres of dark wood. But, even if it is not a haven of particular jollity, the short menu will strike a chord among those who want something novel and enterprising. How do yellow split-pea fritters provençale, mushroom ravioli with mussel sauce and spring onions, or salmon fish-cakes with basil vinaigrette grab you? This is a latter-day brasserie – no white sauce here. People have enjoyed the couscous, the poached eggs on potato pancake with leeks and courgettes, the chicken with apricots, and lambs' kidneys with prosciutto. Among the sweet things, spotted dick and custard, crème caramel with kumquats, and watermelon and Cassis jelly have pleased. The combinations may sometimes be unlikely, but they work. The Brasserie opens daily at 10am (11am Sunday) for coffee, croissants and the like. The wine list is short, but changes as often as the menu, and is as fully in the swim. Konocti Chardonnay, Collard's Sauvignon and Minini's Montepulciano were current in the summer; if they disappear, the replacements will be as keenly priced and as decent. House wines start at £7.75.

CHEF: Noel Ashbourne   PROPRIETOR: Philip McMullen   OPEN: all week, exc Sun D; 10am (11 Sun) to 11pm (4 Sun)   CLOSED: bank hols   MEALS: alc. Sun brunch   SERVICE: not inc (12.5% for 11 or more)   DETAILS: 39 seats. 8 tables outside. Private parties: 40 main room, 40 private room. Vegetarian meals. Children's helpings. Wheelchair access (1 step). Music. Air-conditioned

Brasserie Faubourg

NEW ENTRY   map 10

28 Queenstown Road, SW8 3RX
071-622 6245

COOKING 1
COST £19–£33

The light, wedge-shaped dining-room of this neighbourhood restaurant opens out on to the street for fine-weather eating; inside, it is simple and neat, with French posters adorning the walls. François Closset used to cook at Mon Plaisir (see entry, London). His style is robustly French provincial, with hefty portions and a few nods to modern fashion in the garnishes and decoration, but basically relying on the sauté pan, hot oven and fast high heat. 'Bravo!' cheered a reporter. Sometimes the results may seem overbearingly rich, but ingredients are fresh and well-handled. The short *carte* is supplemented by blackboard specials, and there is a bargain two-course lunch menu. A complimentary glass of Kir more than justifies the cover charge. Excellent starters have included scallop mousse in a creamy citron sauce; gigantic stuffed mussels redolent of butter, parsley and garlic; and salad of sauté chicken livers. Main courses, such as pavé of beef and carré of lamb with mint, are served with 'unusual' vegetables. The French cheeseboard has 'suffered badly from new cheese-keeping regulations – under-ripe, dry and tasteless,' according to one reporter. Sorbets are good and convincingly home-made. Bread is baked in a nearby delicatessen. Nicole Closset runs the front-of-house with great kindness, charm and tact. A short, comprehensive French wine list offers fair value. House wine is £8.10.

CHEF: François Closset   PROPRIETORS: François and Nicole Closset   OPEN: Mon to Sat, exc L Mon and Sat; 12 to 2.30, 7 to 11   CLOSED: 2 weeks from 10 Aug, bank hols   MEALS: alc. Set L £9.50. Cover 95p   SERVICE: not inc   CARDS: Access, Amex, Visa   DETAILS: 30 seats. Private parties: 30 main room. Vegetarian meals. Children's helpings. Wheelchair access (1 step). Music

Bu San £

map 11

43 Holloway Road, N7 8JP
071-607 8264

COOKING 1*
COST £12–£50

Young Hyung Lee's restaurant has changed a great deal in the last 12 months. The tiny dining-room has been renovated and doubled in size; the menu has also been extended, with more emphasis on first courses and vegetarian dishes. Lee's cooking centres on specialities from his native Korea, but he also delivers some individual interpretations of Japanese classics such as sashimi and shabu-shabu. Presentation is a high point and dishes come flamboyantly embellished with sculpted vegetables and fruit ('It is quite incredible what they can do with a carrot,' observed one reporter). The 100-dish repertoire ranges from starters such as che namul (radish with red chilli and vinegar), yuk hoe (Korean-style steak tartare) and deep-fried aubergine with soy sauce, to classic bulgogi and ya chae woo dong (mixed vegetables and white noodles cooked at the table). Visitors have approved of the friendly atmosphere. To drink there are tea and saké, Japanese beer and ginseng brandy as well as a modest wine list. House French is £6.85.

CHEF: Young Hyung Lee PROPRIETORS: Young Hyung Lee and Tea Sun Lee OPEN: all week, exc L Sat and Sun; 12 to 2.30, 6 to 11 CLOSED: 2 days Christmas, 1 Jan, L bank hols MEALS: alc. Set L £6.90, Set D £12.25 to £22.75 SERVICE: 10% DETAILS: 50 seats. Private parties: 55 main room, 56 private room. Vegetarian meals. Children's helpings. Music

Buzkash £

map 10

4 Chelverton Road, SW15 1RH   COOKING 1
081-788 3182 and 0599   COST £18–£36

Putney is soon left behind for the North-West Frontier. Oh! Flashman, where are you now? Two restaurants, Buzkash and Caravan Serai (50 Paddington Street, W1M 3RQ, Tel: 071-935 1208), offer the same menu, and are tended by the same apparently infinitely extended family. Appointments are immaculate and service is attentive. This cuisine is rarely found in Britain: it draws from Persian and Indian traditions, allying a certain sweetness and fondness for fruit with the heat of the subcontinent. The food is spiced rather than curried, though, and this can lead to blandness. Dishes that have pleased include the little potato-cake appetisers, pancakes filled with prawns, pasta served with minced lamb and seasoned yoghurt, and veal grilled then finished with cream and almonds. Other recommendations are a vegetable stew of aubergines, green peppers and onions, veal with a dipping sauce of cherries, pine-kernels and olive oil, some of the rice dishes and the bread from the tandoor. House wine is £9.95; and there are Afghan coffee and green tea.

CHEF: Mr Padsha PROPRIETOR: Mr Natebkhail OPEN: all week, exc Sun L; 12 to 3, 6 to 11 (11.30 Fri and Sat) CLOSED: 25 and 26 Dec MEALS: alc. Cover 75p SERVICE: 10%, card slips closed CARDS: Access, Amex, Diners, Visa DETAILS: 56 seats. 9 tables outside. Private parties: 50 main room, 30 private room. Vegetarian meals. Children welcome. Music

Le Cadre

NEW ENTRY map 10

10 Priory Road,
Priory Park, N8 7RD   COOKING 1*
081-348 0606   COST £18–£34

On the one hand this is every inch an engaging French bistro with maps of Paris and posters on the walls, a bare wood floor, a blackboard menu announcing dishes of the day and tasteful details such as brass Art Deco lamps. On the other, the Muzak might be American and the enthusiastic owner's accent is very English. This split personality seems to extend to the cooking, where 'ambitions are clearly defined, but the execution may fall short': a good buttery brioche filled with wild mushrooms would have benefited from more fungal intensity; bouillabaisse had excellent saffron-flavoured liquor, but overcooked fish. However, this is a place with high aspirations and everything is done with gusto. A short *carte* along the lines of feuilleté of langoustines, rack of lamb, magret of duck with cherry sauce and strawberry vacherin is supplemented by a regularly changing fixed-price menu, featuring dishes such as grilled sardines and blanquette de veau. The details are commendable: well-timed vegetables, strong coffee, plus impressive petits fours including fine pastry tuiles and sumptuous chocolate truffles ('like having another espresso', according to one reporter). The modest, Gallic wine list is boosted by bargains displayed on a blackboard. House wine is £8.50.

CHEF: Yannick Fhuart   PROPRIETORS: David Misselbrook and Marie Fedyk   OPEN: Mon to Sat, exc Sat L; 12 to 2.30, 7 to 11   CLOSED: 25 to 30 Dec, bank hols   MEALS: alc. Set L £10.50, Set D £14.50   SERVICE: not inc   CARDS: Access, Amex, Visa   DETAILS: 45 seats. 4 tables outside. Private parties: 50 main room. Vegetarian meals. Children's helpings. Wheelchair access. Music

Café Fish

NEW ENTRY   map 13

39 Panton Street, SW1Y 4EA
071-930 3999

COOKING 1
COST £22–£39

Café Fish is an asset. Downstairs is the 'cramped' wine bar, which offers snacks and light meals; on the ground floor is a high-ceilinged, bustling dining-room open to the pavement in fine weather. The colour scheme is white and sea-green; every inch of the wall space is taken up with piscatorial and maritime photographs, prints and paintings. Andrew Magson has given the cooking a sharp, modern cosmopolitan edge. Flavours are fresh and forthright. A standard menu offers mighty seafood platters, bouillabaisse, platefuls of French-style fish and chips and well-reported dishes such as scallops with Chinese vegetables, ginger and lime butter, and roast monkfish with fine ratatouille and provençal herbs. A separate menu of *plats du jour* might include unusual fish such as Chinese perch, as well as sweet red pepper gazpacho, and leek and smoked salmon terrine with a 'sharp/sweet/oily' tomato vinaigrette. To finish, pear and almond tart with a blackcurrant coulis has been 'thoroughly good and enjoyable'. The French cheeseboard is worth investigation. Cover charge includes an appetiser of fish pâté, plus freshly guillotined French bread and butter. Whites dominate the short, catholic wine list. House Blanc de Blancs is £7.75. A branch has recently opened at 16 St Barnabas Street, Pimlico, SW1W 8QE, Tel: 071-730 2572 – reports, please.

CHEF: Andrew Magson   PROPRIETORS: Groupe Chez Gérard Ltd   OPEN: Mon to Sat, exc Sat L restaurant; restaurant 12 to 3, 5.45 to 11.30; wine bar 11.30am to 11pm   CLOSED: Christmas, 1 Jan, bank hols   MEALS: alc. Set meals for 10 to 50 by arrangement. Cover £1.25   SERVICE: 12.5%, card slips closed   CARDS: Access, Amex, Diners, Visa   DETAILS: 90 seats. 3 tables outside. Private parties: 100 main room. Vegetarian meals. Children welcome. No-smoking area. Wheelchair access (1 step). Music. Fax: 071-436 5227

Café Normand

NEW ENTRY   map 10

507 Kingston Road,
Raynes Park, SW20 8SF
081-542 4838

COOKING 1*
COST £16–£28

This converted terrace house has two small dining-rooms, a tiny bar and a clear view from the entrance hall of Eric Lecras at work in the kitchen. 'I stopped doing a menu card, as I believe in my blackboard, which changes every day,' he writes. The French staff happily translate. This is Normandy cooking ('lots of cream, calvados and apples') and is dependable, if not very exciting. An inspection meal of crêpes dieppoises with 'a lovely, light creamy sauce' could have done with more seafood filling, and a pintade aux pleurottes, which was a properly cooked breast of guinea-fowl in a good cream and calvados sauce, was described as 'short on pleurottes'. Salade chaude – an enormous plate of salad leaves, croûtons and chicken with a sound dressing – was pronounced good. Others have enjoyed onion soup, moules normande, entrecôte bordelaise and poulet normand. Tarte Alexandra, the house version of tarte Tatin, is star of the desserts. French bread is of good quality, though cafetière coffee is on the weak side. The set lunch offers good value for money. The all-French wine list is short and acceptable. House wine is £7.35.

CHEF/PROPRIETOR: Eric Lecras   OPEN: Tue to Sun; 12 to 2, 7 to 10   MEALS: alc. Set L £9.55 to £11.75   SERVICE: 12.5%   CARDS: Access, Visa   DETAILS: 45 seats. 6 tables outside. Private parties: 30 main room, 25 private room. Vegetarian meals with prior notice. Children's helpings on request. Children welcome. No cigars/pipes in dining-room. Music

Café Royal Brasserie £

NEW ENTRY   map 13

68 Regent Street, W1R 6EL
071-437 9090

COOKING 1
COST £20–£38

The Café Royal is part of history. A giant spread at the bottom of Regent Street, it takes in bar, café, Grill Room (the restaurant proper) and Brasserie. On floor after floor above are banqueting suites. Although there have been structural alterations, particularly in the Brasserie (which was once a double-decker of a room), the original decorative scheme – all mirrors, wall sconces, gilding, painted ceilings, naked ladies and putti – survives. This makes the Grill Room one of the great eating spaces in London. The Brasserie is more of the same, but will miss its mark without refurbishment. January 1992 saw the arrival of Herbert Berger, a good chef, with the brief to revitalise the food here. He has started with the Brasserie; early signs are encouraging. The menu is firmly set in current taste, but execution is often acute and could make this a good bet in an area not blessed with many restaurants. A terrine of provençal vegetables was held together by pressure, not woolly panada or forcemeat: it tasted as fresh as a daisy and was sharpened correctly with a little balsamic. Baked potato with soft-boiled quail's eggs, smoked salmon and sour cream was a sound café dish, even if the eggs were not soft. Confit of duck with lentils was rich, sticky and well-made; a variation on tandoori chicken was given a flush of taste with sun-dried tomatoes; choucroute with black pudding and dried ham was acceptable. Desserts could have better pastry. In operations as large as this, control is everything. Perhaps Herbert Berger will prove a good general. The wine list won't bankrupt, but the choice shows the hand of corporate buying, not a rummage through the lists of the sharpest merchants. Prices start at £10.

CHEF: Herbert Berger   PROPRIETORS: Forte Restaurants   OPEN: all week, exc Sun D; 12 to 3, 6 to 11.30   CLOSED: Good Fri and 26 Dec   MEALS: alc. Set L and D £14.75   SERVICE: net prices   CARDS: Access, Amex, Diners, Visa   DETAILS: 90 seats. Private parties: 180 main room. Vegetarian meals. Children's helpings. No-smoking area. Wheelchair access. Music. Air-conditioned. Fax: 071-439 7672

▲ Capital Hotel ♀

map 12

Basil Street, SW3 1AT
071-589 5171

COOKING 4
COST £25–£60

'I can't remember exactly what we had, but some sort of fish pie with a crumble topping and absolutely perfect vegetables. The whole meal was beautifully judged, service spot-on, wine at the right temperature, fantastic desserts. And I like the way that two elderly ladies doing their shopping in Knightsbridge were given the same attention as an obviously wealthy Italian family with children in designer jeans.' Thus one encomium among many. Of course, the two ladies may have been European royal duchesses in disguise – it's the sort of thing that might happen at this well-set jewel of a hotel. Everything at the Capital is in the best possible taste, from the dining-room to the food. If there was ever a move towards greater intensity or greater flamboyance, it has been checked. Philip Britten avoids over-working for appearance's sake, and steers clear of strident flavours. His palette is that of classical cuisine. A consistent remark has been that sauces have not stood up to the main ingredients, or have not enhanced them sufficiently: 'a little too buttery', or 'The Riesling sauce did nothing for the whiting, which wanted some snappier flavour.' The consensus, however, is that the kitchen has fairly perfect pitch, working with exactitude and not overstepping the mark, so deficiencies are liable to surprise. A lunch that included steak and kidney (and morels) pie where the kidneys drowned out the rest (and the morels were hang-dog affairs), and a piece of pheasant so tough it was inedible in a ceps sauce that needed much more pep (and mushroom), shows that it can nod. Counter this with a mille-feuille of halibut and cucumber with an orange butter sauce, garnished with asparagus. 'The delicacy of the vegetable worked well with the strong citrus of the sauce, and neither overpowered the halibut, which appeared to have been steamed and gently seasoned. Lightness was vitiated only by slightly greasy pastry.' Mr Britten can manipulate flavours when he wants to: the lobster bisque is as good as when he was in Battersea (at the old Chez Nico). 'Roast leg of lamb was soft and melting, with subtle and persistent flavour, and texture from the thin crackly skin. The rosemary and thyme in the sauce gave it all the lift it needed.' He can also deliver simplicity: a salad of foie gras with good brioche was exactly cooked, dressed and presented – remarkable value for a £23 lunch. Service is usually enjoyed; the hall staff positively brim with enthusiasm. Sweets are also appreciated: a dark-chocolate mousse with gooey macaroons, a perfect marquise, excellent hot soufflés, ice-creams of deep tastes. Coffee is hot and strong, and the florentines that may be part of the petits fours are not to be resisted. Wines are serious, with pedigree names, perhaps a touch conservative, and no duff vintages. If vertical tastings are your fancy and price no object, a run through five years of Ch. La Lagune or four of the Ch. Cos-d'Estournel can be enjoyed. Otherwise, the 'Capital Selection' offers fair range, some at affordable prices; there are good half-bottles. House wines start at £9.50. This is one of the more considerate of the London hotel wine lists. CELLARMAN'S CHOICE: Rully, Dom. de la Folie 1985, £17; Chablis 1990, Fèvre, £20.

CHEF: Philip Britten   PROPRIETOR: David Levin   OPEN: all week; 12.30 to 2.30, 7 to 11   MEALS: alc. Set L £20 to £23, Set D £25. Minimum £25 D   SERVICE: net prices, card slips closed   CARDS: Access, Amex, Diners, Visa   DETAILS: 35 seats. Private parties: 6 main room, 4 and 24 private rooms. Car park. Vegetarian meals. Children's helpings. Smart dress preferred. Wheelchair access (3 steps; also WC). No music. Air-conditioned   ACCOMMODATION: 48 rooms, all with bath/shower. Rooms for disabled. Lift. B&B £185 to £285. Deposit: 1 night. Children welcome. Baby facilities. Pets welcome. Afternoon teas. Air-conditioned. TV. Phone. Confirm by 4. Fax: 071-225 0011. (*The Which? Hotel Guide*)

Le Caprice

map 13

Arlington House,
Arlington Street, SW1A 1RT   COOKING 3
071-629 2239   COST £25–£51

The room is glass, black and white; monochrome pictures; a long bar; simple table-settings. 'You have to admire this place,' wrote a devotee. 'It continues to be reasonably priced for the area; it is always fully booked; the staff are nice to you even if you are not important or beautiful. The eggs Benedict are simply the best. Duck was also cooked to perfection, though the vegetables were nothing special.' The food may be unambitious – it is simply not haute cuisine – but it is 'precise, deliberate and very effective'. Every care is taken with ingredients, and art is deployed to make them taste good. The menu is a master-document of modern brasserie cooking: those eggs, bang-bang chicken, wild mushrooms with country bread, risotto, pasta, famous fish-cakes, steak tartare, cod with pea purée, grilled chicken with sweetcorn fritters. The output is consistent, and the efforts to impart flavour – for instance, the Parmesan in the polenta with the grilled rabbit with rosemary – are apposite and successful. Chips are great. Choose rice pudding or rich Brillat-Savarin cheese with olive chutney to finish. Coffee is hot and strong. The ornament is the clientele. The movement is the staff – well-trained to a fault: 'The only way to stop them topping up my wine glass was to drink from it'; then again, 'The waiters are like London's buses, they either don't come at all or they descend in twos and threes.' The wine list is as carefully thought out as the menu: lots of good bottles, lots under £20, mark-ups that do not shock. House wines start at £7.

CHEF: Mark Hix   PROPRIETORS: Christopher Corbin and Jeremy King   OPEN: all week; 12 to 3, 6 to 12   MEALS: alc. Cover £1.50   SERVICE: not inc   CARDS: Access, Amex, Diners, Visa   DETAILS: 70 seats. Vegetarian meals. No children under 5. Wheelchair access. Music. Air-conditioned. Fax: 071-493 9040

The 1994 Guide will be published before Christmas 1993. Reports on meals are most welcome at any time of the year, but are extremely valuable in the spring. Send them to The Good Food Guide, FREEPOST, 2 Marylebone Road, London NW1 1YN. No stamp is needed if posted in the UK.

Casale Franco £

map 11

134–137 Upper Street, N1 1TQ
071-226 8994

COOKING 1
COST £19–£46

This Italian restaurant shares a courtyard off Upper Street with a Citroën garage. On summer nights, as the mechanics lock up, so tables spread outwards. It must itself have been something of a warehouse, and it can hold many people (on two floors, in corridor and circulation spaces) who flock to eat the pizza, or range more widely over pasta, a handful of grills, and salads like octopus and celery, San Daniele and melon, or mixed seafood. It's busy, noisy and efficient (no booking, except at lunch-time). The pizzas (not served at lunch) are large, the toppings workmanlike, and the dough is good. Otherwise, not everything is perfect even if the sausages are spicy; the polenta is unseasoned, the salads come undressed, and the tiramisù is cold but not boozy. Coffee is good. House wines, from a list that offers a couple of dozen serviceable Italian bottles, cost £8.50.

CHEFS: Mario Pensa and Franco Pensa PROPRIETORS: Gisella and Franco Pensa OPEN: L Fri to Sun, D Tue to Sun; 12.30 to 2.30, 6.30 to 11.30 MEALS: alc. Cover £1. Minimum £6.50 SERVICE: not inc (10% for 5 or more) CARDS: Access, Visa DETAILS: 126 seats. 10 tables outside. Private parties: 35 main room. Vegetarian meals. Children welcome. Wheelchair access. Music. Air-conditioned

Chanterelle

map 12

119 Old Brompton Road, SW7 3RN
071-373 5522

COOKING 1
COST £16–£28

'The ambience remains one of elderly ladies and youngish men; the food reflects somehow the penurious sophistication of the eaters.' Thus commented a visitor from Wiltshire who returns time and time again for the value, the politeness and amiability, and the continuity of it all. 'Not the obvious place for attracting family parties, but it does' was the observation of another. Lunch is cheap; dinner is fairly priced; the wine list is not dear. The cooking may go up and down, but dishes such as salt-cod with sweet peppers and avocado, parcels of vegetables with chilli, mustard chicken with salsa, or wild boar with pickled plum sauce show that Messrs Provan and McKenzie have not been sleeping while fashions have changed, and their clients are happy to move along with them. House wines are £6.80.

CHEF: James McKenzie PROPRIETOR: D.F. Provan OPEN: all week; 12 to 2.30, 7 to 11.15 CLOSED: 5 days Christmas MEALS: Set L £11, Set Sun L £13, Set D £19.50 SERVICE: not inc (12.5% for 6 or more, card slips closed) CARDS: Access, Amex, Diners, Visa DETAILS: 45 seats. 2 tables outside. Private parties: 10 main room. Vegetarian meals with prior notice. Children welcome. Smart dress preferred. No cigars/pipes in dining-room. Wheelchair access (2 steps). No music

£ indicates that it is possible to have a three-course meal, including coffee, a half-bottle of house wine and service, at any time the restaurant is open (i.e. at dinner as well as at lunch, unless a place is open only for dinner), for £20 or less per person.

Cheng-du £

9 Parkway, NW1 7PG   COOKING 1
071-485 8058   COST £17–£43

A bronze gong with a huge red mallet is spotlit on one wall of this chic Camden Town restaurant. The décor may be cool and spartan, but it is offset with touches of colour in the plants, wooden lattice work, fresh flowers and prints of Chinese characters and folk heroes. A menu of around 70 dishes specialises in an accessible version of Peking/Szechuan cooking, along the lines of bang-bang chicken, Kung Po prawns, General Tseng's chicken and double-cooked pork with Chinese cabbage and peppers. There is little to challenge the palate or test the kitchen, but the ingredients are good and the cooks deliver creditable versions of popular dishes. West Lake sour prawns with wood ear mushrooms in a vinegar sauce and crispy aromatic duck have been particularly good. Other well-reported items include grilled dumplings with minced pork; sauté squid with hot bean sauce; and quick-fried beef with spring onions and oyster sauce. Toffee bananas with sesame seeds and sweet bean-paste pancakes have been better-than-average desserts. Service is sharp, professional and unobtrusive. Prices are reasonable, although there have been warnings about small portions. House Italian is £7.

CHEF: Mr Nim   PROPRIETOR: Mr N. Wong   OPEN: all week; 12 to 2.30, 6.30 to 11.30
CLOSED: bank hols, 25 and 26 Dec   MEALS: alc. Set L and D £17.20 (minimum 2 people)
SERVICE: 12.5%, card slips closed   CARDS: Access, Amex, Visa   DETAILS: 80 seats. 3 tables
outside. Private parties: 30 main room. Vegetarian meals. Children welcome. No-smoking
area. Wheelchair access. Music

Chez Liline

map 10

101 Stroud Green Road, N4 3PX   COOKING 1*
071-263 6550   COST £21–£41

'Some of the zing has gone, but still a beacon in Finsbury Park' was the comment of a Chez Liline old-stager convinced that the cabinet of Pacific fish that greets you on entry had not changed for years, that the staff are sweet-natured but slow, that portions had got a tad smaller, but that value was still tip-top. The restaurant is Mauritian, the fish often warm-water (vacqua, bourgeois, capitain, snapper), and the methods are a cross between European and oriental. Ginger, chilli, coriander and soy mingle with garlic, saffron, mustard and lemon. Sometimes the mingling and saucing is so emphatic as to douse the essential taste of the fish itself, and there is not the emphasis on plain cooking usually found in London fish restaurants. Lobster does not come boiled with mayonnaise. The shellfish is good, the fish soup is rusty and gutsy, and the Mediterranean stews and plateaux will stand you in garlic for a week. Vegetables are undistinguished, as are puddings. This is a great place, high on atmosphere and smoke, low on comfort. Sylvain Ho Wing Cheong is mostly at the sister restaurant, La Gaulette (see entry, London). The wine list is short but cheap, with house wines at £8.

Report forms are at the back of the book; write a letter if you prefer.

CHEFS: Sylvain Ho Wing Cheong and Mario Ho Wing Cheong   PROPRIETOR: Liline Ng Yu Tin   OPEN: Mon to Sun, exc Sun L; 12 to 2.30, 6.30 to 11   MEALS: alc. Set L £15. Minimum £10.95   SERVICE: not inc   DETAILS: 52 seats. Private parties: 52 main room. Vegetarian meals. Music

Chez Moi

map 10

1 Addison Avenue, W11 4QS
071-603 8267

COOKING 3
COST £22–£41

Chez Moi has been home for Richard Walton and Colin Smith for a quarter-century, and home from home for faithful regulars for as long. New acolytes are accepted; they come to recognise the qualities of good service and consistent cooking as well as the intangible pleasures of a neighbourhood restaurant that knows its business. The pair of dining-rooms glows with gilt and deep reds; the genius loci, a bronze smoking putto rescued from a tobacco divan in Paris, looks over the clientele; the waiters are formal in their address; and customers study a menu that splits between old faithfuls on the left-hand side and 'Quelque chose de différent' on the right. This arrangement gives Richard Walton the opportunity to allow Chez Moi traditions (carré of lamb two ways, saddle of hare with an orange-flavoured game sauce, 'sea urchins' of seafood, or quail's eggs with smoked salmon) their continuance, and his own invention, daily shopping and current fashion some space as well. 'Différent' dishes may be John Dory with basil, a poached chicken with vegetables, kidneys and mash, brains with black butter or some pasta dish. The sweet course has always sported the little pots of chocolate with liquor floated across the top, and expect to see an apple tart, a mixture of sorbets and maybe a crème brûlée amongst the dozen choices. Base standards do not fluctuate, though reports come in of fugitive flavours on some days, excess seasoning on others. The partners created their vision in times past and have kept it well burnished. Although the lunchtime set menu is fair value, the evening total may creep beyond expectation after adding in the vegetables and odd extras. The wine list is predominantly French and by no means over-priced. Decent clarets and red burgundies may weigh down the bill, but Rhônes and Loires will keep it light. House wine is £8.

CHEF: Richard Walton   PROPRIETORS: Richard Walton and Colin Smith   OPEN: Mon to Sat, exc Sat L; 12.30 to 2, 7 to 11   CLOSED: bank hols, Christmas to New Year   MEALS: alc. Set L £14   SERVICE: not inc   CARDS: Access, Amex, Diners, Visa   DETAILS: 45 seats. Children's helpings. No pipes in dining-room. Wheelchair access. Air-conditioned. No music

Chiang Mai

map 14

48 Frith Street, W1V 5TE
071-437 7444

COOKING 1
COST £23–£30

This restaurant that specialises in food from northern Thailand has sparked a northern sister: Vatcharin Bhumichitr has opened the Chiang Rai at 16 Princess Street, Manchester. People still come to eat his food in Soho, however, even if they wonder whether portions have got smaller, prices higher, and that there has been little investment in decoration or smartening up in recent years. 'I like it for its adherence to the spiciness of its Thai originals' is one comment that may be balanced by another's relief that his party had plenty of chillis to scatter over rather bland and characterless lu chin tod beef balls fried in batter with a sweet sauce. Vatcharin Bhumichitr's books on Thai cooking are a great help to Western would-be imitators, and his restaurant is a good place to try out things like gai pad prik hang – chicken with chilli and peanuts – or the pad ped, a dry beef curry which should be as hot as hot. Noodles with bean curd, dried prawns, peanuts and bean sprouts have been well received. Perhaps the effort of moving north has left Soho feeling a mite forlorn and in need of more love. The wine choice is exiguous. Drink Thai whisky or beer.

CHEF/PROPRIETOR: Vatcharin Bhumichitr   OPEN: all week; 12 to 3, 6 to 11.30   MEALS: alc. Set L and D for 2 £34.20 to £41.55   SERVICE: 12%, card slips closed   CARDS: Access, Amex, Visa   DETAILS: 60 seats. Private parties: 12 main room, 20 and 25 private rooms. Vegetarian meals. Children welcome. Music. Fax: 081-985 1767

Chinon
map 10

25 Richmond Way, W14 0AS
071-602 4082 and 5968

COOKING 3*
COST £27–£49

A supporter writes: 'This is serious cooking, with huge attention paid to the quality of ingredients, execution and presentation. The menu is exciting and inspiring. The sauces are deep, not overly rich yet with proper consistency. The bread always presents unusual choices. The dessert plate is a triumph: each individual part gets full care and attention – no dump-all here. The cheese plate would satisfy any *amateur de fromage*. Jonathan Hayes ploughs his own furrow in this little street south of Shepherd's Bush Green, well protected by every form of traffic restriction. Yet he does move with the times. A new gusto and expressiveness have come into dishes such as squid stuffed with pesto, shellfish pilaff with oriental spices, lamb with aubergine, sweet peppers and buffalo mozzarella or osso buco. He has caught the Mediterranean bug, but the essential approach remains the same: fine technique, more than careful presentation, and an adept way with flavours – these are not overstated. The other good news is that prices have moderated. There is a good-value no-choice set menu, and no longer need people worry that the bill will run away with them. Chinon has a very particular atmosphere; it is a personal restaurant: 'The maître d' was wearing carpet-slippers, a grey sweatshirt and black lipstick. The more I think about it the more I believe I went to eat with the Addams family,' wrote one bemused but happy client. The wine list offers plenty of halves. The general range is idiosyncratic. House wine is £9.50.

CHEF: Jonathan Hayes   PROPRIETORS: Barbara Deane and Jonathan Hayes   OPEN: Tue to Sat, exc Sat L; 12.30 to 2, 7 to 10.30 (D pre- or post-theatre, and parties, by arrangement) CLOSED: most bank hols   MEALS: alc. Set L and D £17.50   SERVICE: not inc   CARDS: Access, Visa   DETAILS: 30 seats. 2 tables outside. Private parties: 34 main room. Vegetarian meals. No children under 7. No cigars/pipes in dining-room. Wheelchair access. Music. Air-conditioned

See inside the front cover for an explanation of the symbols used at the tops of entries.

Christopher's

NEW ENTRY   map 14

18 Wellington Street, WC2E 7DD
071-240 4222

COOKING 1
COST £26–£59

It was originally a casino, but has been transformed into a restaurant attracting enough press coverage to have murdered a forest for the paper. Go for the interior, above all the staircase: 'stone steps twirling gently round like a twist of unfolding orange peel'. The intention is to reproduce an authentic American restaurant and the setting is nicely theatrical. Reports of the food are less enthusiastic than about the decoration. The menu is an emulation of those great New York spots where the world comes to watch and be watched and eat good, sassy food – mostly plain with high flavour spots – that is reliable without being demanding. This is a reasonable objective. It has not yet been met by consistent quality. The experience is further vitiated by service that is sometimes arrogant and unsmiling. Popularity should not breed contempt. Perhaps the custom has been judged aright by having more clarets than anything else on the wine list. The American choices are interesting as far as they go, but more of them would be welcome, and lighter on the pocket. House wines start at £9.

CHEF: Adrian Searing   PROPRIETORS: Christopher Gilmour and Alan Crompton-Batt
OPEN: Mon to Sat, exc Sat L; 12 to 3, 5.30 to 11.45   MEALS: alc   SERVICE: not inc   CARDS:
Access, Amex, Diners, Visa   DETAILS: 110 seats. Private parties: 100 main room, 30, 100
and 100 private rooms. Vegetarian meals. Children welcome. Smart dress preferred. Music.
Fax: 071-240 3357

Cibo

map 10

3 Russell Gardens, W14 8EZ
071-371 6271 and 2085

COOKING 3
COST £25–£53

Despite its tendency to be a fashion arena surrounded by wacky modern paintings, Cibo appears 'a little dated and slightly frayed at the edges. The art is delightfully vulgar and overpowering but the menus are grubby. Late in the evening when it is full, the atmosphere is 1970s King's Road.' The oversized plates may be gimmicky but the cooking is serious: the change of chef has sparked renewed confidence. The *carte* tenders a sweeping array that is ostensibly rustic. Flavours, particularly in the saucing, are direct and uncompromising without being heavy-handed. Broad black pasta is served with a garlic butter sauce tasting of roasted shellfish. A huge plate of carefully sautéed langoustines, clams, mussels, squid and scallops is married with a sauce of langoustine shells, garlic, tomato and parsley; the flavours are fresh and easily discernible. Long slices of calf's liver are sautéed with fine strips of grilled vegetables; a gravy of liver juices, garlic, wine and herbs binds sweet roasted red pimento, sharp tomato and slightly bitter courgette and aubergine. Tiramisù and zabaglione of good consistency and lightly coloured under the grill are creditable and approved desserts. Wines are exclusively Italian and good. Prices start moderately, but fashionable vini da tavola may stretch the finances, although not unfairly. The less certain should decide a price and seek help from the always friendly staff. House wine is £8.90.

CHEF: Enzo di Matteii   PROPRIETOR: Gino Taddei   OPEN: all week, exc Sat L and Sun D;
12 to 2.30, 7 to 11   CLOSED: bank hols   MEALS: alc. Set Sun L £17.95   SERVICE: not inc
(10% for 5 or more)   CARDS: Access, Amex, Diners, Visa   DETAILS: 55 seats. Private
parties: 60 main room. Children's helpings. Music. Air-conditioned. Fax: 071-602 1371

Circle East £   [NEW ENTRY]   map 11

The Circle,
Queen Elizabeth Street, SE1 2JN   COOKING 1*
071-403 9996   COST £16–£36

The Circle development just behind Butlers Wharf is one of London's most
'surreal and stunning' architectural creations, and this restaurant follows suit.
Ceramic figures of guardian deities mark the entrance. Inside, it is pure
designer: two huge aquariums, containing a coral-reef display and exquisite
tropical fish, dominate the bar area; there are blinds 'after Miró', intense yellow
and blue tiles on the floor, and brick-orange distressed walls. The staff are all
young Thais: one in a green smoking-jacket plays 1950s hits on a grand piano
(for which you pay £2 extra if you spend less than £20). The menu straddles the
Far East, taking in Thailand, Malaysia, Singapore and Indonesia; a Chinese
chef has been brought in also to add a Szechuan dimension to the cooking. The
current head chef has worked at Chiang Mai and the Blue Elephant (see
entries, London) and cooks convincing, authentic food with subtle spicing.
This shows in the plate of mixed hors d'oeuvre – half a dozen different items
such as Thai fish-cakes, grilled mussels, katon thong (little pastry vol-au-vent
filled with spiced vegetables) and dainty spring rolls, with appropriate dips
and sauces. Whole curried crab with a rich and creamy coconut sauce has been
'ambitious and interesting', although a knowledgeable reporter found the pad
thai (mixed stir-fried noodles with dried shrimps and prawns) 'a little
disappointing'. Coconut rice is authentically sticky. The décor and the cooking
are undoubted attractions, but the 'ghost town' location may explain a
noticeable lack of customers. To drink there are imported beers and cocktails,
and wine from a short list. House French is £7.

CHEFS: Visanu Plapplatong, Adrian Kor and Ching Quin   PROPRIETOR: Christopher
Greene   OPEN: all week, exc Sat L; 12 to 2.30 (12.30 to 3 Sun), 6 to 11.30 (midnight Sat)
CLOSED: bank hols, exc Good Fri   MEALS: alc. Set L £9.50 to £13.50, Set D £17.50 to £22.95.
Cover £2   SERVICE: not inc   CARDS: Access, Amex, Diners, Visa   DETAILS: 80 seats.
Private parties: 100 main room. Car park. Vegetarian meals. Healthy eating options.
Children's helpings. Smart dress preferred. Music. Air-conditioned. Fax: 071-403 7315

Clarke's ▮   map 11

124 Kensington Church Street, W8 4BH   COOKING 4
071-221 9225   COST £26–£41

'We tottered in loaded with assorted breads and olive oil; the welcome was
warm, the parcels whisked away and we settled to a delightful lunch.' A visit
to Sally Clarke's bounteous bakery-delicatessen adjoining the ground-floor
dining-room is an effective stimulus to appetite. Many readers prefer to
assuage their hunger seated amid crisp linen and fresh flowers in the

uncluttered basement. The meat and fish chargrilled in the open kitchen are as unmuddled as the environment. 'Suppliers dictate her no-choice menus and the exceptionally fine raw materials are the reason for success,' surmises an inspector. Not quite; the technique may be simple, but imaginative combination of ingredients, some of them organic, and exact preparation play no small part. A winter lunch beginning with marinated salmon with rocket and mustard honey sauce was an adept sweet and sour contrast: 'The huge mound of dark green, slightly bitter leaves provided another contrast of crisp texture.' There followed a fillet of brill 'so fresh it could not have been long parted with the sea'. This lay across a jumble of pale orange carrots, crisp broccoli and beside paper-thin golden crisps that were still sizzling. A relish of onion rings, fresh-torn basil and tarragon added further depth of flavour. Desserts continue to attract acclaim, among them a 'wickedly rich' moist dark chocolate and hazelnut cake and a fresh apricot tart served with fromage frais. The unfading popularity of the restaurant is witness of success in manipulating flavours but there is a body of opinion that will observe that simplicity is sometimes carried to excess; that dishes are elements in proximity, notes in an arpeggio, not chords of harmony; that the style is too close to careful domestic to rise into the financial spheres necessary to ensure commercial survival. We have always commended the care and intelligence of the wine-buying here. This year our enthusiasm is reinforced by the addition of a number of interesting wines available by the glass (from £2); these change by the month, but the list we received included a Joseph Phelps Chardonnay and a Côtes du Ventoux from Perrin. The succinct main list is a good balance, but Californian, Burgundian and Italian bottles particularly impress. Our award is for interest, dependability and fair price. CELLARMAN'S CHOICE: California, Ridge Vineyards, Chardonnay 1989, £21.50; Napa Valley, Il Podere Dell'Olivos, Nebbiolo 1989, £18.

CHEFS: Sally Clarke and Elizabeth Payne   PROPRIETOR: Sally Clarke   OPEN: Mon to Fri; 12.30 to 2, 7 to 10   CLOSED: 2 weeks Aug, 10 days Christmas, 4 days Easter, bank hols   MEALS: Set L £22 to £26, Set D £37   SERVICE: net prices, card slips closed   CARDS: Access, Visa   DETAILS: 90 seats. Private parties: 10 main room. Vegetarian meals. Children welcome. Wheelchair access. Air-conditioned. Fax: 071-229 4564

▲ *Connaught* map 13

Carlos Place, W1Y 6AL	COOKING 4
071-499 7070	COST £42–£131

If you wish to recreate things as they used to be, the best bets are the Connaught restaurants. Modern life has not penetrated very far. Are you anxious to play out the setting of a William Cooper novel of the British establishment? Or do you want to sort out the social niceties of Anthony Powell's *Dance to the Music of Time*? Here's the place to do it. It still polishes, it still serves, it still cooks as it used to. One reader commented, 'It doesn't do to go too often' – not just a reflection on his wallet, more a fear that the illusion might be punctured. Michel Bourdin labours hard to maintain it. His repertoire starts with *oeuf en gelée Stendhal* and *croustade d'oeufs de caille Maintenon*, but has actually come as close to us in time as to take in *consommé en gelée Cole Porter*, and even *paillard de saumon Jean Troisgros*. Present tastes may have imposed a tagliatelle dish (with fresh peas) on the main courses, but this is fine classical cooking – and all in French. Some people feel intimidated by it – the style, the service, the endless worry of whether they are doing the right thing: 'I shouldn't really have been there until I was 50.' Others value it for definitive quenelles (saffron, smoked salmon, pike or salmon), for rich and masterly braises (oxtail, guinea-fowl, even chicken), for grills and plain English meats that may be served within an inch of their life but do have style, or for the chance to indulge in the luxuries (caviare and foie gras) in pukka fashion. Don't go there for bruschetta with extra virgin. Our rating reflects that this is a unique experience. The wine list is replete with serious clarets and burgundies, from the best established sources. If anxious for adventure, look at the Italian section. The rest of the world hardly gets a look-in. Don't expect bargains. The alternative course is to drink house wine and save your money for the vintage ports. This must be the only place in the world to have three vintages of Tuke Holdsworth (1934, 1947 and 1955). House wines are £11 for 20 fluid ounces. They've forgotten to go metric; it must be all those Americans. The Connaught has notched up 40 consecutive years in the *Guide*; doubtless it reckons to repeat the achievement.

CHEF: Michel Bourdin   PROPRIETORS: Savoy Hotel plc   OPEN: restaurant all week, Grill Room Mon to Fri; restaurant and Grill Room 12.30 to 2, restaurant 6.30 to 10.15, Grill Room 6 to 10.30   CLOSED: Grill Room bank hols   MEALS: alc. Set L restaurant Mon to Sat £25, Sun £30. Minimum £25   SERVICE: 15%, card slips closed   CARDS: Access, Visa   DETAILS: restaurant 75 seats, Grill Room 35. Private parties: 10 and 20 private rooms. No children under 6. Jacket and tie. No pipes. Wheelchair access (3 steps; also male WC). No music. Air-conditioned   ACCOMMODATION: 90 rooms, all with bath/shower. Rooms for disabled. Lift. Room prices on application. Children welcome. Afternoon teas. TV. Phone. Fax: 071-495 3262. (*The Which? Hotel Guide*)

Cork & Bottle ▼ £ map 14

| 44–46 Cranbourn Street, WC2H 7AN | COOKING 1 |
| 071-734 7807 | COST £18–£30 |

Refurbishment is over, and the twenty-first year of business rolls on. Don Hewitson has lost none of his enthusiasm: for New Zealand wines (Te Mata), Californian wines (Jordan's), 1982 and 1986 clarets (lots of stocks), and champagnes (sales up, bucking the trend for 1991). 'My mother always likes lunching there if we go shopping in the West End,' writes one dutiful daughter. 'Once ensconced it is difficult to move her, and she is 80.' All the world goes to this wine bar ('I have never been offered a bad bottle'), and the cooking of grilled fish, the regular appearance of some dish or other from south-western France, the salads, the better cheese and the pavlovas still get lots of support. Hours are longer, service is less frantic. Mr Hewitson claims – incorrectly – to offer the first-ever 'No Muscadet List'. What is in no doubt is its strength and sheer value for money, and a proper pride in its antipodean selection. A wine bar which repays a visit for the wine is a rarity in London; cherish it. House wines are from £8.50. CELLARMAN'S CHOICE: Mâcon-Lugny 1990, Paquet, £10.95; Margaux, Ch. Labégorce-Zédé 1986, £18.95.

CHEF: Louie Egham PROPRIETORS: Cork & Bottle 1991 Ltd OPEN: all week; 11am to midnight (noon to 10.30 Sun) MEALS: alc SERVICE: not inc CARDS: Access, Amex, Diners, Visa DETAILS: 80 seats. Private parties: 20 main room, 20 private room. Vegetarian meals. Children restricted. No pipes. Music. Air-conditioned. Fax: 071-483 2230

La Croisette   map 11

168 Ifield Road, SW10 9AF	COOKING 2
071-373 3694	COST £25–£51

Spin down the spiral stair into maritime France – neither fish nor francophone waiters are avoidable in this other branch of the Pierre Martin empire (see entry under Le Suquet, London). Nor is that desirable, as it is fresh supplies of the first (direct from the Channel ports) and the cooking style of the second that draws people back. The menu runs on the same lines as the other outposts, and the plateau de fruits de mer is what gets the most mail. Otherwise, plain fish cookery is best pursued. Even in such a place as this, 'nouvelle cuisine' has been espied – by which the reader meant tablespoonfuls, not helpings, of vegetables, and pleasant food but not a lot of it. For one customer, the service charge was written in after the bill had been through the computerised till. It's a steep 15 per cent and the stamp says it's discretionary. House wines are £9.50.

CHEF: Robin Bertrand PROPRIETOR: Pierre Martin OPEN: Tue to Sun, exc Tue L; 12.30 to 2.30, 7.30 to 11 CLOSED: Aug, 25 Dec MEALS: alc. Set L £16 to £24, Set D £26 to £35. Cover £1 SERVICE: 15%, card slips closed CARDS: Access, Amex, Diners, Visa DETAILS: 55 seats. 3 tables outside. Private parties: 25 main room. Children welcome. Smart dress preferred. No pipes in dining-room. Wheelchair access (1 step; also WC). Music

Crowthers   map 10

481 Upper Richmond Road West,	
SW14 7PU	COOKING 2
081-876 6372	COST £23–£31

Crowthers is a small, smart set-up in a converted suburban shop, but with young trees growing opposite and a 'country living' interior of flower paintings and Laura Ashley-style fabrics. Philip Crowther has introduced a more flexible pricing policy for two or three courses (with coffee marked up separately), although reporters have commented that the menu itself remains fairly static. Gruyère cheese ramekin with tomato and chervil, and tortellini of seafood with cream and basil sauce continue to get endorsements, along with Mediterranean fish soup ('with the best rouille I have ever had,' according to one reader), shiitake mushrooms in filo pastry with red pepper sauce, venison with orange and madeira sauce, and crisp-skinned confit of duck with ginger and lime sauce. Vegetables are always a well-chosen assortment. To finish there are home-made ice-creams served in brandy baskets, and desserts such as 'deliciously fattening' brandy Alexander shortcake with raspberry sauce. Crowthers is doing nothing wrong: it continues to offer good value for money, ingredients are well chosen, cooking and presentation are 'admirable'. Yet the regularly reported sight of empty tables in the dining-room suggests that the recession may be taking its toll. 'In France the place would be full,' observes one visitor. There are around three-dozen wines, including house French at £8.50.

CHEF: Philip Crowther   PROPRIETORS: Philip and Shirley Crowther   OPEN: Mon to Sat and Mother's Day, exc Mon and Sat L; 12 to 2, 7 to 10   MEALS: Set L £12 to £14.50, Set D £14.50 to £19   SERVICE: not inc   CARDS: Access, Amex, Visa   DETAILS: 32 seats. Private parties: 32 main room. Vegetarian meals. Children welcome. Wheelchair access. Music. Air-conditioned

Daphne £ | NEW ENTRY | map 11

83 Bayham Street, NW1 0AG   COOKING 1
071-267 7322   COST £18–£28

'The most remarkable aspect of this restaurant is its friendly and warm atmosphere,' observes a reporter. The setting is a terraced house on a busy thoroughfare just off Camden High Street, but it manages to create a mood that 'makes customers imagine they have been magically transported to a village in Greece'. There is much camaraderie, handshaking and hugging between the long-serving waiters and customers, many of whom are regulars. The décor is typical taverna, but there is also a luxuriant roof-garden for summer eating. A short printed menu deals in all the favourite Greek-Cypriot staples, from hummus and aubergine salad to grills, stews and casseroles such as tavvas – these, though, have drawn mixed reports. Most interest centres on the blackboard specials, which are dominated by fish and vegetarian dishes. Pourekakia (a deep-fried ball of aubergine and feta cheese) and koukia-anginanes (a warm salad of broad beans and artichoke bottoms with olive oil and lemon) have been excellent. There are also good reports of intensely flavoured cuttlefish casserole – a 'superb' dish served with pourgouri (cracked-wheat pilaff). Fish meze supplement the standard versions. To finish there are locally made Greek sweets and pastries, plus ice-creams from Marine Ices. The wine list includes a handful of Greek-Cypriot bottles, although the house wine (£8.50) is French.

CHEF: Lambros Georgiou   PROPRIETORS: Panikos and Anna Lymbouri   OPEN: Mon to Sat; 12 to 2.30, 6 to 11.30   MEALS: alc   SERVICE: not inc   CARDS: Access, Visa   DETAILS: 85 seats. 10 tables outside. Private parties: 30 main room. Car park. Vegetarian meals. Children's helpings. Wheelchair access (1 step; also WC). Music

dell'Ugo £ | NEW ENTRY | map 14

56 Frith Street, W1V 5TA   COOKING 1*
071-734 8300   COST £19–£39

Everyone has heard of Antony Worrall-Thompson. He did that great little place where they served only first courses, Ménage à Trois; then in 1989 he moved on to 190 Queensgate where his style, emerging into the new boldism of the '90s, was richness and multiplication of layer upon layer. A year later, and Bistrot 190 (see entry, London) was the talk of the town. If the fashion was *fauve*, then he was *fauve* and *pauvre*. It was cheap, cheerful and very busy. He has taken it a step further with this three-decker in Soho – once the Braganza. Downstairs is a bar, offering 'consequential nibbles'; the next floor is no-bookings in much the same way as Bistrot 190; the top is more conventionally a restaurant. The energy cannot be denied. The long menu reads like a summation of every fashion of the last two years, and creates some of its own into the bargain. The overwhelming impression is the importance of pulses – there is a whole section entitled 'one-pot dining', where white beans and flageolets vie with polenta, potatoes and cracked wheat to provide the bulk. Another section is devoted to breads, bruschetta, crostini and panini. Then there is the receptivity to the world's eating habits: sashimi, salsas, blackened this and that, foie gras northern fashion, and lots and lots of Italy and the Mediterranean. Put it in a pot and stir, and the mixture is enticing. When it hits form, it is hearty and highly flavoured, though not so often delicate. Service will usually be amiable, but may take its time. The skill with places like this is keeping the standards. There are many who would say Bistrot 190 has not managed it, will dell'Ugo? While finding out, enjoy. The wine list takes a selection from a chosen merchant which changes every month. It also has its own core choice, graded in price bands – up to date, not badly priced and worth drinking around. House wine is £7.95.

CHEF: Antony Worrall-Thompson   PROPRIETORS: Simpsons of Cornhill plc   OPEN: Mon to Sat, exc Sat L restaurant; 11am to 12.30am (ground floor); 12 to 3, 6.30 to 12.30 (restaurant)   MEALS: alc   SERVICE: not inc   CARDS: Access, Amex, Visa   DETAILS: 200 seats. 4 tables outside. Private parties: 60 main room, 14 private room. Vegetarian meals. Children's helpings. Wheelchair access ground floor (also WC). Music. Air-conditioned. Fax: 071-734 8784

Diwana Bhel-Poori £   map 11

121 Drummond Street, NW1 2HL   COOKING 1
071-387 5556   COST £9–£19

Hard seats, queues at prime times, and quick and friendly service (but no wasted words) are all part of this brand leader on a street filled with Asian sweet shops, grocers and restaurants. People return again and again, value remains absolute, and standards are remarkably consistent. An American reflects: 'It is unusual food, light and fresh by comparison to most Indian cooking in the US.' An Indian celebrates that 'the dosas were hot and crisp and fried golden brown, the like of which is difficult even back home. The bhel poori and kulfis have all the hallmarks of their originals in Bombay.' This restaurant is vegetarian and serves pooris or dosas (patties or pancakes) with various fillings or accompaniments. It sometimes takes on the character of a New Age healthy food centre – reinforced by the bare pine furniture – but for the most part is enjoyed for its high flavour-to-price ratio. Leave room for the kulfis, and drink lassi or tea. There is no booking, and it is not licensed. A second branch can be found at 50 Westbourne Grove, W2 5SH, Tel: 071-221 0721.

CHEF: V.A. Qadir   PROPRIETORS: the Patel family   OPEN: all week; noon to 11.30 CLOSED: 25 Dec   MEALS: alc. Unlicensed, but bring your own: no corkage   SERVICE: not inc   CARDS: Access, Amex, Diners, Visa   DETAILS: 72 seats. Vegetarian meals. Children welcome. Wheelchair access (1 step). Music. Fax: 071-383 0560

▲ *Dorchester* ♥

map 13

Park Lane, W1A 2HJ
071-629 8888

COOKING 3
COST £28–£75

'The Dorchester's clients are the world's top business people, generally over 40 and at the top of their profession,' goes the hotel's own publicity. This does not make for a bubbly atmosphere in any of the three restaurants, though a patent toe or two may step out on the floor at the Terrace to the live music played of an evening, or a wrinkled knee may jig to the piano that tinkles in the brashly mirrored bar. The hotel succeeds in maintaining a high profile for each of its restaurants and a level of performance ahead of many of its rivals. This must be due to the overall control of Willi Elsener, and is itself an achievement. The Grill, which is open for all meals, functions as the hotel dining-room, and revels in Britain and plain food. Reports are not consistent, though the roast beef is well praised. The Terrace is the restaurant, open only five evenings a week, that cooks in refined modern international mode. Meats will be no more exciting than carré of lamb with a brioche mustard crust, rosette of beef first marinated in soy sauce and ginger, a parcel of veal fillet and foie gras, and duck with blueberries and kumquats (the leg a confit, of course). Daily dishes, on a separate sheet, may have more allure. Reports of this have been satisfactory, but it is expensive. The Oriental is the Dorchester's international Chinese restaurant, and it does Chinese food in style. It is worth having the dim-sum for lunch to see how they can be served – no trundling trolley of baskets here. The cooking is accomplished, but the range very restricted and the flavours are etiolated. It is almost best to go for the lunchtime fixed-price menu, or to hang the expense and try some of the well-sourced luxury ingredients – abalone or shark's fin, for instance. The desserts are also worth a pause and the tea ceremony is grand. If the wine list is combed carefully, various things below £20 drop out. It is an impressive list, strongest in claret, with plenty of maturity, and also ranges through China, Russia, and even Yugoslavia. It would be foolish to call it good value, but prices are no higher than in other major London hotels. House wines start at £14.50.

CHEFS: Willi Elsener (Grill and Terrace) and Simon Yung (Oriental)   PROPRIETORS: Dorchester Hotel Ltd   OPEN: Grill all week; Terrace Tue to Sat, D only; Oriental Mon to Sat, exc Sat L; 12 to 2.30, 7 to 11 (11.30 Terrace)   CLOSED: 25 Dec Oriental, bank hols Terrace   MEALS: alc. Grill Set L £27, Set D £28. Terrace Set D £28 to £48. Oriental Set L £20 to £25, Set D £28 to £35   SERVICE: net prices, card slips closed   CARDS: Access, Amex, Diners, Visa   DETAILS: Grill 80 seats, Terrace 81 seats, Oriental 77 seats. Private parties: 6, 10, 12 and 14 private rooms. Vegetarian meals. Healthy eating options Grill and Terrace. Children welcome Grill and Oriental. Jacket and tie. Music. Air-conditioned ACCOMMODATION: 250 rooms, all with bath/shower. Rooms for disabled. Lift. B&B £212 to £1,175. Deposit: 100%. Children welcome. Baby facilities. Afternoon teas. Sauna. Air-conditioned. TV. Phone. Confirm by 6. Fax: 071-409 0114

'We were a little surprised to find that horse-riding for two hours on Sunday had been booked for us (our cost – £64); we thoroughly enjoyed it. Some folk would have been disconcerted at not being consulted. Horses can be dangerous!'
On eating in Leicestershire

Eagle £

map 11

159 Farringdon Road, EC1R 3AL   COOKING 2
071-837 1353   COST £18–£29

Once a pub, the Eagle is still a bit of a pub, but the greatly improved stainless steel back-bar grill and range show the emphasis now to be on the food. The high-ceilinged room appears to be almost a cube. It is always packed – Clerkenwell photographers, *Guardian* journos and lots of leather-jacketed aficionados of the arts mix with the power dressers (but no pin-stripes), and struggle to find a place to perch at the peak of lunch hour. It presents a rough and ready face and the cooking can be that too, revelling in its Portuguese or Italian inspiration. There are lots of grilled meats and sauces, and marinades with punchy flavours. Italian spicy sausages are high-voltage; the grilled veg on focaccia can be great. Risottos have been criticised for low protein; soups – field mushroom, tomato, lentil or minestrone – are everyone's favourite. Stews are hearty enough to fuel the ploughing of Clerkenwell Fields. You may doubt that your order will be absorbed, but the system works most of the time. Potent coffee comes from little Vesuviuses. The wines are chalked up every day and don't cost more than £11. Here is good value. House wine is £7.80.

CHEF: David Eyre PROPRIETORS: Michael Belben and David Eyre OPEN: Mon to Fri; 12.30 to 2.30, 6.30 to 10.30 CLOSED: bank hols, 3 weeks from 23 Dec MEALS: alc SERVICE: not inc DETAILS: 40 seats. 4 tables outside. Vegetarian meals. Children's helpings. Wheelchair access (1 step). Music

Efes Kebab House £

map 13

80 Great Titchfield Street, W1P 7AF   COOKING 1
071-636 1953   COST £14–£23

'Lively, colourful and interesting atmosphere. First-class cooking' sums it up for one enthusiast. Much of the success of the place is due to the personal stamp and presence of the owners. The menu divides equally between hot and cold starters, with a strong vegetarian bias, and main courses which are dominated by generous hunks of animal protein cooked on the chargrill. Bread, sticky sweets and Turkish coffee provide the back-up. Efespilsen (Turkish beer) and a few Turkish wines and liqueurs supplement the short wine list. House Italian is £7.90 a litre. Efes II is at 175–177 Great Portland Street, W1N 5FD, Tel: 071-436 0600.

CHEFS/PROPRIETORS: Kazim Akkus and Ibrahim Akbas OPEN: Mon to Sat; noon to 11.30 MEALS: alc. Set L and D £14 to £15 SERVICE: not inc (10% for 8 or more) CARDS: Access, Amex, Visa DETAILS: 140 seats. 12 tables outside. Private parties: 150 main room. Vegetarian meals. Children welcome. Music. Air-conditioned. Fax: 071-323 5082

See the inside of the front cover for an explanation of the 1 to 5 rating system for cooking standards.

London round-ups listing additional restaurants that may be worth a visit can be found after the main London section.

Eleven Park Walk

map 12

11 Park Walk, SW10 0AJ
071-352 3449 and 8249

COOKING 1
COST £21–£24

There is no lack of people happy to stroll down Park Walk. The restaurant has been popular for a long time and is almost an archaeological type in its decoration of green plants, mirrors, tiled floor and cream walls. There is an intention to remodel, to be hauled into the '90s, but this had not begun as we went to press. The menu splits between old and new favourites: on the one hand, prosciutto San Daniele, ravioli with tomato and basil, liver with sage, and veal milanese; on the other, goose carpaccio with rocket, bagna cauda, cod with balsamic vinegar, and warm salad of scallops with rocket, mushrooms and balsamic. The menu changes slowly, and the boys still whirl round with their pepper mills. The coffee is good, so is the tiramisù. The wine list is no more overpriced than the food: some of the makers are tip-top fashionables, others more pedestrian. House wine is £7.50.

CHEF: Giancarlo Moeri   PROPRIETORS: G. Movio, G. Lotto and J. Manuel-E-Sà   OPEN: all week, exc Sun D; 12.30 to 3, 7 to 12   MEALS: alc. Set L and D £12.50. Cover £1.50
SERVICE: not inc, card slips closed   CARDS: Access, Amex, Visa   DETAILS: 100 seats.
Private parties: 100 main room. Vegetarian meals. Children's helpings. Wheelchair access (1 step). Music. Air-conditioned. Fax: 071-351 5473

Emile's £

map 10

144 Wandsworth Bridge Road, SW6 2UH
071-736 2418

COOKING 1
COST £19–£24

Two floors of bistro – sometimes with bistro levels of housekeeping – keep Wandsworth residents happy with lowish prices. There is a good-value fixed-price blackboard menu, with some more adventurous à la carte dishes. Starters include excellent salads, including one of undyed smoked haddock interleaved with slices of apple, with a finely judged cider vinaigrette. People speak kindly of quail marinated with ginger, honey and coriander and then chargrilled, and pan-fried liver and bacon, but sometimes less charitably about a beef Wellington lacking its mushroom stuffing. Performance may move up and down. Crèmes brûlées are good, coffee is fine, the service makes you welcome. The short wine list keeps to suburban rather than inner-city prices, and house wines cost £6.95. There is a second, more spacious, branch at 96–98 Felsham Road, SW15 1DQ, Tel: 081-789 3323 – reports, please.

CHEF: Paul Duvall   PROPRIETORS: Emil Fahmy and Andrew Sherlock   OPEN: Mon to Sat, D only; 7.30 to 11   CLOSED: 24 to 30 Dec, 2 Jan, bank hols   MEALS: alc. Set D £13.50
SERVICE: not inc (10% for parties)   CARDS: Access, Visa   DETAILS: 60 seats. 6 tables outside. Private parties: 42 private room. Vegetarian meals. Children welcome. Wheelchair access (1 step). Music

Prices quoted in the Guide are based on information supplied by restaurateurs. The prices quoted at the top of each entry represent a range, from the lowest meal price to the highest; the latter is inflated by 10 per cent to take account of likely price rises during the year of the Guide.

English Garden

map 12

10 Lincoln Street, SW3 2TS
071-584 7272

COOKING 2
COST £21–£49

The garden is a conservatory, with foliage like chintz – in bulk. The Englishness of the place produces words like 'ragoo' on the menu and flavourings such as liquorice with hare, sorrel with watercress mousse, and plum and orange with duck. Other countries, now adopted by Albion, contribute goats' cheese and green peppercorns with mushrooms, crab ginger and coriander with a halibut roulade, or, for dessert, filo-pastry parcels of prunes and almonds with sour cream. Service may go awry, but readers find this a steady, if not demonstrative, restaurant. The price range of the wine list is generous and mark-ups are not excessive. The accent is French, to the near-exclusion of choice from other countries, but the list of clarets particularly is worth a careful read. The sister-restaurant, English House, 3 Milner Street, SW3 2QA, Tel: 071-584 3002, is 'just the place to bring your great-aunt from the country'. It has more chintz, lots of crockery and similar food. Some of it works, some of it doesn't, and the tables are close enough to let you talk to your neighbours about it. House wine is £9.

CHEF: Brian Turner   PROPRIETOR: Malcolm Livingston   OPEN: all week; 12.30 to 2.30 (12 to 2 Sun), 7.30 to 11.30 (7 to 10 Sun)   CLOSED: 25 and 26 Dec   MEALS: alc. Set L £14.75
SERVICE: not inc   CARDS: Access, Amex, Diners, Visa   DETAILS: 60 seats. Private parties: 30 main room, 30 private room. Vegetarian meals. Children welcome. Jacket and tie. Music. Air-conditioned. Fax: 071-581 2848

L'Escargot Doré

| NEW ENTRY | map 11

2–4 Thackeray Street, W8 5ET
071-937 8508

COOKING 1
COST £24–£45

This is a basement restaurant that changes its chefs too often for the *Guide* to keep up, hence disappearance from last year's edition. However, Sr Sanchez is always there, and he charms the world. Daniel Delagarde has arrived from Le Cadre (see entry, London) and recommendations have ensued. Cooking is competent and French, and indulges in no surprises. Dishes mentioned have included scrambled eggs and smoked salmon croustade, prawns with basil and saffron, scallops with celeriac, venison with green peppercorns and lamb with rosemary. Old standards like crème caramel and apple tart show the training coming out. The *carte* is priced according to the neighbourhood (rich); the set meal – giving a choice of two in each course – is more popular, less elaborate and also approved. The wine list, like the food, stays in France. House Duboeuf is £8.50.

CHEF: Daniel Delagarde   PROPRIETOR: Modesto Sanchez   OPEN: Mon to Sat, exc Sat L; 12 to 2.30, 6.30 (7 Sat) to 11.30   CLOSED: last 2 weeks Aug, bank hols   MEALS: alc. Set L and D £14.90. Cover £1.20   SERVICE: 10%, card slips closed   CARDS: Access, Amex, Diners, Visa   DETAILS: 60 seats. Private parties: 50 main room, 15 private room. Vegetarian meals. Children's helpings. Smart dress preferred. Music. Air-conditioned

See the back of the Guide *for an index of restaurants listed.*

Est £ NEW ENTRY map 14

54 Frith Street, W1V 5TE
071-437 0666

COOKING 1
COST £18–£33

Wander up Frith Street at night and it begins to look like fun. Alastair Little, dell'Ugo, Soho Soho, Bar Italia, L'Hippocampe, Chiang Mai and Bahn Thai will be variously occupied – or not, as the case may be – and give ample scope for scoffing, adoration, mere observation or participation. Est is the restaurant that looks more like a bar where you can eat (it does have a separate bar menu). Touch elbows with your neighbours, don't go for an intimate dinner, enjoy the fair buzz ('noise' to the sensitive) that comes from a full house. The setting is cool; the chef used to do the food at Emporio Armani. He should therefore know what slender dudes want to eat on the street. It's mostly chargrills, with endless Italian influence. Who would have thought we would be eating 'chargrilled polenta with salsa of the day' as our chosen snack food in 1993? Performance is uneven, not helped by fairly spasmodic attention from the waiting staff. The wine list is as state-of-the-art as the place. House wines are £8.50.

CHEF: Edward Bains   PROPRIETOR: Mogens Tholstrup   OPEN: Mon to Sat, exc Sat L; 12 to 3, 6 to 11 (11.30 Fri and Sat)   CLOSED: bank hols, Christmas   MEALS: alc. Bar meals   SERVICE: 12.5%, card slips closed   CARDS: Access, Amex, Visa   DETAILS: 45 seats. 2 tables outside. Private parties: 80 main room. Vegetarian meals. Children's helpings. Wheelchair access (1 step). Music. Air-conditioned

L'Estaminet NEW ENTRY map 14

14 Garrick Street, WC2E 9BJ
071-379 1432

COOKING 1*
COST £26–£41

The site once housed Inigo Jones, resort of epicures from the late 1960s until recently. Now it is a French-formula special, good at its self-limited task. The brick, the shape of the rooms and the stained glass remain; otherwise the transformation is complete, and satisfactory. That the owners and chef have worked their passage through the far reaches of the Chez Gérard empire may come as no surprise: they know a good system when they see one. The menu is unchanging, supplemented by a handful of daily extras. Quite where pheasant comes from for a menu in May is uncertain. The most consistently reported items are the salad of marinated herrings with potatoes, the hot lyonnais sausage, the seafood pancakes (good pancakes, good sauce, but a pity seafood meant white fish and tuna), sometimes the charcuterie, and the grills. 'The lamb cutlets were of extremely high quality, with plenty of meat, so good that you wanted to pick them up and chew the bones.' Chips are mostly crisp and succulent. Cheese is excellent, puddings are simple and adequate. Coffee is a good finish, with bitter chocolates direct from Paris. Most of the details have been thought out. There have been days when the formula seems to outweigh any skill, but the consensus is more encouraging. This may be due to the staff – monoglot French for the most part – who get many plaudits for a welcome and enthusiasm that come rare these days. No one quibbles about the value, but the total may be a surprise, even if service is included (watch the cover charge). There is a wine bar in the basement for various sandwiches and simple boudin/

sausage-like foods. The wine list could be a whole lot better. House wine is £8.50.

CHEF: Philippe Tamet   PROPRIETORS: Cassis Rest plc   OPEN: Mon to Sat; 12 to 2.30, 6.30 to 11.30   MEALS: alc. Cover £1.50   SERVICE: net prices, card slips closed   CARDS: Access, Amex, Visa   DETAILS: 60 seats. Private parties: 40 main room, 20 private room. Vegetarian meals. Children welcome. No pipes in dining-room. Wheelchair access (1 step). Music

Faulkner's £
map 11

| 424–426 Kingsland Road, E8 4AT | COOKING 1 |
| 071-254 6152 | COST £9–£24 |

This fish restaurant is no longer eponymous, as John Faulkner is no longer a partner, but it carries on the standards set since opening as a branch of the Seashell on Lisson Grove. The fish is fresh, varies according to supplies and may seem dear by contrast to your normal chippie, but quality is assured and portions large. There is plenty of tea, a short list of white wines plus a Beaujolais, and better-than-usual music. House white is £5.20.

CHEF: Michael Webber   PROPRIETOR: Mark Farrell   OPEN: Mon to Sat; 12 to 2, 5 to 10 (12 to 9 Sun)   CLOSED: bank hols, 1 week Christmas to New Year   MEALS: alc. Minimum £2.50   SERVICE: not inc   DETAILS: 65 seats. Children welcome. No-smoking area. Music. Air-conditioned. Fax: 071-249 5661

First Floor
map 11

| 186 Portobello Road, W11 1LA | COOKING 2 |
| 071-243 0072 | COST £25–£33 |

'Trendy' is a word that crops up often in reports on this jam-packed venue above a Victorian pub. It is stuffed full to the brim with bric-à-brac, a hotch-potch of furniture, odds and ends – rather like a version of the nearby market. The menu follows suit. It is all jazzy eclecticism; ingredients, ideas and influences are tossed into the global melting pot seemingly at will. In an unskilled kitchen, this could be the gastronomic kiss of death. But here, it succeeds because there is genuine flair plus a respect and awareness for ingredients and the seasons. Regulars reckon that the place is on the up. The menu changes daily. Recommended dishes speak for themselves: Tuscan bean salad; Thai fish-cakes; seared red snapper with sun-dried tomatoes; chicken with ginger, honey and peppers. Fusilli might be served with tomatoes, chickpeas, olive oil, Parmesan, goats' cheese and rocket ('a wonderful amalgam of ingredients'), or with lamb, ginger, broccoli, olives and tomatoes. To finish, there might be sticky toffee pudding or chocolate mousse with cream and strawberries ('the best I've ever had,' according to one reporter). Cocktails are wacky and weird: 'Ecstasy' is strawberries with vodka, fraise d'Anjou and champagne. Otherwise, there is a short, in-tune wine list. House wine is £8.50. At lunch, the place has a 'café format'.

'Service was either faintly camp or Northern brash as in ''Be careful, luv, this plate is red *'ot''.'*   On eating in Greater Manchester

CHEF: Phil Wright   PROPRIETORS: Simon Rose, Benny Neville and Pip Wylie   OPEN: all
week; 8am (12.30 Sat and Sun) to 4pm, 7.30 to 12.30 (11.30 Sun)   CLOSED: 25 and 26
Dec   MEALS: alc. Cover £1   SERVICE: 15%, card slips closed   CARDS: Access, Amex,
Visa   DETAILS: 55 seats. Private parties: 60 main room, 14 and 40 private rooms. Vegetarian
meals. Children welcome. No cigars/pipes in dining-room. Music. Fax: 071-221 8387

Florians ♥ £

map 10

4 Topsfield Parade,
Middle Lane, N8 8RP
081-348 8348

COOKING 2
COST £15–£32

If only every bit of London could deliver up a Florians; it's a happy place, well
set in its neighbourhood. Drop into the wine bar at the street-front, eat a simple
meal of soup and pasta; progress up the stairs, pass through a small top-lit
dining-room and then to a big room, doubtless once a garage, looking on to the
mews behind. The cooking is Italian: tuna carpaccio with balsamic vinegar, a
basil and oil dip for the bread, parcels of aubergine and mozzarella with spiced
tomato sauce, garlic sausages from the chargrill with polenta and lentils,
chargrilled pork with sun-dried tomatoes, good risottos, calf's liver with sage,
spinach and pine-nuts, lots of home-made pasta. The menu is long and changes
regularly; it is also reinforced by a peripatetic blackboard of daily dishes. The
down-side to all this is that things can fluctuate and not every meal has been a
success. Either there are too many customers or the kitchen nods off. Arnie
Onisto coddles his regulars and serves good espresso, even if the cappuccino
has been weak as can be. His all-Italian wine list is excellent and is
supplemented by short-term shipments and a formidable selection of grappe.
Prices are very fair, for instance for the Super-Tuscan from Vinattieri, the Barolo
from Contratto or Il Cerro's Vino Nobile di Montepulciano. Many of the wines
are shipped direct by the restaurant. House Sicilian is £8. CELLARMAN'S
CHOICE: Ribollo Gialla, Torre Rosazzo 1990, £14.50; Chianti Classico, Rocca di
Castagnoli 1988, £13.75.

CHEF: Jillian Onisto   PROPRIETORS: Franco Papa and Arnie Onisto   OPEN: all week; 12 to
3 (3.30 Sun), 7 to 11 (10.30 Sun); bar meals all day   CLOSED: bank hols   MEALS: alc. Set L
and D £5.95. Minimum £12 restaurant   SERVICE: not inc   CARDS: Access, Visa   DETAILS:
70 seats. 4 tables outside. Private parties: 35 main room, 18 and 35 private rooms.
Vegetarian meals. Children's helpings with prior notice. Music

Four Seasons £

NEW ENTRY   map 11

84 Queensway, W2 3RL
071-229 4320

COOKING 2
COST £15–£30

Aficionados rate this small, respectable Chinese outpost in busy, cosmopolitan
Queensway as the best venue in town for one-plate dishes. Glistening roast
meats hang in the window behind the glass frontage, and visitors can watch
the 'chopper' at work, expertly dissecting carcasses. A plate of roast duck with
warm soy-gravy was pronounced by one visiter as 'the flavouriest, moistest,
crispest-skinned duck I've had in years'. Other recommended items on the
standard 100-dish menu have included sizzling stuffed aubergine, savoury ma

po bean curd, and crisp, succulent Chinese broccoli in a ginger and garlic sauce. There is also a separate menu written in Chinese; one knowledgeable reporter's advice is to ask for a translation and investigate some of these more esoteric specialities. Twice-cooked braised belly pork with pickled vegetables is a classic from the mountain area of Guanzghou province: it is a 'most calorific casserole' with a rich, potent gravy. Steamed cutlet of turbot with pickled garlic has also been good, although it would have benefited from better seasoning. To finish, crisp, crunchy toffee bananas have been handled with skill. Service can seem rather cheerless and indifferent. Drink jasmine tea. House wine is £7.

CHEF: Mr N.L. Lee   PROPRIETOR: Mr H. Lim   OPEN: all week; noon to 11   CLOSED: 24 to 26 Dec   MEALS: alc. Set D £10.50 to £16   SERVICE: 12.5%   CARDS: Access, Amex, Diners, Visa   DETAILS: 80 seats. Private parties: 40 main room. Vegetarian meals. Children welcome. Music. Air-conditioned

Fung Shing £

map 14

15 Lisle Street, WC2H 7BE
071-437 1539

COOKING 2*
COST £19–£48

Fung Shing manages comfort and an 'inviting aspect' to a greater degree than its Lisle Street competitors. There are also many who say it has the edge on cooking as well. 'The art is in the undercooking; the cost is reflected by the freshness of all ingredients,' wrote one who had feasted on steamed sea bass with ginger and coriander; fresh abalone, scallops and clams marinated with sesame oil, chilli, soy and spring onions; steamed prawns served with oil, spring onions and vinegar; and Chinese chives stir-fried with pickled Szechuan cabbage. There have also been reports of less successful meals, of off-hand service and of muddles due to overcrowding. The menu is long and the shellfish and Cantonese duck are usually excellent. There are supporters of the casserole dishes: duck with yams, belly pork with yams, bean curd with soup. The 'special' section includes some of the more out-of-the-way dishes, such as deep-fried squid with prawn balls, chicken with preserved clams and eel with coriander, but more reports concentrate on the quality of the straightforward cooking. Upstairs is more claustrophobic than the ground floor. Wines there are aplenty, and at fair prices. Ch. Larrivet-Haut-Brion, white and red, is an unexpected find on a Chinese wine list, and the substitution of Sancerre by the cheaper Quincy is a social service. There is beer too, and fragrant tea. House wines are £8.50.

CHEF: Fu Kwun   PROPRIETORS: Traceflow Ltd   OPEN: all week; noon to 11.45   MEALS: alc. Set L £12 to £15, Set D £15 to £30. Minimum £8.50   SERVICE: not inc   CARDS: Access, Amex, Diners, Visa   DETAILS: 85 seats. Private parties: 50 main room, 30 private room. Vegetarian meals. Children welcome. Music. Air-conditioned

Not inc *in the details at the end of an entry indicates that no service charge is made and any tipping is at the discretion of the customer.*

Healthy eating options *in the details at the end of an entry signifies that a restaurant marks on its menu, in words and/or using symbols, low-fat dishes or other healthy eating choices.*

La Gaulette

map 13

53 Cleveland Street, W1 5PQ
071-580 7608 and 323 4210

COOKING 2
COST £16–£56

The more central of Sylvain Ho Wing Cheong's duo of Mauritian fish restaurants (see entry for Chez Liline), La Gaulette has a seemingly constant supply of exotic tropical fish: bourgeois, snapper, capitain, vacqua, dorade, parrot fish. This is balanced by the more familiar wild salmon, squid, prawns, mussels and lobster. Lemon grass, ginger, spring onion, coriander and chilli feature in many of the sauces, giving a strong flavour of south-east Asia; but the use of garlic, saffron and fennel, and the appearance on the menu of fish soup, asparagus with hollandaise sauce, feuilleté d'homard and Mediterranean prawns grilled on a bed of herbs in a garlic sauce, more than hint at a tempering French colonial influence. The downstairs bistro offers an inexpensive three-course menu with a choice of 10 first and main courses in fairly cramped surroundings. House red is £9, house white is £10.95.

CHEF: Sylvain Ho Wing Cheong PROPRIETORS: Sylvain and Shirley Ho Wing Cheong OPEN: Mon to Sat, exc Sat L; 12 to 3, 6.30 to 11 CLOSED: bank hol Mons MEALS: alc. Set L and D £10.95 (bistro) to £16.95. Minimum £12.75 SERVICE: not inc CARDS: Access, Amex, Diners, Visa DETAILS: 70 seats. Private parties: 40 main room, 30 bistro/private room. Vegetarian meals. Children welcome. Music. Fax: 081-697 7255

Le Gavroche ♥

map 13

43 Upper Brook Street, W1Y 1PF
071-408 0881 and 499 1826

COOKING 5
COST £38–£106

The transformation of this restaurant into a hotel dining-room (with the opening of the sumptuous apartments at 47 Park Street on the floors above) has had no obvious effect. Not much does affect Le Gavroche, even if the cutesy urchin that has haunted the Roux brothers with its image on the menu since the beginning has converted into a more Dickensian ragamuffin sitting on the front steps. Le Gavroche goes on and on: 'There is an atmosphere of knowing it's an institution and therefore doesn't need to try' is one harsh comment. 'The style of the cooking is heavy and old-fashioned' is another. Heaviness is by no means inevitable, though the gross scale of a slab of calf's liver that overpowered the light and herby gravy might act as denial, even if the same lunch (from the fixed-price short menu that some find a bargain) yielded baked sea bass with a champagne cream sauce that avoided excess by careful seasoning and management. Constant visitors to this and similar restaurants can so easily fall into the trap of ennui – witness the large cigar that was toted by one diner next to a party of seven despite the plea on the menu to smoke such things in the lounge area beyond. (In the event, on representations being made to the staff, the message was that the complainant would have to make his addresses to the smoke-stack in person. He must have been a *very* big cigar-smoker.) But first-timers can still feel the shock of admiration for subtlety, ability and style. 'If it is a restaurateur's ambition to achieve an ambience where diners walk in but float out, not one jot overfed, knowing they have eaten really fresh, wholesome food that has been transformed by skill into a delicious feast, then this place has achieved it for two of us.' Tradition at Le

Gavroche means both that methods of service and presentation are assured, and that certain aspects of French cooking that shorthand dubs traditional are given weight equal to that afforded to the more fanciful or extravagant. Hence ox cheek 'à la ficelle', fricassee of chicken with tarragon, and saddle of rabbit stuffed with spinach and with a thyme gravy rub shoulders with sauté of ever-so-lightly spiced scallops and strips of fried vegetables, terrine of vegetables glimmering on its plate, and the old-lag 'Caneton Gavroche' in two services. The cooking can still yield great dividends: a simple salad of lobster, frisée, diced tomato, gull's egg and pale-green herbed mayonnaise shows exactitude, discretion and a fine palate. Salmon poached with vegetables might be boring, but it has also been described as 'ethereal'. Even white chocolate is managed well: the passion-fruit sauce that accompanied the tall mousse cut through the sweetness and brought out the cacao. 'Food is never handed to you at Le Gavroche, it makes an entrance. The maître d' encourages a stripling of a lad to the table, bearing a vast tray. Dish-covers are whisked away and the plates wait until the correctly sensual sigh is heard from both diners.' It is a place that runs smoothly and in relative silence. Slips that show the petticoat's hem are the worse because there are so many troops. The wine list here remains an unhelpful, if very impressive and very extended, jumble of bottles. Careful search will reveal the odd thing under £20, although the Vins Régionaux offer a more sustained attempt to provide modest pleasures. In essence, this is a list of great seriousness with prices higher even than in comparable establishments. House wine is £16.50. CELLARMAN'S CHOICE: Chablis, St Martin 'Cuvée Albert Roux' 1989, Laroche, £29.50; Margaux, Ch. Gisours 1986, £35.

CHEFS: Albert Roux and Michel Roux Junior   PROPRIETORS: Le Gavroche Ltd   OPEN: Mon to Fri; 12 to 2, 7 to 11   CLOSED: 23 Dec to 2 Jan   MEALS: alc. Set L £29.50, Set D £59. Minimum £50 D   SERVICE: net prices   CARDS: Access, Amex, Diners, Visa   DETAILS: 60 seats. Private parties: 80 main room, 20 private room. No children under 6. Jacket and tie. No pipes in dining-room. No music. Air-conditioned. Fax: 071-491 4387 and 409 0939

Gavvers
map 12

61–63 Lower Sloane Street, SW1W 8DH
071-730 5983

COOKING 2
COST £20–£39

The location, next to the Rose & Crown, was the original site of Le Gavroche (see entry above). People still wonder how such a restaurant could live happily in these cramped surroundings. When the menu (and drink if you wish) is at an all-in price (cheaper, and the food skimpier, at lunch), then comfort is not so vital, even if the tables could be of a better size and more well-spaced. The price draws the crowds. The food and the service are emphatically French and usually appreciated. The cooking is, however, subject to vagaries. This may have something to do with Bruno Valette's apparent absence from the stoves for many months. It is possible to order substantial bourgeois choucroutes, garbures and cassoulets here – often the 'proposals' of the brothers Roux – or else be treated to fairly straight French productions along the lines of stuffed saddle of lamb, hare with chocolate and red wine, salmon with a fish mousse and parsley broth, terrine of smoked fish, or a feuilleté of salmon with cucumber, tomatoes and herbs. Vegetables are on the plate, potatoes are notable by their scarcity, and trimmings and endings make for weight but not for clarions of delight. It is a good formula, of evident service, that can really go or just amble. The wine list is short and all French. House Duboeuf is £11.

CHEF: Bruno Valette PROPRIETORS: Roux Restaurants Ltd OPEN: Mon to Sat, exc Sat L; 12 to 2.30, 7 to 11 CLOSED: bank hols MEALS: Set L £13 to £15.50, Set D £23.50 to £30 (inc wine) SERVICE: net prices, card slips closed CARDS: Access, Diners, Visa DETAILS: 54 seats. No children under 10. Wheelchair access. Music. Air-conditioned. Fax: 071-622 5657

Gay Hussar   map 14

2 Greek Street, W1V 6NB   COOKING 2
071-437 0973   COST £22–£38

Here is Soho's enduring homage to *mitteleuropa*. The plush-benched ground floor is also a monument to what Soho restaurants looked like before the war, as more and more old names fall to new owners. The large menu is deliberately unchanging, aware of loyalties to old customers and its attractions to new ones. Yet people have thought a fine level of performance has run through the kitchen this year. 'A spiced Hungarian sausage served hot with cold horseradish was, in fact, quite delicious,' according to one reader. Another reaffirmed that 'soups are the pinnacle, perhaps thanks to all the duck and smoked goose carcasses that must go into the pot'. Garlic, onions and paprika suffuse almost everything. The style of dishes such as the pâtés of freshwater fish, the smoked goose with scholet, chicken paprikash with dumplings, and baked minced veal with vegetable purée is authentic enough to cause acute nostalgia in yesterday's travellers to the Danube and beyond. The best pudding is always said to be poppy seed strudel. Its greater freshness and reduction in sweetness is held in its favour this year. Fruit pudding or home-made cream cheese stay in the Hungarian mode, just as will some of the choices on the wine list. Victor Sassie, the past owner, now devotes his time to horse-racing. The performance of his steed at Ayr left much to be desired, to the eternal impoverishment of the staff who are as loved by old Soho as their food and locale. Value remains fair for these days and portions are enormous. House wine is £8.

CHEF: Laszlo Holecz PROPRIETORS: Restaurant Partnership plc OPEN: Mon to Sat; 12.30 to 2.30, 5.30 to 11 CLOSED: bank hols and public hols MEALS: alc. Set L £15 SERVICE: not inc L, net prices D CARD: Amex DETAILS: 70 seats. Private parties: 12 main room, 12 and 22 private rooms. Vegetarian meals. Children's helpings. Wheelchair access (1 step). No music. Air-conditioned

Gilbert's ▮   map 12

2 Exhibition Road, SW7 2HF   COOKING 1
071-589 8947   COST £20–£37

A small parade of shops that must have been put up at the same time as the Underground station is host to a tiny – never too comfortable – restaurant with a big wine list (big in ideas rather than length). There has been adjustment between the partners: Ann Wregg's son takes more responsibility for wines and front-of-house, Julia Chalkley and Anne now share the cooking, which is sometimes described as 'women's cooking'. Does this mean careful? Or lacking panache? For sure, it draws on that line of 'French provincial' for much inspiration, but is leavened by many modern touches and a true British view of puddings. Many reports are full of praise for crab soufflé with mushrooms and ginger, baked red peppers with salt cod brandade, tagliatelle with a spring vegetable ragoût, saucisse en brioche, pot au feu à la faouda, pork dijonnaise, beef bourguignonne, and spiced date pudding and chocolate tipsy cake. Unfortunately, all is not entirely consistent. Meat-buying tends to favour the tough; production can be slow, and seems slower on a hard bench; vegetables are not always as they could be; and sometimes the intention of a dish out-runs the capacity to cook it. Value for money is a strong point, especially at lunch, and the wines are glorious. The intelligent wine list continues to encourage experiment and eschews geographical classification for varietal, making for an interesting enforced neighbourliness – Margaux brushes with Napa. Informative and precise though the notes are, their absence or pruning might be considered as a concession to slow readers; six good house wines by the glass, though, aid quick, reliable selection. Prices are fair throughout and half-bottles are provided liberally. House wines are from £8.90.

CHEFS/PROPRIETORS: Julia Chalkley and Ann Wregg   OPEN: Mon to Sat, exc Sat L; 12.30 to 2, 7 to 10.15   MEALS: Set L £9.50 to £16.50, Set D £12.50 to £23   SERVICE: not inc   CARDS: Access, Amex, Visa   DETAILS: 32 seats. 2 tables outside. Children welcome. Wheelchair access (2 steps). Air-conditioned. No music

Gopal's of Soho £

map 14

12 Bateman Street, W1V 5TD
071-434 1621 and 0840

COOKING 1
COST £17–£34

Gopal's still has the power to please, although – like so many new-wave Indian restaurants – there are signs that it has 'gone off the boil'. Even so, customers continue to pack into the modest dining-room to sample a distinctive version of Indian cooking with regional overtones. Murg jalfrezi spiked with hot green chillies, meenu curry (fish cooked with coconut), boigan masala and south Indian nariyal pilau rice have all been good. Some specialities, such as achar gosht, have potency but they lack individuality on the plate. They are 'dishes in search of an identity'. Vegetarian and non-vegetarian thalis offer a varied assortment of different flavours and levels of spicing. Service is generally congenial. The reasonable wine list, put together in consultation with David Wolfe, has one or two additions from Alsace and the Loire; otherwise drink lassi or lager. House wines are £7.90.

CHEF/PROPRIETOR: N.P. Pittal   OPEN: all week; 12 to 3.15, 6 to 11.45   CLOSED: 25 and 26 Dec   MEALS: alc. Set L and D £9.75 to £10.75   SERVICE: not inc   CARDS: Access, Amex, Diners, Visa   DETAILS: 48 seats. Private parties: 50 main room. Vegetarian meals. Children's helpings. Wheelchair access (1 step). Music. Air-conditioned

The text of entries is based on unsolicited reports sent in by readers, backed up by inspections conducted anonymously. The factual details under the text are from questionnaires the Guide sends to all restaurants that feature in the book.

Grahame's Seafare £

map 13

38 Poland Street, W1V 3DA
071-437 3788 and 0975

COOKING 1
COST £15-£40

'We eat here regularly, nothing fancy – grilled haddock and chips, followed by cheesecake if they have it, apple strudel if they don't. We cannot believe there is a better fish and chip place; we love the atmosphere: a kosher restaurant owned by a Turk and staffed by Spaniards and a Finn.' It may be an unexpected mix, but it works, and the cheesecake is fab. There is good fish fried, grilled, steamed or cooked in butter and milk at extra charge, good chips, and saucy things if you want them. House wines start at an affordable £7.25.

CHEF/PROPRIETOR: Chetin Ismet   OPEN: Mon to Sat; 12 to 2.45, 5.30 to 9.30 (8 Fri and Sat)   CLOSED: bank hols, Jewish New Year, 2 weeks from 24 Dec   MEALS: alc. Set L and D £9.95   SERVICE: not inc, card slips closed   CARDS: Access, Amex, Visa   DETAILS: 86 seats. Children's helpings. Wheelchair access. No music. Air-conditioned. Fax: 081-294 1808

Great Nepalese £

map 11

48 Eversholt Street, NW1 1DA
071-388 6737 and 5935

COOKING 1*
COST £13-£26

'Reassuringly unchanged' is a devotee's verdict on this amiable restaurant across the road from Euston Station. It is an ever-popular bolt-hole for early-evening commuters, and the congenial mood of the place is sustained by the unfailing good humour of the waiters. The strong showing of Nepalese specialities draws most praise: masco bara (deep-fried black lentil pancakes), kalezo ra chyau (chicken livers with mushrooms), bhutuwa chicken, prawn jhalphiraji, toriko sag, pulses and dhals. Cold dishes such as vivid green coriander pickle and aloo kerauko achar (potatoes with chillies and powdered sesame seeds) are worth investigating as accompaniments. Basmati rice and breads are generally up to the mark. The owner is promising to introduce Tibetan noodle dishes which, he says, 'should appeal to children and anyone who is unenthusiastic about curries'. The food seldom disappoints, although there are occasional lapses: curries overdosed with garlic, greasy pilau rice, and dishes that sometimes taste as if they have been re-heated. Drink lassi or lager. House Spanish is £5.95 a carafe.

CHEF: Ishad Ali   PROPRIETOR: Gopal Manandhar   OPEN: all week; 12 to 2.45, 6 to 11.45
CLOSED: 25 and 26 Dec   MEALS: alc. Set L £5.50, Set D £9.95. Minimum £5.   SERVICE:
10%   CARDS: Access, Amex, Diners, Visa   DETAILS: 48 seats. Private parties: 34 main room. Vegetarian meals. Children's helpings. Music

Green Cottage £

NEW ENTRY   map 11

9 New College Parade,
Finchley Road, NW3 5EP
071-722 5305 and 7892

COOKING 1
COST £16-£47

Some of the best-value ethnic food in the area is to be had in this well-established Chinese restaurant (opposite Fairfax Road) marked by a large green canopy. At the front of the dark dining-room a chef cleaves meats for the roast dishes – a common sight in Soho, but almost unknown in Swiss Cottage. The menu is Cantonese. The kitchen works best in the old style: roast pork and duck have been succulent and tender; steamed belly of pork with preserved cabbage has been 'brilliant', full of flavour and rustic, with authentically fatty meat. Stuffed crab claws, and steamed scallops with soy and ginger, have been less enthusiastically received. Vegetarian dishes are worth exploring: 'Buddha's cushion' is a pile of stewed black moss with mushrooms on a bed of white Chinese leaves; Zhai duckling should be layers of deep-fried soya bean sheet, but batter was included on one occasion. These sound intriguing, but a knowledgeable reporter warns that 'those used to the brilliant standards of Buddhist food will be disappointed'. The limited choice of sweets reflects the restaurant's intentions: it is not a place for lingering. Even so, chilled sago with fresh melon has been a refreshing finale. Drink tea, Tsing-Tao or Tiger beer. House French is £6.50.

CHEF: T.S. Lok   PROPRIETOR: S.M. Li   OPEN: all day; noon to 11.30   MEALS: alc. Set L and D (minimum 2) £11.50 to £15   SERVICE: 10%   CARDS: Access, Amex, Visa   DETAILS: 80 seats. Private parties: 40 main room, 30 private room. Vegetarian meals. Children welcome. Wheelchair access. No music. Air-conditioned

Greenhouse

map 13

27A Hay's Mews, W1X 7RJ
071-499 3331

COOKING 3
COST £25–£58

Gary Rhodes must be rather bored. Although his menus are daily dated, they do not *really* change at all from month to month – a bit, of course, but not radically. And the customers are such dyed-in-the-wool besuited supporters of everything conservative in Great Britain that they would die themselves if faggots came off the menu. Even the wine list of 20-odd bottles (not a lot for a place of this calibre) is pretty much the same from one year to the next. Regulars must cheer the arrival of a new vintage, as the management cannot steel itself to change the label. This all sounds as if the Greenhouse, after a spectacularly successful re-opening last year, is really a formula affair – a good formula, but there it is. When you eat a piece of haddock topped by Welsh rarebit, on a bed of plum tomatoes, you wish that you had had the chive vinaigrette that some other diners have had, that the haddock was warmed through and that the tomatoes had been tasted before purchase. When you taste the burning raw garlic in the garlic mayonnaise (not pounded in a mortar but chopped in a machine), you wonder what the chef had for breakfast. Machines seemed to be in evidence when it came to the mash, too. It would help if the crumble on top of the bananas were cooked, and if the crèmes brûlées were not held in storage for so long that the tops had softened. Formulas need constant maintenance. A resident of France, who wished to revisit his British roots, complained that the faggots were bland, 'not like Mynan's of Tooting 40 years ago', but then butchers will tell you that they have been decreasing the amount of seasoning in their sausages since the Second World War. The restaurant does many things really well; it is not merely a solid British repertoire, and there are crostini, scallops with vegetables, sea bass with ratatouille, and confit of duck to prove otherwise. But you should try the oxtail, the salmon fish-cakes, the calf's liver and the mushy peas, as well as the steamed puddings, the hot apple fritters, or the rice pudding. Plenty of people do, approve and come back for more. The service, occasionally nannying, often comforting and pleasantly adult, is another reason for returning. The wine list is not – it is acceptable, no more. House wines are from £9.50.

CHEF: Gary Rhodes   PROPRIETOR: David Levin   OPEN: all week, exc Sat L and Sun D; 12 to 2.30, 7 to 11   MEALS: alc. Set Sun L £17.50. Cover £1   SERVICE: not inc   CARDS: Access, Amex, Amex   DETAILS: 100 seats. Private parties: 120 main room. Vegetarian meals. Children's helpings. Smart dress preferred. Wheelchair access (3 steps). No music. Air-conditioned. Fax: 071-225 0022

Green's   **NEW ENTRY**   map 11

Marsham Court,
Marsham Street, SW1P 4LA   COOKING 1
071-834 9552   COST £27–£57

Green's nestles under a large 1930s-style block of flats. A clubby restaurant, within the division bell, full of mahogany panelling, old prints and leather banquettes, it is 'basically a chaps' place'. The food, as old-school-tie as the clientele, is solidly English, served in comforting large portions with lots of vegetables and nursery puddings – to wit, the ideal place to recommend to tourists if they want to see how the country is run. All, led by the quality of the ingredients, is reassuringly familiar and well-prepared: oysters, smoked salmon, dressed crab (which can also be had at the oyster bar, which you encounter on first entering), fish-cakes, grilled Dover sole, an exemplary mixed grill of calf's liver, lamb cutlet, steak, kidneys, mushrooms, tomato and sausage, Arbroath smokies, fresh kippers with poached egg on toast. Forays into more adventurous cooking – sea bass with a sweet onion sauce – have also been enjoyed. Jam pudding with custard or a good old-fashioned gooseberry fool are examples of desserts. The short, mainly French, wine list has some half-dozen pricey half-bottles, and a few wines by the glass. House wine is £10.

CHEF: Beth Coventry   PROPRIETOR: Simon Parker Bowles   OPEN: Mon to Fri; 12.30 to 2.45, 6 to 11   CLOSED: bank hols   MEALS: alc. Cover £1   SERVICE: not inc   CARDS: Access, Amex, Diners, Visa   DETAILS: 80 seats. Private parties: 80 main room, 30 private room. Vegetarian meals. Children's helpings. Wheelchair access (3 steps). No music. Air-conditioned. Fax: 071-233 6047

Gurkha Brasserie £   map 10

756 Finchley Road,
Temple Fortune, NW11 7TH   COOKING 1
081-458 6163   COST £9–£23

North Indian and Nepalese specialities share the bill in this cheerful restaurant bedecked with Gurkha artefacts. The Nepalese dishes get most votes for their distinctive, 'noticeably different' flavours, and the Nepalese thali is a helpful introduction to the cuisine. Momo (steamed meat dumplings) and chow-chow (noodles with meat, prawns and vegetables) have been particularly good. Other intriguing dishes include aloo ko achar (a cold dish of spiced potatoes with fresh coriander) and golbhenda ko achar (grilled pickled tomatoes). Readers have also liked the chicken tikka and lamb biriani. Portions are daunting: 'We had trouble finishing the large thali,' comments one visitor, 'but asked for a bag to take home the rest, which was provided as a matter of course with great friendliness.' Drink lassi or lager. House wine is £5.65.

CHEF/PROPRIETOR: Hari Kc   OPEN: all week; 12 to 2, 6 to 12 (12.30am Fri and Sat)
MEALS: alc. Set L £5 to £10, Set D £7 to £12   SERVICE: 10%, card slips closed   CARDS: Access, Amex, Visa   DETAILS: 32 seats. Private parties: 35 main room. Vegetarian meals. Children's helpings. Music

▲ The Halkin

NEW ENTRY   map 12

Halkin Street, SW1X 7DJ
071-333 1234

COOKING 3
COST £32–£68

Most new hotels that open in London are kitted out with some form of British heritage, especially when they are sited in central Belgravia. The surprise is all the greater, therefore, when the doors slide open for you and you find the Halkin is as modern as can be – north Italian style. It is not large; the bedrooms are luxurious but would worry many people with their great sweeps of expensive hardwoods with not a pediment in sight, and the dining-room is equally handsome. It is also quiet, save for the nightly performance from a harpist. When the hotel opened, Paul Gayler was chef. No sooner was he installed than he was poached by the Lanesborough and the Halkin was left to find a new formula. In came Gualtiero Marchesi, Milan's answer to nouvelle cuisine and darling of the Michelin set. This move certainly has produced a different line to the re-creations of Tuscan farmhouse kitchens that have sprung up over London in the last few years. This restaurant is refined, sophisticated, expensive (but not so dear at lunch), sometimes good, and sometimes not very good at all. Dishes to eat are the risotto with saffron, glowing from large black plates that cool it in under five seconds; some of the pasta with cream sauces, such as the macaroni with foie gras sauce and white truffle, or the gomiti with langoustine and curry sauce; and a simple meat dish such as calf's liver with onion fondant, or roasted calf's kidney. Everything should be perfect, but unfortunately it is not. A tempura of langoustines with sweet-and-sour sauce showed slavish admiration for the Orient, used wonderful langoustines, but ran a sauce that would not impress. It was served with a half-moon dish of standard chef's vegetables, inappropriate in the extreme. Other main courses have not had the interest of starter dishes – perhaps delicacy works with the latter but not the former: an 'ethnic' production such as veal milanese proved to be too heavy and fatty for success. The rosewater sorbet on a lake of almond milk is a dessert to try. In sum, there are enjoyable appetisers such as a roulade of rabbit with the clearest of stock sauces, rather boring bread, good coffee, and impeccable service. But the Halkin is one of the most pleasant places to sit for a meal. Italian wines predominate on the list and very good they are. But with Favorita del Piemonte by Deltetto, an enjoyable enough lightweight, at £18.50 a bottle many customers would be stuck for choice and rightly feel aggrieved. Half-bottles are thin on the ground, but otherwise this is a wonderful list. House wine is £16.

CHEF: Gualtiero Marchesi   PROPRIETORS: Beng Seng and Christina Ong   OPEN: Mon to Sat, exc Sat D; 12.30 to 2.30, 7.30 to 10.30   MEALS: alc. Set L £18 to £24, Set D £24.50 to £28.50   SERVICE: net prices, card slips closed   CARDS: Access, Amex, Diners, Visa DETAILS: 50 seats. Private parties: 10 main room, 30 private room. Car park. Vegetarian meals. Children welcome. Smart dress preferred. No cigars/pipes in dining-room. Wheelchair access (also WC). Music. Air-conditioned   ACCOMMODATION: 41 rooms, all with bath/shower. Rooms for disabled. Lift. B&B £220 to £282. Children welcome. Baby facilities. Afternoon teas. Air-conditioned. TV. Phone. Fax: 071-333 1100 (*The Which? Hotel Guide*)

Harveys   map 10

2 Bellevue Road, SW17 7EG   COOKING 4*
081-672 0114 and 0115   COST £39–£80

Hard by Wandsworth Common, in Tooting no less, is one of Britain's better restaurants. The room is simple, even if the veneer of cream and white plaster lends it a certain opulence. The customers can sometimes be described as cheerful, young, local and noisy; at other times, the perception changes to brash and loud. Noise is a problem because the tables are closely set, and bookings follow hard behind each other of an evening. The brashness may come because you may need to allow about £140 for two people, made up of the £48 for three courses, £4 each for coffee (no refills necessarily offered), a tip, and something for the wine. This total was reached with half a bottle of a poor year of Châteauneuf-du-Pape and one fresh orange juice. The service is disjointed – few have a good word to say for it. At these prices it would help if it were better. The wine waiter, asked about the half-bottles of Rhône on the list, admitted that none was available. His suggested substitute, when delivered, turned out to be a different property to that described. But three months before, another party had found the first three halves chosen were unavailable. The wine waiter proposed a fourth, but returned to admit that this was out of stock too. Practicalities matter; genius is not all. The cooking often pleases, even if the lack of balance does not. A stuffed pig's trotter of giant proportions, filled with truffles, chicken mousseline and sweetbreads, with a morel-perfumed sauce, needed more than a smear of rich potato purée – very fine this – to help it down, especially when the first course was a brandade with langoustines, tapénade, caviare and gazpacho sauce where the creaminess (not much garlic) of the brandade was barely offset by the creaminess of the gazpacho (also not much punch) and merely enriched by the langoustines, topped with a minuscule tapénade. The caviare was good, as was the toasted leaven bread. Richness had kicked the meal off with an appetiser of foie gras and chicken liver parfait. Lack of balance, for many English diners at least, is found in the fine new addition to the repertoire of sea bass generously spread with caviare – pure protein that would be helped by alleviation. Mixtures that do not exclude all padding are evidently well thought out – witness the oyster dish with noodles, or oysters again but this time with girolles and noodles. Witness too the daube of beef, the meat so tender it could be cut with a spoon, the sauce deep yet not as vinous or rich as it might be, the vegetables and micro mushrooms adding breadth to the composition, and the buttery parsleyed noodles in a knot adding bulk. Some of the cookery is light: that of fish, for instance, speaks of an effort to reduce the weight of sauces so as to allow the fish its full value. Desserts read less unusually than the savoury courses. They seem to be a repertoire of old favourites, but the execution is faultless, and this stage in the meal is often termed the best. Lemon tart 'about as runny as possible without failing to set and with a strong flavour of pleasantly bitter peel' comes with a lemon soufflé, also nicely sharp, in a lemon shell. Mille-feuille of raspberries is a crisp and light pie. 'Breaking the golden cover brought forth a puff of steam containing a wonderful fragrance of butter and fruit. It was surrounded by the foamiest kirsch sabayon.' Hot chocolate soufflé with chocolate sauce is another sweet to die for. Petits fours show the same skill at work. The wine list is heavy with antiques – wide-ranging in France, thin elsewhere, with prices to match the food. Lunch is cheaper, but still more expensive than most of the competition. House wines are from £15.

CHEF/PROPRIETOR: Marco Pierre White   OPEN: Tue to Sun, exc Sun D; 12.30 to 2, 7.30 to 11.15   MEALS: Set L £24, Set D £48   SERVICE: not inc   CARDS: Access, Visa   DETAILS: 45 seats. No children under 16. No pipes in dining-room. Air-conditioned

Harveys Café £   NEW ENTRY   map 11

358 Fulham Road, SW10 9UU   COOKING 1
071-352 0625   COST £15–£24

Harveys Café has the air of an adult schoolroom: chipboard tables, painted wooden chairs, white walls, and lots of pictures (for sale) to take advantage of the light flooding through the windows of the first floor above the Black Bull pub. The view is pleasing, but the immediate prospect when Chelsea Football Club is playing at home may be less so. Harvey Sambrook has opened one of 1992's breed of café/restaurants: low prices, intelligent food, an informal ambience, but operated with commitment even when relaxation rules – *décontracté* the French might call it. The cooking may be up and down – haphazard seasoning, varying performance of things like pizza – but it is honest of intent. You pay for bread (and olives) which you can nibble while ordering a fish soup (that needed its rouille to pep it up), or Tuscan bean soup (that needed a stronger stock base), before marinated lamb fillet with harissa and cracked wheat – a sort of Italian couscous, and lo! the cook that day came from Sardinia. Another main course sampled during that meal was vegetable risotto, which held its own; this before orange and lime rice pudding served cold with some prunes soaked in armagnac. Coffee would benefit from an espresso machine. The short wine list will not break the bank; it has less allure than some of the very adventurous West End short lists, but no one will cavil at a Zind-Humbrecht Gewurztraminer or Ch. Court-les-Muts from Bergerac, even if details are somewhat sparse. House wines are £7.95 for Côtes de Duras.

CHEFS: Harvey and Polly Sambrook, and Tracey Cooper   PROPRIETOR: Harvey Sambrook   OPEN: Tue to Sun, exc Sun D; 12.30 to 3, 7.30 to 11   CLOSED: Christmas and New Year, Aug   MEALS: alc. Minimum £10.50 for 6 or more   SERVICE: 12%   DETAILS: 65 seats. Private parties: 35 main room. Vegetarian meals. Children welcome. Music

'''Our chef can't be expected to put your dessert in the oven now. He's busy with the main courses.'''   On eating in Sussex

Hilaire ▼

map 12

68 Old Brompton Road, SW7 3LR
071-584 8993

COOKING 3
COST £30–£60

The pair of bow windows on the street and the columns at the back of the
dining-room give the impression of a Georgian shop. There is also a basement,
but ground level is best unless for a private party. Bryan Webb works in the
abbreviated modern mode: lots of high flavours, interesting conjunctions, and a
varied attack on the menu – from the classic gravlax, steak au poivre or rack of
lamb with a herb crust to the unexpected angle such as oysters with laverbread
and Stilton (good, that), crispy crab pancake with a Thai dip (shades of the
Walnut Tree Inn, see entry, Llandewi Skirrid, Wales), scallops with lentils and
coriander (shades of Shaun Hill at Gidleigh Park, see entry, Chagford), or veal
with polenta, onion confit and mushrooms, or turbot with mustard sauce,
broad beans and pancetta. That Thai sauce appeared again in a dish of deep-
fried brains and baby corn. Things may not always hang together, or the
flavours we looked forward to from the menu may not arrive on the plate:
hence a spinach and ricotta pancake seemed gutless, and a dish of guinea-fowl
was not enhanced by a very greasy smoked sausage and flavourless sauce; but
the general opinion is that the cooking is sound. There are a number of menu
options, while the *carte* remains fully West End in price. Our criticisms in the
last edition have seen the wine list put into more customer-friendly shape; also,
the addition of a few wines under £12 puts all else into perspective. If a
quality-against-value equation exists, then Hilaire now looks more right than
wrong, especially for Old Brompton Road. It is a commendably interesting and
catholic list. Dessert wines repay study, and halves generally are well-chosen
and abundant. House wines start at £11.50. CELLARMAN'S CHOICE: Mâcon-
Peronne 'Dom. des Légères' 1988, £16.50; Givry, Cuvée Traditionelle 1988,
Mouton, £18.85.

CHEFS: Bryan Webb and Denise Dunn   PROPRIETOR: Bryan Webb   OPEN: Mon to Sat, exc
Sat L; 12.30 to 2.30, 7 to 11.30   MEALS: alc. Set L £20, Set D £26.50   SERVICE: not inc
CARDS: Access, Amex, Diners, Visa   DETAILS: 35 seats. Private parties: 8 main room, 25
private room. Vegetarian meals. Children's helpings. No music. Air-conditioned

L'Hippocampe

map 14

63 Frith Street, W1V 5TA
071-734 4545

COOKING 3
COST £26–£46

This is a fish-only restaurant. It has stuck to its guns and now, with new chef
Marc Williamson fresh from Australian experience, is producing some
entertaining fishy cookery. He has the sense to make tastes vivid and
sometimes novel in order to dress up the base material for customers who
might otherwise hanker for steak – perverse, but true. Mussels come with
chilli, smoked salmon has pungent guacamole and salsa, and grilled scallops
and sardines come with a mixture of hot salami and artichoke and a herb
beurre blanc. Sea bass may be studded with three peppers, and John Dory
home-salted and marinated in lime, then grilled and served with spinach and
red pepper sauce. The tastes do work; plainer stuff is there for the asking, and
although sometimes execution may go awry, it is stimulating. Oysters, usually

creuses from Cancale, are among the cheapest in town. There is a cheaper lunch and pre-theatre menu, but the *carte* reflects the price of fish with a vengeance. The weak spots are puddings and disconcerting service. The wine list is short and fashionable, with makers such as Goyard, Leflaive, Delegat's, Au Bon Climat, and de Villaine. Whites, of course, outnumber reds. House wine is from £8.75.

CHEF: Marc Williamson   PROPRIETORS: Pierre and Kathleen Condou   OPEN: Mon to Sat, exc Sat L; 12.15 to 2.30, 6.15 to 11.15   CLOSED: 25 Dec to New Year, bank hols   MEALS: alc. Set L and D until 8pm £18.50   SERVICE: not inc   CARDS: Access, Amex, Diners, Visa DETAILS: 40 seats. Children's helpings. No cigars/pipes in dining-room. Wheelchair access. Music. Air-conditioned. Fax: 071-287 1027

Ikkyu £
map 13

67 Tottenham Court Road, W1P 9PA   COOKING 1
071-436 6169 and 9280   COST £10–£39

As the number of cheaper Japanese restaurants grows, the unique selling point of Ikkyu diminishes. But don't ignore it. The basement premises are lively, the staff are heterogeneous and young, the menu is long and infinitely adaptable – without the need to take one or other set meal that often seems the only way to deal with eating Japanese food – and, best of all, the place is cheap. It can be hectic, with all the problems that stem from that, but it is worth trying the tofu with oyster mushrooms, the cuttlefish – grilled or salted – the sushi, and the skewers of grilled chicken and offal such as heart and tongue. Other recommendations have included fried pork with leeks, salad of four seaweeds with contrasting colours and textures, and sometimes the soups. This place is more robust, perhaps even more real if you seek Japan, than fancier spots. Tea (stewed, someone acidly remarked) is free, otherwise there is Kirin beer. House wine is £7.50.

CHEF: Y. Sato   PROPRIETOR: M. Kawaguchi   OPEN: Mon to Fri; 12.30 to 2.30, 6 to 10.30 MEALS: alc. Set L and D £4.60 to £9.30   SERVICE: 10%   CARDS: Access, Amex, Diners, Visa   DETAILS: 65 seats. Private parties: 30 main room, 12 private room. Vegetarian meals. Children welcome. Music. Air-conditioned

Inaho £
NEW ENTRY   map 11

4 Hereford Road, W2 4AA   COOKING 2
071-221 8495   COST £12–£35

'A jewel of a neighbourhood restaurant,' enthuses a reporter. 'The most pleasant little restaurant I have been to for years. So good, yet totally unpretentious,' seconds an inspector. The setting is a tiny wooden-fronted shop off Westbourne Grove, but inside it is a near-perfect example of Japanese home-style décor and atmosphere. The modest dining-room seats only 20, at polished wooden tables decorated with baskets of dried flowers. The menu is short and conventional – taking in yakitori, sashimi, tempura and teriyaki. There is also a list of seasonal specialities – all 'small dishes' – advertised on boards. Wednesday to Saturday are sushi nights. Highlights from one seasonal menu included edamame (salted steamed soya beans in the pod), hiyayako (iced silky tofu in soya sauce with ginger), and cubes of fresh tuna stewed in soya sauce. Sashimi has been outstandingly good, generous and chilled to the right temperature; tempura have been 'light and clean in flavour'. Rice, noodles and pickles are exceptional. Portions are quite large by Japanese standards. The cooking tends towards delicacy and a few dishes could be more highly seasoned, but the verdict is that the kitchen succeeds 'triumphantly'. The wine list is non-existent, although there is saké at £5.50, and Japanese green tea comes free.

CHEF: S. Ohtsuka   PROPRIETOR: H. Nakamura   OPEN: Mon to Sat, exc Sat L; 12.30 to 2.30, 7 to 11   MEALS: alc. Set L £7 to £9, Set D £18 to £20   SERVICE: 10%   CARDS: Access, Visa   DETAILS: 20 seats. Private parties: 22 main room. Vegetarian meals. Children welcome. Music

L'Incontro ♥

map 12

87 Pimlico Road, SW1W 8PH
071-730 6327

COOKING 2
COST £23–£62

This place is punishingly smart – grey on grey, plus mirrors and splats of colour from upholstery – and killingly expensive. People love it, and flock to be seen in it. They may also flock to eat. Some concession to loss of income at Lloyds may have been made by a lunchtime menu at lower prices than Pimlico expects. The cooking is all-Italian – the frittata is said to be made of farm eggs from the homeland – with a tilt towards the north-east and Venice. The pasta can be good, so can the risottos. Much else can be patchy. L'Incontro is better than its sister restaurant, Santini. On the wines front, Italians precede the few French bottles on the list. That apart, it is difficult to discern structure or logic from an unhelpful arrangement. Quality and age, such as a 1961 Barolo of Conterno, are in abundance and prices are high, but with so many restaurants now won over to Italy there is less reason for making the pilgrimage just for the wines. House wine is £12.50. CELLARMAN'S CHOICE: Pinot Grigio, Santa Margherita 1990, £16.50; Venegazzù della Casa 1988, £19.50.

CHEFS: D. Minuzzo and I. Santin   PROPRIETOR: G. Santin   OPEN: all week; 12.30 to 2.30 (1 to 3.30 Sun), 7 to 11.30 (10.30 Sun)   MEALS: alc. Cover £1.50   SERVICE: 12%   CARDS: Access, Amex, Diners, Visa   DETAILS: 65 seats. Private parties: 30 private room. Vegetarian meals. Children's helpings. Wheelchair access. Music. Air-conditioned. Fax: 071-730 5062

▲ Inn on the Park, Four Seasons

map 13

Hamilton Place,
Park Lane, W1A 1AZ
071-499 0888

COOKING 4*
COST £31–£79

Once the hotel recovers from jibes like 'Inn on the Car Park', the view is nearly, but not quite, as pastoral as the floreate pinks and blue-greens of the columned dining-room itself. 'It swarms with good-humoured staff' was an encouraging report, often confirmed. Asked if it was good value, a reader swiftly replied, 'Yes, compared with similar meals elsewhere, it seemed almost cheap.' Bruno Loubet is riding a high. At present, he seems to be cooking bolder food, with less apparent complication, than any of his colleagues also working in hotel kitchens in London. For the money, therefore, you get character as well as plush. Start with an appetiser that may be mussels in a saffron soup with a little turnip and carrot, or melon consommé. Then move perhaps to scallops with a rösti potato for texture and bottom, and onion marmalade for 'spicy attack that made the flavours catch fire'. Alternatively, three blinis topped with shellfish (cockles and queenies) and caviare with a sea urchin sauce will be at once more sophisticated, yet evincing mastery of flavour balance. Main courses will have vegetables built in – a little purée of something, torpedoes of something else. This may be insufficient for British appetites – certainly starch is not inevitable, and bread gets approval but not wild applause. Fish is brilliant: lobster with bay leaves and vegetables, sea bass with seaweed and salt crust and an artichoke purée, red mullet on rice with red pepper and 'a block of olive paste'. 'This was full of peasant feel, bold flavours, deceptively simple, generous in presentation; it was a brave and splendid course for a restaurant of this quality.' Meat, too, benefits from broad panache: hare arranged round an endive tart on a reduced game stock given sweet-and-sour edge; succulent duck with its fattiness on a bed of wild mushrooms, plus celeriac and spinach and a fairly neutral light gravy. (If the menu sometimes has a fault, it is the over-emphasis on mushrooms and fungi.) Beef last year was treated with capers and bacon dumplings; lamb this year has had couscous accompanying poached fillet and spiced pumpkin. Invention remains for the desserts. A kumquat mousse is not too sweet, even if the fruit itself seems to overpower the confection that should be the centrepiece; soft chocolate cake with a fig mousse shows a novel approach; orange and cardamom parfait and chocolate sauce hints at this chef's eagerness to work with spices at this stage as well as earlier in the meal. Coffee is good, and the petits fours are as excellent as the cheeseboard. Wait for stage three of the post-prandial goodies – it will be the sorbet bombs enrobed in chocolate. With an adequate St-Nicolas-de-Bourgeuil offered at the 'very special' price of £17, be warned that there are few economies on the wine list. The range and quality are undoubtedly good; although Italy receives barely a nod, Spain is well represented. There are many magnificent classics, but with curtailment of the page of wines offered by the glass, endorsement must remain muted. House wines are from £12.75.

CHEF: Bruno Loubet   PROPRIETORS: Four Seasons, Inn on the Park   OPEN: all week; 12.30 to 3, 7 to 11   MEALS: alc. Set Mon to Sat L £25, Set Sun L £28, Set D £40   SERVICE: net prices, card slips closed   CARDS: Access, Amex, Diners, Visa   DETAILS: 62 seats. Private parties: 10 main room. Car park. No children under 5. Jacket and tie. No pipes in dining-room. Wheelchair access (also WC). Music. Air-conditioned   ACCOMMODATION: 228 rooms, all with bath/shower. Rooms for disabled. Lift. B&B £211 to £275. Children welcome. Baby facilities. Pets welcome. Afternoon teas. Air-conditioned. TV. Phone. Fax: 071-493 1895

Net prices *in the details at the end of an entry indicates that the prices given on a menu and on a bill are inclusive of VAT and service charge, and that this practice is clearly stated on menu and bill.*

Card slips closed *in the details at the end of an entry indicates that the total on the slips of credit cards is closed when handed over for signature.*

▲ Inter-Continental Hotel, Le Soufflé

map 12

1 Hamilton Place, W1V 0QY
071-409 3131

COOKING 4
COST £29–£74

It is difficult to recommend the Inter-Continental as a place of beauty. It has many of the attributes of a modern luxury hotel, in a modern block. The cool dining-room, albeit windowless, is one of the better spaces, with a lightness about it enhanced by the super-keenness of the staff. What needs to be recommended, however, is the cooking. Peter Kromberg is a fine cook. He works on the hazardous dividing line between delicacy and boldness, between richness and vapidity, and he often gets it right. His is a more individual voice than many allow. The food is not cheap here, nor is the wine, although there is some concession at lunch-time. The menu is a long one, involving a whole section of *cuisine de vie*, which might be defined as dishes light in fats, and is not afraid to tackle the mega-luxuries (caviare and foie gras) head-on. It may be rewarding to ignore them, though – Peter Kromberg has more to offer. A set 'Choix du Chef' menu shows off his talents well. A first course of timbale of lobster set in aspic with vegetables and wrapped with smoked salmon shared the plate with a fine moneybag of filo pastry encasing a well-seasoned oyster and a heap of saladings. Seasoning was very exact, balancing the flavours of the main ingredients, with an eye also to keeping textural variety. Next was a piece of halibut seared on the grill, given some richness by spices – not just salt. The sauce was a saffron vinaigrette, and the fish was partnered by artichoke and tomato. Again, balance and harmony were there with clarity of flavours. A pause, then, for orange sorbet with Campari before a choice of main courses, the first of which was a breast of chicken with potato scales and chanterelles and tomatoes. The sauce was a light reduction of chicken stock flavoured with tarragon. The alternative was venison with a rich game-stock sauce. The plate was filled by apple, thin slices of sprout, new carrots and a spätzli layered with creamed potato 'of almost unbelievable lightness'. This was described as 'consummately rich without being indigestible, the meat brilliantly timed to retain a blush at the centre, ensuring maximum flavour without sacrificing moistness'. On to cheese, not brilliant, and an intermediate course of hot sabayon flavoured with green and pink peppercorns, before a dessert of cherries in kirsch with amaretto ice-cream. The meal may have been dear, but the extras piled on, yet avoiding overload, made it surprising value. Petits fours are first-rate, coffee is not invariably so. The wine list is long, the prices are high, and the choice is not adventurous – clarets are perhaps the best-selected. House wines are £14.

CHEF: Peter Kromberg   PROPRIETORS: Inter-Continental Hotels Group   OPEN: all week, exc Sat L; 12 to 3.30, 7 to 11   MEALS: alc. Set L inc wine £25.50, Set Sun L £26, Set D £43   SERVICE: not inc, card slips closed   CARDS: Access, Amex, Diners, Visa   DETAILS: 80 seats. Private parties: 10 main room. Car park. Vegetarian meals. Children welcome. Jacket and tie. Wheelchair access (also WC). Music. Air-conditioned   ACCOMMODATION: 467 rooms, all with bath/shower. Rooms for disabled. Lift. B&B £223 to £317. Children welcome. Baby facilities. Small dogs welcome. Afternoon teas. Swimming-pool. Sauna. Air-conditioned. TV. Phone. Fax: 071-409 7460

Isohama

map 11

312 Vauxhall Bridge Road, SW1V 1AA
071-834 2145

COOKING 1
COST £23–£47

This simple room divided by black screens, with vivid purple upholstery, is conveniently close to Victoria station. It is busy at lunch for the shorter menu; go at night to range through a bigger choice of soundly prepared Japanese food. High points remain jellyfish in vinegar with cucumber strips and spinach, salmon roe and vinegar rice, and excellent sushi. Saké is £4.50 for a large pot.

CHEF: Yukio Saito PROPRIETORS: Senko (UK) Ltd OPEN: Mon to Sat, exc Sat L; 12 to 2.30, 6 to 10.30 MEALS: alc. Set D £25 to £30 SERVICE: 10%, card slips closed CARDS: Access, Amex, Diners, Visa DETAILS: 35 seats. Vegetarian meals. Children's helpings. Wheelchair access (1 step). No music. Air-conditioned

Ivy

map 14

1 West Street, WC2H 9NE
071-836 4751

COOKING 2*
COST £23–£50

'Glad to see the Ivy doing well again,' writes a reporter who was first taken to the place by his father in the 1940s. Much has changed since then: in its new incarnation the establishment has a vibrant atmosphere – 'heaving and throbbing', according to one report. It is a venue where stars of stage and screen come out to play, and it capitalises on the fact by opening early for pre-theatre meals. Links with Le Caprice (see entry, London) show in the distinctive style of the menu, which is equally at home with fashionable, old-fashioned dishes such as ham hock and lentils, Lancashire hotpot and bubble and squeak, as well as trendy Mediterranean and oriental flourishes – grilled sardines on black olive toast; rocket with shaved Parmesan salad; warm scallop and shiitake mushrooms; and duck breast with Chinese pears. Reporters regularly mention grilled red peppers with aubergine and anchovy paste, roast pheasant with polenta, and sticky toffee pudding. The regime copes with the crowds, and staff are professional and polite, although there is a tendency to keep the operation moving at pace. Prices are generally fair. Occasionally the set-up misfires: 'What a disappointment after all the hype. The service was as cold as the food' was one complaint. Here and there dishes are not quite up to the mark, but this place is good news for theatreland. It is also one of the few West End venues open on Sundays (free valet parking): the brunch menu is recommended. The wine list is racy and up to the minute. House wine is £7.

CHEF: Nigel Davis PROPRIETORS: Jeremy King and Christopher Corbin OPEN: all week; 12 to 3, 5.30 to 12 MEALS: alc. Cover £1.50 SERVICE: not inc CARDS: Access, Amex, Diners, Visa DETAILS: 110 seats. Private parties: 8 main room, 20 and 80 private rooms. Vegetarian meals. No children under 5. Wheelchair access. Air-conditioned. Fax: 071-493 9040 and 497 3644

Restaurateurs justifiably resent no-shows. If you quote a credit card number when booking, you may be liable for the restaurant's lost profit margin if you don't turn up. Always phone to cancel.

Jade Garden £

map 14

15 Wardour Street, W1V 3HA
071-437 5065 and 439 7851

COOKING 1*
COST £16–£46

A stalwart survivor among flashy Soho neighbours, even if its consistency does seem sometimes to lapse. At lunch-time it draws the local Chinese community, and diverse and carefully prepared dim-sum attract the capacity crowd to downstairs and balcony seating. No trolleys here: items such as steamed beef and ginger dumplings, pork-filled pancake rolls, paper-wrapped king prawns and stuffed bean curd rolls are delivered direct from the busy kitchen. The main menu features Canton and Peking, and may include lobster. 'Really fresh flavours are the key,' judges an inspector who observed 'friendly waitresses in green waistcoats and white lacy-collared blouses keeping everything under control'. A pot of tea arrives automatically, along with a small dish of chilli sauce and chilli oil. House French wine is £7.50.

CHEF: Raymond Bignold PROPRIETORS: L.S. Man, P.W. Man and F.T. Man OPEN: all week; noon (11.30am Sat and Sun) to 11.30 (10.30 Sun) CLOSED: 25 Dec MEALS: alc. Set L and D £9.50 to £17 (minimum 2). Minimum £6 after 5pm SERVICE: not inc CARDS: Access, Amex, Visa DETAILS: 160 seats. Private parties: 70 main room. Vegetarian meals. Children's helpings. No music. Air-conditioned. Fax: 071-494 1336

Jin £

map 14

16 Bateman Street, W1V 5TB
071-734 0908

COOKING 1*
COST £14–£31

Tony Wee's Soho restaurant provides an elegant setting for authentic Korean food. The décor is defined by strong modern colours. Tables are black and each incorporates a grill in the centre and panelling at the sides: 'It is rather like sitting in a large cube,' commented one visitor. The grill is used for barbecued specialities such as bul kal bee, bulgogi and dahk gui (chicken in chilli and saké sauce), which are marinated and cooked at the table. Spicy soups such as 'lip-numbing' yuk ke jang make potent starters; other well-reported dishes have included seng sohn chun (pan-fried fish in egg batter) and yache pokum (vegetables with beef, shrimps and fish-cake cooked in sesame oil). Service is quick and helpful. 'Most dishes are quite filling,' notes one reporter, although another thought that prices were high in relation to the size of portions. Drink saké or Korean barley tea. House wine is £7.50.

CHEF: Mr Ro PROPRIETOR: Tony Wee OPEN: all week, exc Sun L; 12 to 3, 6 to 11 CLOSED: 25 and 26 Dec, 1 Jan MEALS: alc. Set L £7.90, Set D £15.50 to £19.50 SERVICE: 12.5%, card slips closed CARDS: Access, Amex, Diners, Visa DETAILS: 70 seats. Private parties: 50 main room. Vegetarian meals. Children welcome. No-smoking area. Wheelchair access (1 step). Music. Air-conditioned

£ *indicates that it is possible to have a three-course meal, including coffee, a half-bottle of house wine and service, at any time the restaurant is open (i.e. at dinner as well as at lunch, unless a place is open only for dinner), for £20 or less per person.*

Joe's Café

map 12

126 Draycott Avenue, SW3 3AH
071-225 2217 and 2218

COOKING 1
COST £27–£45

The self-conscious style and design of this 'Sloane bolt-hole' is a talking-point: it has been described as 'moderately executed techno-chic with witty references to 1930s ocean liners'. A green stacked-glass pillar takes centre stage in the raised eating area. Monochrome photos line the walls and tiny fairy-spots glitter in the ceiling. This is not a café in the strictest sense, although most people choose one or two courses from the flexible brasserie menu. The repertoire is a familiar jazzy cosmopolitan mix, with lots of salads, exotic dressings and fish: green lentils with warm croustade of preserved duck, grilled prawn salad with coriander dressing, wild mushroom ravioli, and seafood brochette with lime dressing are all typical. Reporters have been particularly impressed by artichoke, asparagus, French bean and foie gras salad, and veal escalope viennoise with a rich sauce that had a distinct nutty aftertaste. Sweets have been less successful: chocolate mousse was too warm and milky and lacked flavour. Value for money is questionable: particularly as one diner found her credit card slip left open when cover and 15 per cent service had already been levied. House French is £10.80

CHEF: Jerome Laugénie   PROPRIETORS: Joseph Ltd   OPEN: all week, exc Sun D; 12 (11 Sun) to 3,30, 7.30 to 11.30   CLOSED: 25 Dec and 1 Jan   MEALS: alc. Cover £1   SERVICE: 15%   CARDS: Access, Amex, Diners, Visa   DETAILS: 95 seats. 2 tables outside. Private parties: 25 main room. Vegetarian meals. Children's helpings. Wheelchair access. Music. Air-conditioned

Kagura

map 14

13–15 West Street,
Cambridge Circus, WC2H 9BL
071-240 0634

COOKING 1
COST £22–£67

Kagura has relocated in the old premises of another restaurant, Azami, in a house where there is also a Japanese nightclub and karaoke club. In general it is not making a pitch for European custom, but is happy to tell you (comprehensibly) about the contents of the Japanese-only menu that supplements the series of set meals. Some of the sashimi and sushi have been made from the very finest materials, even if the wasabi with the sushi was lacking bulk or punch. A certain blandness was also found in the pickled vegetables, just as the grilled duck under a dullish brown sauce could be ignored if taste was your goal. Soups are generally excellent. There is a teppanyaki bar and a sushi bar. The menu of the Kagura of last year seems to have shortened while increasing in price.

CHEF: H. Shiraishi   PROPRIETORS: Tavisdawn Ltd   OPEN: Tue to Sun, exc L Sat and Sun; 12 to 3, 6 to 11.30   MEALS: alc. Set L £14 to £18, Set D £24 to £50. Cover £1 (D only) SERVICE: 12%, card slips closed   CARDS: Access, Amex, Diners, Visa   DETAILS: 40 seats. Private parties: 8, 9 and 10 private rooms. Vegetarian meals. Children welcome. Music. Air-conditioned. Fax: 071-240 3342

Kalamaras £

map 11

76–78 Inverness Mews, W2 3JQ
071-727 9122

COOKING 2
COST £17–£27

'This is one of the few restaurants I know which manages to conjure up the atmosphere of its home country' is a typical view of this basement in a mews off Inverness Place. Over the years, Stelios Platonos has turned the flower-filled, low-ceilinged room into a very special venue for genuine Greek cooking. The printed menu – in Greek with English translations – steers a course that bypasses most clichés, backed up by daily specials scrawled in handwriting on the page. Starters are highly recommended: deep-fried aubergines with intensely garlicky skordalia; grilled octopus; tyropites (little filo pastry parcels); agginares me koukia (artichoke hearts casseroled with broad beans and dill). Excellent fresh seafood is a star attraction: crab, red mullet, salmon and baby squid have all been praised. Meaty main courses – often slow-cooked rather than chargrilled – seem to be suffused with an abundance of fresh mint, although the results can sometimes pale in comparison with the starters. Twenty Greek wines include house red at £7.20. Micro-Kalamaras, at 66 Inverness Mews, is unlicensed and delivers food of similar quality.

CHEF/PROPRIETOR: Stelios Platonos OPEN: Mon to Sat, D only; 7 to 12 CLOSED: bank hols MEALS: alc. Set D £14.50. Cover £1 SERVICE: 10%, card slips closed CARDS: Access, Amex, Diners, Visa DETAILS: 78 seats. Private parties: 10 main room, 28 private room. Vegetarian meals. Children's helpings. Wheelchair access (also WC). Music

Kastoori £

map 10

188 Upper Tooting Road, SW17 7ER
081-767 7027

COOKING 1
COST £12–£20

The Tankis queried our reference to the plaster mouldings of cherubs on their walls – in fact, 'upright female dancing figures, as far removed from Renaissance cherubs as curry is from Caravaggio,' they commented. Inspectors' eyes may fail them, but their taste-buds do not. This vegetarian restaurant has a fine hand with baking, an interesting though short menu, and very fair prices. Some dishes are prepared on Sundays alone, rotlo (millet bread) and oro (roast aubergine with spring onions) among them. The bhajias 'bear no resemblance to the leaden fritters you usually get, nor do the samosas; dahi puri is excellent, and the chana bhatura, a fairly hot chickpea curry with light deep-fried dumplings, is a knock-out.' The Sunday thali is 'more than anyone can eat'. The formula is evidently successful: a branch has opened in Croydon at 466 London Road. House wines are £6.75.

CHEFS/PROPRIETORS: Dinash and Kanchan Tanki OPEN: all week, exc L Mon and Tue; 12.30 to 3, 6 to 10.30 (11 Fri to Sun) CLOSED: 25 Dec MEALS: alc. Set L and D £7.25 to £11.25. Minimum £4 SERVICE: not inc, card slips closed CARDS: Access, Visa DETAILS: 76 seats. Private parties: 40 main room. Vegetarian meals. Children welcome. Wheelchair access. Music

'Not the place to take an appetite – we have enjoyed more to eat at a child's birthday party.' On eating in Cheshire

Kensington Place ♥

map 11

201 Kensington Church Street, W8 7LX
071-727 3184

COOKING 3*
COST £19–£46

'This, I'm afraid, was a shamelessly sozzled Saturday night blur. I remember excellent rabbit and hilariously good coffee' is a report which goes to show that it takes all sorts to make a restaurant swing. Kensington Place swings. 'The glass cage at the top of Kensington Church Street' is how a Scot seemed to dismiss it, who then admitted it was 'a user-friendly canteen' that, despite the 'clinking, clanking and chattering', provided wonderful service – friendly, speedy, intelligent – and excellent value for money. It is noisy. The counsel is to sit at the edge if you are a couple; the reassurance is that the noise inhibits being overheard. It is also on the bare side, but those chairs are more comfortable than they look. Rowley Leigh manages to combine classical technique with the immediacy and boldness of 'brasserie' food. He has often licked the numbers problem too: 'The foie gras with sweetcorn pancake was delicate and delicious; the chicken and goats' cheese mousse up to standard. How do they manage to turn out so much properly cooked food of such variety to so many people so consistently?' So asked one contented diner who went after the theatre and found the place still packed and turning people away. He went on to one of the day's specials, 'hake and potato torte, which was a cross between fish pie and Swiss roll, tasting like one, looking like the other. It was utterly magnificent.' The menu produces many points of praise: oyster and creamed leek soup, soupe au pistou, red mullet with shrimp jelly, or with lentils, tomato and cumin, partridge with spiced cabbage (another firm favourite), pheasant ('the best I have ever eaten') with salsify and green peppers; the dauphinois with ceps, the tarte Tatin, lemon tart, and on, and on. There have to be failures, even when the success rate is high. Chicken often seems rather boring; portions can be out of kilter; there can be glitches in a booking system that insists on two or more sittings to a table on busy nights; there are times when the comment is 'acceptable but not memorable', but this may be the result of over-expectation as well as under-performance. Olives are 'as good as Bibendum's', breads are Italian (with the odd slice of toasted Innes sourdough) and coffee is strong. The wine list is changed as often as the menu and is a modern listing, not helpful for beginners, but full of excellent things at prices that are definitely low enough to admit a try-out or two. Burgundy growers are invariably interesting and expect to see any of the fashionable names you read about in last Sunday's wine columns. There are not many halves. House wines are from £7.95. CELLARMAN'S CHOICE: New Zealand, Sauvignon Blanc 1990, Collard, £16.75; Cornas 1986, Lionnet, £24.25.

CHEF: Rowley Leigh   PROPRIETORS: Nick Smallwood and Simon Slater   OPEN: all week; 12 to 3.30, 6.30 to 11.45 (10.15 Sun)   MEALS: alc. Set L £12.50   SERVICE: not inc   CARDS: Access, Visa   DETAILS: 90 seats. Private parties: 90 main room. Children's helpings. Music. Air-conditioned. Fax: 071-229 2025

Several sharp operators have tried to extort money from restaurateurs on the promise of an entry in a guidebook that has never appeared. The Good Food Guide *makes no charge for inclusion and does not offer certificates of any kind.*

Langan's Brasserie

map 13

Stratton Street, W1X 5FD
071-493 6437

COOKING 2*
COST £25–£44

A couple running a tiny restaurant in Dorset come to London. They visit this monster of an eating-house – two floors, open to nearly midnight (try Dorset for that), scene of 'constant commotion' – and wonder at how it is done. There is an analogy in the small boy, new to the giant scale of London hotels, gawping at the mountains of spuds needed each day to keep the place from hunger. Londoners take the quality and logistical skill of their favourites too much for granted. Where outside the capital would somewhere like Langan's either survive or produce such food? It may not be brilliant food, but it can be very fair (for the plainer, most traditional recipes, strangely enough). And who can resist the hubbub, the competition for tables, and the chance to see the world in many guises? 'The onion sauce with the bangers and mash is out of this world, though you have to order more of it,' writes someone who adores the old waiters recalling old times (other people have encountered their fractious side) and who revisits even if some of the dishes misfire. And an old-timer who has reported to the *Guide* for decades, not years, reflected on the quality of an autumn meal of smoked goose breast and celery and apple salad, roast grouse, skate with black butter, bubble and squeak, spinach and then a summer pudding with caramel sauce (just as good as cream, he maintained). House wines are £7.75.

CHEFS: Richard Shepherd, Dennis Mynott and Roy Smith PROPRIETORS: Michael Caine and Richard Shepherd OPEN: Mon to Sat, exc Sat L; 12.30 to 3, 7 to 11.45 (8 to 12.45 Sat) CLOSED: bank hols, 25 Dec, 1 Jan, Easter MEALS: alc. Cover £1 SERVICE: 12.5% CARDS: Access, Amex, Diners, Visa DETAILS: 200 seats. Private parties: 12 main room. Vegetarian meals. Children's helpings. Wheelchair access (1 step). Music. Air-conditioned

Launceston Place ♥

map 12

1A Launceston Place, W8 5RL
071-937 6912

COOKING 2*
COST £23–£46

The purchase of next door has given extra room – a space for waiting, drinking and turning around – and has not affected standards one jot. A partnership of two effective managers, and competent staff, also mean that running a pair of busy restaurants (this is the older sister of Kensington Place, see opposite) can still have that personal touch. If all London treks to the younger sibling, this one has put down deep local roots. You even feel that the place is done out like a friendly Kensington drawing-room. A daily set menu keeps customers coming with fair prices; the *carte* strikes all the modish notes. 'Crab flan had a good fresh flavour, braised ox tongue had rounder tastes than a similar dish taken at the other branch, a salad of artichoke and salt cod was an unusual combination of textures that married well,' reported one happy visitor, while others endorse starters such as griddled scallops with red onion salsa, deep-fried oysters with chilli and coriander, or poached quail's eggs with sorrel and green peppercorns, followed by duck with a béarnaise and salsify fritter, pigeon with leeks and foie gras, or grilled Dover sole. There are roast joints for Sunday lunch. A refreshingly succinct and intelligent wine list has wines from

£9 and a few cleverly chosen half-bottles – makes one wonder why some people make such a fuss. CELLARMAN'S CHOICE: Gigondas 1986, Jaboulet, £17.50; Ch. La Lagune 1982, £35.

CHEF: Charles Mumford   PROPRIETORS: Nick Smallwood and Simon Slater   OPEN: all week, exc Sat L and Sun D; 12.30 to 2.30, 7 to 11.30   MEALS: alc. Set L and D £12.50 to £15.50   SERVICE: not inc   CARDS: Access, Visa   DETAILS: 80 seats. Private parties: 25 main room, 14 private room. Vegetarian meals. Children's helpings L. No pipes in dining-room. Wheelchair access. No music. Air-conditioned. Fax: 071-938 2412

Laurent £   map 11

| 428 Finchley Road, NW2 2HY | COOKING 1* |
| 071-794 3603 | COST £18–£25 |

Couscous gets ever more popular and Laurent is the best place in London to test its delights. This restaurant, dropped on the street side beyond the arterial section of the Finchley Road, is never fancy. Laurent Farrugia concentrates on the subtle perfume and correct fluffy dryness of his couscous, rather than the beauty of table ornaments. The menu is studiously short: brique à l'oeuf and couscous three ways. The merguez sausages are good, the harissa sauce is hot and the Algerian wine is very drinkable. House wines are £9.

CHEF/PROPRIETOR: Laurent Farrugia   OPEN: Mon to Sat; 12 to 2, 6 to 10.30   CLOSED: first 3 weeks Aug   MEALS: alc. Minimum £6.50   SERVICE: not inc   CARDS: Access, Visa   DETAILS: 36 seats. Private parties: 50 main room. Vegetarian meals. Children's helpings. No music

Leith's ▮   map 11

| 92 Kensington Park Road, W11 2PN | COOKING 3 |
| 071-229 4481 | COST £33–£60 |

'It all runs as smoothly as the trolleys (hors d'oeuvre, puddings, cheese).' Leith's trots along: its style is most easily compared to that of classic hotel dining-rooms, yet it carries this off with such assurance and aplomb that the dominant mood is one of pleasant relaxation. 'Service is impeccable, even when in error. It is never ham-fisted, at once punctilious and unexpectedly witty' was one comment; 'We were enveloped in warmth and concern, a nice restaurant, not *too* perfect' was another; '"Tell your friends about us," the maître d' called as we left, quite as if we were walking out of Burger King' was a third. The success of the *mise-en-scène*, even if aspects of the decoration strike the young as old hat, is supported by that of the cooking. The trolley at the first course contained some good things one May evening: soft-boiled gull's eggs with spinach, pointedly seasoned mushrooms à la grecque, spinach, bean sprout and bacon salad, haddock and leek mousse, marinated monkfish with a chive vinaigrette. The main courses from the seasonal menu (and don't forget the real effort put in for the vegetarian) include a braised poussin with vegetables and morels that is simple yet could even be called sublime. A loin of lamb with tomato coating, with an aubergine charlotte and finely judged sauce won prizes all the way except for the meat (too many toothpicks afterwards). The cheese trolley is not as big, bold or ripe as such a place might command, yet the sweets (unless you go for baked Alaska and the trimmings) have palpable high points as well as the low of a lemon tart that got stuck, then fell apart. Ancillaries, from olives to very little petits fours, are up to the mark, though bread is boring. Leith's is on a good curve. The wine list marches on. It is absolutely classic. You can even defend the £395 for 1970 Petrus – just compare it to the £775 plus service at Bibendum (see entry, London). Many margins are generous to the drinker. Nicholas Tarayan is an enthusiast and his advice should be sought. It may be worth spending a little; or just hunt among the bin-ends. House wines start at £13.75, and remember that Leith's is pukka about the service-included. CELLARMAN'S CHOICE: Tursan, Ch. de Bachen 1990, £19.75; Piedmont, Pais, Colle Manora 1988, £19.50.

CHEF: Alex Floyd PROPRIETORS: Leith's Restaurant Ltd and Prue Leith OPEN: all week, D only; 7.30 to 11.30 CLOSED: 3 or 4 days Christmas, 2 days Aug bank hol MEALS: Set D £26.50 to £47.50 SERVICE: net prices, card slips closed CARDS: Access, Amex, Diners, Visa DETAILS: 85 seats. Private parties: 24 main room, 10, 24 and 36 private rooms. Vegetarian meals. Children welcome. Wheelchair access (3 steps). No music. Air-conditioned

Lobster Pot £ 　　　　　　　　　　 NEW ENTRY 　 map 11

3 Kennington Lane, SE11 4RG 　　　　　　　　　　　 COOKING 1*
071-582 5556 　　　　　　　　　　　　　　　　　　　 COST £17–£53

The location is surprising in itself; the matelot uniforms that everyone seems to wear, the restaurant done out like a ship's cabin, the tremendous willingness of the staff to discuss and explain everything make this place even more bizarre. 'Service is slow but friendly (it improves if you repeat requests in French), the ambience is like Hastings in the 1960s – brass portholes, old photos, a portrait of someone who resembles Captain Birdseye, a room entirely lined in pitchpine,' ran one report. The Lobster Pot specialises in fish (though next to a good fish shop, it buys independently) and offers a long *carte* and a more changeable pair of tables d'hôte. Meat is not forgotten. Some dishes have gained excellent reports: a plate of shellfish was suitably generous and varied; a bouillabaisse bretonne was enormous and powerful; salmon was described as tender, plump and flavourful; prawns with garlic butter were eyed enviously by other diners. Not much is left to its own devices: fish comes emphatically sauced, the chargrill and the herbs and oil are not important. Sometimes people find this ill judged: to one, the skate with raspberry vinegar was more like raspberry coulis. Vegetables are not always well suited to fish (red cabbage?), and desserts pass muster. This is a brave venture that deserves to survive. The wine list is very short. House wines are £8.50.

CHEF: Hervé Régent PROPRIETORS: Hervé and Nathalie Régent OPEN: Tue to Sun; 12 to 3, 7 to 11.30 MEALS: alc. Set L and D £12.50 to £18.50 SERVICE: net prices, card slips closed CARDS: Access, Amex, Diners, Visa DETAILS: 28 seats. Vegetarian meals with prior notice. Children's helpings. No cigars/pipes in dining-room. Wheelchair access (1 step). No music. Air-conditioned

CELLARMAN'S CHOICE: *Wines recommended by the restaurateur, normally more expensive than house wine.*

Lou Pescadou

map 11

241 Old Brompton Road, SW5 9HP
071-370 1057

COOKING 1
COST £24–£40

'A genuine piece of French *jouissance* in Earls Court' is one reader's opinion of this fish restaurant (the cheapest of a small chain). Inside it looks and feels nautical, with prints of boats and maritime memorabilia. At the front it is bare-boarded bistro; at the back there are pink cloths and carpets. Downstairs is the Rugby Bar, dedicated to stars of the French game. The short menu centres on daily supplies of fresh fish from Brittany: true flavours are not masked or spoilt by fussy cooking or complex sauces. 'The taste is all-consuming,' writes a convert. The freshness of the raw materials shows in dishes such as monkfish served on ratatouille with basmati rice, and salmon en papillote (although this has seemed to lack seasoning on occasion). Menu fixtures have also drawn enthusiastic praise: fish soup has been 'magnificent, as good as anything one would get in Marseille'; pissaladière has been 'sumptuous'. There are also mussels, various Gallic salads (including a fresh langoustine version), pâtés, omelettes and pizzas, plus steaks. Desserts are the likes of peach melba and apple tart flamed in calvados. Service has been praised this year, but the wine list has not. House wine is £8.90.

CHEF: David Laurent   PROPRIETORS: Lou Pescadou Ltd   OPEN: all week; 12 to 3, 7 to 12   CLOSED: 2 weeks Christmas   MEALS: alc. Cover £1   SERVICE: 15%, card slips closed   CARDS: Access, Amex, Diners, Visa   DETAILS: 60 seats. 8 tables outside. Private parties: 20 main room, 40 private room. Vegetarian meals. Children's helpings. Wheelchair access (1 step). No music

Malabar £

NEW ENTRY   map 11

27 Uxbridge Street, W8 7TQ
071-727 8800

COOKING 1
COST £17–£36

The Malabar is slick, the waiters are sassy, the crowd is happy to be there. The menu is clearly and intelligently devised, with a south-west Malabar coastal theme diluted with a few north Indian tandoori choices. The cooking does not always hit the mark, and there is an element of compromise in the spicing that may negate the point of devilled chicken livers on a skewer – where's the devil, then? – or undistinguished prawns with undistinguished spinach. But the freshness of fried pumpkin, and a dish of fried banana with ginger, gave sign of what the place can do. Portions are not enormous; nans are fluffy; the cover charge brings poppadums (one spiced, one plain). Drink lager, lassi or house wine at £8.50.

CHEF: Anil Bist   PROPRIETORS: Jo Chalmers and Anil Bist   OPEN: all week; 12 to 2.45, 6 to 11.30   CLOSED: 1 week end Aug, 4 days Christmas   MEALS: alc. Set L and D £11.75 to £29.75 (for 2). Sun buffet £7.95. Cover 80p   SERVICE: net prices   CARDS: Access, Visa   DETAILS: 60 seats. Private parties: 12 main room, 20 private room. Vegetarian meals. Children welcome. No music. Air-conditioned

Dining-rooms where live and recorded music are never played are signalled by No music *in the details at the end of an entry.*

Mandalay

map 10

100 Greenwich South Street, SE10 8UN
081-691 0443

COOKING 2
COST £16–£34

'The combination of Gerald Andrews' enthusiasm for Burmese food and his off-the-wall front-of-house style are part of the attraction of this functional restaurant,' according to one reporter. There's not much décor, apart from some photographs on the walls: food is the main talking point. The menu covers unfamiliar territory, but Gerald Andrews' notes and descriptions are helpful. Satisfying one-plate meals such as mohinga (rice noodles in a fish-based soup served with fried onions in batter) have impressed with their 'wonderful play of texture and flavour'. Powerfully spiced main-course dishes, such as marinated fish balls or pork in a thick lentil and tamarind sauce, are served with bowls of soothing soup. Flavours are generally authentic. Onion oil rice is an excellent accompaniment. Hsa-nwin-makin (semolina cake with raisins and almonds) is the pick of the sweets. Prices may seem high, but set Sunday lunch is excellent value. House French is £7.

CHEF/PROPRIETOR: Gerald Andrews   OPEN: Tue to Sat, D only, and Sun L; 12.30 to 3, 7 to 10.30   MEALS: alc. Set Sun L £9.50. Minimum £9.50   SERVICE: not inc   DETAILS: 58 seats. Private parties: 26 main room, 26 private room. Vegetarian meals. Children welcome. Music

Mandarin Kitchen £

map 11

14–16 Queensway, W2 3RX
071-727 9012 and 9648

COOKING 1*
COST £15–£50

'A first visit, delighted to have found it,' writes one who enjoyed a pot of crab with dried shrimps, spring onion and vermicelli ('as good a Chinese dish as I have eaten in the West'), beautifully cooked sea bass with ginger and spring onion, and roasted fillets of eel with chilli. This is the place for seafood rather than meat dishes. Better order lobster with noodles ('a marvellous way of eating noodles') or bean curd stuffed with prawns. This is a popular restaurant, noted for 'hordes of pretty Chinese waitresses' who remain unruffled despite the press of custom. On occasion, standards have been known to slip, with popular dishes such as sea bass served overcooked and tasting as average as the meat dishes. Piped music can be a little too loud for comfort. Drink Chinese or Japanese rice wines or Tiger beer. House wine is £6.80.

CHEFS: Kwong Wing Man and D.D. Ly   PROPRIETORS: Stephen and Helen Cheung   OPEN: all week; noon to 11.30   MEALS: alc. Set L and D £8.90 to £15   SERVICE: not inc   CARDS: Access, Amex, Diners, Visa   DETAILS: 110 seats. Private parties: 110 main room. Vegetarian meals. Children welcome. Wheelchair access. Music. Air-conditioned

---

An asterisk (*) after the 1 to 5 cooking mark at the top of an entry signifies that the Guide *and its readers think that the restaurant is a particularly fine example within its rating.*

All entries in the Guide *are rewritten every year, not least because restaurant standards fluctuate. Don't trust an out-of-date* Guide.

Mandeer £

map 13

21 Hanway Place, W1P 9DG
071-323 0660

COOKING 1
COST £9–£21

Hanway Place – a Dickensian alleyway curving round the back of Tottenham
Court Road – is an unlikely setting for an Indian vegetarian restaurant. Down
in the basement is a long dining-room, dimly lit by lamps over each circular
table. 'The overall effect is one of rootlessness rather than romance,' notes a
visitor. 'It could have been in any strange corner of the globe.' The owners'
philosophy of natural food as a life-fulfilling, holistic key to health translates
into a short menu that includes brown rice and tofu as well as the expected
range of vegetables, spices and herbs. Five thalis – including a vegan version
and one without garlic or onions – are excellent value. Otherwise there is a
good choice of Gujarati-style starters, such as delicate sev puri, freshly made
bhajias, kachori and masala dosai. Some of the curries, such as Bombay aloo
and paneer korma ('Cheese and ghee and cream is pretty heavy-going,'
comments one reporter), are slightly less successful. Basmati rice tastes freshly
cooked; breads such as puris and stuffed parathas are excellent. Sweets range
from various kulfis to Loseley ice-creams. Good-value self-service lunches are
available in the adjoining Ravi Shankar Hall. Drink lassi, masala tea or lager.
Organic German house wine is £7.60.

CHEF: Mr Daudbhai   PROPRIETORS: Mr and Mrs Patel   OPEN: Mon to Sat; 12 to 3, 5.30 to
10   CLOSED: bank hols   MEALS: alc. Set L £2.75 to £3.65, Set D £7.50 to £11.50. Minimum
£7. Self-service L   SERVICE: 10%   CARDS: Access, Amex, Diners, Visa   DETAILS: 75 seats.
Private parties: 100 private room. Vegetarian meals. Children's helpings. No-smoking area.
Music

▲ Manzi's

map 14

1–2 Leicester Street, WC2H 7BL
071-734 0224

COOKING 1
COST £21–£54

'Why exactly is this seafood restaurant still in the *Guide*?' asked one perplexed
reader. 'Atmosphere and ambience (downstairs) are splendid still; starters of
asparagus and Colchester oysters were very promising; so was the coffee at the
end. In between, two main dishes of scallops Mornay and Dover sole tasted as
if they had been lying around all day under their thick and tasteless blankets of
sauce. The extremely expensive vegetables were overcooked. The Niersteiner
was just about drinkable. Service was charming from Emilio.' The answer was
supplied by an inspector: 'The place seems the same as 20 years ago; there is a
nice old-fashioned feel, and professional waiters convey a good balance of
efficiency and informality; the menu has not changed for ages, though prices
have, and some of the fish is of excellent quality; but don't eat the sauces.'
Although the age charms, it also irritates: our tastes have altered, and perhaps
Manzi's should move a little with the times. Embark on the wine list at your
peril; the only firm information seems to be the prices. House wine is
from £7.90.

▲ *This symbol means accommodation is available.*

CHEF: Vincenzo Frappola PROPRIETORS: the Manzi family OPEN: all week, exc Sun L; 12
to 2.30, 5.30 to 11.30 (Sun D 6 to 10.30) CLOSED: 25 and 26 Dec, Good Fri L MEALS: alc.
Cover £1.50 SERVICE: not inc, card slips closed CARDS: Access, Amex, Diners, Visa
DETAILS: 150 seats. Private parties: 15 main room. Vegetarian meals with prior notice. No
children under 6. Wheelchair access (2 steps). Music ACCOMMODATION: 16 rooms, all
with bath/shower. Lift. B&B £40 to £63. Deposit: £30. Children welcome. Phone. Confirm
by midnight. Fax: 071-437 4864

Maroush III

map 11

62 Seymour Street, W1H 5AF   COOKING 2
071-724 5024   COST £25–£43

'It's only slightly gaudy', with an unstuffy atmosphere, 'not a place that
requires jacket and tie'. Friendly staff, generous portions, good ingredients and
authentic Lebanese cooking: this is the place to go for good-value meze, chosen
from a huge list that can provide an entire meal. Tabouleh and hummus are
popular, but some of the more unusual dishes are worth trying: mouhamara
(chopped nuts in olive oil and paprika – 'delicious with pitta bread'), basturma
(smoked fillet of beef), simply fried sweetbreads, chargrilled chicken wings
with garlic and lemon sauce, fried lambs' kidneys. Raw fresh meat, puréed
with various spices, adds a sense of adventure. Main courses have sometimes
been less successful, with unimaginative but competent cooking. House
Lebanese wine is £13.50.

CHEF: F. Ladkani PROPRIETOR: M. Abouzaki OPEN: all week; noon to midnight
CLOSED: 25 Dec MEALS: alc. Cover £1.50 SERVICE: not inc, card slips closed CARDS:
Access, Amex, Diners, Visa DETAILS: 60 seats. 5 tables outside. Private parties: 60 main
room. Vegetarian meals. Children welcome. Smart dress preferred. Music. Air-conditioned

Mayflower £

map 14

68–70 Shaftesbury Avenue, W1V 7DF   COOKING 2
071-734 9207   COST £18–£40

'Very busy, with mainly Taiwanese customers,' observes a reporter about this
big restaurant on the fringes of Soho's Chinatown. The menu of some 170
dishes makes challenging reading, with specialities from mainland China
including Canton, as well as from Hong Kong. There are some esoteric items,
such as crispy milk balls, stewed yam with coconut chicken, and stuffed sea
cucumber with prawn and crab-meat sauce. A range of more accessible,
familiar dishes is also available – and these tend to draw most reports.
Szechuan prawns and sizzling chicken with black-bean sauce have been
notable for 'good strong flavours and generous portions'. Law-hon chai
(Chinese dry vegetables) has been an interesting selection. There is also a
decent showing of one-plate rice and noodle dishes (although these are only
available after 11pm). Portions are generous, and value for money is reckoned
to be 'excellent'. House wine is £9.

*'''We bought a lot of lamb but people just won't order it, so we run out of other things''
(said without humour).'* On eating in Sussex

CHEF: F. Chung   PROPRIETOR: Patrick Tsang   OPEN: all week, D only; 5pm to 4am
CLOSED: 23 to 25 Dec   MEALS: alc. Set D £11.50 to £13 (minimum 2)   SERVICE: not inc
CARDS: Access, Amex, Diners, Visa   DETAILS: 120 seats. Private parties: 40 main room.
Vegetarian meals. Children welcome. Music. Air-conditioned

Melati £ map 14

21 Great Windmill Street, W1V 7PH COOKING 1
071-437 2745 COST £16–£32

The cosmopolitan buzz of this jam-packed Malaysian venue in the heart of
strip-club Soho, the irrepressible friendliness of the waiters and the big
platefuls of authentic food make it a gem among London's ethnic restaurants.
This year's crop of recommendations is as forthright as ever: satays with
excellent peanut sauce, sup sayur (hot-and-sour vegetable soup), fish with
strong thick tamarind sauce, fried chicken in lemon sauce and Malaysian
chicken curry have all been recommended, although one reader felt that the
'greasy' fried aubergine with pungent dried fish was probably 'an acquired
taste'. For quick, cheap meals there are big bowls of laksa soup, noodles and
composite rice dishes such as nasi ramas (embellished with fried chicken, fish
cutlet and vegetables). Finish with exotic fresh fruit or try one of the
extraordinary desserts, such as Sam's Triple (layers of puréed avocado, mango
and pineapple). Drink Indonesian Bintang or Singapore Tiger beer. House
French is £7.15. Melati's younger brother Minang (11 Greek Street, W1V 5LE,
Tel: 071-434 1149) serves similar dishes.

CHEFS: S. Alamsjah and H. Hasyem   PROPRIETORS: M.C.W. Ong and S. Alamsjah   OPEN:
all week; noon to 11.30 (12.30 Fri and Sat)   CLOSED: 25 Dec   MEALS: alc. Set L and D for 2
inc wine £39.50   SERVICE: 10%, card slips closed   CARDS: Access, Amex, Diners, Visa
DETAILS: 120 seats. Private parties: 50 main room. Vegetarian meals. Children welcome.
Wheelchair access. Music. Air-conditioned

▲ Le Meridien Hotel,
Oak Room map 13

21 Piccadilly, W1V 0BH COOKING 4
071-734 8000 COST £34–£70

Diners in the spring might have been perplexed by the choice of first courses at
this exemplary grand-hotel restaurant which may, in its own way, be the
steadiest example of modern French haute cuisine in the capital. A gazpacho of
langoustines or a warm salad of lobster would take care of shellfish lovers; foie
gras with wild mushrooms, or a tourte of quail with foie gras and white port
jelly, are the alternatives for devotees of liver, or, if it's offal that takes you, a
little calf's cheek and sweetbread salad; rabbit and frogs' legs salad, again with
wild mushrooms and truffle oil to dress them, would solve any problem if you
think frogs essential to a study of French cookery, which would leave as the
final offerings a salad of a fish called 'lisette' with aubergine and tomato confit,
or salmon and tomato set in jelly with parsley and herbs. The plain-food
brigade, the people who like something hot and simple, who don't like fish or
funny things like calf's cheek, frogs' legs or rabbit, would have to comb the

simpler table d'hôte, or go elsewhere. The dining-room is, of course, magnificent. Limed oak panelling, lofty ceilings, lots of space and comfort, immense flower displays and a brigade of padding servants combine in a crescendo of sober calm. Shoot the pianist or go at lunch-time. At tea in the lounge, there's a harpist. The cooking here is the result of joint discussions between David Chambers, the resident chef, and Michel Lorain of La Côte Saint-Jacques in Burgundy, who acts as visiting consultant. It is a stable relationship that works. The deed of accord, the menu, is complicated: sections of 'traditional' and 'creative' dishes, dishes cooked for that day alone, gastronomic set menus and a shorter lunch card. Balance, perhaps because of the two minds at one object, is not always a strong point. A winter meal began, on the one hand, with appetisers of smoked perch before a warm salad of venison with foie gras on a galette of potato, and, on the other, wafer-thin slices of smoked duck breast with shavings of Parmesan. Main dishes were a breast of pheasant with wild mushrooms, and monkfish with an unexpected blueberry sauce. Fish cooking often works the contrast of fish with strong sauces (red wine with bream, or red wine and girolles with oysters) or with spices (turbot with cloves, tartare of salmon with spices). Game is a strong point here. An autumn dinner saw the day's specials of venison with fresh figs and celeriac, partridge with red cabbage and truffle gravy, or roast grouse with potato and truffle galette and trimmings of spinach, wild mushrooms and salsify. An arrangement of vegetables comes separately. The last half of the meal is the realm of the waiting staff: a fine trolley of cheese, and a better-than-usual trolley of sweets, the sauces lovingly feathered at table. Coffee is strong. Bread is good. Service is *comme il faut*. It is an impressive operation. This year, the price and range of the wines seem to have hardened in favour of the wealthy. Although quality remains excellent, more modest bottles such as Ch. Cissac 1983 at £32 or a good St-Nicolas-de-Bourgeuil for £23 must give pause for thought. House wines are £13.

CHEF: David Chambers   PROPRIETORS: Meridien Hotels   OPEN: Mon to Sat, exc Sat L; 12 to 2.30, 7 to 10.30   MEALS: alc. Set L £24.50, Set D £46   SERVICE: not inc   CARDS: Access, Amex, Diners, Visa   DETAILS: 50 seats. Children welcome. Jacket and tie. No pipes in dining-room. Wheelchair access (also WC). Music. Air-conditioned   ACCOMMODATION: 263 rooms, all with bath/shower. Rooms for disabled. Lift. B&B £200 to £256. Deposit: 1 night. Children welcome. Baby facilities. Afternoon teas. Swimming-pool. Sauna. Snooker. Air-conditioned. TV. Phone. Confirm 1 day ahead. Fax: 071-437 3574

Meson Don Felipe £

map 11

53 The Cut, SE1 8LF
071-928 3237

COOKING 1
COST £15–£23

There is always discussion as to the best tapas bar, especially when so many are as bad as they are in London. The Diments' place gets fair support: noisy, crowded, impossible to talk when the guitarist gets under way, but cheerful, fast and usefully placed. It is not too dear. There are extras on the blackboard as well as the printed sheet, *and* the display at the bar is there for you to study before coming to a decision. The Riojas are of interest, but the wine list is not a monument to Spanish viticulture. House wines are from Valencia, cost £7.65, and have been selected for the Spanish pavilion restaurants at Expo '92.

CHEF: Ana Diment   PROPRIETORS: Philip and Ana Diment   OPEN: Mon to Sat; noon to 11
MEALS: alc   SERVICE: not inc   CARDS: Access, Visa   DETAILS: 50 seats. Private parties:
10 main room. Vegetarian meals. Children's helpings. Wheelchair access (also WC).
Music. Fax: 071-386 0337

Mijanou ▮ ⁵✳   map 12

143 Ebury Street, SW1W 9QN   COOKING 2*
071-730 4099   COST £29–£55

Ring the door to gain entry to this bijou restaurant. Bijou, because it is on two
floors, with the kitchen on view on the half-landing between, with a tiny yard
behind for fresh-air summer eating. 'The intimacy derives from its smallness,
for the staff are correct and responsive rather than warm, and the view of the
backstage is of a quietly, earnestly efficient operation in progress in near-
Trappist conditions' was a first-time visitor's assessment. The monastic analogy
was taken up again by someone who was given a table in the basement. Sonia
Blech's cooking is quite complicated, though exact terrines of foie gras and
game cookery of a high order show that the undiluted classics are within her
grasp. There are a lot of terrines and 'cakes' (for instance, of veal sweetbreads,
liver and fillet); puff pastry is used to wrap things, or enthrone a fillet of beef;
steak and kidney is put in a herby potato rather than in suet pudding. This
makes the food substantial. If it is badly handled, or technique goes slightly
awry, it can also aggravate failure. The lentil sauce made the puff pastry around
a fillet of veal too soggy, and overcooking drained the meat itself of character.
Desserts, too, have lots of substance, and are major constructions in their own
right. The cassata of three ice-creams with marrons glacés, the soufflé pancakes,
and a large gratin of fruits with a passion-fruit and orange muscat sauce and a
ginger and lavender sorbet, all get more than a mention. Ginger on the one
hand, endives or bitter chicory on the other, seem to be two flavours that entice
Sonia Blech. The menu is annotated with 'Winematch' numbers, indicating
which section of the list would go best with each dish. The dozen or so wines
offered by the glass are so good as to render further exploration superfluous.
Neville Blech has assembled a knowledgeable selection that knows no
geographical bounds; bottles are arranged by style, so exploration is
encouraged when such as Vouvray and Western Australia rub shoulders.
Prices are fair with much enjoyable drinking below £15. There are good
halves. This is one of the best lists that we see. CELLARMAN'S CHOICE: Alsace,
Gewurztraminer, 'Bergweingarten' 1986, Rieflé, £15.75; Coonawarra,
Cabernet/Shiraz 1989, Penley Estate, £15.50.

CHEF: Sonia Blech   PROPRIETORS: Neville and Sonia Blech   OPEN: Mon to Fri; 12.30 to 2,
7 to 11   CLOSED: 1 week Easter, 2 weeks Christmas, 3 weeks Aug   MEALS: Set L £17 to
£21, Set D £28 to £34.50   SERVICE: not inc   DETAILS: 30 seats. 6 tables outside. Private
parties: 20 main room. Children welcome. No smoking upstairs. No music. Fax:
071-823 6402

*All details are as accurate as possible at the time of going to press, but chefs and owners
often change, and it is wise to check by telephone before making a special journey. Many
readers have been disappointed when set-price bargain meals are no longer available.
Ask when booking.*

Mirabelle

NEW ENTRY   map 13

56 Curzon Street, W1Y 8DL   COOKING **3**
071-499 4636   COST £34–£66

The news that this hallowed establishment (which went under after 50 years of trading in 1988) was to be reopened by Japanese owners gave rise to column-inches in newspapers, but little evident response from people anxious for a good night out. The restaurant itself is deep under an apartment block in Mayfair, reached by labyrinth. It could be the last-ditch command centre of a high-living regime. Contact with the real world is through skylights, one of which retracts to give that al fresco feel. The service, table settings and flower displays are those of a luxury cruise liner floating through a never-never land. Michael Croft changes his menus every six months. This should give good practice. On one side are the things that aristos have for supper: smoked salmon, chateaubriand and the like. On the other is a set of modern dishes, with a nod here and there to distinguished colleagues, that yields a mixture of good and bad. Cannon of lamb with a basil and garlic mousse is not actually so modern – Raymond Blanc was doing it in the 1970s – and current taste would perhaps have ditched the mousse for the pleasant gravy that was also on the plate; especially as the excellent potatoes (soufflé and dauphinois) would have been ample accompaniment. A minestrone of langoustine with noodles is hardly a soup – the liquid was reduced to sauce consistency – but it was fair-flavoured even if the langoustines had lost their texture. The Pierre Koffmann classic galettes of potatoes sandwiching foie gras is here accompanied by madeira, not Sauternes, sauce. But no matter, it tastes good. An escabèche of red mullet was not so successful, nor was the aubergine caviare that accompanied it. A chibouste of lemon starts with a puff pastry case, then lemon curd, then crème pâtissière, then meringue, then caramel. Gosh! It's great! The strawberry sauce, however, is really no help. The coffee and petits fours would save any meal, even from anaemic bread and heavy appetisers. People will want to come here, but competition in this sector is intense. It will not be helped by the wine list, which out of 380 bins has a half-dozen below £20 and not many under £30. Clarets from 1982 kick off with Ch. Beychevelle at £75. House wines are from £17.

CHEF: Michael Croft   PROPRIETOR: Mr Sekine   OPEN: Mon to Sat, exc Sat L; 12 to 2.30, 6 to 10.30   CLOSED: bank hols, 25 to 30 Dec   MEALS: alc. Set L £19 to £25, Set D £45   SERVICE: net prices, card slips closed   CARDS: Access, Amex, Diners, Visa   DETAILS: 90 seats. Private parties: 100 main room, 8, 10 and 30 private rooms. Vegetarian meals. Children's helpings. No children under 4. Music. Air-conditioned. Fax: 071-499 5449

Mr Kong £

map 14

21 Lisle Street, WC2H 7BA   COOKING **2**
071-437 7341   COST £13–£30

As with so many Chinese restaurants, performance over a wide menu – with many worthwhile specialities to explore – can go up and down. Criticisms undermine confidence. Yet the queues at Mr Kong are testimony that some things are done right, and the general view is of a reliable and dynamic kitchen. Prawns with chilli spices, prawns and chicken with melon, and chicken with jellyfish are some of the specials that have been enjoyed, as have fried intestines, salty spiced squid and boiled tripe. More conventional dishes are also done well. Choose a table on the ground floor, for preference. A notional wine list may be sacrificed for tea throughout. House wine is £6.80.

CHEF: K. Kong PROPRIETORS: K. Kong, Y.W. Lo, M.T. Lee, W.C. Lee and C.Y. Chau OPEN: all week; noon to 1.45am CLOSED: 4 days Christmas MEALS: alc. Set L and D £8.60 to £18. Minimum £7 after 5pm SERVICE: net prices CARDS: Access, Amex, Diners, Visa DETAILS: 115 seats. Private parties: 40 main room, 40 and 50 private rooms. Vegetarian meals. Children welcome. Wheelchair access (1 step). Music. Air-conditioned

Mitsukoshi
map 13

Dorland House,
14–20 Regent Street, SW1Y 4PH
071-930 0317

COOKING 2*
COST £36–£150

The restaurant in the basement of the Mitsukoshi department store was once a well-kept Japanese secret. Now, Westerners are discovering what it has to offer. The menu is based on a series of set meals, centring on shabu-shabu, sukiyaki and the like, plus lavish kaiseki banquets and a house special that spans the traditional Japanese repertoire. There is high praise for the sushi-course set dinner, which has included freshly prepared seaweed, sashimi with 'excellent' rice, and tempura with an interesting choice of vegetables and very light batter. Portions are generous. The *carte* features elegantly presented dishes such as salmon roe on minced mooli; light, vinegary sunomono; and chawan mushi – a savoury custard with an assortment of tiny morsels such as black mushroom, fish-cake, daikon pickle and lotus nut. Delicacy is the keynote, although the kitchen can deliver strong flavours when required. Service by waitresses in formal kimonos is attentive and dignified. Soup and tea are included in meal prices; there are also saké, Japanese beer and a creditable list of mostly French wines.

CHEF: Mr Shimada PROPRIETOR: Mr Mitsukoshi OPEN: Mon to Sat; 12 to 1.50, 6 to 9 MEALS: alc. Set L and D £20 to £120. Cover £1.50 SERVICE: 15%, card slips closed CARDS: Access, Amex, Diners, Visa DETAILS: 56 seats. Private parties: 24 main room, 12 and 24 private rooms. Vegetarian meals with prior notice. Children Sat only. Music. Air-conditioned. Fax: 071-839 1167

Miyama
map 13

38 Clarges Street, W1Y 7PJ
071-499 2443

COOKING 3
COST £19–£57

An austere modern interior sets the tone of this highly rated Japanese restaurant in Mayfair. Many people – especially Westerners – opt for the set meals, although the quality is not always consistent: one visitor's tempura dinner was considered top-quality, and the raw fish has been 'exceptional', but on another occasion both the sashimi and tempura lunches were 'disappointing'. The *carte* is shorter than in many comparable places and the emphasis is on teppanyaki, sukiyaki, shabu-shabu and other theatrical specialities cooked at the tables. There are also classic zen-sai starters such as yakitori and kani su (crab-meat and cucumber in rice vinegar), plus grilled eel, teriyaki and ton katsu (deep-fried loin of pork). Noodles, rice, soups and pickles form the back-up. Despite 'less than brilliant service', one reporter rated this as 'some of the best Japanese food I have eaten'. Saké, Japanese beers and Suntory whisky support a short, mainly French, wine list. House wine is £8. The City branch, City Miyama, is at 17 Godliman Street, EC4V 5BD, Tel: 071-489 1937; it is best for lunch (just as Clarges Street is best for dinner).

CHEFS/PROPRIETORS: F. Miyama and T. Miura   OPEN: Mon to Sat, exc Sat L; 12.30 to 2.30, 6.30 to 10.30   MEALS: alc. Set L £9 to £16, Set D £30 to £36   SERVICE: 15%   CARDS: Access, Amex, Diners, Visa   DETAILS: 75 seats. Private parties: 25 main room, 8 and 12 private rooms. Vegetarian meals. Children's helpings L. Jacket and tie. Wheelchair access (1 step; also WC). Music. Air-conditioned

Mon Petit Plaisir
map 11

33C Holland Street, W8 4LX
071-937 3224

COOKING 1
COST £21–£35

This younger brother of Mon Plaisir (see entry below) follows the same pattern as its mentor, with all its virtues and occasional drawbacks. One problem seems to be the cramped surroundings and the severe lack of comfort – which does not make for a relaxed meal. The food can compensate. A short regular *carte* is supplemented by a set lunch. A selection of recommended dishes shows the staunchly French provincial bias: grilled crottin on a bed of spinach leaves; fish terrine wrapped in smoked salmon; tender coq au vin with 'a good rich sauce'; and rare, tender lamb fillet with tarragon sauce. Crème brûlée is a favourite sweet, although the top was not crisp enough for one reporter. Cafetière coffee comes with petits fours. Some have found the service 'laid-back', others consider it 'quick, excellent and very courteous'. A short list of French wines includes a few halves. House wine is £7.80.

CHEF: Christophe Hariot   PROPRIETOR: Alain Lhermitte   OPEN: Mon to Fri; 12 to 2.30, 7 to 10.30   CLOSED: 4 days Easter, Christmas to New Year   MEALS: alc. Set L £13.80, Set D £13.70 (6.30 to 7)   SERVICE: 12.5%, card slips closed   CARDS: Access, Amex, Diners, Visa   DETAILS: 36 seats. 4 tables outside. Private parties: 20 main room. Children's helpings. No cigars/pipes in dining-room. Music. Air-conditioned. Fax: 071-738 7045

Mon Plaisir
map 14

21 Monmouth Street, WC2H 9DD
071-836 7243

COOKING 1*
COST £21–£37

'This restaurant is a treasure. It welcomes diners to an authentic experience of French cooking and service' is one view of Alain Lhermitte's archetypal bistro. Flavours are rich, helpings generous and the cooking is accurate, although the kitchen works best with simple ideas and classic provincial favourites. 'Wonderful' broccoli soup, blanquette de veau, roast pigeon, coq au vin and various fruit tarts have pleased reporters. Details such as the French bread, the cheeseboard and the excellent coffee are up to the mark. The general feeling is that 'the cooking does its level best in chaotic surroundings'. In the early evening it can be full to bursting with theatre-goers taking advantage of the special fixed-price menu. M. Lhermitte deals equally well with staff and customers, switching with the utmost facility from French to English and back. Generally the 'unfailingly concerned service makes up for an absence of elbow-room'. A short French wine list represents the major growing regions. House wine is £7.50.

CHEF: Michel Dubarbier   PROPRIETOR: Alain Lhermitte   OPEN: Mon to Sat, exc Sat L; 12 to 2.30, 6 to 11.15   MEALS: alc. Set L £13.70, Set pre-theatre D inc wine £13.95   SERVICE: 12.5%, card slips closed   CARDS: Access, Amex, Diners, Visa   DETAILS: 95 seats. Private parties: 26 main room, 30 private room. Vegetarian meals. Children's helpings. Wheelchair access. Music. Fax: 071-379 0121

Monkeys
map 12

1 Cale Street,
Chelsea Green, SW3 3QT   COOKING 3
071-352 4711   COST £20–£50

Familiarity has bred popularity and the customers who inhabit this Chelsea backwater know a good Anglo-French neighbourhood restaurant when they find one. The pine-panelled front room may remind some of their terraced homes around the corner and the flowers and crisp napery confirm propriety. The Anglo emphasis is on game – pheasant, partridge, snipe, woodcock and wild duck. Grouse is bedded on sweet braised red cabbage and cooked 'just right'. The French element amounts to a hot foie gras salad, sea scallops served with Puy lentils and Bresse pigeon. Otherwise there is accurate cooking of staples such as grilled fillet steak, roast rack of lamb and sauté calves' kidneys. A separate pudding menu features fruit brioche and crème Anglaise, treacle tart and home-made sorbets. The set-price lunch is good value. House wine is £11.

CHEF: Tom Benham   PROPRIETORS: Tom and Brigitte Benham   OPEN: Mon to Fri; 12.30 to 2.30, 7.30 to 11   CLOSED: 2 weeks Easter, 3 weeks Aug   MEALS: alc. Set L £12.50 to £35, Set D £22.50 to £35. Minimum £17.50 D   SERVICE: not inc   CARDS: Access, Visa   DETAILS: 50 seats. Private parties: 10 main room, 10 private room. Children welcome. No pipes in dining-room. No music. Air-conditioned

Mulligans of Mayfair
NEW ENTRY   map 13

13–14 Cork Street, W1X 1PF   COOKING 3
071-409 1370   COST £26–£46

If Irish address there had to be in Mayfair, it had to be in Cork Street. A pub has been recreated at Mulligans, with a restaurant down the stairs. Oysters are to be had upstairs, while a daily menu of Ireland, the Mediterranean and modern Britain is found down below (Richard Corrigan was chef at Stephen Bull's – see entry, London – and it shows). The choices are often enticing, and the menu gets longer as confidence is gained. It is essential to eat the black pudding with apples and a calvados cream, and it is worth trying the oyster, beef and Guinness casserole. Crubeens (pig's trotter fish-cakes) with a pickled accompaniment is another Irish success. You will often be served champ or colcannon; the latter – mashed potato and curly kale – is a regular partner of boiled ham and parsley sauce. But Richard Corrigan chases other flavours than these and puts together really heartwarming food like best end of lamb with a pesto crust, field mushrooms and garden peas, or fillets of plaice (fish is well-bought here) with broad beans and a mussel cream. Stewed squid is another regular that should not be missed. There is a lot going for the cooking, so it is a pity the place does not match it, even if the staff are grand. The wine list will not excite. House wines are from £8.75.

CHEF: Richard Corrigan PROPRIETORS: Mulligans Irish Whiskey Emporiums Ltd OPEN: Mon to Sat, exc Sat L; 12 to 2.15, 6.15 to 11.15 CLOSED: bank hols MEALS: alc SERVICE: 12.5%, card slips closed CARDS: Access, Amex, Diners, Visa DETAILS: 60 seats. Private parties: 12 main room. Vegetarian meals with prior notice. Children's helpings before 12.30 L/6.30 D. Smart dress preferred. Music

Museum Street Café ✸✳

47 Museum Street, WC1 1LY
071-405 3211

map 13

COOKING 3
COST £17–£25

You can start to think that this is a bit of a 'no' restaurant: no credit cards, no smoking, no decoration to speak of, not much choice on a menu of two or three items per course. Most people, however, love it (although a few don't). The real value, the genuine intent, the freshness of approach, the lack of fandango, the slight seriousness are manna, though one comment about the service – 'a bit more interaction and movement of the face muscles would have been nicer' – puts the problem in a nutshell. This small room by the British Museum is home to a pair of fine cooks. The breads and baked items (Gail Koerber's department) share the glory with the grill (Mark Nathan). 'The walnut bread a knock-out, the rye good too', 'an especially interesting artichoke tart', 'walnut and wholemeal bread possibly the best I have ever tasted, superbly moist yet crusty, still warm from the oven' are some remarks of the first. 'My salmon was attractive, a scent of fresh fish about it, not dried out anywhere', 'lamb with tapénade was a joy', 'chargrilled leeks and peppers with an olive oil dressing and a scattering of hard-boiled egg were so juicy, with flecks of burning to add flavour' are endorsements of the second. Not everything is done like this; there are soups (minestrone), baked fish (brill in paper on root vegetables), and precise, simple cooking of vegetables. Sauces tend to be scanty, even if garlic sauce with chicken (pesto on other days), and a saffron mayonnaise with salmon get much applause: 'I just wish there had been more.' Desserts may be rich – double chocolate pots – or bulky like the apple and rhubarb crumble or the chocolate and almond tart with chocolate sauce: 'I do not expect to eat such a good dessert, even at Christmas.' The counter-argument is that the food is too plain for an 'evening out': that depends on your view of plain, or how much value you set on a perfect dressing to a simple salad. The place is unlicensed, but the bergamot tea is good, so is the coffee.

CHEFS: Gail Koerber and Mark Nathan PROPRIETOR: Mark Nathan OPEN: Mon to Fri; 12.30 to 2.15, 7.30 to 9.15 MEALS: Set L £11 to £14, Set D £19.50. Unlicensed, but bring your own: no corkage SERVICE: not inc DETAILS: 23 seats. Vegetarian meals with prior notice. Children's helpings with prior notice. No smoking. No music

The Guide *always appreciates hearing about changes of chef or owner.*

Nakano

map 12

11 Beauchamp Place, SW3 1NQ
071-581 3837

COOKING 2
COST £23–£73

The Japanese never seem to go for the cosy or the picturesque in their restaurant designs, and the plain, even bleak, Nakano is no exception. The mind is on the food alone – and its deft and seemly service. Nakano conceals an enterprising and worthwhile menu, cooked with style. Beyond the set menus there are several dishes that repay ordering, including a flight of bean curd appetisers (with cod's roe and chilli, or deep fried with grated yams), some ochazuke (rice with green-tea soup), and 'chef's recommendations' that offer chikuwa fish-cake with ume wasa sauce (pickled plum, green mustard, bonito flakes and sesame), grilled tongue with garlic sauce, or dried herring with mirin. The wine list is short and dear, but there is saké. House wine is £13.

CHEF: Mr Kikuchi   PROPRIETORS: Meadowdawn Ltd   OPEN: Tue to Sun, exc Sun L; 12.30 to 2.30, 6.30 to 11   CLOSED: bank hols, 1 week Aug bank hol, 25 Dec and 1 Jan   MEALS: alc. Set L £8.50 to £18, Set D £26.50 to £42.50. Cover £2 D. Minimum £20 D   SERVICE: 15%   CARDS: Access, Amex, Diners, Visa   DETAILS: 30 seats. Private parties: 30 main room. Vegetarian meals. Children's helpings. Music. Air-conditioned. Fax: 071-357 7315

Neal Street Restaurant

map 14

26 Neal Street, WC2H 9PS
071-836 8368

COOKING 2
COST £39–£61

The question of the cost of it all occupies the minds of reporters this year, taking precedence over enjoyment of the food and the pleasant atmosphere. We are, after all, in a recession. 'To pay £12 for a starter consisting of noodles with truffle flavour, £16.50 for a vegetarian main course and £24 for one bottle of Chianti Classico – not again. On the other hand the rabbit casserole was excellent and the other starter of mixed wild mushrooms, exquisite.' Antonio Carluccio's stylish restaurant, famous for wild mushrooms, offers a menu which on face value is Italian but the execution is more international in style and influence: dandelion tart or giant prawns with chilli and garlic, lamb cutlets with egg and lemon sauce, sweetbread meunière. Reports have been positive about the cooking. What does upset is the practice of charging separately for individual vegetables. The customer is expected to dig deep into the pocket if he or she wishes to choose from the wine list, nor is it particularly adventurous; Italy could be better explored. House wine is £11.

CHEF: Santiago Gonzalez   PROPRIETOR: Antonio Carluccio   OPEN: Mon to Fri; 12.30 to 2.30, 7.30 to 11   CLOSED: Christmas to New Year, bank hols   MEALS: alc   SERVICE: 15%, card slips closed   CARDS: Access, Amex, Visa   DETAILS: 65 seats. Private parties: 24 private room. Vegetarian meals. Children welcome. Wheelchair access. Air-conditioned. No music. Fax: 071-497 1361

The Guide *office can quickly spot when a restaurateur is encouraging customers to write recommending inclusion – and sadly, several restaurants have been doing this in 1992. Such reports do not further a restaurant's cause. Please tell us if a restaurateur invites you to write to the* Guide.

Neshiko

map 11

265 Upper Street, N1 2UQ
071-359 9977

COOKING 2
COST £16–£70

Although outside the main run of Japanese restaurants, this offers a mighty interesting menu, executed with skill and enjoyment. Have the sushi, sashimi, tempura set meals if you will, but it is far better to delve among the range of dishes reminiscent of Japanese home-cooking. Japanese omelette, vinegared squid and seaweed, simmered chicken and spring onion, duck with plum sauce, and rice in soup with pickled plums are some that repay exploration. There are decent wines at sensible prices (house wine £8.95), or saké or whisky.

CHEF: Shinji Akamatsu PROPRIETORS: Kawab Ltd OPEN: Mon to Sat, exc Sat L; 12 to 2.30, 6 to 11 CLOSED: 25 Dec to 1 Jan MEALS: alc. Set L £8 to £49, Set D £35 to £49 SERVICE: 10%, card slips closed CARDS: Access, Amex, Diners, Visa DETAILS: 55 seats. Private parties: 30 main room, 25 private room. Vegetarian meals. Children welcome. Smart dress preferred. Wheelchair access. Music. Fax: 071-226 8863

New World £

map 14

Gerard Place, W1V 7LL
071-734 0677 and 0396

COOKING 1
COST £11–£31

'Really on peak form during a frantic Friday lunch-time,' comments a fan. This sprawling dim-sum arena performs best when it is running at a pace. Legions of trolley girls, waitresses and waiters are the main characters in the action. Turnover is fast. Devotees have their favourites from the challenging assortment of morsels on offer. King prawn cheung-fun (slithery, white rice-flour rolls moistened with rice vinegar and soy), pungent, deeply flavoured stuffed aubergine, beef dumplings with ginger and spring onion, spring rolls with sweet-and-sour sauce, and steamed siu mai dumplings have all been memorable. Gigantic helpings of noodle soups with barbecued pork or duck are prepared at the table. Added to this there are plates of roast suckling pig and barbecued pork, exemplary roast duck sliced and piled on a bed of peanuts, and 'wondrous' custard tarts. The weak point is deep-fried dishes, such as squid with sweet-and-sour dip, which really need to come direct from the kitchen to the plate. The evening menu (dim-sum are served from 11am to 6pm) draws few reports, although it offers some intriguing chef's specials. House French is £6.05.

CHEFS: L. Diep, T.W. Man and W.L. Wong PROPRIETORS: New World Restaurant Ltd OPEN: all week; 11am to 11.45pm (11pm Sun) MEALS: alc. Set L and D £6.60 to £10.50 SERVICE: not inc CARDS: Access, Amex, Diners, Visa DETAILS: 600 seats. Private parties: 200 main room, 20, 80 and 100 private rooms. Vegetarian meals. Children welcome. Wheelchair access (also WC). Music. Air-conditioned

£ *indicates that it is possible to have a three-course meal, including coffee, a half-bottle of house wine and service, at any time the restaurant is open (i.e. at dinner as well as at lunch, unless a place is open only for dinner), for £20 or less per person.*

Nico Central

NEW ENTRY map 13

35 Great Portland Street, W1N 5DD
071-436 8846

COOKING 3
COST £27–£45

Step one of Nico Ladenis' repositioning fell into place as the *Guide* went to press. Step two, which is the reopening of Chez Nico under the umbrella of the Grosvenor House Hotel on Park Lane – to be called Nico at Ninety (90 Park Lane, W1A 3AA, Tel: 071-409 1290) – is imminent. Nico Central is where Chez Nico used to be. The chef is Andrew Jeffs, who cooked at Simply Nico in Rochester Row (see entry, London), a restaurant that was itself a result of fission as Nico moved from Victoria to the rag trade district of Great Portland Street. If it all reads like a soap opera, that's because it is; but there is a thread of continuity. Nico Central runs the same menu as Simply Nico, with a few extra dishes. It also prices them individually, not as a whole meal deal. This allows the streetwise to rest with a couple of first courses. Equally, it enables Nico to raise a few more sous from the normal diners to pay the extra overheads. It still works out as fairly costed, even though there are pitfalls such as the charge for vegetables and the upper reaches of the wine list. Service is firmly included, and the wine list has good range below £20. The carpets and walls are just as Chez Nico used to be. The tables are also the same, though with oilcloths under the linen, and the chairs are now bentwood simplicity. There is a certain dissonance between one set of fittings and the relics of the old which will doubtless settle down. The menu affords steady cooking of consistent quality (see the Simply Nico entry). You get classy details from old hands. Thus the potato purée, heavy with the scent of olive oil, is yet as light as a feather. The crème caramel is rich but lifted by the sharpening with citrus. The boudin blanc is refined, as is the mustard sauce. The guinea-fowl cooked with baked beans smells of poultry, as it should do, and makes one appreciate the bird more than many 'haute cuisine' treatments. The coffee is strong; the bread is from one of London's gutsier bakeries; the service is proper. The formula developed in Victoria worked well, whether it bears repetition remains to be seen. House wine is £10.

CHEF: Andrew Jeffs PROPRIETORS: Nico and Dinah-Jane Ladenis OPEN: Mon to Sat, exc Sat L; 12 to 2.15, 6.30 to 11 MEALS: alc SERVICE: net prices, card slips closed CARDS: Access, Amex, Diners, Visa DETAILS: 70 seats. Private parties: 60 main room, 12 private room. Vegetarian meals. No children under 10. No pipes in dining-room. Wheelchair access (1 step). No music. Air-conditioned. Fax: 071-355 4877

Now & Zen

map 14

4A Upper St Martin's Lane, WC2 9EA
071-497 0376, 0377 and 0378

COOKING 1*
COST £23–£42

Dazzling modern architecture and design are features of all restaurants in the Zen chain. This branch, between Soho Chinatown and Covent Garden, conveys a sense of sheer visual exhilaration, with its white walls, mirrors and water in the form of a spiral fountain of saucers. On the ground floor is a sushi bar. The menu makes exotic reading: soft-shell crabs with peppercorn salt; Ching dynasty chicken broth with fresh chrysanthemum petals; Szechuan-style French beans with minced meat and shredded courgettes cooked with dried chilli in a clay pot. Vegetarian options are equally appealing: crispy seaweed topped with pine-kernels; spring rolls given extra piquance with pickled vegetables in the filling; succulent peeled aubergines with spices; braised bean curd with Chinese mushrooms and mange-tout. Like the décor, dishes are 'high on art', but exhibitionism can sometimes be at the expense of taste. It is possible to eat good-value meals, although specialities such as lobster and abalone will inflate the bill. Best value on the 70-strong wine list is from the New World bottles. House wines are from £10.50.

CHEF: Michael Leung   PROPRIETORS: Blaidwood Company Ltd   OPEN: all week; noon to 11.30   MEALS: alc. Set D £16   SERVICE: 12.5%, card slips closed   CARDS: Access, Amex, Diners, Visa   DETAILS: 200 seats. Private parties: 100 main room, 40 private room. Vegetarian meals. Children welcome. Smart dress preferred. Wheelchair access (also WC). Music. Air-conditioned. Fax: 071-437 0641

Odette's 🍾

map 11

130 Regent's Park Road, NW1 8XL
071-586 5486 and 8766

COOKING 3
COST £22–£42

The shift in the emphasis of the cooking from old to new that was inaugurated last year has been continued, with greater steadiness of performance, by the new chef Paul Holmes in this restaurant within reach of a fast-bowler's long run-up when Lord's is in play, or a short stroll from Primrose Hill. The village atmosphere of the street is echoed by the open doors and tables on the pavement on sunny days, though the principal dining-room is a hallowed shrine of dark-green paint and gilt-framed mirrors, with an airier conservatory room in what was once the garden behind. Odette's is neighbourhood-plus: the prices are fair enough to keep a strong local band of regulars, the cooking is good enough to gather them in from further afield. The menu, changing at lunch and dinner, is usually longer on starters than main courses, sometimes more interesting for fish than for meat. It has embraced modern idioms. Cooking is robust, arrangements are simple, and flavours are often strong. A spring meal took in cream of scorzonera soup with rocket leaves wilting in the hot liquid. Stock was not so strong as to drown out the vegetable, and the rocket gave bite and seasoning. Oysters were served with spicy wontons (all lemon grass and a bit of chilli); sometimes they come with red-hot Thai sausages. Calf's kidney, properly trimmed and nicely pink, was served with a shallot purée and round-flavoured red wine and stock sauce. Vegetables were broccoli with strips of roasted pimento, baked potato, roast turnips and roast carrots. It's a change to see some effort and seasonality applied to vegetables. Apple sponge proved to be an upside-down affair with caramelised apple and prune, with rich vanilla ice-cream. Puddings here are good, unusual without being wayward, with a line of heavy things in the winter, fruit in the summer – the peaches poached with basil put another perspective on the form. The repertoire as a whole is happily wide-ranging, and the materials are carefully bought. Bread is another strong suit, and there are those who eat the fudge with the coffee (it's richer than most). The wine list is mostly from Bibendum, occupying premises at the bottom of the road. The choice is from all over the world, the properties and growers are among the most fashionable and prices are realistic. House wines are from £7.50, and there are half a dozen better things by the glass. CELLARMAN'S CHOICE: Bergerac, Ch. Court les Muts 1990, £11.50; California, Pinot Noir 'Carneros' 1989, Saintsbury, £18.85. Down in the cellar is a wine bar, though brasserie is the preferred description. Its food has improved by leaps and bounds, and the prices have not increased, making it a good bet for lunch or something quicker.

CHEF: Paul Holmes PROPRIETOR: Simone Green OPEN: all week, exc Sat L and Sun D; 12.30 to 2.30, 7 to 11 MEALS: alc SERVICE: not inc, card slips closed CARDS: Access, Amex, Diners, Visa DETAILS: 55 seats. Private parties: 8 and 28 private rooms. Children welcome. No music

---

192 🍾

map 11

192 Kensington Park Road, W11 2ES
071-229 0482

COOKING 1*
COST £27–£38

The immediate neighbourhood, apparently mostly made up of singles and young families, keeps this place on its feet and running. People from outlying districts may find the welcome 'brusque to the point of dismissive', but service is often keen. The ground floor is the wine bar (food available), while the main seat of action is down below where the side room extends beneath next door. The place has been around a time, has seen many campaigns, and is not as fresh-faced as a new recruit, even if it is an early example of post-modernism. The new chef returns to his master's haunts, for here Alastair Little first made his mark, and Dan Evans was his assistant in Soho before trying his own wings at Odette's (see entry, above). The menu bears the hallmarks of modern Italianate cooking, agglomerations of things rather than careful compositions, enthusiasm, and a keenness to seek out supplies. A duck platter consists of galantine, confit, parfait, croûtons, truffle oil and some pickles: 'It would be great for a picnic, more trouble as a first course.' Sun-dried tomato risotto comes with piedmontese peppers and pesto. Roast mushrooms are served with tapénade, spinach, feta and tsatsiki. Even at main course, fish comes as a trio in a dish of salmon, halibut and John Dory pan-fried with garlic and herbs, and chicken and minted couscous has some hummus to help it all down. The execution can be mixed, and the enthusiasm leads to an unbalanced menu. Puddings are not so fine and coffee lacks aroma. The wine list is full of savvy. It is short, the bottles are good and there's plenty by two sizes of glass. The prices are fairness made manifest. House wine is £8.20. CELLARMAN'S CHOICE: California, Sauvignon Blanc 1990, Groth, £14.75; Côteaux Varois, Dom. de Triennes 1990, £11.

CHEF: Dan Evans PROPRIETORS: Anthony Mackintosh, John Armit and Tchaik Chassay OPEN: all week, exc Mon L; 12.30 to 3 (3.30 Sat and Sun), 7.30 to 11.30 (11 Sun) CLOSED: bank hols MEALS: alc SERVICE: not inc CARDS: Access, Amex, Visa DETAILS: 70 seats. 3 tables outside. Private parties: 28 main room. Children's helpings. No cigars/pipes in dining-room. Music. Fax: 071-727 7133

The 1994 Guide will be published before Christmas 1993. Reports on meals are most welcome at any time of the year, but are extremely valuable in the spring. Send them to The Good Food Guide, *FREEPOST, 2 Marylebone Road, London NW1 1YN. No stamp is needed if posted in the UK.*

Orso ♥

map 14

27 Wellington Street, WC2E 7DA
071-240 5269

COOKING 1*
COST £28–£38

This giant basement has a large door on to the street, but there is little warning as you go down that this is the resort of legions of trendy people, all chattering ten to the dozen and all happily eating sound, modern Italian food at acceptable prices. Popularity has its drawbacks: the staff get battle fatigue, you are asked to vacate your table two hours after your booking time, some of the handsome pottery from Italy, giving gay colour in muted surroundings, is showing the scars of its own battle. The menu is large and changes all the time. Small pizzas and pasta have their own sections and first courses revolve around many salads (these are not insipid collections of leaves, however). Main dishes, when successful, are bolder than any trattoria's range of veal. Pasta – for instance, spaghetti with scallops, parsley and garlic, penne with tomato, aubergine and mozzarella, or tagliatelle with spiced sausage, tomato and herbs – comes well recommended. Position and hours make Orso convenient for the theatre; early dinners, however, seem a less sound bet than those at prime time. The ideas are all there but execution has lacked energy. The wine list occupies a page, encompassing a range to please any Italophile – a Valpolicella from Allegrini at £11, a 1987 Sassicaia for £47.50 and a trio of Spumantis, for instance. House wine is £9 a litre.

CHEF: Martin Wilson PROPRIETORS: Orso Restaurants Ltd OPEN: all week; noon to midnight CLOSED: 25 and 26 Dec MEALS: alc SERVICE: not inc DETAILS: 110 seats. Vegetarian meals. Children welcome. No music. Fax: 071-497 2148

Osteria Antica Bologna £

map 10

23 Northcote Road, SW11 1NG
071-978 4771

COOKING 1*
COST £12–£29

No one disputes the good value here, or the need to book in advance. It tries to oblige all comers, though there may be two sittings of an evening as a result. The Clapham interpretation of a Bolognese inn seems to be small tables crowded together with uncomfortable chairs and benches in the main room and a conservatory. But the spirits are kept high because of everyone's pleasure at having got here – and not needing to spend too much into the bargain. Aurelio Spagnuolo was born in Sicily then raised in Bologna, and his cooking reflects the mix of north and south. The trademark is the assaggi – small dishes in the manner of tapas – but there is also a full range of pasta or clean-tasting salads, before main courses evenly spread between meat and fish. Recommendations have included cuttlefish risotto; prawns with chilli; spinach with Gorgonzola, or with pine-nuts and sultanas; octopus with black olives and tomatoes; oxtail with tomato and celery; and kid with lemon, egg and asparagus. Standards may fluctuate on impossibly busy nights. The all-Italy wine list is an excellent accompaniment, and would that all lists were so reasonably priced. House wine is £6.90.

🍾 *denotes an outstanding wine cellar;* ♥ *denotes a good wine list, worth travelling for.*

CHEF: Aurelio Spagnuolo   PROPRIETORS: Rochelle Porteous and Aurelio Spagnuolo
OPEN: all week, exc L Mon and Tue; Mon and Tue 6 to 11, Wed to Sat noon to 11, Sun 12.30
to 10.30   MEALS: alc. Set L £6.50   SERVICE: not inc (10% for 5 or more, card slips closed)
CARDS: Access, Amex, Visa   DETAILS: 70 seats. Private parties: 40 main room. Vegetarian
meals. Children welcome. Music. Air-conditioned

Panda Si Chuen £

map 14

56 Old Compton Street, W1V 5PA
071-437 2069

COOKING 1
COST £15–£35

'A very friendly, comparatively cheap Chinese restaurant where one can get
some spicy food,' sums up the appeal of this spick-and-span Soho venue. The
menu of around 100 dishes shows signs of Westernisation in dishes such as
chicken and sweetcorn soup, lemon chicken and sweet-and-sour pork, but it
can also deliver some authentic Szechuan specialities. Pelmeni with hot chilli
oil is regularly mentioned. Otherwise the repertoire takes in stewed croaker
fish, tea-smoked duck, red-cooked aubergines, sam-sin soup noodles and
steamed bread rolls. The cooking is adequate and consistent, although the
predominance of chilli, garlic and other ingredients may result in repetitive
flavours and a lack of individuality in some dishes. Service is first-rate, ultra-
efficient and attentive. Drink saké or tea. House French wine is £7.

CHEF: Ping Tzue   PROPRIETOR: K.C. Chew   OPEN: Mon to Sat; noon to 11.30   MEALS: alc.
Set L and D £9 to £16.50   SERVICE: 10%   CARDS: Access, Amex, Diners, Visa   DETAILS:
60 seats. Private parties: 40 main room, 15 private room. Vegetarian meals. Children
welcome. Music. Air-conditioned

Il Passetto £

map 13

230 Shaftesbury Avenue, WC2H 8EG
071-836 9391 and 379 7962

COOKING 1
COST £17–£39

'Young ladies beware' was the sage advice of a seasoned customer, who enjoys
the 'pregos and grazies galore' in this long-running theatre of trattoria cooking.
The portions, he also suggested, may have been trimmed with the coming of
harder times, but the cooking is a good example of its kind, and the zuppa
inglese would fill a lake. The menu does not actually change; if it did, people
might not know what to eat. There is a quick list of inexpensive Italian wines;
house wine is £7.95.

CHEF: Jesus Sanchez   PROPRIETORS: Domenico Forcina and Jesus Sanchez   OPEN: Mon to
Sat, exc Sat L; 12 to 3, 6 to 11.30   CLOSED: 25 and 26 Dec, bank hols   MEALS: alc. Cover
£1   SERVICE: not inc   CARDS: Access, Amex, Diners, Visa   DETAILS: 46 seats. Private
parties: 50 main room. Children welcome. Wheelchair access. Music. Air-conditioned

*London round-ups listing additional restaurants that may be worth a visit can be found
after the main London section.*

🚭 *indicates that smoking is either banned altogether or that a dining-room is maintained
for non-smokers. The symbol does not apply to restaurants that simply have no-smoking
areas.*

Pearl　　　　　　　　　　　　NEW ENTRY　map 12

22 Brompton Road, SW1X 7QN　　　　　　　　　COOKING 2
071-225 3888　　　　　　　　　　　　　　　　　COST £18–£70

Taking over the Sabatini spot on Knightsbridge Green has put Pearl in an unenviable position of having to live up to its predecessor's self-conscious modishness. The interior, almost under-designed, works well; the few tables at the front are a pleasant window on the lunchtime world of shoppers. Waiting, too, avoids cliché, being well drilled and amiable under proprietorial eye. Dim-sum are excellent: for example, a generous prawn filling for the har gau, fine translucent wrappings for the other steamed dumplings and well-flavoured lotus leaf-wrapped rice and carefully cooked glutinous rice. Quality comes at bargain prices given the location and ambience. The menu also avoids tedium when the main meal is in question. Braised beef tendons in a light soy soup flavoured with bitter orange peel have a wonderful gelatinous texture, hot-and-sour lobster soup is a de luxe version of a standard, noodles are good, and the fresh crab has been well reported. Whole sucking pig is a speciality at £150 a throw. House wines are £11; saké, shao-sing or chia fan chien are £17 a bottle.

CHEF: Felix Yiu　PROPRIETORS: the Lam family　OPEN: all week; 12 to 3, 6 to 11.30 (noon to 11.30 Sat and Sun)　CLOSED: 25 and 26 Dec　MEALS: alc. Set L £8.50 to £12.50, Set D £25 to £40. Cover £2. Minimum £15　SERVICE: not inc　CARDS: Access, Amex, Diners, Visa　DETAILS: 90 seats. Private parties: 100 main room, 20 private room. Vegetarian meals. Children welcome. Smart dress preferred. Music. Air-conditioned

Le P'tit Normand　　　　　　　　NEW ENTRY　map 10

185 Merton Road, SW18 5EF　　　　　　　　　COOKING 1
081-871 0233　　　　　　　　　　　　　　　　COST £16–£27

Resolutely Norman – beams, candles, gingham, copper and brass, travelogue posters – this place knocks out sound bistro food with a will and a generous heart ('monster ducks had been bred for the confit'), though in the eyes of some reporters, it falls down on the details. The short printed menu grows in range if you take account of the dailies chalked on the blackboard. Black pudding, artichoke soufflé, stuffed leg of duck, confit of duck, duck Vallée d'Auge, a slightly cheesy panaché of seafood, very generous seafood pancakes, a light brown tarte Tatin, apple sorbet well dosed with calvados, Grand Marnier soufflé: these are some of the items mentioned this year, as also is the magnificent French cheeseboard. Service runs along and M. Herrard is there to supervise. The wine list has only 16 choices, but there is interest none the less, and no overcharging. Menetou-Salon from Henry Pellé, Chardonnay de St-Bris from Hervé Félix, and Sauvignon de Touraine from Michel Antier are three worth drinking. There is also an excellent selection of vintage calvados. House wines are £7.35.

CHEF/PROPRIETOR: Philippe Herrard　OPEN: all week, exc Sat L; 12 to 2, 7 to 10.30 (11 Sat, 10 Sun)　MEALS: alc. Set L £9.75 to £16.75, Set D £16.75　SERVICE: 12.5%, card slips closed　CARDS: Access, Amex, Visa　DETAILS: 30 seats. Private parties: 25/30 main room, 20 and 30 private rooms. Vegetarian meals. Children's helpings. No pipes in dining-room. Wheelchair access (1 step). Music

Pied-à-Terre

NEW ENTRY map 13

34 Charlotte Street, W1P 1HJ
071-636 1178

COOKING 3*
COST £27–£50

Devotees of things Indian will recognise the former premises – and chairs, and fittings – of Jamdani. The conversion from tandoori to avant-garde European cooking was rapidly effected. The stone-coloured roughcast walls were washed in white. Richard Hamilton lent some arresting works of pop art, as well as 'a strange still-life of knees and tins of tomato soup,' according to one reader mystified by it all, but who liked the hand-painted plates that make up the place-settings, and the plain, elegant china and glassware. David Moore and Richard Neat come young to owning restaurants and have made no bones about going for the quality market. Their background (and backers like Raymond Blanc) is right: Jamin, Harveys and Le Manoir aux Quat'Saisons for Neat, Adlard's and Le Manoir for Moore. Their prices do not leave much doubt either. Richard Neat's cooking is as current as can be: everything arrives with strips of something (beans, leeks, fennel). All the ingredients are there – mash, dried légumes, olive oil, offal and cabbage, and when he is on song, the flavours are upstanding, though not invariably. The pricier menu changes within fairly close parameters and runs to about seven items per course. A summer meal gives an idea of the character. Roasted scallops with baby artichokes and coriander are just stiffened and caramelised, the corals sliced to one side. Tiny artichokes give texture and have sufficient flavour; more variety and balance come from tomato flesh and a pile of tissue-thin courgettes. The coriander avoids over-intrusiveness. In another first course, foie gras is served with fresh lime. The offal is laid over a crisp pile of paper-thin potato, and onion and lime in the sauce cut through the richness. A main course of red mullet is crisped on top of the stove and served on a pile of tomato, fennel and basil, then given a mop of angel-hair threads of fried leek. The plate is ringed with punchy tapénade. Pigeon comes as breast ('crisp, moist, almost livery') over thin slices of crisp celeriac, and there are parcels of cabbage holding an earthy confit of the rest of the bird. Lentils give padding, in three colours, and add the peasant dimension. It is now that you get your freebie: a deeply rich tub of crème brûlée with a pralined topping. If you can stagger to the last course, a mille-feuille of raspberries gets more votes than any of the other desserts. Coffee and petits fours are extremely superior. Other things that have been enjoyed include soups and veloutés involving oysters, a giant exercise in offal with braised pig's head and root vegetables, a salad of skate with purée of broccoli and fondant potatoes, John Dory with a foie gras sauce (this really worked) and peas, and various tarts at the finish. The effort seems worth it, though many wish that production could be more rapid. You can study economy with the half-price lunch, which is fair value, though materials are less exciting. You will not have much saving from the wine list, which manages only a baker's dozen of bottles at less than £20, though the choice is very fashionable (Quenard's Chignin, Juillot, Rousseau, Guigal, Vincent and others), and there are a dozen New Worlders (but nothing from Italy or Spain) to give balance. You can get by with a fair choice of wines by the glass. If the economy allows Pied-à-Terre to survive, and if Richard Neat could hasten some of his cooking, then we will have something worthy of the list of top 20 restaurants.

CHEF: Richard Neat   PROPRIETORS: David Moore and Richard Neat   OPEN: Mon to Sat,
exc Sat L; 12.15 to 2.30, 7.15 to 10.30   CLOSED: last week Dec, first week Jan, last 2 weeks
Aug   MEALS: Set L £17.50 and £36, Set D £36   SERVICE: net prices, card slips closed
CARDS: Access, Amex, Diners, Visa   DETAILS: 40 seats. Private parties: 40 main room.
Vegetarian meals with prior notice. Children welcome.
No cigars/pipes in dining-room. No music. Air-conditioned

Pizzeria Castello £

map 11

20 Walworth Road, SE1 6SP
071-703 2556

COOKING 1
COST £11–£16

To find the Castello, smell the air for garlic. When found, expect no comfort, no
quiet, no beauty – just pizzas. Thin-based, soggy from the weight of tomato,
with generous fillings, the pizzas are cooked in impressive ovens at the front of
the shop, where you queue and hope for someone to leave. Eating goes on
beyond. People like the garlic bread, the minestrone, the trifle and the tiramisù,
and like still more the pizzas. Output is consistent. An outpost, a beacon, a
pathfinder for the Elephant and Castle, say many. Drink Italian beer or gulp the
house wine at £5.50.

CHEF: Cicero Calogero   PROPRIETORS: Renzo Meda and Antonio Proietti   OPEN: Mon to
Sat, exc Sat L; noon (5 Sat) to 11   MEALS: alc   SERVICE: not inc   CARDS: Access, Visa
DETAILS: 180 seats. Private parties: 30 main room. Vegetarian meals. Children's helpings on
request. Wheelchair access (also WC). Music. Air-conditioned

Pizzeria Condotti £

map 13

4 Mill Street, W1R 9TE
071-499 1308

COOKING 1
COST £15–£26

The discreet charm of the Condotti: 'Wishing to eat after the theatre, we
attempted to gain a table at a fashionable Covent Garden place – for the
atmosphere, not the food. It was full. Walked past the Condotti: at first it
appeared closed, but it wasn't, just emptying at the end of a long night. It was
worth the diversion: excellent pizza bases.' The menu and cooking style are
closely related to those of Peter Boizot's Pizza Express chain. There are many
who find it a very consistent example of the art, like the pictures and enjoy the
location. The pizzas are thin, the toppings in proportion, and the service is fast.
There is also a range of salads and ice-creams. House Italian is £7.50.

CHEFS: Mahmoud Eskendry and Nacevr Hammami   PROPRIETORS: Enzo Apicella and
Peter Boizot   OPEN: Mon to Sat; 11.30am to midnight   MEALS: alc   SERVICE: not inc
(12.5% for 6 or more)   CARDS: Access, Amex, Diners, Visa   DETAILS: 130 seats. Private
parties: 70 main room, 50 private room. Children's helpings. Wheelchair access (2 steps).
No music. Air-conditioned

'''I'm sorry to rush you but everyone seems to want service at the same time.'''
On eating in Sussex

*'Whilst we were left without service for long periods, the owner/manager sat down to eat
his own meal at a nearby table.'*   On eating in Nottinghamshire

Poissonnerie de l'Avenue

map 12

82 Sloane Avenue, SW3 3DZ
071-589 5774 and 2457

COOKING 1
COST £26–£50

An old-fashioned fish restaurant, with old-fashioned ambience and service that marks the point which London fish cookery had reached before the revolution of the '70s. The materials can be very good, their rendition cream-laden and old-style. People like this place best who have a long-standing acquaintance with the maître d' and his cohorts. If you are not so privileged, reported one irritated reader, matters may not be so seamlessly perfect. The wine list is mainly white and more affordable than might be expected. House wines are £9.

CHEFS: Fernando Tomassi and J. Roses   PROPRIETOR: Peter Rosignoli   OPEN: Mon to Sat; 12 to 3, 7 to 11.30   CLOSED: 23 Dec to 3 Jan, 4 days Easter, bank hols   MEALS: alc. Cover £1.25   SERVICE: 15%, card slips closed   CARDS: Access, Amex, Diners, Visa   DETAILS: 90 seats. 8 tables outside. Private parties: 24 private room. Children's helpings. Smart dress preferred. No-smoking area. Wheelchair access. No music. Air-conditioned. Fax: 071-581 3360

Pollyanna's 🍾

map 10

2 Battersea Rise, SW11 1ED
071-228 0316

COOKING 1
COST £38

The breathlessly modern decoration and arrangement of the place is rather successful: a long dining-room on a mezzanine with broad blocks of colour, spot lighting and a sense of perspective (even if narrowing here and there). To old hands who have witnessed the transformation over the years from a jolly bistro with wines into this quite serious-looking restaurant, it must be disconcerting. The cooking is in keeping with the decoration, but is less uniformly successful. Bits are good: a roast pigeon on potatoes, salmon with a sole mousse and champagne and chive sauce, calf's liver and mash – sometimes on dauphinois – or guinea-fowl with red wine. Other bits have misfired. There is a degree of simplification this year, which is no bad thing. Norman Price is a good host and he knows his wines. His staff can be less impressive. Wine-buying is strictly Francophile; but within that boundary, which by the year becomes harder to defend, there is enthusiasm as well as consideration. The clarets alone offer a range of quality and maturity second to none, from many good bourgeois growths to familiar second growths. Half-bottles are abundant. House wines are from £12.95. CELLARMAN'S CHOICE: Santenay Blanc 1989, Leflaive, £28.50; St-Emilion, Ch. de Lisse 1986, £16.50.

CHEF: Richard Aldridge   PROPRIETOR: Norman Price   OPEN: Mon to Sat, D only; 7 to 12   CLOSED: 4 days Christmas   MEALS: Set D £18.50 to £22.50   SERVICE: 10%, card slips closed   CARDS: Access, Visa   DETAILS: 35 seats. Private parties: 20 main room, 35 private room. Vegetarian meals. Children's helpings. Music

Prices quoted in the Guide *are based on information supplied by restaurateurs. The prices quoted at the top of each entry represent a range, from the lowest meal price to the highest; the latter is inflated by 10 per cent to take account of likely price rises during the year of the* Guide.

Le Pont de la Tour 🍾

36 Shad Thames,
Butlers Wharf, SE1 2YE
071-403 8403

COOKING **2***
COST £25–£56

'My petit salé with lentils had a fine, rustic, earthy taste and moist texture to the
meat,' wrote one who welcomed this gastrodome. Sir Terence Conran has
developed a series of ventures along this terrace overlooking Tower Bridge:
restaurant, bar and grill, bakery, wine shop and food store. The ambition is
impressive; Le Pont de la Tour is marketed, and enjoyed, as an experience.
People like the buzz, the smart set, the view, the open-air dining in fine
weather, the chance to slum it (with elegance if not comfort) in the bar – the
whole package. They even write about the lavatories. The restaurant is a long
room in good modern taste but without much fun to it, where there is
emphatically a front row (views) and a back (nothing). A set-price menu is
offered at lunch and a long *carte* at dinner; and there is a shift in culinary mood
between lunch, which emphasises the virtues of fish and chips, black pudding
and other simple things of life, and dinner, which gets into fillet steaks, foie
gras, venison and oysters. Make no bones, dinner is dear: add 15 per cent for
service and you'll probably hit £40 for food alone. The implications of
simplicity apply at dinner too, and there is little by way of needless
elaboration. The problem lies with performance. Too many meals have been
flawed. A plate of Bayonne ham with celeriac rémoulade was faultless, but
quantities were minimal. The potatoes for champ, mashed on a machine, were
gluey. A green salad came with raw onion. Saffron risotto lacked saffron and
seasoning, and was stodgy to boot. Arbroath smokies with tomato and Gruyère
were fine tasting but cold. Oxtail was undercooked. Rabbit was tough, though
the prunes, bacon and wild mushrooms with it were matchless. Fish soup
lacked garlic. But when everything hums, praise flows: best end of lamb with a
parsley cream was 'the best dish' ever served to a man from the City;
aubergines with pesto avoided bitterness and had great depth of flavour; bread
(from their own bakery) and butter were first-class; and the bread-and-butter
pudding was rich and creamy. Portions are generous. Shellfish is as good as
should be expected with the care taken about supplies; bourgeois dishes like
tripe with lyonnais sausage, onions and parsley have been appreciated; so, too,
have desserts such as crème brûlée, tarte Tatin, lemon tart and apple and
almond tart. Service goes up and down. Everyone speaks well of the bar, and
the wine list demands great concentration. Fastidious buying has assembled an
intelligent list which is fairly priced, with bottles like Allegrini Valpolicella at
£10.75 and many good mid-range burgundies and Loires around £15. There are
majestic clarets and two mouthwatering columns of dessert wines. House wine
is £8.50. CELLARMAN'S CHOICE: Gewurztraminer 1990, Preiss-Zimmer, £16.50;
Corbières, Ch. de Lastours 1988, £11.50.

CHEF: David Burke PROPRIETORS: Sir Terence Conran, Joel Kissin and David Burke
OPEN: all week; 12 to 3, 6 to 12 (10.30 Sun) CLOSED: 25 Dec MEALS: alc. Set L £22.50.
Grill menu SERVICE: 15%, card slips closed CARDS: Access, Amex, Visa DETAILS: 105
seats. 33 tables outside. Private parties: 10 main room, 20 private room. Vegetarian meals.
Wheelchair access (also WC). No music. Fax: 071-403 0267

Poons £

map 14

4 Leicester Street, WC2H 7BL
071-437 1528

COOKING 2
COST £12–£23

Refurbishments are in train, but this is still, one reader remarked, 'the best café in the area'. 'Great wind-dried meats and sausages. Chinese hotpots are genuine and hearty,' says another. 'Boldly flavoured and fresh' was a comment after a noodle lunch. Pork and preserved vegetable soup 'had a deeply flavoured gutsy stock, good meat and great chunks of intriguingly flavoured, pungent, preserved Chinese cabbage'. King prawn chow-mein was made memorable by the sheer quality of the prawns. A loyal following for this place keeps standards high and perhaps the smiles on the waiters' faces. It's worth looking at the scallop, squid, eel and bean curd dishes on the menu. Tsingtao beer or jasmine tea should be just the ticket. House French wine is £6.

CHEF/PROPRIETOR: W.N. Poon OPEN: all week; noon to 11.30 CLOSED: 25 Dec MEALS: alc. Set L £7 to £11, Set D £7 to £15 SERVICE: not inc DETAILS: 100 seats. Private parties: 30 main room. Children welcome. No music. Air-conditioned. Fax: 081-458 0968

Poons £

map 14

27 Lisle Street, WC2H 7BA
071-437 4549

COOKING 2
COST £9–£18

This is 'not a restaurant where customers rate the décor highly', but it offers 'excellent authentic Chinese cooking', according to one enthusiastic visitor. The cramped downstairs room has been described as 'definitely seedy', with its Formica-topped tables and elbow-to-elbow seating. Upstairs is almost posh by comparison. Two types of speciality dominate the hard-core Cantonese menu: renowned wind-dried ducks, sausages and Chinese bacon; also 'original' hotpots, such as stewed eel with crispy pork and garlic, which are cooked and served in lidded metal pots. One-plate rice and noodle dishes are some of the best and some of the cheapest in Chinatown. Many dishes continue to draw recommendations: wun-tun soup made with 'lovely fresh clean stock'; outstanding char siu pork and roast duck; fried scallops with oyster sauce; beef with ginger and pineapple. Choi-sum greens with oyster sauce are juicy and slithery. Drink Jasmine tea.

CHEFS: Mr B.T. Ly and Mr Chiu PROPRIETORS: Mr and Mrs Kit Chuen Chiu OPEN: all week; noon to 11.30 CLOSED: Christmas MEALS: alc. Set D £7.50. Minimum £2.20. Unlicensed, but bring your own: no corkage SERVICE: not inc DETAILS: 40 seats. Private parties: 30 main room. Vegetarian meals. Children welcome. No music. Air-conditioned

Quality Chop House £

map 11

94 Farringdon Road, EC1R 3EA
071-837 5093

COOKING 2*
COST £16–£32

'Progressive working-class caterer' is Charles Fontaine's description of his up-market café. Here, egg, bacon and chips are served alongside confit of duck to customers packed in 'uncomfortable' pine-settled booths, surrounded by bottled sauces and gas lamps on the walls. Most people love the atmosphere, the flexibility of the menu and the good humour of the place. Many dishes have met with approval: warm asparagus with slivers of Parmesan; bang-bang chicken; rigatoni ai quattro formaggi; rib-eye steak; salmon fish-cake with sorrel sauce. Other fish specials are well reported, vegetables are generally 'crunchy and simple', and chips are A1. Sweets, ranging from kiwi sorbet to bread-and-butter pudding, draw mixed reports. As one American visitor noted: 'This is capable and interesting food, but not so good that you can stop worrying about the preparation.' Indeed, regulars have noticed some disconcerting signs of late, a suggestion that 'there are things being cut back' – 'The starters are more simple; liver is now lamb's, not calf's'; and steaks can be tough, especially 'if you hit a thin one'. The restaurant no longer serves breakfast, although Sunday brunch remains. Teas, coffees and bottled beers provide a choice of drinks. House French is £7.75.

CHEF/PROPRIETOR: Charles Fontaine   OPEN: all week, exc Sat L; 12 to 3 (3.30 Sun), 6.30 to 12 (11.30 Sun)   MEALS: alc   SERVICE: not inc   DETAILS: 48 seats. Vegetarian meals. Children's helpings. No music

Ragam £

map 13

57 Cleveland Street, W1P 5PQ

071-636 9098

COOKING 1*

COST £10–£23

The tiny, cramped dining-room across the road from the Middlesex Hospital retains its special place as one of the most consistent Indian restaurants in this part of London. 'Honest cooking with clear distinct flavours' is one reporter's verdict. The menu continues to offer intriguing south Indian and Keralan vegetarian specialities pointed up with the elemental flavours of chilli, coconut and curry leaves. There are excellent dosai of various shapes and sizes – including a 'ghee roast' version (a burnished, golden brown, foot-long tube filled with mashed potato and fried onion). Fiery uthappam (a south Indian pizza) demands the mollifying coolness of coconut chutney, while avial is a Keralan vegetable stew with an almost 'cheesy' sauce of yoghurt and coconut. The full range of standard curries and vegetable dishes is notable for fresh spicing and a lack of oiliness: chicken malabar with 'searing hot-and-sour overtones' has been recommended. Rice and breads are outstanding. Service is courteous and prices are fair, although one regular noted that the décor now seems to be verging on the 'tacky'. Drink mango lassi or lager. House wine is £6.70.

CHEFS: J. Dharmaseelan and Mojid Ullah   PROPRIETORS: J. Dharmaseelan, T. Haridas and S. Pillai   OPEN: all week; 12 to 3, 6 to 11.30   CLOSED: bank hols, 25 and 26 Dec   MEALS: alc. Minimum £6   SERVICE: 10%, card slips closed   CARDS: Access, Amex, Diners, Visa DETAILS: 38 seats. Private parties: 34 main room, 25 private room. Vegetarian meals. Children's helpings. Wheelchair access (also WC). Music. Air-conditioned

The Guide *relies on feedback from its readers. Especially welcome are reports on new restaurants appearing in the book for the first time.*

All letters to the Guide *are acknowledged with an update on latest sales, closures, chef changes and so on.*

Rani £

map 10

7 Long Lane, N3 2PR
081-349 4386 and 2636

COOKING 2
COST £10–£27

'It is not only the best Indian food I have eaten in London, it is also the best
vegetarian food,' writes a reporter impressed by the Pattnis' bright, functional
restaurant. 'The reassuring impression of wholesomeness created by home
cooking sans meat, sans fish, sans vindaloo is one thing, but this food is hugely
exciting as well.' Vivid home-made chutneys give 'an invigorating kickstart to
the palate' and set the tone of authenticity which is the hallmark of the kitchen.
Starters such as samosas with date chutney, vegetable bhajia with a pile of pale
green shredded coconut, and aloo papri chat have all been excellent. The range
of curries includes stuffed aubergine and potato, gently spiced mushroom and
pea, and 'sublime' banana methi flecked with slivers of sticky date. Daily
specials take the cooking into even more fascinating territory: undhia (gram
flour and fenugreek dumplings cooked with spices) and tindora (baby
cucumbers with potato and yoghurt) have been endorsed. Accompanying
breads, rice, dhal and raita are stunningly good: the overall impact is one of
colourful profusion. Sweets are generally applauded. Prices are not 'bargain
basement', but few doubt the value for money. Drink lassi, herbal teas or lager.
House wine is £8.

CHEFS: Kundan Pattni and Sheila Pattni   PROPRIETOR: Jyotindra Pattni   OPEN: all week,
exc L Mon, Tue and Sat; 12.30 to 2, 6 to 10.30   CLOSED: 25 Dec   MEALS: alc. Set L £6 to
£12, Set D £11.50 to £19. Minimum £8   SERVICE: net prices, card slips closed   CARDS:
Access, Visa   DETAILS: 90 seats. Vegetarian meals. Children's helpings. No children
under 6. No-smoking area. Music. Fax: 081-349 4386

Riva

map 10

169 Church Road, SW13 9HR
081-748 0434

COOKING 3
COST £22–£37

Riva rocketed to stardom when people found that this small restaurant in
Barnes offered a style of Italian cooking, and ingredients, rarely seen in
London. With a couple of proud exceptions, it was the first surge of a new
wave. The cost of discovery was popularity. It's wise to book for a table in this
unassuming, but cannily decorated, room which sets no store by luxury, and
avoids charging too much into the bargain. 'It reminded me strongly of a place
near the duomo in Milan' was one well-travelled response, which went on to
compare the tiramisù with one habitually ordered in Volterra. The meal
described started with smoked goose breast on grilled chicory with slivers of
pecorino cheese ('the richness of the meat and cheese offset by the tartness of
the chicory') and a bruschetta which was deemed the best yet eaten outside
Italy ('marvellous extra-virgin, and tomatoes sweet and Mediterranean'). The
main dishes were calf's liver with wild mushrooms and polenta (this a little
heavy) and halibut with anchovy sauce. A course is steered between the simple
– grilled vegetables, mixed grill – and the more complex, such as pike with
salsify purée and a green sauce, rabbit with wild mushrooms, and duck with
juniper and grappa. Some dishes come in groups: a fine plate of charcuterie
including goose salami, pancetta and venison bresaola, or three toppings on

polenta. If there is something seasonal to be had from Italy – for instance, white truffles even after a bad year in Piedmont – this place may well be offering it. There are two reservations to all this success. The first is that the cooking is not always accurate; and when it's simple, it shows. The second is the service. This gets more than brickbats. When the most obvious quality of restaurants in Italy is their open and unaffected enjoyment in dealing with customers, it's strange that a London Italian should be so bad at it. It is worse when there is a service charge. The wine list is short but sweet. Names like Jermann, Lageder, Pasolini, Negri and Maculan demonstrate that it deals with the best. The coverage is not complete, but things change. House wine comes in half-litre pichets at £5.80.

CHEF: Francesco Zanchetta   PROPRIETOR: Andrea Riva   OPEN: all week, exc Sat L; 12 to 2.30, 7 to 11 (11.30 Fri and Sat, 9.30 Sun)   CLOSED: Christmas, Easter, bank hols   MEALS: alc   SERVICE: 10%, card slips closed   CARDS: Access, Visa   DETAILS: 50 seats. 2 tables outside. Private parties: 40 main room. Vegetarian meals. Children's helpings. No cigars/pipes in dining-room. Wheelchair access. Music. Air-conditioned

River Café ♟   map 10

Thames Wharf Studios,
Rainville Road, W6 9HA   COOKING 3
071-381 8824   COST £25–£43

'How did we cook before the chargrill?' asks a veteran of the River Café, once the staff canteen for Sir Richard Rogers' architectural practice, now resort of glitterati, with valet parking and high prices. The decoration, however, remains starkly original. 'I loved it, a teachers' dining-room of a state secondary school complete with canteen glass and cutlery' was the reaction of one reporter. River Café offers Italian food, not all of it chargrilled. It was one of the first to change our perception of this cuisine, and was not afraid to do it simply, with good ingredients brought to life by stabs of flavour. And it was among the first to attempt interpretation of slow-cooked farmhouse dishes that gave a new slant to the potential of a trattoria. If you can bring off 'charred scallops with a pesto dressing, real mozzarella with sun-dried tomatoes and bruschetta, chargrilled lamb with cannellini beans, and calf's liver with sage and polenta' without stumbling at any point, perhaps you can justify the prices. Unfortunately, stumblings there are – in timing of simple cooking, in materials, or in making a dish hang together as more than the sum of its parts. Slow-cooked dishes such as beef with aubergines, peppers and tomatoes can be great: 'the meat had taken up all the vegetable flavours, and was sumptuously tender,' remarked one who also appreciated the grilled salmon with enough salsa verde to set it off, and the crisply battered zucchini that came with it. Although the staff do not indulge in Italian habits of hunting anything that flies, the restaurant enjoys cooking game. 'My partridge was dense with a strong sauce and a very concentrated thyme flavour,' said one customer, even if another found teal too dense to eat. The full force of success comes in blindingly simple dishes like the chargrilled squid with chilli ('meltingly tender, sizzlingly striped and searingly hot'). Desserts include good sorbets and a repertoire that is less Italian than the rest. Torte di Gorgonzola is an exception, as is the generous use of mascarpone. The waiting is as modern as the decoration: the staff look like actresses on holiday and vary from nice to off-hand. Physically, the place seems to be fraying round the edges. Most reports feel that it is too dear by comparison with its competitors. It is also very noisy. Wine prices take off rapidly here but there are some decent choices below £15 and quality is impeccable. For the curious, succinct notes are provided at the end of the list. If you are prepared to pay, this must now be one of the best places to try Italian wines. House wine is £9.50. CELLARMAN'S CHOICE: Frascati, 'Villa Simone' 1990, Constantini, £18.50; Freisa delle Langhe 1989, Vajra, £18.

CHEFS: Rose Gray and Ruth Rogers PROPRIETORS: Richard and Ruth Rogers, and Rose Gray OPEN: all week, exc Sat and Sun D; 12.30 to 3.15, 7.30 to 9.15 CLOSED: bank hols MEALS: alc SERVICE: 12.5%, card slips closed CARDS: Access, Visa DETAILS: 75 seats. 8 tables outside. Private parties: 75 main room, 16 private room. Car park. Vegetarian meals. Children's helpings. No cigars/pipes in dining-room. Wheelchair access (also WC). No music

Rotisserie £

map 10

56 Uxbridge Road, W12 8LP
081-743 3028

COOKING 1
COST £20–£27

The spits keep turning on Shepherd's Bush Green, and as there are not so many establishments within walking distance that will lighten the spirits, this is a really useful neighbourhood place. The menu hardly changes at all, though performance can have its ups and downs – perhaps depending on how much business has been seen. The reliable aspect of it all is the rotisserie and the chargrill: simple food filling large gaps. The short wine list takes in Argentina as well as Chinon (which somehow gets called a Beaujolais). House vins de pays are £7.95.

CHEF: Emanuel Schandorf PROPRIETOR: Ian Davies OPEN: Mon to Sun, exc L Sat and Sun; 12 to 3, 6.30 to 11 (7 to 11.30 Fri and Sat) MEALS: alc SERVICE: not inc CARDS: Access, Visa DETAILS: 76 seats. Vegetarian meals. Children welcome. Music

Royal China £

map 10

3 Chelverton Road, SW15 1RN
081-788 0907

COOKING 2
COST £19–£44

This is glitz. Black enamelled walls decorated with waves and birds, perspex-edged pillars and a black ceiling divided into squares by gold lines combine for an eye-catcher. The particular interest of the menu lies in the list of appetisers, which concludes with a handful of chilli-hot wonders. Lobster is a good and varied option, too. The Chinese community, restaurateurs and all, are to be seen taking Sunday lunch here, and if it's a party you want, Royal China will cater for it. House wine is £7.50.

CHEF: Simon Man PROPRIETORS: Ken Poon, Simon Man, Martin Man and Pui Tsoi OPEN: all week; 12 to 2.30, 6 to 11 CLOSED: 25 to 27 Dec MEALS: alc. Set D £20 to £26 (minimum 2) SERVICE: not inc CARDS: Access, Amex, Diners, Visa DETAILS: 80 seats. Private parties: 80 main room. Vegetarian meals. Children welcome. Smart dress preferred. Wheelchair access (also WC). Music. Air-conditioned. Fax: 081-785 2305

Royal China

[NEW ENTRY] map 11

13 Queensway, W2 4QJ
071-221 2535

COOKING 2
COST £21–£52

This high-class Bayswater Chinese restaurant has the same dazzling décor and distinctive menu as its relative in Putney (see previous entry). It draws a cosmopolitan crowd of Chinese families and Westerners. 'Hong Kong chic' is one description of the large L-shaped dining-room, with its black and gold lacquered walls, glass partitions and elegantly clothed tables. The menu is quite long and wide-ranging, with fancy names and a slight bias towards deep-fried dishes – especially among the starters. Many items have been recommended: Peking dumplings in 'very hot' chilli sauce, Vietnamese spring rolls, 'frilly squid balls', jellyfish with marinated pork, 'dragon' prawns sautéed with scallops, lobster with yellow-bean sauce. 'Royal China fish' is a whole Dover sole, deep-fried, sliced and topped with lightly breaded fillets of other fish. Stir-fried vegetables and lotus-leaf rice have been good accompaniments. The kitchen makes few compromises, although occasionally a dish may be 'changed to accommodate Westerners' taste', according to one diner. Set menus (for two sharing), including one for vegetarians, are excellent value. Dim-sum are served until 5pm, but expect long queues on Sundays. Attractively dressed waitresses provide smooth, skilled service. The wine list is good, short and modestly priced. House French is £8.50.

CHEFS: Simon Man and Wai Hung   PROPRIETORS: Playwell Ltd   OPEN: all week; noon to 11.15   CLOSED: 24 and 25 Dec   MEALS: alc. Set D £20 to £26 (minimum of 2)   SERVICE: 12.5%   CARDS: Access, Amex, Diners, Visa   DETAILS: 100 seats. Private parties: 80 main room, 10 private room. Vegetarian meals. Children welcome. Wheelchair access (1 step). Music. Air-conditioned

RSJ ▮ £

map 11

13A Coin Street, SE1 8YQ
071-928 4554 and 9768

COOKING 2
COST £19–£34

For those who have braved the broken paving stones, the litter and boarded-up properties of this part of the South Bank RSJ offers a comfortable haven, very acceptable Anglo-French cooking and willing staff. 'I enjoy being able to eat well *before* the Festival Hall' was one comment, and staff and kitchen are geared to performance times. Enjoyed as much for the fair price as for the cooking was a winter menu of chicken almond soup; a country pâté of pork and chicken livers; tartare of smoked haddock; suprême of salmon with basil and white wine sauce; breast of pheasant with cranberries, chestnuts, apple and a rich game sauce; cutlet of pork with morels and prunes plus a cream and mushroom sauce; coffee and apricot gâteau; and chocolate fudge cake. There were endorsements, too, for halibut with grapes and walnuts in a white wine sauce; and red mullet with coriander, sorrel and spinach and a citrus sauce. Slips can occur: vegetables just 'competently, although not excitingly, cooked' or 'only adequate', or a sauce appearing twice in the same meal with a change of name but not of taste. The basement brasserie offers a short card that lists vegetable fettuccine, truffle and pistachio sausage, and duck confit among the options. Our bottle award is normally handed out for balance, as much as anything. At

RSJ there is no such pretence: the few concessions that stray beyond the Loire Valley appear to diminish by the year. Anyone who risks two pages of the marvellously complex wines of Bourgueil is a hero. If we awarded magnums, Mr Wilkinson would be an early recipient. House wine is £9.25. CELLARMAN'S CHOICE: Vouvray, Dom. des Aubuisières 1989, Fouquet, £14.25; St-Nicolas-de-Bourgueil, Cuveé Prestige 1985, Mabileau, £19.95.

CHEF: Ian Stabler PROPRIETOR: Nigel Wilkinson OPEN: Mon to Sat, exc Sat L; 12 to 2, 6 to 11 CLOSED: 3 days Christmas MEALS: alc. Set L and D £13.75 to £15.25 SERVICE: 10%, card slips closed CARDS: Access, Amex, Visa DETAILS: restaurant 60 seats, brasserie 40 seats. Private parties: 40 main room, 20 private room. Children's helpings on request. Music. Air-conditioned

---

Rue St Jacques

map 13

5 Charlotte Street, W1P 1HD   COOKING 3
071-637 0222   COST £33–£70

Refugees from another restaurant – 'where we were put off by the smell of stale fish' – had no fears when their booking was accepted at short notice at Gunther Schlender's suave, svelte and attractive restaurant on Media Street, W1. It still glows, it still glints, the succession of small rooms gives intimacy and comfort, and the upstairs has space for meetings or parties; this is one of the West End's more romantic settings. How long the romance will last depends on the receivers, alas, but for the time being things rub along. Service is endlessly solicitous. That might describe the cooking too. None of the new brutalism of ingredients or presentation has been adopted. When the cooking is on form, it is very accurate, if sometimes rich; its fault will only be that of lack of punch. Good dishes have included grilled scallops with lentils and coriander – scallops are sometimes smoked, as may be white fish like sea bream, served with a warm vinaigrette – a fish soup, guinea-fowl (also on lentils), venison wrapped in hazelnut pancakes, or straight fillet steak with shallots and red wine; there are good cheeses to finish, or bubbling-hot fruit soufflés. The wine list is a classic French collection, though New Worlders come in to help out the poorer among us. There are old clarets, plenty of halves, some very good burgundies including runs of Meursaults and Montrachets, three Sancerres to choose between, well-sourced Rhônes, and enough range to reconcile us to those three-figure prices that crop up too often once the really impressive names are wheeled out. House wines start at £11.50.

CHEF: Gunther Schlender PROPRIETORS: J. Jessop, T. Boyce and G. Schlender OPEN: Mon to Sat, exc Sat L; 12 to 2.30, 7 to 11 CLOSED: Christmas, Easter, bank hols MEALS: alc. Set L £19.50 SERVICE: 15%, card slips closed CARDS: Access, Amex, Diners, Visa DETAILS: 60 seats. Private parties: 36 main room, 10, 20 and 24 private rooms. Vegetarian meals. Children's helpings on request. Jackets preferred. No pipes in dining-room. Wheelchair access (1 step). Music. Air-conditioned. Fax: 071-637 0224

All details are as accurate as possible at the time of going to press, but chefs and owners often change, and it is wise to check by telephone before making a special journey. Many readers have been disappointed when set-price bargain meals are no longer available. Ask when booking.

Sabras £

map 10

263 Willesden High Road, NW10 2RX
081-459 0340

COOKING 2
COST £10–£25

After a spell in the doldrums, this unassuming little café/restaurant is once again back on form, delivering some of the best Indian vegetarian food in the capital. The menu is long and wide-ranging, with a challenging assortment of snacks and specialities from many parts of the subcontinent. Memorable items have included samosas, aloo papri chat, khamans (steamed squares of lentil and gram flour), patras and bhel poori. Masala dosai was 'quite superb', according to one expert: 'a perfect blend of crisp (but not overcooked) shell with a delightful vegetable filling'. Another reporter waxed ecstatic over sev puris – 'the savoury equivalent of a Swiss liqueur chocolate! Wonderful!' There is also a fascinating list of Gujarati vegetable dishes such as ravaiya (stuffed baby aubergines, bananas and potatoes) and ugavela moong (home-sprouted mung beans with chilli and lemon). One visitor praised the 'excellent' surati undhiu, a winter speciality of slow-cooked ethnic vegetables with garlic. Excellent pickles and kulfi are made on the premises. Service is very friendly and knowledgeable. Cut-price dishes are available at lunch-time. To drink there is good lassi and an impressive choice of imported beers. The short wine list includes House French at £5.50.

CHEFS/PROPRIETORS: Hemant and Nalinee Desai OPEN: Tue to Sun, exc Sat and Sun L; 12.45 to 2.45, 6.15 to 10; bank hol Mons 6 to 10 MEALS: alc. Set L and D £5.75 (exc Sat) to £11 SERVICE: not inc, card slips closed CARDS: Access, Visa DETAILS: 32 seats. Private parties: 32 main room. Vegetarian meals. Children welcome. No-smoking area. Wheelchair access. Music

▲ St James's Court Hotel, Auberge de Provence

map 11

41 Buckingham Gate, SW1E 6AF
071-821 1899

COOKING 3
COST £30–£79

'An effort has been made, with whitewash and brick alcoves, to recreate an auberge de Provence in the unlikely setting of Buckingham Gate,' observes a reporter. The Auberge continues as the British off-shoot of L'Oustau de Baumanière in the French village of Les Baux. Provence is the inspiration, although the cooking is refined rather than native, and looks well beyond France for ideas and influences. The range shows in the fish dishes; not only red mullet provençale, warm oysters with winkles in the shell served with samphire, and steamed sea bass with tomato, basil and olive oil, but also mahi-mahi cooked with lemon grass and tropical fruit. Reporters have enjoyed salade Baussenque (artichoke hearts and French beans with pine-kernels), fillet steak with Roquefort sauce, chicken breast with aubergines, and rack of lamb. There has also been praise for the selection of cheeses and desserts such as rich chocolate mousse with vanilla custard, and colourful confections of fruit, pastry and ice-cream. There is much theatricality in the lifting of silver domes. The formality is not to everyone's taste and, despite the legions of waiters, it is sometimes difficult to attract attention: 'I had to get up in search of bread to supplement my nouvelle cuisine portions,' commented one diner. All of this comes at a high price – although set lunch is something of a bargain at this level. The restaurant, despite its name, does not offer a great sweep of provençal wines. Prices are high, and quality is good, but this is not a wine list to travel for. House wine is £11.

CHEF: Bernard Brique   PROPRIETORS: TAJ International Hotels   OPEN: Mon to Sat, exc Sat L; 12.30 to 2.30, 7.30 to 11   MEALS: alc. Set L £21.50, Set D £30 to £45   SERVICE: not inc CARDS: Access, Amex, Diners, Visa   DETAILS: 80 seats. Private parties: 40 main room. Vegetarian meals. Children welcome. Jacket and tie. No music. Air-conditioned ACCOMMODATION: 391 rooms, all with bath/shower. Rooms for disabled. Lift. B&B £183.50 to £267. Children welcome. Baby facilities. Afternoon teas. Garden. Sauna. Air-conditioned. TV. Phone. Confirm by 6. Fax: 071-630 7587

Salloos   NEW ENTRY   map 12

62–64 Kinnerton Street, SW1X 8ER   COOKING 2
071-235 4444   COST £26–£51

The restaurant is part of a mews house; it has been in business since 1977, and the dark décor gives it away. Although the cuisine is described as Pakistani, it would be more accurate to say that it represents a certain high-class domestic cooking to be met with in 'good families' of the north-west of the subcontinent. The secret of Salloos' success lies in the use of immaculate ingredients and ultra-fresh spices backed up by meticulous preparation. This is sophisticated cooking, but it comes at a high price, even for Belgravia. 'Sensational' tandoori lamb chops are one of the highlights: the meat is succulent and properly marinated without artificial colour, spicing is first-rate, timing is spot-on. Chicken karahi has been correctly prepared with no short-cuts, while pilau rice cooked in stock with aromatic spices was the 'best pilau I've ever had', according to one visitor. Nan bread is authentically light and buttery. Some specialities, such as haleem akbari (shredded lamb cooked with wheatgerm, lentils and spices), are classics of the repertoire. Service is knowledgeable and enthusiastic. The wine list includes a special selection from Corney & Barrow. House French is £10.50.

CHEF: Abdul Aziz   PROPRIETOR: Muhammad Salahuddin   OPEN: Mon to Sat; 12 to 2.30, 7 to 11.15   CLOSED: bank hols   MEALS: alc. Set L £16, Set D £25. Cover £1.50   SERVICE: 15%, card slips closed   CARDS: Access, Amex, Diners, Visa   DETAILS: 65 seats. Private parties: 65 main room. Vegetarian meals. No children under 6 D. Music. Air-conditioned

San Martino ✳   NEW ENTRY   map 12

103–105 Walton Street, SW3 2HP   COOKING 1
071-589 3833   COST £16–£40

Expansion has come to San Martino, but the 1970s trattoria look (West End-style) remains. The waiters are fairly unreconstructed as well: a lot of good-natured bombast that needs a firm approach. More bombast on the menu, but the prices are not high, the range is wide, and the promise is great. Many things are very satisfactory: salads are good; game in season is lustily, if not brilliantly, cooked; braised goat has flavour. The pasta is very acceptable.

Service, when everything works, is faster than an Olympic sprint. It does not, however, always function as it should, and the bill has a habit of running away from you, too. The cover charge, 'suggested 15 per cent gratuity', and high-priced ancillaries dent the good impression of prices such as £4.35 for pasta and chanterelles. The wine list contains some excellent Italians, new-wave as well as old. House wines are £8.20.

CHEF: Alfonso Cestaro   PROPRIETOR: Costanzo Martinucci   OPEN: all week, exc Sun D; 12 to 3, 6.30 to 12 (11 to 8 Sun)   CLOSED: bank hols   MEALS: alc. Set L £11.50 (inc wine), Set Sun L £12.50. Theatre menu £10.50. Cover £2. Minimum £8.50   SERVICE: 15%   CARDS: Access, Amex, Visa   DETAILS: 130 seats. 7 tables outside. Private parties: 165 main room, 48 private room. Vegetarian meals. Children's helpings. Jacket and tie. No smoking in 1 dining-room. Wheelchair access (2 steps). No music. Air-conditioned. Fax: 071-584 8418

I Sardi   NEW ENTRY   map 11

112 Cheyne Walk, SW10 0DJ   COOKING 2
071-352 7534   COST £21–£45

One attraction of this large, bustling restaurant is the courtyard at the back for fine-weather eating – although it can get packed on hot days. As the name I Sardi suggests, the food and cooking are Sardinian, with authentic specialities such as bottarga (dried tuna and mullet roe), broad beans with bacon and onions, wild boar chops and roast sucking pig. One regular mentions the 'remarkable selection of fresh, clear-eyed fish brought to your table for selection as daily specials'. The menu also features a handful of dishes from mainland Italy, such as escalope of veal with wine and mushrooms. Appetisers are familiar grilled morsels, but elevated to a new level and noticeably 'unoily'. Likewise, good timing, lightness and a lack of grease are the hallmarks of frittura of prawns, squid and aubergines. Other impressive items have included razor shells and clams cooked with wine, herbs and garlic, and golden-orange coloured pasta stuffed with cheese and saffron in a light tomato sauce. Cassoba has 'all the richness one expects from a Mediterranean fish stew'. A trolley of sweets might contain moist almond cake and sliced fresh mango. Service is cheerful and friendly. The wine list reinforces the Sardinian theme, with some well-chosen, reasonably priced bottles. House wine is £7.25.

CHEF: Giovanni Brancu   PROPRIETOR: Graziano Lecca   OPEN: all week; 12 to 2.45, 7 to 11.45   CLOSED: bank hols   MEALS: alc. Cover £1.25   SERVICE: not inc   CARDS: Access, Amex, Diners, Visa   DETAILS: 100 seats. 11 tables outside. Private parties: 25 main room. Vegetarian meals. Children's helpings. Wheelchair access (2 steps). Air-conditioned

Les Saveurs   NEW ENTRY   map 13

37A Curzon Street, W1Y 8EY   COOKING 3*
071-491 8919   COST £35–£68

In a basement on Curzon Street is a fairly characterless room that is lifted from the luxurious ordinary only by the quality of the table settings, china and glassware. Les Saveurs is a full-blown international haute cuisine restaurant, working closer than most in London to standards set in Paris. The chef is a Frenchman who has done time with several three-star employers as well as at

the Oriental, Bangkok. The owner is a Japanese corporation. It seems all rather
unlikely. What is more, the staff are remarkably keen to please – there is none
of that stuffy Gallic superiority. The cooking is clearly very skilled; whether the
prices, or the fashions, please British customers is another point altogether.
While it is possible to find a dish that explores the contrasts between luxury,
insubstantiality and earthiness – such as the light lettuce and bacon soup with
a soft-boiled egg and white truffle – there are also likely to be compositions
that remind one of the days of oversweet savoury dishes, and arrangements
redolent of nouvelle cuisine. Thus many dishes are fabricated into neat
roundels, sandwiched and layered by apple or celeriac. Others come complete
with compotes or chutneys (or so they are called), which may be clever, but
often overload the palate with sweetness. And some productions may appear to
have validity for a chef, but a tartare of salmon with a cauliflower cream was
difficult to justify either in taste or texture. There is affinity with oriental
seasonings, but they are not often allowed to come out with sufficient zest.
There is also a lack of balance to main courses: thus, sweetbreads are given no
makeweight of pasta or potato, just wafers of apple and some spinach. The
cooking is clever and interesting, but reports will make clear over the next year
whether it is successful. The concessionary lunch menu could be the easiest
way into this repertoire. The wine list has flights of single properties; there is
complete coverage of French classics, and there are high prices. It is impressive
in its way. House wines are £15.

CHEF: Joël Antunès PROPRIETORS: Fujikoshi UK Ltd OPEN: Mon to Fri; 12 to 2.30,
7 to 10.30 CLOSED: 2 weeks Aug, 2 weeks Dec MEALS: alc. Set L £21, Set D £39.50
SERVICE: not inc CARDS: Access, Amex, Diners, Visa DETAILS: 50 seats. Private parties:
50 main room, 10 private room. Vegetarian meals on request. No children under 6. Jacket
and tie. No pipes in dining-room. No music. Air-conditioned. Fax: 071-491 3658

▲ Savoy Grill and River Restaurant

map 14

Strand, WC2R 0EU
071-836 4343

COOKING 3
COST £32–£90

The two restaurants are quite separate: entrances, chefs, kitchens, menus and
all. The Grill Room is on the left as you approach the hotel; the River
Restaurant is the hotel dining-room, with views over the Thames and the
Embankment, and earfuls of music in the evening. They serve their functions
rather well. The Grill is full of power-brokers and City gents, the River
Restaurant copes with the multifarious clientele of a giant hotel (not without
power themselves, you'll observe). Both restaurants deal in classic traditional
cooking, whether it be international haute cuisine or the British specials. The
Grill Room menu develops rather like a chapter from *Repertoire de la Cuisine*; a
different trimming goes on to the same mix of prime materials, but it is
heartening to note that the chill winds of recession have meant prices have
gone up very little over the past year. Cooking in the Grill can be first-rate,
though admirable largely for its willingness to do things properly, be that a
sauté of lamb with aubergine and parsnip mousse and a grain mustard sauce,
or steak Diane. The River Restaurant does not displease either. The foie gras en

gelée was first-class; Cheddar and lobster soup was a new and impressive combination; wild mushroom consommé with quail's eggs was all that should be expected; turbot in red wine sauce was of impeccable provenance; good roast beef came off the trolley; and there were outstanding petits fours. Disappointments have been the sweets trolley and a feeling one Sunday lunch that not much cooking goes on in those giant kitchens, more food manufacturing to a specification. This, of course, is the problem with the big places that do things to a budget. The wine list goes round most of the world, even if the glory is largely kept to the classic areas and champagne. The list is manageable in length, and some people maintain there are bargains to be had on the Grill list in particular. With Sancerre at nearly £25, it's difficult to see what these can be. House wines are from £10.50.

CHEFS: David Sharland (Grill) and Anton Edelmann (River Restaurant) PROPRIETORS: Savoy Hotel plc OPEN: Grill Mon to Sat, exc Sat L; 12.30 to 2.30, 6 to 11.15. River Restaurant all week; 12.30 to 2.30, 7.30 to 11.30 (7 to 10.30 Sun) CLOSED: Grill Aug MEALS: Grill alc. River Restaurant alc, Set L £20.25, Set D £30.50 to £42.30 SERVICE: Grill not inc. River Restaurant net prices, card slips closed CARDS: Access, Amex, Diners, Visa DETAILS: Grill 80 seats, River Restaurant 150 seats. Private parties: 6 to 60 private rooms. Vegetarian meals. Children's helpings Sat and Sun L River Restaurant. Children restricted. Jacket and tie. No pipes in dining-room. Wheelchair access (2 steps). Music River Restaurant. No music Grill. Air-conditioned ACCOMMODATION: 200 rooms, all with bath/shower. Rooms for disabled. Lift. B&B £197 to £678. Children welcome. Baby facilities. Afternoon teas. Swimming-pool. Sauna. Air-conditioned. TV. Phone. Confirm 1 day ahead. Fax: 071-240 6040 (*The Which? Hotel Guide*)

La Sémillante
NEW ENTRY map 13

5 Mill Street, W1R 9TF
071-499 2121

COOKING 2*
COST £21–£37

The address is Mayfair, down a discreet alleyway, opposite the Rolls Royce showroom. The basement site was once occupied by an Indian restaurant, and there are still some exotic touches in the carved wooden screens and arches, the tiled floor and smoked plate glass frontage. Elsewhere, the style is post-modernist chic: a wall of small mirrors decorated with starfish shapes, and high-backed upholstered chairs draped in bright silks. Chef Patrick Woodside has a typically pedigree curriculum vitae, having worked at Harveys, Tante Claire and, most recently, Claridge's. He is a thorough-going modern cook, working to a fixed-price menu that treads a path between overt luxury and refined peasantry: tarte of sea scallops and caviare, and mille-feuille of quail's eggs and foie gras might appear alongside roast breast of pigeon with aubergines. Pan-fried fillet of John Dory comes as strips of fish twisted together with strands of courgette set in a sauce of pan juices decorated with broad beans. The kitchen is versatile and can create unexpected items for vegetarians, such as tian of aubergines and peppers with cold carrot sauce. Reporters have praised a 'fabulous' nougat dessert of pear William resting on 'flower-petals' of carmelised pear and decorated with alcoholic macerated raspberries. Accessories, such as the excellent range of breads, French farmhouse cheeses, strong espresso and petits fours, show serious intent. Service is extremely keen, attentive and very formal. The two-page wine list is as modern as the menu. House wine is £8.50.

CHEF: Patrick John Woodside   PROPRIETORS: Patrick John Woodside and Donald Gay
OPEN: Mon to Sat, exc Sat L; 12.15 to 2.30, 7.15 to 11.15   CLOSED: last 2 weeks Aug, last
week Dec, first week Jan   MEALS: Set L £14.50, Set D £26   SERVICE: not inc, card slips
closed   CARDS: Access, Diners, Visa   DETAILS: 40 seats. Private parties: 65 main room,
20 private room. Vegetarian meals. Children's helpings. No-smoking area. No music.
Air-conditioned. Fax: 071-499 4042

Simply Nico   map 11

48A Rochester Row, SW1P 1JU   COOKING 3
071-630 8061   COST £30–£36

This restaurant offers a three-course lunch and dinner menu at a set price. The
repertoire doesn't change much. If you have a good formula, stick to it. When
the price is compared to that of suburban restaurants, small country houses and
provincial places, the diner should jump for joy. This is a bargain. The cooking
is assured, reliable, palatable, in tune with modern tastes, and delivered with
pleasure in an environment which can be noisy and overcrowded, but does not
lack for comfort. Many not-so-hot chefs and cooks might come and take a
lesson or two. It is by no means complicated or continually imaginative, but the
materials are good and performance is consistent. There are nights when heads
nod and the mirror seems tarnished, but the consensus is very favourable.
Mediterranean fish soup, a thin escalope of salmon with a herb mayonnaise,
fresh noodles with tomatoes and feta cheese, confit of duck with potato salad
and mustard dressing, brochette of calf's liver and bacon, chicken stuffed with
wild mushrooms, shin of veal with madeira, and melting confit of duck with
lentils and herb dumpling are some of the list of dishes enjoyed this year by
readers. At the end there are pear crumble, crème brûlée, fair apple tart as well
as decent coffee. The wine list is short and dear. This is the black mark; the
range at Nico Central (see entry, London) is wider and more considerate of
limited pockets. House wine is from £10.50.

CHEF: Andrew Barber   PROPRIETORS: Nico and Dinah-Jane Ladenis   OPEN: Mon to Sat,
exc Sat L; 12 to 2, 7 to 11   CLOSED: 10 days Christmas, 4 days Easter   MEALS: Set L £23,
Set D £25   SERVICE: net prices, card slips closed (exc Amex)   CARDS: Access, Amex,
Diners, Visa   DETAILS: 48 seats. Private parties: 24 main room. Vegetarian meals. Children
welcome. Smart dress preferred. No pipes in dining-room. Wheelchair access (1 step). No
music. Air-conditioned

Singapore Garden Restaurant £   map 11

83–83A Fairfax Road, NW6 4DY   COOKING 1*
071-328 5314   COST £18–£32

'I have bumped into half Malaysia and Hong Kong passing through,' writes
one expatriate from the Peninsula, 'so they must be getting something right.'
Here is 'traditional Singapore/Malaysian cuisine with no compromising for the
Western palate'. The elder Mrs Lim, who has cooked for more than 30 years,
knows her job. Malay cooking is the least chauvinist of styles; the territory
plays host to countless peoples, so Chinese dishes sit happily next to those of
Indonesia or the Straits. Chilli lobster, satays, beef rendang, soft-shell crabs
and skate from a daily list of specials and Singapore noodles have all had their

words of praise, as has the service and attention from the Lim family and their helpers. Careful choosing will keep the price down. There are wines if you want, beers if you prefer. House French wine is £7.45.

CHEF: Mrs S. Lim PROPRIETORS: the Lim family OPEN: all week; 12 to 2.45, 6 to 10.45 (11.15 Fri and Sat) MEALS: alc. Set L and D £14.85. Minimum £9 SERVICE: 12.5% CARDS: Access, Amex, Diners, Visa DETAILS: 100 seats. Private parties: 60 main room, 60 private room. Vegetarian meals. Children welcome. Music. Air-conditioned. Fax: 071-624 0656

Snows on the Green

| NEW ENTRY | map 10

166 Shepherd's Bush Road, W6 7PB COOKING 2
071-603 2142 COST £21–£33

Snows are the owners; the Green is Brook Green. The restaurant brings metropolitan chic to the benighted villages of Shepherd's Bush and Hammersmith. Sebastian Snow was assistant to Antony Worrall-Thompson at 190 Queensgate, and the menu shows signs of lessons absorbed. Yet there is a strong sense of neighbourhood to the place, of owner-occupation, even if other parts of its mood derive from the coming and going of questing fashionables. The dining-room takes its light from Provence. Vibrant photographs of lavender fields and Mediterranean scenes give high tones to the warm yellows, terracottas and greens of walls and floors. The basement, with a giant mural and side-glances of chefs working, allows extra seating. Foie gras with fried egg and balsamic vinegar, bollito misto, salmon with pancetta, squid ink casserole with saffron risotto – these are dishes that take inspiration from Italy, peasants, the south, California and not a little romance. Early steps were faltering but many things have settled down, even though there may be an air of experiment – and some ventures don't work – about a number of dishes, or even an evening's output. The main drawback has been an excess of richness through lack of balance. Hence a pumpkin ravioli with brown butter, mint and almonds ended up too greasy; a pecorino and lamb broth had too little broth for the giant slices of bread and the strips of boiled lamb. Other dishes have been approved: for instance, a salad of smoked haddock and spinach with a chive beurre blanc; rump of lamb with a multi-layered aubergine and mozzarella tower leaning next to it, and a baked head of garlic for the strong of breath; or cod baked with a herb crust; finishing with charlotte of apples, or prune tart, or sound crème caramel. They also do a great steak and chips. Service is full of smiles. Wine prices are held firmly below £20 and the choice is as modish as the food. House wines are £7.95.

CHEF: Sebastian Snow PROPRIETORS: Sebastian and Melissa Snow OPEN: all week, exc Sat L and Sun D; 12 to 3, 7 to 11 CLOSED: last 2 weeks Aug, 2 weeks after 25 Dec, Easter weekend, bank hols MEALS: alc. Set L £10.50 to £14.50 SERVICE: not inc (10% for six or more) CARDS: Access, Visa DETAILS: 65 seats. Private parties: 12 main room, 20 private room. Vegetarian meals. Children's helpings. No pipes in dining-room. Wheelchair access. Music. Air-conditioned

If a restaurant is new to the Guide *this year (did not appear as a main entry in the last edition)* NEW ENTRY *appears opposite its name.*

Soho Soho £

map 14

11–13 Frith Street, W1V 5TS
071-494 3491

COOKING 1*
COST £17–£35

'The attractions of the place are the lively atmosphere, opportunities for serious people-watching (body language running riot all over the place) and the always adequate and sometimes excellent food.' This assessment by a regular visitor encompasses the cheaper downstairs café-bar/rotisserie as well as the upstairs restaurant. Busy it certainly is, and rendered lively by the Miróesque decoration and intensively provençal trimmings. Whether the menu itself is provençal might be debated, but 'new-wave Mediterranean' would gather in most aspects of the dishes on offer and alert you to plenty of modern ingredients (chickpeas, lentils, swordfish, balsamic vinegar, pasta and tuna) cooked with some panache: the calf's liver with capers, tomatoes and sage is cut in a slice thick enough for it to be cooked properly rare, the sauce 'richly flavoured, stock-based, and not reduced to syrupy stickiness; the capers added just the right note of sharpness'. So busy a place can hardly be without fault – sometimes heinous – or problems associated with necessary batch-cooking or semi-mass production, but at least you're not overcharged. The staff busy themselves and when they are 'ignorant, at least they are amiably ignorant'. The wine list keeps the prices low and strikes a southern blow: the list is divided into wines east or west of the Rhône. There are not the new-wave wonders from Italy, Spain or even France that we have come to expect of trendy London openings, but some of the country wines such as the reds from Rasteau or Vacqueyras or the white from Dom. de Mas Carlot in Provence deserve exploration. House wines are £8.75 in the restaurant.

CHEF: Tony Howorth PROPRIETORS: Neville Abraham and Laurence Isaacson OPEN: Mon to Sat, exc Sat L; restaurant 12 to 3, 6 to 12; café-bar/rotisserie 8am to 1am CLOSED: bank hols MEALS: alc. Cover £1.50 SERVICE: 12.5% (not inc restaurant), card slips closed CARDS: Access, Amex, Diners, Visa DETAILS: restaurant 70 seats, café-bar/rotisserie 70 seats. Private parties: 50 private room. Vegetarian meals. Children welcome. Music. Air-conditioned. Fax: 071-436 5227

Sonny's

map 10

94 Church Road, SW13 0DQ
081-748 0393

COOKING 1
COST £21–£32

Well established, popular, successful, Sonny's should be a model for other London neighbourhoods to follow. It provides modern, sassy food at convenient hours and at prices many people can afford. The restaurant is no-frills, with bare boards, and is bustling: through the bar (and a few tables) and down to a long room that echoes with Barnes in full song on frenetic Saturdays or Sundays. The menu is à la carte, or a stripped-down table d'hôte at a friendly price for two courses and coffee. The *carte* changes a lot, and shows affection for the chargrill (salmon with orange aïoli, figs with Parma ham) and the current favourites of London such as lentils (with roast salt-cod, rosemary crust and salsa verde), sausages (veal sausage with a mustard sauce), spices (spicy aubergine hors d'oeuvre with feta, hummus and roasted peppers) and the Far East (deep-fried squid with Thai dipping sauce). Puddings could be a crumble (rhubarb), or a tart (almond and caramel), or ice-cream, or crème brûlée. Coffee is cafetière and decent. It sounds good, yet the crop of reports suggests it could be better: that muddled service (through press of business) may vitiate good timing in the kitchen; that portions can be on the lean side; that the cooking is not always accurate – in timing or in construction of flavour combinations. If unsuccessful, the value-for-money equation becomes suspect. The wine list is well matched to the surroundings and the food: decent sources, reasonably priced examples, a good range of types and origins. There are even enough half-bottles for the most choosy. House wines are £7.50.

CHEF: Nikki Barraclough PROPRIETOR: Rebecca Mascarenhas OPEN: all week, exc Sun D; 12.30 to 2.30, 7.30 to 11 CLOSED: bank hols, 1 week Christmas MEALS: alc. Set L and D £12.50 SERVICE: not inc CARDS: Access, Visa DETAILS: 70 seats. Vegetarian meals. Children welcome. Baby facilities. Smart dress preferred. Wheelchair access. Music. Air-conditioned. Fax: 081-748 2698

▲ Spice Merchant   NEW ENTRY · map 11

Coburg Hotel,
13 Bayswater Road, W2 4RJ   COOKING 1
071-221 2442   COST £15–£38

A new look to Indian restaurants has come into being over the last few years. It is the grand-hotel school – an authentic export from the subcontinent – of large dining-rooms, a high if rather corporate level of decoration and appointment, and sometimes good cooking. What it lacks in character it may make up in comfort. The menu is interesting, involving dishes not often found in the suburbs. The chicken and potato curry called kuku paaka has been drawn from Indian regional cuisines as well as from Indian colonies such as East Africa. Vegetables, too, get unusual treatment in, for example, allo dum (potatoes hollowed out and stuffed with cashews and sultanas), gobi hara masala (cauliflower with mint and spring onions), and sweetcorn with coconut. Reports have spoken highly of the treatment of standards like king prawn masala and rogan josh, as well as the poppadum and nan incidentals. Spicing can be interesting but can also miss the mark: the menu-reads-better-than-it-eats syndrome. Success, however, comes in dhokri chat, lentil cakes filled with date and coriander chutney, and in the mild, sweetly nutty sauce accompanying kuku paaka. The wine list is short and undistinguished, but the stuff is poured as if to quench thirsts in a drought. A cheaper set-price three-course 'tiffin' is offered at lunch-time. House French is £9.25.

CHEF: B.S. Rao PROPRIETORS: Spice Merchant Ltd OPEN: all week; 12.30 to 2.30, 6.30 to 11.30 CLOSED: 25 Dec MEALS: alc. Set L £8.95 SERVICE: not inc, card slips closed CARDS: Access, Amex, Diners, Visa DETAILS: 100 seats. Private parties: 120 main room. Vegetarian meals. Children's helpings. Music. Air-conditioned ACCOMMODATION: 132 rooms, all with bath/shower. Lift. B&B £94 to £129. Deposit: 1 night. Children welcome. Baby facilities. Pets by arrangement. Afternoon teas. TV. Phone. Fax: 071-229 0557

Healthy eating options *in the details at the end of an entry signifies that a restaurant marks on its menu, in words and/or using symbols, low-fat dishes or other healthy eating choices.*

The Square ♥

NEW ENTRY map 13

32 King Street, SW1Y 6RJ
071-839 8787

COOKING 3
COST £29–£44

If you go to the London Library, or pop into Christie's to hock the family silver, this is a godsend. The room is large, light and full of slightly inexplicable interwoven wall panels, blocks of gold, magenta and puce abstracts, and big stretches of mirror. Don't worry: the cooking is substantial, vibrant, Mediterranean, modern and often good. One meal began with shallot soup and a blob of thyme Chantilly cream sitting in the middle of the steaming bowl. (Philip Howard likes this conceit – for instance, a mullet soup with a 'tapénade Chantilly'.) The soup had body and sweetness, but not too much; the thyme gave it nice point. Grilled venison sat on broad beans and green beans: a salad, but only just cooked, the dressing of truffle oil. The meat was succulent and had enough flavour to do battle with the truffle. Brill and oysters were cooked with lemon grass and lime leaves. The sauce was light – some might say watery – and seemed to dilute the flavours, not enhance them. Rump of veal was served with excellent mash and buttered vegetables. The mash was not the gluey paste that so many lazy chefs deliver (by using a fast mixer). The veal had a caramelised and salty crust from the fastest of ovens, to give it more flavour than veal usually has. Again, there was a thin gravy that almost spoiled the intensity of the rest. Philip Howard can cook, and it doesn't have to be way-out. Interesting items have included parsnip soup with foie gras croûtons; roast aubergine, one half smeared with herbs and garlic, the other stuffed with cumin-flavoured ratatouille vegetables; skate with carrot and coriander; sausage of oxtail and pig's trotter; caramelised banana tart; and roast figs, lemon fritters and pecan crunch. Some of the grace notes are missing or awry, but the heart is all there. Service, so far (and perhaps the cooking speed), has been very mixed. The place has suffered from too many customers, especially at lunch-time. From the 'Square Selection', a dozen bottles (from £9.50) carefully edited from the main list, through a catholic range of bourgeois bottles and their antipodean equivalents, to 'Fine Wines', selection is fastidious and up to date. Prices, especially for St James's, are really not bad. Half-bottles, though, are rather limited. CELLARMAN'S CHOICE: David Wynn, Chardonnay 1990, £16.50; Reuilly Pinot Noir 1990, Beurdin, £14.50.

CHEF: Philip Howard   PROPRIETORS: Dailyrare Ltd   OPEN: all week, exc Sat L and Sun D; 12 to 2.30, 6 to 11.45   CLOSED: Christmas   MEALS: alc   SERVICE: not inc   CARDS: Access, Amex, Diners, Visa   DETAILS: 65 seats. Private parties: 20 main room. Vegetarian meals. Children's helpings. Smart dress preferred. No pipes in dining-room. Wheelchair access (also WC). No music. Air-conditioned. Fax: 071-321 2124

Sree Krishna £

map 10

194 Tooting High Street, SW17 0SF
081-672 4250

COOKING 1
COST £10–£23

Consistency is the hallmark of this popular Indian restaurant south of the river. The place is under the same ownership as Ragam (see entry, London) and the menus are very similar. Vegetarian dishes and specialities from the Keralan coast are the highpoints, although the kitchen also delivers vividly spiced versions of stalwarts such as chickens dhansak, Madras and dupiaza (with crisp fried onions). Reporters have approved, too, of onion bhajias, masala dosai and mushroom korma. Look for interesting items such as avial (a mixed vegetable curry with coconut, yoghurt and curry leaves) and iddly (a steamed cake of rice and black lentil flour). Breads and rice are excellent. Drink lassi or lager. House wine is £6.

CHEF: Mullath Vijayan   PROPRIETORS: T. Haridas and family   OPEN: all week; 12 to 3, 6 to 12   MEALS: alc. Set L and D £7.50. Minimum £2.50   SERVICE: 10%   CARDS: Access, Amex, Diners, Visa   DETAILS: 120 seats. Vegetarian meals. Children welcome. Wheelchair access (also WC). No music. Air-conditioned

Sri Siam
map 14

14 Old Compton Street, W1V 5PE   COOKING 2
071-434 3544   COST £16–£38

'Thai restaurants blow hot and cold,' observes a reporter, 'and I don't just mean the taste of the food.' However, this Soho venue has maintained its standards and most reckon it now has the edge on its neighbours around Old Compton Street. The 70-dish menu is wide-ranging and there is much to recommend: stuffed chicken wings, king prawn satay, hot-and-sour tom yum soup with squid, scallops and mussels, roast duck curry with pineapple and grapes, 'red' chicken curry flavoured with Kaffir lime leaves, 'green' curry with baby Thai aubergines, and spot-on Thai noodies have all been good. The restaurant also has a full vegetarian menu with some impressive dishes, such as deep-fried bean curd 'golden bags' filled with vegetables and curried bean curd in coconut milk. Kong wan – a special Thai sweet of little palm leaf parcels filled with a sweet jelly topped with coconut cream – is 'so unusual and so good'. Occasionally there are mishaps: 'tough, gristly' marinated beef; 'insipid' soup; 'soggy' noodles. Reporters also question the practice of leaving credit card slips open when 12.5 per cent service is included in the bill. Singha Thai beer suits the food. House French is £7.75. There is also a sister restaurant in the City – Sri Siam City, 85 London Wall, EC2M 7AD, Tel: 071-628 5772.

CHEF: Ora Won   PROPRIETORS: Thai Restaurants plc   OPEN: all week, exc Sun L; 12 to 3, 6 to 11.15 (10.30 Sun)   CLOSED: Christmas and New Year   MEALS: alc. Set L £9, Set D £14.95   SERVICE: 12.5%   CARDS: Access, Amex, Diners, Visa   DETAILS: 75 seats. Private parties: 40 main room. Vegetarian meals. Children welcome. Wheelchair access. Music. Air-conditioned

Stephen Bull ♥
map 13

5–7 Blandford Street, W1H 3AA   COOKING 3
071-486 9696   COST £28–£44

'It's so nice to be comfortable in a top London restaurant where at others it is all just a little pomp and circumstance,' writes someone who appreciates the spare lines of Stephen Bull's first restaurant, in Marylebone, still running after the successful opening of his bistro in the City (see next entry). The operation is on auto-pilot. The gyros have been carefully set, the crew is personable, and passengers will rarely notice the captain is not on board, though mistakes will quickly be diagnosed as the result of inattention. The original objectives are still being met. It is a restaurant without pretension, or indeed any ornament, which serves original food at prices just below top whack, without ever masquerading as a brasserie or some such subordinate art form. The menu changes all the time, but the style is consistent. Materials are very carefully bought – though little evident fuss is made of this on the menu – and flavourings and recipes are just so angled as to take them into the unexpected or unfamiliar. The palette is slightly more limited this year than last, so the repertoire seems more mainstream than it did. The two strengths here are fish cookery – for instance, skate with chillis, salmon with lentils and sherry vinegar, and home-salted cod, but rarely shellfish apart from mussels – and stews. These are not treated as receptacles for trimmings, but good chunks of meat in deep sauces, cooked to tenderness yet not losing succulence. Though the cooking sometimes borrows the language of peasant food, the results are far more refined – some think too much so. Hence focaccia is dainty, pasta elegant, and portions are delicate. Seekers after comfort food will not always be satisfied, though salad lovers will. Desserts can be serious. Variations on a theme of chocolate still gets consistent votes; blockbusters like brown-sugar meringues with bananas and hot fudge sauce are enjoyed; demoulded hot soufflés often work well. Cheeses are chosen for you. The bread is excellent, some of the most palatable around. Close on 100 wines are offered; the house wines alone are an object lesson in good sense and economy. Alsace, though, a standby for any Parisian establishment of similar ambitions, remains dull here but is more than compensated for by burgundies and antipodean bottles from the simple to the very fine. Prices remain modestly provincial. House wines are from £10.50.

CHEF: Jon Bentham   PROPRIETOR: Stephen Bull   OPEN: Mon to Sat, exc Sat L; 12 to 2.30, 6.30 to 10.45   CLOSED: 1 week Christmas   MEALS: alc   SERVICE: not inc, card slips closed   CARDS: Access, Visa   DETAILS: 60 seats. Private parties: 50 main room. Vegetarian meals. Children's helpings. Wheelchair access (1 step). Air-conditioned

Stephen Bull's Bistro and Bar ♥

NEW ENTRY   map 11

71 St John Street, EC1M 4AN
071-490 1750

COOKING 2*
COST £21–£32

There was a spate of new openings in London during spring 1992. Good cooking at fair prices seemed to be their common aim. One of the best examples is Stephen Bull's venture, to the north of Smithfield. His restaurant in Blandford Street (see entry above) has provided the conceptual framework: a daily menu, cutting expense to a minimum; a 'light yet tasty' style of cooking; a clean, even gaunt, decorative schema. The bistro is large, with a main floor and a mezzanine, reached by stairs as well as by a bridge from the kitchen zone. The antics of waiters carrying things to and fro or up and down add an element to the theatre. Giant grey walls, flat planes, stabs of colour from three-dimensional 'constructions', and hard floors, tables and chairs do little to relieve the noise or quieten the eyes. 'A works canteen' was one description – stylish, though. The menu works with good, but of course not luxury, materials. It has not pursued the usual bistro path, or the revival of old English plain cooking. Early impressions have been that attention to detail has had a good effect on tastes and seasonings: a focaccia of grilled vegetables uplifted by lemon was very lively; a stir-fry of beef with sesame, ginger and coriander was arresting, without being over-strong; even carpaccio of beef with almonds, capers and Parmesan, or pasta with basil, olives and tomatoes have outshone equivalents elsewhere. It is risky cooking. Everything depends on accuracy and verve, without which dishes such as home-cured salmon with lemon crème fraîche, aubergine and sweet pepper salad, fennel, broccoli and summer savoury tart, and the plethora of first-course salads become insubstantial. Choice in the main courses, split between fish and meat, is not extensive. Bull's beef stews are a revelation of light intensity coupled with good meat. Some of the simple desserts like brown-sugar meringue with a fudge sauce and lots of banana will leave sugar fiends in ecstasy. Some other sweet things have seemed pale in colour and taste: rhubarb parfait, lemon and lime curd pots (with really good lemon biscuits) are two which appeared to miss. Double chocolate cake is ace. Coffee is espresso; breads have not been thrilling. This is a grand place for lunch, so long as you don't mind the crowds; not so obvious a choice for a gentle dinner. The value is excellent. The wine list is short and strong, not unfairly priced, and includes very good makers from all over: Quady, Au Bon Climat, Moss Wood, Bonny Doon, Talenti. The emphasis is away from France and there are lots of choices by the glass. There are good beers, too. CELLARMAN'S CHOICE: Côtes de Thongues, Chardonnay 1990, Dom. Boyer, £11.50; Capello di Prete Rosso del Salento 1988, Candido, £11.50.

CHEFS: Stephen Bull and Stephen Carter   PROPRIETORS: Stephen Bull Restaurants Ltd
OPEN: Mon to Sat, exc Sat L; 12 to 2.30, 6 to 11   CLOSED: 10 days Christmas to New Year
MEALS: alc   SERVICE: not inc, card slips closed   CARDS: Access, Visa   DETAILS: 90 seats.
Vegetarian meals. Children's helpings. No cigars/pipes in dining-room. Wheelchair access
(1 step). No music. Air-conditioned

Suntory

map 13

72 St James's Street, SW1A 1PH
071-409 0201

COOKING 3*
COST £29–£107

Japanese restaurants come and go, but Suntory remains a bastion of quality and tradition. This is the formal, conservative face of Japanese expense-account eating in London. The main dining-room is furnished with impeccable taste, while the austere, politely hushed atmosphere is eminently suited to discreet business discussions. Downstairs, in the teppanyaki bar, the mood is exuberant and the eating area is full of businessmen with bibs tucked into their collars. Western customers are greeted by a Western waitress, although service was interminably slow and 'inefficient' at an inspection meal. At first glance this may not seem like a place for 'inspired cuisine', but the menu offers plenty of unusual and exciting dishes – particularly among the list of chef's suggestions. One reporter appreciated the seasonal rightness of an early summer menu which included a 'river' of soy milk and jelly; cold shabu-shabu; plum-flavoured wheat noodles served cold; and cold savoury egg custard with shreds of lobster meat set in agar-agar ('a stunning combination of flavours'). Other highlights have included a visual treat of fresh sardine and burdock tempura bound with a strip of nori seaweed, and another archetypal summer dish of grilled sea eel with sweet soy sauce, served correctly in a rectangular lacquered box, red inside, black outside. Some other specialities have been acceptable rather than dazzling: sushi, in particular, has suffered from too-soft rice and average fish – despite very proper arrangement. Desserts include a variety of fresh fruits, plus Japanese extravaganzas adorned with cubes of red aduki bean jam. The wine list pulls no financial punches. House French is £14.

CHEF: Mr K. Kato   PROPRIETORS: Suntory Ltd   OPEN: Mon to Sat; 12 to 1.30, 7 to 9.30   CLOSED: 25 Dec, 1 Jan, bank hols   MEALS: alc. Set L £22 to £80, Set D £48 to £90   SERVICE: net prices, card slips closed   CARDS: Access, Amex, Diners, Visa   DETAILS: 120 seats. Private parties: 4, 7 and 14 private rooms. Children restricted. No music. Air-conditioned. Fax: 071-499 7993

Le Suquet

map 12

104 Draycott Avenue, SW3 3AE
071-581 1785

COOKING 2
COST £30–£48

One reporter, who had not visited this French seafood restaurant for a decade, found that little had changed. There is still a small vivier and the décor is a mixture of 'giddy Mediterranean fishscapes', with lots of deep blue colours, huge flower arrangements and white cloths. 'It is casual, cheerful and fishy – not an easy combination to find in central London.' The menu has remained much the same over the years: fresh fish and shellfish are done half a dozen ways; there are also daily specials, plus a handful of meat dishes including rabbit and tripe. Ingredients are fresh, but the kitchen seems to work best when it keep things simple. Rich, herby sauces can be overbearing and may have a 'bludgeoning' effect, masking true flavours. Even so, the cooking generally succeeds, as in sweet-tasting scallops cooked *à point* with a perfectly judged saffron sauce, and turbot neatly arranged and presented with a buttery champagne sauce. Vegetables have undergone a transformation: a bright, well-timed colourful assortment – although not always appropriate to the fish on the plate. To finish, the selection of sorbets is refreshing, tart and fruity. Service is very French – sometimes verging on the familiar – although one visit was ruined by off-hand treatment and bad manners. House wine is £9.50.

CHEF: Jean Yves Darcel   PROPRIETOR: Pierre Martin   OPEN: all week; 12.30 to 3, 7 to 11.30   MEALS: alc. Cover £1   SERVICE: 15%, card slips closed   CARDS: Access, Amex, Diners, Visa   DETAILS: 50 seats. 4 tables outside. Private parties: 14 private room. Vegetarian meals. Children's helpings. Wheelchair access (1 step; also WC). Music

Surinder's

map 11

109 Westbourne Park Road, W2 5QL
071-229 8968

COOKING 1
COST £24

Surinder himself may sit out at a table during quiet times, but he is no chef-prop in spotless whites just doing the tour of the punters. The restaurant is a survival from bistro days: good value, straight cooking and a lack of stiff ceremony. It has not reproduced the gloom and candle-grease of 1960s bistros, but the simple French-inspired cooking (some dishes carry supplements) that offers chicken terrine, salmon mousse, rack of lamb, calf's liver and little pots of chocolate at the end retains the mood of those days. Its failings can be heinous and even the staff can exude less than their usual charm, but the airy little room is a neighbourhood resource of value. A short wine list has enough under £15, although, given the price of the food, it could have more and from a wider range. House wines are £7.95.

CHEF/PROPRIETOR: Surinder Chandwan OPEN: Tue to Sat, D only, and Fri L; 12 to 3.30, 7 to 11 MEALS: Set L and D £14.95 SERVICE: 10%, card slips closed CARDS: Access, Amex, Visa DETAILS: 45 seats. Private parties: 45 main room, 40 private room. Vegetarian meals. Children welcome. Wheelchair access (2 steps). No music

Surya £ map 11

59–61 Fortune Green Road, NW6 1DR COOKING 1
071-435 7486 COST £10–£22

This is a family business. Mrs Tiwari cooks, while her husband runs the smart dining-room, which is adorned with prints and Indian paintings on silk. The owners point out that their style is north Indian vegetarian with a strong emphasis on ethnic vegetables. Starters such as samosas and dahi vadai precede dosas and an assortment of curries and dhals. Reporters provide consistent recommendations for the crunchy bhel poori, aloo papri chat, baigan bhartha with a dark, smoky flavour, mushroom bhaji and mater paneer. Each day there are specials highlighting particular vegetables: loki bhaji (a marrow-like gourd) and banana, methi and tomato curry have been highly recommended. Side dishes and accompaniments are impressive: coriander chutney with poppadums, light fluffy puris, 'excellent' pilau rice. The home-made kulfi is usually a winning sweet. Service is invariably cheerful and attentive. Drink lassi, lager or the house wine at £5.95.

CHEF: Mrs H. Tiwari PROPRIETOR: Mr R.C. Tiwari OPEN: all week, D only, and Sun L; 12 to 2.30, 6 to 10.30 CLOSED: 24 to 26 Dec, 31 Dec, 1 Jan MEALS: alc. Set L £4.95, Set D £6 to £11 SERVICE: 10%, card slips closed CARDS: Access, Visa DETAILS: 32 seats. Private parties: 32 main room. Vegetarian meals. No children under 6 after 7pm. Wheelchair access. Music. Air-conditioned

Tageen £ NEW ENTRY map 14

12 Upper St Martin's Lane, WC2 9DL COOKING 1
071-836 7272 COST £19–£37

The building was once a pub, and there are echoes of its past in the big clock, the dark heavy bar and the wooden floor. But the tiles, hanging brass lamps, draped fabrics and hand-stitched leather seat covers are evidence that it now functions as a Moroccan restaurant. The menu focuses on eponymous tageens, served in conical glazed earthenware dishes, the lids of which are removed with a flourish: chicken with pickled lemon and olives, and lamb with prunes and fried almonds in a honey and saffron sauce have both been enjoyable ('competent' rather than exciting). The restaurant also serves bastela – the national Moroccan dish – a sweet pigeon pie (chicken is used here) with layers of filo pastry topped with icing sugar and cinnamon. To start there is a range of appetisers, such as briwat (little pastry triangles filled with chicken and lamb), as well as salads and soups (although these have been thin and lacking in flavour). Sweets include not only sticky pastries, but also a sweetened version of couscous. The Moroccan bread covered with sesame seeds is excellent. Service tries to be smartly up-market, although it is 'uninformed'. The short, mainly French wine list also has a few Moroccan bottles. House wine is £8.50.

CHEF: Maitre Idrissi   PROPRIETORS: the Samane family and I. Aylwin   OPEN: Mon to Sat, exc Sat L; 12.30 to 2.45, 6.30 to 11   MEALS: alc. Set L £12, Set D £12 to £16. Minimum £12 SERVICE: not inc   CARDS: Access, Amex, Diners, Visa   DETAILS: 80 seats. 2 tables outside. Private parties: 60 main room. Vegetarian meals. Children's helpings. Music. Air-conditioned. Fax: 071-379 0759

Tante Claire ♥
map 12

68–69 Royal Hospital Road, SW3 4HP
071-352 6045

COOKING 5
COST £30–£79

One is not often moved to sentimentality about London's luxury restaurants. They may cook well, serve glossily, afford comfort, but they never give it away. At Tante Claire, a restaurant that seems to have relaxed in recent years without ever dropping its vigilance or quality, the lunch is consistently described by grateful customers as a bargain. 'Top-quality ingredients were transformed by top-quality skill into tastes never previously experienced' was one inscription to a report. Similarly, the wine list actually has a choice of wines under £15 a bottle. You may have to save up for the experience, but it is within the bounds of many, and there is no stinting by the restaurant, even if your first course is not *foie gras truffé*. 'The sunlight breezes in and the yellows and blues of the watercolours and dressed chairs of the dining-room are brought gaily to life,' wrote an aficionado. At night, the Biedermeyer furniture, deep linen cloths and soft pastels of the walls glow with warm solidity. Tante Claire remains a restaurant, not a monument, though some old hands actually regret the days when it was less grand, less formal. The main business revolves round the *carte*, supplemented by extras, especially game in the season. Pierre Koffmann seems able to turn his hand to several modes: an haute cuisine reworking of robust and comforting dishes, such as the pig's trotter stuffed with morels; dazzling presentation and invention as in the scallops with squid-ink sauce; tradition, as in a straight roast woodcock done properly; or modern classicism as in the venison served with a chocolate and raspberry vinegar sauce, garnished with raspberries (out of season, as they were in the vacherin that occurred later in the same Christmas meal). His touch is sure, and his materials are fantastic. Matters are not complicated by mousses or modifications imposed by conventional grand cooking, but each menu affords plenty of variation in methods: for example, a braise of spring lamb with parsley, a tournedos Rossini, grilled venison, daube of beef, blanquette of bass and John Dory. There is an affection (harking back to the ancestors again) for fish with meat support, hence garbure of turbot with duck confit, or salmon with goose fat. Spices, too, which have swept into the larders of ambitious European chefs in the last decade, get their outing in squab with 'exotic' flavours, as well as lobster roast with spices. Many aver that the best bit of the meal is at the end. 'Tarte fine aux figues is a wonderful, buttery yet thin puff-pastry base filled with slices of figs that have been lightly grilled to bring out the sweetness of the fruit; crème brûlée is seriously rich and eggy; to offset the cream a scoop of sorbet in a glass of champagne is served.' Feuilleté of pear with caramel sauce, a plate of citrus confections, and a similar collection of apple desserts win superlatives. 'The sweets were on another level of achievement' was one happy conclusion. Coffee is strong, and petits fours are good, as are the warm-ups to the meal proper. Once, the head waiter was away; it was the only time one set of regulars experienced less than perfect service. The wine list is exceptional. Quality is as good as you will find anywhere at this level, and there is no shortage of very grand bottles at commensurate prices. Here, though, there is genuine effort to seek out decent but modest wines. The only qualification is that everything is French. House wines are from £11.70. CELLARMAN'S CHOICE: Mâcon-Viré 1989, Bonhomme, £25.80; Ch. Clerc-Milon 1983, £47.50. The black mark comes at the very end. Service is included, according to the menu and the bill. Why, then, are credit card slips left open?

CHEF: Pierre Koffmann   PROPRIETORS: Mr and Mrs Pierre Koffmann   OPEN: Mon to Fri; 12.30 to 2, 7 to 11   CLOSED: bank hols   MEALS: alc. Set L £23.50, Set D £55. Minimum £40   SERVICE: net prices   CARDS: Access, Amex, Diners, Visa   DETAILS: 38 seats. Children welcome. Jacket and tie. Wheelchair access. Fax: 071-352 3257

Tatsuso
map 11

32 Broadgate Circle, EC2M 2QS
071-638 5863

COOKING 2
COST £21–£93

The scenes of animation in the wine bars and restaurants that skirt Broadgate Circle are not reflected in this proper Japanese restaurant. In any case, unless you are having teppanyaki, the action is in the windowless basement. This produces adequate and competent stuff, though an evening spent trying to coax the staff into admitting that there might be scope for something more seasonal, more varied, than the fairly pedestrian menu has proved unsuccessful. This is not cheap; it deals with the City, not the private individual out for pleasure. House wines are £9.90.

CHEFS: Mr Maehara and Mr Hirai   PROPRIETORS: Terriibroadgate Ltd   OPEN: Mon to Fri; 11.30 to 3, 6 to 9.30   CLOSED: bank hols   MEALS: alc. Set L £13 to £65, Set D £13.80 to £70. Minimum £15 L, £25 D   SERVICE: 12.5%, card slips closed   CARDS: Access, Amex, Diners, Visa   DETAILS: 130 seats. Private parties: 30 main room, 6 and 8 private rooms. Vegetarian meals. Children welcome. Music. Air-conditioned. Fax: 071-638 5864

Thai Garden ✳ £
NEW ENTRY   map 10

249 Globe Road, E2 0JD
081-981 5748

COOKING 2
COST £10–£28

'A delightful addition to London's ever-growing family of Thai restaurants' is one reporter's view. This place is different because it deals solely in vegetarian and seafood specialities. The brightly lit, cheerful dining-room is something of an oasis in the rather forbidding, inauspicious surroundings close to Bethnal Green tube station. The mainly black and white décor is offset by pictures of exotic vegetables, brightly painted jars and a striking Chinese mask on the bar.

Innovative ideas, an accurate use of spices and beautifully judged flavours are typical of the kitchen's output. Reporters have been impressed by 'superb' prawn tom yum soup served in a handsome clay pot; a version of satay using marinated oyster mushrooms; stir-fried prawns with garlic and pepper; outstanding vegetable curry; and a classic version of pomfret served with a genuine sweet-and-sour sauce. Desserts include Thai custard and chopped banana in coconut milk, which is 'hot rather than tepid – a rare treat', according to one aficionado. The waiters are friendly and helpful in explaining what goes into particular dishes. Booking is essential. Set lunches are excellent value. House French is £5.50 on the minimal wine list, or drink Singha Thai beer.

CHEF: Mrs Pensri Vichit   PROPRIETORS: Suthinee and Jack Hufton   OPEN: Mon to Sat; 12 to 2.45, 6 to 10.45   CLOSED: bank hols   MEALS: alc. Set L £6.50, Set D £14.50 to £19   SERVICE: 10% D, net prices L, card slips closed   CARDS: Access, Visa   DETAILS: 32 seats. Private parties: 20 main room, 14 private room. Vegetarian meals. Children's helpings with prior notice. No smoking in upstairs dining-room. Wheelchair access (1 step). Music

Thailand £

map 10

15 Lewisham Way, SE14 6PP
081-691 4040

COOKING 2*
COST £19–£30

'It goes from strength to strength,' says one who finds Khamkhong Kambungoet's cooking as good as any in the capital; and unusual, too, in so far as it offers the cuisine of ethnic Laos from Thailand's north-east border. The Laotian dishes are the ones to make for: sticky rice; chicken with black pepper and garlic; hot-and-sour papaya, lime, garlic, chilli and mudfish; and steak chargrilled with lime juice, pounded toasted rice and chillis. There is no stinting the chilli, but some have also noted no shortage of sugar-sweetness. Portions are giant ('our soup shared between three'), service is charming and, with the sensitive interpretation of Thai cooking by Victor Herman, highly informed. The wine list may be short but it's chosen by Master of Wine Nicholas Belfrage, and the bottles make sense in the context of the cooking. Lucky Lewisham. House wine is £6.75.

CHEF: Khamkhong Kambungoet   PROPRIETORS: Victor and Khamkhong Herman   OPEN: Tue to Sat, D only; 6 to 11   CLOSED: 25 and 26 Dec, 1 Jan   MEALS: alc. Set D £15 to £17   SERVICE: not inc   CARDS: Access, Amex, Diners, Visa   DETAILS: 25 seats. Private parties: 25 main room. Vegetarian meals. Children by arrangement. Music

Thistells £

map 10

65 Lordship Lane, SE22 8EP
081-299 1921

COOKING 1*
COST £16–£31

Having built his reputation – first with Nico Ladenis, later at L'Auberge – Sami Youssef has moved away from the world of high sophistication and has adopted a more accessible, affordable style. This converted wine bar is now the setting for a menu that brings together classic French and Middle Eastern specialities: warm salad of chicken livers, moules marinière and sauté rabbit with calvados and apples share the stage with falafel, ful medames and dizi (lamb casserole with beans, chickpeas and tomatoes). The cooking is favourably reported and sweets such as banoffi pie have met with approval ('as good as my wife's,' noted one – 'a big compliment'). The atmosphere tends to the relaxed – confirmed by the portable Calor gas heater trundled in one spring evening. House French is £6.80.

CHEF/PROPRIETOR: Sami Youssef   OPEN: all week, exc Sun D; 12 to 3, 7 to 10.30   MEALS: alc. Set L £10   SERVICE: 10%, card slips closed   CARDS: Access, Visa   DETAILS: 40 seats. Private parties: 50 main room. Vegetarian meals. Children's helpings. Wheelchair access. Music

La Truffe Noire £

map 11

29 Tooley Street, SE1 2QF

071-378 0621

COOKING 2

COST £19–£74

La Truffe Noire gets no prize for location: a fancy restaurant in this churning section of the south side of the river is as unexpected as a lido. But it has the merit of convenience for City lunchers – if it can get its service into gear in the time allocated. There is a bewildering series of deals, from brasserie fast food to set meals at this price or that. And people have reported baffling escalation from an apparently low base, though the general sense is that the main standards of cooking are sound indeed. Lentil soup, gazpacho with lots of fresh basil, thin strips of marinated tuna with root ginger, duck breast with celeriac and apple, scallops layered between game chips and bacon then dusted with sesame seeds, breast of goose with figs and a red wine sauce, three large truffle ravioli with a light fennel cream which were 'aromatic, delicious, subtle', an apple tart with a pancake base, and a chocolate parfait 'so pretty the diner wanted to just sit there and admire it' are some of the dishes that have been well reported on this year. The kitchen is French and works in the modern classic mode. It is unfortunate that it is not supported by the ancillaries to the operation. There have been stories of muddle and incompetence. The wine list offers but five half-bottles, a lot of very expensive clarets, and a good set of burgundies. The range at lower prices, however, is not adequate. House wines are £8.

CHEFS: Pascal Lucas and Patrick Lalor   PROPRIETORS: Mr and Mrs M. Alam-Ahmed OPEN: Mon to Sat, exc Sat L (also Sun during local festivals); 12 to 2.30, 6.30 to 10.30 CLOSED: bank hols (exc during local festivals)   MEALS: alc. Set L and D £10 to £21 SERVICE: 12.5%, card slips closed   CARDS: Access, Amex, Diners, Visa   DETAILS: restaurant 46 seats, brasserie 30 seats. 10 tables outside. Private parties: 46 main room, 16 and 30 private rooms. Vegetarian meals. Children welcome. Smart dress preferred. No cigars/pipes in dining-room. Wheelchair access (1 step). Music. Air-conditioned. Fax: 071-403 0689

Turner's

map 12

87–89 Walton Street, SW3 2HP

071-584 6711

COOKING 3*

COST £26–£56

There is a steadiness about Brian Turner's restaurant that seems to defy criticism. 'It's a good place for lunchtime meetings; the price at that time is not high; the service is quiet and good; the place is restful.' So writes one among many. Not quite the same degree of satisfaction is felt by evening customers, for whom the cost may be much greater, and who find that the *carte* evolves at a snail's pace. Better, again, to look at the short menu of the day for signs of change and variety. The appeal may be timeless, but care has been taken this year to spruce the image by refurbishment, while avoiding radical change. Brian Turner's presence, too, is often appreciated; his cheffing is executive, leaving time to season the service. 'There is a welcome matter-of-factness about the style; one doesn't feel pressurised to worship, merely assisted to enjoy' is how one regular visitor expressed it. The cooking is conventional, yet light; it mobilises good materials and treats them carefully in dishes such as a terrine of duck and foie gras, timbale of salmon and crab with a feathered crab sauce of unmistakable shellfish flavour but yet not too heavy, venison with Puy lentils and a classic demi-glace sauce, or lamb with a black olive sauce on a mound of mange-tout. The cheeses may be French (as, inexplicably, is the whole menu), but the desserts show an enjoyment of English tastes in a firm bread-and-butter pudding, or a light raspberry pie, both on superlative custards. Petits fours, canapés, coffee and bread and butter are all up to the mark. The paint-job in the restaurant has evidently given new gloss to the kitchen's performance. The wine list is all French and not very enterprising. The prices are more in line with the evening *carte* than the bargain lunch. There is a range of Fèvre Chablis, but only a single claret below £20. House wines start at £14.

CHEFS: Brian Turner and Peter Brennan   PROPRIETOR: Brian Turner   OPEN: all week, exc Sat L; 12.30 to 2.30, 7.30 to 11 (10 Sun)   CLOSED: 25 to 31 Dec (exc D 31 Dec)   MEALS: alc. Set L £15.75 to £18.50, Set D £23.50 to £29.50   SERVICE: net prices, card slips closed CARDS: Access, Amex, Diners, Visa   DETAILS: 52 seats. Private parties: 22 private room. Children's helpings Sun L. Smart dress preferred. Wheelchair access (2 steps). Music. Air-conditioned. Fax: 071-584 4441

Upper Street Fish Shop £

map 11

324 Upper Street, N1 2XQ
071-359 1401

COOKING 1
COST £9–£20

One viewpoint is that the Conways' bistro-style fish and chip restaurant is 'consistent and friendly. An example of what you get if owners and staff enjoy what they're doing.' It is always packed: 'As usual we had to be shoe-horned in,' comments a regular. Olga Conway is the life and soul of the place, supervising the crowds and chatting during rare quiet moments. Alan Conway chooses the fish and oversees the frying. Lemon sole has been singled out for praise; otherwise there is cod, haddock, skate and plaice, backed up by specials such as halibut. Fish can be grilled for an extra charge. Home-made fish soup, fish lasagne and old-fashioned sweets are popular, although not everyone agrees about the quality of the chips or value for money. Unlicensed.

CHEF: Stuart Gamble   PROPRIETORS: Alan and Olga Conway   OPEN: Mon to Sat, exc Mon L; 12 to 2 (3 Sat), 5.30 to 10   CLOSED: bank and public hols   MEALS: alc. Unlicensed, but bring your own: no corkage   SERVICE: not inc   DETAILS: 50 seats. Children welcome. Wheelchair access. No music. Air-conditioned

See inside the front cover for an explanation of the symbols used at the tops of entries.

Villandry Dining Room ✳

map 13

89 Marylebone High Street, W1M 3DE
071-224 3799 and 487 3816

COOKING 1
COST £23–£34

If Jean-Charles Carrarini had realised how popular his lunchtime dining-room would be, perhaps he would never have bothered with a delicatessen, good though that is. Customers would also find that the kitchen had not run out of main courses by 2pm, and there might have been a little more space in the schoolroom-like dining area. But success speaks for itself. The place serves honest food, at apparently fair prices that may end up, once the bill is done, as a *little* more than you first thought, but the epithets remain valid. There are constants of oysters, charcuterie and smoked salmon on the *carte*, and there is usually an omelette (very good). Main dishes such as roast chicken with lemon and oregano, fish stew of mainly squid with saffron rice, or pasta with sorrel, lovage, chilli, garlic and Parmesan are served in well-judged quantities. Soups are always a decent bet. Unlike the shop, which is endlessly Gallic, the dining-room does not just offer a French experience but concentrates on plain good food. Some of the desserts are worth a mention: arborio rice pudding and apricot frangipane tart are skilful, tarte Tatin is well reported. Coffee is first-rate and strong; the cappuccino is good. The wine list is short, fluid and French, comes direct from Legrand in Paris and thus includes unfamiliar and worthwhile makers. House wines are £9.90.

CHEF: Caroline Symonds   PROPRIETORS: Jean-Charles and Rosalind Carrarini   OPEN: Mon to Sat, L only (D once a month, and by arrangement for private parties); 12.30 to 2.30   MEALS: alc   SERVICE: net prices, card slips closed   CARDS: Access, Visa   DETAILS: 50 seats. Private parties: 50 main room, 40 private room. Vegetarian meals. Children's helpings. No smoking in dining-room. Wheelchair access. No music. Air-conditioned. Fax: 071-486 1370

Wagamama ✳ £

NEW ENTRY   map 13

4 Streatham Street, WC1A 1JB
071-323 9223

COOKING 1
COST £10–£15

The formula has had immediate response from a willing public. This giant restaurant is in a basement in central museum-land, within walking distance of Covent Garden, theatres, west-central offices and the university. Its prices are pitched low, and the flim-flam is kept to a minimum in a minimalist setting – high fashion, this. The staff are ultra-keen and responsive, and they take your order on computer terminals hooked up to the kitchen, which is open for all to see. There is no smoking, and not a lot of comfort. It is a feeding station, Japanese-style. Much of the cooking is bright and cheerful, but not distinguished. The noodles, however, in soup or fried, with various extras, make a decent one-pot meal. It is worth visiting the British Museum just to have the excuse to pop out for a bowl. House wine is £6.80.

CHEF: Ayumi Maeda   PROPRIETOR: Akitoshi Handa   OPEN: Mon to Sat; 12 to 2.30, 6 to 11   MEALS: alc   SERVICE: not inc   DETAILS: 104 seats. Vegetarian meals. Children welcome. No smoking. No music. Air-conditioned

Wakaba

map 11

122A Finchley Road, NW3 5HT
071-722 3854 and 586 7960

COOKING 2*
COST £16–£63

A sheer off-white façade broken by a curved frosted glass window sets the tone of austere modernity that characterises this Japanese restaurant. The output of the sushi bar at the far end of the dining-room has been mightily impressive – a fascinating selection of beautifully fresh fish in clever architectural constructions ('reminded me of town planners' models,' observed one reporter). Sukiyaki has been described as 'a maelstrom of contrasting textures: slithery yam noodles, tender wafer-thin beef, crunchy bamboo and Chinese leaf', although the accompanying sauce was 'unmemorable'. Other well-reported dishes have included udon noodle soup with king prawn tempura, and perfectly grilled lemon sole. Set dinners are satisfying, very good value and provide the opportunity to explore many different cooking styles. The food clearly generates much enthusiasm, but visitors have been unmoved by the high-tech, minimalist décor. It may work best when the place is full and bustling. Drink green tea, saké or Kirin beer. House Soave is £8.50.

CHEF/PROPRIETOR: Minoru Yoshihara   OPEN: Mon to Sat; 12 to 2.30, 6.30 to 11   CLOSED: 1 week Aug, 5 days Christmas, 4 days Easter   MEALS: alc. Set L £11 to £15, Set D £24 to £33. Minimum £16   SERVICE: net prices   CARDS: Access, Amex, Diners, Visa   DETAILS: 55 seats. Private parties: 60 main room. Vegetarian meals. Wheelchair access (also WC). Air-conditioned

Waltons

NEW ENTRY   map 12

121 Walton Street, SW3 2HP
071-584 0204

COOKING 2*
COST £21–£63

A restaurant of the 1970s, and one look at the swagged yellow and grey dining-room – 'archetype of the boudoir' – confirms it. It may wear a tiny bit thin, but enthusiasm is not lacking in service or commitment. Classics like home-cured salmon, terrine of foie gras, calf's liver and bacon, medallions of beef and roast Norfolk duckling sit next to the more popular of modern ideas: wild mushroom ravioli, a cabbage parcel of sweetbreads and chicken with saffron sauce, or duck with lime, courgette and ginger and a wheatgerm sauce. Waltons has often been associated with 'English' cooking, but it is a carefully modulated emphasis, coming out in hot puddings or liver and bacon rather than cod Englishry. Good things have been experienced, though not unmixed with error. Salmon and lobster fish-cakes (with intelligent use of tarragon and dill, and even a bit of gin), a layered chicken and walnut terrine, accurate vegetable cookery, a chocolate mille-feuille that might be a poor man's dream of a banana split, and a great apricot custard were all highlights of a summer meal characterised overall as 'thoughtful, yet a little "one-note" to be truly memorable'. Lunch comes cheaper – on Sundays, too. Good clarets, especially petits châteaux, at reasonable prices are the high spot of the long wine list. House wines are £9.

Report forms are at the back of the book; write a letter if you prefer.

CHEF: Paul Hodgson   PROPRIETOR: Roger Wren (Waltons Restaurants Ltd)   OPEN: all week; 12.30 to 2.30 (2 Sun and bank hols), 7.30 to 11.30 (7 to 10 Sun and bank hols)   CLOSED: 25 and 26 Dec   MEALS: alc. Set L £14.75, Set Sun L £16.50, post-theatre supper £21 (Mon to Sat)   SERVICE: not inc, card slips closed   CARDS: Access, Amex, Diners, Visa   DETAILS: 65 seats. Private parties: 40 main room, 25 private room. Vegetarian meals. Children's helpings. Wheelchair access (1 step). No music. Air-conditioned. Fax: 071-581 2846

Wiltons   map 13

55 Jermyn Street, SW1Y 6LX   COOKING 2
071-629 9955   COST £29–£77

Wiltons does not change much: Edwardian dining-room with alcoves, many well-dressed waiters who 'listen to one's order so that what comes back is what was originally requested', 'characterful' waitresses, a facility to buy fine fish, game and meat and to cook it simply or traditionally, but not a place to go for ambitious or imaginative cooking. You pay for the privilege, but many people like its apparently authoritative Englishness. Dressed crab, grilled turbot, salmon fish-cakes and Welsh rarebit were a recipe for gastronomic heaven for one inspector. Slightly overcooked soles, no extra sherry with the turtle soup, and food a mite on the cool side meant 'overpriced' for another. Wiltons does not have much time for complicated techniques. The wine list is in keeping: dear and traditional but jolly good. House wine is from £12.50.

CHEF: Ross Hayden   PROPRIETORS: Wiltons (St James's) Ltd   OPEN: Mon to Sat, exc Sat L; 12 to 2.30, 6 to 10.30   CLOSED: 2 weeks Aug   MEALS: alc. Cover £1. Minimum £12.50   SERVICE: not inc   CARDS: Access, Amex, Diners, Visa   DETAILS: 90 seats. Private parties: 20 main room, 16 private room. Children welcome. Jacket and tie. Wheelchair access (1 step). Air-conditioned. No music. Fax: 071-495 6233

Wódka   map 12

12 St Albans Grove, W8 5PN   COOKING 2
071-937 6513   COST £20–£37

'It's the vodkas that set the tone,' comment reporters about this Polish restaurant a stone's throw from Leith's School of Food and Wine in a Kensington backwater. New chef Mirek Golos takes his cue from the liquor and offers a menu ranging from blinis and pierogi filled with lentils, mushrooms and truffles to beef olives with dill cucumber and golonka (pork shank glazed with honey and orange). It may sometimes seem like 'Poland-meets-Paris' (or at least Western Europe), particularly when *plats du jour* include marinated mozzarella and anchovy salad, and osso buco. Creamy chilled leek and potato soup, leniwe (cheese dumplings in a sauce dotted with chopped, sun-dried tomatoes and black olives), and classic salmon koulibiaca have all been fresh and enjoyable, with true, distinct flavours. Caraway-seed bread makes a convincing staple accompaniment to the meal. One visitor felt that the authentic robustness of the food is 'softened' for English palates, and that there is 'a tendency to retreat on the vegetables, to keep the pickle jars at arm's length and to over-sophisticate the ingredients'. Even so, the chef knows his trade and the restaurant holds its niche well. Sunday brunch is now available. In addition to the seductive range of flavoured vodkas, there is Polish Zywiec beer and a useful wine list – although Eastern Europe is notable by its absence. House French is £7.90.

CHEF: Mirek Golos   PROPRIETOR: Jan Woroniecki   OPEN: all week, exc Sat L; 12.15 to 2.30 (12.30 to 4.30 Sun L), 7 to 11   CLOSED: bank hols   MEALS: alc. Sun brunch SERVICE: not inc   CARDS: Access, Amex, Diners, Visa   DETAILS: 60 seats. Private parties: 10 main room, 30 private room. Vegetarian meals. Children welcome. Music. Fax: 071-937 6513

Yoisho £

map 13

33 Goodge Street, W1P 1FD
071-323 0477

COOKING 1
COST £10–£35

It won't win prizes for elegance, nor will the food win awards for high fashion. Indeed, one man's thought was that it resembled a dockland eating den for sailors. In fact, most of the clientele are Japanese, and they come for the noodles – these are good. Some of the cooking is more rustic and homely than in more expensive restaurants, yet the sashimi is still as fresh as a daisy.

CHEF: Mr Takayama   PROPRIETOR: Mr Watanabe   OPEN: Mon to Sat, D only; 6 to 11 CLOSED: bank hols   MEALS: alc. Minimum £8   SERVICE: 10%   DETAILS: 70 seats. Private parties: 40 main room. Children's helpings. No children after 8, exc Sat. No-smoking area. Music. Air-conditioned. Fax: 071-323 0477

Zen Central ♥

NEW ENTRY   map 13

20 Queen Street, W1X 7PJ
071-629 8089 and 8103

COOKING 1*
COST £25–£70

Though offering salmon, sea bass and Dover sole at so much a pound and cooked in one of five possible ways, 'we didn't see any live fish brought out to tables and weighed in front of the customer as happens in Hong Kong,' reported one visitor from the colony. Zen is too chic for that, its clientele perhaps unused to face-to-face encounters with raw life. The menu, however, is as smart as the Rick Mather interior design – smooth, white and clever – and gives a new angle on Chinese cooking. Smoked chicken imbued with spices, pork with dried scallops, lobster with tangerine and garlic are not often met with on Anglo-oriental dish lists, even if sweet-and-sours, monks' vegetables or Singapore noodles are more commonplace. What Zen does well are hot appetisers and dumplings, what is not so good is the lack of attack in the spicing and flavouring (though MSG is mercifully banned from the kitchen). The ambience is endlessly smart and service good. You pay for that privilege. The wine list expands the bill, but the choice is very suave. House wine is £12.

CHEF: Michael Leung   PROPRIETORS: Blaidwood Co Ltd   OPEN: all week; 12.15 to 2.30, 6.30 to 11.30 (11 Sun)   MEALS: alc. Set D £30 to £45. Cover £1. Minimum £20 D   SERVICE: not inc   CARDS: Access, Amex, Diners, Visa   DETAILS: 90 seats. Private parties: 90 main room, 20 private room. Vegetarian meals. Children's helpings. Smart dress preferred. Wheelchair access. Music. Air-conditioned. Fax: 071-437 0641

London round-up

'Where should we go then?' is sometimes as impossible a question as 'Who is your favourite composer?' and the *Guide's* full entries may not always supply the answer. You live in the wrong part, your pocket cannot stretch so far, you can't stand curries, fish, liver or vegetables. This supplementary listing is 100 places that may help your decision. They have gained approval of other readers, but they may not fit the *Guide's* specifications, or approval is too guarded for complete description or recommendation. Read on.

Price guide
For a three-course meal, including half a bottle of house wine, coffee and service, per person.

  £ = £20 or under
 ££ = £20–£30
£££ = £30 or over

Accademia Italiana   SW7
24 Rutland Gate   map 12
071-225 3474
For the price of a pound, non-members of the Italian Academy for arts and applied arts can visit the bookshop, gallery and lunchtime restaurant. Traditional, homely Italian dishes at affordable prices. Unlicensed, but bring your own.   £

Andrew Edmunds   W1
46 Lexington Street   map 13
071-437 5708
Packed-out Soho joint that's certainly fun. Cooking is variable, the menu changes weekly and includes such comforting things as couscous, cassoulet and home-made pasta. A popular lunchtime spot.   £

Aroma   W1
1B Dean Street   map 14
071-287 1633
Upbeat café doused in Technicolor; wacky crockery and furniture and a cool crowd. The perfect pit-stop for take-out or eat-in gourmet sandwiches, savouries and sweet sundries. Coffee is fortifying; choose from espresso, cappuccino, ristretto or café melange (among others).   £
Another branch at: 36A St Martin's Lane, WC2, 071-836 5110.

Arts Theatre Café   WC2
6 Great Newport Street   map 14
071-497 8014
Tucked away beneath the theatre, this is all too easy to miss. Modern Mediterranean cooking, together with a cosmopolitan atmosphere and low prices. Great Italian breads, pasta and polenta.   £

Au Provençal   SE24
293–295 Railton Road   map 10
071-274 9163
Inexpensive, popular, rough and ready French cooking that pleases some, but can be let down by materials and approximate finish.   ££

Balzac Bistro   W12
4 Wood Lane   map 10
081-743 6787
Long-standing French bistro in the BBC locality. Reliable cooking of average ingredients; moules, wild mushroom crêpes, cassoulet, figs in Pernod.   ££

Belvedere   W8
off Abbotsbury Road,   map 11
Holland Park
071-602 1238
While not exactly al fresco – although several terrace tables do exist – the pretty

157

park location is this restaurant's best feature. Modern décor and menu to match, but uneven cooking can let down the side. Popular in summer and for Sunday lunch. ££–£££

Ben's Thai   W9
The Warrington,   map 11
93 Warrington Crescent
071-266 3134
Glorious room on first floor of large pub. Very fair Thai cooking, including good hot-and-sour soups. Charming service. £

Beotys   WC2
79 St Martin's Lane   map 14
071-836 8768/8548
Very long-standing Greek family-run restaurant. The *carte* might appear schizophrenic, with one half devoted to bland, international dishes, but ignore this and go for the Greek-Cypriot selection. Here find decent dolmades, taramasalata, kleftiko; finish with sweet pastries and authentically sludgy coffee. ££

Bloom's   E1
90 Whitechapel High Street   map 11
071-247 60001
Old-fashioned, East End Jewish restaurant. Kosher cooking that can be variable; homely soups, bortsch, potato latkes and dumplings may be more reliable than meat dishes. £
Another branch at: 130 Golders Green Road, NW11, 081-455 1338.

Books for Cooks   W11
4 Blenheim Crescent   map 11
071-221 1992
Small space at the back of this specialist cookery bookshop. Open only for lunch but worth making the trip for interesting recipes and fair prices. Almost possible to read – from the overflowing shelves – about food and eat it at the same time. Unlicensed. £

La Bouchée   SW7
56 Old Brompton Road   map 12
071-589 1929
Basic bistro fare that's comparatively cheap, especially early evening. A long menu lists expected peasant staples, plus good oysters and snails. Serves a purpose in South Kensington. £

Bouchon Bordelais   SW11
9 Battersea Rise   map 10
071-738 0307
French restaurant-with-bistro. Buzzy atmosphere, popular with the young. Shellfish a speciality, also crêpes and salads. ££

La Bouffe   SW11
13 Battersea Rise   map 10
071-228 3384
Busy Clapham bistro cooking French country fare. Don't mind cramped surroundings for set-price mix-and-match menus that offer choice and value. Good range of vintage calvados. ££

Busabong Too   SW10
1A Langton Street   map 11
071-352 7414
Bright, pleasant Thai with interesting menu. Specialities include softshell crab in chilli, green chicken curry, stir-fried prawns and satays. There is also an upstairs room where diners can relax on cushions before low tables. ££

Café de Colombia   W1
Museum of Mankind,   map 13
6 Burlington Gardens
071-287 8148
After you have perused ethnic artefacts, this small, stylish café makes for a welcome refuelling spot. Open for lunch, morning coffee and afternoon tea. Light meals, speciality breads, good cakes and excellent cappuccino presented with chocolate-covered coffee beans. £

Café Delancey   WC1
32 Procter Street,   map 13
Red Lion Square
071-242 6691

Continental-style café where you can choose anything at any time. That said, weekend breakfasts are what count. Typical brasserie menu; popular meeting spot.   £
Another branch at: 3 Delancey Street, NW1, 071-387 1985.

Café des Arts   NW3
82 Hampstead High Street   map 11
071-435 3608
Fashionable joint with a modern, Mediterranean menu. Grilled vegetables, seafood, warm and cold salads and inventive puddings all feature.   ££

Café du Marché   EC1
22 Charterhouse Square   map 11
071-608 1609
High marks for location and atmosphere; lower ones for some undistinguished cooking in the French manner that has lacked substance.   £££

Café Flo   NW3
205 Haverstock Hill   map 11
071-435 6744
Relaxed base for small brasserie chain. Modern and provincial French dishes including warm salads, onion tart, good steak and chips, freshly baked bread.   £
Branches also at: 51 St Martin's Lane, WC2, 071-836 8289
334 Upper Street, N1, 071-226 7916
127–129 Kensington Church Street, W8, 071-727 8142.

Café Rouge   SW19
26 High Street, Wimbledon   map 10
081-944 5131
Popular espresso pit-stop that's used as much for its brasserie menu. Croque-monsieurs, Normandy fish stew, hot smoked sausage with warm potato salad and decent desserts on offer.   £
Branches also at: 6–7 South Grove, N6, 081-342 9797
19 Hampstead High Street, NW3, 071-433 3404
855 Fulham Road, SW6, 071-371 8371
200 Putney Bridge Road, SW15, 081-788 4257

46 James Street, W1, 071-487 4847
31 Kensington Park Road, W11, 071-221 4449
7A Petersham Road, Richmond, Surrey, 081-332 2423.

Camden Brasserie   NW1
216 Camden High Street   map 11
071-482 2114
Relaxed, popular venue close to the market, that gets very busy at weekends. Chargrilling a speciality, large bowls of matchstick frites to accompany. Stick to Häagen-Dazs ice-cream for sweets.   £

Canal Brasserie   W10
Canalot Studios,   map 11
222 Kensal Road
081-960 2732
Former Fry's chocolate factory now home to music and film studios and this suitably fashionable restaurant with, as yet, unrealised potential. Modern British cooking of a watered-down formula – flavours are mild, too – but a fabulous space with a funky atmosphere.   ££

Carapace   NW3
118 Heath Street   map 11
071-435 8000/5773
Pretty, old Hampstead cottage now an intimate French restaurant. Peasant bread, fresh vegetables, simple marinades and straightforward main courses. Like dining in a private house.   ££

Caruso   SW6
585 Fulham Road   map 10
071-381 3422
Contemporary Italian cooking matched with fashionably stripped-down surroundings. Good results, especially pastas, smooth service; conservatory addition.   ££

Le Cassis   SW15
30 Putney High Street   map 10
081-788 8668
Unpretentious French, popular with Putney locals. Fair home-cooking takes in fish soup, snails, steaks, venison with wild mushrooms and fresh fish.   ££

159

Cecconi's   W1
5A Burlington Gardens   map 13
071-434 1509
A lot of money for simple food, but look
at the customers. Probably the first
carpaccio in London, good pasta, but
the cooking barely matters.   £££

Cherry Orchard   E2
241–245 Globe Road   map 10
081-980 6678
Buddhist-run vegetarian restaurant in the
East End. Daily-changing menu includes
much for vegans and is also available for
take-away. Low prices.   £

Chez Gerard   W1
8 Charlotte Street   map 13
071-636 4975
Charming, lively French bistro renowned
for its good steak frites. Popular
lunchtime rendezvous.   ££
Branches also at: 31 Dover Street, W1,
071-499 8171
119 Chancery Lane, WC2, 071-405 0290.

China China   W1
3 Gerrard Street   map 14
071-439 7511
Chinese café that's fast, pacy and full of
buzz. Try and eat on the ground floor for
maximum action. Big bowls of noodle
soup, roast meats, one-plate rice and fried
noodle dishes. Have an accompanying
helping of choi sum with oyster
sauce.   £

Christian's   W4
1 Station Parade,   map 10
Burlington Lane
081-995 0382/0208
Another neighbourhood restaurant –
with greenhouse feel – that charges more
than the cooking deserves. But pleasant
enough.   ££–£££

Chuen Cheng Ku   W1
17 Wardour Street   map 14
071-437 1398
Enormous Chinese recommended for its
lunchtime dim-sum wheeled round on
trolleys. Good char siu stuffed buns, spare
ribs and sucking pig. Evening menu is less
interesting.   £–££

Chutney Mary   SW10
535 King's Road   map 10
071-351 3113
Jewel in the crown, lauded as London's
first Anglo-Indian restaurant. Large,
comfortable, with pretty
conservatory.   ££

Claridge's Causerie   W1
Brook Street   map 13
071-629 8860
The intimate side of Claridge's. You sit on
dainty tables round a central smorgasbord
(one of the first in London). There is a full
menu as well, costs can be kept within
bounds, and people-watching is
interesting.   £££

Czech Club   NW6
74 West End Lane   map 11
071-372 5251
Czechoslovak National House is also
home to a dining-room. Here, sustaining
fare takes in soups, Debrecin sausage,
roast meats, sauerkraut. Dumplings with
everything. Faded, austere surroundings
have a peculiar appeal.   £

Daphne's   SW3
112 Draycott Avenue   map 12
071-589 4257
Agreeable French restaurant in the heart
of Kensington. Properly cooked cheese
and spinach soufflé; roast partridge
with bread sauce, breadcrumbs and
bacon; braised sweetbreads with morels.
Sweet soufflés make ideal
desserts.   ££–£££

Deals   SW10
Chelsea Harbour   map 10
071-376 3232
Its fun approach and provision of high
chairs make this a likely spot for
entertaining children. Thai flavours are
mixed in with a more mainstream,
American menu.   £

La Dordogne W4
5 Devonshire Road map 10
081-747 1836
French; more expensive than
neighbourhood; eat oysters. **£££**

Eatons SW1
49 Elizabeth Street map 12
071-730 0074
Dependable neighbourhood restaurant
that's inexpensive for Belgravia. Pleasant,
airy dining-room with lots of plants and
prints. Familiar Anglo-French cooking
and a traditional sweets trolley. **££**

Emporio Armani SW3
191 Brompton Road map 12
071-823 8818
Lunch venue in the Armani shop that's
strictly for serious shoppers. Linger over
modern, immaculate food before settling
the bill and homing in on The Purchase.
Chic, pared-down surroundings, mostly
Italian cooking, brief wine list. **££**

Enoteca SW15
28 Putney High Street map 10
081-785 4449
Interesting Italian with a modern menu,
managing to avoid trattoria clichés.
Regional cooking; grilled aubergine and
smoked mozzarella, swordfish escallopes,
tagliatelle in duck and pepper
sauce. **££**

La Famiglia SW10
7 Langton Street map 11
071-351 0761
Long-standing, popular World's End
trattoria. Its attractively tiled yard and
garden is a corner worth knowing about
for sunny, summer eating. Traditional
and modern Italian fare. **£££**

Fleet Tandoori Two N10
346 Muswell Hill Broadway map 10
081-882 8252
Quiet, standard Bangladeshi restaurant in
the High Street. Fish curry and tandoori
fish depart from the norm, otherwise
there's a run-of-the-mill selection

including vegetarian and meat thalis.
Service is pleasant. **£**

Galicia W10
323 Portobello Road map 11
081-969 3539
Spanish restaurant that's frequented by
the local Iberian community. This is its
degree of authenticity, the food may not
be so true to form. Octopus, hake and all
things fishy. Great coffee, smoky
atmosphere; you can just go to sit at
the bar. **£**

Geales W8
2 Farmer Street map 11
071-727 7969
Superior fish and chip shop where the
fresh fish is delivered daily. Old-fashioned
style, good atmosphere and gargantuan
portions. A blackboard menu takes in
cod, plaice, salmon, skate and shark.
Brilliant fruit crumbles; no booking. **£**

Gonbei WC1
151 King's Cross Road map 11
071-278 0619
Japanese café that's convenient for
travellers using King's Cross. Basic
surroundings, fresh ingredients and a
menu taking in tempura, sushi and
sashimi. Cheap prices. **£**

Greek Valley NW8
130 Boundary Road map 11
071-624 3217
Good-value Greek-Cypriot with
interesting and peculiarly authentic
cooking. Great kleftiko, calamari and king
prawns baked in a tomato and feta sauce.
Vegetarians can choose from dolmades, a
moussaka and a bean casserole. **£–££**

Grill St Quentin SW3
2 Yeoman's Row map 12
071-581 8377
Bustling Knightsbridge brasserie in
subterranean surrounds. A meat-
dominated menu also has salad starters
and a shellfish platter. Decent wines at
drinkable prices. **££**

Haandi   NW1

161 Drummond Street   map 11
071-383 4557

Indian; mostly carnivorous menu takes in tandooris, tikkas, lamb pasanda and Goan fish curry. Some vegetarian offerings. The lunchtime buffet offers the best value.   £

Halcyon Hotel   W11

129 Holland Park Avenue   map 11
071-221 5411

Elegant hotel with an extremely pretty, romantic dining-room and small, well-run bar. Popular hang-out for the famous and the discreet. Salmon fish-cakes, ravioli with ricotta and white chocolate terrine are typical offerings. Good for Sunday brunch.   £££

Hyde Park Hotel   SW1

Park Room,   map 12
Knightsbridge
071-235 2000

Go for the views of Hyde Park and a grand interior, done out in coloured marbles, with fancy ceilings and chandeliers. Cooking is less spectacular but competent enough Italian fare that's aiming at the health-conscious.   £££

Joe Allen   WC2

13 Exeter Street   map 14
071-836 0651

Lively basement restaurant with an American-influenced menu. From burgers, barbecue ribs and brownies to gravlax and good salads. Booking is essential, as is punctuality. Upbeat service.   £–££

Julie's   W11

135 Portland Road   map 11
071-229 8331

A Holland Park institution, hidden amid a backwater of antique shops. Inside, a confusing labyrinth of wildly decorated rooms and lots of corners ideal for private trysts. The menu is English vernacular with nods to passing fashion. Sunday teas in the wine bar.   £££

Kaspia   W1

18–18A Bruton Place   map 13
071-493 2612

Wood-panelled caviare house for the well-heeled. Can work out exceptionally expensive, although set menus offer some price guidelines. Good choice of flavoured vodkas. Smoothly run, smart dress and suits required.   £££

Káthmandu Inn   W12

6–7 Seven Stars Corner,   map 10
Padenswick Road
081-743 7192

Neighbourhood friendly Nepalese; try the king prawn dhansak, brinjal bhaji, chicken phal. Always reliable.   £

Kenny's   NW3

70 Heath Street   map 11
071-435 6972

Happy American restaurant with strong Cajun/Creole overtones. Big portions, youthful atmosphere and obliging service creates a successful formula.   £
Another branch at: 2A Pond Place, SW3, 071-225 2916.

Kettners   W1

29 Romilly Street   map 14
071-437 6437

Old Soho building that has character. Pizzas are the thing here and they do not disappoint. Otherwise, a straightforward menu lists garlic bread, burgers, chocolate fudge cake and ice-cream. No-booking policy makes it handy for the area.   £

Lahore Kebab House   E1

2 Umberston Street   map 11
071-488 2551

Busy, cheap, one of the East End's better Indian bets, where 'authentic' may not always carry the charm it might.   £

Lal Qila   W1

117 Tottenham Court Road   map 13
071-387 4570

Once new-wave, now looking more standard tandoori. Mixed reports but reasonable murgh makhani, lamb pasanda and baigan masala. Breads and thalis can be disappointing.   ££

Lanesborough Hotel   SW1

1 Lanesborough Place,   map 12
Hyde Park Corner
071-259 5599
Grandiose hotel, formerly St George's Hospital. Seriously over-blown, sumptuous decorations, striving to be stately. Two expensive dining-rooms: the main is British and formal, the conservatory more fun and, cooking oriental dishes, more successful.   £££

Lemonia   NW1

89 Regent's Park Road   map 11
071-586 7454
New premises for a long-standing Primrose Hill restaurant. A standard but well-presented Greek-Cypriot repertoire. The wine list has been expanded to include a good choice of half-bottles. The dauntingly large space has been cleverly lit, managing to create islands of intimacy.   £–££

Lilly's   W11

6 Clarendon Road   map 11
071-727 9359
Low-key Holland Park place that mostly pleases. Well-presented, tending towards fussy food and a modern British menu. Polite service.   ££

Los Remos   W2

38A Southwick Street   map 11
071-723 5056/706 1870
The basement tapas bar is a likelier bet than the upstairs restaurant. Lively atmosphere, friendly Spanish staff, lots of choice, generous portions.   ££

Magno's   WC2

65A Long Acre   map 14
071-836 6077
Brasserie popular with the Royal Opera House crowd. Set-price pre-theatre menu is good value and delivers straight-forward, acceptable French food. Quick and efficient service.   ££

Mangal   E8

10 Arcola Street,   map 11
off Stoke Newington Road
071-275 8981
Small, blue-tiled Turkish restaurant in the East End. Grilled and spiced meats freshly prepared are accompanied by bread baked on the premises. Unlicensed, but bring your own.   £

Martin's   NW1

239 Baker Street   map 11
071-935 3130/0997
Down a peg to a brasserie style of operation but early reports say not bad. Risotto with wild mushrooms, confit of duck with salt pork and haricot beans, peach tart with caramel sauce.   ££

May's Café   NW10

1030 Harrow Road   map 10
081-960 8268
Daytime greasy spoon transforms into Thai food café by night. Fundamental décor, good menu selection, lots of lemon grass and chilli. Bring your own wine (no corkage) or drink Singha lager. Also does take-away.   £

Le Mesurier   EC1

113 Old Street   map 11
071-251 8117
Small restaurant in an unprepossessing, ill-served area. Open for lunch; dinner is only by arrangement, for parties. Modern British menu; main courses are better than starters or sweets.   £££

Metro Wine Bar   SW3

28 Basil Street   map 12
071-589 6286
Basement wine bar that's intimate and relaxing, in contrast to the heady abundance of nearby Harrods. A great wine list with much to interest has many by the glass. The best bet is to stay with satisfying snacks like croque-monsieur and cheeses.   ££

Mildred's · W1
58 Greek Street · map 14
071-494 1634
Cheap and cheerful vegetarian café
that's a central London find for the
impecunious. Modern art on the walls,
hard seats and some tables shared.
Wholesome cooking, tempting
cakes. £

Le Muscadet · W1
25 Paddington Street · map 11
071-935 2883
Well-established French bistro that's
popular as a lunch venue. A blackboard
menu offers a familiar range: mussels,
foie gras, steaks, fish and duck. Puddings
can be predictable, cheese is a better bet.
Service can be haughty, the bill (with
unexpected charge for bread and a service
charge) can be high. £££

Navigator · SW5
Polish Air Force Club, · map 11
14 Collingham Gardens
071-370 1229
Basement dining-room with cold war
décor but full marks for warm service and
authentic Polish food. Eat bortsch, blinis
and potato and walnut latkes, drink
Polish lager or vodka. £

Ninjin · W1
244 Great Portland Street · map 13
071-388 4657
Japanese basement restaurant, now with
added sushi bar. Set meals at lunch offer
best value; meal-boxes might include
miso soup, tempura beautifully presented
in baskets, deep-fried tofu with bean
sprouts or a sushi selection. The upstairs
Japanese supermarket sells ingredients to
the newly inspired. £££

Norma Café · W4
183 Acton Lane · map 10
081-994 1093
Very much a night-time activity in
fundamental surroundings, but the word
is of high-grade Thai cooking. It's a caff by
day. Unlicensed. £

Noughts 'n' Crosses · W5
77 The Grove · map 10
081-840 7568
Quietly successful neighbourhood
restaurant ensconced in Ealing. A
Chinese chef cooking all manner of
things, from Eastern noodle and crabmeat
balls to rack of lamb to modern
Mediterranean recipes. An admirable
formula that partly works but flavours
need balancing out. ££

Ognisko Polskie · SW7
Polish Hearth Club,
55 Exhibition Road · map 12
071-589 4670
Open to non-members, this discreetly
disguised restaurant is home to Polish
exiles and lovers of East European
food. Hot, filled bagels, blinis, bortsch,
through to pancakes with swee
cheese. Great selection of flavoured
vodkas. ££

Patisserie Valerie · SW3
215 Brompton Road · map 12
071-823 9971
New sister to Soho café-cum-cake shop.
Sit on stools at the stately marble bar or
make comfortable at back-room tables.
Light lunches, although afternoon tea is
its *raison d'être*. Peerless eclairs and choux
buns. Good espresso. £
Another branch at: 44 Old Compton
Street, W1, 071-437 3466.

Phuket · SW11
246 Battersea Park Road · map 10
071-223 5924
Straightforward Thai that's good for spicy
soups made with coconut milk, red
chicken curry and simple puddings. Drink
Singha lager or cocktails. £

Piccolo Mondo · WC2
31 Catherine Street · map 14
071-836 3609
Elegant Italian boasting fine
surroundings. Green, shot-silk walls,
crystal chandeliers and, as focal point,
a cast-iron spiral staircase. Good

minestrone, seafood pancake and chicken breast stuffed with foie gras, in a lobster sauce. **£££**

Pomegranates SW1
94 Grosvenor Road map 11
071-828 6560
Basement restaurant with a long and interesting menu. Global cooking that can be variable but pleases the curious. Equally eclectic wine list. **££–£££**

La Pomme d'Amour W11
128 Holland Park Avenue map 11
071-229 8532
Classically decorated French restaurant, complete with sylvan murals and rear conservatory. An equally classical menu, pleasant service and a quietly romantic atmosphere. **££**

Le Poulbot EC2
45 Cheapside map 11
071-236 4379
This is the Roux brothers' answer to eating in the City. Plush red banquette seating, slick service for fast turnover. Expensive, daily-changing three-course menu of reliable classics. Pricey wine list with no house wine. Cheaper upstairs brasserie. Only open for lunch. **££–£££**

La Poule au Pot SW1
231 Ebury Street map 12
071-730 7763
Romantic, candle-lit, long-surviving '60s restaurant with lace-edged tablecloths. Classic menu, plus wonderful garlic bread and an admirable selection of vegetables. Pleasant service with genuine Gallic charm. **££–£££**

Primates NW1
257 Royal College Street map 11
071-284 1059
Nice garden, pretty restaurant, lots of stuffed apes, food that might be cooked in the provinces. Neighbourhood, maybe, cross London, no. **££**

Quincy's NW2
675 Finchley Road map 11
071-794 8499
Pleasant neighbourhood restaurant cooking straightforward English food. Expect oxtail soup, choice of fresh fish and game, accompanied by crunchy vegetables and good dauphinois potatoes. **££**

Raoul's W9
30 Clifton Road map 11
071-289 7313
Italian restaurant bringing rustic Mediterranean cooking to the backwaters that are Little Venice. An emphasis on pastas, backed up by pulses, fish and grilled vegetables; this is fashionable eating. Décor, too, is modern. **£**
Another branch at: Raoul's Café, 13 Clifton Road, W9, 071-289 7313.

Rasa Sayang W2
38 Queensway map 11
071-229 8417
Modern, neon-lit showcase for Malaysian/Singaporean cooking. Fresh ingredients, generous portions and an interesting menu. Hot soups and noodle dishes are a good bet. **££**
Branches also at: 10 Frith Street, W1, 071-734 8720
Kingswell Shopping Centre, Heath Street, NW3, 071-435 6508
3 Leicester Place, WC2, 071-437 4556
146 The Broadway, W13, 081-840 4450.

Rebato's SW8
169 South Lambeth Road map 11
071-735 6388
Go for the tapas bar rather than the restaurant. Pleasant atmosphere, authentically Spanish. Good fish dishes, drinkable house wine. **£**

La Reserve SW6
422–428 Fulham Road map 11
071-385 8561
Modern, fashionable hotel on the fringes of Fulham. A designer dining-room done

out in black and white and a menu betraying Mediterranean, Californian and Thai influences. Interesting results, laid-back service.   ££

Rive Gauche
SE1
61 The Cut   map 11
071-928 8645
French that is useful for the location, seems good for its materials, but can miss on its cooking. Set price is not dear.   ££–£££

Rules
WC2
35 Maiden Lane   map 14
071-836 5314
Purported to be London's oldest restaurant. Certainly the food is old-fashioned fare and the panelled décor has the feel of an institution. Steak and kidney pudding and game dishes attract a solid business crowd.   ££

San Frediano
SW3
62 Fulham Road   map 12
071-584 8375
Stylish South Kensington trattoria with a winning atmosphere. Italian staples backed up by a good selection of daily specials. Booking is recommended.   ££

San Lorenzo
SW3
22 Beauchamp Place   map 12
071-584 1074/4633
Star-spotting opportunities abound at this still-fashionable haunt. Italian cooking, decent wines, rather too many potted palms. Expensive.   ££–£££

San Remo
SW13
195 Castelnau   map 10
081-741 5909
Good neighbourhood Italian, unsophisticated décor, friendly service and serious cooking. Fish soup, pasta with ink-fish, aubergine fritters. Sweets are from the trolley.   ££

Satay House
W2
13 Sale Place   map 11
071-723 6763
Modest family business that's cheap and authentic. Good, peppery Thai soup, satays and rice sticks. Useful for the area and for an alternative Sunday lunch.   £

Smokey Joe
SW18
131 Wandsworth High Street   map 10
081-871 1785
Bright yellow, bright Caribbean cooking. Ask Charlie Phillips for his specials, or get him to cook you something to order. No luxury, lots of sounds. Bring your own wine.   £

Smollensky's Balloon
W1
1 Dover Street   map 13
071-491 1199
American, fun food and perfect for entertaining children. Book for the weekend lunchtime puppet shows and clowns.   ££

Soho Brasserie
W1
23–25 Old Compton Street   map 14
071-439 9301
Chiefly a watering-hole for Soho trendies but a good venue for a casual meal, if a lively atmosphere is called for. Good olives and vegetables, espresso coffee, pleasing service.   £

Spread Eagle
SE10
1–2 Stockwell Street   map 10
081-853 2333
Old, rambling coaching-inn, convenient for Greenwich Theatre. Show-goers may eat their starter before the play and their main course after it. French menu: langoustine bisque, pigeon breast with grapes and raisins, chocolate marquise. Atmosphere does get smoky.   £

Sumos
W6
169 King Street   map 10
081-741 7916
Very plain and simple Japanese with acceptable noodles. Cheap.   £

Sweetings   EC4
39 Queen Victoria Street   map 11
071-248 3062
Traditional City establishment, open only
for lunch. Fish is the thing, as are the
excellent oysters: West Mersey,
Colchester and natives. Those with
simpler appetites can sit at the bar with
a sandwich.   ££

Swiss Centre   WC2
Restaurant Marché,   map 14
Leicester Square
071-434 1791
Swiss restaurant laid out like a market-
place, with a choice of several seating
areas. Room for 500 and open until
midnight makes it useful for shoppers,
and cinema- and theatre-goers. Fondue
and raclette through to salads, pasta,
burgers or what you will.   £

Sydney Street   SW3
4 Sydney Street   map 12
071-352 3433
Antipodean restaurant occupying an
arrestingly designed space. Modern and
airy, complete with Aboriginal murals
and exotic fish tanks. Way-out menu
mixes influences of Australasia, the
Americas, Italy and Thailand. Exotic fish,
crocodile, kangaroo and emu feature.
Mostly successful cooking, more reports,
please.   £££

Tandoori Lane   SW6
131A Munster Road   map 10
071-371 0440/4844
Above-average curry house with a
standard menu but decent ingredients
and preparation. Specialities include
murgh bhaza, on-the-bone tandoori
chicken cooked with vegetables and
minced meat, and vegetarian and meat
thalis. Smoking at nearby close tables can
be a nuisance.   £

Tiny Tim   NW1
7 Plender Street   map 11
071-388 0402
Popular, unpretentious Camden Town
bistro serving elegantly presented, real

French home-cooking. Informal
atmosphere, reasonably priced Sunday
lunch. Excellent fresh fish and much-
praised île flottante for dessert.   £–££

Tui   SW7
19 Exhibition Road   map 12
071-584 8359
Traditional Thai that's not cheap. Short,
to-the-point menu, with fish and shellfish
dishes the speciality. Freshly spiced soups
are also good.   £££

Twenty Trinity Gardens   SW9
20 Trinity Gardens   map 10
071-733 8838
Modern British cooking in Brixton.
Terrine of tropical fish is a local trend but
better choices might be crêpes filled with
salmon and almonds and well-dressed
salads. Nice wines, reasonable prices,
relaxed service.   ££

White Horse on Parsons Green   SW6
1–3 Parson's Green   map 10
071-736 2115
Sloane bolt-hole and a well-patronised
pub. Decent choice of wines, quiches and
meats from the cold-display cabinet or
hot daily specials. Outside tables, good
vantage point.   £

Wilds   SW10
356 Fulham Road   map 11
071-376 5553
Theatrical fabric swathes, firmly
fashionable menu attracting a chic
clientele. Californian/Italian cuisine,
South African-run; many influences at
work striving to achieve an adventurous
amalgam. Some good New World
wines.   ££

Willoughby's Café-Bar   N1
26 Penton Street   map 11
071-833 1380
Simple, good English food in modest,
quiet surroundings close to Chapel
Market. All-day menu with blackboard
specials. Lamb with good vegetables,
tagliatelle, decent coffee and successful
desserts.   £

Wong Kei   **W1**
41–43 Wardour Street   map 14
071-437 8408
Large, multi-tiered, fast-food operation
that's one of the cheapest places to eat in
Chinatown. Good for one-plate meals
and groups not minding frantic service.
Cash only, means just that.   **£**

Zen Cargo   **W1**
St Christopher's Place,   map 13
3–5 Barrett Street
071-224 1122
Smart joint that's not cheap. Western
cooking by a Chinese chef.   **££**

England

▲ The Elms

Abberley WR6 6AT
GREAT WITLEY (0299) 896666
on A443 between Worcester and   COOKING 2*
Tenbury Wells, 2m W of Great Witley   COST £19–£48

The building stands, all symmetry, before you – 'Designed by Gilbert White, a
pupil of Sir Christopher Wren, in 1710,' the brochure proudly states. The inside
is more a case of this-and-that – some eighteenth century, for sure, with
fireplaces worth a second look, but also the carpets, comforts, colour schemes,
curtains, and the well-padded upholstery of the country-house hotel. The
cooking, too, is well-padded, cushioning customers from the shock of the new.
Traditionalists may delight in avocado or smoked salmon or a sweets trolley,
but the new traditionalists, looking for signs of revival, may be more interested
in braised ox liver, lambs' offal with black and white puddings, or a casserole
of pulses and roots with cider, that form a regular subsection of the daily menu
partnering the seasonal *carte*. In a cooking style that tends to understate
flavours, the fire may not always catch, but it is reliable: 'I have been going for
15–20 years and now, far more than in the recent past, it does deliver what its
customers expect.' This comes with a smile from the always willing staff, and is
framed by sound incidentals from the appetisers onwards, even if there have
been moments of vegetables being more al dente than old molars enjoy.
Changing patterns of spending have led to a whole series of deals: lunchtime
simplicity in the Library Bar every day except Sunday; in the Brooke Room,
one set price for fancy cooking – such as bouillabaisse of salmon and monkfish
flavoured with basil, or chicken breast with sage and leek – another (lower) for
the new revivalists' steak and kidney pie, or chicken, mushroom and bacon
pie; a vegetarian menu; a fairly priced Sunday lunch, and so on. The Elms is not
suffering any disease of indifference. A sound rather than exciting wine list is
headed by an 'Elms Selection', which is helpfully wide-ranging and includes
house wine at £11.50. Prices, though, are on the high side, with an anonymous
Sancerre offered at £23.25.

'Presented with the Amex voucher with the customary blank total, I commented, ''Service is
included, yes?'' Hurriedly the waiter entered the total and muttered, ''Yes.'''
On eating in Edinburgh

CHEF: Michael Gaunt PROPRIETORS: Queens Moat Houses plc OPEN: all week; 12.30 to 2, 7.30 to 9.30 MEALS: Brooke Room and Library Bar alc. Brooke Room Set Sun L £14.95, Set D £16 to £22 SERVICE: not inc, card slips closed CARDS: Access, Amex, Diners, Visa DETAILS: 70 seats. 5 tables outside. Private parties: 42 main room, 12 and 30 private rooms. Car park. Vegetarian meals. Children's welcome. Jacket and tie in Brooke Room. No cigars/pipes in Brooke Room. Wheelchair access (1 step; also WC). No music ACCOMMODATION: 25 rooms, all with bath/shower. B&B £82 to £128. Children welcome. Baby facilities. Afternoon teas. Garden. Tennis. TV. Phone. Fax: (0299) 896804 (*The Which? Hotel Guide*)

ABINGDON Oxfordshire   map 2

▲ *Thame Lane House* ⁑✳

1 Thame Lane, Culham,
Abingdon OX14 3DS   COOKING 2
ABINGDON (0235) 524177   COST £24–£32

'What a find!' exclaimed a reader who, walking beside the Thames, lit upon this guesthouse down a lane branching off the Abingdon to Dorchester road. He then recounted a meal of scallops en feuilleté, followed by monkfish with garlic and white wine sauce, and strawberries macerated with orange juice. Marie-Claude Beech, who is French, produces thoughtful modern cooking for a small number of outsiders (who need to telephone a day in advance for a reservation). Overnight guests may feel they get shorter shrift.The recited menu is short (for residents it is even shorter), but the food is fresh and well handled. The cooking of new classics, such as soufflé suissesse, is as adept as that of civet of hare or skate with capers and mustard. The dishes one winter's night were tartare of salmon with sour cream, dill and cucumber, terrine of game with a celery and orange salad, and wild duck with mushrooms (both pleurottes and trompettes de mort) accompanied by mashed celeriac, broccoli and aubergine with garlic; desserts included an ice-cream bombe with stem ginger and mango sauce, and meringue with chestnut purée dosed with rum, 'which seemed to bring out the chestnut flavour'. Some evenings are evidently more interesting than others: one resident found a meal of melon with port, salmon trout with beurre blanc, and an apple tart neither brilliantly executed nor excitingly chosen. Since there are no staff apart from the Beeches themselves, planning and forethought are necessary for an evening to go without hitches such as delays before the meal or between courses. As prices are not low, a greater sense of 'do it all for fun and love' might be welcome. The wine list still admits only France (save one Bulgarian), but some of the choices are admirable if not earth-shattering. Wine service and offering of pre-dinner drinks are rudimentary. House wines are from £10.

CHEF: Marie-Claude Beech PROPRIETORS: Michael and Marie-Claude Beech OPEN: all week, exc Sun D and Mon L; 12.30 to 1, 7 to 8.30 CLOSED: 3 to 17 Jan MEALS: Set L and D £18.50 to £24.50 SERVICE: net prices, card slips closed CARDS: Access, Visa (3.5% surcharge) DETAILS: 16 seats. Private parties: 16 main room. Car park. Children's helpings on request. No children under 3. Smart dress preferred. No smoking. No music ACCOMMODATION: 5 rooms, 1 with shower. B&B £29 to £52. Deposit: £15. No children under 3. Garden. TV. Doors close at 11.30. Confirm by 6

ALDEBURGH Suffolk   map 3

▲ *Austins*

243 The High Street,
Aldeburgh IP15 5DN   COOKING 1
ALDEBURGH (0728) 453932   COST £19–£28

Robert Selbie is 'a gentle troubleshooter', avers one supporter of this hotel,
who finds it a real boon when visiting Aldeburgh. Mr Selbie's past as an actor
is clear from memorabilia on every wall: a positive shrine to Thespis. There is
no suspension of disbelief at table, however, for Julian Alexander-Worster will
produce the cream of local produce in a dinner of asparagus and lobster, or
work more complex magic in a hot cheese soufflé or smoked eel koulibiac.
Essentially, though, the cooking stays simple, and when it stays fresh and
flavoursome it is good. A menu will usually carry a fair complement of steaks
berthed alongside salmon quenelles, or chicken with tarragon, or Austins'
Peking widgeon, and sound, fresh fish. Desserts (the choice is legion) have
included light lemon sponges that floated down happily. There is not one half-
bottle on the wine list and the choice of the rest is not going to win awards, but
the prices are not dear. House wines are £7.15.

CHEF: Julian Alexander-Worster   PROPRIETORS: Robert Selbie and Julian Alexander-
Worster   OPEN: Tue to Sun D, and Sun L (other days by arrangement); 12.30 to 2, 7.30 to 11
CLOSED: first 2 weeks Feb   MEALS: Set L £13.75, Set D £19.50   SERVICE: not inc   CARDS:
Access, Amex, Diners, Visa   DETAILS: 30 seats. Private parties: 30 main room. Children's
helpings. No children under 12. No cigars/pipes in dining-room. Music
ACCOMMODATION: 7 rooms, all with bath/shower. B&B £47.75 to £70. No children under
12. Pets welcome. TV. Phone. Doors close at 1am. Confirm by noon. Fax: (0728) 453668
(*The Which? Hotel Guide*)

ALNWICK Northumberland   map 7

John Blackmore's 🌟✳

1 Dorothy Foster Court, Narrowgate,
Alnwick NE66 1NL   COOKING 3
ALNWICK (0665) 604465   COST £22–£33

History is evident from the stone fabric of this charming house set in a narrow
alley close to the castle, though modern furnishings give an overlay of comfort,
and gentle service makes for happier evenings than when Alnwick suffered
raids from marauding Scots. John Blackmore is consistent in his approach.
Cooking is complicated and mobilises several elements so that even soups will
have their own accompaniments – cheese and almond scones with the cream of
broccoli or generous croûtons with the smoked haddock, for example. Mousses
– often good – still rule: vegetarian dishes may be a fennel mousse with
mushrooms and a Stilton sauce on one night, a carrot and coriander mousse
with the same support another; a broccoli mousse may come with sweetbreads;
a sole mousse will be served with baked smoked salmon and a parsley sauce.
If, however, the dish has too many things, the failure of one may affect the rest.
A mixture of monkfish and lobster with coriander, baked in a pastry case with
a Pernod sauce, would have been excellent had the monkfish been less tough.

Some details may lack finish – a salad with no dressing, a less-than-rich crème brûlée – but that day was saved by classic profiteroles. The wine list is short and could be better. House wine is £6.20.

CHEF: John Blackmore   PROPRIETORS: John and Penny Blackmore   OPEN: Tue to Sat, D only; 7 to 9.30   CLOSED: Jan   MEALS: alc   SERVICE: not inc, card slips closed   CARDS: Access, Amex, Diners, Visa   DETAILS: 25 seats. Private parties: 30 main room. Vegetarian meals. Children's helpings. Smart dress preferred. No smoking in dining-room. Wheelchair access (1 step). Music

---

AMBERLEY West Sussex   map 3

▲ Amberley Castle, Queen's Room ✷

| NEW ENTRY |

Amberley BN18 9ND   COOKING 1*
BURY (0798) 831992   COST £28–£68

The castle may be compared to Bodiam or Herstmonceux. It's on flat lands, defending river access from the south coast. Its turreted and gated walls form a square courtyard within which there now stands a house. The dining-room has its own seventeenth-century fresco at the end of a barrel-vaulted great hall that may give the client delusions of grandeur. The chef certainly has grand ideas. The *carte* is so long and so dear that one must wonder how he keeps the food in trim all the time. However, it is an achievement to produce very good asparagus soup, excellent home-smoked lobster with a chervil butter sauce, and well-timed and decently flavoured best end of lamb with a mustard coating that had exactly the right piquancy, even if the butchery was apprentice stuff. The ancillaries need a lot of work to bring them to the level of price or ambition. Service is keen and eager. It's rather fun to stay here. The wine list is as ambitious as the menu, so are the prices. House wines are £14.50.

CHEF: Nigel Boschetti   PROPRIETORS: Joy and Martin Cummings   OPEN: all week; 12 to 2, 6.30 to 9.45   MEALS: alc. Set L £18.50, Set D £25.50 to £37.50   SERVICE: not inc, card slips closed   CARDS: Access, Amex, Diners, Visa   DETAILS: 38 seats. 4 tables outside. Private parties: 38 main room, 12, 12 and 35 private rooms. Car park. Vegetarian meals. Children's helpings. Jacket and tie. No smoking in dining-room. No music   ACCOMMODATION: 14 rooms, all with bath/shower. B&B £100 to £225. Deposit: 50%. Children welcome. Afternoon teas. Garden. TV. Phone. Doors close at 1am. Confirm by 6. Fax: (0798) 831998

AMBLESIDE Cumbria   map 7

▲ Rothay Manor ♈ ✷

Rothay Bridge,
Ambleside LA22 0EH
AMBLESIDE (053 94) 33605   COOKING 2
                                                                     COST £17–£36

Mob-caps and pinnies give that old-fashioned look to the staff, but do not detract one jot from the friendliness, decent appointments and general success of this long-running hotel, still in the hands of the Nixon families. The cold buffet at lunch-times goes on and on, so does the sweets trolley at night, and the five-course dinner with the smallest of choices, and helpful wine suggestions down one side of the menu. People come back from year to year and are comforted: 'The atmosphere is relaxed yet slightly formal, without the extreme quiet of some of the smaller hotels.' A criticism may be that some of the food just misses: meat a little overcooked, pastry a little heavy, sauces a tad mild. There are plenty who dispute this and cite in their defence dishes such as leg of lamb stuffed with anchovies, ham, herbs and parsley, then braised with onions and carrots, or Windermere char with a cucumber hollandaise, or halibut with a prawn sauce. People also applaud the sweets: orange and hazelnut cheesecake, two-tone chocolate mousse, raspberry tart, as well as the sound British cheeses. The answer may lie in interpreting 'intensity', but the Manor does appear to produce steady English food of a certain character. The useful wine list shows commitment to quality as well as value: evidence of careful buying from good merchants is as apparent for Burgundy as for the Barossa Valley. House wine is £8. CELLARMAN'S CHOICE: Chardonnay d'Oc 1990, Ryman, £10; Givry, 'En Choué' 1989, Lespinasse, £16.40.

CHEFS: Jane Binns and Colette Nixon   PROPRIETORS: the Nixon families   OPEN: all week; 12.30 to 2 (12.45 to 1.30 Sun), 8 to 9   CLOSED: last 3 weeks Jan, first week Feb   MEALS: buffet weekday L £5.80. Set Sun L £14, Set D £19 to £25   SERVICE: not inc   CARDS: Access, Amex, Diners, Visa   DETAILS: 70 seats. Private parties: 12 main room, 30 private room. Car park. Vegetarian meals. Children's helpings. Smart dress preferred. No smoking in dining-room. Wheelchair access (also WC). No music. Air-conditioned   ACCOMMODATION: 18 rooms, all with bath/shower. Rooms for disabled. B&B £64 to £140. Deposit: £50. Children welcome. Baby facilities. Afternoon teas. Garden. Air-conditioned. TV. Phone. Doors close at midnight. Confirm by noon. Fax: (053 94) 33607 (*The Which? Hotel Guide*)

AMERSHAM Buckinghamshire   map 3

King's Arms

30 High Street, Old Amersham HP7 0DJ	COOKING 1
AMERSHAM (0494) 726333	COST £19–£38

History looms large in this old beamed inn at the bottom of the hill. This is the Old Town. Inside, the spaciousness of the lounge and bar seem at odds with the cramped conditions in the small dining-room. Gary Munday's cooking inhabits the world of duck breast with rhubarb and ginger wine, sirloin of beef with celeriac and oyster mushrooms, and grilled haddock on vegetable galette. There have been favourable reports of mushroom and smoked bacon pithiviers with peppercorn sauce, oak-smoked duck, fillet of lamb stuffed with chicken and tarragon mousseline, and exemplary roast beef with Yorkshire pudding. The general feeling seems to be that the kitchen has good ideas, but that it promises more than it achieves. Dish descriptions are not always accurate: one reporter's confit of duck with rich Cassis sauce was little more than 'duck in Cassis'. Set lunch is clearly a better bargain than the full-price evening *carte* and it is worth booking for Sunday lunch. Around 70 fairly priced wines include house Chilean at £7.40.

CHEF: Gary Munday   PROPRIETOR: John Jennison   OPEN: Tue to Sun, exc Sun D; 12.30 to 2, 7 to 9.30   CLOSED: Christmas, 1 day after bank hols   MEALS: alc. Set L £11.50 to £16.50, Set Sun L £14.50, Set Sat D £23. Minimum £11.50   SERVICE: not inc   CARDS: Access, Amex, Diners, Visa   DETAILS: 30 seats. Private parties: 48 main room, 12 private room. Car park. Vegetarian meals. Children welcome. No cigars/pipes in dining-room. No music

---

APPLETHWAITE Cumbria

map 7

▲ *Underscar Manor* ✲

NEW ENTRY

Applethwaite, nr Keswick CA12 4PH
KESWICK (076 87) 75000

COOKING 2
COST £24–£37

The beleaguered weaving industry of Lancashire must have jumped for joy when decorating began at Underscar. There are enough curtains for the owners to dispense with walls. Luxury is not in question in this striking Italianate villa set against the slopes of Skiddaw, with views over Derwent Water, and red squirrels in the garden. The Harrisons embarked on the conversion after 18 years of owning and running Moss Nook in Manchester (see entry). Tyre manufacturers must be watching their stocks with interest as the Harrisons and Robert Thornton zip up and down motorways to tend their flock of two. The swags and drapes, the seasonless silk flower arrangements, and thick-pile carpets are relentlessly pursued, and this luxury is matched in the style of service, guaranteed to include synchronised dome-raising. 'It tends to raise expectations' was the first reaction, and time will tell if they are met. Some encouraging aspects have been a decent soufflé suissesse with a mustard sauce, nicely roasted quail on a salad with raspberry dressing, and a good combination of white chocolate fondant, mint and mango. Red mullet with potato, spinach and tarragon and a sauce maltaise may mix many flavours, and calf's liver with bacon, onions and a red wine sauce may sound like a main course, not a starter, but they were definitely enjoyed, as was fillet of beef with oxtail, and duck breast wrapped in a 'pithiviers' of pastry then served with apples and calvados sauce. The solid wine list will probably suit the constituency – an awful lot of champagnes – and commits no indiscretions. House wines are from £9.90. Symbiotic assistance from the cellar of Moss Nook should give added buying power.

CHEFS: Robert Thornton and Stephen Yare   PROPRIETORS: Pauline and Derek Harrison, and Gordon Evans   OPEN: all week; 12 to 1.30, 7 to 8.30 (9 Sat)   MEALS: Set L £16.50, Set D £25   SERVICE: not inc, card slips closed   CARDS: Access, Amex, Visa   DETAILS: 60 seats. 5 tables outside. Private parties: 40 main room, 16 private room. Car park. Vegetarian meals. No children under 12. Smart dress preferred. No smoking in dining-rooms   ACCOMMODATION: 11 rooms, all with bath/shower. D,B&B £75 to £250. Deposit: 25%. No children under 12. Afternoon teas. Garden. TV. Phone. Doors close at 12.30am. Fax: (076 87) 74904 (*The Which? Hotel Guide*)

'It does seem somewhat odd that they served fish soup for two in one bowl (two spoons – they're not that extreme!). It wasn't a mistake – we asked. It was good soup but under-seasoned. The trouble was that we disagreed on remedial action. I wanted more salt and he wanted more pepper. It's a bit awkward when you're sharing a bowl!'
On eating in East Sussex

ASHBOURNE Derbyshire   map 5

▲ *Callow Hall*

Mappleton Road, Ashbourne DE6 2AA	COOKING 1
ASHBOURNE (0335) 43403	COST £18–£39

The grey Derbyshire-stone manor emerges at the end of a long lime tree-lined drive; its elevated position reveals stretches of woodland along the Dove Valley. Inside, David Spencer is disclosed as an affable host, 'both formal and friendly'. He may introduce himself in the grandly furnished no-smoking dining-room, which is replete in deep-red wall coverings, brocade, carpet and chairs. Food quality is recommended as being congruous with the décor. 'Good ingredients, carefully prepared, professionally sauced and attractively presented,' writes one reporter. Fish retrieved at dawn from Birmingham is the anchor; home-smoked salmon with lemon and dill, turbot with fresh herbs, sea bass with pink peppercorns and brill with tomato and garlic all serve as starters or mains. The anthology of French wines is weighted to Burgundy with a nod to Alsace. House wine is £7.50.

CHEF: David Spencer PROPRIETORS: David and Dorothy Spencer OPEN: Mon to Sat, D only, and Sun L (other days L and Sun D by arrangement); 12.30 to 2.30, 7.30 to 9.30 MEALS: alc. Set L £12.50, Set D £27 SERVICE: not inc, card slips closed CARDS: Access, Amex, Diners, Visa DETAILS: 80 seats. Private parties: 50 main room, 40 private room. Car park. Vegetarian meals. Children's helpings Sun L. No smoking in dining-room. No music ACCOMMODATION: 12 rooms, all with bath/shower. B&B £65 to £120. Children welcome. Baby facilities. Garden. Fishing. TV. Phone. Doors close at 11.30. Confirm 2 days ahead. Fax: (0335) 43624 (*The Which? Hotel Guide*)

ASTON CLINTON Buckinghamshire   map 3

▲ *Bell* ▮

Aston Clinton HP22 5HP	COOKING 3
AYLESBURY (0296) 630252	COST £26–£65

The big news from Aston Clinton is that the chef is David Cavalier, who has vacated his restaurant in Battersea and returned to native pastures round Aylesbury. It is still early days in his tenure, and developments are tentative. There is a shift away from the more florid aspects of cooking that had ruled the Bell of late, but one can expect refined neo-classicism as the dominant motif, tempered by a vein of British cooking that has always been part of the hotel's appeal. A meal that included roast scallops with a fennel, parsley and tarragon vinaigrette, squab pigeon with a parsley purée, then hot Grand Marnier soufflé suffered many a technical fault, mainly that of being too fatty at every turn, but this was not the experience of a summer lunch party who enjoyed salmon and halibut terrine, chicken breast stuffed with spinach and another Grand Marnier soufflé, while luxuriating at intervals in the sun-filled garden. The old inn has spawned various outliers of bedrooms and banqueting suites (and car parks) across major and minor roads (it stands at an intersection). There is much to be said for the atmospheric lounges and private rooms, rather less for the lugubriously green series of dining-rooms with uncomfortable benches. The problem at the Bell is time. It takes time for the kitchen to deliver; it takes time for the waiting staff to wake up to your presence; and it has taken up to three hours to complete a meal on an evening when there were no more than a dozen customers. The wine list here is very good but a copy has not been sent us this year, so we can only applaud the range while regretting some of the prices. House wines start at £11.20. More reports, please. David Cavalier took a long time to get new menus in place, and the expectation should be that matters will improve.

CHEF: David Cavalier PROPRIETORS: the Harris family OPEN: all week; 12.30 to 2, 7.30 to 10 MEALS: alc. Set L £18 to £20, Set D £22 to £38 SERVICE: not inc, card slips closed CARDS: Access, Amex, Visa DETAILS: 100 seats. Private parties: 20 and 200 private rooms. Car park. Children welcome. Smart dress preferred. No smoking in 1 dining-room. Wheelchair access (also WC). No music (exc piper at New Year) ACCOMMODATION: 21 rooms, all with bath/shower. Rooms for disabled. B&B £92 to £133. Children welcome. Baby facilities. Pets welcome. Afternoon teas. Garden. TV. Phone. Doors close at 12.30am. Confirm by 6. Fax: (0296) 631250 (*The Which? Hotel Guide*)

AYLESBURY Buckinghamshire   map 2

▲ *Hartwell House*

Oxford Road, Aylesbury HP17 8NL
AYLESBURY (0296) 747444   COOKING 2*
on A418, 3m S of Aylesbury   COST £28–£50

'It's like being in heaven,' rhapsodised a visitor one lunch-time, visibly overcome by the setting, the plasterwork, the giant public rooms ('too large for atmosphere' is a countervailing thought) and even the carpets. He also thought the food overpriced, and the skills mobilised in the kitchen inadequate for the pretension of the undertaking. Price does have an effect on one's perception, and the cost of dinner here, for cooking that may be sound, but is rarely inspired, is very high. Lunch is the cheaper option. The main *carte* shows little willingness to take risks: game pâté, crab ravioli, confit of duck, quail salad, scallop mousse, plus foie gras, haddock soup and smoked salmon are not earth-moving choices. A summer stay revealed many technical faults, but the underlying problem was lack of 'challenging and subtle flavours', perhaps because the kitchen has decided that this is unsuitable for the potential clientele. Good things recorded include ravioli of crab with its own sauce, a terrine of quail with smoked bacon and prunes and a little foie gras, a vegetable summer pudding as a first course, squab with red cabbage and a raisin and walnut sauce, venison with figs and game sauce and breast of guinea-fowl with creamed endive, honey and citrus fruits. Desserts are in keeping with the style of the place: a hot soufflé, perhaps, lots of little scoops of sorbet, caramelised pears, a chocolate marjolaine given edge by a kumquat confit. Service is universally praised, from front to back of the house. A reader fairly considered £43 for 1981 Ch. Cissac outrageous. It is a pity that the prices are so multiplied, however well-bought the wines. Virtually nothing is below £15; even the antipodes fail to provide the often expected financial relief. House wine is £11.

▲ *This symbol means accommodation is available.*

CHEF: Aidan McCormack   PROPRIETORS: Historic House Hotels Ltd   OPEN: all week;
12.30 to 2, 7.30 to 9.45   CLOSED: 24 to 26 Dec, exc to residents   MEALS: Set L £16.50 to
£22.40, Set Sun L £28, Set D £38   SERVICE: net prices, card slips closed   CARDS: Access,
Amex, Diners, Visa   DETAILS: 60 seats. Private parties: 30 main room, 16 and 30 private
rooms. Car park. Vegetarian meals. No children under 8. Jacket and tie. No cigars/pipes in
dining-room. Wheelchair access (also WC). Music (Fri and Sat)   ACCOMMODATION: 48
rooms, all with bath/shower. Rooms for disabled. Lift. B&B £97.75 to £316. No children
under 8. Dogs by arrangement. Afternoon teas. Garden. Swimming-pool. Sauna. Tennis.
Fishing. TV. Phone. Fax: (0296) 747450 (*The Which? Hotel Guide*)

BAKEWELL Derbyshire   map 5

▲ *Biph's* £ | **NEW ENTRY** |

Bath Street, Bakewell DE45 1BX   COOKING 1*
BAKEWELL (0629) 812687   COST £13–£35

Dried hops and flowers hang from the beams that support a pretty, albeit
homespun, stone dining-room. Reports repeat that Ian Patrick is hard-pressed
to serve the room efficiently on busy nights and that he will have to manage
success better. 'The cooking makes a consistent, decent and careful impression,'
records a visitor. Another praises 'an honest, straightfoward menu'. Duck
breast, slow roasted and served with a peach purée and blackberries, and lamb
cutlets pan-fried with a glaze of greengage, peppercorns and vermouth have
pleased. If the temptation to over-elaborate is not resisted, results suffer.
Vegetables are fresh and 'full with flavour'. Desserts are fruit-based. The new
Biphery Bistro is a separate venture to get the spread of custom, trading in
pasta, liver, bubble and squeak, and chicken and ham pie. The wine list at
Biph's is sound indeed. Prices are fair and makers reliable. House wines are £6.
Book ahead for a Victorian champagne breakfast served on Sundays.

CHEF: Susan Hoult Brooksbank   PROPRIETOR: Ian G. Patrick   OPEN: Wed to Sat
(restaurant); all week, exc Tue (bistro); 12 (bistro 11.30 Sun) to 2, 7 to 10 (bistro 9 Sun)
MEALS: alc. Set D £14.50 to £17.50   SERVICE: not inc   CARDS: Access, Amex, Visa
DETAILS: 40 seats. 2 tables outside. Private parties: 100 main room. Car park. Vegetarian
meals. Children's helpings. Wheelchair access (1 step). Music   ACCOMMODATION: 3
rooms. B&B £24 to £35. Deposit: £10. Children welcome. Garden

---

BARNET Hertfordshire   map 3

Mims

63 East Barnet Road, Barnet EN4 8RN   COOKING 2
081-449 2974 and 447 1825   COST £20–£32

Mims sits in an unprepossessing suburban shopping parade. Inside is 'a calm
oasis of green, white and pink' in the eyes of one, mildly uncomfortable to
others. The ambience is so calm, in the eyes of many, that a bomb under the feet
of the staff might make the waiting less interminable. That said, to find braised
tongue with coriander, monkfish with cumin and garlic, steamed rabbit with
courgette vinaigrette, grilled scallops with grilled vegetables or open ravioli of
spinach and cream cheese in Barnet is pretty unlikely. Everyone concurs that

there is superior cooking in dishes such as tuna with two contrasting vinaigrettes of tomato and anchovy, roast pigeon accompanied by a red pepper stuffed with rice and mushrooms, and roast quail with a little nest of pasta as a cusp for the quail's eggs. Very good lemon tart, banana pancakes, or pear terrine with white chocolate are some desserts that have honourable mention. The wine list is short but well thought out; half-bottles there are aplenty. House wines are from £8.50.

CHEF: Ali Al-Sersy   PROPRIETORS: M. Abouzahrah and Ali Al-Sersy   OPEN: Tue to Sun, exc Sat L; 12 to 3, 6.30 to 11 (noon to 10.30 Sun)   CLOSED: 1 week Christmas   MEALS: Set L £8.50 to £15, Set D £17 to £20.50   SERVICE: not inc   CARDS: Access, Visa   DETAILS: 50 seats. Private parties: 50 main room. Car park. Children welcome L and Sun. No cigars/pipes in dining-room. Wheelchair access (1 step). Music

---

BARNSLEY South Yorkshire   map 5

Armstrongs

6 Shambles Street, Barnsley S70 2SQ   COOKING 2
BARNSLEY (0226) 240113   COST £19–£33

The sign above the door now says 'Restaurant' rather than 'Café Bar', suggesting that Nick Pound is a man with gastronomic aspirations. Reports confirm that the kitchen has moved up a gear and into new territory. 'We have seen him go from strength to strength, steadily refining his culinary skills and achieving greater reliability,' comments a regular visitor. Nick Pound offers a monthly-changing *carte*, light lunches and what he calls a 'recession buster' (a good-value three-course menu served early on Tuesday to Friday evenings). The modern repertoire covers a lot of territory, mixing influences and styles with confidence. 'Reconstructed' British dishes, such as black pudding with mustard sauce and bread-and-butter pudding, share the stage with soul-food chicken with black-eyed beans and sweet potato, roast monkfish with estate-bottled olive oil and rosemary, and braised salt-beef with salsa verde and pickled vegetables. The Italian renaissance is much in evidence. Reporters have approved of the timbale of courgette and Stilton with spring onions and tomato sauce, fish soup, saffron chicken with almonds and fromage frais, and tarte Tatin. Vegetarian specials are also mentioned. Nick Pound now makes his own breads using flour from a local watermill. Helpful staff understand the food. The wine list has been upgraded to give more choice and better value. Prices are very fair and growers excellent: Natter's Sancerre, Oxford Landing Chardonnay, Rolly-Gassmann's Auxerrois among them. House wines are £8.

CHEFS: Nick Pound, Ron Widdowson and Lee Hammond   PROPRIETOR: Nick Pound   OPEN: Tue to Sat, exc Sat L; 12 to 2, 7 to 10   CLOSED: bank hols   MEALS: alc. Set D £12.95 (7 to 8, Tue to Fri only)   SERVICE: not inc   CARDS: Access, Visa   DETAILS: 60 seats. Private parties: 40 main room, 18 and 40 private rooms. Vegetarian meals. Children welcome. Wheelchair access. Music

---

Restaurateurs justifiably resent no-shows. If you quote a credit card number when booking, you may be liable for the restaurant's lost profit margin if you don't turn up. Always phone to cancel.

Restaurant Peano

102 Dodworth Road, Barnsley S70 6HL
BARNSLEY (0226) 244990

COOKING 2*
COST £14–£39

Michael and Tracey Peano's converted Victorian house a mile from the M1 has helped to put Barnsley firmly on the food map, and there is much to celebrate in their enterprise. Michael's half-Italian background shows in his monthly-changing menus: Tuscan white bean soup; risotto with porcini mushrooms; saltimbocca in puff pastry with sage sauce; fillet of beef served on polenta with pesto. But his style also encompasses the urbane classicism of sauté lamb's liver and kidney with green bean salad and lime sauce, and roast saddle of lamb with aubergine gâteau. Meals end on a high note: there is praise for first-rate sweets such as the mixed platter of chocolate desserts and a mille-feuille with fresh kiwi fruit and lemon mousse on a raspberry coulis. Bread, pasta and petits fours are made on the premises. Some reports suggest that the burden of publicity and popularity seems to have taken its toll. Michael Peano has, however, recently recruited a chef from the Old Vicarage, Ridgeway (see entry), whose hands should help to smooth out any problems. The professional aspirations of the kitchen often jar with the amateurism of the service, although Tracey Peano is a 'welcoming lovely host'. The short wine list divides its loyalties between France and Italy. House wines are from £7.95.

CHEF: Michael Peano PROPRIETORS: Michael and Tracey Peano OPEN: Mon to Sat, exc Mon and Sat L; 12 to 2, 7 to 9.30 MEALS: alc. Set L £9 to £11 SERVICE: not inc, card slips closed CARDS: Access, Amex, Visa DETAILS: 45 seats. Private parties: 45 main room. Car park. Children's helpings. Wheelchair access. Music

---

BARNSTAPLE Devon

map 1

▲ Lynwood House 🍴✹

Bishops Tawton Road,
Barnstaple EX32 9DZ
BARNSTAPLE (0271) 43695

COOKING 1
COST £18–£53

There is much emphasis on the help given to the elder Roberts by two of their three sons: a real family enterprise. Continuity and consistency are valued in this Victorian house slowly converted and refurbished by John Roberts. Shellfish and fish are constants from a menu that changes very slowly. Mussels with white wine and parsley, prawns with garlic butter, 'pot of seafood' with wine, tarragon and cheese sauce, and various plainer fish according to supplies are satisfactory. Fresh crab pancakes, terrine of seafood, and excellent local lobster were the main part of a meal that ended happily with first-class double cream crème caramel, lemon sorbet with vodka and plain strawberries. The wine list canters round the world and back again, not overcharging, misspelling quite a lot, but supplying a good workmanlike range. House wines are from £8.25.

'The service was excellent and also very friendly; we followed dinner the second night with a game of croquet with the waiter.'   On eating in Scotland

---

CHEFS: Ruth Roberts and Matthew Roberts   PROPRIETORS: John, Ruth, Matthew and Christian Roberts   OPEN: Mon to Sat (Sun D residents only); 12 to 2, 7 to 10   MEALS: alc. Set L £9.75 to £11.95   SERVICE: not inc   CARDS: Access, Visa   DETAILS: 70 seats. Private parties: 70 main room, 24 and 70 private rooms. Car park. Vegetarian meals. Children's helpings. No smoking in dining-room. Wheelchair access (also WC). Music ACCOMMODATION: 5 rooms, all with bath/shower. B&B £47.50 to £67.50. Children welcome. TV. Phone. Confirm by 6. Fax: (0271) 79340 (*The Which? Hotel Guide*)

BARWICK Somerset   map 2

▲ *Little Barwick House*

Barwick, nr Yeovil BA22 9TD
YEOVIL (0935) 23902
off A37, taking second left
opposite Red House Pub

COOKING 2*
COST £29–£35

'This is Christopher and Veronica's home,' emphasises one reader, which neatly sums up the charm and appeal of the Colleys' comfortable Georgian house. The welcome is friendly, Christopher is an excellent host, breakfast is wonderful and the food must be the best value for miles around, according to one satisfied visitor, who can't wait to go back again. Veronica Colley has provided chapter and verse about her search for local ingredients: venison is from the Melbury estate, fish comes from Bridport and Lyme Bay, lamb is from Somerset, cheese and butter are from nearby farms. This translates into a menu with a strong British backbone, but an open-minded attitude. A couple who stayed for three nights approved of much they tried: parsnip and curry soup; avocado and chicken tikka salad; marinated grilled trout with cumin and dill sauce; Sussex steak and mushroom pie; roast loin of venison with damson, port and orange sauce; loin of lamb with mint crust. There is a full menu for vegetarians. Reported desserts have been treacle sponge, crème caramel, chocolate pot, and pear and almond tart. Christopher Colley provides willing advice from his not over-long wine list. Selection is careful and unstuffy, and prices are fair. There are a few interesting halves, but generally it is a list that eschews great depth and age. House wine is £8.30.

CHEF: Veronica Colley   PROPRIETORS: Christopher and Veronica Colley   OPEN: Mon to Sat, D only; 7 to 9   MEALS: Set D £20.90 to £22.90   SERVICE: not inc, card slips closed CARDS: Access, Amex, Visa   DETAILS: 40 seats. Private parties: 50 main room. Car park. Vegetarian meals. Children's helpings. No music   ACCOMMODATION: 6 rooms, all with bath/shower. B&B £47 to £72. Deposit: £20. Children welcome. Pets welcome. Garden. TV. Phone. Doors close at 11. Fax: (0935) 20908 (*The Which? Hotel Guide*)

'Pre-dinner drinks were enlivened by a dispute in the bar with a young couple who were early arrivals. The young lady stormed into the bar declaring loudly, ''I will not put up with that language'', closely followed by her husband demanding their coats and repeating the same words. What was going on? It soon became obvious that they were complaining not about fellow diners but the language from the kitchen. We only heard the F-word once, during the second course. Obviously the loss of two customers curbed the kitchen.'
On eating in Bedfordshire

BASLOW Derbyshire   map 5

▲ Fischer's at Baslow Hall ♔ ✻

Calver Road, Baslow DE45 1RR   COOKING 2*
BASLOW (0246) 583259   COST £23–£45

In this substantial Edwardian mansion in the Jacobean style, Max Fischer has converted one of the ground-floor dining-rooms to café format (Café Max). The junior repertoire here extends to carpaccio of beef and chicken stuffed with a julienne of vegetables. The principal salon has injured the aesthetic sensibilities of some reporters, but few consider the cooking as flawed. Just as two epochs are joined in the architecture, old-fashioned rich flavours share the *carte* with modern advances. Breast of chicken stuffed with lobster and with lobster sauce was 'overwhelming; sometimes a combination of flavours is too powerful'. Alternatively, the combination of roast monkfish with calf's liver, gravy and lemon juice was 'outlandish but astounding'. Approval is signalled, also, for braised fillets of Dover sole in a chive sauce as well as a saddle of lamb with globe artichokes, thyme and rosemary. A separate dessert menu might offer a chocolate marquise with vanilla custard or mille-feuille of fresh strawberries. Sandwiched between a few very good sherries and a delectable collection of spirits is a wine list that shows acquaintance with all that is good and new. The Californian Chardonnay of Kistler, the gamey Givry of Lespinasse alongside Sauzet's Montrachet and classic clarets allow excitement and reassurance in equal measure. Prices are neither high nor low, and there are some good halves. House wines are from £9.50. CELLARMAN'S CHOICE: St-Véran 1990, Corsin, £15; Pomerol, Vieux Château Certan 1987, £45.

CHEF: Max Fischer   PROPRIETORS: Max and Susan Fischer   OPEN: all week, exc Mon L and Sun D (Mon to Sat Café Max); 12 to 1.30 (2 Sun), 7 to 9.30 (10 Sat); 10am to 10pm Café Max   MEALS: alc Café Max. Set L £18.50, Set D £31.50 restaurant   SERVICE: not inc, card slips closed   CARDS: Access, Amex, Visa   DETAILS: 35 seats. Private parties: 35 main room, 10 and 25 private rooms. Car park. Children's helpings L. No children under 10 in restaurant. No smoking in restaurant. Wheelchair access (also WC). No music   ACCOMMODATION: 6 rooms, all with bath/shower. B&B £65 to £120. Children welcome. Afternoon teas. Garden. TV. Phone. Doors close at midnight

---

✻ *indicates that smoking is either banned altogether or that a dining-room is maintained for non-smokers. The symbol does not apply to restaurants that simply have no-smoking areas.*

The text of entries is based on unsolicited reports sent in by readers, backed up by inspections conducted anonymously. The factual details under the text are from questionnaires the Guide sends to all restaurants that feature in the book.

The 1994 Guide will be published before Christmas 1993. Reports on meals are most welcome at any time of the year, but are extremely valuable in the spring. Send them to The Good Food Guide, FREEPOST, 2 Marylebone Road, London NW1 1YN. No stamp is needed if posted in the UK.

Beaujolais

5A Chapel Row, Queen Square,
Bath BA1 1HN   COOKING 1*
BATH (0225) 423417   COST £15–£32

The many postcards and bijou bistro atmosphere of the front room hardly
prepare the visitor for the small barn-like extension to the rear. The Beaujolais
is as French as the wine, the humour occasionally as Clochemerlish, but, as a
supporter maintains, Phillipe Wall is serious in pursuit not only of wild
mushrooms on the Mendips but of decent bourgeois/bistro cookery, a step up
from what we disdainfully (but most people don't treat it as such) called *routier*
last year. Indeed, partridge with wild mushrooms, goose liver terrine with
onion marmalade, or squid fried with coriander would be a surprise in a *routier*,
just as they come as a pleasant shock to visitors to Bath – a city not graced with
too many decent restaurants. The place bubbles with popularity, prices are not
high and the wine list gives fair, and not chauvinistic, support. Lunch seems
cheaper than dinner on a *carte* of maybe eight dishes in each course, but the
style does not change, save in elaboration.

CHEFS: Jean-Christophe Larras and Jacque Dubinni PROPRIETORS: Jean-Pierre Auge and
Phillipe Wall OPEN: all week, exc Sun D; 12 to 2, 6 (7 Fri to Sun) to 10 (11 Fri and Sat)
CLOSED: first 2 weeks Jan MEALS: alc. Set L £9. Minimum £6 L SERVICE: not inc (10%
for 5 or more), card slips closed CARDS: Access, Amex, Visa DETAILS: 80 seats. 5 tables
outside. Private parties: 50 main room, 25 private room. Vegetarian meals. Children's
helpings. Wheelchair access. Music

Garlands

7 Edgar Buildings, George Street,
Bath BA1 2EE   COOKING 1
BATH (0225) 442283   COST £23–£39

A small restaurant that works hard to produce mainstream modern food of fair
quality. Set in a couple of rooms opening off the broad pavement at the top of
Bath's main shopping street, it is a welcome haven: 'It was the best thing about
a day out in Bath,' said one who had tried the set-price lunch. First courses and
fish get more approbation than meat: a salad of red mullet, or simple wild
salmon with a beurre blanc, are two things particularly mentioned. There is a
sensible range of dishes and the perils of oversweetness or over-reduction are
avoided in sauces such as shallot and thyme for venison, basil cream for lamb,
tomato and chive with chicken, or orange and Dubonnet with duck. Service can
slow down proceedings, and muddles seem to be a leitmotif of reports this
year. The wine list has some thoroughbreds among its pricey clarets or more
reasonable Bodegas Ochoa Tempranillo, Umani Ronchi's Le Busche, Iron Horse
Cabernet Sauvignon as well as burgundies and Rhônes from Jean Mathias,
Henri Clerc or Ch. de Beaucastel. House wines from Duboeuf are £9.75.

The Guide *always appreciates hearing about changes of chef or owner.*

CHEF: Tom Bridgeman PROPRIETORS: Tom and Joanna Bridgeman OPEN: all week, exc
Mon L; 12.15 to 2.15, 7 to 10.30 CLOSED: 26 Dec MEALS: alc. Set L £12.95 to £14.95
SERVICE: not inc CARDS: Access, Amex, Visa DETAILS: 30 seats. Private parties: 14 main
room. Vegetarian meals. Children welcome. No cigars/pipes in dining-room. Wheelchair
access. Music

▲ Olive Tree

NEW ENTRY

The Queensberry Hotel,
Russel Street, Bath BA1 2QF
BATH (0225) 447928

COOKING 1
COST £20–£36

Stephen and Penny Ross used to have Homewood Park, outside Bath. They
restored and reopened the Queensberry, above the present restaurant, as a
comfortable, stylish and well-positioned town hotel; but it had no place in
which to dine. The lack is now remedied in a fairly spare pair of rooms in the
basement with four steps between (which give watching customers heart
failure as they watch the waitresses run up and down). On a bright summer's
day, the colours glow. At night, the white starched linen sets up its own dazzle.
This is no hotel dining-room purveying delicate or fancy cooking – a lunch of
provençal fish soup, venison sausages with bubble and squeak and onion
gravy, and bread-and-butter pudding is hardly that. Evening menus, though,
tend to grander, more expensive things, even if in the same spirit, such as
chicken baked with garlic and lemon, veal fillet with goats' cheese and madeira
sauce, or steamed John Dory with spinach purée. These are early days, but the
feeling at the moment is that performance is ragged, while the menu promises
much. Thus grilled monkfish salad with sauce mojo picon-red chilli had little
taste of the grill and the sauce was more pimento-ish than chillified (just as the
rouille was too mild with the fish soup). Food has been left cooking too long,
risottos have not always been perfect and gravies have drowned their principal
item. Given the track records of Stephen Ross and his colleagues, there is no
reason why practice should not make more perfect. On Thursdays, fish is the
major item. The wine list is short and sensible. Prices start at £8.50.

CHEFS: Stephen Ross, Rupert Pitt and Janice Wilmot PROPRIETORS: Stephen and Penny
Ross OPEN: Mon to Sat, exc Mon L; 12 to 2, 7 to 10.30 CLOSED: Christmas week, D bank
hol Mons MEALS: alc. Set L £12.50 SERVICE: not inc CARDS: Access, Amex, Visa
DETAILS: 42 seats. 4 tables outside. Private parties: 25 main room. Vegetarian meals.
Children's helpings with prior notice. Music ACCOMMODATION: 22 rooms, all with bath/
shower. Rooms for disabled. Lift. B&B £75 to £130. Children welcome. Baby facilities.
Afternoon teas. TV. Phone. Fax: (0225) 446065

▲ Priory Hotel 💱✖

Weston Road, Bath BA1 2XT
BATH (0225) 331922

COOKING 3
COST £33–£54

This suburban house built in the first Victorian flush of Bath's expansion is not
'country', yet its reputation has been for many 'country-house' qualities. These
have continued despite Select Country Hotels, the owners, being in
receivership. Public statements have maintained that the hotel does good

business, the receivership is corporate and reflects nothing on individual establishments. Perhaps the increased profits reported were due to prices in the restaurant, for these are never low. For what you pay, you get a professional operation. There is an element of conference business, as in many hotels these days, which punctures the illusion of gracious living, but Michael Collom's cooking may reconcile you to that. It has plenty of classical stature and treads carefully towards innovation in main courses such as quail with lentils, baby onions and bacon, best end of lamb with a herb crust, or entrecôte Café de Paris. His terrine of vegetables is light, his tartare of salmon is fresh, grilled sardines with a red pepper sauce are lively, and red mullet and scallops with fennel and tarragon are perfumed. The menu changes seasonally, but there is a daily set meal, though expensive, which draws on more interesting fish than the salmon that is constant tenant of a place on the *carte*. The wine list remains seriously classic, and seriously priced. House wines are from £12.50.

CHEF: Michael Collom   PROPRIETORS: Select Country Hotels plc   OPEN: all week; 12.30 to 2, 7 to 9.30   MEALS: alc. Set L £20.50, Set D £29   SERVICE: not inc, card slips closed CARDS: Access, Visa   DETAILS: 64 seats. Private parties: 40 main room, 22 and 40 private rooms. Car park. Vegetarian meals. Children welcome. Smart dress preferred. No smoking in dining-room. Wheelchair access. Music   ACCOMMODATION: 21 rooms, all with bath/ shower. B&B £80 to £195. Deposit: 1 night. Children welcome. Baby facilities. Afternoon teas. Garden. Swimming-pool. TV. Phone. Fax: (0225) 448276

▲ Royal Crescent Hotel

16 Royal Crescent, Bath BA1 2LS   COOKING 3
BATH (0225) 319090   COST £29–£61

The hotel merges seamlessly into the giant façade of the Royal Crescent itself. Only little tree-tubs warn you of a different function. In fact the restaurant is in the dower house, a detached villa at the bottom of the short garden, reached by a serpentine concrete path. The villa is wonderful, particularly for its hall and staircase, though less exciting are the lounge and the dining-room, which have been thoroughly done up in the best possible taste. Steven Blake has come here from Le Talbooth in Dedham (see entry) and is capable. As he gets into his stride, this could become a distinguished restaurant. Experiences have produced disparate results. On the one hand a first course of pigeon with bean sprouts, Chinese leaves and raspberry dressing was quite brilliant. The sauce had just the right level of acid, fruit and sweetness, yet never betrayed its origins in the bird itself. Very good too was quail bound with a wood mushroom mousse on braised cabbage with a sherry gravy – almost too complicated for a first course, but showing great balance, deep flavours and impeccable technique. Not so a velouté with seafood that was too sweet by half, nor a cannon of lamb bound in caul and mousseline that had the vapid flavours and under-seasoning of too much country-house cooking. Much, much better was a piece of salmon poached in olive and pimento stock, served with lots of micro-ratatouille, chervil and a great sauce. Vegetables are not brilliant, nor are desserts as interesting as the rest. The wine list is all that you feared: long and very expensive. Whichever way you look at it, the set menus are worth having, for the dishes are very similar, if not identical, to those on the *carte*. It is a pity that this restaurant, and this chef, have to play at luxury rest-homes. It would be more fun if they could inject enthusiasm and zip into the operation, leave conferences and rich touring parties to other people and try wooing Bath to come out and eat and make merry.

CHEF: Steven Blake PROPRIETORS: Queens Moat Houses plc OPEN: all week; 12.30 to 2, 7 to 9.30 (10 Sat) MEALS: alc. Set L £18.50, Set D £25 SERVICE: not inc, card slips closed CARDS: Access, Amex, Diners, Visa DETAILS: 70 seats. 8 tables outside. Private parties: 70 main room, 45 and 48 private rooms. Car park. Vegetarian meals. Children's helpings with prior notice. No children under 7. Smart dress preferred. No cigars/pipes in dining-room. Wheelchair access (1 step). Music ACCOMMODATION: 42 rooms, all with bath/shower. Rooms for disabled. Lift. B&B £98 to £187. Children welcome. Baby facilities. Pets welcome. Afternoon teas. Garden. TV. Phone. Confirm by 6. Fax: (0225) 339401 (*The Which? Hotel Guide*)

Tarts ▼ £

8 Pierrepont Place, Bath BA1 1JX   COOKING 2
BATH (0225) 330280 and 330201   COST £18–£32

The name dates from whacky younger bistro days; the approach now is modern but grown-up. The cellar dining-rooms are called 'snug and cosy' or 'primitive' depending on the reporter. Michel Lemoine's cooking deserves applause. Regular commendation is attached to seaweed-wrapped sushi, and the addition of miso soup to the *carte* confirms the kitchen's easterly direction. Daily dinner specials demonstrate an urge to experiment: poached fillet of veal on a bed of braised lentils comes with a salsa of blanched parsley, capers, Dijon mustard, anchovies, garlic and virgin olive oil. Cheaper lunch menus feature Caesar salad and pan-fried salmon with chive butter sauce. 'Knowledgeable, attentive and hospitable' service keeps the place swinging. Puddings do not let the side down, even if they contain less to raise the eyebrows. Cheeses are decent, and a two-tone chocolate parfait cake left people recumbent with bliss. The good, sensible wine list seeks to inform rather than intimidate. Selection is reliable but far from tedious; there is special enthusiasm for Rioja, and an intelligent aim to provide fair range of price and quality shows itself particularly well in the Cabernet Sauvignons. House wines are £8.30. CELLARMAN'S CHOICE: Hawke's Bay Sauvignon Blanc 1991, Delegats, £12.80; Chianti Classico 1988, Isole e Olena, £16.

CHEF: Michel Lemoine PROPRIETOR: John Edwards OPEN: all week, exc Sat L; 12 to 2.30, 6.45 to 10.45 (11 Fri and Sat) CLOSED: 3 days Christmas MEALS: alc. Set L and D £9.60 to £12.05 SERVICE: not inc (10% for six or more) CARDS: Access, Amex, Visa DETAILS: 50 seats. Private parties: 25 main room, 8 and 12 private rooms. Vegetarian meals. Children welcome. No cigars/pipes in dining-room. Music

---

▐ *denotes an outstanding wine cellar;* ▼ *denotes a good wine list, worth travelling for.*

£ *indicates that it is possible to have a three-course meal, including coffee, a half-bottle of house wine and service, at any time the restaurant is open (i.e. at dinner as well as at lunch, unless a place is open only for dinner), for £20 or less per person.*

Woods £

9–13 Alfred Street, Bath BA1 2QX
BATH (0225) 314812

COOKING 1
COST £16–£28

The restaurant is opposite the Assembly Rooms in a broad street that, were it
not for the cars, would give strong vibes of eighteenth-century elegance. There
is elegance within doors, either in the brasserie to the fore or the restaurant
beyond, where David Price's enthusiasm for horse-racing stands out from every
wall. Mary Jane Alley's cooking takes a 'small-world' route, offering Thai beef
casserole or monkfish with hijiki seaweed and rice noodles next to chicken
stuffed with basil and pine-kernel mousse, or salmon with tomatoes, coriander
and green ginger. There is a series of set menus but mix and match is permitted,
and bargain hunters turn up for the early 'happy supper hour'. There are
crudités on the table to get you through the waiting, but service is invariably
cheerful and there is often a buzz from good business. High flavours are
promised though not invariably delivered; this place is a useful watering-hole
none the less. The wine list has enough at under £15 to avoid worry about the
clarets and burgundies. House wines are £7.20.

CHEFS: Mary Jane Alley and Kirk Vincent   PROPRIETORS: David and Claude Price   OPEN:
Mon to Sat; restaurant 12 to 2.15, 6.30 to 10.15; brasserie 11 to 11 (Sat 11 to 3)   CLOSED: 24
to 29 Dec   MEALS: alc. Set L £10, Set D £12 to £18.95 (Sat)   SERVICE: not inc   CARDS:
Access, Visa   DETAILS: 70 seats. 8 tables outside. Private parties: 70 main room, 38 private
room. Vegetarian meals. Children's helpings. No cigars/pipes in dining-room. Wheelchair
access (2 steps; also WC). Music. Fax: (0225) 443146

BEAMINSTER Dorset   map 2

▲ Bridge House ⁵⅟✳ £

Prout House, Beaminster DT8 3AY
BRIDPORT (0308) 862200

COOKING 1
COST £19–£36

The house itself is medieval and sports some big fireplaces and good features –
as well as sprouting modern rooms and conservatory round the courtyard. The
dining-room is a variation on pink, not a very medieval colour, but the
Adamesque fireplace that was inserted at some later date is probably
justification for that. If you stay, the place will relax you, but the menu may not
change for a week. The cooking avoids the 'flash-Harry' approach, preferring to
present good materials simply. This may founder if the essential techniques
misfire, the materials are not so special, or the flavours are insufficiently
pronounced. Duck breast with a berry coulis had not only a coulis but whole
strawberries, cranberries, raspberries and grapes; the tomato sauce with a slice
of steamed turbot was not lively enough to revive the fish. The wine list is short
but intelligently chosen and not heavy on the mark-ups. House wine is £8.25.

---

*'He left the card slip open – I wrote in the money, i.e. £20. I never leave a tip – I need it
much more than they do currently. The waiter said I should draw a line because ''people
can write in hundreds in front''. ''You wouldn't do that, would you?'' I replied.'*
On eating in London

CHEFS: Peter Pinkster and Lindsay Wakeman   PROPRIETOR: Peter Pinkster   OPEN: all
week; 12.30 to 2, 7 to 9 (9.30 Sat)   MEALS: alc   SERVICE: not inc, card slips closed
CARDS: Access, Amex, Diners, Visa   DETAILS: 42 seats. 3 tables outside. Private parties: 24
main room, 18 private room. Car park. Vegetarian meals. Children's helpings with prior
notice. No smoking in dining-room. Wheelchair access. No music   ACCOMMODATION: 14
rooms, all with bath/shower. Rooms for disabled. B&B £35 to £92. Deposit: £10. Children
welcome. Pets welcome. Afternoon teas. Garden. TV. Phone. Doors close at 11.30. Confirm
by 6. Fax: (0308) 863700 (*The Which? Hotel Guide*)

BECKINGHAM Lincolnshire   map 6

Black Swan ✳ £

Hillside, Beckingham LN5 0RF   COOKING 3
NEWARK (0636) 626474   COST £20–£36

'We drove there in the fog but it was worth it, and the restaurant was full,'
wrote a couple who made a January pilgrimage to this Lincolnshire country
restaurant. Had they arrived in summer they might have been able to eat in the
new garden area overlooking the river. One major attraction is the value for
money – especially in the set menus – although regulars have noticed prices
creeping upwards. The menu reads well and the kitchen keeps its finger on the
pulse: seafood ravioli with ginger and spring onion sauce, roast guinea-fowl
served on aubergine purée with aniseed sauce, and vegetable and coriander
fricassee in filo pastry with tomato vinaigrette are thoroughly in line with the
trends. At its best the kitchen can produce 'main dishes of exuberant vitality
and balance'; vegetables, however, receive perfunctory treatment and become a
predictable selection. There have also been signs of inconsistency. Well-
reported dishes such as smoked salmon and cucumber and chervil sauce, beef
perfumed with lavender, and pork in a filo parcel stuffed with a light but
intense Stilton mousse have been offset by rather tasteless roast pheasant in
pastry and Dover sole stuffed with a salmon and watercress mousse that did
not live up to expectations. 'Sweets are devastating,' warns one regular:
sponges and soufflés are a highlight, but hazelnut parfait with brandy sauce
has also been praised. Light lunches are available, and Sunday lunch is a new
feature. Around 50 wines include some fairly priced red and white burgundies.
House French is from £6.20.

CHEF: Anton Indans   PROPRIETORS: Anton and Alison Indans   OPEN: Tue to Sun, exc Sun
D; 12 to 2, 7 to 10   MEALS: alc. Set L and D £13.50   SERVICE: not inc   CARDS: Access,
Visa   DETAILS: 30 seats. Private parties: 24 main room, 12 and 24 private rooms. Car park.
Children's helpings L. No smoking in dining-room. Wheelchair access (also WC). Music

---

*Several sharp operators have tried to extort money from restaurateurs on the promise of an
entry in a guidebook that has never appeared.* The Good Food Guide *makes no charge
for inclusion and does not offer certificates of any kind.*

*Healthy eating options in the details at the end of an entry signifies that a restaurant
marks on its menu, in words and/or using symbols, low-fat dishes or other healthy eating
choices.*

BERWICK-UPON-TWEED Northumberland

map 7

Funnywayt'mekalivin

41 Bridge Street,
Berwick-upon-Tweed TD15 1ES
BERWICK-UPON-TWEED (0289) 308827 and 86437

COOKING 2*
COST £25

The restaurant occupies a former plumber's shop in a street in the old town being restored by the Berwick Preservation Trust, so it has charm. This is increased by the miscellany of pictures, plants, a collage of old printers' letters, tables by Coldstream craftsman Iain McGregor, and all the other things that people came to love at Elizabeth Middlemiss' former premises. She stamps the place with her personality, and it remains a one-woman show – if she is ill, it shuts. The formula is a long meal, kicking off at a single time, of tremendous value and capable cooking. Here's one from February: you start with a glass of Muscat with Roquefort and sesame-seed biscuits, then carrot and apple cream soup from a tureen, with hot crusty bread; spinach- filled pancakes; underdone fillet of beef with madeira sauce, potatoes and stir-fried cabbage with juniper and garlic; iced orange soufflé with passion-fruit sauce; Teviotdale cheese; finally coffee, with shortbread (in heart-shapes for St Valentine). 'We requested a sliver of Bonchester to sample before departing, and the proprietor presented us with a whole cheese for coming such a long way. Guests were all given souvenir felt-tip pens as they left,' reported one bemused but contented traveller from Birmingham. This is a very particular place and is worth a visit. A score of wines marks the start of licensed status. All are satisfactory choices and none is overpriced. House wines are £6.95.

CHEF/PROPRIETOR: Elizabeth Middlemiss OPEN: Wed to Sat, D only (L by arrangement); 7.30 for 8 MEALS: Set D £17.50 SERVICE: not inc, card slips closed CARDS: Access, Visa (4.5% surcharge) DETAILS: 34 seats. Private parties: 34 main room, 8 private room. Vegetarian meals. Children welcome. No smoking during meals. Music

BEXHILL East Sussex

map 3

Lychgates

5A Church Street, Old Town,
Bexhill TN40 2HE
BEXHILL (0424) 212193

COOKING 2
COST £16–£28

At the white clapboard house hard by the church, John Tyson has not paused in his effort to bring professional cooking and value to the seasiders of Sussex. There is something about the place that encourages regulars: perhaps the prospect of clean air, a brisk walk and then dinner makes a good day out. Menus change monthly: lunch is particularly good value, but even the most highly priced dinner menu, of five courses and coffee, with no service charge made or expected, offers proper ingredients and careful treatment. John Tyson trained at the Dorchester and has continued to keep abreast of things by reading and noticing; hence, perhaps, dishes such as quail's eggs on a bed of tomato, leek and mushrooms 'à la Tovey', or calf's liver roasted with vegetables and madeira 'à la Guèrard'. Shopping is indefatigably pursued, evidenced in the appearance of Romney lamb, good fish and excellent crab. This is a one-man kitchen, which may show if too many people order at once. The wine list is short and looks everywhere for its sources. At least half its 30 bins are available in half-bottles. A supplementary short choice of more interesting things comes and goes with spot purchases. Prices are as fair as can be. House wine is £8.45.

CHEF: John Tyson PROPRIETORS: John and Sue Tyson OPEN: Tue to Sat, exc L Tue and Sat (by arrangement only); 12.30 to 2, 7.15 to 10.30 MEALS: Set L £10, Set D £17.25 to £20.50 SERVICE: net prices, card slips closed CARDS: Access, Visa DETAILS: 26 seats. Private parties: 18 main room. Vegetarian meals. Children's helpings. No children under 8 D. No cigars/pipes in dining-room. Wheelchair access. No music

---

BILBROUGH North Yorkshire   map 5

▲ *Bilbrough Manor* ╬╳ | NEW ENTRY |

Bilbrough Y02 3PH   COOKING 3
TADCASTER (0937) 834002   COST £23–£49

'First-class old-fashioned hotel providing butler service and top-class cooking,' comments a reporter about this lavishly refurbished manor house in a conservation village between Leeds and York. The popular view is that there has been a marked change for the better in terms of comfort, atmosphere, service and food. Despite a certain formality, there is no stuffiness – the wine waiter has even been known to provide vocal renditions in concert with the resident pianist. Chef Andrew Pressley can deliver an assured version of modern Anglo-French cooking, with fresh fish as the main attraction on the *carte* and the short 'menu exceptionnel'. The cooking particularly impresses with the quality of its ingredients, high-class sauces and gravies, and details such as the fresh home-made bread rolls, nibbles and petits fours. The high point of one meal was pan-fried loin of lamb – generous, sweet, tender meat with a natural gravy spiked with chopped parsley. Other star dishes have included grilled marinated tuna fillet with deep-fried spinach and tomato vinaigrette, parrot fish with lemon butter sauce, and full-flavoured wild salmon with creamy vermouth and chive sauce. Vegetables are plain and crisp. Puddings such as savarin ring with spicy syrup and baked bananas, and sweet pastry filled with fresh blueberries have been notable for the quality of the pâtisserie. Service is excellent: 'Nothing was too much trouble,' notes a visitor. The wine list is very extensive and well-chosen. House wines are £11.95.

CHEF: Andrew Pressley PROPRIETORS: Mr and Mrs Colin Campbell Bell OPEN: all week; 12 to 2, 7 to 9.30 CLOSED: 25 to 29 Dec MEALS: alc. Set L £10.50 to £14.50, Set D £20 to £30 SERVICE: not inc CARDS: Access, Amex, Diners, Visa DETAILS: 70 seats. Private parties: 45 main room, 10 and 20 private rooms. Car park. Vegetarian meals. Children's helpings Sun L. Jacket and tie. No smoking in dining-room. Wheelchair access (also WC). Music ACCOMMODATION: 12 rooms, all with bath/shower. B&B £77 to £150. No children under 10. Afternoon teas. Garden. TV. Phone. Fax: (0937) 834724

The Guide *relies on feedback from its readers. Especially welcome are reports on new restaurants appearing in the book for the first time.*

BILLESLEY Warwickshire map 2

▲ *Billesley Manor* 🍷

Billesley B49 6NF
STRATFORD-UPON-AVON (0789) 400888 COOKING 2*
off A422, 2m W of Stratford-upon-Avon COST £24–£56

Heavy oak panelling, velvet curtains and green Chesterfield-style chairs lend the main restaurant of this many-gabled, mullioned manor house/hotel the air of a gentlemen's club, which can become painfully real if 'a party of about 20 bankers' enters. This highlights one of the hazards facing the lone couple who venture to dine in a hotel offering conference facilities and a health centre. Furthermore, they may feel that the high *carte* prices are not justified by the general ambience. The table d'hôte does offer a cheaper alternative. Mark Naylor continues to maintain good, consistent standards in the kitchen. One sound winter dinner produced duck terrine with foie gras pâté, roast pheasant with caramelised apples and a chocolate marquise with winter fruits and praline sauce. Generous portions elicit as much praise as the 'good and unobtrusive service'. There has been comment on 'tough and flavourless' saddle of rabbit and 'excessively fat' roast Gressingham duckling, but niggles are outweighed by the praise. This is no place for bargain wines, with only the very modest offered below £14. What remains, though, is of quality, with fine Alsaces, a good range of clarets and among the best of Burgundian growers. A sprinkling of interest from the New World rounds off the picture. There are good half-bottles, so economy of sorts is possible. House French is £10.50. CELLARMAN'S CHOICE: Montagny premier cru Les Monts Cuchot 1989, Dom. Steinmaier, £21.50; St-Nicolas-de-Bourgueil 1988, Taluau, £15.75.

CHEF: Mark Naylor PROPRIETORS: Queens Moat Houses plc OPEN: all week; 12.30 to 2, 7.30 to 9.30 (10 Fri and Sat) MEALS: alc. Set L £17, Set D £25 SERVICE: not inc, card slips closed CARDS: Access, Amex, Diners, Visa DETAILS: 75 seats. 6 tables outside. Private parties: 8 main room, 100 private room. Car park. Vegetarian meals. Children's helpings. No children under 12. Jacket and tie. No cigars/pipes in dining-room. No music
ACCOMMODATION: 41 rooms, all with bath/shower. B&B £99 to £160. Children welcome. Baby facilities. Afternoon teas. Garden. Swimming-pool. Tennis. TV. Phone. Doors close at 1am. Confirm by 6. Fax: (0789) 764145

BIRDLIP Gloucestershire map 2

▲ *Kingshead House* 🍷

Birdlip GL4 8JH COOKING 2
GLOUCESTER (0452) 862299 COST £24–£36

'Still pleasant and comfortable,' affirms one regular. This unfussy Cotswold stone house continues to supply undimmed satisfaction to an undiminished following. Warren Knock is a gallant host, and service under his tutelage is adept and obliging. Judy Knock regularly recharges her repertoire but is, at heart, a careful conservationist. A typical spring four-course dinner listed among main choices rosettes de boeuf, with sauce tapénade, and Gressingham duck with kumquats. The rounds of fillet steak were pan-fried and finished with anchovies, capers, olives and red wine. In general, beef arrives rare.

Vegetables are mainly organic and sometimes of superior quality, as are most soups. Here is capable English cooking despite the *carte*'s tendency to use French descriptions. A modest and intelligent wine list neither intimidates the novice, nor disappoints the discerning. Ch. Léoville-Poyferre 1981 at £25.50 is one of the grander wines; this is a list which deters prodigality. Half-bottles are abundant and pricing throughout is very fair. House wines are from £8.75. CELLARMAN'S CHOICE: Azay-le-Rideau 1990, Pibaleau, £11.50; Chianti Montalbano 1988, Capezzana, £10.25.

CHEF: Judy Knock PROPRIETORS: Warren and Judy Knock OPEN: Tue to Sun, exc Sat L; 12.30 to 2 (1.45 Sun), 7.30 to 10 CLOSED: 25 and 26 Dec, 1 Jan MEALS: Set L £14 to £16, Set D £22.50 to £24.50 SERVICE: not inc (10% for six or more) CARDS: Access, Amex, Diners, Visa DETAILS: 32 seats. 3 tables outside. Private parties: 36 main room. Car park. Vegetarian meals. Children's helpings. No cigars/pipes in dining-room. Wheelchair access (1 step). Music ACCOMMODATION: 1 room, with bath/shower. B&B £35 to £50. Deposit: £10. Children welcome. Pets by arrangement. Garden. Doors close at midnight. Confirm by 6

BIRKENHEAD Merseyside
map 5

Beadles

15 Rosemount, Oxton,
Birkenhead L43 5SG
051-653 9010

COOKING 1
COST £21–£28

The Gotts are now into their fifteenth year here. Bea Gott cooks to a 'sort of regional Masterchef final level and at the end of the evening sits inscrutably sipping one glass of wine', while Roy Gott continues his discourses to customers on food and wine, which are always good value. The menu is straightforward, offering Anglo-French cooking with Italian overtones. It is not without interest, such as warm goats' cheese salad, roasted red pepper stuffed with anchovies, pine-kernels and lots of garlic, warm duck salad, sliced woodpigeon breast on a bed of crisp green lentils, lamb on a bed of rosemary-infused leeks, vitello tonnato, and home-made lavender ice-cream, well balanced by a bitter chocolate sauce and meringue. The service can be put under a strain if the place is full. House wine is £6.50.

CHEF: Bea Gott PROPRIETORS: Roy and Bea Gott OPEN: Tue to Sat, D only; 7.30 to 9 CLOSED: Aug MEALS: alc SERVICE: not inc (10% for 6 or more), card slips closed DETAILS: 34 seats. Private parties: 30 main room. Vegetarian meals. Children welcome. Wheelchair access (1 step). Music

---

BIRMINGHAM West Midlands
map 5

Chung Ying £

16–18 Wrottesley Street, B5 6RT
021-622 5669 and 1793

COOKING 2
COST £16–£36

'Warning, parking may damage your wealth,' reads the message on the menu as Birmingham's tow-trucks ply a merry trade at all hours. Your eyes, of course, may never recover from the eight-page listing of what can be had from the kitchens of this giant restaurant. Start with the dim-sum: deep-fried squid with sweet-and-sour sauce, Shanghai dumplings with vinegar dip, stuffed green pepper and paper-wrapped prawns are examples. Move on to fish: a whole sea bass, king prawns with ginger and spring onions, perhaps. Essay a few of the wilder things: goose webs, fish lips, ox tripe. If on economies, be satisfied with a one-plate meal. 'I met my first Chinese waiter with a sense of humour here,' wrote one who fared well. Many others do, too. House wine is £7.50 per litre.

CHEF/PROPRIETOR: Siu Chung Wong   OPEN: all week; noon to midnight (11 Sun)   MEALS: alc. Set L and D £10 to £16   SERVICE: 10%   CARDS: Access, Amex, Diners, Visa   DETAILS: 200 seats. 48 tables outside. Private parties: 100 main room, 100 private room. Car park. Vegetarian meals. Children welcome. Smart dress preferred. Music. Air-conditioned

Days of the Raj £

| 51 Dale End, B4 7LS | COOKING 1 |
| 021-236 0445 | COST £12–£30 |

Pink overwhelms, and bamboo and rattan support the happy eater in a restaurant pitched at a different market to the balti-houses of Sparkbrook. Despite its name and fading sepia photographs, this is no revival of Anglo-Indian cuisine, rather a competent yet mainstream all-India tandoori house. People speak well of the spicing, the fragrant herbs and the produce of the oven. Its proximity to the law courts is an asset. At lunch-time, and three evenings a week, there is a buffet. The breads are good. House wine is £6.95.

CHEF: Ramesh Chander   PROPRIETOR: Balbir Singh   OPEN: all week, exc L Sat and Sun; 12 to 2.30, 7 (6 Fri and Sat) to 11.30   CLOSED: L bank hols   MEALS: alc. Set L £6.45 to £8, Set D £8.90 to £20.15. Minimum £7.50   SERVICE: not inc   CARDS: Access, Amex, Diners, Visa   DETAILS: 120 seats. Private parties: 100 main room, 30 private room. Vegetarian meals. Children's helpings with prior notice. Smart dress preferred. Wheelchair access (also WC). Music. Air-conditioned. Fax: 021-200 2879

Henrys £

| 27 St Pauls Square, B3 1RB | COOKING 1 |
| 021-200 1136 | COST £18–£32 |

'The cooking outshines the decor,' comments one reporter about this smartly appointed restaurant in Birmingham's revitalised jewellery quarter. Although the menu is pitched towards Western tastes, the kitchen puts its faith in fresh ingredients, sauces are good and MSG levels seem to be kept in check. The list of recommended dishes shows the style: sweet-and-sour wun-tun, crispy duck with plum sauce, stir-fried squid with garlic, and sizzling chicken with black-bean sauce. The repertoire also takes in assorted seafood in crispy bird's nest, loin of lamb with chilli and pepper, and aubergine stuffed with minced prawn. Fried noodles and special fried rice are creditable accompaniments. Service is attentive. A new 40-seat extension has recently been added for private parties. Drink tea, saké or wine. House French is £7.50.

See the back of the Guide for an index of restaurants listed.

CHEF: C.W. Choi PROPRIETORS: Henry Wong and C.W. Choi OPEN: Mon to Sat; 12 to 2,
6 to 11 (11.30 Fri and Sat) CLOSED: 1 week Aug MEALS: alc. Set L and D £13 SERVICE:
not inc CARDS: Access, Amex, Diners, Visa DETAILS: 140 seats. Private parties: 40 main
room. Vegetarian meals. Children welcome. Music

Maharaja £

23–25 Hurst Street, B5 4AS
021-622 2641

COOKING 1
COST £15–£27

A few minutes from New Street, this is one of the most consistent Indian
restaurants in the city centre. The menu is entrenched in classic north Indian
and Punjabi cooking, using freshly mixed spices and achieving some intensity
to the sauces. The range does not extend beyond chicken and lamb dishes with
a few simple prawn and vegetable extras. House wine is £6.50.

CHEF: Bhupinder Waraich PROPRIETOR: N.S. Batt OPEN: Mon to Sat; 12 to 2.30, 6 to 11.30
MEALS: alc SERVICE: 10%, card slips closed CARDS: Access, Amex, Diners, Visa
DETAILS: 60 seats. 18 tables outside. Private parties: 30 main room. Vegetarian meals.
Children welcome. Wheelchair access. Music. Air-conditioned

Sloans

27–29 Chad Square, Hawthorne Road,
Edgbaston, B15 3TQ
021-455 6697

COOKING 2*
COST £23–£48

The major change at Sloans is that Roger Narbett, the young chef, has gone to
seek his fortune in London, at the Dorchester Hotel (see entry). He retains an
interest here (his father is the other owner), but day-to-day cooking is in the
hands of Simon Booth, once the sous-chef, with time at Le Gavroche as a
feather in his cap. Sloans has ever been a restaurant that delighted in the 'art of
cooking'. This means that techniques are often sound, even if the product is
over-worked for some palates. Fashion's passage is noted in recipes like
salmon with asparagus, broad beans and green pea sauce, while the
timelessness of haute cuisine is celebrated in a first course of prawns, sole and
salmon wrapped in salmon mousse flavoured with dill, with a white wine and
chive sauce. Classic ingredients such as wild mushrooms get an outing in
several dishes, but true luxuries like foie gras, caviare and truffles are left to the
glory-boys. 'The best in Birmingham; I find I can take people here without
disappointment,' went one endorsement of the kitchen. The price for lunch,
and the fixed-price dinner menu, indicate that not all of Birmingham catering is
designed to drain expense accounts: a fair bargain here. Consistently fine
quality and reasonable prices on the wine list – our benchmark for greediness
is the £20-plus charged by some restaurateurs for Cloudy Bay Sauvignon, but
Sloans falls the right side – are matched by informed range and cannily
selected half-bottles. The choice of French regional wines is of exceptional
value and interest. House wines are from £8.75. CELLARMAN'S CHOICE:
Jurançon Sec, Dom. Cauhape 1990, £14.75; Côtes du Jura, Pinot Noir 1988,
Boilley, £13.85.

CHEF: Simon Booth   PROPRIETORS: John and Roger Narbett   OPEN: Mon to Sat, exc Sat L; 12 to 2, 7 to 10 (10.30 Sat)   CLOSED: bank hols, 1 week after Christmas   MEALS: alc. Set L £14.50 to £16.50, Set D £23 to £25   SERVICE: not inc (10% for 8 or more)   CARDS: Access, Amex, Diners, Visa   DETAILS: 62 seats. Private parties: 80 main room. Car park. Vegetarian meals. Smart dress preferred. No-smoking area. Wheelchair access (1 step; also WC). Music. Air-conditioned. Fax: 021-454 4335

▲ Swallow Hotel, Sir Edward Elgar

12 Hagley Road, Fiveways, B16 8SJ
021-452 1144

COOKING 3
COST £27–£56

An Edwardian block houses a hotel, the restaurants of which are dedicated to eminent Edwardians: Elgar and Lillie Langtry. The composer's dining-room is calm and plush. The staff are solicitous rather than pompous, and the ceremony of raising the silver cloche is low-key. The menu suggests a familiar variation on unenigmatic British cooking, but Idris Caldora marshals flavour and texture in precise terms and with handsome results. Few reports fail to mention the canapés and petits fours that are dispatched to boost a sense of being well looked after. Dinner itself – available as two, three or four courses – might start with 'an unfussy medley of sea fish and scallops' or 'rather rich' braised leeks filled with ricotta and dressed with avocado, tomato and basil. Fish is subject to care but also invention: medallions of salmon are topped with wild mushroom mousse and olive and nutmeg sauce. Black sea bass with diced tomatoes and caviare boasts 'terrific flavour'. Otherwise, it's chicken pot-roasted with Parma ham, sauté calf's liver with herbs and trumpet mushrooms, or an entrecôte of beef glazed with shallots that 'bursts with flavour'. Desserts, such as a meringue disclosing fresh berries or alternate layers of shortbread biscuits and fresh raspberries, are classical. The wine list is full of classic names at classic prices. The heart sinks at house wines for £14. Some of the Italians are most drinker-friendly – purse-wise, that is.

CHEF: Idris Caldora   PROPRIETORS: Swallow Hotels   OPEN: all week, exc Sat L; 12.30 to 2.30, 7.30 to 10.30   MEALS: alc. Set L £15.50 to £23.50, Set D £17.50 to £30 (Sat)   SERVICE: not inc, card slips closed   CARDS: Access, Amex, Diners, Visa   DETAILS: 50 seats. Private parties: 5 private room. Car park. Vegetarian meals. Children's helpings. Jacket and tie. No-smoking area. Wheelchair access (also WC). Music. Air-conditioned   ACCOMMODATION: 98 rooms, all with bath/shower. Rooms for disabled. Lift. B&B £60 to £130. Children welcome. Baby facilities. Pets welcome. Afternoon teas. Swimming-pool. Sauna. Air-conditioned. TV. Phone. Doors close at midnight. Confirm by 6. Fax: 021-456 3442 (*The Which? Hotel Guide*)

The Guide *office can quickly spot when a restaurateur is encouraging customers to write recommending inclusion – and sadly, several restaurants have been doing this in 1992. Such reports do not further a restaurant's cause. Please tell us if a restaurateur invites you to write to the* Guide.

All letters to the Guide *are acknowledged with an update on latest sales, closures, chef changes and so on.*

BIRTLE Greater Manchester

map 5

▲ *Normandie*

Elbut Lane, Birtle BL9 6UT
061-764 3869 and 1170

COUNTY OF THE YEAR RESTAURANT

COOKING 3*
COST £19–£46

Once upon a time it was the Crown Inn, high up the lane towards the hills, away from Bury. Then a Frenchman, Yves Champeau (whose brother cooks at Delph – see entry), bought it and transformed it into a restaurant-with-rooms – utterly Norman. Twenty-five years or more on, it was sold to the Moussas, a really effective mother-and-son team. They preserved its Frenchness, against all odds; they added to it, they installed (latterly) a Frenchman to cook for it, and this year Edward Denny has joined the team as consultant and co-chef. The Normandie is not a pretty sight: the buildings are a strange gathering of this and that but, once inside, the visitor is struck by the serious intentions, borne out by the very sound cooking and the correct and complete service. There are set menus (at fair cost) and a *carte*. The style is modern classicism, which is able to absorb the composition of a good salad (for instance, langoustines and sea perch with a nicely cut tomato concassé and a parsley vinaigrette) as well as the production of a faultless eggs florentine. The range is wide: British puddings among the parfaits, mille-feuilles and sorbets (good); fresh noodles (with asparagus, oyster mushrooms and madeira) alongside beef béarnaise. There can be quite a lot of eggs, butter and cream – but that is how M. Champeau would have wished it, and it is easy to avoid them. The cooking touches on the luxuries – foie gras, morels and truffles – but it is not ostentatious. Some people find the set meals less appealing than the *carte*, but the usual choice is not ungenerous for the price. There has been consistency about the cooking, which may be the result of strengthening the team. It may also be the consequence of the place being a resort for visiting businessmen during the week, giving it a steady and sometimes quality-conscious public. Bread and butter are good; the appetiser, one night a perfect gazpacho, may be excellent; the petits fours are acceptable. It is a very professional place. The wine list, stretching from carefully selected Beaujolais and Australians to magnificent burgundies, is strong on quality as well as range. Half-bottles are well provided and prices throughout are fair, with a collection of decent French country wines from £9.50. CELLARMAN'S CHOICE: Rosemount Semillon/Chardonnay 1989, £11.40; Margaux, Ch. d'Issan 1983, £45.10.

CHEFS: Pascal Pommier and Edward Denny PROPRIETORS: Gillian Moussa and Max Moussa OPEN: Mon to Sat, exc L Mon and Sat; 12 to 2, 7 to 9.30 CLOSED: 26 Dec to first Sun Jan, 1 week Easter MEALS: alc. Set L £12.50 to £15, Set D £18.95 SERVICE: not inc, card slips closed CARDS: Access, Amex, Diners, Visa DETAILS: 60 seats. Private parties: 70 main room. Car park. Vegetarian meals. Children's helpings with prior notice. Smart dress preferred. No cigars/pipes in dining-room. Wheelchair access. Music ACCOMMODATION: 22 rooms, all with bath/shower. Rooms for disabled. Lift. B&B £49 to £79. Children welcome. TV. Phone. Confirm by noon. Fax: 061-764 4866

'Marvellous value, in fact, and an authentic feel from the scent of herbs and a little Greek music from the player. (Unfortunately the bouzouki-player had had trouble with his strings and though there could only eat, not play. Shame.)' On eating in Wales

---

BISHOP'S TACHBROOK Warwickshire

map 2

▲ Mallory Court

Harbury Lane,
Bishop's Tachbrook CV33 9QB
LEAMINGTON SPA (0926) 330214
off A452, 2m S of Leamington Spa

COOKING 3*
COST £32–£70

Professional pampering in established English country-house hotel style continues to elicit eulogies for Mallory Court. A reader vows to return 'whenever possible' after a 'weekend of luxury'. The regulation chintzy drawing-room wrests approbation. The fires that warm the library comfort Midlands business personnel and well-heeled travellers alike. 'Excellent' canapés arrive on cue. In the dining-room Allan Holland's high standards of execution claim praise: roast loin of pork with peeled apricot halves atop an apple purée was pronounced 'very good – pink, juicy pieces of meat'; Dover sole was 'beautifully filleted off the bone and not overcooked'. Precision rather than invention is the benchmark. There is more meat than fish on a typical menu, but beef has not fared well in reports: 'My main course was tough, tasteless and swimming in watery gravy.' Indeed, querulousness has crept into recent accounts, with suggestions of vegetables being less than well-bought. Service is 'attentive and efficient'. It may need more than accuracy and efficiency to justify the very high prices here. A basic charge will buy you the daily table d'hôte. Various individual supplements are made to the minimum cost if you eat off the *carte*, which is long and changes much less frequently. This may land you with a food bill in excess of £45: major league stuff. The wine list is distinguished by top-flight clarets and burgundies with matching prices. House wines are from £8.95.

CHEF: A.J.G. Holland   PROPRIETORS: A.J.G. Holland and J.R. Mort   OPEN: all week; 12.30 to 2, 7.30 to 9.30 (10 Sat)   MEALS: alc. Set L £24, Set D £29.50   SERVICE: net prices, card slips closed   CARDS: Access, Visa   DETAILS: 50 seats. Private parties: 50 main room. Car park. No children under 9. Jacket and tie. No cigars/pipes in dining-room. No music ACCOMMODATION: 10 rooms, all with bath/shower. B&B £95 to £220. Deposit: 1 night for overseas reservations. No children under 9. Afternoon teas. Garden. Swimming-pool. Tennis. TV. Phone. Fax: (0926) 451714

BLACKPOOL Lancashire

map 5

September Brasserie

15–17 Queen Street, Blackpool FY1 1PU
BLACKPOOL (0253) 23282

COOKING 2*
COST £17–£37

Book your party conferences now. Blackpool can feed you with imagination and economy, for among the tack and the junk is this first-floor brasserie. The hairdresser's below belongs to Pat Wood, who turns to serving meals in the evening. Our last year's comment that views from the tables are of the 'open sea' was qualified by one visitor as being rather more that of a bridal outfitter's opposite. Don't worry, the place has enough interest of its own, including the view of Michael Golowicz cooking in the semi-open kitchen. His menus pack tremendous variety into a short list: fillet of sea trout marinated in orange, honey, ginger and tamarind, served with Jamaican chutney; pink rack of lamb encrusted with an olive and mustard tapénade and served on basil and tomato sauce; knuckle of naturally reared pork with haricot beans and mustard sauce. An autumn meal that included endive poached in chicken stock then wrapped in smoked ham and cheese sauce, crispy crab and scallop pancake with a sweet sauce, poached chicken with fresh asparagus spears in a watercress sauce, and sliced calf's liver with wild mushrooms in a madeira sauce showed the cooking in a fair light. It was all well done, though a bit short on stand-up flavour (no evidence of watercress in the watercress sauce, endive lacking bite through being slightly overcooked). Desserts and cheese are as intelligent as the rest. Michael Golowicz may offer a selection of Welsh farmhouse cheeses with walnut bread, or just some fine fresh Parmesan with pickled walnuts and figs. A walnut tart proved a bit tough, but think about trying a mille-feuille made with brandy-snaps and strawberries on a stem ginger sauce. Details such as vegetables show the real keenness of the man even if bread could be better. Lunch is cheaper and shorter; a blackboard menu gives the running order. The wine list, like the cooking, shows loyalty to the organic concept. A short choice from round the world is usefully annotated and not expensive. There is even a list of six organic dessert tipples by the glass. House wines are £8.95 and upwards.

CHEFS: Michael Golowicz and Mark Coulton   PROPRIETORS: Michael Golowicz and Pat Wood   OPEN: Tue to Sat; 12 to 2.30, 7 to 9.30   CLOSED: 2 weeks summer, 2 weeks winter   MEALS: alc. Set L £9.50 to £14.50, Set D £17.75 to £23.50   SERVICE: not inc, card slips closed   CARDS: Access, Amex, Diners, Visa   DETAILS: 34 seats. Private parties: 40 main room. Vegetarian meals. Children's helpings. Music

---

BLACKWATER Cornwall   map 1

Long's

Blackwater TR4 8HH   COOKING 2
TRURO (0872) 561111   COST £17–£36

The house stands proud by the old road out of Blackwater, its granite walls firm against the moorland blasts, sheltering a striking conversion from residence to restaurant. Ann Long's cooking may be in similar style to the decoration: lots of personality, multi-layered, anxious for effect. Wrappings and stuffings are given full vent: guinea-fowl with a chicken and ham mousse stuffing; crab meat and shredded courgettes topped with a tarragon mousse; salmon wrapped in spinach and puff pastry; duck wrapped in bacon. Fruit sauces and dressings may often give accent to the savoury: passion-fruit dressing with a pressed terrine of chicken and leeks, or plum purée with duck – but more robust flavours such as 'pease pudding sauce' or spiced red cabbage are not forgotten. This may be complicated cooking that satisfies a Cornish person's ideal of a 'good night out', eating food that emphatically would never be cooked at home. Desserts are more homely – substantial, that is – but of disarming richness. This is the stage in the meal when Ann Long herself may forsake the stove for the dining-room, otherwise the domain of her husband, a forceful and characterful host. Prices have not mushroomed, and the Longs have been careful to tailor their offerings to Cornish tastes. The same can be said for the wine list: very fairly costed, with most bottles below £15, ignoring the high-priced regions and offering instead bottles from Israel and the New World. House wine is £7.75.

CHEF: Ann Long   PROPRIETORS: Ian and Ann Long   OPEN: Wed to Sat, D only, and Sun L; 12.30 to 1.45, 7.30 to 10   CLOSED: 4 weeks winter   MEALS: alc. Set L Sun L £11.25, Set D (Wed only) £14.95   SERVICE: not inc   CARDS: Access, Amex, Visa   DETAILS: 30 seats. Private parties: 10 main room, 10 and 12 private rooms. Car park. Children's helpings. No children under 12. Smart dress preferred. Wheelchair access (also WC). No music

Pennypots

Blackwater TR4 8EY   COOKING 2*
REDRUTH (0209) 820347   COST £27–£35

The old road out of Blackwater towards Redruth goes straight past the village's two restaurants. Pennypots is the further west and looks much as if it were an extended cottage with lean-to and porch to serve teas to scurrying motorists on their way to the family holiday before the foreign package took over. The locale is unexpected, and the determinedly cottagey decoration may appear at odds with Kevin Viner's correct and elaborate productions such as brill roasted with coriander, capers, shallots and brown butter. Jane Viner is an excellent hostess: welcoming, loyal, an eager interpreter of her husband's efforts in the kitchen. The framework of the short menu is supplemented by daily specials, particularly of fish. Kevin Viner can cook this well, and the raw materials are first-rate, as in a simple first course of scallops in a salad with a Chinese-style sauce that tasted of soy, tomato, fish and sugar. The scallops were plump and juicy, their sweetness enhanced by the sauce. That elaboration is enjoyed is seen from the trimmings of deep-fried strips of leek and leaves of basil. Such ancillaries will probably grace a main course too, for example, duck with citrus and green ginger, or venison with spiced pears and a game sausage, the sauce composed of hazelnut oil (in which the meat was fried) and juices and vinegar. The Viners may overload at the pudding stage when technique and flavour may be masked by too many elements, as in a pear poached with cinnamon that arrives with a chocolate ice-cream, caramelised whole peanuts, caramel sauce, a piece of shortbread and a whole lot of chocolate shavings. The extras – little kebabs of peppers, mushroom and sesame, a piece of tandoori chicken, intriguingly flavoured deep-fried shavings of coconut for appetisers, bread, sweets with coffee, well-flavoured sorbet after the first course – are what might be expected from a place that looks much grander. The restaurant is like the mythic fat boy who is housed in skeletal frame. The wine list is not long, but range comes from a set of New World bottles, and prices are fair. House wines are £6.95.

CHEF: Kevin Viner   PROPRIETORS: Kevin and Jane Viner   OPEN: Tue to Sat, D only; 7 to 10   CLOSED: 3 weeks winter   MEALS: alc   SERVICE: not inc, card slips closed   CARDS: Access, Amex, Diners, Visa   DETAILS: 30 seats. Private parties: 18 main room, 12 private room. Car park. Vegetarian meals. Children's helpings on request. No smoking before 10pm. Wheelchair access (1 step). Music

---

BLANDFORD FORUM Dorset　　　　　　　　　　　　　　　map 2

▲ *La Belle Alliance* ✚✳

White Cliff Mill Street,
Blandford Forum DT11 7BP　　　　　　　　　　　COOKING 1*
BLANDFORD FORUM (0258) 452842　　　　　　　　COST £16–£30

The restaurant and comfortable rooms occupy a Victorian house – an island of
flowers set in a lake of tarmacadam – on the Shaftesbury Road beyond the
baroque core that is the fairground attraction of Blandford. Phil Davison's
cooking excites a loyal following, and his wife's sense of pride is infectious –
'Relaxed, yet refined' is one person's dictum. The refinement comes from the
generously modest curtains and drapes and the propriety of the decoration; also
from the feeling of occasion that many reckon is imparted to a meal here. There
is choice on the seasonal menu though the price is fixed, and dishes such as
spinach pancake with prawn and white fish stuffing, mushroom terrine with
pine-kernels and a basil dressing, monkfish with grapefruit and a lobster
butter, and duck breast with orange and apple served on lentils may serve as
markers of the style. Desserts are often praised ('The vanilla and almond tart
with amaretto ice-cream was the best thing I have tasted') and usually include
a hot British pudding – step forward bread-and-butter. La Belle Alliance is a
steady country restaurant, satisfying a steady band of customers, and avoids too
much lolling on its laurels. Hence this year much time has been put into the
wine list's improvement. It has a decent range (with not a little from merchant
Christopher Piper) at fair prices, with acceptable French house wines and a
couple of vintage ports standing ready in decanters. House wines are £8.95.

CHEF: Philip Davison　PROPRIETORS: Lauren and Philip Davison　OPEN: Mon to Sat, D
only, and Sun L (Tue to Sat L by arrangement); bank hol Sun and Mon D; 12.30 to 2, 7 to
9.30 (10 Sat)　MEALS: Set L £11.50, Set D £22.50　SERVICE: net prices, card slips closed
CARDS: Access, Amex, Visa　DETAILS: 32 seats. Private parties: 36 main room. Car park.
Children by arrangement. No smoking in dining-room. Wheelchair access. Music
ACCOMMODATION: 6 rooms, all with bath/shower. B&B £40 to £68. Children welcome.
Baby facilities. Pets welcome. TV. Phone. Doors close at midnight. Confirm by 6

BOLLINGTON Cheshire　　　　　　　　　　　　　　　map 5

Mauro's £

88 Palmerston Street,
Bollington SK10 5PW　　　　　　　　　　　　　COOKING 1*
BOLLINGTON (0625) 573898　　　　　　　　　　　COST £14–£31

'The Mauros have managed to sustain their good intentions and reproduce a
friendly, mid-range, neighbourhood trattoria experience,' comments an
inspector. 'The place steers its own course mid-way between the bogus world
of old Chianti bottles, checked tablecloths and oversized peppermills and the
"new" Italian designerland of bruschetta, polenta and sun-dried tomatoes.'
The results are enjoyable, uncomplicated and unfussy. This is no-frills,
conventional Italian cooking – and none the worse for that. The menu has its
share of trattoria favourites, but high points are the antipasti, fresh pasta and

fish dishes. The trolley of hot and cold starters has provided marinated carrot salad, red peppers in oil, tuna and borlotti beans, squid, 'exceptionally light' ravioli filled with cheese and ham, and grilled sardines. Other approved dishes have included crisp deep-fried frittura del golfo, veal escalopes with lemon sauce, good-quality steaks and grilled veal chop with rosemary. The sweets trolley 'tends more towards Middle Britain than Little Italy', but there's praise for the amaretto cream and tiramisù. Some reporters feel that the food is slightly over-priced, but the wine list compensates with well-chosen, affordable Italians. House wine is £7.60.

CHEF/PROPRIETOR: V. Mauro   OPEN: Tue to Sat, exc Sat L; 12 to 2, 7 to 10   MEALS: alc. Set L £8.20, Set D £22.50   SERVICE: not inc (10% for 6 or more)   CARDS: Access, Amex, Visa   DETAILS: 50 seats. Vegetarian meals. Children's helpings. Wheelchair access (also WC). Music

---

BOTLEY Hampshire   map 2

Cobbett's

15 The Square, Botley SO3 2EA   COOKING 1
BOTLEY (0489) 782068   COST £28–£43

'In spite of ventures into parallel forms of revenue (i.e. La Causerie Bistro and the piano bar) we have found that the demand is not there for these alternatives,' writes Charles Skipwith. 'We are known essentially for our cuisine in the main restaurant that we have maintained for 17½ years.' The kitchen's inspiration comes mainly from France, and this translates into a mix of modern and provincial: roast leg of lamb sauced with white wine, saffron, garlic and paprika; a sauté of sweetbreads, ducks' livers and kidneys in a lemon, soya, honey and ginger sauce served on a pasta nest; a 'light, subtly seasoned, melt-in-the-mouth' boudin blanc à la périgourdine. Fresh fish from the south coast boats includes plump fillets of red mullet and sea bream ('each had its own distinctive flavour and texture'). Desserts can lack enthusiasm. The recession has forced a reduction in staff front-of-house, but not in the kitchen, and Sunday lunch is now available. The wine list is short and concentrates on the major French growing regions. House wine is £9.20.

CHEFS: Lucie Skipwith, Peter Hayes and Giles Hester   PROPRIETORS: Charles and Lucie Skipwith   OPEN: all week, exc Sun D and L Mon and Sat; 12 to 2, 7 to 10   MEALS: alc SERVICE: not inc   CARDS: Access, Visa   DETAILS: 40 seats. Private parties: 50 main room, 8 and 14 private rooms. Car park. Vegetarian meals. Smart dress preferred. No cigars/pipes in dining-room. No music. Fax: (0489) 799641

Net prices *in the details at the end of an entry indicates that the prices given on a menu and on a bill are inclusive of VAT and service charge, and that this practice is clearly stated on menu and bill.*

The 1994 Guide will be published before Christmas 1993. Reports on meals are most welcome at any time of the year, but are extremely valuable in the spring. Send them to The Good Food Guide, *FREEPOST, 2 Marylebone Road, London NW1 1YN. No stamp is needed if posted in the UK.*

BOUGHTON LEES Kent   map 3

▲ *Eastwell Manor*

Eastwell Park,
Boughton Lees TN25 4HR   COOKING 3
ASHFORD (0233) 635751   COST £26–£61

This is a mixed report for a giant of an Edwardian castle set amid acres and acres of grassland. What should be, and often is, first-rate, has had derelictions, and the management of the hotel has not been warmly praised. A spring meal began with an appetiser of a cep mousse with caramelised onion, on chicory with a stock gravy; then a quail stuffed with herbed and nutty breadcrumbs on a heap of spring onions and sweet peppers with a rich girolle sauce, and a warm sole mousseline with lobster and ginger on a lobster sauce. For main courses there were fillet of brill with scallops in a slightly sweetened and very rich chicory sauce, and breast of duck with garlic polenta and braised shallots with a deep brown gravy; vegetables were varied with each dish; desserts came as caramelised apple flan with butterscotch sauce and vanilla ice-cream, and poached pear coated with chocolate, filled with rice and sultanas, and set on a poire William ice-cream with a red wine sauce. In this last rather complex dish, the cinnamon in the sauce and the rum with the sultanas contributed to a wholly successful conclusion. Elaborate cookery (though not petits fours or canapés) is essayed by Mark Clayton and his able team, using good ingredients to effect. It does come at a price, however, and there have been periods in the year when success was not achieved. Some have noticed that the housekeeping lacks verve; still more think the waiting staff should be better trained. At around £40 for a dinner of three courses and coffee, the meal should be perfect. The wine list may be large, but it is also dear. House wines are £11.50.

CHEF: Mark Clayton PROPRIETORS: Queens Moat Houses plc OPEN: all week; 12.30 to 2, 7.30 to 9.30 (10 Sat) MEALS: alc. Set L £12.75 to £18, Set D £24.50 SERVICE: not inc CARDS: Access, Amex, Diners, Visa DETAILS: 70 seats. Private parties: 50 main room, 40 private room. Car park. Vegetarian meals. Children's helpings. Jacket and tie. No cigars/pipes in dining-room. Wheelchair access (2 steps; also WC). Music ACCOMMODATION: 23 rooms, all with bath/shower. Rooms for disabled. Lift. B&B £92 to £143. Children welcome. Baby facilities. Pets by arrangement. Afternoon teas. Garden. Tennis. Snooker. TV. Phone. Confirm by 6. Fax: (0233) 635530 (*The Which? Hotel Guide*)

BOURNEMOUTH Dorset   map 2

Sophisticats

43 Charminster Road,
Bournemouth BH8 8UE   COOKING 2
BOURNEMOUTH (0202) 291019   COST £25–£34

Twelve years down, how many to go? Sophisticats rides out the recession, though John Knight wonders why all Britain eats out on Saturday and no other night: 'Midweek, a patronising gent remarks, "You're rather quiet, how long have you been open?" Then at the weekend, when efficient chaos reigns, an order to the kitchen is greeted by "What do you think this is, a hamburger bar?"' Consistency is the restaurant's forte. The cats remain a decorative theme – kitsch kittens, you might say. Some dishes are old favourites. Steak follows a route through Dorchester (peppered) to Bordeaux ('marchand de vins') and Java (soy sauce and spices); veal may be Yugoslav (stuffed with ham, mushrooms, tomatoes and cheese) or Norman (with apples, calvados and cream). Messrs Knight and Calligan are well-travelled. Extras on the day are mostly fish, and well worth it: 'the best meal of our holiday'. Very old friends will recognise the crab gratin starter from the proprietors' days as publicans in Dartmouth. Desserts embrace cream, liqueurs and meringue; hot soufflé is recommended too. The owners have judged their market well and intend to stick around. The wine list will neither cause surprises nor break the bank. House wines are £7.25.

CHEF: Bernard Calligan PROPRIETORS: John Knight and Bernard Calligan OPEN: Tue to Sat, D only; 7 to 9.30 CLOSED: 2 weeks Feb, 1 week June, 1 week July, 2 weeks Nov MEALS: alc SERVICE: not inc DETAILS: 32 seats. Private parties: 12 main room. Vegetarian meals. Children welcome. Wheelchair access (also WC). Music

---

BOWNESS-ON-WINDERMERE Cumbria   map 7

Porthole Eating House 🍾

3 Ash Street,
Bowness-on-Windermere LA23 3EB   COOKING 2
WINDERMERE (053 94) 42793   COST £22–£44

The entertainment value is one reason why reporters enthuse about this idiosyncratic restaurant set in a quaint street described as the Lakes equivalent of the Blackpool prom. Wine bottles, maps and cycling memorabilia are dotted around the dining-room, reflecting Judy and Gianni Berton's interests. For more than 20 years they have been offering what they call 'a cocktail of Italian, French and English dishes'. Some of the best items are on the list of weekly specialities, including examples of Venetian cuisine. Vegetarian dishes are beginning to show up more strongly: as in a 'cake' of six kinds of wild mushrooms or tortellini stuffed with pine-kernels, leeks and Stilton. Pasta, bresaola, ice-creams and 'totally irresistible' brown bread are made on the premises – and the Bertons make full use of Lakeland produce such as Windermere char. Reporters have approved of tripe cooked with white wine and vegetables, goujons of chicken with curry mayonnaise, osso buco, grilled salmon with cream, shallots and herbs, and meringues with fresh raspberries. Occasional quibbles about value for money do not extend to the wine list. Our enthusiasm is undimmed; the owners are especially proud of their 'Mosel, Alsace, Rhône, Bordeaux, Australia...'. Spain isn't bad, and there are some particularly good New Zealand wines. Prices are fair, although there is a certain coyness about the grander appellations for which 'price on application' is deemed necessary. A fondness for collecting gives opportunities for comparison across the years: four vintages of Moss Wood Chardonnay, three of Ch. de Beaucastel. A serious list. House wines are £9.50.

Not inc *in the details at the end of an entry indicates that no service charge is made and any tipping is at the discretion of the customer.*

CHEFS: Michael Metcalfe, Tim Dalzell and Greame Wells   PROPRIETORS: Judy and Gianni Berton   OPEN: Wed to Mon, D only (L parties by arrangement); 6.30 to 11   CLOSED: mid-Dec to mid-Feb   MEALS: alc. Set D £13.50 to £27   SERVICE: not inc, card slips closed   CARDS: Access, Amex, Diners, Visa   DETAILS: 36 seats. 8 tables outside. Private parties: 36 main room, 8 and 20 private rooms. Vegetarian meals. Children's helpings. Wheelchair access. Music. Fax: (053 94) 88675

BRADFIELD COMBUST Suffolk   map 3

▲ Bradfield House

Sudbury Road,
Bradfield Combust IP30 0LR   COOKING 2
SICKLESMERE (0284) 386301   COST £21–£30

'If it wasn't for our bedrooms, we could well have been joining the ranks of restaurants that have not survived,' writes Sally Ghijben after a hard year for country places. Those bedrooms have forceful decoration – 'heavy, large floral wallpaper' – and 'tremendous' fireplace surrounds, plus the occasional plumbing difficulty. The house is a good piece of half-timbering, and the garden is appreciated. Roy Ghijben enjoys baking; on a menu this summer he had a couple of pastry lids, a puff-pastry 'hat', a pair of tartlets and a slice of toasted brioche. His style is English country. Rack of lamb (with those tartlets), beef with mustard sauce, chicken breast stuffed with a mushroom duxelles on a tarragon cream sauce, turbot and salmon with a prawn and lobster sauce are main dishes; haddock soufflé with a spinach sauce, sauté chicken livers, and garlic mushrooms are first courses. Reporters have found first and last courses outshine the central, and some have queried Roy Ghijben's butcher, though none has doubted his skill at making ice-cream and sorbet. Satisfactory cooking is enhanced by the good service and sound wine list, much from Lay & Wheeler, which includes most countries in order to give fair price range as well as a few impressive names such as Michel Ampeau, Antinori, Simi, and Schlumberger from Alsace. House wines are £6.95.

CHEFS/PROPRIETORS: Roy and Sally Ghijben   OPEN: Tue to Sat, D only (also Mon to Fri supper for guests); 7 to 9.45   MEALS: alc   SERVICE: net prices, card slips closed   CARDS: Access, Visa   DETAILS: 36 seats. 2 tables outside. Private parties: 24 main room, 16 private room. Car park. Children's helpings. No children under 5. No pipes in dining-room. Wheelchair access (1 step; also WC). Music   ACCOMMODATION: 4 rooms, all with bath/shower. B&B £40 to £60. Deposit: 10%. Children welcome. Baby facilities. Garden. TV. Phone. Doors close at midnight. Confirm by 6 (The Which? Hotel Guide)

'The food was so slow in arriving that I and my three companions had nearly finished the bottle of Mâcon-Lugny when the first course was served. There was enough wine left for half a glass each and I was in the process of pouring it when a waiter insisted on taking over the task. He contrived to leave my glass bare, no doubt expecting me to order another bottle. At that moment the owner came to the table and asked if everything was satisfactory. I explained why it wasn't. ''Leave this to me,'' the owner said grandly and with a flourish picked up my friend's full glass and emptied two-thirds of it into my empty glass.'
On eating (or drinking) in Oxfordshire

BRADFORD West Yorkshire   map 5

▲ *Restaurant Nineteen* ♟

North Park Road,
Bradford BD9 4NT   COOKING 4
BRADFORD (0274) 492559   COST £26–£46

The sweeping avenues with mature trees, broad pavements, long views over
the city, and giant houses built by a rich and confident bourgeoisie make one
realise the charms of suburbia or inner-city countryside – no threats, all
comfort. That's true of this restaurant-with-rooms, where you drink in rather
cosy surroundings but move on to a wedding-cake of a dining-room. Robert
Barbour's quiet discretion, gentle friendliness and skill make sure that neither
the surroundings nor the experience overawe. The prices confirm this. The
cooking, however, is thoroughgoing and successful: 'not bland in texture, but
imaginative and enterprising,' as one person put it. It is also substantial: 'I was
flagging by the soup course. Perhaps they should serve fewer appetisers.' An
autumn meal had as first course a roast teal on red cabbage with orange. Then
there was a rich soup of smoked haddock and pumpkin. Third came sea bass
baked with a herb crust, fresh and full-flavoured, the vegetables plain so as not
to clash (and cooked specifically for this dish). Spiced lamb kebabs with
couscous is sign that the Mediterranean revolution has reached these parts,
even if the spicing has been tremulous. Other dishes that confirm this are
pigeon with tagliatelle, red wine sauce and shiitake mushrooms, and a
brochette of salmon and monkfish with couscous and sweet pepper sauce. First
courses often tend to be miniature main dishes. Though everything may have
substance, this does not mean clumsiness, even in something so liable to this
fault as fillet of beef with a ragoût of kidneys (or, on other occasions, with a
mille-feuille of kidneys and mustard sauce). Another main dish – leg of lamb
lightly smoked, with a soubise sauce, and the nut of lamb roasted, with an
apple and mint jelly – gives an idea of the potential complications that are
tamed by intelligence and accurate cooking. Do not think enjoyment lapses
come the sweets: banana and walnut pudding with maple syrup and vanilla
sauce will build up many a northern breast; poached pears with honey-and-
brandy ice-cream and a caramel sauce is more delicate. Details are good:
changing varieties of bread, decent canapés; but less exciting petits fours, and
passable coffee. Service is willing, if just occasionally unsure. A complaint by a
reader that a Californian Chardonnay recommended by Robert Barbour was
'too modest' is encouraging. A restaurant that is proud of its lower-priced
offerings is to be trusted. Here the list has good range and carefully selected
growers; the house selection of a dozen, ranging from Simi Chardonnay to a
Cornas from Jaboulet, gives the flavour. Italy and Spain draw the short straw.
House wines are from £10.25. CELLARMAN'S CHOICE: Muscat d'Alsace, Grand
Cru Goldert 1989, Zind-Humbrecht, £17.50 (half-bottle only); Côte Rôtie,
Brune et Blonde 1985, Guigal, £28.50.

*See the inside of the front cover for an explanation of the 1 to 5 rating system
for cooking standards.*

CHEF: Stephen Smith   PROPRIETORS: Stephen Smith and Robert Barbour   OPEN: Mon to Sat, D only; 7 to 9.30 (10 Sat)   MEALS: Set D £16.50 to £28   SERVICE: not inc   CARDS: Access, Amex, Visa   DETAILS: 40 seats. Private parties: 10 main room. Car park. Children welcome. No pipes/cigars in dining-room. Music   ACCOMMODATION: 4 rooms, all with bath/shower. B&B £60 to £70. Children welcome. TV. Phone. Doors close at midnight. Confirm by 6 (*The Which? Hotel Guide*)

BRADFORD-ON-AVON Wiltshire   map 2

▲ *Woolley Grange*

Woolley Green,
Bradford-on-Avon BA15 1TX
BRADFORD-ON-AVON (022 16) 4705
on B3105, 1m NE of   COOKING 3
Bradford-on-Avon   COST £15–£31

'The gardeners certainly respond to a chef who wears wellies' is the encouraging comment of Nigel Chapman when announcing the arrival of Colin White as the new man in charge of the cooking. 'His cooking is perhaps more rustic than his predecessor's,' he continues. It is early days yet to see how things will shake down, but it is sure that Colin White can cook (after long stints as his own boss, and lately two years at Sharrow Bay, Ullswater – see entry). The evident strengths of Woolley Grange are its situation (if you can find it, on the north side of Bradford-on-Avon), the cleverly adapted architecture (even if some of the bedrooms may be a trifle small), the facilities in summer, and the positive willingness of the place to cope with children. This may mean that a summer visit reminds you of a middle-class playgroup more than country-house weekend, but how refreshing that someone is prepared to attack the problem. Sanity and peace return at dinner. The daily menus are a compromise between traditional and modern. Calves' kidneys and sweetbreads come with Marsala and sage and a slice of polenta; scallops are coriandered and lentilled with a push of ginger; pigeon is with tomato and olives rather than the usual liquorish reduction; sole comes with saffron mash; and lots of items have a salsa trotting along beside them. The Terrace menu – full of risotto, pizzetta and omelette Arnold Bennett – is cheaper and shorter. Some of our admonishments of the wine list in the last edition have been met; halves have been augmented and prices relaxed a little, although £21 for a straight Bourgogne Chardonnay still looks steep, whatever the grower's pedigree. The promised Italians are a curiously unrepresentative bunch. Wine, as well as food, shows promise here, but at least we have yet to be convinced that the list's balance of reliability, quality and value is a happy one. House wines are from £9.85.

CHEF: Colin White   PROPRIETORS: Nigel and Heather Chapman   OPEN: all week; 12 to 2, 7 to 10   MEALS: Set L £24, Set Sun L £16, Set D £26. Terrace menu (inc Set L £10) SERVICE: not inc, card slips closed   CARDS: Access, Amex, Diners, Visa   DETAILS: 54 seats. 5 tables outside. Private parties: 30 main room, 14 and 22 private rooms. Car park. Vegetarian meals. Children's helpings. Wheelchair access (1 step; also WC). No music ACCOMMODATION: 20 rooms, all with bath/shower. B&B £80 to £165. Children welcome. Baby facilities. Pets welcome. Afternoon teas. Garden. Swimming-pool. Tennis. Snooker. TV. Phone. Fax: (022 16) 4059 (*The Which? Hotel Guide*)

BRAITHWAITE Cumbria   map 7

▲ *Ivy House* ✦✦

Braithwaite CA12 5SY	COOKING 1
BRAITHWAITE (076 87) 78338	COST £26

The dining-room is done out in unrelenting dark green – 'rather like being under the sea,' remarked one visitor. A strict, brisk regime is at work here: dinners must be ordered between 7 and 7.30pm and diners have found themselves being rushed. The menu is fixed-price, and a number of items such as pork satay and sticky toffee pudding are fixtures. The cooking makes few demands on the palate, with dishes such as avocado and raspberry vinaigrette, steak au poivre and breaded escalope of pork with curry sauce; but there have been good reports of seafood pancake, salmon and monkfish cooked with sherry and coriander with paprika cream, duck breast with black cherries and madeira sauce, and venison with port wine and redcurrant sauce. Others mention overcooked steaks, dry venison and annoying garnishes. A useful list of around 50 wines includes a few organics. House wine is £6.95.

CHEF: Wendy Shill   PROPRIETORS: Nick and Wendy Shill   OPEN: all week, D only; 7 to 7.30   MEALS: Set D £17.95   SERVICE: not inc, card slips closed   CARDS: Access, Amex, Diners, Visa   DETAILS: 36 seats. Private parties: 10 main room. Car park. Vegetarian meals. Children's helpings. No smoking in dining-room. Music   ACCOMMODATION: 12 rooms, all with bath/shower. B&B £31 to £74. Deposit: £20. Children welcome. Baby facilities. Dogs by arrangement. TV. Phone. Doors close at 11.30. Confirm by 4.30 (*The Which? Hotel Guide*)

BRAMLEY Surrey   map 3

Le Berger

4A The High Street,	
Bramley GU5 0HB	COOKING 1
BRAMLEY (0483) 894037	COST £23–£28

The shepherd continues to excite different cries from his flock. Some find it enterprising (though sometimes serious and self-important), others find it lacking the necessary. The restaurant is well-appointed, behind its unassuming shop-front, and it offers a set of mainstream modern French dishes at a set price – with the added incentive that parties of more than six get a free carafe of house wine. Pâté de campagne, a croissant stuffed with spinach, *crottin en feuilleté*, or breast of chicken with spring vegetables, salmon sauce Choron, and lamb with white beans, garlic and red wine will not raise any eyebrows for their adventure, but Peter Hirth cooks them carefully – even if one reporter found the breasts of guinea-fowl too tiny and the vegetables too sparse to form a proper judgement. Reports of various gastronomic evenings, encompassing meals such as warm oysters in champagne sauce, fillet of lamb with a mousseline of wild mushrooms, then a 'Caribbean' soufflé, have been enthusiastic. The wine list is short, even shorter if you want to spend less than £20. House wine starts at £6.50.

CHEF/PROPRIETOR: Peter Hirth   OPEN: Tue to Sat; 12.30 to 2, 7 to 9.30   CLOSED: 2 weeks Jan, bank hols   MEALS: Set L and D £15 to £18.50   SERVICE: not inc, card slips closed CARDS: Access, Amex, Diners, Visa   DETAILS: 24 seats. 2 tables outside. Private parties: 15 main room. Children welcome. Jacket and tie. No-smoking area. Music

---

BRAMPTON Cumbria   map 7

▲ *Farlam Hall*

Brampton CA8 2NG
HALLBANKGATE (069 77) 46234
on A689, 2m from Brampton   COOKING 2*
(not at Farlam village)   COST £34–£38

'The very model of a small country-house hotel. Mr Quinion greets you; Mrs Q. does the menus and aperitifs; Master Q. does the cooking.' Q is for quality here. 'My only Q for quibble was a certain air of gracious living, but that is all a matter of taste' – emphasised, no doubt, by the sub-Victorian uniforms worn at dinner. The cooking is more resolutely twentieth-century, though not invariably modern, mind you, with dishes such as monkfish with mushrooms, white wine, cream and vegetables, chicken with mushrooms and white wine, or roast pheasant with the trimmings. The fixed price gets you five courses (one a sorbet) and coffee, with a short choice throughout – though the selection of desserts is long. The food is often cooked exactly as it should be: beef was well hung, tender and richly flavoured, its sauce a subtle combination of sage and madeira; brill had a basil and mustard crust and another fine sauce of vermouth and red peppers. 'Gourmet salad' may be no more exciting here than elsewhere, but a pastry cornet of fish with dazzling green watercress sauce had finesse, colour and flavour. Vegetables are plain and decent. Country-house trimmings like varied rolls and bread (including apricot and walnut), canapés and petits fours help to justify the price. The service remains North Country in its freshness. The wine list is short and could be better. House wines are £8.75. There is a request on the wine list that guests should not smoke 'pipes, cigars, or exotic cigarettes in the dining-room'.

CHEF: Barry Quinion   PROPRIETORS: the Quinion and Stevenson families   OPEN: all week, D only (L 25 Dec and Easter Sun); 8   CLOSED: part Feb   MEALS: Set D £26 to £26.50   SERVICE: not inc, card slips closed   CARDS: Access, Visa   DETAILS: 40 seats. Private parties: 30 main room. Car park. No children under 5. Smart dress preferred. Wheelchair access. No music   ACCOMMODATION: 13 rooms, all with bath/shower. D,B&B £92 to £190. No children under 5. Pets welcome. Afternoon teas. Garden. TV. Phone. Doors close at midnight. Confirm by noon. Fax: (069 77) 46683 (*The Which? Hotel Guide*)

County round-ups listing additional restaurants that may be worth a visit are at the back of the Guide, *after the Irish section. Reports on round-up entries are welcome.*

Prices quoted in the Guide *are based on information supplied by restaurateurs. The prices quoted at the top of each entry represent a range, from the lowest meal price to the highest; the latter is inflated by 10 per cent to take account of likely price rises during the year of the* Guide.

BRAY Berkshire

map 2

▲ *Waterside Inn* ♟

Ferry Road, Bray SL6 2AT
BRAY (0628) 20691

COOKING 3*
COST £37–£80

It was once a village pub, with a garden down to the river and weeping willow in the corner. Now, the building – still humble on the entrance side – gives on to a glazed dining-room, with the Thames a picture spread before it. There is a small riverside terrace, with tiny, yet heated, pavilions for taking coffee. (There is even a river boat if you want a picnic.) People come to the Waterside for a day out. It is an institution, but has gone through a face-lift. The long curved backdrop to the dining-room, once pergola of fake flowers and leaves, has been spruced up, new chairs and carpet installed, and more space afforded between tables. It has regained freshness. More important as sign of the times are new guest bedrooms on the floor above the restaurant. The cooking itself is a defensive work, throwing a protective screen around French haute cuisine. It is almost an historic experience which leaves you wondering where delicacy stops and blandness sets in. A first course of poached eggs with puff pastry, asparagus tips and light hollandaise sauce arrives at the table. The eggs are exact, the puff is light and buttery (the very best), the sauce is eggy, too, and lacks any sharp seasoning to mask its richness, and the asparagus are delicate, and only six slenderest tips. Yet filling the pastry case is the largest element of the dish (but not mentioned on the menu): a wonderful mushroom cream. Again bland, as mushrooms can be, but unctuous, comforting, luxurious and desirable. Eat this and die. Before burial, there is a lobster and truffle ravioli, sauce vierge. Two tender ravioli; two large slices of truffle; a lobster claw; a ravioli filling that looks as if it were made with lobster (pink) but is essentially a mousse, rich, comforting, luxurious and desirable. The sauce is olive oil, a few strands of basil (tasteless) and several chunks of tomato flesh (likewise). In taste terms this is too mild; the olive oil has a back-kick, but not enough to jigger up the weight of richness. Then, there are two breastlets of pigeon wrapped in caul, the meat on top, and a forcemeat underneath. Also on the plate is a small tower of solid mushroom, this by no means bland, but rich. On either side, two ovals turn out to be tiny pancakes made from mashed potato. Each carries a little pile of diced olive. The sauce is fatty, as if it has not been skimmed. It has a lemon/olive flavour. The pigeon meat is dry, almost overcooked, but tastes absolutely first-class. It really didn't need a forcemeat. To accompany this, a salad is delivered. Cheese is excellent: Philippe Olivier, lots of choice, good condition. First class, too, is a pithiviers and the vanilla ice-cream that accompanied it. The pastry work here is very fine, with great ability to handle sugar content. The ice-cream also shows real class. Coffee is aromatic and rounded in flavour. Petits fours are piled high, but are simply redundant after all that food. Some things here are very fine, some are too fussy, and some may seem badly cooked. This is a restaurant that aspires to the highest, but often does not meet it. Service, lots of it, is generally good, but that does not justify printing a special line labelled 'gratuity' on the credit card slip when the bill and menu have already proclaimed that service is included. It is an event, the set-price lunch is affordable to many, and you will often eat well.

The cellar remains almost unremittingly French. Quality is expectedly high, with multi-vintage selections of first-growth clarets – there are 10 Ch. Latour alone – and all the swanky burgundies you could name. Prices are very high, but reassuring consideration for the less wealthy is shown with many good bottles such as Baumard Clos du Papillon, most of the Beaujolais and the odd Alsace under £20. There is a good range of half-bottles.

CHEF: Michel Roux   PROPRIETORS: Roux Waterside Inn   OPEN: Tue to Sun, exc Tue L; 12 to 2, 7 to 10   CLOSED: 26 Dec for 6 weeks, Sun D end Oct to mid-Apr   MEALS: alc. Set L £27 to £54.50, Set D £54.50. Minimum £30   SERVICE: net prices   CARDS: Access, Diners, Visa   DETAILS: 80 seats. Private parties: 80 main room, 8 private room. Car park. Vegetarian meals. Children restricted. Smart dress preferred. No cigars/pipes in dining-room. Wheelchair access (2 steps; also WC). Music. Air-conditioned   ACCOMMODATION: 6 rooms, all with bath/shower. B&B £105 to £145. Deposit: £60. No children under 6. TV. Phone. Fax: (0628) 771966

BRIDPORT Dorset   map 2

Will's

4–6 Barrack Street,
Bridport DT6 3LY   COOKING 2
BRIDPORT (0308) 27517   COST £21–£30

'An oasis in fairly barren country,' writes a convert to 'this delightful little restaurant tucked away in the centre of Bridport.' It is indeed an oasis of fairly priced, effective cooking served in a folksy pine habitat. William Longman's cookery is intelligent and fine-tuned; creative rather than derivative. Best results accrue from fish, much of it caught locally. Whole black bream is served with an uplifting tomato vinaigrette; monkfish, scallops and crevettes are stir-fried with pungent garlic, ginger, spring onions and chillies. There is a lot of chargrilling; boned leg of lamb gets this treatment after being marinated in olive oil, garlic and herbs. 'Out of the 90 or so courses that we must have consumed over the past two years there has never been a dud,' testifies a mightily satisfied diner. The wine list is short, sweet and very fairly priced, taking in a remarkable range within its 30 bins. House wines are £6.95.

CHEF: William Longman   PROPRIETORS: William Longman and Robyn Huxter   OPEN: Tue to Sat, D only; also Mon D bank hols and summer; 7 to 9.45 (10.15 Sat)   CLOSED: 2 weeks end Oct to early Nov   MEALS: alc   SERVICE: not inc   CARDS: Access, Visa   DETAILS: 30 seats. Private parties: 30 main room. Vegetarian meals. Children's helpings. Wheelchair access (2 steps; also WC). Music

---

'We had lobster salad with good new potatoes. However, we had first been asked by the waitress if we would like roast potatoes.'   On dining in Fife

'The restaurant was given 24 hours' notice that I have an intolerance to milk products. They were reminded of this when we ordered. The potatoes and mange-tout still arrived swimming in butter and the braised celery covered in melted cheese. A subsequent request for some plain celery could not be met, although some plain potatoes and a salad were eventually produced.'   On eating in Cornwall

---

map 3

Black Chapati

12 Circus Parade, New England Road,
Brighton BN1 4GW   COOKING 1*
BRIGHTON (0273) 699011   COST £17–£31

'Not so much stark or elegant, more prison-like' was the full and frank
appraisal of this unique restaurant where Indian food is cooked and explored
with enthusiasm and originality by a pair of English people. It is the nearest
thing to different that Indian cooking in Britain has felt these last few years.
Surroundings are neither spacious nor full of comfort, but the intentions are
genuine, though they may be masked by inexpert service. The evening menu
(there is a Sunday lunch buffet) has now reverted to a *carte*. One critic felt that
there was over-use of cumin and coriander, not the most subtle of spices; but
generally one of the advantages here is that spicing is varied, fresh and strong.
Some recommendations mentioned the dhal, the Goan pork sausages with
lentils (there are other Goan dishes often cooked here), the Tamil chicken dish
with coriander and cumin, and the onion bhajia. We would like to record that
all has gone swimmingly this year, but there have been objections raised to the
ambience, service and sometimes apparently missed objectives of individual
dishes. These problems may stem from popularity, which is sometimes a mixed
blessing. House wines are £7.95 and there are good beers.

CHEFS: Stephen Funnell and Lauren Alker   PROPRIETORS: Black Chapati Ltd   OPEN: Tue
to Sun D, and Sun L (Wed to Fri L by arrangement); 1 to 3.30, 7 to 10.30   CLOSED: 1 week
Christmas   MEALS: alc. Set Sun L £7.95 to £8.95. Minimum £14.50 or £16.50   SERVICE:
10% (not inc Sun L), card slips closed   CARDS: Access, Amex, Visa   DETAILS: 30 seats.
2 tables outside. Private parties: 30 main room. Vegetarian meals. No children after 9.
Wheelchair access. Music

Food for Friends £

17A–18 Prince Albert Street,
The Lanes, Brighton BN1 1HH   COOKING 1
BRIGHTON (0273) 202310   COST £9–£15

'Food for Friends has never used artificial additives,' say the owners. 'We
believe food should be fresh, innovative and loved.' The philosophy is put into
practice with organic produce (flour, fruit, vegetables and wine), free-range
eggs, unrefined oils and grains, vegetarian farmhouse cheddar, yoghurts and
ice-creams, and filtered water. The café is invariably busy, and there are
queues, no bookings and closely-packed tables. Freshly baked breads and
cakes, salads with unusual dressings, quiches and stir-fried vegetables are
bolstered by daily specials such as re-fried beans in a filo pastry parcel,
buckwheat and cheese strudel, and masala dosai with coconut and coriander
dhal and mango chutney. The kitchen occasionally cracks under pressure at
peak times and service has been described as 'brusque'. To drink there are teas,
coffees, barleycup, beers and wines. House French is £4.95. There is also a
pâtisserie at 41 Market Street and a second restaurant/take-away at 12 Sydney
Street, North Laines, Tel: (0273) 571363 – reports please.

CHEFS: Karen Samuel PROPRIETORS: Simon Hope and Jeremy Gray OPEN: all week; 9am (9.30 Sun) to 10pm MEALS: alc. Set L and D £3 to £6 SERVICE: not inc, card slips closed CARD: Visa DETAILS: 50 seats. Vegetarian meals. Healthy eating options. Children's helpings. Baby-changing facilities and high chairs available. No-smoking area. Wheelchair access. Music. Fax: (0273) 571363

▲ Hospitality Inn, La Noblesse

Kings Road, Brighton BN1 2GS COOKING 3
BRIGHTON (0273) 206700 COST £26–£50

La Noblesse restaurant at the back of the building has serious aspirations and is one of the few places in Brighton where it is possible to get a high standard of cooking and inventive ideas. Chef Richard Lyth now has an executive role in proceedings, but his kitchen continues to impress. Bold, creative set menus supplement a short, interesting *carte*, and many dishes have won over reporters. Some of the best items appear on the set menus: warm salad of steamed skate wing sharpened up with a salad of assorted leaves; 'gamey' roast woodpigeon with honey and thyme sauce and 'delectable' baby turnips; calf's liver on a bed of purée potatoes with a lime sauce (which seemed to intensify, rather than complement, the offal); strawberry pavlova. From the *carte*, clear smoked pigeon soup garnished with slices of rare meat and halved morels has been outstanding. The cheeseboard is excellent: some 20 types, mostly French rarities, but all in peak condition, accurately identified and described by the waiter. Occasionally a dish is 'ill-judged', as in 'bland walnut parfait with oversweet caramel sauce', sampled by one reporter. Portions are delicate, prices are not low. The wine list may have been revamped, with more halves and bottles from the New World, but – according to one expert – it is 'nothing to write home about, and it is pricey'. House French is £12.50.

CHEF: Richard Lyth PROPRIETORS: Mount Charlotte Investments plc OPEN: Mon to Sat, exc Sat L; 12 to 2.30, 7 to 10.30 MEALS: alc. Set L £13.50 to £16.95, Set D £21.95 to £31 SERVICE: not inc, card slips closed CARDS: Access, Amex, Diners, Visa DETAILS: 45 seats. Private parties: 45 main room. Car park. Vegetarian meals. Children welcome. No pipes in dining-room. Wheelchair access (also WC). Music. Air-conditioned ACCOMMODATION: 204 rooms, all with bath/shower. Rooms for disabled. Lift. B&B £115 to £135. Children welcome. Baby facilities. Pets welcome. Afternoon teas. Swimming-pool. Sauna. Air-conditioned. TV. Phone. Doors close at 11. Confirm by 6. Fax: (0273) 820692 (*The Which? Hotel Guide*)

Langan's Bistro

1 Paston Place, Brighton BN2 1HA COOKING 2
BRIGHTON (0273) 606933 COST £20–£34

'It feels very London, with something of the image of Odin's and Langan's Brasserie,' wrote one who thanked the gods for its existence on a Sunday morning in Brighton. The place was chock-a-block full. Another reader, entering as the first customer and leaving when every other table was occupied, described how 'the sinking orange sun bathed the room in a warm light, highlighting the clear sparkle of the glasses on white linen'. Fresh flowers and gleaming cutlery complete the encouraging picture. The cooking lives up to the image: it is very passable, not expensive, and is served with willingness in a happy atmosphere. It is not complicated – calf's liver with sage sauce, baby chicken with herbs, halibut with samphire, entrecôte vin rouge – but it works. The *carte* is short and the lunch menu is cheap and shorter. The wine list is fine, as is the house wine at £7.35.

CHEF: Mark Emmerson PROPRIETORS: Michael Caine and Richard Shepherd OPEN: Tue to Sun, exc Sat L and Sun D; 12.30 to 2.30, 7.30 to 10.30 CLOSED: first 2 weeks Jan, last 2 weeks Aug MEALS: alc. Set L £13.50. Cover 75p SERVICE: 10% CARDS: Access, Amex, Diners, Visa DETAILS: 48 seats. Vegetarian meals with prior notice. Children's helpings. Wheelchair access. Music. Air-conditioned

Shifting Sands

NEW ENTRY

11B Kensington Gardens,
Brighton BN1 4AL
BRIGHTON (0273) 609830

COOKING 2
COST £20–£41

The sands of time have filled this site with up to seven restaurants in as many years. Let's hope the Daniels can hang in there with a place that serves as a café in the day and a restaurant at night (which may close if there are no reservations). Decoration is spare: 'simple varnished tables, tiled floor, glass round the kitchen so you can watch the preparation; it verges on, but avoids, the empty feeling', but is probably not a place for romance. Any shortcomings will be made up by the Daniels, happy to talk, cook and serve until all hours. They seem to have a mission. This comes through on the self-conscious menus and in the sort of food cooked. It has an angle. Dishes that have gained honourable mention include charlotte of aubergine baked with thyme and served with tomato basil sauce; mussels (stuffed as an appetiser) with white wine, tomato, basil and leek, or in a pesto-based sauce; eels with herb and cream sauce; pigeon on a bed of spinach and ginger; duck with mustard and tarragon cream sauce; rabbit with mustard and cream with a side dish of lentils, the rabbit's liver and apricots; and zabaglione made with lemon and Muscat. An inspection meal revealed faults in execution that vitiated the evident thought that had gone into the cooking but, with encouragement, this place may enliven a lacklustre Brighton scene. 'Character' persists as far as the wine list. Short, with long notes, it offers a desirable and interesting choice: Carmenet 1983, fair-priced Sancerre from Bonnard, Kreydenweiss Riesling 1985 from Alsace, even Ch.'Y', the dry wine of Yquem. House wines are £8.50.

CHEF: Ricky Daniel PROPRIETORS: Agnes D. Ltd OPEN: Tue to Sat (pre- and post-theatre D, and Sun L by arrangement); 12.30 to 2.30, 7.30 to 10.30 CLOSED: bank hols, 25 Dec MEALS: alc. Set L £12.50, Set D £15.50 SERVICE: 10%, card slips closed CARDS: Access, Amex, Visa DETAILS: 24 seats. 4 tables outside. Private parties: 40 main room. Vegetarian meals. Children's helpings with prior notice. No-smoking area. Wheelchair access. Music. Fax: (0273) 681820

Report forms are at the back of the book; write a letter if you prefer.

▲ *Poppies* ❦

The Roebuck,
Brimfield SY8 4WE
LUDLOW (0584) 711230

COOKING 3
COST £19–£50

'The restaurant is elegant, light, and has a conservatory feel with its palms and cane and bamboo chairs, light-wood floor and summery pictures,' writes one who visited in hazy days of sun. It might be a world away from the bar of the pub – copper ashtrays, gaudy carpet and clumsy chairs – though but a corridor divides them. There is a single mind behind the food, however, which makes eating in the bar a refreshing experience. Who would not rather try a savoury bread-and-butter pudding with onion and watercress sauce than another tired shepherd's pie? In the restaurant, matters get more formal and more elaborate. A fillet of sole is wrapped round a spinach soufflé and served with anchovy hollandaise, John Dory is served with rhubarb and coriander sauce (an old favourite), and quail are boned then stuffed with a pistachio and truffle mousse. Carole Evans is a self-taught chef. This may account for the sometimes inadvised complication: a dessert of over-cinnamoned brown bread ice-cream under a pyramid of caramel is given far too many sauces and trimmings; but this will also be the reason for the individuality of the cooking – a mind untainted by convention. Nothing detracts from the quality of the cider and pink peppercorn sauce served with duck breast: 'stock plus cider, excellent consistency, and balance between sweet, sharp and fruity,' go the notes. Complexity is not pursued for its own sake. A summer diner who enjoyed split baby lobster grilled and served with hazelnut garlic butter will witness that. He would also vouch for Carole Evans' ambition to do a proper restaurant, not just a pub with food: appetisers, bread, fine slightly salted butter, and excellent sweetmeats are all trappings of quality, even if the coffee was weak that night. Cooking in general seems to like high flavours with main dishes, often working on the sweet-and-sour contrast: for instance, roe deer with port sauce and brandied kumquats, lamb with redcurrant and mint sauce, pork with lovage and mustard, or hake with tomatoes and saffron. It is a sadness to record that John Evans died early in 1992, so Carole has necessarily been diverted from attending to just the cooking. Jane Malcolm is an able lieutenant, and the service in the restaurant has by no means suffered. Regulars will miss John in the bar, which was his particular domain. 'Poppies' continues. The wines are very sound, with much supplied by restaurant specialists Reid Wines. The range is good, the notes are instructive, and the prices are firm but not exorbitant. Growers and properties, from the New World as well as French country districts, are among the most prestigious.

CHEFS: Carole Evans and Jane Malcolm   PROPRIETOR: Carole Evans   OPEN: Tue to Sat; 12 to 2, 7 to 10   CLOSED: 2 weeks Feb, 25 and 26 Dec   MEALS: alc. Bar meals   SERVICE: not inc, card slips closed   CARDS: Access, Visa   DETAILS: 40 seats. Private parties: 40 main room. Vegetarian meals. Children welcome. No-smoking area. Wheelchair access. No music   ACCOMMODATION: 3 rooms, all with bath/shower. B&B £40 to £65. Deposit: £30. No children under 10. Pets by arrangement. TV. Phone. Doors close at 12.30am. Confirm by 6. Fax: (0584) 711654 (*The Which? Hotel Guide*)

Bistro Twenty One

21 Cotham Road South, Kingsdown,
Bristol BS6 5TZ
BRISTOL (0272) 421744

COOKING 1
COST £22–£37

The recent enlargement of Alan Dubois' successful enterprise has drawn a mixed response. Most feel it an improvement on the original, rather cramped set-up, that the service is knowledgeable and friendly as ever and the place retains its relaxed mood. Another view is that refurbishment has been at the expense of atmosphere: cheery waiters replaced by dignified waitresses and a slower, less sharp pace. The Muzak is still uncomfortably loud. The food is good-value bistro, but the output of the kitchen can be uneven: reporters have mentioned overcooked lamb and duck, and a certain blandness here and there. Even so, the consensus is firmly in favour, with endorsements for snails and mushrooms in garlic butter; cream cheese and spinach pancakes; perfectly cooked steaks and grilled Dover sole; and roast salmon wrapped in bacon with lemon cream sauce. Everyone approves of the big platters of vegetables. Sweets can sometimes disappoint, but choux-pastry 'swans' of white and dark chocolate mousse have been 'out of this world'. House French is £7.50.

CHEF/PROPRIETOR: Alain Dubois OPEN: Mon to Sat, exc Sat L; 12 to 2.30, 7 to 11.30
MEALS: alc. Set L and D £12.95 to £16.50 SERVICE: not inc (10% for 8 or more) CARDS:
Access, Amex, Visa DETAILS: 75 seats. Private parties: 45 main room, 25 private room.
Vegetarian meals. Children's helpings. No-smoking area. Wheelchair access. Music

Howards

| NEW ENTRY |

1A–2A Avon Crescent, Hotwells,
Bristol BS1 6XQ
BRISTOL (0272) 262921

COOKING 1
COST £20–£32

The restaurant is on two floors of a one-time càfé on the edge of the Cumberland Basin, with views of ships and the Clifton Suspension Bridge from window tables. Husband-and-wife team Chris and Gillian Howard offer good value: Anglo-French bistro cooking along the lines of duck terrine with pistachio nuts; roast Barbary duck with raspberry vinegar sauce; and apple tart with calvados sabayon. There are distinct oriental overtones in Thai chicken in filo pastry, pork tenderloin with ginger and spring onions, and chicken marinated in yoghurt, coconut and spices. A seasonally changing *carte* is supplemented by a three-course table d'hôte including similar dishes, and there are daily specials such as whole baby hake cooked with butter, parsley and fennel. Ingredients (including Cornish fish) are fresh and the cooking is honest, although the results can sometimes be 'rather dull'. Successful dishes have included hot goats' cheese pastry parcel with pine-kernels, basil and garlic; venison and pheasant cooked with red wine and mushrooms under a pastry crust; and a duo of iced honey and walnut parfait with poire William sorbet. Two-dozen wines are sensibly priced. House French is £7.25. Howards Bistro, run by the same team, is at Nailsea, Tel: (0275) 858348 – reports please.

CHEF: David Roast PROPRIETORS: Christopher and Gillian Howard OPEN: Mon to Sat,
exc Sat L; 12 to 2.30, 7 to 11.30 CLOSED: 25 and 26 Dec MEALS: alc. Set L £13, Set D £15
SERVICE: not inc (10% for 8 or more), card slips closed CARDS: Access, Amex, Visa
DETAILS: 65 seats. Private parties: 25 main room, 25 private room. Vegetarian meals.
Children welcome. No-smoking area. Wheelchair access. Music

Hunt's

NEW ENTRY

26 Broad Street,
Bristol BS1 2HG
BRISTOL (0272) 265580

COOKING 3
COST £21–£39

Andy Hunt's restaurant opened just too late for inclusion in the last *Guide*. He
was once the Hunt in Markwick & Hunt, but the partnership has split into two.
Hunt has remained in Bristol's 'city' quarter, occupying a former tea and coffee
merchant's (the mahogany fittings make a pleasant ante-room and bar area)
opposite the brilliant art nouveau building by Edward Everard. The restaurant
has a 'quartier' feel. Supporters of Stephen Markwick (from Bistro Twenty One
days, too) will recognise many dishes on the crisp menu that changes every day
but explores a relatively short-range repertoire. People suggest that Andy
Hunt's flavourings are bolder – or that Stephen Markwick's are more refined.
Whatever the truth of it, Hunt's has pleased many for good materials and
expressive cooking of Anglo-French country classics like mussels with garlic
and herb crust, tagliatelle with bacon, saffron and cream, smoked haddock
soufflé with dill cream, guinea-fowl with apples and calvados, beef with
shallots, mustard and tarragon, and venison with gherkins and sour cream as
well as beetroot. Gutsy fish dishes like the monkfish with leeks and garlic have
also been well received, as have the charcuterie, the breads and the sweet iced
nougat, hot cranberry and kirsch soufflé and the prune and armagnac tart.
Espresso coffee is grand. Service is charming, if not entirely experienced. The
wine list kicks off with Billecart-Salmon champagne and some really
interesting French country wines. Prices are excellent, the choice nicely
balanced and not too long. An affair well-suited to the requirement. House
wines start at £8.50.

CHEFS: Andrew Hunt and Haydn Neal PROPRIETORS: Andrew and Anne Hunt OPEN:
Tue to Sat, exc Sat L (Mon by arrangement for private parties); 12 to 2.15, 7 to 10 (pre- or
post-theatre by arrangement) CLOSED: 1 week Christmas, 1 week Easter, 1 week Aug
MEALS: alc. Set L £11.95 SERVICE: net prices, card slips closed CARDS: Access, Visa
DETAILS: 40 seats. Private parties: 26 main room. Vegetarian meals with prior notice.
Children welcome. Wheelchair access (1 step). Music

Net prices *in the details at the end of an entry indicates that the prices given on a menu
and on a bill are inclusive of VAT and service charge, and that this practice is clearly stated
on menu and bill.*

*All details are as accurate as possible at the time of going to press, but chefs and owners
often change, and it is wise to check by telephone before making a special journey. Many
readers have been disappointed when set-price bargain meals are no longer available.
Ask when booking.*

Jameson's

30 Upper Maudlin Street,
Bristol BS2 8DJ
BRISTOL (0272) 276565

COOKING 1*
COST £17–£30

This is an attractively converted Victorian house with a dining-room on two levels, which seems to make people feel comfortable. 'It was like coming back from a decent dinner with friends, with lots of memories of what you had just eaten, and a sense of good company' was one thought. The menu is set-price for two courses, plus a dessert if you want one. One night, it was offering leek, mushroom and sage Derby pie for a vegetarian, and a choice of pigeon, venison, trout or sole for other people, together with spinach and cream cheese pancakes, onion soup, avocado mousse and moules marinière from the first courses. There is also a *carte*. Cooking is competent, with good flavours. Dishes that have been recommended include chicken breast stuffed with spinach and cream cheese, with a white wine sauce containing tomatoes and chives; noisettes of lamb with blackcurrant and pink peppercorn sauce which gave sweetness and heat at one fell swoop; orange crème brûlée; and a lemon soufflé with raspberry sauce. The value is fair. The wine list also offers acceptable value, with house wines at £8.25 a litre.

CHEFS: Carole Jameson and Thierry Rouvrais PROPRIETOR: Carole Jameson OPEN: all week, exc L Mon and Sat, and Sun D; 12 to 2.30 (5 Sun), 6 to 11 CLOSED: 25 and 26 Dec MEALS: alc. Set L £10, Set D £14.95 SERVICE: not inc, card slips closed CARDS: Access, Amex, Diners, Visa DETAILS: 70 seats. Private parties: 40 main room. Vegetarian meals. Children's helpings. Wheelchair access (2 steps). Music

Lettonie ▼

9 Druid Hill, Stoke Bishop,
Bristol BS9 1EW
BRISTOL (0272) 686456

COOKING 4
COST £25–£41

It looks like a shop and it *was* a shop. Next door are shops. Press on, it's a very good restaurant. As one with the sense to be intrepid remarked, 'Once through the door, you know that it will be good.' It radiates serious intent; the cutlery and table settings mean business; the young waiters (in attendance when Mrs Blunos isn't there) are effective. Martin Blunos does not curb his ambition to small shop size. The champion dish of the year seems to be scrambled duck egg popped back into its shell, crowned with sevruga caviare and surrounded with a flaming moat of vodka. The blinis that come with it are the lightest possible. That's new classicism. The old version gets its outing with a chicken liver parfait and madeira sauce: faultless technique. It's a pity that on the same menu another madeira sauce comes with pig's trotter stuffed with morels and chicken mousse. Most of the sauces are in the classic mode: juniper with pigeon, Pineau des Charentes with guinea-fowl, sherry with oxtail, dill with salmon. The composition of main courses can start to overload. Breast of guinea-fowl has been served with chestnuts and leeks, a potato cake, Brussels sprouts and carrots; trotter, stuffed this time with sweetbreads, is served with potato cake, red onions and green beans (which serve well to cut the richness). If the meal has begun with a fluffy quiche with onion marmalade as complementary dish, then takes in pan-fried salmon with red pimento sauce before passing on to plum and cardamom compote with poppy seed and vanilla ice-cream, as well as good friandises, there's quite a lot to get through. Details are appreciated: the bread, the vegetables that are often in mousse form, the spun sugar work with desserts, the chocolate-coated Cape gooseberries for coffee. So many things are right. Lunch is a bargain. An intelligent emphasis on good, middle-range wines – Fronsac, Givry, St-Joseph – but without denying the more profligate the chance to make an impression, puts this list in the running for one of the most appropriate small restaurant wine lists in the country. Very fair prices, interesting range and lots of halves confirm the impression. House wines are from £10.20. CELLARMAN'S CHOICE: Ch. Thieuley 1989, £15.15; California, Au Bon Climat, Pinot Noir 1989, £23.50.

CHEF: Martin Blunos   PROPRIETORS: Martin and Siân Blunos   OPEN: Tue to Sat; 12.30 to 2, 7 to 9.30   CLOSED: 2 weeks Aug, 1 week Christmas, bank hols   MEALS: Set L £15.95 to £25.95, Set D £25.95   SERVICE: not inc   CARDS: Access, Amex, Visa   DETAILS: 24 seats. Private parties: 16 main room. Vegetarian meals with prior notice. Children's helpings on request. Wheelchair access (1 step). Music

Markwicks

43 Corn Street, Bristol BS1 1HT
BRISTOL (0272) 262658

COOKING 3*
COST £22–£38

The city centre of Bristol, home of banks, medieval churches and markets, is a world away from the Georgian terraces of Clifton or the heaving shopping malls of Broadmead. The buildings have variety, substance and character, which might also be said of Stephen Markwick's cooking, on show in the elegantly converted basement of a Victorian building that started life as a safety deposit. If you don't pay, you could end the evening in one of the barred and railed rooms. Meals here can excite superlatives of surprise and affirmation: 'closer to perfection than any we can remember since the great days of Perry-Smith', 'crab soup the best for two years in the UK and in France'. The cooking is neither complex nor simplistic; at its best, it allows sufficient interest while never forgetting the predominant flavour that was intended at the outset. There is little truck with high fashion, and the habits retained are good ones, not frills, fripperies or nonsense. The carte is not long, perhaps six dishes at each course, and there is a set-price menu at each meal. Lunch is a bargain – for the taste of it. Many things have been reported upon, but an early summer menu that included cucumber fritters with dill and sour cream, provençal fish soup, a simple pigeon salad with bacon and pine-nuts, duck with polenta and wild mushrooms, fillet of beef with tarragon and mustard, venison with gherkins and beetroot, and brill with basil mash, tomatoes and olive oil, may give pointers to the character. Desserts may include hot soufflés, or a walnut and treacle tart. Portions are 'never meagre but avoid the gross'. Bread, cheese straws and other ancillaries are to the point without excess show. Bad days occur, but usually service is friendly and relaxed. The wine list is a pleasure. France gets the major treatment, but other regions have some good examples: a Lungarotti or Avignonesi from Italy, a Simi from California, or a Heggies from Australia. The main quality seems to be solid dependability of choice, allied to range and a very fair set of prices. Wine service is adequate without fulsome attentiveness. House wines start at £8.50. CELLARMAN'S CHOICE: Wairau River, Sauvignon Blanc 1991, £15; Chianti 1989, Tenuta Farneta, £12.

CHEFS: Stephen Markwick and Sara Ody   PROPRIETORS: Stephen and Judy Markwick
OPEN: Mon to Fri; 12 to 2, 7 to 10.30   MEALS: alc. Set L £14.50 to £25, Set D £21.50 to £25
SERVICE: net prices, card slips closed   CARDS: Access, Amex, Visa   DETAILS: 50 seats.
Private parties: 6 and 14 private rooms. Children's helpings. No music

Melbournes £

74 Park Street, Bristol BS1 3AF
BRISTOL (0272) 226996

COOKING 1
COST £13–£22

This split-level restaurant is invariably packed, boisterous and thriving, equally suited to young people, students and families. The secret of success is a commitment to decent food at fair prices, backed up by an Australian-style bring-your-own wine policy. Lunch and dinner menus are fixed-price for two or three courses and the repertoire is boosted by daily specials. The kitchen delivers a competent version of cosmopolitan bistro cooking: Spanish tortilla with home-made relish; pasta and vegetable salad; breast of duck with lemon and honey glaze; chicken with prawns and lobster cream sauce; best end of lamb with garlic and herb sauce. Filled pancakes are popular, vegetables are fresh and plentiful, and sweets range from orange roulade with raspberry sauce to brandy-snap basket with honey and ginger ice-cream. Most people bring their own, but there's also a creditable list of affordable wines and antipodean beers. House Australian is £6.

CHEFS: C. Cowpe and M. Read   PROPRIETORS: A. Wilshaw, N. Hennessy, C. Cowpe and M. Read   OPEN: Tue to Sun, exc Sat L and Sun D; 12 to 2, 7 to 10.30   CLOSED: week between Christmas and New Year   MEALS: Set L £8 to £9.50, Set D £12.25 to £14.25. Licensed, also bring your own: no corkage   SERVICE: 10%, card slips closed   CARDS: Access, Visa   DETAILS: 70 seats. Private parties: 40 main room. Vegetarian meals. Children's helpings. No cigars/pipes in dining-room. Wheelchair access (1 step; also WC). Music

Michael's ✺

NEW ENTRY

129 Hotwell Road,
Clifton, Bristol BS8 4RU
BRISTOL (0272) 276190

COOKING 1*
COST £19–£34

Michael McGowan has been cooking here for more than a decade. Once a pair of Victorian shops, Michael's, done up originally in deep reds, greens and rich fabrics, has now mellowed with age. It glows out of the evening fog that billows in from the river. There is a longish set-price *carte* firmly into current restaurant orthodoxies. Artichoke bottom with crab, pink grapefruit and an avocado cream, warm salad of pigeon with pine-kernels, and Stilton and watercress soup with Stilton profiteroles are some first courses; main dishes include duck with green peppercorns, guinea-fowl with blackcurrant sauce, and chicken stuffed with watercress mousse and served with a Pernod cream sauce. 'There is an emphasis on butter and cream,' commented one reporter; but execution is very competent and presentation well judged. Service and atmosphere are universally admired. The wine list is useful and not overpriced. Halves are not forgotten. House wines cost £7.95.

CHEF/PROPRIETOR: Michael McGowan   OPEN: Tue to Sat, exc Sat L; 12 to 2, 7 to 11
CLOSED: 26 Dec, 1 Jan   MEALS: Set L £12.50 to £17.50, Set D £22.50   SERVICE: not inc
(10% for 5 or more)   CARDS: Access, Diners, Visa   DETAILS: 50 seats. Private parties: 56
main room, 38 private room. Vegetarian meals. Children welcome. No smoking in dining-
room. Wheelchair access (1 step; also WC). Music in bar. Fax: (0272) 253629

Muset ▼

12–16 Clifton Road, Clifton,
Bristol BS8 1AF   COOKING 1*
BRISTOL (0272) 732920   COST £20–£25

The restaurant occupies a set of Victorian terraced houses, and the dining-
rooms are a cleverly interlocking set of spaces at different levels, offering
multiple perspectives on a single fact: it's always busy. 'We continue to have
too many customers and not enough seats,' write the owners. Customers
suggest the reason is good value and enjoyable food, allied to support
(although there is a licence) of the Australian B(ring) Y(our) O(wn) policy on
wine. The menu is long, yet is further extended by daily specials written up on
blackboards. The price is set. A summer meal began with avocado pear with
poached salmon and a lemon dressing, and mushrooms topped with goats'
cheese and breadcrumbs, then went on to pigeon breast with a piquant sauce
and a breast of chicken stuffed with prawns with a tomato and crab sauce.
Subsequent offerings, such as mushrooms with garlic and a nettle-cheese glaze,
pickled salmon with prawns and tomato mayonnaise, salmon and sole with
sorrel cream sauce, or pigeon with a black pudding croûton and garlic and
cream, have also met with approval. The restaurant is refreshing in that it does
not try to be what it is not. It also runs a straight and honest line on service, and
on the whole business of being in business. There is almost a crusading zeal
motivating the whole. The wine list is not long, but it is good and very cheap. It
deserves some sort of prize for Ch. Léoville Poyferré 1985 at £18.50 and Clos du
Val Cabernet Sauvignon 1988 at £10.50. House wines are £6.25. Keep an eye on
the blackboard for 'Bankrupt Stock'. CELLARMAN'S CHOICE: Victoria, Ch.
Tahbilk, Chardonnay 1990, £10.50; Yarra Valley, Yarra Yering No.1 Cabernet
1988, £18.50.

CHEF: D. Wheadon   PROPRIETORS: A.J. Portlock and D. Wheadon   OPEN: Mon to Sat, D
only; 7 to 10.30   MEALS: Set D £13.50 to £15.50   SERVICE: 10%, card slips closed   CARDS:
Access, Visa   DETAILS: 130 seats. Private parties: 30 main room. Children's helpings. No
children under 10 after 8pm. Music. Air-conditioned

*'When I got home I was so hungry that I had a double Welsh rarebit followed by a large
piece of cake.'*   On eating in London

*'The soup was only lukewarm and when a request was made to have it heated, we were
told that if we stirred it, it would be hot at the bottom!'*   On eating in London

Rocinantes £

85 Whiteladies Road,
Bristol BS8 2NT
BRISTOL (0272) 734482

COOKING 1
COST £14–£29

Up the road from the BBC is this cheerful – 'haphazard,' said one who experienced there an enjoyable Sunday lunch – tapas bar, full of colour, tiles, music and people. Generally, there is care for the food and its origins, using organically produced meat (and vegetables, wherever possible). Squid, prawns, lamb, chicken and chorizos are done with chilli, garlic mayonnaise, cumin and other arresting flavours. Spicy meatballs in a sweet red pepper sauce, and chargrilled sardines, have been reported to be good. Salads are enjoyable. There is also a cheap set menu. Wines are not dear, the list is not long. House wines start at £7.50.

CHEF/PROPRIETOR: Barny Haughton   OPEN: all week, exc Sun D (by arrangement only); 12 to 3, 6 to 11   MEALS: alc. Set L and D £6.95 to £8.25. Minimum £7.50 (bookings only) SERVICE: not inc (10% for 6 or more)   CARDS: Access, Visa   DETAILS: 80 seats. 6 tables outside. Private parties: 40 main room, 30 private room. Vegetarian meals. Children's helpings. Wheelchair access (3 steps; also WC). Music

---

BROADHEMBURY Devon

map 1

Drewe Arms

Broadhembury EX14 0NF
BROADHEMBURY (040 484) 267

COOKING 2*
COST £24–£37

This thatched pub still has atmosphere, even if sometimes it is crowded out with country lunchers from Exeter, Torquay or Tiverton. The draw is the fish cooked by Kerstin Burge – a good range, including shellfish, and a good repertoire of cooking methods beyond just plain, or seafood platter. There's steak too, and bar meals, and cheese, and a more than adequate wine list. Not everyone leaves happy – perhaps the cost is more than expected, perhaps the setting more rustic, perhaps the various blackboards are hard to fathom. Sweet dishes are more rustic than fish or fowl. House wine is £6.99.

CHEF: Kerstin Burge   PROPRIETORS: Kerstin and Nigel Burge   OPEN: all week, exc Sun D; 12 to 2, 7 to 10   MEALS: alc. Set L and D £16.95   SERVICE: not inc, card slips closed CARDS: Access, Visa   DETAILS: 24 seats. 11 tables outside. Private parties: 24 main room. Car park. Vegetarian meals with prior notice. Children's helpings L. No pipes in dining-room. Wheelchair access (1 step; also WC). No music

---

An asterisk (*) after the 1 to 5 cooking mark at the top of an entry signifies that the Guide *and its readers think that the restaurant is a particularly fine example within its rating.*

£ *indicates that it is possible to have a three-course meal, including coffee, a half-bottle of house wine and service, at any time the restaurant is open (i.e. at dinner as well as at lunch, unless a place is open only for dinner), for £20 or less per person.*

▲ Collin House

Collin Lane, Broadway WR12 7PB
BROADWAY (0386) 858354   COOKING 2
on A44, 1m NW of Broadway   COST £16–£33

'Gratifying lack of designer theme with comfortable old furniture,' sighs one
reporter with apparent relief. Traditionalists will find the food at Collin House
equally reassuring. To start, black pudding in whole-grain mustard sauce
'worked very well'. Principal dishes may feature cod, fresh from Birmingham
market and served with mussels and leeks; beef, grilled and with a red onion
marmalade or braised as oxtail; and duck, reared locally and offered with
spiced red cabbage and glazed apple. The separate and distinctly patriotic
pudding card is regularly saluted, even if treacle tart was as heavy as the bread-
and-butter pudding was good. A separate reasonably priced lunch menu
applies to the seventeenth-century bar and to a few seats in the adjoining
garden. Accommodation is basic but this is an attractive place at which to stay.
The wine list takes in good sources from the New World, Italy and Spain as
well as France, and does not charge too much for it all. House French is £8.65.

CHEFS: Judith Mills and Mark Brookes PROPRIETORS: John and Judith Mills OPEN: all
week; 12 to 1.30, 7 to 9 CLOSED: 5 days Christmas MEALS: bar L. Set L £15.50, Set D
£18.50 to £21 SERVICE: not inc, card slips closed CARDS: Access, Visa DETAILS: 24
seats. 4 tables outside. Private parties: 32 main room. Car park. Vegetarian meals.
Children's helpings. No cigars/pipes in dining-room. Wheelchair access (1 step; also WC).
No music ACCOMMODATION: 7 rooms, all with bath/shower. B&B £43 to £96. Deposit:
£40. Children under 6 by arrangement. Garden. Swimming-pool (The Which? Hotel Guide)

▲ Dormy House   [NEW ENTRY]

Willersey Hill,
Broadway WR12 7LF   COOKING 1*
BROADWAY (0386) 852711   COST £23–£55

Isolated on the steep, wooded escarpment above Broadway, this Cotswold
yellow-stone seventeenth-century farmhouse has suffered modern extensions.
John Sanderson's menu has contracted and results are more even. 'A pleasing
lack of luxury ingredients,' notes an inspector, 'and no discrepancy between
the quality of table d'hôte and à la carte.' Dinner might begin with a feuilleté of
baby leeks on a white butter sauce with pan-fried scallops or Cornish crabmeat
served on a bed of finely cut gherkin with a sweet red pepper coulis. Main-
course roast fillet of English lamb on a pipérade of peppers, onion and tomato
with roast garlic and a light jus is recommended. The kitchen is driving in the
direction of sound yet elegant cooking with robust flavour as the destination.
Vegetables have improved. Desserts remain weak, but plates of cheese sourced
from Pierre Androuet have been praised. Tighter management of the dining-
room has helped nurture attentive service. Although an inspector's glass of
house white was judged poor, there are sufficient good bottles for the
knowledgeable to ponder over. House wines are from £8.95.

CHEF: John Sanderson PROPRIETOR: Jorgen Philip-Sorensen OPEN: all week, exc Sat L;
12.30 to 2 (2.30 Sun), 7.30 (7 Sat) to 9.30 CLOSED: 25 and 26 Dec MEALS: alc. Set L £16,
Set D £25.50 SERVICE: not inc CARDS: Access, Amex, Diners, Visa DETAILS: 80 seats.
Private parties: 40 main room, 8 and 14 private rooms. Car park. Vegetarian meals.
Children's helpings. Jacket and tie. No-smoking area. Music ACCOMMODATION: 49
rooms, all with bath/shower. Rooms for disabled. B&B £55 to £110. Children welcome.
Baby facilities. Pets welcome (not in public rooms). Afternoon teas. Garden. TV. Phone.
Doors close at 12.30am. Confirm by 6. Fax: (0386) 858636 (*The Which? Hotel Guide*)

Hunters Lodge

High Street, Broadway WR12 7DT   COOKING 2
BROADWAY (0386) 853247   COST £20–£38

The plant-clad house runs on well-oiled bearings, Kurt Friedli being as
professional a chef, as his wife is an effective hostess. A short *carte* is reinforced
by a two-course set-price menu, and cooking here is a step up from English
country traditional. A warm salad of scallops, fish- and crab-cakes, hot cheese
and mushroom tarts, followed by guinea-fowl with sage and cider vinegar,
steak with red wine and tarragon, or pork with Roquefort and rosemary are
dishes that set the style; the sweet course is laid out on the sideboard. Wines
are sound, if conventional. House wines are £7.

CHEF: Kurt Friedli PROPRIETORS: Kurt and Dottie Friedli OPEN: Tue to Sun, exc Sun D;
12.30 to 2, 7.30 to 9.45 CLOSED: first 2 weeks Feb, first 2 weeks Aug MEALS: alc. Set L
£12.85, Set D £12.50 SERVICE: not inc CARDS: Access, Amex, Diners, Visa DETAILS: 55
seats. 6 tables outside. Private parties: 35 main room, 22 private room. Car park. Vegetarian
meals. Children's helpings. No children under 8 D. No cigars/pipes in dining-room.
Wheelchair access (also WC). Music

▲ Lygon Arms

Broadway WR12 7DU   COOKING 2*
BROADWAY (0386) 852255   COST £29–£57

This Cotswold coaching-inn has become an idealised English country manor
and a *grand luxe* interpretation of country life. The suits of armour might
encourage an impression of contrived heritage, and the Savoy Group has
certainly applied metropolitan polish to the crooked beams and worn
flagstones. Historically and geographically situated between the Elizabethan
entrance and the recently constructed health spa is an Edwardian barrel-
vaulted living-room titled the Great Hall, surveyed by several stag's heads
mounted above the stone fireplace. Here Clive Howe parades food described by
one reporter as having 'character and style – modern British but with
conviction'. Evidently he is well in his stride and working with first-rate
ingredients. A meal that started with a superlative appetiser went into decline
with a table d'hôte Stilton and chicken mousse, but recovered with roasted
scallops and monkfish with orange and ginger, which was 'inspired'. Then two
medallions of mature Scottish beef arrived with 'two interesting shallot sauces.
The pale sauce was fresh, creamy and flecked with chives, the dark was
sweetish and caramelised.' Vegetables may be a modern chef's medley, but

intelligence returns with dessert. Here was offered an orange-flower water and honey curd tart – good pastry, not quite enough taste. Then came apricot fritters round a cone of marzipan ice-cream: brilliant ice, but a pity about the unsoaked dried apricot in one of the fritters. Elements such as the bread show that the corporation outweighs the chef, and the service is not as keen as the cooking, but generally this deserves a wider public than mere one-nighters on the way to Stratford. The wine list is good, and fairly distributed between cheap and dear. House wines are £10.50.

CHEF: Clive Howe   PROPRIETORS: The Savoy Group   OPEN: all week; 12.30 to 2, 7.30 to 9.30   MEALS: alc. Set L £18.25 to £19.25, Set D £27.75 to £34.95   SERVICE: not inc, card slips closed   CARDS: Access, Amex, Diners, Visa   DETAILS: 90 seats. Private parties: 90 main room, 20, 40 and 76 private rooms. Car park. Vegetarian meals. Children's helpings. Smart dress preferred. Wheelchair access (also WC). Music   ACCOMMODATION: 65 rooms, all with bath/shower. Rooms for disabled. B&B £95 to £195. Deposit: 1 night. Children welcome. Baby facilities. Pets welcome. Afternoon teas. Garden. Swimming-pool. Sauna. Tennis. Snooker. TV. Phone. Confirm by 6. Fax: (0386) 858611

BROCKENHURST Hampshire   map 2

Le Poussin ✦✕

The Courtyard, Brookley Road,
Brockenhurst SO42 7RB   COOKING 4
LYMINGTON (0590) 23063   COST £22–£42

The Aitkens' move from larger to smaller premises (from *poularde* to *poussin*) has received much approval, the strengthening of the team with the addition of Mark Wilkinson, previously at Rondelle near Birkenhead, much speculation. As the number of covers reduced, so did the size of menu (and the price remained excellent value). There is usually a choice of two hors d'oeuvre, two fish, two meat and two puds. This promotes the sense that everything is done for you, that everything receives equal care. A May meal took in a medley of grilled seafoods with a herb butter sauce. The fish were rock salmon, sea bream and squid. The alternative was a chicken and sweetbread sausage with a light asparagus sauce and a rich stock reduction. The main course was fish once more: sea bass with red peppers and saladings, a vinaigrette sauce based on the cooking juices and the most fragrant olive oil. To finish, a caramelised apple tart with a cinnamon ice-cream showed off the pastry skills of the kitchen. This was fine stuff and many report similar experiences. There are days when one dish or another is not quite up to par: a menu this short must fire on all cylinders. Another thought was that a spring meal had insufficient contrasts built into it. A main course of oxtail wrapped in caul and cabbage had caramelised vegetables as accompaniment: 'The caramelising meant they all tasted the same, I longed for some meat which was not cooked to a pulp, and some relief from the overall, sweet syrupy effect.' Counter this with another person's account: 'I started with home-made tagliatelle with a cream and wild mushroom sauce; my companion took pigeon breast with smoked lentils – a stunning combination. For the main course, pig's trotter stuffed with chicken, vegetables and wild mushrooms with lightly caramelised swede and turnip was on one side of the table; chicken leg with wild mushroom risotto was on the other, and astonishingly tasty. Featherlight passion-fruit soufflé finished the whole thing off.' Wild mushrooms are something of a passion, as are local supplies in general. Service comes from Caroline Aitken and her son Justin, the sommelier of the family. It reinforces the sense of intimate scale and his knowledge of wine apace, no doubt with paternal advice. A good tranche of house wines gives eight possible glasses from Priorato Gran Reserva 1985 to Wairau River Sauvignon Blanc 1991. The main list is longest in claret, short in red burgundies and very soundly based for the rest. House wines are from £9.95.

CHEF: Alexander Aitken PROPRIETORS: Alexander and Caroline Aitken OPEN: Tue to Sun, exc Sun D; 12 to 2, 7 to 10 MEALS: Set L £10 to £16, Set D £20 to £25 SERVICE: not inc CARDS: Access, Visa DETAILS: 25 seats. Private parties: 25 main room. Vegetarian meals on request. Children welcome. No smoking in dining-room. Wheelchair access. No music. Fax: (0590) 22912

BROXTED Essex   map 3

▲ *Whitehall*   NEW ENTRY

Church End, Broxted CM6 2BZ   COOKING 2
BISHOP'S STORTFORD (0279) 850603   COST £28–£48

There has been a succession of chefs here since the days of young Gary Rhodes. So fast have they come and gone that the *Guide* has not been able to keep up: a putative entry would always refer to the last but one. It is hoped that Paul Flavell gives it steadiness. The site is worth it: a remarkable set of half-timbered rooms – some, like the barn used for conferences, unembellished, others done out cleverly in pastel shades. If the price is no barrier, there is some fair cooking here. The cost is justified for some by a profusion of extras – appetiser and mid-meal sorbet – and for others by a willingness to use some luxury ingredients, such as foie gras on a bed of lentils with a raspberry vinegar dressing, at no extra cost. The cooking is by no means bad, even if the menu reads as if it is just another country-house affair. A delicate smoked chicken broth (bland, perhaps) came with wild mushrooms but none of the advertised tortellini; langoustines with truffles were to the exact point – delicate flavours, good texture, nice combination; chicken with wild mushrooms and cream underlined the kitchen's love affair with fungi; salmon and scallops with under-seasoned chive sauce showed better scallop cookery than salmon. Vegetables were tedious. Caramelised apple was greatly improved by the touch of candied lemon peel to give it edge and guts (not really enough caramelisation). Here is mixed achievement, therefore, at a price, but with potential for delicacy rather than abandoned verve. The service has improved of late, and it is hoped that, for the sake of freshness, so long a menu can be supported by sufficient customers. The wine list is well supplied with lots from Corney & Barrow but has a supplement of high-grade wines from Australasia and the USA including Simi, Lake's Folly, Stag's Leap, Frog's Leap, St Helena and Hungerford Hill. Prices are not impossible. House wines are £12 and £13.50.

CHEF: Paul Flavell PROPRIETORS: the Keane family OPEN: all week; 12.30 to 1.30, 7.30 to 9.30 MEALS: Set L £19, Set D £33.50 SERVICE: not inc, card slips closed CARDS: Access, Amex, Diners, Visa DETAILS: 120 seats. Private parties: 120 main room, 15 and 40 private rooms. Car park. Vegetarian meals. Children's helpings with prior notice. No cigars/pipes in dining-room. Wheelchair access (also WC). No music ACCOMMODATION: 25 rooms, all with bath/shower. Rooms for disabled. B&B £75 to £155. No children under 5. Afternoon teas. Garden. Swimming-pool. Tennis. TV. Phone. Doors close at midnight. Fax: (0279) 850385 (*The Which? Hotel Guide*)

BRUTON Somerset   map 2

▲ *Claire de Lune* £

2–4 High Street, Bruton BA10 0EQ	COOKING 1*
BRUTON (0749) 813395	COST £14–£33

The cold draught of the economy has had repercussions in Bruton High Street and the Stewarts have seen fit to convert their restaurant into a brasserie. This does not mean great alteration to the fabric: still a garish carpet, beams and knick-knacks, but now a bar (for shorter meals) and a restaurant. Kate Stewart remains a cheerful and intelligent presence at front-of-house, and Thomas shows that he can cook, even if the evidence is sometimes obscured by too many slices of cucumber or trimmings, by overcooked vegetables, or by items suspiciously like prawn cocktail on the menu. Never fear; eat plain poached salmon with a proper mayonnaise (but characterless oil), or a steak with decent port sauce and some melted Stilton, and a really good summer pudding. This will not cost too much, and the materials (fish and beef especially) are still properly bought. Simplification has happened on the plate, not in the larder, which is the right order. The wine list is keen on guidance and on countries other than France. It is not overpriced. House wine is £7.95.

CHEF: Thomas Stewart PROPRIETORS: Thomas and Kate Stewart OPEN: Tue to Sat, D only, and Sun L (also bank hol Mon D); 12 to 2, 7 to 10 (10.30 Sat) MEALS: alc. Set L £5.50 to £7.95, Set D £7.95 to £20. Minimum £5 SERVICE: not inc CARDS: Access, Visa DETAILS: 40 seats. Private parties: 40 main room, 25 private room. Children's helpings. Smart dress preferred. Wheelchair access (2 steps). Music ACCOMMODATION: 3 rooms, 2 with bath/shower. B&B £25 to £40. Children welcome. TV. Doors close at 10. Confirm by 7

Truffles

95 The High Street, Bruton BA10 0AR	COOKING 2
BRUTON (0749) 812255	COST £20–£31

'Here you have a young couple creating a friendly and pleasant atmosphere in cramped surroundings,' observed a visitor from France who enjoyed his guinea-fowl with morels served in this cottage restaurant. Cramped it may be, but it does not lack local colour from Bruton's fine townscape, nor is it devoid of comfort even when packed with supporters. Martin Bottrill has not abandoned his standards, of cooking or ingredients, and continues to produce a set-price monthly menu of country-modern slant with dishes such as quenelles of crab with grapefruit and orange, venison sausage with red cabbage and apple, turbot on a bed of vegetables with a tarragon and mustard sauce, or quail stuffed with a game mousse and served together with breast of pigeon 'on a nest of celeriac' with a piquant sauce. Elaboration is not ignored here – even tomatoes come stuffed with cubes of courgette. The balance of tastes and the skill in execution, however, are sufficient to bring off most conceits, though some reflect that the imagination's palate has occasionally outstripped reality. Desserts get very good lines: a bavarois of honey and Greek yoghurt with vanilla sauce was a summer delight, so was banana terrine with wafer-thin chocolate layers. The wine list has plenty of halves, a short selection of second labels from the Bordeaux big league, a fair essential range from around the world and no untoward prices. House Duboeuf is £7.95.

CHEF: Martin Bottrill PROPRIETORS: Martin and Denise Bottrill OPEN: Tue to Sun, exc Sun D; 12 to 2, 7 to 9.30 MEALS: Set L £12.95, Set D £18.50 SERVICE: not inc DETAILS: 20 seats. Private parties: 20 main room. Vegetarian meals. Children restricted. Smart dress preferred. Wheelchair access (1 step). No music

---

BUCKLAND Gloucestershire | map 2

▲ *Buckland Manor* 🍷

Buckland WR12 7LY
BROADWAY (0386) 852626
off A46, 1m SW of Broadway

COOKING 2*
COST £23–£51

At 9am on a Sunday, expect to hear church bells. Being a full Cotswold manor house, with gables, honeyed stone, mullions and all, Buckland Manor is bang next to the belfry. For atmosphere it can't be beaten. 'For fancy food, fancily served, we'd give it high marks, though let down by being lukewarm and, for quantity, expensive' was one view. The cooking is in the vein of restrained modern classical simplicity. It is mercifully free of mousses and stuffings and relies on meat and sauce *tout court*. Fillet of beef with claret sauce and bone marrow, lamb with two tarragon sauces, calf's liver with Cointreau sauce or chicken with basil and tomato do not overload the stomach, and when exactly performed will please the hotel's likely constituency. Service is described as efficient, friendly and unfussy. The prices here are high. Those at the top end would get you a room and meal at the best in Knightsbridge. The wine list is excellent. Of course prices are not give-away, but care has been taken to offer fair range and there are some classic items. The Italian section has some of the exciting new makers, some of the Americans are good, and the mid-range clarets are worth considering. The presentation is vastly improved. House wines start at £7.95. CELLARMAN'S CHOICE: Wairau River, Sauvignon Blanc 1991, £14.30; Hermitage 1983, Guigal, £36.

CHEF: Martyn Pearn PROPRIETORS: Roy and Daphne Vaughan OPEN: all week; 12.30 to 1.45, 7.30 to 8.45 MEALS: alc. Set Sun L £17.25 SERVICE: not inc CARDS: Access, Amex, Visa DETAILS: 38 seats. 6 tables outside. Private parties: 10 main room. Car park. No children under 8. Smart dress preferred. No cigars/pipes in dining-room. Wheelchair access (also WC). No music ACCOMMODATION: 10 rooms, all with bath/shower. Rooms for disabled. B&B £135 to £270. No children under 12. Afternoon teas. Garden. Swimming-pool. Tennis. TV. Phone. Fax: (0386) 853557 (*The Which? Hotel Guide*)

BURFORD Oxfordshire   map 2

▲ *Lamb Inn*

Sheep Street, Burford OX18 4LR   COOKING 1
BURFORD (0993) 823155   COST £16–£34

The inn is a picture: stone, beams, mullions, flagstones, warmth, candlelight –
the catalogue continues. The garden is a delight: flowers are everywhere. The
de Wolfs bring everything off with skill and purpose: popularity is a certainty.
Many people recommend this place for an overnight stay: pretty rooms and 'the
breakfast was as good as dinner'. Others recommend it for the honest and
plentiful bar food. The romantic restaurant, open for dinners and Sunday
lunch, offers a daily menu of acceptable food. One person observed that it is
'neither over-ambitious nor unsuccessful'; on the other hand, there is very little
plain and simple on a menu that may offer oyster mushrooms with Stilton
cream; terrine of salmon, sole and scallops; chicken filled with garlic prawns;
or salmon with mussels and a prawn sauce. The sweets section seems the
weakest part. Staff are enthusiastic, even if sometimes confused by the press of
Saturday night business. The wine list limits its extension into price
hyperspace of fine clarets or burgundies and offers a sound selection. House
wines are £7.50.

CHEFS: Pascal Clavaud and David Partridge   PROPRIETORS: Richard and Caroline de
Wolf   OPEN: all week; 12 to 2, 7.30 to 9   CLOSED: 25 and 26 Dec   MEALS: Set Sun L
£16.50, Set D £17.50 to £23. Bar meals L   SERVICE: not inc   CARDS: Access, Visa
DETAILS: 55 seats. 8 tables outside. Private parties: 20 main room. Car park. Children's
helpings. No pipes in dining-room. Wheelchair access (1 step; also WC). No music
ACCOMMODATION: 15 rooms, 14 with bath/shower. Rooms for disabled. B&B £30 to £75.
Children welcome. Baby facilities. Pets welcome. Garden. TV. Phone. Doors close at 11.
Fax: (0993) 822228 (*The Which? Hotel Guide*)

BURGH LE MARSH Lincolnshire   map 6

Windmill £

46 High Street, Burgh le Marsh PE24 5JT   COOKING 2
SKEGNESS (0754) 810281   COST £13–£24

The wind comes straight from the Urals that drives the sails that mill the flour
that crosses the car park to make the dough that Tim Boskett bakes each day to
serve his customers in the small house with homely bar and dining-room. 'We
did not believe this sort of place existed in the wilds of East Lincs,' went one
happy report. By keeping the monthly menu short, the Bosketts may guarantee
the immediacy of ingredients that is difficult to achieve in regions where
restaurant-going is not a major leisure activity; by keeping the cooking style
restrained, they keep hitting the bull's-eye of timing and flavour. Good chicken
came with a simple cream sauce spiked with mushrooms and bacon. Tim
Boskett extends his repertoire with the occasional rogue dish from beyond
these shores – for example, feijoada, a Brazilian casserole of pork, chorizo,
bacon and beans. More usually, there will be perhaps a couple of steaks,
chicken, a substantial British pie such as venison or game, rack of lamb with a
rosemary gravy and, for sure, one fish dish, such as plaice with mushroom

stuffing and a lobster sauce. Sunday lunch does not alter the repertoire – good roasts, nicely baked hot starters or sometimes a fried thing such as bacon, onion and potato fritters with tomato sauce. A cottage industry that deserves reward. The wine list is short and fair-priced. House wines are a selection from André Daguin in south-western France at £6.40 a bottle.

CHEF: Tim Boskett   PROPRIETORS: Tim and Janette Boskett   OPEN: Tue to Sat, D only, and Sun L; 12 to 1.45, 7 to 9.15   CLOSED: 1 week Christmas, first week Sept   MEALS: Set Sun L £7.50, Set D £12.50 to £17   SERVICE: not inc   DETAILS: 50 seats. Private parties: 40 main room. Car park. Vegetarian meals. Children's helpings Sun L. Wheelchair access. Music

---

BURNHAM MARKET Norfolk   map 6

Fishes' £

Market Place, Burnham Market PE31 8HE   COOKING 1
FAKENHAM (0328) 738588   COST £17–£36

Gillian Cape's informal country restaurant in 'a recession-immune Norfolk village' makes a virtue of simplicity. In high summer it creaks with tourists and holidaymakers, but it remains one of the few places in the area that offers fresh food for adults and children, without compromises. Even on a November evening it can deliver the goods: 'We got what we expected,' writes a visitor, 'enjoyable plain fresh fish.' Dishes inspired by the catch from the local boats are undoubtedly the main attraction: for instance, rich crab soup ('there must have been a whole crab in it'); mussels with cider, apple and celery; scallop and prawn gratin; and halibut steak with garlic butter. Everyone raves about the salmon fish-cakes with crab sauce. There is also an impressive output from the smokehouse (including goose and duck breast), plus home-baked ham for meat-lovers. Sweets are home-made ice-creams, meringues and pancakes; cheeses might include Welsh Pencarreg or single Gloucester. The wine list is short and sharp. House French is £6.50.

CHEFS: Gillian Cape, Carole Bird and Paula Ayres   PROPRIETOR: Gillian Cape   OPEN: Tue to Sun and bank hol Mons (Sun D July and Aug only); 12 to 2, 6.45 to 9 (9.30 in summer) CLOSED: 24 to 27 Dec and 3 weeks mid-Jan to Feb   MEALS: alc. Set L £10.80 to £11.95 SERVICE: not inc   CARDS: Access, Amex, Diners, Visa   DETAILS: 48 seats. Private parties: 12 main room. Children's helpings. Children under 5 before 8.30 D. Wheelchair access (1 step). No music

---

BURY ST EDMUNDS Suffolk   map 3

Mortimer's £

30 Churchgate Street,
Bury St Edmunds IP33 IRG   COOKING 1
BURY ST EDMUNDS (0284) 760623   COST £15–£34

This long-standing popular restaurant is done out in shades of white and green, with ferns, patterned oilcloth table-tops and watercolours by the nineteenth-century painter Thomas Mortimer lining the walls. Mortimer's is all about fish, much of it from the East Coast boats. The menu has an old-fashioned ring to it: crab pâté, grilled sardines, skate with black butter and capers, salmon meunière, steamed halibut with tomato and basil sauce. Meals are excellent-value and the emphasis on fish is in tune with current nutritional thinking: it is food 'of the kind which it would be wise to eat every day,' writes a devotee. Puddings such as lemon syllabub and melon sorbet have 'successfully served to refresh the palate'. Service is polite and well-paced. The wine list may be short on information, but prices are fair and there are plenty of halves. House French is £7.25. The sister restaurant, Mortimer's on the Quay in Ipswich (see entry), is run along similar lines.

CHEF: Kenneth Ambler   PROPRIETORS: Kenneth Ambler and Michael Gooding   OPEN: Mon to Sat, exc Sat L; 12 to 2, 7 to 9 (6.45 to 8.15 Mon)   CLOSED: bank hols and day after, 23 Dec to 5 Jan, 2 weeks Aug   MEALS: alc   SERVICE: not inc   CARDS: Access, Amex, Diners, Visa   DETAILS: 60 seats. Private parties: 8 main room. Children's helpings on request. No-smoking area. Wheelchair access (1 step). No music. Fax: (0284) 752561

CALSTOCK Cornwall   map 1

▲ Danescombe Valley Hotel 🍷 ⭐✳

Lower Kelly, Calstock PL18 9RY   COOKING 2*
TAVISTOCK (0822) 832414   COST £36

The Smiths continue to plough their particular furrow in this handsome villa overlooking the Tamar: views to the left, right, and straight ahead. Setting is never all, neither is careful attention to one's needs (toys in the bath), but every year sees some improvement: a redecorated hall and a restored clinker rowing boat to allow you to experience the views close-up start the roster this year. While Martin (it's first names here) tells you what you need to know – about the shopping, the sights, the wine list, the furniture, you name it – Anna is slaving over the hot stove to produce a no-choice dinner of three courses and cheese. The food is disarmingly simple, sometimes not involving too much cooking at all, but it can be very exactly judged. The danger is that if the shopping falls below par, then the eloquence disappears. An autumn meal of three melons (one good and two poor), then breast of chicken wrapped with bacon and cabbage (an Anglicisation of Italy, Anna's chief inspiration, which would have been better had the chicken been more flavourful), before local cheeses (some good, some truly boring) and a hot lemon pudding (the star of the show) points up this defect. On the other hand, everything frequently slots into place: fine balance from course to course, no over-emphasis on display or complication, just exact and careful craftsmanship. What you will never lack for is dialogue – this is a proactive establishment. A didactic approach to wines is insisted upon here, so allow time for a lengthy read. Quality is very high, prices are almost embarrassingly generous, and Italy is an enthusiasm.

CHEF: Anna Smith   PROPRIETORS: Martin and Anna Smith   OPEN: Fri to Tue, D only; 7.30 for 8   CLOSED: Nov to 1 Apr   MEALS: Set D £27.50   SERVICE: net prices, card slips closed   CARDS: Access, Amex, Diners, Visa (3% surcharge)   DETAILS: 12 seats. No children under 12. No smoking in dining-room. No music   ACCOMMODATION: 5 rooms, all with bath/shower. B&B £65 to £120. Deposit: £50. No children under 12. Garden. Doors close at midnight. Confirm by 6. Fax: (0822) 832414 (*The Which? Hotel Guide*)

CAMBRIDGE Cambridgeshire | map 3

Midsummer House

Midsummer Common,
Cambridge CB4 1HA
CAMBRIDGE (0223) 69299

COOKING 2*
COST £27–£55

Oarsmen and oarswomen glide on the Cam beneath willows, in view of the gardens surrounding Midsummer House. On a midsummer evening the effect has infused reports with a warm glow of satisfaction. The principal dining-room is a double-aisled conservatory bordered on three sides by flowers; the upstairs 'can seem claustrophobic'. Hans Schweitzer has evolved a wide-ranging repertoire geared to modern preference but honed with classical technique. Readers approve dishes such as a terrine of salmon and turbot in a light pimento sauce, tea-smoked Barbary duck breast with a marinated vegetable salad on a hoisin dressing, and venison with woodland mushrooms and juniper berry sauce. Scallops were 'wonderful', lamb was 'very good', but criticism surfaces in reports of slow service. The dessert stage may be the highlight: the pear tart with honey ice-cream has claimed an enthusiastic following; 'coffee excellent'. The wine list has some high prices and wide range. House wines are £9.50.

CHEF: Hans Schweitzer PROPRIETORS: Hans Schweitzer and Chris Kelly OPEN: Tue to Sun, exc Sat L and Sun D; 12.30 to 2, 7 to 9.30 MEALS: Set L £12.95 to £38, Set D £23 to £38 SERVICE: not inc CARDS: Access, Amex, Diners, Visa DETAILS: 60 seats. 10 tables outside. Private parties: 30 main room, 8 private rooms. Vegetarian meals. Children's helpings. Smart dress preferred. Wheelchair access (also WC). No music

Twenty Two ♦

22 Chesterton Road, Cambridge CB4 3AX
CAMBRIDGE (0223) 351880

COOKING 2
COST £29

A favourite among academic families spending their own money, the cheerful front and back rooms of this small house are 'fresh and homey' and can be busy with the buzz of doubtless elevated conversation. Michael Sharpe's weekly menu is kept short with four choices at each course, a pause for salad between the first two, and the option of 'cheese of the week' rather than dessert. Dishes may range from crisp green apple filled with herbed cream cheese to pakoras, from fillet of beef with red wine or rack of lamb with rhubarb (more rosemary, actually) to burritos. Vegetables show the same breadth of approach: one night saw both red cabbage with currant jelly and shredded courgettes with Parmesan. The cooking is not elaborate and may be spot-on. Home-made ices, such as ginger in a brandy-snap basket, are always enjoyed. Tea is stronger than is wise, but there is espresso. House wines have not always hit the spot, but the generously priced wine list as a whole affords pleasure and encourages experiment. No blockbuster of a list with 50-plus bins, it negotiates an intelligent path through the wine world, taking in the classics as well as offering diversions to Italy and Australia. In its quiet way this is a very

remarkable list, as satisfying for the expert as the novice. House wine is £7.95.
CELLARMAN'S CHOICE: St Romain 1990, Jaffelin, £14.75; Tignanello 1985,
Antinori, £23.

CHEF: Michael Sharpe   PROPRIETORS: Michael and Susan Sharpe   OPEN: Tue to Sat, D
only (L by arrangement); 7.30 to 9.30   MEALS: Set D £19.50   SERVICE: not inc   CARDS:
Access, Visa   DETAILS: 28 seats. Private parties: 25 main room. Vegetarian meals. No
children under 12

CAMPSEA ASH Suffolk   map 3

▲ *Old Rectory* ♥

Campsea Ash IP13 0PU
WICKHAM MARKET (0728) 746524   COOKING 1
on B1078, 1m E of A12   COST £29

This is Stewart Bassett's kingdom. You may find him, as did some new arrivals
in the spring, sitting reading in the garden in sun hat and shorts; or he will be
cooking, plastic pinny and all, single-handedly in the kitchen; or he will be
exercising his dog, which you will get to know later. Bedrooms are
comfortable, the drawing-room has a large fire, deep chairs, board games and
magazines; there is a very landed-gentry private dining-room, all silver and
polished wood; the bar is serve-yourself and own up to it; and most meals are
served in a large conservatory painted wonderful colours. It all has a British
style without evident pretension. People love it, yet because it is so relaxed and
individual, there are those who don't know what to make of it. Devotees are
very much part of the scene. There is a no-choice set menu, including a fish
dish, meat (often roast, often a joint), cheese on a plate, then a somewhat
British pudding. Cooking may be magical, but it may also misfire if timing goes
awry or confections such as mousses are not made with an eye to light texture
and high flavour. Sound reports come for halibut with watercress sauce, sea
trout with spinach and butter sauce, duck with ginger and apricot, roast
venison marinated (almost too long) in red wine, good crèmes brûlées, and
strawberry tarts topped with hot meringue. Coffee is plentiful afterwards. The
wine list is good enough for customers to ignore everything else and prices are
not high. The clarets are certainly worth exploring as there are old as well as
new, but all sections are given thought, even if red burgundies are slightly
short due to high prices at the merchants. House wine is £9.40.

CHEF/PROPRIETOR: Stewart Bassett   OPEN: Mon to Sat, D only; 7.30 to 9   MEALS: Set D
£18.50   SERVICE: not inc   CARDS: Access, Amex, Diners, Visa   DETAILS: 35 seats. Private
parties: 18 main room, 20 private room. Car park. Vegetarian meals. Children's helpings.
Wheelchair access. No Music   ACCOMMODATION: 6 rooms, all with bath/shower. B&B £30
to £51. Deposit: £20. Children welcome. Garden. Doors close at midnight (*The Which? Hotel
Guide*)

---

*'For dessert we had one of their bought-in ice-creams. A rock-hard coconut-dusted
snowball, rather how one pictures the nucleus of a comet. Perhaps left to thaw for another
15 minutes it might have revealed some flavour, but they did need the table.'*
On eating in Edinburgh

George's Brasserie £

71–72 Castle Street,
Canterbury CT1 2QD   COOKING 1
CANTERBURY (0227) 765658   COST £20–£37

George's wears three hats: first and foremost a cheerful brasserie, but there is also a crêperie next door plus the Garden Café serving snacks, ices and afternoon teas. Reports centre on the Brasserie, which has recently had a face-lift. Two fixed-price menus – backed up by good-value daily specials – provide plenty of options. The style is Franco-Mediterranean, along the lines of lentil soup with crispy onions, grilled lamb cutlets with flageolet beans, wild salmon with local watercress sauce, and roast duck with green olives and rosemary. Reporters have enjoyed pea and lettuce soup, home-made pasta with truffle cream and pecorino sauce, grilled swordfish steak with lemon and garlic, strawberry tart and 'magnificent' gâteau St-Emilion. It would be better if simple things were attempted more often than the complicated, and if production were more even. A short, carefully selected list of French wines has house wines at £6.95.

CHEFS/PROPRIETORS: Simon Day and Beverley Holmes OPEN: Mon to Sat; 11am to 10pm (10.30 Fri and Sat) CLOSED: 25 Dec, 1 Jan MEALS: alc SERVICE: not inc, card slips closed CARDS: Access, Amex, Diners, Visa DETAILS: 90 seats. 15 tables outside. Private parties: 30 main room, 25 and 30 private rooms. Car park. Vegetarian meals. Children's helpings. Wheelchair access (3 steps). Music. Fax: (0227) 700777

▲ Sully's   NEW ENTRY

County Hotel, High Street,
Canterbury CT1 2RX   COOKING 2
CANTERBURY (0227) 766266   COST £20–£41

The hotel has been refuge to generations of parents visiting their schoolboy offspring, tourists and travellers to the Continent when motors did not move so fast. It is a town hotel in the old mode. Sully's has had recommendations over the years but suffers from changes of personnel. The new chef was owner/chef at Le Chausson on the river in London, and his arrival has prompted a late flurry of support. Inspection revealed a classic arrangement of *carte* and table d'hôte, and some proficient cooking. Eric Marin Gavignet does not dodge complexity or an urge to dress things up: for example, lamb wrapped with leaf vegetables, a mousseline in a parcel of trout, a savarin of fish with a vanilla-tasting lobster sauce. Indeed, pastry is one of his strengths. But his ability to work things up is done in a pleasantly light manner and sauces do not bludgeon and are not essence-ridden, even if excess salt was a fault one summer evening. Whether the sight of breakfast cereals being wheeled in at the end of dinner will endear you to this restaurant is a moot point. This chef needs every support from the service if he is to rid the setting of its persistent undertones. The wine list, not cheap, is a mixture of this and that: Jadot burgundies, some dubious vintages in claret, a Grants of St James's Sancerre, and a 1955 Haut-Brion. House wine is £7.80.

CHEF: Eric Marin Gavignet PROPRIETORS: Laughing Water Hotels Ltd OPEN: all week; 12.30 to 2.30, 7 to 10 MEALS: alc. Set L £12 to £14.50, Set D £14.50 to £18.50 SERVICE: not inc, card slips closed CARDS: Access, Amex, Diners, Visa DETAILS: 50 seats. Private parties: 18 main room, 30, 100 and 130 private rooms. Car park. Vegetarian meals. Children's helpings. No pipes in dining-room. No music. Air-conditioned ACCOMMODATION: 73 rooms, all with bath/shower. Rooms for disabled. Lift. B&B £75.50 to £106. Deposit: 1 night. Children welcome. Baby facilities. Afternoon teas. TV. Phone. Confirm by 6. Fax: (0227) 451512

CARTMEL Cumbria   map 7

▲ Aynsome Manor 🏮✷

Cartmel LA11 6HH   COOKING 1
CARTMEL (053 95) 36653   COST £16–£29

Cartmel Priory can be seen across the fields from the dining-room of the Varleys' handsome eighteenth-century manor house, set far, in Lakeland terms, from the madding crowd. The five-course dinner menu offers just three choices of first and main courses, punctuated by soup, finishing with cheese and the sweets trolley. The style is unreconstructed country hotel: chicken liver pâté with redcurrant, orange and port jelly served with melba toast; deep-fried devilled local whitebait; avocado pear and kiwi fruit with mango and raspberry coulis; lemon sole fillets with prawn and cucumber sauce; roast duckling with peach and brandy sauce; sautéed escalope of veal with Marsala sauce. Vegetables can be unimaginative, although correctly cooked ('successive days yielded Brussels sprouts, batons of carrots and swede, courgettes provençale and broccoli with almonds'). The sweets trolley 'must both disturb the advocates of low-cholesterol food and delight those with a sweet and creamy tooth'. A fairly priced wine list offers some good names from a spread of countries. House wine is £7.50.

CHEFS: Tony Varley, Victor Sharratt and Christopher Miller PROPRIETORS: Tony and Margaret Varley OPEN: Mon to Sat, D only, and Sun L; 1 (Sun), 7 to 8.15 CLOSED: 2 to 25 Jan MEALS: Set Sun L £10, Set D £18 SERVICE: not inc CARDS: Access, Amex, Visa DETAILS: 35 seats. Private parties: 35 main room. Car park. Children's helpings. No children under 5 D. Smart dress preferred. No smoking in dining-room. Wheelchair access. No music ACCOMMODATION: 13 rooms, 12 with bath/shower. D,B&B £46 to £102. Children welcome. Baby facilities. Pets welcome. Afternoon teas. Garden. TV. Phone. Doors close at midnight. Fax: (053 95) 36016

▲ Uplands 🏮✷

Haggs Lane, Cartmel LA11 6HD   COOKING 3*
CARTMEL (053 95) 36248   COST £20–£35

'Even on a miserable, wet, misty Good Friday, the view from the windows restores the spirit,' wrote someone of this small country house. It is full of warm comfort, while still sporting bare pine tables, and is run by Tom and Diana Peter with ease and informality, despite the single time for eating. 'As a total experience, it was as good an example of how it should be done as one is likely to find,' wrote another, who hates that constant enquiry and undertow of intrusion that often surrounds fancy meals out. John Tovey's spirit is discernable in the short menus offering dishes that seem impossibly complicated and yet find harmony from disparate notes, like a gathering of quail's eggs, cheese and mushroom and herb pâtés, pepper and onion marmalades and cream and chives. Another example of this *multum in parvo* approach might be loin of veal roasted with mustard and rosemary, served with fried pineapple and a mustard and honey cream sauce. Dinner is five courses, with limited choice. A paradigm evening may run through a hot sole soufflé with mushroom pâté and a watercress sauce; followed by what many consider an Uplands trademark, the generous tureen of soup (tomato and basil or fennel and almond, perhaps), served with a loaf of 'hot, sweet and malty' bread all your own to slice at table. Then up comes the main course, a choice of salmon with chive and vermouth sauce or chicken with cheese and herb pâté and tomato and mustard sauce; accompanying it is a harvest festival of vegetables ('not just plate fillers'). Finally there is the choice of sweet things: apricot pie, chocolate Grand Marnier mousse, strawberry and passion-fruit coffee meringue. Prime ingredients, treated with respect, are allowed their chance to shine. Not everything is larded, layered or laced. Flavourings are usually well handled, despite a comment that a mustard and tomato sauce was swamped by the herbs in a stuffing. Lunch is cheaper and shorter, but no less good. Portions are generous: 'They would suit a weight-lifter in training.' Diana Peter is all a host should be, while Tom stays mainly in the kitchen. The wine list, like that at Miller Howe, has a strong Australian presence. Value, therefore, is palpable and the up-front flavours seem to suit the food very well.

CHEF: Tom Peter PROPRIETORS: John J. Tovey, and Tom and Diana Peter OPEN: Tue to Sun and Mon bank hols; 12.30 to 1, 7.30 to 8 CLOSED: 1 Jan to 24 Feb MEALS: Set L £13.50, Set D £24 SERVICE: not inc, card slips closed CARDS: Access, Amex, Visa DETAILS: 34 seats. Private parties: 34 main room. Car park. Vegetarian meals. No children under 8. No smoking in dining-room. Wheelchair access. Music ACCOMMODATION: 5 rooms, all with bath/shower. D,B&B £70 to £124. No children under 8. Pets welcome. Garden. TV. Phone. Doors close at 11. Confirm by 3 (*The Which? Hotel Guide*)

CHADDESLEY CORBETT Hereford & Worcester   map 5

▲ *Brockencote Hall* | NEW ENTRY |

Chaddesley Corbett DY10 4PY   COOKING 1
CHADDESLEY CORBETT (0562) 777876   COST £21–£45

The Hall was built early this century by brewers with taste. It has been kept up to the mark and is a lovely place to visit. Most things glow, rooms shine and the park dazzles. The menus, French and potentially pricey, carry English subtitles like 'a salad of prawns and pink grapefruit enrobed with a dill dressing'. This can put people off. Didier Philipot's cooking has had favourable reports, despite raw edges. Sweetbreads and foie gras in crisp pastry had a sherry vinegar sauce sharp enough to do good to the liver, if not to the sweetbreads. Seafood pasta showed sound technique though flavours were better handled in sirloin with a wild mushroom sauce and sea bass on a spicy, salty beurre blanc. The conventional neo-classical repertoire of the savoury dishes is confirmed at the sweet course. It would all be better if it had more character, and more *taste*.

Details such as vegetable cookery, bread and butter and coffee have not overwhelmed. The wine list has a serious collection of clarets and burgundies, and the makers generally are good ones. Prices are not greedy, though the imbalance towards classic names makes the overall cost seem high. The house selections start at £9.50.

CHEFS: Didier Philipot and Eric Bouchet   PROPRIETORS: Alison and Joseph Petitjean   OPEN: all week, exc Sat L and Sun D; 12.30 to 2, 7.30 to 9.30 (10 Sat)   CLOSED: bank hol Mons, 27 Dec to 17 Jan   MEALS: Set L £15.50 to £33.50, Set D £19.50 to £33.50   SERVICE: net prices, card slips closed   CARDS: Access, Amex, Diners, Visa   DETAILS: 50 seats. 4 tables outside. Private parties: 50 main room, 18 and 40 private rooms. Car park. Vegetarian meals with prior notice. Children's helpings. Smart dress preferred. No cigars/pipes in dining-room. Wheelchair access. No music   ACCOMMODATION: 8 rooms, all with bath/shower. B&B £75 to £90. Children welcome. Baby facilities. Afternoon teas. Garden. TV. Phone. Doors close at midnight. Confirm by 6. Fax: (0562) 777872

CHADLINGTON Oxfordshire   map 2

▲ *Manor* 🍷 ✳

Chadlington OX7 3LX   COOKING 1
CHADLINGTON (0608) 76711   COST £32–£36

The house and its setting with views of the village and the surrounding countryside can be seductive: 'The sheer tranquillity of the place for a weekend after a hard week was wonderful,' writes one contented visitor. The Cotswold-stone manor is surrounded by formal gardens complete with pond and ha-ha. Chris Grant cooks, while her husband runs the front-of-house and advises on the prodigious wine list. Her straightforward five-course menus show a deal of care, ingredients are good and dishes are attractively presented, although the cooking is not always technically on target. A penchant for sweet flavours runs through the repertoire, but the results can be pleasing: two 'Dick Whittington bags' of quail in filo pastry with redcurrant sauce, and lemon tart with good shortcrust pastry have met with approval. David Grant maintains one of those long-as-your-arm wine lists. Fortunately he does not demand a matching pocket, as many bottles are still around the £10 mark; if economy is not the object then exceptional clarets and burgundies abound. This is a classic list which extends to many fine older Mosels, but eschews anything beyond Europe. House Duboeuf is £8.

CHEF: Chris Grant   PROPRIETORS: David and Chris Grant   OPEN: all week, D only; 7 to 9   MEALS: Set D £25.50 to £26.50   SERVICE: net prices, card slips closed   CARDS: Access, Visa   DETAILS: 24 seats. Private parties: 6 and 10 private rooms. Car park. Children welcome. No smoking in dining-room. Music   ACCOMMODATION: 7 rooms, all with bath/shower. B&B £65 to £125. Children welcome. Baby facilities. Garden. TV. Phone. Doors close at 11

Prices quoted in the Guide *are based on information supplied by restaurateurs. The prices quoted at the top of each entry represent a range, from the lowest meal price to the highest; the latter is inflated by 10 per cent to take account of likely price rises during the year of the* Guide.

CHAGFORD Devon   map 1

▲ Gidleigh Park ▮

Chagford TQ13 8HH   COOKING 4
CHAGFORD (0647) 432367   COST £42–£70

Gidleigh Park was once apparently undistinguished – a rambling piece of
Edwardian half-timbering, buried beneath rhododendrons. Energetic
landscaping, now continued behind the house, has revealed the site as
magnificent, and the house as passable, nay impressive strung along a ledge on
the slopes up to Dartmoor. The hotel itself runs well, rooms improve (not every
one is as spacious as may be wished), and the machine is oiled by some years'
practice. Shaun Hill still cooks like an angel, or a slightly portly leprechaun. He
manages individual dishes, interesting flavours and high technique. There are
moments when visitors have wished that a few things were more
straightforward – that 'Brixham crab salad' was just Brixham crab rather than
'a mould of herb mayonnaise with white crabmeat and three asparagus heads'
– but the handling of components usually occasions praise. A new dish, open
ravioli with foie gras, lemon and garlic was 'so good I could have had three of
them instead of a meal', and has those elements of luxury, high flavour and
gutsiness that Shaun Hill seems to enjoy. Scallops with lentil and coriander
sauce continues to be a firm favourite, and has spread through Britain as a
modern standard. Steamed, then crisply fried duck gets taste out of a duck,
though the finish is rather dry. Ragoût of vegetables with morels, broad beans,
carrots, turnips and leeks in a buttery sauce shows a cook more interested in
vegetables than most (they appear as a separate course on the speciality menu).
His easy familiarity and curiosity is revealed in sea bass with five-spices ('eat
your heart out most Chinese restaurants'), with a shining fillet of bass set in a
bowl of fish broth reinforced by chicken stock. Turbot with fried leeks was
proclaimed by one elderly customer as the 'best turbot dish in 87 years', the fish
still in firm curds, topped by hair-thin leeks and an oil emulsion sauce with
asparagus, slivers of spring onion, mange-tout, broad beans and potatoes
boiled with saffron. The dinner menu has about eight choices in each course, at
a single price; there is a long set menu for the whole table, and there are light
lunches. Gidleigh is not cheap. Ancillaries are excellent, as are desserts: lemon
tart with caramelised banana, apple tart with caramel ice-cream, passion-fruit
and other sorbets, a 'life threatening' plate of chocolate goodies. Cheeses, on a
double-decker trolley, have always been a strong point here, and the staff
know what's what. Breakfasts have improved according to one very regular
reporter. For a twosome, the most intelligent route through the wine list might
be the shortest. With eight top wines offered by the glass – the current list
includes Au Bon Climat Reserve Chardonnay and Guigal Côtes Brune et
Blonde – the modest premium over and above the bottle price seems small
sacrifice. As for the rest, Paul Henderson oversees one of the more remarkable
cellars in the country, with a clear vision and a missionary zeal that steers
drinkers towards his own favoured regions – Alsace, Rhône, Italy and the
antipodes. Classic areas are handled with reassuring concern for age, with the
youngest red burgundies on offer from 1985. Prices start high, but do not be put
off; value is good, especially in the upper reaches where mark-ups are eased.

House wines are from £17.50. CELLARMAN'S CHOICE: Chassagne Montrachet 1989, Latour, £28; Tignanello 1985, Antinori, £24.50.

CHEF: Shaun Hill   PROPRIETORS: Kay and Paul Henderson   OPEN: all week; 12.30 to 2, 7 to 9   MEALS: Set L £33 to £43, Set D £43 to £50   SERVICE: net prices, card slips closed   CARDS: Access, Visa   DETAILS: 35 seats. Private parties: 18 main room. Car park. Children welcome. Smart dress preferred. No cigars/pipes in dining-room. Wheelchair access   ACCOMMODATION: 14 rooms and cottage, all with bath/shower. D,B&B £165 to £350. Children welcome. Pets welcome. Afternoon teas. Garden. Tennis. Fishing. TV. Phone. Doors close at 12.30am. Fax: (0647) 432574 (*The Which? Hotel Guide*)

CHEDINGTON Dorset   map 2

▲ *Chedington Court* ▼

Chedington DT8 3HY
CORSCOMBE (0935) 891265   COOKING 2
off A356, 4m SE of Crewkerne   COST £33

More like 'a country-house weekend party' than a hotel, affirms a regular visitor to Philip and Hilary Chapman's comfortable Victorian stone pile. In summer the surrounding gardens and fine lawns cast a deeper spell. The kitchen has worked some magic since the promotion of Hambleton Hall-trained Christopher Ansell-Green, but there is no trickery. Rather, confidence is asserted in simple starters such as brioche filled with mussels in a saffron and leek sauce, and prawn and cucumber salad with 'really fresh prawns tasting of the sea'. Fish takes the lead in main courses, as demonstrated by John Dory glazed with champagne sabayon and baked brill with sweet curry sauce and toasted almonds. The dinner menu (four courses, cheese and coffee) admits of little choice; perhaps a pair of starters and a vegetarian or meat alternative for the main dish before the dessert trolley. Sweets load on calories, cheese can have class. On the wine side this is a place that encourages happy experiment; half-bottles are liberal and prices are generous throughout. Our remarks last year suggesting some editing of the cellar still stand; it helps no one to have a list clogged up with wines which offer no discernable differences. So many good wines of tremendous value are on offer here, it is a pity not to make them more accessible. House wine is £7.50. CELLARMAN'S CHOICE: Brouilly, Ch. des Tours 1990, £14.50; Mercurey, Ch. de Chamirey 1989, £19.50.

CHEFS: Christopher Ansell-Green and Hilary Chapman   PROPRIETORS: Philip and Hilary Chapman   OPEN: all week, D only; 7 to 9   MEALS: Set D £26.50   SERVICE: net prices, card slips closed   CARDS: Access, Amex, Visa   DETAILS: 30 seats. 2 tables outside. Private parties: 32 main roo.n, 40 private room. Car park. Vegetarian meals. Children's helpings. High tea for children under 10. Smart dress preferred. No cigars/pipes in dining-room. Wheelchair access (also WC). No music   ACCOMMODATION: 10 rooms, all with bath/shower. D,B&B £73 to £162. Deposit: £30. Children welcome. Baby facilities. Pets welcome. Afternoon teas. Garden. Golf. Snooker. TV. Phone. Doors close at midnight. Confirm by 6. Fax: (0935) 891442 (*The Which? Hotel Guide*)

The text of entries is based on unsolicited reports sent in by readers, backed up by inspections conducted anonymously. The factual details under the text are from questionnaires the Guide sends to all restaurants that feature in the book.

Le Champignon Sauvage ▼

24–26 Suffolk Road,
Cheltenham GL50 2AQ   COOKING 2*
CHELTENHAM (0242) 573449   COST £24–£37

This modest, almost plain, buttermilk-coloured dining-room is in danger of
being eclipsed by a burgeoning collection of fungi-related souvenirs. 'Most of
our mushroom mementoes are presents from customers,' explains Helen
Everitt-Matthias. Visitors who have repaid a debt of gratitude for an evening of
fungi-sponsored entertainment are clearly legion. They may have enjoyed brill
with morels, noodles and spring onions in a reduced butter and wine sauce
(though the morels can be gritty), or, as you might expect, a wild mushroom
ravioli poached in its stock, thickened with cream and garnished with more
fungi. David Everitt-Matthias is, however, skilled in most of the non-
mushroom departments as well. A spring lunch starter of smooth pork terrine
with fresh spinach dressed with hazelnut oil and garlic croûtons was reported
as 'superb'. A summer dinner main course of salmon with green cabbage and
crisp potatoes was 'exceptional'. Desserts recommended include an iced terrine
of white chocolate and gingerbread served with a caramel sauce and fresh
dates, and a lemon crème brûlée and home-made lemon ice-cream served with
a lemon balm syrup. There is an urge to complexity in the cooking that might
be curbed in favour of more direct presentation. Slow service has been
commented on, and it doesn't help for late arrivals for a 9pm booking (arriving
by 9.30pm, but not telephoning in advance) to be told last orders are at 9pm.
Wine selection is very sound; the antipodean range is particularly fine with
Leeuwin, Redwood Valley and Stoneleigh represented. Mark-ups at the
expensive end can be high; otherwise, prices are fair with many good bottles
below £15. House wine is £7.75. CELLARMAN'S CHOICE: Beaujolais Blanc
1988, Brun, £14.75; New Zealand, Marlborough Pinot Noir 1987, Hunter's,
£16.95.

CHEF: David Everitt-Matthias PROPRIETORS: David and Helen Everitt-Matthias OPEN:
Mon to Sat; 12.30 to 1.30, 7.30 to 9.30 MEALS: Set L £17.50, Set D £24 SERVICE: not inc
CARDS: Access, Amex, Visa DETAILS: 30 seats. Private parties: 26 main room. Children
welcome. Smart dress preferred. Wheelchair access (1 step; also WC). Music. Air-
conditioned

Epicurean

On the Park Hotel, 38 Evesham Road,
Cheltenham GL52 2AH   COOKING 3
CHELTENHAM (0242) 222466   COST £22–£60

The restaurant occupies a section of the ground floor of a small Regency hotel,
once an elegant villa, that overlooks Pittville Park. The cool yellow and grey
colour scheme of restaurant and bar sits easily in large, gracious rooms. Patrick
McDonald has not deviated from his pursuit of haute cuisine perfection among
Cheltenham's crescents and terraces, though he has moderated his prices in an
effort to secure more custom – full marks for determination. All the frills

remain: that appetiser of black pudding on an apple purée, those excellent nibbles with drinks, very fine petits fours, and a granita (often grapefruit and champagne) between first and second courses. Foie gras and truffles may have taken a seat further back in the auditorium, but the skills mobilised have not lessened in dishes such as salmon tortellini with chive butter sauce, a parsley soup with scallops and oysters, very good stuffed pig's trotter, or a neo-British fillet of beef served with haggis and clapshot. It is quite encouraging that even for the lower-priced Sunday lunch, Patrick McDonald can produce ravioli of fish with little round pancakes of celeriac and small onions with a café-au-lait sauce, before a very fine joint of ham boiled in chicken stock, the moist slices surrounded by a medley of shaped vegetables, and a pleasing ending of 'winter fruit trifle', where the dried fruits were set in sweet aspic. His mind does not run on luxuries alone. 'My meal was better technically and in taste than most in the region' was the reaction of one who chanced upon the place after its relocation from Stow-on-the-Wold. It needs customers to give it experience and a chance to relax. The wine list shows signs of the old affection for making too much money – £70 for a 1975 Dow's vintage port is too much for a bottle that is available wholesale at £15 before VAT. There is some superior stuff in the cellar, but this is insufficiently balanced by interesting and cheaper material. House wines start at £9.75.

CHEF: Patrick McDonald   PROPRIETORS: Patrick and Claire McDonald   OPEN: Tue to Sun, exc Sun D; 12.30 to 2.30, 7 to 10.30   MEALS: Set L £15 to £25, Set D £25 to £45   SERVICE: not inc   CARDS: Access, Amex, Visa   DETAILS: 30 seats. Private parties: 18 private room. Vegetarian meals. Children's helpings. Wheelchair access. No music

Mayflower £

32–34 Clarence Street,
Cheltenham GL50 3NX
CHELTENHAM (0242) 522426 and 511580

COOKING 1
COST £15–£40

Mr Kong and his mother have taken over the kitchen and plan to reconstruct the menu, with more emphasis on vegetarian dishes. This well-liked venue currently supplies a familiar mixed bag of Cantonese, Pekinese and Szechuan specialities along the lines of paper-wrapped spicy ribs, spring rolls, crispy aromatic duck, sizzling beef with ginger and spring onion, and Szechuan king prawns. Mixed seafood hotpot has been particularly enjoyable. The list of around 120 wines is above the usual Chinese average. House Australian is £7.75.

CHEFS: Mr C.F. Kong and Mrs M.M. Kong   PROPRIETORS: the Kong family   OPEN: all week, exc Sun L; 12 to 1.45, 5.45 to 10.45 (11.15 Fri and Sat)   CLOSED: 25 to 27 Dec   MEALS: alc. Set L £7 to £8.50, Set D £15 to £27.50   SERVICE: not inc   CARDS: Access, Amex, Diners, Visa   DETAILS: 130 seats. Private parties: 90 main room, 40 private room. Vegetarian meals. Children welcome. Wheelchair access (1 step). Music. Air-conditioned. Fax: (0242) 251667

'The orange and kiwi pavlova appeared to be nothing more than a solid round of whipped cream, from which strenuous excavations unearthed the odd shard of meringue and sliver of fruit.'   On dining in Cumbria

CHESTER Cheshire   map 5

Abbey Green ♥ ⅝✳

1 Rufus Court, Northgate Street,
Chester CH1 2JH   COOKING 1
CHESTER (0244) 313251   COST £11–£27

'We should all have vegetarian meals from time to time,' comments a visitor to
this relocated restaurant which, for him, combines 'wonderful service with
inventive cooking and good-value wines'. 'Clean, smart, but perhaps lacking
the character of the older house' was the reaction of one who passed through a
second time. Latest reports reflect that the place is settling down now the move
to a conservationist shopping development is over. The evening is more serious
than lunch-time, when the crowds may provoke hasty cooking and deserts
among the desserts. The recipes have invention, avoiding the heavy-as-lead
school of vegetarian cookery. The Middle East, Caribbean and the Orient each
contributes its tithe in dishes such as tabouleh, green banana and coconut
curry, and Thai soup, while Italy and the Mediterranean are never far away in
dishes such as aubergines and olives with lemon couscous, or a layering of
pancakes with spinach, fromage frais and ratatouille. The desserts – raspberry
charlotte, fruit and nut flan, or fruit mousses on sponge bases – have plenty of
calories. Note that when Abbey Green moved, it also bifurcated. Meat- and
fish-eaters are catered for in the Garden House restaurant on the floor above.
Those who enter from Rufus Court will be faced with the choice of going up the
stairs or down them. Duncan Lochhead assures us that kitchens are separate, so
that beef stock does not rub shoulders with vegetables. Grandeur is not the
hallmark of the wine list, but that is no bad thing. Everything here is selected
purposefully and priced generously. It is a good list that invites experiment.
House wine is £6.50. CELLARMAN'S CHOICE: Cloudy Bay Sauvignon Blanc
1989, £18.80; St-Joseph, Clos de L'Arbalestrier 1985, £16.25.

CHEFS: Kevin Woods and Roger Hyde   PROPRIETOR: Duncan Lochhead   OPEN: Mon to
Sat, exc Mon D; 12 to 2.30, 6.30 to 10.15   MEALS: alc L. Set D £16.50   SERVICE: not inc,
card slips closed   CARDS: Access, Visa   DETAILS: 55 seats. 12 tables outside. Vegetarian
meals. Healthy eating options L. Children's helpings. No-smoking downstairs. Music

▲ *Chester Grosvenor Hotel, Arkle* ♥

Eastgate Street, Chester CH1 1LT   COOKING 4
CHESTER (0244) 324024   COST £27–£67

Curry bread, tomato and cheese bread, herb bread that tasted overwhelmingly
of dusty dried herbs: there surely is a variety of them, each cut for you on the
'chariot'. The Arkle has flounce and pretension. Although the menus say no
smoking, the tables are laid with ashtrays. Unexpectedly, once you cut through
the sing-song recitation of the menu and ignore the over-performance, the
waiters are excellent: well informed, helpful and efficient. Most people start in
the panelled, book-lined library bar (ignore the pianist at this point) before
going through to a pillared, windowless room with lots of pictures of horses on

the walls. Although the phrasing of the menu may put you off, persevere to try food that is much more expressive, more strident even, than the surroundings. A cassoulet of duck means a duck breast, game sausages, haricot beans and garlicky, crusted tomato sauce. Powerful stuff, it needed the plain but accurate vegetables. Terrine of bream layered with jellied fish stock was supported, if not knocked flying, by a strong rouille sauce that needed something firmer than wettish bream to stand up to it. This style may be contrasted with the more classic flavours of scallops with thin slices of Jerusalem artichoke and slim spears of asparagus in a light herby broth: first-rate, save for the rubbery snails that came along with it. There is ability to work in several modes: venison with bread mousseline and cranberries, chicken with truffles, wild mushrooms and spinach, osso buco with noodles and sweet wine sauce, or turbot à la basquaise. Puddings seduce the sweet-toothed, especially when they include things like an iced white chocolate soufflé with warm cherries and kirsch, or a parfait of white chocolate with 'quenelles' of white and dark chocolate and a passion-fruit coulis. Coffee and mignardises are good. Prices, regrettably, are very high. Lunch is better value and much enjoyed. Scratch the wine waiters' veneer of pretension and, it is reported, they show knowledge and enthusiasm – fortunately, since even the best-read oenophile might struggle with this 500-plus list. Eight vintages of Ch. Léoville-Barton from 1976 back to 1945 indicate the quality and depth, but there is ample evidence of interest elsewhere with carefully chosen Loires and Italians. Prices are dear, although there is concern to provide decent drinking under £15. House wine is from £9.50.

CELLARMAN'S CHOICE: Pouilly-Fuissé 1989, Gruber, £24; Pommard 1989, Clerget, £34.

CHEFS: Paul Reed and Simon Radley   PROPRIETORS: Grosvenor Estate Holdings   OPEN: Mon to Sat, exc Mon L; 12 to 2.30, 7 to 10.30   CLOSED: bank hols, 25 Dec to 1 Jan   MEALS: alc. Set L £16.50 to £20, Set D £37   SERVICE: not inc   CARDS: Access, Amex, Diners, Visa   DETAILS: 40 seats. Private parties: 10 main room. Car park. Children's helpings. Jacket and tie. No cigars/pipes in dining-room. Wheelchair access (also WC). Music. Air-conditioned   ACCOMMODATION: 86 rooms, all with bath/shower. Rooms for disabled. Lift. B&B £124 to £209. Deposit: 1 night. Children welcome. Baby facilities. Afternoon teas. Sauna. Air-conditioned. TV. Phone. Confirm by 6. Fax: (0244) 313246

CHICHESTER West Sussex   map 3

Thompsons

30A Southgate,
Chichester PO19 1DR   COOKING 1
CHICHESTER (0243) 528832   COST £17–£36

Masses of paintings give interest to this high-ceilinged and 'difficult' room on the first floor, reached from a 'nondescriptly Georgian' Chichester shopping street. Shoppers may be the reason why Jonas Tester is able to vary his repertoire from bangers and mash at lunch to *poularde agenaise* at dinner. Menus for both are quite long and do not change that frequently, but they show a chef's training in dishes like rillette of skate La Chapelle and darne of cod Dugléré at lunch, or turbot Medard (set on root vegetables, with a madeira sauce) at dinner. Most comments, other than about the rather hard bread, have

241

been favourable, slips tending to occur in the dead of winter. For sure the welcome is good, and the cooking is better than most experienced in Chichester these years past. The wine list is not long but is very nicely chosen. Pacherenc du Vic-Bilh, Natter's Sancerre, Coche's Meursault and Goyard's Mâcon: these are fashionable and potable names. Prices are not out of the way. House wines are £8.50.

CHEF: Jonas Tester   PROPRIETORS: Elly and Jonas Tester   OPEN: Mon to Sat, exc Mon L; 12.30 to 2, 7.30 to 11   CLOSED: first 2 weeks Jan   MEALS: alc. Set L £10, Set D £18.50 SERVICE: not inc   CARDS: Access, Visa   DETAILS: 45 seats. Private parties: 60 main room. Vegetarian meals. Children's helpings. Music

---

CHILGROVE West Sussex

map 3

White Horse Inn 🍷

Chilgrove PO18 9HX
EAST MARDEN (024 359) 219

COOKING 1*
COST £24–£37

Wistaria, beams, small-paned bows, ingles, nooks and crannies are all attributes of the place – and a wine list. 'Where someone serves me good wine, I happily stay longer' is one motto on the immense list compiled by Barry Phillips for this inn in the lee of the South Downs. The food is enjoyed as well. Neil Rusbridger steers a course between country classics (braised leg of lamb with rosemary-scented gravy) and more restaurant fare (pork fillet with green peppercorns and noodles). And he puts on a more elaborate set of dishes for dinner. Daily fish is recommended – it may be striped bass, Dover sole or lobster; game makes its appearance at night; ice-creams and good home-made desserts fill many human crannies. One remark was that the food was fair match for the wine, but that steadier service and more frills and furbelows to the setting would make for more of an event. The Phillipses have kept close to the original intentions of the house, and praise be for their consistency. Even an enthusiast might be daunted by the blockbuster wine list, now an institution. Close reading reveals bargains and many good half-bottles. Slow readers should stray no further than the very adequate house selection (from £8.50), while the profligate are well served with an abundance of £100 clarets. CELLARMAN'S CHOICE: Muscadet, Cuvée de Millenaise 1989, Marquis de Goulaine, £11.25; Bordeaux, Dom. de Cambes 1989, £12.50.

CHEF: Neil Rusbridger   PROPRIETORS: Dorothea and Barry Phillips, and Neil Rusbridger OPEN: Tue to Sat; 12 to 2, 7 to 9.30 (10.30 during Chichester theatre season)   CLOSED: 3 weeks Feb, 1 week Oct   MEALS: Set L £16.50, Set D £22 to £23.50   SERVICE: 10% (12.5% Sat), card slips closed   CARDS: Access, Diners, Visa   DETAILS: 65 seats. Private parties: 30 main room, 12 and 30 private rooms. Car park. Vegetarian meals. Children's helpings. No cigars/pipes until after meals. Wheelchair access (also WC). Music. Air-conditioned. Fax: (024 359) 301

All details are as accurate as possible at the time of going to press, but chefs and owners often change, and it is wise to check by telephone before making a special journey. Many readers have been disappointed when set-price bargain meals are no longer available. Ask when booking.

CHINNOR Oxfordshire   map 2

Sir Charles Napier Inn ▮

Sprigg's Alley,
nr Chinnor OX9 4BX   COOKING 1
RADNAGE (0494) 483011   COST £26–£41

Take the Sprigg's Alley lane off the Bledlow Ridge out of Chinnor. Although
only 10 minutes from the motorway, and past wide quarrying gashes, the inn is
in deep country. This is a former pub that excites regulars to great loyalty and
also inspires some irritation. The cooking is often good. An autumn meal took
in ceps in puff pastry with truffle sauce, grilled sardines with olive oil, liver
and bacon with a bordelaise sauce, roast grouse with a port gravy, grilled
swordfish in smoked salmon parcels with a lobster sauce ('a bit contrived and
out of character'), mundane vegetables, and then summer (autumn) pudding,
chocolate gâteau and some well-kept cheese. Sunday roasts are pronounced
good. Lunch is a shorter and sometimes scrappier menu. Service is informal, as
is the whole place, which can lead to long waits. You take this according to
your preferences. Another problem for new customers is the price, which
seems to be high, particularly as portions can be small: 'I think bread-and-
butter pudding should be a helping, not a rectangular portion.' The wines are a
joy; prices, apart from at the upper end where mark-ups seem to push
unreasonably, are very fair. Half-bottles abound, and there are many very
decent bottles well below £12. California and Australasia receive especially
good treatment, with Leeuwin Chardonnay and the Santa Barbera Nebbiolo 'Il
Podere' catching the eye. The 'House Selection' is rather more than the usual
collection of modest bottles; most customers would do well to go no further.
House wine is £9.25. CELLARMAN'S CHOICE: New Zealand, Chardonnay 1990,
Redwood Valley Estate, £16.50; Haut-Médoc, Ch. Lanessan 1985, £18.75.

CHEF: Batiste Tolu   PROPRIETORS: the Griffiths family   OPEN: Tue to Sun, exc Sun D (also
L bank hol Mons); 12 to 2 (3 Sun), 7.30 to 10 (10.30 Fri and Sat)   MEALS: alc. Set L £15, Set
D £17.50   SERVICE: 10% L, 12.5% D, card slips closed   CARDS: Access, Visa   DETAILS: 65
seats. 10 tables outside. Private parties: 45 main room, 25 and 45 private rooms. Car park.
Vegetarian meals. Children's helpings L. No children under 7 D. No cigars/pipes in dining-
room. Wheelchair access. Music. Air-conditioned

CHOBHAM Surrey   map 3

Quails | NEW ENTRY |

1 Bagshot Road,
Chobham GU24 8BP   COOKING 1*
CHOBHAM (0276) 858491   COST £18–£37

The Wale family run this pleasant restaurant in a converted shop in the centre
of town. Outside, it is dark blue and red; inside, the colours are cream, pink
and green with paintings on the walls and a circular bar dividing the two
dining areas. A modern *carte* featuring dishes such as green-lipped mussels in
pesto butter, aromatic crispy duck with orange and ginger, and seafood
brochette with tomato and red pepper coulis is backed up by monthly-

changing fixed-price menus devoted to French regional cooking. A Normandy menu that included salad of fresh prawns and mussels with new potatoes, 'brilliant' Camembert tartlet with melt-in-the-mouth pastry, and suprême of chicken with tarragon sauce and pork chop in cider sauce was enjoyed on one evening. Dishes are served with glasses of French country wines. Other recommendations have included smoked salmon parfait, saddle of wild rabbit, and game sausages with bubble and squeak. Desserts are the likes of steamed pecan pudding with butterscotch sauce, and chocolate truffle torte. Service is efficient, although the waitresses seem to lack knowledge. A wide-ranging list of around 100 wines includes 11 French country wines from £8.50.

CHEF: Christopher Wale   PROPRIETORS: the Wale family   OPEN: Tue to Sun, exc Sat L and Sun D; 12 to 2, 7 to 10   MEALS: alc, Set Sun L £12.95, Sct L and D £14.95   SERVICE: not inc   CARDS: Access, Amex, Diners, Visa   DETAILS: 46 seats. Private parties: 46 main room. Car park. Vegetarian meals. Children welcome. Wheelchair access. Music. Air-conditioned

---

CLAYGATE Surrey   map 3

Les Alouettes

7 High Street,
Claygate KT10 0JW   COOKING 3
ESHER (0372) 464882   COST £28–£48

The house must once have been a bijou residence in half-timber, bang on the road junction in the centre of Claygate, next to the Royal British Legion. The inside has not sacrificed plush comfort to any stark modernity, and the main room with small mezzanine is a restful place to talk, listen and dine. Michel Perraud continues to explore modern haute cuisine by means of a long seasonal *carte* supplemented by a daily *prix fixe* – we write in French to warn you that it is the language of the restaurant. However, 'my *poussin* was chicken,' remarked one who also hunted for the named langoustines in a fish terrine, so perhaps when you read '*Cannette du Gressingham Rôtie Crispy*' you won't report the owner to the Académie Française. Follow appetisers of mussels in a light curry butter sauce and smoked salmon toasts with perhaps a warm potato and haddock salad or a papillote of wild mushrooms. First courses on the spring menu sort out as six fish or shellfish, one foie gras and one mushroom and asparagus feuilleté: not good planning. Main courses may, for instance on the daily menu, include slow-cooked daube of beef, though the *carte* wields frying-pan or roasting-tray almost to the exclusion of the casserole. Flavours, such as endive with pigeon, ginger with chicken stuffed with prawns, basil with lamb or cranberries with liver, are deployed with conviction and skill. They surface again in the classically inclined sweet course – a Grand Marnier soufflé given an exact point by caramelised orange segments and texture by well-executed *tuile d'amandes*. Service does not do well here – 'leisurely at best' is one view. 'My request for either duck, venison, pigeon or lamb was flatly refused because I requested them well-done. Eventually I was grudgingly allowed carré of lamb.' This person's dilemma is referred to in 'Your rights in restaurants' at the end of this book. The menu makes no allusion to the chef's insistence on cooking meats lightly. It is difficult to know what the customer should do. The wine list is French and not cheap. House wine is £11.50.

CHEF: Michel Perraud PROPRIETOR: Steve Christou OPEN: Mon to Sat, exc Sat L; 12.15 to 2, 7 to 9.30 (10 Fri and Sat) CLOSED: 12 to 28 Aug MEALS: alc. Set L and D £22.50 SERVICE: net prices, card slips closed CARDS: Access, Amex, Diners, Visa DETAILS: 75 seats. Private parties: 85 main room. Children's helpings. Smart dress preferred. Wheelchair access (3 steps). Music. Air-conditioned. Fax: (0372) 465337

Le Petit Pierrot

4 The Parade, Claygate KT10 0NU   COOKING 2
ESHER (0372) 465105   COST £16–£30

The Brichots' restaurant, designed to resemble a circus tent, is a favourite with readers: it is one of the few venues in the area that opens on Monday, a full menu is available lunch and dinner, and the food retains its authentic French accent. The atmosphere is congenial, although the Muzak is not to everyone's taste and the rather cramped dining-room can cause problems and irritation for non-smokers. Fish dishes earn a lot of recommendations: for example, fish soup with sherry and crab dumplings; grilled sea bream with thyme; 'magnificent' scallops and scampi in saffron and ginger sauce with wild rice. Otherwise, there have been votes for wild mushrooms baked in filo pastry with a pool of avocado sauce, navarin of lamb, 'succulent' roast squab pigeon in black cherry sauce, and roast rack of lamb. Desserts seem to be the stars of the show: coconut parfait with praline sauce, gâteau maison and crème caramel have been enthusiastically reported. The wine list is patriotically French. House wine is £7.95.

CHEF: Jean-Pierre Brichot PROPRIETORS: Jean-Pierre and Annie Brichot OPEN: Mon to Sat, exc Sat L; 12.15 to 2.30, 7.15 to 10.30 MEALS: Set L £9.95 to £16.85, Set D £18.95 SERVICE: not inc CARDS: Access, Amex, Diners, Visa DETAILS: 30 seats. No children under 9. Smart dress preferred. Wheelchair access. Music. Air-conditioned

---

CLEEVE HILL Gloucestershire   map 2

▲ Redmond's ▮ ⁵✳

Cleeve Hill, Cheltenham GL52 3PR   COOKING 3*
CHELTENHAM (0242) 672017   COST £22–£45

Last year was not a good one for the Haywards, but it gets better. For sure, the tone of reports in 1991/1992 warmed by several degrees as winter turned to spring, and all hopes are for a return to form as the months pass. The view is wonderful, and the dining-room – a happy blend of country and sophistication – is a good space in which to eat. The rooms for staying in are a boon, avoiding hotel luxury and hotel prices. An autumn meal began with mozzarella and basil tart with a varied and well-dressed salad. Then there was chicken with ginger and lemon butter sauce ('clear, clean flavours, an appetising harmony') accompanied by a very good crisp potato galette with melting interior, cabbage and almonds, parsnip purée and grated courgette. Hot ginger soufflé came with apple and calvados ice-cream. Cheeses arrived with three sorts of home-made biscuits. Redmond Hayward likes to bake tarts – they sometimes pop up in every course – and spices, ginger particularly, with cinnamon running it a close second. Hot soufflés are a passion too, and go down well with the public. A prune and armagnac one with hot chocolate sauce is especially remembered – as fondly as the bread-and-butter pudding or the queen of puddings, also strong favourites. The flavours deployed throughout the menu may threaten coarse strength but they are handled with care, though not usually with cowardice. This means the cooking has character, yet is light, and also has variety. One group in the winter praised first the little pizza appetisers and then a meal that included chicken liver parfait with apricot chutney, scallop and squid salad, ragoût of rabbit with celeriac, madeira and rosemary, red mullet with ginger, brill stuffed with a scallop mousse, and best end of lamb with a light curry sauce: a good range involving several tastes and techniques, though generally avoiding the 'hearty plenty' of new-wave peasant cooking. Things can run quite slowly on busy nights. Pippa Hayward looks after the customers, the wines and the babies (her own) with considerable aplomb. The wine list went through a fallow patch but now seems back on form. The new-look presentation dispels any lingering doubts; this is now one of the clearest as well as one of the best-structured restaurant lists to be found. Half-bottles are plentiful, and prices are very fair; a half-dozen house wines, available by the glass, add to customer-friendliness as does Mrs Hayward's frequently reported helpful advice. House wines are from £8.95. CELLARMAN'S CHOICE: Washington State, Chardonnay 1988, Stewart Vineyards, £16.25; Mercurey 1987, Juillot, £18.

CHEF: Redmond Hayward   PROPRIETORS: Redmond and Pippa Hayward   OPEN: all week, exc L Mon and Sat, and Sun D; 12.30 to 2, 7.15 to 10   CLOSED: first week Jan   MEALS: Set L £17.50 to £23, Set D £32 to £36   SERVICE: net prices, card slips closed   CARDS: Access, Visa   DETAILS: 36 seats. Private parties: 24 main room, 12 private room. Car park. Children's helpings on request. No smoking in dining-room. No music ACCOMMODATION: 5 rooms, all with bath/shower. B&B £49 to £75. Children welcome. Baby facilities. Garden. TV. Doors close at midnight. Confirm by 6

CLITHEROE Lancashire   map 5

Auctioneer

New Market Street, Clitheroe BB7 2JW   COOKING 2
CLITHEROE (0200) 27153   COST £17–£42

The old cattle market, the ruins of Clitheroe Castle and magnificent hills further away make a good set of views from the conservatory extension of this popular and fairly priced restaurant. Inside, the tables are close-packed and business is normally quite brisk, but there is no discomfort. Lunch offers a short *carte*, at dinner the price is fixed, but the choice is flexible and the dishes more complicated. Sundays are set-price and notable value. Henk Van Heumen has not given up a wish to elaborate: chicken is wrapped round fillet of beef, chicken breast is stuffed with crab mousse, lamb is wrapped in filo. Fruit flavourings are also enjoyed: grapes and almonds with brill, pear with a Stilton and walnut mousse, avocado with liver, apricot with chicken or nectarine with crab. Flavours often meld, but not invariably: the nectarine and crab was an unequal contest, for instance. But an assured technique means flavours are enjoyed, sauces competent and overcooking is rare. Good supply lines have led to praise for Basque fish soup, fish in general, Lancashire duck, and wild boar from South Wales. Some visitors have felt vegetables could be better, but criticism is stilled when they taste a dish of spinach with shallots and cream. Method and complexity do not dominate everything; the chefs are quite capable of letting the raw materials shine through. Service may be good, or it may be flighty: it depends who is on duty. The wine list is sound and not dear. House wine is £9.

CHEFS: Henk Van Heumen and Michael Heathcote PROPRIETORS: Henk and Frances Van Heumen OPEN: Tue to Sun; 12 to 1.30, 7 to 9.30 MEALS: alc L. Set Sun L £10.75, Set D from £18.50. Minimum £5.75 L SERVICE: not inc CARDS: Access, Visa DETAILS: 44 seats. Private parties: 24 private room. Vegetarian meals. Children's helpings L. Smart dress preferred. Music

Brown's Bistro

10 York Street, Clitheroe BB7 2DL COOKING 1
CLITHEROE (0200) 26928 COST £22–£36

A wall of menus from famous chefs, complete with autographs, is no guide to the cooking at Brown's, a bistro resplendent. Good value is to be had from a menu that works the old repertoire of stuffed mushrooms, chicken livers and madeira sauce, duck with orange, chicken Kiev, plenty of vegetables and puddings, and sweets that may include a steamed sponge. No nonsense, plenty of welcome and an appreciative audience all add to the picture. The wine list is affordable, though details are scant. Prices are as fair as those for the food. House wines are £6.50.

CHEFS: David Brown, Ian Brown and Nick Warf PROPRIETORS: David and Carole Brown OPEN: Mon to Sat, exc Sat L; 12 to 1.45, 7 to 10 MEALS: alc SERVICE: not inc, card slips closed CARDS: Access, Visa DETAILS: 68 seats. Private parties: 30 main room. Vegetarian meals. Children's helpings. Wheelchair access (2 steps; also WC). Music. Air-conditioned

---

CLUN Shropshire map 4

▲ Old Post Office ▮

9 The Square, Clun SY7 8JA COOKING 2*
CLUN (0588) 640687 COST £21–£40

Clun has a lot going for it: frontier town, the last bit of home before pressing on towards the bare hills beyond. Savour the roofscapes, the winding streets and the castle mound. Enjoy a night at the Old Post Office; you won't be charged a lot, and almost everyone agrees that the Arbuthnots make good hosts. The restaurant is in the post office; then comes a small sitting area; finally there are more tables in an extension. Richard Arbuthnot is not out of touch with the wider world. His short menu, therefore, reads well, with dishes such as monkfish with sesame and ginger vinaigrette; chicken sausage with truffle, wild rice and stock sauce; guinea-fowl on sauerkraut with madeira sauce and black and white pudding; or grilled lamb with polenta. People have also approved the execution of sauté scallops with coriander, a hot mousse of scallop and crab, well-turned-out lamb baked in filo with garlic, a remarkable collection of British cheeses, decent vegetables, and desserts such as lemon tart (a favourite), damson ice-cream (another favourite) or chocolate 'slab' with mango coulis. Performance, however, is not entirely even. At lunch, there is a sensible listing of real food at realistic prices. Nothing is *too* large – you can have starter-size portions if that's what you want – but if the wind has blown too cold of a morning, it will set you up for the last lap to dinner. The wine list is one of the most enjoyable and intelligent: neither over-long nor overpriced, it sets the New Zealand Martinborough Pinot Noir between the bourgeois Ch. Cissac and a Tuscan Sangiovese. The focus is on the growing number of excellent middle-range wines that combine individuality with quality. Prices are all very fair, and good half-bottles allow further economy and abstinence (if you are not occupying one of the two rooms, that is). House wines are from £6.95. CELLARMAN'S CHOICE: Côtes-du-Rhône-Villages, Seguret Blanc 1989, Meffre, £12.25; Victoria, Bailey's Shiraz 1986, £14.75.

CHEF: Richard Arbuthnot   PROPRIETORS: Anne and Richard Arbuthnot   OPEN: Wed to Sun, exc Wed L (bookings only L); 12.30 to 1.30, 7.15 to 9.30   CLOSED: 1 week after Aug bank hol, 24 Dec to 3 Jan, 22 Jan to 14 Mar   MEALS: alc   SERVICE: not inc   CARDS: Access, Visa   DETAILS: 30 seats. 2 tables outside. Private parties: 25 main room. Vegetarian meals. Children welcome. No cigars/pipes in dining-room. Music   ACCOMMODATION: 2 rooms. B&B £22 to £44. Children welcome. Baby facilities. Doors close at midnight. Confirm by 6 (*The Which? Hotel Guide*)

COCKERMOUTH Cumbria   map 7

Quince & Medlar ⚡✳ £

13 Castlegate, Cockermouth CA13 9EU	COOKING 1
COCKERMOUTH (0900) 823579	COST £16–£21

The house is at the end of a terrace. By purchasing next door, the Le Vois have added a sitting area to their dining-room. Many come to try the serious vegetarian cooking at none too high a price. Meat-eaters come too. Cooking is substantial, and the recipes are creative and sometimes very successful. Where last year we had the comment that sauces seemed too spare, this had an inspector reflecting that sometimes it was the very sauce that made the dish – otherwise perhaps too heavy or lacking variety of flavour. He also remarked that some advertised tastes did not really come through. Contrast this with one visitor heady with relief that her teenage daughter, never easy to please, had got what she wanted after they had eaten blinis with mushrooms and courgettes, roasted hazelnut crown with lemon, cheese and parsley stuffing and an asparagus sauce, then finished with a ginger and pear crunch. The wine list is short, yet acceptable and inexpensive. There are lots of fruit cordials. House wine is £5.80.

CHEF: Colin Le Voi   PROPRIETORS: Louisa and Colin Le Voi   OPEN: Tue to Sun, D only; 7 to 9.30   CLOSED: 3 weeks Feb, 1 week Nov   MEALS: alc   SERVICE: not inc, card slips closed   CARDS: Access, Visa   DETAILS: 26 seats. Private parties: 14 main room. Vegetarian meals. Children restricted. Smart dress preferred. No smoking. Music

---

The Good Food Guide *is a registered trade mark of Consumers' Association Ltd.*

COGGESHALL Essex   map 3

Baumann's Brasserie

4–6 Stoneham Street, Coggeshall CO6 1TT   COOKING 1
COGGESHALL (0376) 561453   COST £15–£40

The brasserie is more of a restaurant, with a *carte*, various cheaper set-price
menus at lunch and dinner, and full-dress table settings and service – even if
the latter is sometimes lacking supervision and attack. Baumann's occupies a
picturesque village position and premises: greens outside, real pictures inside
(from the late Peter Langan, who founded the restaurant in the first place). The
cooking is not brasserie either. It takes in some modern standards like pesto,
pastrami, gravlax and grilled meats, and it harks back to early times with some
fruit accompaniments like the peach and onion sauce offered in the spring with
duck. The promise of the menu is not always met by performance. This can be
catastrophic. Everyone praises the vegetable cookery and the desserts; many
comment on the hit-and-miss of sauces and on the timing of meat and fish. The
generally happy welcome is enhanced by the sound wine list, which groups by
colour and weight and has very good materials to work from. Prices are
distinctly drinker-friendly. House wines are from £8.

CHEFS: Mark Baumann, Doug Wright and Lee Cousins   PROPRIETORS: Baumann's
Brasserie Ltd   OPEN: Tue to Sun, exc Sat L and Sun D; 12.30 to 2 (2.30 Sun), 7.30 to 10
MEALS: alc. Set business L £9.95, Set Sun L £12.95, Set D £14 to £25   SERVICE: not inc, card
slips closed   CARDS: Access, Amex, Visa   DETAILS: 75 seats. Private parties: 75 main
room. Children's helpings. Music

COLCHESTER Essex   map 3

Warehouse Brasserie £

12A Chapel Street North,
Colchester CO2 7AT   COOKING 2
COLCHESTER (0206) 765656   COST £15–£25

Nothing changes in this admirable brasserie close to the ABC Bingo Hall and
the multi-storey car park. The founder-owners have sold to their chef, who has
been joined in partnership by Mel Burley, but principles do not shift and the
chefs and most of the staff are familiar faces. Value for money is remarkable,
and the cooking is an eclectic mix, with a noticeable vegetarian bias and
influences from the Far East and the Mediterranean as well as Britain. Meals
are flexible: have a couple of starters, a single dish or a three-course meal.
Soups such as tomato and basil or carrot and coriander come with excellent,
dark home-made bread. Chicken satay, chargrilled duck and pigeon breasts
with juniper berries and blackcurrants have been well reported. Among the
vegetarian dishes there have been votes for spinach gnocchi in fresh tomato
sauce, and nut and cheese puff-pastry parcels with mushroom and sherry
sauce. Vegetables are reliably fresh and cooked to perfection. Desserts
sometimes fade, but ever-popular brown bread ice-cream, and passion-fruit
sorbet with home-made almond biscuits, have pleased. The wine list may be
short but, given the choices of makers and countries of origin, it is very sound

and prices are admirably fair. It does help to have good merchants in the district, but the list rises above that to include nice little extras unfamiliar to Essex-Man. House wine is £6.95.

CHEFS: Anthony Brooks, Stuart Mott and Gillian Griffith   PROPRIETORS: Anthony Brooks and Mel Burley   OPEN: Mon to Sat (pre- and post-theatre D by arrangement); 12 to 2, 7 to 10   MEALS: alc   SERVICE: not inc   CARDS: Access, Visa   DETAILS: 80 seats. Private parties: 100 main room. Children's helpings. Wheelchair access. No music. Air conditioned

---

COLERNE Wiltshire   map 2

▲ *Lucknam Park*

Colerne SN14 8AZ   COOKING 3*
BATH (0225) 742777   COST £30–£52

Everyone must have heard of Lucknam Park: the board of governors of the BBC seem to have spent much of the year in semi-public colloquy here. No doubt they number trenchermen; they must also be millionaires. The house is a mixture of classical motifs, surrounded by flat grounds and a plateau of land occupied by an airfield (only used in time of war, the management assures you). There has been much restoration: conference suites and accommodation in the stables, a spacious front hall and public rooms, and a dining-room that is nearly successful with its painted ceiling of gold-tinged clouds but does not have the flair of the rest of the house. Michael Womersley seems set to make his mark here, though he seems intent on doing it with a regularly repeated set of dishes. A panaché of fish with red pepper sorbet has been a firm favourite since his arrival; a meal eaten in the summer of 1991 could be nearly replicated from a spring menu of 1992. It does not speak loudly of responding to the markets. The style is advanced neo-classical, as befits a graduate of the schools of Raymond Blanc, Marc Meneau and Michel Guérard. Dishes such as a gâteau of foie gras, truffle, chicken and pistachio with a morel Chantilly cream and brioche, and a salmis of pigeon with aubergine and mozzarella are careful, elaborate and successful. Elaboration comes also into a dessert of strawberries where the fruit is stuffed with its ice-cream, plus strawberries Eton Mess-style in a tuile basket, and a soufflé to finish the plate off. Bags of spun sugar, of course. Fish cookery gets varied treatment, from the meaty brill with an Hermitage and star-anise sauce, to skate with an artichoke mousse and a light chicken stock sauce. Long gone are the days of everything sweet and sour, even if the confit of duck is lusciously tender with figs, sultanas and almonds in a small pastry case beside the breast. Flavours are more sophisticated than that: hence the liquorice sauce with hot chocolate pudding – 'subtle and delicious', as the commentator said. Service is of course a ballet of synchronicity, but people have found the prices depressing. The wine list shows this particularly, with high mark-ups removing many bottles that might otherwise be affordable. The cellar is a good one, for France at least, but the usual assistance on the fiscal front from the New World is hardly forthcoming. House wines are £14.95.

See inside the front cover for an explanation of the symbols used at the tops of entries.

CHEF: Michael Womersley PROPRIETOR: Robert Carter OPEN: all week; 12.30 to 2, 7.30 to 9.30 MEALS: Set L £17.50 to £19.50, Set D £35 SERVICE: not inc, card slips closed CARDS: Access, Amex, Diners, Visa DETAILS: 75 seats. Private parties: 75 main room, 10, 20 and 25 private rooms. Car park. Vegetarian meals. No children under 10. Jacket and tie. No pipes in dining-room. Wheelchair access (also WC)

CONSETT Co Durham   map 7

Pavilion £

2 Station Road, Consett DH8 5RL   COOKING 1
CONSETT (0207) 503388   COST £10–£37

'Very consistent and highly commended. The only fault I can find is that you need to plan a visit so far ahead because it's always booked up,' writes a Tyneside reporter. The Westernised Cantonese menu of around 150 dishes has its quota of sizzlers and bird's nests, but also includes some Peking and Szechuan specialities, such as fried beef in fish-flavoured sauce and chicken with preserved cabbage. It has also adopted the idea of a 'health and vegetarian menu' from restaurants in Newcastle's Chinatown with everything from rainbow soup to sweet-and-sour cashew-nuts. Set meals and special banquet menus may include some dishes not on the standard menu, such as chicken breast with Cointreau and orange sauce. House French is £6.30.

CHEF: Wan Yip PROPRIETORS: the Yip family OPEN: all week D, Thur to Sat L; 12 to 1.30, 6.30 to 10.30 CLOSED: 24 to 26 Dec, 1 Jan MEALS: alc. Set D £12.50 to £17 SERVICE: not inc CARDS: Access, Amex, Diners, Visa DETAILS: 100 seats. Private parties: 100 main room. Vegetarian meals. Healthy eating options. Children welcome. Smart dress preferred. Music. Air-conditioned

---

CORSE LAWN Gloucestershire   map 2

▲ Corse Lawn House Hotel

Corse Lawn GL19 4LZ
GLOUCESTER (0452) 780479 and 780771   COOKING 3
on B4211, 5m SW of Tewkesbury   COST £19–£51

An elegant Queen Anne house, Corse Lawn has latterday neo-elegant wings appended. There is less lawn than water: a big ornamental pond in front, a swimming-pool at the back. An accusation that 'the place has got too large and impersonal' is countered by affirmations of Denis Hine's sociability. 'The battle with the recession has taught us a lot,' he says. Apart from moderated prices, the lesson appears to be stronger management insistence on diligent service – as substantiated in a report from the dining-room: 'They were unusually knowledgeable about what went on in the kitchen. Very professional without being robots.' Indeed, accounts this year launch a return to consistent quality. The handsome vanilla and dark-wood dining-room is well served by Baba Hine's efforts; faintly *ancien régime*, and none the worse for that. 'This style of cooking is a welcome relief from the standard modern menu,' comments a reader. Sauce is king – hot crab tart was abetted by a 'subtle hollandaise'; 'beautifully timed' pigeon breasts were baked in 'a fruity sauce made with

251

gravy and good-quality red wine: something other than the endlessly repeated stock reduction'. Guinea-fowl, duck, veal, venison and oxtail make regular appearances. Cheeses are well-sourced and properly maintained. Cheaper bar meals are available, lunch and dinner. The excellent wide-ranging wine list is marred by old-fashioned mark-ups; there is little of stature below £16, although some relief is provided by a decent selection available by the glass, and good half-bottles, albeit scattered unevenly with little sense of structure. House wine is £8.50. CELLARMAN'S CHOICE: Mâcon Fuissé 1989, J.J. Vincent, £17.90; Fronsac, Ch. Plain-Point 1986, £16.50.

CHEF: Baba Hine   PROPRIETORS: Denis, Baba and Giles Hine   OPEN: all week; 12.30 to 2, 7 to 10   MEALS: alc. Set L £10 to £15.95, Set D £12.50 to £23.50. Bar meals   SERVICE: not inc, card slips closed   CARDS: Access, Amex, Diners, Visa   DETAILS: 45 seats. 8 tables outside. Private parties: 55 main room, 24 and 35 private rooms. Car park. Vegetarian meals. Children's helpings. Wheelchair access (also WC). No music   ACCOMMODATION: 19 rooms, all with bath/shower. Rooms for disabled. B&B £70 to £90. Children welcome. Baby facilities. Pets welcome. Afternoon teas. Garden. Swimming-pool. Tennis. TV. Phone. Doors close at midnight. Confirm by 6. Fax:(0452) 780840 (*The Which? Hotel Guide*)

COSHAM Hampshire   map 2

Barnards

109 High Street, Cosham PO6 3BB   COOKING 2
COSHAM (0705) 370226   COST £17–£34

Cosham remains home to a restaurant that other parts of Solent City might envy. David Barnard cooks, his wife Sandie provides a welcome the warmth of which lifts the visitor above the humdrum surroundings – already subject to nice touches of crisp linen, flowers, table settings, even hand-carved butter pats. The menu, once all in French, has turned to our native tongue but has not deserted the kitchen's identification with mainstream classic French cooking. This is manfully interpreted, often (as with soufflés, which are a strong point) with style. Positive reaction has been recorded for flavourful onion soup; rough cut, strong-tasting duck terrine; chicken pancakes; cheese soufflés; salmon or brill with watercress sauce; or fancy puddings – even baked Alaska and strawberry fritters. Items such as ice-creams, truffles and bread are home-made here, and all those sounds from the kitchen bear witness to the effort that goes into the rest of it. As one reader urged, 'May there be more places with such careful attentiveness, value (especially the lunch menu) and consistency.' Once a month there is a gastronomic evening with a set menu inclusive or exclusive of wine. The wine list is not long, but offers decent value. House wines are £7.95.

CHEF: David Frank Barnard   PROPRIETORS: Mr and Mrs D.F. Barnard   OPEN: Tue to Sat, exc Sat L; 12 to 2, 7.30 to 10   MEALS: alc. Set L £12.95, Set D Tue to Fri £18.50   SERVICE: net prices, card slips closed   CARDS: Access, Visa   DETAILS: 20 seats. Private parties: 20 main room. Children's helpings. Wheelchair access. Music

---

Card slips closed *in the details at the end of an entry indicates that the total on the slips of credit cards is closed when handed over for signature.*

CRANLEIGH Surrey   map 3

Restaurant Bonnet

High Street, Cranleigh GU6 8AE   COOKING 2
CRANLEIGH (0483) 273889   COST £19–£36

'It looks understated,' says one visitor who finds this encouraging, which denotes, perhaps, a certain French acceptance of the inevitability of decent cooking. The Surrey architecture houses Anglo-French restaurant food, with very French service. Parking is difficult. Prices are set; at night they include an aperitif and can take in house wine as well. Feuilleté of wild mushrooms, mussel, apple and curry soup, chicken breast with watercress sauce or leg of duck with honey sauce place the style firmly in the context of the conventions of the 1980s, but execution and presentation are sensitive and well-accepted. Desserts are enjoyable, too: a meringue with the right degree of crunch and chew, a regular pine-kernel tart with egg custard, excellent petits fours. The wine list is short, but many will want to take up the offer of house wine in the cost of dinner.

CHEF: Jean Pierre Bonnet   PROPRIETORS: Jean Pierre and Ann Bonnet   OPEN: Tue to Sun, exc Sat L and Sun D; 12 to 2, 7 to 10   MEALS: Set L £11.50 to £15.50, Set D £20.50 to £29.75   SERVICE: not inc, card slips closed   CARDS: Access, Amex, Visa   DETAILS: 50 seats. Private parties: 35 main room. Children welcome. Smart dress preferred. No pipes in dining-room. Wheelchair access (1 step). Music

CROYDE Devon   map 1

▲ Whiteleaf at Croyde ▼ £

Croyde EX33 1PN   COOKING 2
CROYDE (0271) 890266   COST £19–£26

The Wallingtons' house looks like, and is, a B&B – but how much more! David Wallington cooks and does the wine, Flo does the service side. It is a small show, and coping with such pressures as random opening and unbooked custom are too much for it. So expect a certain amount of gentle organisation. Most customers stay the night, but there is room for a couple of outsiders who will be gently organised as well. The cooking is unexpected: a strong vein of British traditional, balanced by an equal head-over-heels love affair with things Italian. So game pie may come up on the same night as osso buco; steak and kidney with venison braised in Barolo. A person who asked for vegetarian food was given eggs en cocotte with a bundle of asparagus followed by five-inch towers of Yorkshire pudding filled with buttered rice and peas and a mushroom sauce, and a range of vegetables that included beetroot and cumin crumble – not bad for a one-man kitchen. There is substance in the food: 'We never made it to the end of the five-course dinners.' There can sometimes be moments when finesse is absent. Breads, croissants and brioches are all home-made; orange juice is fresh. Mr Wallington knows his wines; the love affair with Italy extends to five vintages of Sassicaia, but most people will be happy to stay with good basic Chianti or one of the fairly priced petits châteaux. Half-bottles are bountiful. House wine is £8. CELLARMAN'S CHOICE: Victoria,

Dry Muscat Blanc 1990, Brown Brothers, £9.60; Brouilly, Ch. des Tours 1991, £11.15.

CHEF: David Wallington PROPRIETORS: David and Florence Wallington OPEN: all week, D only; 7.30 to 8.30 CLOSED: 2 weeks Apr, 2 weeks July, 2 weeks Oct MEALS: Set D £15 to £19.50 SERVICE: net prices, card slips closed CARDS: Access, Visa DETAILS: 16 seats. Car park. Children's helpings. Smart dress preferred. No music ACCOMMODATION: 3 rooms, all with bath/shower. B&B £34.50 to £54. Deposit: £25. Children welcome. Baby facilities. Pets welcome. Garden. TV. Phone. Doors close at midnight. Confirm by 5 (*The Which? Hotel Guide*)

CROYDON Surrey — map 3

34 Surrey Street £

34 Surrey Street, Croydon CR0 1RJ
081-686 0586

COOKING 1
COST £18–£32

A little bit American, little bit Cajun, little bit steak house, little bit fish restaurant, number 34 is civilised, cheerful, loud and some relief from the pavements of Surrey Street itself – awash with squashed fruit from the daytime market. Listen to jazz, sit in the conservatory and watch waiters in short trousers. Eat from a daily menu offering 10 fish specials – from marlin, barracuda and swordfish to shark – or from the *carte* that runs through many ways with salmon (hash, broiled with a Texas sauce), lots of prawns (deep-fried with chilli, called Cajun popcorn, or butterflied with garlic, lemon and polenta) and lots of steaks. Mexico and the American south are the chief inspirations. Puddings may be a 'refrigerated afterthought'. The wine list is more than adequate, has some drinkable Californians, and won't damage the wallet. Amiable service can be overwhelmed by business. House wine is £6.95.

CHEF: Malcom John PROPRIETOR: Mr Patel OPEN: all week, exc Sat L and Sun D; 12 to 2.45, 6 to 10.45 CLOSED: Christmas MEALS: alc SERVICE: not inc (12% for 5 or more, card slips closed) CARDS: Access, Amex, Diners, Visa DETAILS: 100 seats. Private parties: 70 main room, 40 private room. Vegetarian meals. Children's helpings. Wheelchair access (also WC). Music

---

CRUDWELL Wiltshire — map 2

▲ *Crudwell Court* ⁑✗

Crudwell, nr Malmesbury SN16 9EP
CRUDWELL (0666) 577194 and 577195

COOKING 1
COST £21–£38

Crudwell Court, a seventeenth-century former rectory, is hard by the church. It has changed hands but new owners Iain Maclaren and Nick Bristow have kept the same team on both sides of the green-baize door, with Chris Amor continuing in the kitchen. An inspection meal produced a duck and pistachio terrine with apricot sauce, poached haddock with chopped bacon and spring onion, a 'nicely pink' shoulder of lamb, and pork fillet wrapped in filo pastry with cheese – all served in 'generous portions'. A Danish apple and cream pudding was poor, but sticky toffee pudding with butterscotch sauce, and pear and cinnamon flan were both good. Details such as amuse-gueules, petits fours, home-made bread rolls, butter and coffee are carefully observed. Service is hard-working and pleasant. The wine list offers a reasonable spread and is not excessively priced. House wine is £8.75.

CHEF: Chris Amor PROPRIETORS: Iain Maclaren and Nick Bristow OPEN: all week, exc Sat L; 12.30 to 1.45, 7.30 to 9.30 MEALS: Set L £14.50, Set D £19.50 to £24.95 SERVICE: not inc, card slips closed CARDS: Access, Amex, Diners, Visa DETAILS: 80 seats. 6 tables outside. Private parties: 50 main room, 30 private room. Car park. Children's helpings with prior notice. Smart dress preferred. No smoking. Wheelchair access (also WC). No music ACCOMMODATION: 15 rooms, all with bath/shower. B&B £47 to £114. Deposit: varies. Children welcome. Baby facilities. Pets welcome. Afternoon teas. Garden. Swimming-pool. TV. Phone. Doors close at midnight. Fax: (0666) 577853 (*The Which? Hotel Guide*)

CUCKFIELD West Sussex   map 3

▲ *Ockenden Manor* ⁝✳

Ockenden Lane, Cuckfield RH17 5LD	COOKING 1
HAYWARDS HEATH (0444) 416111	COST £20–£40

True-blue Sussex: the architecture reflects the length of tradition, and the style of the hotel buttresses it further. 'Warm colour schemes and warming log fires complement an oak-panelled dining-room with ornate plaster ceiling that manages to be civilised yet intimate, with staff that do not obtrude, yet never fail to be there.' Half a dozen choices per course in the fixed-price menu do not offer hostages to daring. Chicken liver parfait (smooth and dull), pigeon salad with citrus fruits, best end of lamb with rosemary and garlic, chicken with wild mushrooms and green peppercorn sauce, prune and frangipane tart, and white chocolate and pistachio parfait are examples of what is on offer. Executed with panache, they might hold the attention, but poor technique in ice-creams and sorbets, meagre slicing of sirloin steak and inadequate vegetables made one meal less than brilliant. Some very fancy drinking goes on here, for the wine list is full of collectors' items, from old Bordeaux to the odd Hugel Vendange Tardive Tokay from 1976. If you wish to be economical, the choice is less dramatic: a lot of Duboeuf and less exciting makers for anything under £15. House Dubeouf is £9.75.

CHEF: Philip Guest PROPRIETORS: Mr and Mrs H.N.A. Goodman OPEN: all week; 12.30 to 2, 7.30 to 9.30 MEALS: Set L £13.50 to £17.50, Set D £25.50 to £28.50 SERVICE: not inc CARDS: Access, Amex, Diners, Visa DETAILS: 50 seats. Private parties: 45 main room, 75 private room. Car park. Vegetarian meals. Children's helpings. Jacket and tie. No smoking in dining-room. Wheelchair access (also WC). No music ACCOMMODATION: 22 rooms, all with bath/shower. B&B £71 to £158. Deposit: £25. Children welcome. Baby facilities. Afternoon teas. Garden. TV. Phone. Confirm 1 week ahead. Fax: (0444) 415549 (*The Which? Hotel Guide*)

Dining-rooms where live and recorded music are never played are signalled by **No music** *in the details at the end of an entry.*

⁝✳ *indicates that smoking is either banned altogether or that a dining-room is maintained for non-smokers. The symbol does not apply to restaurants that simply have no-smoking areas.*

DARLINGTON Co Durham

map 7

Victor's

84 Victoria Road, Darlington DL1 5JW
DARLINGTON (0325) 480818

COOKING 1*
COST £12–£26

Peter Robinson is a North Countryman whose girth and amiability are personal tributes to his cooking: honestly prepared, familiar food, not over-ambitious, served in generous portions. The fixed-price menus have ensured a loyal following. From the many notes of satisfaction, salmon mousse in parsley sauce, carrot and orange soup, red mullet fillet with ginger sauce, steak with chestnut purée in a port wine sauce served with roast potatoes and pepper, mashed potatoes and garlic, sliced carrot and lemon juice, Brussels sprouts with cashew, and eight different local cheeses with home-made biscuits are all soundly endorsed. Home-made bread, ice-creams, sorbets, petits fours and biscuits show the kitchen's attention to detail. Writes Jayne Robinson: 'If either of us were to take time away from the restaurant we would not be able to open ... we have been involved in every meal eaten in our restaurant and to our customers that means a great deal.' The short wine list offers fair prices from £7.

CHEFS: Peter and Jayne Robinson, and Trudie Doig PROPRIETORS: Peter and Jayne Robinson OPEN: Tue to Sat; 12 to 2.30, 7 to 10.30 MEALS: Set L £7.50, Set D £18 SERVICE: not inc, card slips closed CARDS: Access, Amex, Diners, Visa DETAILS: 30 seats. Private parties: 30 main room. Vegetarian meals. Children's helpings. Wheelchair access (2 steps). Music

---

DARTMOUTH Devon

map 1

▲ Billy Budd's £

7 Foss Street, Dartmouth TQ6 9DW
DARTMOUTH (0803) 834842

COOKING 1
COST £12–£30

'Simple and friendly' is one reader's endorsement of this bistro, which is casual at lunch and candle-lit by evening. 'Wonderful ambience,' comments a regular recipient of Gillian Webb's hospitality. The warm demeanour is matched by generous fish cookery. 'Our fish pie, with a huge variety of seafood, was orgasmic.' Few restaurateurs receive brighter compliments. Treatment is simple: fresh-caught wing of skate comes with black butter; fillet of turbot has a sorrel sauce. The same light touch is applied to noisettes of lamb and a sauté of calf's liver. Praise is heaped on vegetables. Few reports resist a paean to the range of home-made ice-creams. Lively service contributes to relaxed enjoyment. The wine list has 30-odd bottles all at very fair prices. House wines are from £7.80.

CHEF: Keith Belt PROPRIETORS: Gilliam Webb and Keith Belt OPEN: Tue to Sat; 12 to 2, 7.30 to 10 CLOSED: 1 month winter MEALS: alc L. Set D £12.95 to £18.95 SERVICE: not inc, card slips closed CARDS: Access, Visa DETAILS: 35 seats. Private parties: 20 main room. Vegetarian meals with prior notice. Children's helpings. No children under 9 D. Smart dress preferred. Wheelchair access (1 step). Music ACCOMMODATION: 2 rooms. B&B £29. Deposit: 20%. No children under 7. TV

Carved Angel 🍴

2 South Embankment, Dartmouth TQ6 9BH	COOKING 4
DARTMOUTH (0803) 832465	COST £30–£55

The restaurant sits bang on the river front. A pavement and a street separates it from the view, which can be enjoyed through the giant shop window of the dining-room, of the scurry of a harbour occupied mostly by pleasure craft, but with some real life to vary the mix. At the back is the kitchen, also on full, but modest, view. 'I was glad to see that the dirty dishes disappeared behind closed doors,' wrote one who spent the evening rubbernecking. This place has assurance born of popularity and habit. It is infectious and has the culinary wit to mix adventure with discretion. It rarely falls into the trap of over-elaboration, yet adds sufficient zip to things to make them interesting and one step beyond many rivals. It quite evidently has lost neither curiosity, nor enthusiasm. Materials, too, remain of a high standard, especially the fish and shellfish; and who could question the greens that are picked that day, the soft fruit or the poultry from local coops? These are ingredients for a potent cocktail of satisfaction: situation, attitude and materials. Add skill, and success is assured. The repertoire does not mirror current fashions or hark back to old fads, but seems to treat every dish at its own face value. Dressed crab with guacamole sits next to scallops with lentil and coriander, or little turnovers of salt cod with a cucumber raita, and a salad of home-cured salt beef with pickled mushrooms and horseradish cream. Simple main courses of noisettes of lamb with rosemary sauce or charcoal-grilled fillet steak with bone marrow might be neighbours to a plate of duck – the breast with spiced apple, the leg stuffed with green olives and mushrooms, and a neck sausage with red cabbage. This is individual stuff, and the flavours sing. Trios and quartets of things are a feature: aubergine as a first course comes as a spiced loaf, a sweet-and-sour caponata, and as a satay; chocolate is served as a cake, as a custard, an ice, a roulade and with pear and almond. It is possible to pick holes. A winter dinner saw the cheese biscuits with aperitifs undercooked; then the salt beef and avocado salad with a walnut dressing was too simple to constitute a dish on its own and became boring. Squid in wonderfully light batter, served with a blackened (from the ink) tomato sauce, was very fine, but there was too much lemon juice – it killed it in the end. Widgeon with Chinese plum and star-anise sauce was a little overcooked, the sauce too sweet, but the pan gravy was great and the noodles were excellent. The vegetables (with both main courses) suffered from undercooked celeriac and potato cakes; some novel purple (black) Brussels sprouts were very undercooked and tasted horrid, while real green sprouts were delicious. Buckwheat pancakes filled with an apple and quince soufflé and served with an apple ice-cream was a pudding which, from its very description, makes one realise why this place is different. Coffee is espresso, fudge is great. On good days there are pleasing appetisers, such as smoked sprats. The service is natural, not fancy. The cost is hideous, but it has the virtue of being truly inclusive (save alcohol). It is like paying top whack for a piece of peasant clothing when haute couture would cost no more. You do it because you like it, but against this you weigh the fact that there was little peasant labour and the fabric cost nothing (there are no luxuries on the Carved Angel menu, beyond fresh food). The wine list is a joy and the layout has improved; although mark-ups remain old-fashioned, there are enough well-chosen bottles below £14 and generous provision of halves to permit economy of sorts. With some of the best merchants provisioning the cellar, quality is consistently excellent. House wines are £14. CELLARMAN'S CHOICE: Sancerre 1990, Vacheron, £20; Médoc, Ch. Chasse-Spleen 1981, £28.

CHEFS: Joyce Molyneux and Nick Coiley   PROPRIETORS: Joyce Molyneux and Meriel Matthews   OPEN: Tue to Sun, exc Sun D; 12.30 to 1.45, 7.30 to 9.30   MEALS: alc. Set L £22.50 to £27.50, Set D £37.50 to £42.50   SERVICE: net prices   DETAILS: 30 seats. Private parties: 30 main room, 15 private room. Children's helpings. Wheelchair access (2 steps). No music

---

The Exchange

NEW ENTRY

5 Higher Street, Dartmouth TQ6 9RB   COOKING 2
DARTMOUTH (0803) 832022   COST £19–£31

Once upon a time, Higher Street was the first real street in Dartmouth after the river front. As the waters have been embanked and tamed, so this little row of late-medieval and Tudor half-timbered buildings has found itself plumb centre of the old town. The most magnificent building – which served as Dartmouth's Labour Exchange for a while, hence the name – now houses this restaurant. Conversion has been intelligent, without affecting the early bits. There are two storeys for eating, a big staircase, and a lot of dark (slightly pubby) wood panelling. Nick Trant is a young chef who has worked with, among others, Jean-Christophe Novelli, now at the Provence at Gordleton Mill (see entry, Lymington). Some of that man's enthusiasms have rubbed off here, hence the air-cured beef and duck, and home-smoked salmon, trout and hams that pop up on the menus. The style makes serious efforts to be streetwise: pressed leek and prawn terrine with a sherry vinaigrette, squid and cucumber salad with cumin and mint dressing, a bourride, sea bass with a herb sauce and ragoût of squid march hand in hand with things that holiday visitors may expect to see – salmon hollandaise, lemon sole stuffed with a salmon mousse, beef with green peppercorn béarnaise and wild mushrooms, or turbot wrapped in spinach and filo. The cooking is as good as it sounds, though so far it has not been often tested at moments of bank-holiday stress. Fish is the obvious prime ingredient and is not mistreated. The staff seem motivated to give everyone a good time. Chips have been appreciated, and children are not victimised. The wine list has a very acceptable spread, starting with house wines at £7.50.

CHEF: Nick Trant   PROPRIETORS: Mr and Mrs Nigel Way   OPEN: Tue to Sat; 12 to 2, 7 to 9.45   CLOSED: Jan   MEALS: alc   SERVICE: not inc, card slips closed   CARDS: Access, Visa   DETAILS: 50 seats. Private parties: 50 main room, 20 and 30 private rooms. Vegetarian meals with prior notice. Children's helpings. Music

---

'The Valentine menu, in our opinion, contained some very unusual choices of food, when you consider that no other menu was available as an alternative. Crab can be a very doubtful meat at the best of times, and we were both extremely ill the last time it was eaten. Rabbit pâté has no appeal at all, the mere mention of the word ''rabbit'' puts most people right off.'   On eating in the West Midlands

---

DEDHAM Essex   map 3

▲ Fountain House 🍷 ✳

Dedham Hall, Brook Street,
Dedham CO7 6AD   COOKING 1
COLCHESTER (0206) 323027   COST £20–£25

'You sit in an oak-beamed room, through the window is a most beautiful
country garden, the easy chairs in the lounges are the sort you sink into: this
must be the foreigner's idea of what England is all about.' That comment may
also apply to the cooking, which eschews 'foreign fare', with choices such as
roast rib, grilled salmon, devilled kidneys, peppered steak and pork with sage
and apple. These are done competently. In true English style, the puddings get
the most attention in reports. Chocolate fondue with fruits for the diners to dip,
is 'a meal in itself'. 'Fountain House is the home of folk who live in great
elegance, and you are a guest,' reports one such, although the welcome was
'uncertain' for another person. The marvellous wine list alone is worth the
journey: a very knowing collection that allows no geographic prejudice, all at
outrageously fair prices. Italy has a fine range, including a Felsina Chianti, a
1982 Barolo from Giacosa, and some nicely mature Barbaresco. The classic
areas are given the same space, with no let-up in quality – for example, 1970
Ch. Gloria and Dauvissat premier cru Chablis. Half-bottles are plentiful and
larger parties should take a careful look at the dozen mature magnums. House
wine is £7.50. CELLARMAN'S CHOICE: Riesling, Herrenweg 1985, Zind-
Humbrecht, £12; Dolcetto d'Alba, Corsini 1990, Mascarello, £13.

CHEF: Wendy Anne Sarton   PROPRIETOR: James F. Sarton   OPEN: Tue to Sat, D only, and
Sun L; 12.30 to 2, 7.30 to 10   MEALS: Set Sun L £14.50, Set D £16.50   SERVICE: not inc,
card slips closed   CARDS: Access, Visa   DETAILS: 32 seats. 3 tables outside. Private parties:
50 main room. Car park. Vegetarian meals. Children's helpings. No smoking in dining-
room. Wheelchair access. Music   ACCOMMODATION: 12 rooms, all with bath/shower.
Rooms for disabled. B&B £38 to £57. Children welcome. Garden. TV. Confirm by 6

▲ Le Talbooth 🍷

Gun Hill, Dedham CO7 6HP   COOKING 3
COLCHESTER (0206) 323150   COST £28–£55

The outlines of this half-timbered house in Constable country – river flowing
past, heavy-limbed trees, big skies – must be familiar to many readers; after all,
Le Talbooth has been in business for 40 years. Whether they enjoy full
floodlighting, Constable reproductions, log-effect gas fires and the suave
couthness of it all depends on taste. There has been a change of chef, though
management flows as strongly as the Essex tides, and kitchen policy has not
altered. Some observe no diminution in skill, others reflect that the impetus of
the recent past has slackened. Perhaps it is just that the sophisticated cooking,
which derives from nouvelle cuisine, can seem lacking fire and brio when
technique falters. The restaurant still meets the demand for elaborate cooking
in cosseted surroundings, but not necessarily that of excitement. Some classic
dishes have pleased immensely: warm skate with tomato and garlic; chicken
strips in spiced sauce; breast of chicken with a herb mousseline and a light port

sauce; calf's liver with balsamic vinegar. Yet that same skate salad, done instead with codling, was felt to be underseasoned, and an inspection meal raised several points of missed objectives. Over-complication, not-so-perfect raw materials, over-reduction of sauces, lack of saffron in a sauce that was said to be saffron, and overcooking of fish were just some. The lunch menu, at a fixed price, is better value than dinner. Notwithstanding a niggle about pretentious wine service – a half-bottle of a simple Beaune unnecessarily decanted – the list is unimpeachable. Classic areas are kept within sensible bounds and the selections of Beaujolais, Alsace and the antipodes show reassuring knowledge. Prices are fair with much decent drinking below £12. The 'Personal Selection' provides a reliable short-cut for all. House wines are from £9.75. CELLARMAN'S CHOICE: Hamilton Russell Vineyards, Chardonnay 1990, £16.25; Cyril Henschke, Cabernet Sauvignon 1987, £23.50.

CHEF: Lee Timmins PROPRIETOR: Gerald M.W. Milsom OPEN: all week; 12.30 to 2, 7 to 9 (9.30 Sat) MEALS: alc. Set L £18.50, Set Sun L £19.95 SERVICE: 10%, card slips closed CARDS: Access, Visa DETAILS: 70 seats. Private parties: 70 main room, 24 private room. Car park. Children welcome. Smart dress preferred. No cigars/pipes in dining-room. No music ACCOMMODATION: 10 rooms, all with bath/shower. Rooms for disabled. B&B £82.50 to £137.50. Garden. TV. Phone. Fax: (0206) 322752

DELPH Greater Manchester   map 5

Cross Keys Inn, Honfleur

Oldham Road, Delph OL3 5RQ   COOKING 1
SADDLEWORTH (0457) 874241   COST £17–£39

Anne Marie and Serge Marlot have run the Cross Keys Inn for several years – their enthusiasm 'actually filters through to the staff,' remarks one convert. Drink Old Peculier, and eat beef and mushroom pie ('the ethereal puff pastry crust was exemplary'), cooked in the ale from the bar menu. Anne Marie's brother, Jean-Pierre Champeau, used to work with her at Yves Champeau's Normandie at Birtle (see entry). They have opened a restaurant extension at Delph where the delights of Norman cooking *à l'ancienne* are on permanent show. The menu doesn't change a lot – why should it, the dishes are nearly timeless? They are heavy on butter and cream, and deal in expectations as well as tradition. Thus snails and frogs' legs come high on the list, but veal chasseur, noisettes of lamb sauce choron, venison with mushrooms and cream, veal kidneys with cognac, and chicken with tarragon may take the votes for real food. This is how restaurants used to be. The largely French wine list offers Drouhin, Ch. d'Issan 1981, Pierre Ponnelle, Clos Frantin and Ropiteau among other properties and négociants. Prices are not excessive. House wine is £8.10 a litre.

CHEF: Jean-Pierre Champeau PROPRIETORS: Paragon Inn OPEN: Tue to Sun, exc Sun D; 12 to 2, 7.30 to 9.30 MEALS: alc. Set L £9.95, Set Sun L £9.15 SERVICE: not inc CARDS: Access, Amex, Diners, Visa DETAILS: 55 seats. Private parties: 65 main room, 20 private room. Car park. Vegetarian meals. Children's helpings. Wheelchair access (2 steps; also WC). Music

DENT Cumbria   map 7

▲ *Stone Close* ⁵⁄✻ £

Main Street, Dent LA10 5QL   COOKING 2
DENT (058 75) 231   COST £11–£17

'As a café it is outstanding,' write travellers from Berkshire, 'a wonderful range
of truly home-cooked food is available all day to walkers and tourists alike, but
what really intrigued us was dinner.' Five evenings a week, guests are able to
enjoy genuine domestic cooking with all its customary benchmarks. Meals
begin with a wholesome soup, while main courses such as chicken marengo or
pork in mushroom sauce are served with spot-on, interesting fresh vegetables.
Home-made puddings, cakes and sweets include hot lemon sponge cake with
clotted cream, sticky date pudding, walnut pie and 'scrumptious' chocolate
cheesecake. To finish, there are at least six local cheeses. During the day, this
beguiling seventeenth-century farmhouse-cum-B&B deals in pâté, salads,
quiches, home-made cakes and dishes such as minced meat and kidney bean
bake. The value for money is excellent, a family atmosphere pervades the place
and the pace is leisurely. The choice of drinks ranges from non-alcoholic
Sheffield Stout and traditional lemonade to 'wines of the month' listed on a
blackboard. House wine is £7.30 a litre.

CHEFS: Patricia Barber and Hazel Haygarth   PROPRIETORS: Graham Hudson and Patricia
Barber   OPEN: all week, exc D Mon and Sun; 10.30 to 5.15, 7.30   CLOSED: Jan and first 2
weeks Feb. Tea-shop closed mid-week Nov to mid-Mar   MEALS: alc (daytime). Set D
£10.50   SERVICE: not inc   DETAILS: 40 seats. Private parties: 25 main room, 20 private
room. Vegetarian meals. Children's helpings. No smoking in tea-shop. Wheelchair access.
Music   ACCOMMODATION: 3 rooms. B&B £15.50 to £27. Deposit: £10. Children welcome.
Baby facilities. Pets welcome. Afternoon teas (*The Which? Hotel Guide*)

DISS Norfolk   map 6

▲ *Salisbury House* ⁵⁄✻

84 Victoria Road, Diss IP22 3JG   COOKING 1*
DISS (0379) 644738   COST £23–£36

This pleasant Victorian-classical house in cool Norfolk brick is on a main road,
but the protective ring of garden plus lashings of double glazing keep
everything peaceful indoors. Salisbury House is comfortable and flower-filled;
a conservatory overlooks the lawn, and the beds are luxurious. There is a
monthly menu with prices depending on the number of courses consumed.
Barry Davies cooks in that style once called 'modern British'. There is
invention, there are quite strong flavours, and some of them may be
unexpected. Pheasant comes with a ginger and whisky sauce; the same spice
also infuses the butter sauce with salmon in the spring; lamb is cooked with
herbs and fresh pears; scallops are set off by chicory and lime; a brioche is filled
with Stilton and pear mousse. Reporters say that these are well-handled, that
flavours remain distinct and pleasing, neither insipid nor mixed
indiscriminately. Desserts may have equal panache, though a prune tart that
gave a chance to play 'tinker, tailor' seemed lax, even if a lemon meringue pie

hit the target beautifully. Service is by Sue Davies, and Barry too if necessary, which gives the right tone to the place. If you want wine advice, refer to the kitchen. You may need guidance because choice is very wide and there are some good things to be had. France is almost the sole concern, but the clarets will have you wondering whether it is worth trying some Toulifaut or Taillefer from Pomerol, a 1970 Citran in magnum, or a Lynch-Bages 1966. Burgundies come from high-grade names like Leroy, Grivelet and Viénot, though Boisset is met most often. House wines start at £7.75.

CHEF: Barry Davies PROPRIETORS: Barry and Sue Davies OPEN: Tue to Sat, D only (Tue to Fri L by arrangement); 12.15 to 1.45, 7.30 to 9.15 CLOSED: 1 week Christmas, 2 weeks July MEALS: Set L and D £17.75 to £25.75 SERVICE: not inc CARDS: Access, Visa DETAILS: 38 seats. 3 tables outside. Private parties: 20 main room, 14 private room. Car park. Children's helpings. No smoking in dining-room. Wheelchair access (1 step). Music ACCOMMODATION: 3 rooms, all with bath/shower. B&B £38 to £65. Children welcome. Baby facilities. Garden. TV. Doors close at 11.30. Confirm by 9 (The Which? Hotel Guide)

DORCHESTER Dorset   map 2

Mock Turtle

34 High West Street,
Dorchester DT1 1UP   COOKING 1
DORCHESTER (0305) 264011   COST £18–£30

The Hodders' open-plan restaurant continues to draw the crowds with its distinctive version of eating out. The regularly changing *carte* may feature dishes such as scallop mousse wrapped in a leek case; sesame-encrusted goose breast with onion and apple confit and calvados sauce; and breadcrumbed breast of chicken with mango and curry sauce. The menu is boosted by daily fish specials along the lines of délice of salmon or suprême of brill garnished with king scallops; there are also simple grills and steaks. Sweets range from hot cherry pancakes to home-made brandy-cake ice-cream with Bénédictine sauce. Service copes well, even at peak times. A short, wide-ranging wine list offers plenty of decent drinking at fair prices. House New Zealand is £7.95.

CHEF: Raymond Hodder PROPRIETORS: Raymond, Alan and Vivien Hodder OPEN: Mon to Sat, exc L Mon and Sat; 12 to 2.30, 7 to 10.30 CLOSED: 28 and 29 Dec, 1 Jan MEALS: Set L £9.50, Set D £14.95 to £20 SERVICE: not inc CARDS: Access, Visa DETAILS: 56 seats. Private parties: 60 main room. Vegetarian meals. Children welcome. No cigars/pipes in dining-room. Wheelchair access (1 step). Music

---

Restaurateurs justifiably resent no-shows. If you quote a credit card number when booking, you may be liable for the restaurant's lost profit margin if you don't turn up. Always phone to cancel.

The 1994 Guide will be published before Christmas 1993. Reports on meals are most welcome at any time of the year, but are extremely valuable in the spring. Send them to The Good Food Guide, FREEPOST, 2 Marylebone Road, London NW1 1YN. No stamp is needed if posted in the UK.

DORCHESTER-ON-THAMES Oxfordshire map 2

▲ *George Hotel* ♀

High Street,
Dorchester-on-Thames OX10 7HH COOKING 1
OXFORD (0865) 340404 COST £20–£32

This unashamedly 'Olde English' former coaching-inn opposite the Abbey
Church turns its back on modern hotel uniformity. Heavy beams support
knotted roof rafters high above the dining-room's collection of skew-whiff
pastoral prints. The set-price menu is genteel but execution is reported as
rough-hewn. A summer dinner that started with a warm salad of pigeon
breasts, bacon and garlic croûtons was 'insufficiently green' although it
contained 'quite good meat'. To follow came fillet of beef on a potato cake with
port wine jus: 'The tournedos were pink with a good crust but the fried, grated
potato cake was over-large.' While quibbling extends to a limited choice of
sweets, there is rapture at the traditional quality. A lone diner complained of
the paucity of half-bottles, aggravated by an otherwise interesting and fairly
priced wine list. So many merchants have responded to demand for halves that
there can be no excuse for restaurants not to follow suit. Good bourgeois clarets
such as Ch. Fourcas-Hosten 1982 at £17, alongside decent Loires, will satisfy
many people. Selection is not totally assured but we maintain the glass award.
House wine is £7.95.

CHEF: Paul Sheriff PROPRIETORS: Neville and Griffin Ltd OPEN: all week; 12 to 2, 7 to
9.45 (9 Sun) MEALS: Set L £14, Set D £18 to £22 SERVICE: not inc CARDS: Access,
Amex, Diners, Visa DETAILS: 40 seats. Private parties: 30 main room, 20 private room. Car
park. Vegetarian meals. Children's helpings. No music ACCOMMODATION: 18 rooms, all
with bath/shower. B&B £62 to £75. Children welcome. Pets welcome. Garden. TV. Phone
(*The Which? Hotel Guide*)

DORKING Surrey map 3

Partners West Street

2, 3 and 4 West Street,
Dorking RH4 1BL COOKING 3
DORKING (0306) 882826 COST £21–£39

The outsides of half-timbered Surrey homes are usually masks on the face of
centrally heated, well-upholstered late-twentieth-century reality. Such is
Partners West Street. The timbering is genuine Tudor, but the inside reveals a
cocooned, swagged and buttoned dining space – with another room upstairs
that gives more muted pleasure than the ground floor. Although there is a
willingness to deploy the fruits of the Mediterranean earth, the kitchen is
perhaps happier with the classical, northern palate. Smoked haddock with a
warm soufflé, or calf's liver with bubble and squeak, butter sauces and
hollandaises (even when the latter are too cold) are the things that get
mentioned more often than red snapper with ratatouille, or bresaola with pink
grapefruit. Skill and sound purchasing are apparent in dishes such as warm
oysters with spinach and vermouth cream sauce (only three oysters, though),

skate fried with Chinese spices, a nage of sole and scallops, veal escalope with wild mushroom risotto and a Marsala sauce, breast of duck with limes and quail with bacon, lentils and new potatoes. This does come at a price (unless one is a member of the promotional dining club with hefty discounts), and when that price is reduced – as at lunch-time – there have been less perfect experiences of the cloth being cut too close to the seams. Habitués of the old Partners, in cosier surroundings, have said that solemnity has triumphed here, but others suggest that better training might promote the smiles. The fairly conservative wine list does a range from the Denbie Estate, Dorking's answer to large-scale viticulture, and has some mixed sources for its largely French selection. There are a few from the New World, but nothing from Italy or Spain. House wines are £9.85. There is also a brasserie – Partners Brasserie, 23 Stonecot Hill, Sutton SM3 9HB, Tel: 081-644 7743.

CHEFS: Tim McEntire, Paul Ager, Adrian Walton and Nathan Darling   PROPRIETORS: Partners Restaurants plc   OPEN: Tue to Sun, exc Sat L and Sun D; 12.30 to 2, 7.30 to 9.30   MEALS: alc L. Set D £17.60 to £29.65   SERVICE: net prices, card slips closed   CARDS: Access, Amex, Diners, Visa   DETAILS: 45 seats. Private parties: 35 main room. Vegetarian meals. Children's helpings Sun L. No children under 5. No-smoking area. Wheelchair access (2 steps). No music

---

DORRINGTON Shropshire   map 4

▲ *Country Friends*

Dorrington SY5 7JD
DORRINGTON (0743) 718707   COOKING 3
on A49, 5m S of Shrewsbury   COST £23–£35

Sniff, and you may miss Dorrington. Country Friends is the most obvious thing about it: a black and white building set on a lawn rising back from the road. Charles Whittaker bought the re-assessment of cooking that ran through country restaurants in the 1980s and it stuck. There are many identifiers: a wish to be self-sufficient in the kitchen; an enjoyment of stuffings and layerings – a first course of sole fillets filled with a Parmesan soufflé shares the menu with breast of chicken with a herb and cheese pâté stuffing, then wrapped in pastry; fairly elaborate vegetable cookery – a frittata of courgettes, cauliflower fritters and plain mange-tout at one meal (the choice may cut across the tastes on offer in the main course); and an apostolic support of British produce – witness the excellent cheeseboard. Small wonder that some weighty, but good, British puddings also figure: banoffi pie, a strawberry and almond variation of summer pudding, and bread-and-butter pudding are instances. People speak highly of the sauces and enjoy the various combinations such as scallop mousse with ginger and saffron, calf's liver with watercress and beetroot, halibut with red pimento and beef with dill. The rooms here are fair value, not elaborate, but there is compensation in the breakfasts of Buck's Fizz, scrambled egg and smoked salmon. Value is also evident in the wine list – written for reading without the help of spectacles. The range is not inspiring, but certainly adequate and there are half bottles aplenty. House wines are £8.50.

CHEFS: Charles Whittaker and Tim Greaves   PROPRIETORS: Charles and Pauline
Whittaker   OPEN: Tue to Sat; 12 to 2, 7 to 9 (9.30 Sat)   MEALS: alc. Set L and D £16.90
SERVICE: not inc   CARDS: Access, Visa   DETAILS: 40 seats. Private parties: 45 main room.
Car park. Children welcome. No smoking while others are eating. Wheelchair access. No
music   ACCOMMODATION: 3 double rooms, 1 with bath/shower. B&B £42 to £45 per room.
Garden (*The Which? Hotel Guide*)

DREWSTEIGNTON Devon   map 1

▲ *Hunts Tor House*

Drewsteignton EX6 6QW   COOKING 2
DREWSTEIGNTON (0647) 21228   COST £25

'Chris Harrison would really like to run a restaurant, but the planners won't let
him' was the surmise of one resident who dined at this guesthouse full of
Edwardian furniture and Clarice Cliff china. Unfortunately, if you are not
resident then food is not available, unless guests bring you in on their coat-
tails, so to speak (given notice). What guests get is a fairly plainly furnished
bedroom and some excellent cooking from a no-choice menu. If you don't like
the other residents, hard luck, but you will have to see and even speak to them.
Sue Harrison is a capable and tactful cook. She may work lightly, using the best
of local materials such as Devon cheeses or local air-dried ham, while a main
course of maize-fed chicken with ginger, soy and maple syrup shows balance
and accuracy in seasoning. Vegetables are good, puddings are excellent. Fruit
can be popular as a main-course accompaniment: thus quail stuffed with
apricots had oranges on the plate as well. This falls outside the category of a
true restaurant, but as many places in mid-Devon seem to fall to the deep-fryer
and the ice-cream cone, its mention seems justified. Don't expect a long wine
list, but accept its low prices and careful choice of things like Lageder's Pinot
Grigio, Ch. Martouret 1986, or Poliziano's Vino Nobile di Montepulciano.
House Duboeuf is £7.

CHEF: Sue Harrison   PROPRIETORS: Sue and Chris Harrison   OPEN: all week, D only;
7.30   CLOSED: Dec and Jan   MEALS: Set D £17   SERVICE: not inc   DETAILS: 8 seats.
Private parties: 12 main room, 8 private room. Vegetarian meals. No children under 14. No
music   ACCOMMODATION: 4 rooms, all with bath/shower. D,B&B £45 to £84. Deposit: £20.
No children under 14. Pets welcome. Doors close at midnight. Confirm by 2 (*The Which?
Hotel Guide*)

EAST BOLDON Tyne & Wear   map 7

Forsters

2 St Bedes, Station Road,
East Boldon NE36 0LE   COOKING 3*
091-519 0929   COST £20–£36

'Please can the *Guide* stop printing the snide remarks of southern journalists
about the North-East?' pleads one report. 'The situation of Forsters is very
pleasant and far better than many we have encountered in the suburbs of
London.' Set in a suburban shopping parade – estate agent, antique shop and

upmarket bathroom shop – Forsters is a tiny place, no more than the size of a good sitting-room and comfortably done out in fashionable light colours and limed wood. East Boldon is a funny place for a restaurant, but as Barry Forster writes, 'The "poor" North-East seems to be coping very well with the recession. If restaurants like mine can survive in East Boldon there could be hope for British cooking.' Not every chef, however, cooks like Barry Forster. The style is uncomplicated, and freshness, high-quality ingredients and neat presentation are all hallmarks of the cooking. An inspection meal that could not be faulted consisted of Thai prawns cooked with chilli oil, ginger and spring onions, oven-baked Swiss cheese and ham soufflé, roast turbot with mussels and saffron, roast venison with walnuts, bacon lardons, mushrooms and piquant sauce, lemon crème brûlée and warm sponge with butterscotch sauce and home-made vanilla ice-cream. Add to that the praiseworthily fair prices and this should be a place that continues to do well. The wine list is not long, perhaps not long enough for the ambition of the cooking, but value is very fair. House wines are £7.50.

CHEF: Barry Forster   PROPRIETORS: Barry and Sue Forster   OPEN: Tue to Sat, D only, and Sun L; 12 to 3, 7 to 10   MEALS: alc. Set Sun L £14.50   SERVICE: not inc   CARDS: Access, Amex, Diners, Visa   DETAILS: 28 seats. Private parties: 28 main room. Car park. Children's helpings. Smart dress preferred. No cigars/pipes in dining-room. Music

---

EASTBOURNE East Sussex   map 3

▲ Grand Hotel, Mirabelle

Jevington Gardens, Eastbourne BN21 4EQ   COOKING 2*
EASTBOURNE (0323) 410771   COST £20–£49

'For many long years have I hoped to make an Eastbourne recommendation to your guide. I do so now with confidence.' Thus wrote one happy resident, impressed by the loss-leading prices at quiet lunch-times. Keith Mitchell has been promoted from mere chef to executive but this does not seem to have caused a dilution of effort. Luxurious the place certainly is: 'Long, ruched curtains falling from three-layered valances,' starts one enthusiast, 'a colour scheme of lemons, soft greys and palest blues complementing white linen, crystal chandeliers and huge windows to ground level.' Cooking matches the setting: artful and elaborate. 'A trio of lamb medallions topped with basil, tarragon and lovage mousselines, served with a tomato jus,' runs the menu. 'A double breast of baby guinea-fowl stuffed with lobster and pistachio, with a vermouth sauce' is another chapter. The success of much of the cooking, especially when it is slightly more simple (as in the set-price menus), is not gainsaid. Good dishes from the winter season have included gratin of mussels with piquant cider sauce and noodles; chicken breast with Dijon mustard and bacon lardons, served with a simple cream sauce; three crisp balls of smoked haddock, salmon and crab, with a tomato and chive sauce; and a raspberry and pear charlotte that gained much from careful deployment of texture contrasts. Raw materials have been well chosen; combinations and composition have been light and true; details, such as coffee and petits fours, have been enjoyable. Service is young and enthusiastic. At the back of the wine list are a couple of pages of brandies and ports. The list is serviceable and fairly priced. There is a house selection of half a dozen bottles at either £11.50 or £12.50.

CHEFS: Keith Mitchell and Neil Wiggins   PROPRIETORS: De Vere Hotels   OPEN: Tue to Sun; 12.30 to 2.30, 7 to 10   CLOSED: 1 to 15 Jan, 1 to 14 Aug   MEALS: alc. Set L £13 to £16.50, Set D £19.50 to £26.50   SERVICE: not inc, card slips closed   CARDS: Access, Amex, Diners, Visa   DETAILS: 60 seats. Private parties: 50 main room, 170 private room. Car park. Vegetarian meals. Children's helpings. Jacket and tie. No cigar/pipes in dining-room. Wheelchair access. Music. Air-conditioned   ACCOMMODATION: 164 rooms, all with bath/shower. Rooms for disabled. Lift. B&B £60 to £150. Children welcome. Baby facilities. Pets welcome. Afternoon teas. Garden. Swimming-pool. Sauna. Snooker. TV. Phone. Fax: (0323) 412233

EAST BUCKLAND Devon   map 1

▲ *Lower Pitt*

East Buckland EX32 0TD
FILLEIGH (0598) 760243
2m N of A361 (North Devon Link Road)   COOKING 2
in East Buckland nr church   COST £22–£29

The Lyons achieve a consistency at this longhouse on the edge of Exmoor, now civilised by the addition of a conservatory, banishing to memory the fairly cramped seating of early times. There is no avoiding rusticity – you first have to get there – but the house is comfortable. Suzanne Lyons has worked out her methods which, like the dishes that are recommended by those who stay or visit, do not vary a great deal from year to year. Pork with cider, venison with Cumberland sauce, prawns with sesame oil, ginger and garlic as a main course or with garlic, mushrooms and cashew-nuts to begin are examples. Materials are carefully sourced and fish can be excellent. People suggest that first and last courses are more fun than the middle: butterscotch coupe, toffiana pie and sticky toffee pudding are a sweet-tooth's delight, just as a salad of kiwi, pineapple, mushrooms and soy can still be made to taste good. People find the value fair, as they do the wine list, where a canter through most wine-producing countries gives something for everyone, soundly based on the offerings of merchant Christopher Piper. House wines are £8.20 a litre.

CHEF: Suzanne Lyons   PROPRIETORS: Jerome and Suzanne Lyons   OPEN: Tue to Sat, D only; 7 to 9   MEALS: alc   SERVICE: not inc, card slips closed   CARDS: Access, Visa DETAILS: 28 seats. Private parties: 14 main room. Car park. Children welcome. No music ACCOMMODATION: 3 rooms, all with bath/shower. D,B&B £55 to £110. Deposit: 10%. No children under 12. Garden. Doors close at 11. Confirm by 6. Fax (0598) 760243 (*The Which? Hotel Guide*)

'They appear to be a rather discriminating lot in Oxford these days, as was made apparent by the young gentleman of seven to my right who was doggedly putting the waitress through her paces. "Do you have Orangina?" "I'm afraid not, though we have ordinary orange juice." "Do you have lemonade?" "Yes, we have lemonade." "Then I'll have orange juice."'   On drinking in Oxford

▲ *Gravetye Manor* ▮ ✻

Vowels Lane, East Grinstead RH19 4LJ
SHARPTHORNE (0342) 810567   COOKING 3
off B2110 at West Hoathly sign   COST £33–£67

The house is magnificent – 'everything old, in good taste and well cared for'
was how a reader put it. He had gone for Sunday lunch (a meal that is not too
expensive Gravetye-style) and doubtless took a turn round the gardens (turn-
of-the-century William Robinson), had a look at the woods (lots of them) and
may even have noted the new rooms on the north wing – in the Elizabethan
style, of course. Gravetye is the epitome of English country-house operations.
The restaurant is softly lit and wainscoted, the lounges are large, the fires huge
and the seats deep. Staff are solicitous. 'The effect was more than ever that of a
charm school, but they were genuinely efficient and willing.' When delays
have been reported, it seems the fault has been the kitchen's. There is a long
carte, supplemented by daily menus. All prices shown in this establishment
have to be increased by the current rate of VAT. Gravetye is conservative. It is
not so much that over-reliance is placed on taste-deadening things like dairy
products, but more that the taste range is in keeping with the location and the
clientele. When modernity comes out, it may appear as a lot of vinegar-
sharpened sauces – a good thing in moderation, but can ruin delicacy in excess.
Simple things are done well: a lunch dish of melon with figs and a fig compote
was exactly chosen and the compote gave the precise lift needed. But a complex
dish such as mixed seafood proved to be mainly salmon, monkfish and one
other fish, but no shellfish and 'a rather unsuitable' red wine sauce –
particularly as the fish was poached, not pan-fried as the menu stated. Game
cookery is worth pursuing here, but vegetables have not been so approved. The
present regime in the kitchen seems still to be finding its feet. The wine list
appears to suffer no such changes. It remains serious, but unlike similar
establishments is not content to restrict its range to Europe. Best value can be
found among the antipodeans. Elsewhere prices are high or very high, quality
good or very good. Genuine effort is made to find interest among half-bottles,
particularly in Alsace. It is a pity about the prices, but as you gaze across the
gardens, reflect that the drawing of every cork has contributed to a little
mowing and digging. House wine is £18.50. CELLARMAN'S CHOICE: Mosel,
Eitelsbacher Karthäuserhofberger, Riesling Auslese 1973, £25.50; Médoc, Ch.
Cissac 1973, £75 (magnum).

CHEF: Stephen Morey   PROPRIETORS: Peter Herbert and Leigh Stone-Herbert   OPEN: all
week; 12.30 to 1.45, 7.30 to 9.45 (10 Sat)   CLOSED: 25 Dec D to non-residents   MEALS: alc.
Set weekday L £19, Set Sun L £22, Set D £22   SERVICE: inc (but VAT added)   DETAILS: 50
seats. Private parties: 10 main room, 20 private room. Car park. No children under 7. Smart
dress preferred. No smoking in dining-room. No music   ACCOMMODATION: 18 rooms, all
with bath/shower. B&B £90 to £190. No children under 7. Garden. Fishing. TV. Phone.
Doors close at midnight. Fax: (0342) 810080 (*The Which? Hotel Guide*)

CELLARMAN'S CHOICE: *Wines recommended by the restaurateur, normally more
expensive than house wine.*

EASTON ON THE HILL Northamptonshire   map 6

Exeter Arms £ | NEW ENTRY |

Stamford Road,
Easton on the Hill PE9 3NF   COOKING 1
STAMFORD (0780) 57503   COST £13–£26

This is not the most beautiful of pubs to look at, even though it is just outside
one of the county's more handsome villages, close to a very special country
house, in a great Midlands landscape. But go through the door and be greeted
by flowers in profusion. The cooking here is not complicated, but the meat
cookery is very good indeed. 'My beef Wellington was the best I've ever had,'
wrote the veteran of more battles than were fought in the Peninsular. This is
simple food, cooked well, giving very good value for money. Fish is not bad
either – try the lobster. There is a short wine list. House wine is £5.95.

CHEF/PROPRIETOR: David Waycot   OPEN: Tue to Sun; 12 to 3, 7 to 10.30   MEALS: alc
SERVICE: not inc   DETAILS: 60 seats. 10 tables outside. Private parties: 60 main room, 10
private room. Car park. Vegetarian meals. Children's helpings. No-smoking area.
Wheelchair access (also WC). Music

EDENBRIDGE Kent   map 3

Honours Mill

87 High Street, Edenbridge TN8 5AU   COOKING 3
EDENBRIDGE (0732) 866757   COST £19–£40

Pulleys, flour bins and water-wheel: the evidence of former use is there, and
has been handsomely restored and petrified for curiosity's sake in this
restaurant. Beams, too, are obvious enough; stoop low if you walk tall. English
building, but French menu, and an Anglo-French nouvelle cuisine that seems to
die hard here: 'I thought I was on a diet when I saw my main course.' There
are cascading prices attached to various menus. Lunch-time is ultra-cheap, but
weekday dinners see a bargain offer too with a price to cover food and half a
bottle of Duboeuf. This gives a useful option where once none existed – a
reflection, perhaps, of the recession. There is a certain enjoyment of dressing
things up: chicken may be stuffed variously with Roquefort and orange, lambs'
sweetbreads and morels, and with lobster; sole may be rolled with crab and
chives; lamb may be wrapped with leeks, just as beans will come as a faggot.
But the techniques of cooking are not lacking (for instance, a good warm terrine
of red mullet with saffron and Pernod) just as a degree of heartiness is admitted
in dishes like a bold onion soup, a braise of oxtail, red wine and shallots, or
flavourful pheasant with red wine. People speak well of the tarte Tatin and of
the chocolate marquise, and there is a Sussex Pond Pudding *nouvelle vague*.
Ancillaries are well considered, as is the service, though on some nights it lacks
fine tuning. The wines are mainly French, with the price range pitched high.
Try the pair of Kentish wines, or consider the Bandol from Dom. de la Noblesse
and the Ch. Bicoty white Bergerac. House wines from Georges Blanc are £9.25.

CHEFS: Martin Radmall and Neville Goodhew   PROPRIETORS: Neville, Duncan and Giles Goodhew   OPEN: Tue to Sun, exc Sat L and Sun D; 12.15 to 2, 7.15 to 10   CLOSED: 2 weeks after Christmas, bank hols   MEALS: Set L £14.50 to £31.75, Set D £20.50 to £31.75   SERVICE: net prices   CARDS: Access, Visa   DETAILS: 40 seats. Private parties: 30 main room. Children's helpings Sun L. No children under 10. No music

---

ELTON Cambridgeshire   map 6

Loch Fyne Oyster Bar £   NEW ENTRY

The Old Dairy, Elton PE8 6SH   COOKING 1
OUNDLE (0832) 280298   COST £15–£33

This is the third, and most recent, branch of the Loch Fyne Oyster venture based in Cairndow, Scotland (see entry). It is housed in a former model dairy to Elton Hall, preserving the cute rusticity, crossed with a slice of Scottish pine. Its philosophy, like its parent's, is simplicity, economy and quality. The shellfish and smoked fish (though not crab) are freighted from Scotland and the menu is a celebration of their flavours. The cooking skills on show are modest. If you want a full meal and do not like smoked fish, your choice will be restricted. If the produce is not in tip-top condition, the point of the thing is lost. A visit in the summer found several things had not got through or were not at their peak, which limited the menu still further. Plump for the hot-smoked salmon, applaud the oysters, enjoy the salty kipper, wish that inappropriate vegetables were not put with everything, think the chowder a mite crude but hearty, and wonder at the great sticky toffee pudding. Service is very willing. The wine list is short but decent, and excellently cheap. House wine is £7.95. The second branch, at Nottingham – 17 King Street, NG1 2AY, Tel: (0602) 508481 – has been going through some sort of identity crisis – reports have been unsatisfactory.

CHEF: Martin Lane   PROPRIETORS: Loch Fyne Oysters Ltd   OPEN: all week; 9am to 9.30pm   MEALS: alc   SERVICE: not inc   CARDS: Access, Visa   DETAILS: 80 seats. 10 tables outside. Private parties: 60 main room. Car park. Vegetarian meals. Children's helpings with prior notice. No-smoking area. Wheelchair access (also WC). Music. Fax: (0832) 280125

ELY Cambridgeshire   map 6

Old Fire Engine House ♥ ✸

25 St Mary's Street, Ely CB7 4ER   COOKING 1
ELY (0353) 662582   COST £21–£32

This eighteenth-century house on the edge of the cathedral close incorporates part of the former fire station. You drink in a tiny snug, and you eat in a large room with uneven tiled floor reached by passing the kitchen. Things have not changed a lot since the place opened in 1968, though redecoration has kept the house and gallery spruce. There is still emphasis on British food and materials; there is still an excellent wine list; service is still by cheerful and welcoming ladies who sometimes make you think that today was the day of the church bazaar. It is unfortunate that cooking borders on the simplistic and that routine seems to have taken over from inspiration. First courses are notional – egg mayonnaise, smoked salmon pâté, a soup or two – and not much cooking is done at all. Main courses like casserole of rabbit and pork, or pigeon breasts wrapped in bacon with black olives and a rich sauce, are very much enjoyed, though on occasion the execution can be faulty and unskilled. Vegetables are copious, if not always good. Raw onion in a giant salad served with cold salmon really does not help the wine, or the tastebuds. The puddings are old-fashioned, and tend to the heavy. This may be pardoned for the fair prices and the wine list, though better glassware would help appreciation. France takes most attention, but other countries are enlisted for breadth and price. Makers are admirable. Watch for bin-ends. Adnams bitter is drawn direct from the cask. House wines are £6.

CHEFS: Ann Ford, Michael Jarman and Terri Kinred   PROPRIETORS: Ann Ford and Michael Jarman   OPEN: all week, exc Sun D; 12.30 to 2, 7.30 to 9   CLOSED: 2 weeks from 24 Dec, bank hols   MEALS: alc   SERVICE: not inc   CARDS: Access, Visa   DETAILS: 36 seats. 8 tables outside. Private parties: 36 main room, 22 private room. Car park. Vegetarian meals with prior notice. Children's helpings. No smoking in 1 dining-room. No music

---

EMSWORTH Hampshire   map 2

Spencers

36 North Street, Emsworth PO10 7DG   COOKING 2
EMSWORTH (0243) 372744   COST £16–£28

On the first floor of this atmospheric cottage, the dining-rooms are full of odd corners, books in alcoves and period touches. The illusion is pursued in the relentless descriptions on the menu, but Denis Spencer's cooking is not without merit and takes in many styles. A duck may be braised and served with peas and onions, but then a fillet of venison may be served with poached pear and raspberries, or lamb cooked on a skewer and marinated with cumin, coriander and garlic. 'Modern British' is the shorthand description. The unusual, such as grilled pike steak with a basil sauce, walks hand in hand with the well-loved, like eggs florentine. Toffee apple crumble will fill any empty nooks in the body, while passion-fruit and lime mousse will lighten the load. A short wine list won't break the bank. House wines are £7.95.

CHEF: Denis Spencer   PROPRIETORS: Denis and Lesley Spencer   OPEN: Tue to Sat, exc Sat L; 12.30 to 2, 7.30 to 10.30   CLOSED: 25 and 26 Dec   MEALS: alc L. Set D £18.50   SERVICE: not inc   CARDS: Access, Visa   DETAILS: 45 seats. Private parties: 24 main room, 10 and 11 private rooms. Vegetarian meals. Children welcome. Smart dress preferred. Music. Air-conditioned

---

The Guide *is totally independent, accepts no free hospitality, and survives on the number of copies sold each year.*

The Guide *office can quickly spot when a restaurateur is encouraging customers to write recommending inclusion – and sadly, several restaurants have been doing this in 1992. Such reports do not further a restaurant's cause. Please tell us if a restaurateur invites you to write to the* Guide.

EPWORTH Humberside

map 5

Epworth Tap 🍾 £

9–11 Market Place,
Epworth DN9 1EU
EPWORTH (0427) 873333

COOKING 2
COST £16–£30

'The "Tap" retains its oasis status in this corner of Humberside,' a reader reports. John and Helen Wynne have been running this wine bar for some time, but neither of them has lost any enthusiasm. The short menu, five choices at each turn, has been well received, its quality making apparently run-of-the-mill ideas more memorable. Moules marinière, oak-house pâté, boeuf provençale and chicken breast in cream and garlic show the range. An inspection meal in the spring turned up disappointing vegetables ('crisply cooked but rather plain') and a lasagne 'excessively drowned in béchamel, giving it a rather untypical bland flavour'. Yet baked spare ribs were 'tenderly cooked' and rib of beef was of high quality, tender and pink, with a naturally reduced red wine sauce. Puddings have always been a strength, with sticky toffee pudding and a 'light yet chewy' meringue with fresh fruit receiving several commendations. For the enthusiastic fast reader the wine list is a delight, supplied as it is by some of the finest merchants and priced with great friendliness. Classic French wines are counterbalanced by majestic Italians, antipodeans and Californians. A more relaxed route is afforded by the intelligent 'recommendations' accompanying the menu, and there are excellent half-bottles. Wine-tasting courses are also available. House wines are from £6.95. CELLARMAN'S CHOICE: Givry 1988, Lespinasse, £18; Hermitage, La Chapelle 1982, Jaboulet, £27.

CHEFS: Helen Wynne and Noreen Smith PROPRIETORS: Helen and John Wynne OPEN: Tue to Sat, D only (Sun L sometimes); 7.30 to 10 (10.30 Sat) MEALS: alc. Set D £14.50 SERVICE: not inc, card slips closed CARDS: Access, Visa DETAILS: 74 seats. Private parties: 50 main room, 24 private room. Vegetarian meals. Children welcome. No-smoking area. Wheelchair access (3 steps). Music

ERPINGHAM Norfolk

map 6

▲ *Ark* 🍷 ✳

The Street, Erpingham NR11 7QB
CROMER (0263) 761535

COOKING 2
COST £17–£33

Running a restaurant in an idyllic rural setting can have its problems: 'We still have the same frustration of never having enough space for all the customers who would like to eat at weekends, while often having very quiet mid-weeks,' write the Kidds. This they hope to remedy with their now completed accommodation and proposed mid-week bargain breaks. However, regulars are consistent in their praise of Sheila Kidd's cooking, of the generous portions and the freshness of the ingredients. Her style is defined as much by the garden as by the inspiration of Elizabeth David. This translates into a menu that packs variety into a short list: shrimp and squid salad with walnuts; basil and aubergine tart; Barbary duck with apple, sage and onion sauce; ragoût of salmon and turbot with cream and basil; herb-crusted roast lamb with flageolet beans. Vegetables are a harvest festival. Puddings are a strength: bramble ice-cream; raspberry, cinnamon and almond torte; iced mocha mousse. 'This is a very homely place; you feel you could ask for anything and it would be brought,' writes one who appreciates Mike Kidd's laid-back approach (too laid-back sometimes, almost curmudgeonly on one occasion, but maybe the barometric pressure banished happiness for a brief instant). Some might describe the wine list as messy; we prefer the epithet dynamic. Mr Kidd's enthusiasm brings frequent changes but his selection is sound, his choice catholic, and prices are fair. It all leads to a wine glass award this year. House wines are from £7.50. CELLARMAN'S CHOICE: Entre-Deux-Mers, Ch. Bel-Air 1991, £10.50; Côtes du Rhône 1990, £12.50.

CHEF: Sheila Kidd   PROPRIETORS: Mike and Sheila Kidd   OPEN: Tue to Sat, D only (Sun and Mon D by arrangement), and Sun L; 12.30 to 2, 7 to 9.30 (10.30 Sat)   MEALS: Set Sun L £11.50, Set D £14 to £22.50. Minimum 2 courses   SERVICE: not inc   DETAILS: 32 seats. Private parties: 38 main room. Car park. Vegetarian meals. Children welcome. No smoking in dining-room. Wheelchair access (also WC). No music   ACCOMMODATION: 3 rooms, 2 with bath/shower. Rooms for disabled. D,B&B £65 to £85. Children welcome. Baby facilities. Garden

---

EVERSHOT Dorset   map 2

▲ *Summer Lodge* |

Evershot DT2 0JR   COOKING 2*
EVERSHOT (0935) 83424   COST £25–£46

There can be few places so well manicured, gardened and carpeted. The Corbetts maintain a spotless house and motivate their staff to the full. The kitchen has continued on its appointed path since Roger Jones steered it away from classic British country cooking towards something a little more up to date and restaurant-like. He still gets the support of his public, though not unqualified. One problem (at dinner) is the high price for food that does not indulge luxury; nor does it go much for quantity. 'They used to have bisques for their soup course, now it seems always to be vegetable-based' was the remark of one who wondered for how much longer he could afford regular visits. Lunch, by contrast, is perceived as good value. The other note that has crept into some accounts is that flavours are not as high, or as exciting, as they might be: for example, in a game terrine that seemed more liverish than gamey, or a duck parfait that would have sunk beneath its apricot chutney had the latter been tried. But the general verdict is one of pleasure for dishes such as crab timbale on a trout mousse, salmon bavarois, trout and crayfish terrine, beignets of smoked fish, guinea-fowl with lentils, lamb with sorrel and mint, Sunday roasts, or venison with endives and spinach. Sauces have been well-constructed; the vegetables are a modern plain array. Puddings and the cheeseboard get more approval: a chocolate mousse in two tones, full of taste, a five-star pavlova, and other cold things from a side-table; but hot numbers are also on offer. Few places beyond Andalusia could offer such a pleasing range of sherries by the glass; half-bottles of dessert wine are plentiful. Between is as broad a sweep as could be hoped for, which shows as much consideration for the thrifty as for the profligate. Clarets and Rhônes are very strong, while in

273

whites Alsace has a fine range from some of the region's best. House wines are from £9.95. CELLARMAN'S CHOICE: Pinot Blanc 1988, Schlumberger, £15.50; Ch. Pontet-Canet 1983, £27.25.

CHEFS: Roger Jones and Tim Ford PROPRIETORS: Nigel and Margaret Corbett OPEN: all week; 12.30 to 1.30, 7.30 to 9 CLOSED: 1 to 16 Jan MEALS: Set L £17.50, Set D £32.50 SERVICE: not inc, card slips closed CARDS: Access, Amex, Visa DETAILS: 48 seats. 10 tables outside. Private parties: 28 main room. Car park. Vegetarian meals. No children under 8. Wheelchair access (also WC). No music ACCOMMODATION: 17 rooms, all with bath/shower. Rooms for disabled. B&B £65 to £205. No children under 8. Pets welcome. Afternoon teas. Garden. Swimming-pool. Tennis. TV. Phone. Doors close at midnight. Confirm by 6. Fax: (0935) 83005 (*The Which? Hotel Guide*)

EVESHAM Hereford & Worcester   map 2

▲ *Evesham Hotel,* *Cedar Restaurant* ? £

Cooper's Lane, Evesham WR11 6DA   COOKING 2 EVESHAM (0386) 765566   COST £15–£33

The Jenkinson family remain irrepressibly good-natured in their work (but the velvet smile has iron teeth of determination behind it). If you enjoy running humour, this is the place to sample it: on the menus, the literature, the wine list and the new vade-mecum to the spirits shelf – essential reading for those who like to extend their drinking into little-known alcoholic corners. This enthusiasm, and the wish to offer fair value, mean that trade has increased, despite the recession. The family must know something others don't. The weekly menus are a document of British creative cooking, tending to the fruity and the unexpected. Chicken is marinated in coconut and lime juice with onion and coriander, then baked in foil. Guinea-fowl is served with strawberries. A beanshoot salad as first course is composed of dates, celery, mushrooms and a honey dressing. Tiger prawns are wrapped in Parma ham. There are also classics and plainer things for the conservative to rest on such as mussels marinière, pâtés and terrines, and grilled meats. At lunch, there is a good buffet where the saladings are not limp leaves. Vegetarians and children have their own menus. The wine list only confirms that this is somewhere unlikely. There are no French or German bottles on the wine list, but every other wine-producing country you can think of gets a chance to air its best. There are plenty of oddities, but the range of Italian, Spanish and New World material is impressive and the prices are very fair indeed. As with the hard stuff mentioned above, it is worth coming here simply to try things. Just remember to wear your smile, too. House wine is £8.40. CELLARMAN'S CHOICE: Chile, Vina Los Vascos, Chardonnay 1990, £11.50; Victoria, Meadow Creek, Cabernet/Shiraz 1987, Brown Bros, £16.

'One of the meals actually had hairs on one of the potatoes. When this was brought to the proprietor's attention, she picked up the potato for closer examination and made a joke, saying nobody had had their hair cut that day. There was no offer of a replacement meal or even the potatoes.'   On eating in Cumbria

---

CHEF: Ian Mann PROPRIETORS: the Jenkinson family OPEN: all week; 12.30 to 2, 7 to 9.30 CLOSED: 25 and 26 Dec MEALS: alc. Buffet L SERVICE: net prices, card slips closed CARDS: Access, Amex, Diners, Visa DETAILS: 55 seats. Private parties: 12 main room, 15 private room. Car park. Vegetarian meals. Children's helpings. Wheelchair access (also WC). No music ACCOMMODATION: 40 rooms, all with bath/shower. B&B £58 to £94. Children welcome. Baby facilities. Pets welcome (not in public rooms). Afternoon teas. Garden. Swimming-pool. TV. Phone. Doors close at midnight. Confirm by 6. Fax: (0386) 765443 (*The Which? Hotel Guide*)

EXETER Devon   map 1

▲ St Olaves Court Hotel   NEW ENTRY

Mary Arches Street, Exeter EX4 3AZ   COOKING 2
EXETER (0392) 217736   COST £27–£34

The mulberry tree still grows in the garden of this merchant's town house hard by the multi-storey car park. The house was converted into a hotel about eight years ago, after a period as a nunnery. The Golsworthy restaurant is in a 'towards Georgian' and 'genteel' extension. The Wyatts came here not long since and have installed a new team to inject life into the kitchen, as well as impressing new visitors with a warm welcome and lots of smiles. Not every meal has been a success. But there is hope. David Mutter has taken lessons from modern masters, so his menu marks a shift for Exeter. First courses may be micro-mains if you order fried breast of pigeon with potato purée and a port jus, though more evidently hors d'oeuvre if you take the gravlax, or plump for feuilleté of John Dory with star-anise and herbs, or perhaps the timbale of crab with sour cream and red caviare. Flavours and technique have been thought good in these examples. Main courses have scored for presentation, but taste is sometimes in question: a pheasant was tender but not gamey, pork bland with a sauce that helped little, though rack of lamb and a port essence were accurately cooked and correctly reduced. Vegetables can be on the hard side – 'shown the hot water' was one person's reaction. Presentation comes up again with desserts: a lot of spun sugar. There is usually one hot pudding, to be ordered early, and a two-tone chocolate mousse and a hazelnut galette with a glazed pear are two others that have gone down well. Petits fours are passed round on a tray, and coffee has varied from good to not so hot. On a short and serviceable list, the wines are not overpriced. House wines are £9.50.

CHEF: David Mutter PROPRIETORS: Raymond and Ute Wyatt, and Peter Collier OPEN: all week, exc Sat L; 12 to 1.45, 6.30 to 9.30 CLOSED: 26 Dec to 5 Jan MEALS: alc SERVICE: not inc CARDS: Access, Amex, Diners, Visa DETAILS: 50 seats. 6 tables outside. Private parties: 50 main room, 15 private room. Car park. Vegetarian meals. Children's helpings. Smart dress preferred. No cigars/pipes in dining-room. Wheelchair access (3 steps). No music ACCOMMODATION: 15 rooms, all with bath/shower. 1 room for disabled. B&B £35 to £90. Children welcome. Baby facilities. Pets by arrangement. Afternoon teas. Garden. TV. Phone. Doors close at midnight. Fax: (0392) 413054

Several sharp operators have tried to extort money from restaurateurs on the promise of an entry in a guidebook that has never appeared. The Good Food Guide makes no charge for inclusion and does not offer certificates of any kind.

EYTON Hereford & Worcester   map 2

▲ *Marsh* ⁵⁄★

Eyton HR6 0AG   COOKING 1
LEOMINSTER (0568) 613952 and 611330   COST £36

Restoring this handsome fourteenth-century timbered house – and nurturing its gardens – has been a labour of love for Martin and Jacqueline Gilleland, a considerate couple with 'unassuming friendliness' and 'an unusually good sense of quality, taste and style'. Their hard work and aesthetic judgement has impressed visitors, who have praised the Marsh's virtues as a country hotel. Fixed-price dinners change regularly, depending on the availability of produce. A typical evening might begin with artichoke and scallop soup or warm chicken liver salad, then a sorbet, before centrepieces such as breast of duck with wild mushrooms or brill à la Bréval. Sweets are along the lines of Alsatian rhubarb tart and caramel ice-cream with butterscotch sauce. Pastry is a forte; imagination is left to the customers. Care rather than sparkle is the real thing here, but the price is high for so diffident a manner. Cheeses are British, and coffee comes with home-made chocolates. Booking, confirmed by 6pm, is essential. A short, well-spread list of around 60 wines has a useful choice of halves. House wines are from £9.50.

CHEF: Jacqueline Gilleland   PROPRIETORS: Martin and Jacqueline Gilleland   OPEN: all week, D only (L by arrangement); 7 to 9.30   MEALS: Set D £27.50   SERVICE: net prices, card slips closed   CARDS: Access, Amex, Visa   DETAILS: 24 seats. Private parties: 24 main room. Car park. Children welcome. Smart dress preferred. No smoking in dining-room ACCOMMODATION: 5 rooms, all with bath/shower. B&B £74 to £100. Deposit: £15. Children welcome in family suite. Baby facilities. Garden. TV. Phone. Doors close at 11. Confirm by 6 (*The Which? Hotel Guide*)

FAVERSHAM Kent   map 3

Read's ▮

Painter's Forstal,
Faversham ME13 0EE
FAVERSHAM (0795) 535344
on Eastling road,   COOKING 3*
1m S of Faversham   COST £23–£42

(County of the Year Restaurant)

It looks a bit of a shoe-box on the outside, but one irregular visitor felt the inside had been done up – 'well-spaced tables, more than just the odd painting on the walls, very satisfactory'. The same visitor hoped the Pitchfords stayed put: 'restaurants of this calibre are thin on the ground in north Kent'. This sentiment is echoed by others, particularly those who profit from the excellent value of lunch or the super-value of children's meals, or just enjoy full dinners and the welcome given by the staff. David Pitchford obviously likes gazpacho, hot cheese soufflés, asparagus, cheesecakes and chocolate desserts. These are regular items on a fixed-price menu that also shows he does not sleep while others cook around him. Parcels of skate with creamed parsley and caper sauce, pigeon with black pudding, or terrine of mullet and sole with ratatouille are dishes that run with the culinary pack. Tradition (even if adjusted) may rule in artichokes stuffed with wild mushrooms, salmon with lemon and chive sauce, two colours of asparagus with Bayonne ham, or duck with orange. Execution is exact, presentation – even of simple things like smoked duck with avocado – is well-judged. Wine-buying continues to be wide-ranging and intelligent, with a steady eye for quality. Pricing is fair throughout. Although the bottle award remains, we urge more consideration for the slow reader and the customer who is simply looking for a decent bottle; our comments last year about 'generous spacing' and over-long notes still stand. House wine is £10.50. CELLARMAN'S CHOICE: Chablis premier cru Vaulorent 1989, Fèvre, £19; Ch. Musar 1981, £16.

CHEF: David Pitchford   PROPRIETORS: David and Rona Pitchford   OPEN: Tue to Sat; 12 to 2, 7 to 10   MEALS: Set L £13.50, Set D £27.50   SERVICE: not inc, card slips closed   CARDS: Access, Amex, Diners, Visa   DETAILS: 60 seats. 3 tables outside. Private parties: 60 main room, 12 private room. Car park. Children's helpings. Wheelchair access (1 step; also WC). Music. Fax: (0795) 591200

FELSTED Essex   map 3

Rumbles Cottage £

Braintree Road, Felsted CM6 3DJ   COOKING 2
GREAT DUNMOW (0371) 820996   COST £18–£33

There is no stopping Joy Hadley. She has successfully opened a new restaurant called Rumbles Castle (see Essex round-up) and continues to develop new dishes – tried out on her Guinea Pig table d'hôte before being moved to the *carte* proper – and she goes on discovering new suppliers. This year's find has been an Italian gentleman who cures his own bresaola and air-dried ham in Saffron Walden. A family visit one Sunday was improved by the invigorating lunch that was available. It might have included things like ackee and prawns, chicken tandoori, duck with an orange and walnut crust and served with a gin and kumquat sauce, or a vegetarian dish of cheese scones. Cooking like this is often disastrous, but Joy Hadley brings it off. The wine list goes round the world, though its resting places do not always yield bottles from the very best sources. It is certainly adequate. House wines are from £7.50.

CHEFS: E. Joy Hadley and Steven Urry   PROPRIETORS: E. Joy Hadley and M. Donovan OPEN: Tue to Sat, D only, and Sun L; 12 to 2, 7 to 9   MEALS: alc. Set Sun L £13, Set D £13 SERVICE: not inc   CARDS: Access, Visa (2% discount for non-card payments)   DETAILS: 46 seats. Private parties: 24 main room, 8 and 10 private rooms. Vegetarian meals. Children's helpings. No-smoking area. Wheelchair access. No music

---

All entries in the Guide *are rewritten every year, not least because restaurant standards fluctuate. Don't trust an out-of-date* Guide.

£ *indicates that it is possible to have a three-course meal, including coffee, a half-bottle of house wine and service, at any time the restaurant is open (i.e. at dinner as well as at lunch, unless a place is open only for dinner), for £20 or less per person.*

FLITWICK Bedfordshire   map 3

▲ *Flitwick Manor* ✻

Church Road, Flitwick MK45 1AE
FLITWICK (0525) 712242   COOKING 1
off A5120, S of Flitwick   COST £26–£56

This is a mellow house, just the right distance for a day-trip from London. Old
hands will recognise much of the furniture and fittings from the days when the
place was first converted by Somerset Moore (now at the Painswick Hotel,
Painswick, see entry). It has recently taken on a new chef/manager in Ian
McAndrew. He used to cook in Canterbury (very well), and most recently in
the Republic of Ireland, where his talents were subverted by too many steaks.
Some initial reactions to his regime have not been encouraging. There is no
doubt that the man can cook – a carrot consommé with carrot and coriander
ravioli is proof of that – but it seems he doesn't yet cook enough of the good
stuff. At least, this is the only explanation we have for the pedestrian, and
sometimes poor, quality of the rest of the meal. Service, though willing, is not
up to scratch. Bread is brilliant. At lunch there is a set-price menu that makes
economic sense; at night the *carte* is very expensive. The potential is there, but it
needs bringing out. The wine list makes no concessions; the range is
acceptable. House wines are from £14.50.

CHEF: Ian McAndrew PROPRIETORS: Greentime Ltd OPEN: all week; 12 to 2, 7 to 10
MEALS: alc. Set L £16.50 to £19.50, Set vegetarian D £29.50 SERVICE: not inc, card slips
closed CARDS: Access, Amex, Diners, Visa DETAILS: 60 seats. 6 tables outside. Private
parties: 65 main room, 10 and 20 private rooms. Car park. Vegetarian meals. Children's
helpings. Smart dress preferred. No smoking in dining-room. Wheelchair access (also WC).
Music. Air-conditioned ACCOMMODATION: 15 rooms, all with bath/shower. Rooms for
disabled. B&B £78 to £190. Deposit: 50%. Children welcome. Baby facilities. Pets
welcome. Afternoon teas. Garden. Sauna. Tennis. TV. Phone. Confirm by 6. Fax: (0525)
712242

FOLKESTONE Kent   map 3

Paul's £ | NEW ENTRY |

2A Bouverie Road West,
Folkestone CT20 2RX   COOKING 1
FOLKESTONE (0303) 259697   COST £19–£23

A block back from the main street, look for the giant Sainsbury – Paul's is
opposite. The restaurant has a feminine touch; perhaps it's the pinks, yellows
and greens added to the well-furbelowed window. Paul Hagger has been
running this for many a year and his menus show continuity from the early
times of British bistros and 1960s cooking: dishes that use cheese – baked crab
topped with Brie, mussels and prawns with Parmesan crust, chicken
cannelloni with dolcelatte; dishes that use fruit – duck with pink grapefruit
and pineapple, liver and lemon, pork and apricot; lots of cream in the
puddings, and giant meringue confections. The food is certainly generous in
quantity, not outrageous in price and comes sizzling in pans (vegetables
included) straight from the kitchen. The waitresses dress in shirts and trousers

that match the carpet. The wines are not dear, and there are some clarets to splash out on at fair mark-ups. House wines are £6.50.

CHEFS/PROPRIETORS: Penny and Paul Hagger   OPEN: all week; 12 to 2.30, 7.30 (7 Sat) to 9.30   MEALS: alc   SERVICE: not inc   CARDS: Access, Visa   DETAILS: 46 seats. 5 tables outside. Private parties: 100 main room. Vegetarian meals. Children's helpings. Wheelchair access (2 steps; also female WC). No music

---

FOWEY Cornwall   map 1

Food for Thought

Town Quay, Fowey PL23 1AT   COOKING 2
FOWEY (072 683) 2221   COST £24–£41

There is a 'waterfront apartment' above this granite-walled restaurant, which boasts deeply swagged curtains contrasting nicely with the stone. You can stay there and get a discount on restaurant prices. Or, ignore the restaurant and go to the Billingsleys' fish and chip shop next door. Reports on Food for Thought imply that more thought is needed. Some meals have been very good, others have suffered from moderate materials, bad balance and defective technique. Pasta was poor on an inspection meal; sticky toffee pudding was not as it should be, say Lake District visitors; pastry has been heavy and soft. Everyone is impressed by Caroline Billingsley's service – intelligent and attentive – just as they are by the fried mushrooms and garlic mayonnaise that come as an appetiser; but there is a feeling that the hand that sauces dips too deep in the sugar bowl, which compounds the problems from elsewhere. A dose of simplification (for example, the hollandaise all over the vegetables is redundant in so rich a repertoire) would be to everyone's benefit. The wine list is perfectly adequate, and not overpriced. The clarets, a dozen of them, perhaps offer the most interest. House wines are from £6.95.

CHEF: Martin Billingsley   PROPRIETORS: Martin and Caroline Billingsley   OPEN: Mon to Sat, D only; 7 to 9.30   CLOSED: Jan to early Feb   MEALS: alc. Set D £18.50   SERVICE: not inc, card slips closed   CARDS: Access, Visa   DETAILS: 38 seats. Private parties: 20 main room. No children under 5. Wheelchair access. No music

---

FRAMPTON ON SEVERN Gloucestershire   map 2

Saverys

The Green,
Frampton on Severn GL2 7EA   COOKING 2
GLOUCESTER (0452) 740077   COST £28–£38

John Savery and Patricia Carpenter continue to attract the most loyal custom. 'Over the past year I have tried every GFG-listed restaurant in Avon and Gloucestershire, and some further afield. I keep coming back to Saverys' were the words of one regular. The setting on the Green of wide vistas, flowering chestnuts and swans, 'even peacocks', the diminutive brick house, the homely dining-room and kind attentions from the owners must contribute; but so does John Savery's steady cooking of seafood pancakes, venison and pork terrine with Cumberland sauce, duck with honey and ginger, loin of lamb with tarragon, and sea bass with red pepper and tomato sauce. Lots of vegetables, as well as a dauphinois, come with main dishes. This is sound country-restaurant cooking, with attention to flavour as well as quantity. Desserts such as warm rice pudding and caramelised bananas win votes; they are not skimped, either. A minimalist wine list starts with house wines at £7.95.

CHEFS/PROPRIETORS: John Savery and Patricia Carpenter   OPEN: Tue to Sat, D only (L by arrangement); 7 to 9.15   MEALS: Set D £19.75   SERVICE: not inc, card slips closed
CARDS: Access, Visa   DETAILS: 26 seats. Private parties: 26 main room. No children under 12. No pipes in dining-room. Wheelchair access. No music

---

FRESSINGFIELD Suffolk   map 6

Fox and Goose ▍

Fressingfield IP21 5PB   COOKING 3*
FRESSINGFIELD (037 986) 247   COST £22–£42

'In Fressingfield? Never! What a mixture: Peking duck, tempura, calamari, carpaccio and cod and chips.' This was the reaction of a Suffolk man, unused to such a liberated approach to cooking and hospitality. Others find the apparently random hopping from country to country gives them putative stomach-lag, but they are in the minority. Ruth Watson is an enthusiast. It shows from the notice on the signboard promising 'the best food for miles', to the notice pinned to the front door to the effect that clothing does not matter but behaviour does. It shows in the long menu and the longer wine list. The pub – a bar and dining-room – remains relatively unimproved. Some new lights for the tables were observed, but otherwise it's paper over linen for the tops, a sideboard of cheese, a roaring log fire, and all the fun of a pub. 'Good Renaudin champagne started a meal that ran through a gazpacho with plenty of kick, excellent egg and anchovy mayonnaise (not often you see that) with the eggs just soft, grilled salmon with champagne and sorrel sauce, plus a saffron mash that made the trip worthwhile, a mixed green salad with walnut dressing, warm treacle tart and a tall glass of raspberry fool, before thick, strong coffee, served with a strainer.' Other dishes include bruschetta with tomato and red peppers, Peking duck with a salad of spring onion and cucumber, chargrilled calamari served with a square of grilled polenta and a lethal tomato and chilli salsa, a superb squid and prawn risotto well-flavoured with saffron, and bresaola with sun-dried tomatoes and a salad. The cooking exemplifies some of the best traits of buying and thinking that are going the rounds today: not just inspiration from reading cookbooks, but nice, yet simple, inventiveness that results in a dish such as the scrambled egg with green garlic and asparagus that was a day's special in the summer. There have been moments when there has been a certain distance between staff and customer – not so great as to be off-hand, but unexpected in a country pub. Most readers will be happy to stray no further than the short wine list: a good catholic selection, modestly priced, with house wines from £8.50. For the adventurous with time to spare, a more weighty 300-plus list is also available; by no means exclusively majestic and expensive, this list will repay more than a glance with many good halves of petits châteaux and interesting Spanish and Italian bottles at modest prices.

CELLARMAN'S CHOICE: Quincy 1990, Dom. Pierre Mardon, £14.90; St-Amour 1990, D. Barbelet, £16.50.

CHEFS: Ruth Watson, Sara Fox and Brendan Ansbro PROPRIETOR: Ruth Watson OPEN: Wed to Sun; 12 to 2.15, 7 to 9.30 CLOSED: 1 week Christmas MEALS: alc SERVICE: not inc, card slips closed DETAILS: 50 seats. Private parties: 36 main room, 20 private room. Car park. Children welcome. No cigars/pipes in dining-room. No music. Fax: (0379) 868107

GATESHEAD Tyne & Wear   map 7

▲ *Eslington Villa Hotel* ╬✕

8 Station Road, Low Fell,
Gateshead NE9 6DR   COOKING 2
091-487 6017   COST £18–£46

This hotel has proved a godsend for visitors to Gateshead. Alan O'Neill's sound cooking produces modern, country-house-style dishes, including pan-fried duck breast with buttered lentils and spiced red cabbage, fricassee of scallops and salmon with home-made noodles and basil sauce, and fillet of lamb baked in filo pastry with a chicken and mint mousse. Lunch is served in the conservatory ('light and airy – white Lloyd Loom chairs and green hues'), a contrast to the dark main dining-room. One reader who enjoyed a three-course set lunch of salmon and vegetable mousse, medallion of beef ('the best I have tasted for a long while') and a raspberry cheesecake felt the experience was 'altogether very good value and the service meant that I was through in an hour without feeling rushed'. Another report on the evening table d'hôte praised a warm salad of fresh scallops, confit of duck and leeks, pecan pie and bourbon ice-cream. All comment favourably on the seven vegetables served at lunch and dinner. The wine list offers a fair spread. House wines are £7.95.

CHEF: Allan O'Neill PROPRIETORS: Mr N. and Mrs M. Tulip OPEN: Mon to Sat, exc Sat L; 12 to 2, 7 to 10 CLOSED: 23 Dec to 2 Jan; bank hols MEALS: alc. Set L £11.95 to £12.95, Set D £19.95 to £21.50 SERVICE: not inc CARDS: Access, Amex, Diners, Visa DETAILS: 50 seats. Private parties: 40 main room. Car park. Vegetarian meals with prior notice. Children's helpings. Smart dress preferred. No smoking in dining-room. Wheelchair access (2 steps; also WC). Music ACCOMMODATION: 14 rooms, all with bath/shower. Rooms for disabled. B&B £49.50 to £79. Pets welcome. Garden. TV. Phone

Fumi £   NEW ENTRY

248 Durham Road,
Gateshead NE8 4JR   COOKING 2
091-477 1152   COST £15–£30

This is a Japanese restaurant, occupying the site of a former Indian restaurant. Presumably the Japanese presence in the British motor industry is the explanation for its existence. The use of some British staff (who may be studying Japanese) does much to mediate between the two cultures. Local visitors cannot believe their luck. The place offers the full range of teriyaki, sushi, sashimi, sunomono, tempura and the like; its prices are not out of the way and it gets plenty of flavour and freshness in where they are required.

After eating deep-fried oysters with plum sauce, one reader was moved to remark that if the inhabitants of Newscatle's Chinatown were to taste this, 'there would be a mass exodus to Gateshead'. Other things that have met the warmest approval have been tako-su (octopus and sliced cucumber in rice vinegar), salmon teriyaki, nanban-zuke (fried fish with vinegar and sesame dressing) and the soups. The drinks list doesn't seem to extend much beyond saké and cokes. House wine is £6.50.

CHEF: Akio Konno   PROPRIETOR: Aki Hiko   OPEN: Tue to Sun, D only; 6 to 10.30
MEALS: alc   SERVICE: not inc   CARDS: Access, Visa   DETAILS: 50 seats. Private parties:
12 private room. Vegetarian meals. Children's helpings. Wheelchair access. Music.
Air-conditioned. Fax: 091-276 2915

GILLINGHAM Dorset   map 2

▲ Stock Hill Country House Hotel ⁵⁄✱

Gillingham SP8 5NR   COOKING 3*
GILLINGHAM (0747) 823626   COST £26–£40

There is word of Austrian-style waitress uniforms for the staff here, but we have not seen them. They might fit with the generally expansive nature of the Hausers, whose every gesture has impact and arouses comment. Stock Hill is a great place to visit. No one could have done it like them. The outside is impressive – woods, flowers and excellent gardening. The inside is highly worked, and the dining-room is almost the plainest room. People like it, just as they like the hospitality dispensed there. Peter Hauser is a cook who does not think you should eat small, so prepare to expand your appetite. Dinner is at a set price, with an intermediate soup and coffee included. Classical technique underlies many of the dishes, but the repertoire is not embedded in Escoffier. A breast of turkey is wrapped in a sorrel mousse and served with olive crostini to give texture and angle to the tastes. Monkfish is roasted and comes with a lovage and garlic butter. Ham is home-cured and offered as a salad with asparagus. Scallops are fresh as a daisy and put into ravioli to be served with spinach. The range is wide, and the points of novelty remain the lovage, sorrel and nettles in the much-loved nettle soup. These English tastes could be dangerous if handled coarsely, but make good seasoning when done well. Desserts go for a bit of old Vienna – Peter Hauser is Austrian – and are really good. A swan tartlet filled with fresh fruit, meringues, *schnitte* and sachertorte are things to cross the street for, as are the petits fours. The only reservation we had for cooking related to a large function, but most find this place a delight. The fair-priced wine list is mostly from Robin Yapp, so the Rhône and the Loire are the real strengths. House wines are £9.75.

CHEF: Peter Hauser   PROPRIETORS: Peter and Nita Hauser   OPEN: Tue to Sun, exc Tue and
Fri L and Sun D; 12.30 to 1.45, 7.30 to 8.45   MEALS: Set L £19, Set D £28   SERVICE: not inc,
card slips closed   CARDS: Access, Visa   DETAILS: 26 seats. Private parties: 12 main room,
12 private room. Car park. Children's helpings L. No children under 7. Jacket and tie. No
smoking in dining-room. No music   ACCOMMODATION: 9 rooms, all with bath/shower.
D,B&B £80 to £240. Deposit: £40. No children under 7. Garden. TV. Phone. Doors close at
midnight. Confirm by 8. Fax: (0747) 825628 (*The Which? Hotel Guide*)

GLASTONBURY Somerset   map 2

▲ No.3 ✻

3 Magdalene Street, Glastonbury BA6 9EW   COOKING 1
GLASTONBURY (0458) 832129   COST £40

A dolls'-house of a house in that every bit is decorated, giving rise to a sense of cosiness. The menu is careful, so is the cooking, and the price is fixed. Gratin of mushrooms with garlic, lambs' kidneys with sherry sauce, or pineapple grilled with some goats' cheese precede chicken filled with avocado mousse, spinach pancakes with two sauces, and lemon sole filled with crab and served with a prawn sauce. It's a family-run place and John Tynan will give you good advice about wines. The cellars must be capacious at No.3 because the list is of generous length and contains some fine French material. Note the mature Vouvrays and the collection of champagnes. House wine is £9.

CHEF: Ann Tynan   PROPRIETORS: John and Ann Tynan   OPEN: Tue to Sat, D only; 7 to 9 CLOSED: Jan   MEALS: Set D £26   SERVICE: not inc   CARDS: Access, Visa   DETAILS: 28 seats. 2 tables outside. Private parties: 12 main room. Car park. Children's helpings on request. No children under 5. Jacket and tie. No smoking in dining-room. No music ACCOMMODATION: 6 rooms, all with bath/shower. Rooms for disabled. B&B £55 to £75. Garden. TV. Phone. Doors close at 11.30. Confirm by 6 (*The Which? Hotel Guide*)

GLOUCESTER Gloucestershire   map 2

Yeung's £

St Oswalds Road, Cattle Market,
Gloucester GL1 2SR   COOKING 1
GLOUCESTER (0452) 309957   COST £16–£33

The former cattle-market site gives space enough for this trellis-framed, neon-lit single-storey chamber filled to the brim with flowers and plants. No, it's not a garden centre but a Chinese restaurant, and a good one, where the none-too-long menu ensures an immediacy and spring to the food served. The location, far from daily marketing in a Chinatown, means there is little out of the ordinary in ingredients, but the accuracy of the cooking makes it a useful spot for the city. The wine list is adequate. House wine is £7.

CHEF: C.H. Voong   PROPRIETORS: Henry and Ivy Soon, C.H. Voong and Peter Lee   OPEN: Mon to Sat, exc Mon L; 12 to 2.15, 6 to 11.15   CLOSED: 25 and 26 Dec   MEALS: alc. Set L and D £12 to £22.50. Minimum £8   SERVICE: 10%   DETAILS: 100 seats. Private parties: 50 main room. Vegetarian meals. Children welcome. Wheelchair access (also WC). Music. Air-conditioned

---

Not inc *in the details at the end of an entry indicates that no service charge is made and any tipping is at the discretion of the customer.*

✻ *indicates that smoking is either banned altogether or that a dining-room is maintained for non-smokers. The symbol does not apply to restaurants that simply have no-smoking areas.*

GOLCAR West Yorkshire
map 5

Weavers Shed

Knowl Road, Golcar HD7 4AN
HUDDERSFIELD (0484) 654284

COOKING 1
COST £15–£35

The restaurant occupies a converted cloth mill, the heavy stone of the outside belied by the cheer and warmth of the welcome. As if to maintain the historical connection, a keenly priced lunch menu is refulgent with British food: Yorkshire pudding with onion gravy, lamb's liver with onions, cod with cheese and parsley sauce. At dinner, the repertoire extends to quenelles of duck liver parfait and an apple and geranium jelly, or scallops with tarragon cream sauce, followed by venison with mushrooms in port wine, or wild boar with a reduced sauce flavoured with sloe gin. The desserts fit each of these stylistic bills: sticky toffee pudding or Eve's pudding on the one hand, blackcurrant mousse with passion-fruit sauce or chocolate terrine with orange and caramel sauce on the other. Now that she has had her baby, Kate McGunnigle has returned to work, but Bernadette McGunnigle, who steered the ship last year, remains to help steady the tiller. The wine list is a catholic range with some sound examples from France (Thevenet's Mâcon Blanc), Spain (Marqués de Murrieta), USA (Phelps' Syrah) and down-under (Stoneleigh's Sauvignon Blanc). The champagne is from Bruno Paillard, and prices are fair. House wines are £7.95.

CHEFS: Peter McGunnigle and Ian McGunnigle PROPRIETORS: Peter and Kate McGunnigle OPEN: Tue to Sat, exc Sat L; 12 to 1.45, 7 to 9 (9.15 Sat) CLOSED: first 2 weeks Jan, last 2 weeks July MEALS: alc. Set L £9.95 SERVICE: not inc CARDS: Access, Amex, Visa DETAILS: 70 seats. Private parties: 40 main room, 30 private room. Car park. Vegetarian meals. Children welcome. Smart dress preferred. Music

GORING Oxfordshire
map 2

Leatherne Bottel

Goring RG8 0HS
HENLEY (0491) 872667

COOKING 2*
COST £28–£44

Depart Goring on the Wokingham road and watch for the sign that commands a left-turn down a narrow lane. Thames waterfowl and perhaps the scent of wild herbs will herald arrival at the riverside. 'The terrace is the nicest setting I've eaten in for some time,' writes an inspector. Few restaurants integrate as effectively with advantageous surroundings. Even on a dull February day the dining-room was flooded with 'beautiful and abundant fresh-cut flowers'. Annie Bonnet is a warm and efficient hostess. Keith Read's cooking is inspired by the seasons, backed by fine local produce and fish from Cornwall and refined by skill. Open-air dishes such as a salad of green rocket leaves with scallops and pleurotte mushrooms stir-fried with ginger, olive oil and mint have satisfied as much as a January Sunday lunch of roast pork with 'lots of crackling', cabbage spiked with garlic and coriander and with roast parsnips. Flavour-matching technique is evinced both in spring woodpigeon, off the bone, marinated in olive oil and fresh red chillies, chargrilled and served with a stew of chickpeas and baby leeks, and in winter hare, the leg stewed with ground coriander and lemon thyme, the saddle chargrilled rare and with noodles tossed with chestnut pesto. Bread, including tomato and black olive varieties, and biscuits are home-baked, and British cheeses are properly maintained. Desserts have improved: for example, warm treacle tart with home-made brown bread ice-cream is rewarding. The wines are good and show a marked enthusiasm for Bordeaux. There is little below £15 apart from house wine (£10.50), but, as it says on the list, 'most bottles we are happy to serve as half-bottles'.

CHEF: Keith Read   PROPRIETORS: Keith Read and Annie Bonnet   OPEN: all week; 12.30 to 2 (2.30 Sat and Sun), 7 to 9.45   CLOSED: 25 Dec   MEALS: alc   SERVICE: not inc   CARDS: Access, Amex, Visa   DETAILS: 60 seats. 20 tables outside. Private parties: 20 main room, 12 and 20 private rooms. Car park. Vegetarian meals. Children restricted. No pipes in dining-room. Wheelchair access. No music. Air-conditioned

---

GRAMPOUND Cornwall
map 1

Eastern Promise £

1 Moor View, Grampound TR2 4RT	COOKING 1
ST AUSTELL (0726) 883033	COST £18–£30

The residents of mid-Cornwall appreciate Liza and Philip Tse's hospitality as well as their proficiency with the wok and the corkscrew. As is the case in many provincial Chinese restaurants far away from daily markets, the menu is not host to the arcane or outlandish ingredient. It runs through pork, chicken, beef, lamb, fish and shellfish with few deviations to innards, cartilage or taboo creatures (but it does have a section on frogs' legs). People enjoy it for immediacy and freshness, for the company, and for the variation it offers to a Cornish diet of pasty and pint. The wine list is very acceptable (you can even have Ch. Giscours 1970) and the prices are eminently fair. House French is £6.50.

CHEF: Liza Tse   PROPRIETOR: Philip Tse   OPEN: Thur to Tue, D only; 6 to 11   MEALS: alc. Set D £16.50   SERVICE: not inc   CARDS: Access, Amex, Diners, Visa   DETAILS: 64 seats. Private parties: 40 main room, 24 private room. Car park. Vegetarian meals. No children under 3. Music. Air-conditioned

---

GRASMERE Cumbria
map 7

▲ Michael's Nook ❢ ✳

Grasmere LA22 9RP	COOKING 3*
GRASMERE (053 94) 35496	COST £37–£63

'There is an air of grandness about this country-house hotel that stops far short of intimidatory,' wrote one satisfied guest. Perhaps it comes from the well-lived-in furniture ('worn gentility', in the words of another), the high-stacked fires, the rosettes won by Reg Gifford's Great Dane – not for cooking – or the grand piano ready for the off in the drawing-room (a spinet is in the hall). The dining-room is equally striking: deep red walls with white cornices, elbow-grease on the table-tops, good flowers, cutlery, china and glassware. Kevin

Mangeolles is the new head chef and, if anything, cooking has improved under him. He is prepared to use a combination of rich and poor: quail and poussin with truffles, oxtail with foie gras, or salmon mousse with caviare (not much of that). He enjoys offal dishes: calf's liver with mash, wild mushrooms and madeira, or kidneys with vegetable strips and mustard sauce (as a first course). He deploys fashionable items: monkfish done as osso buco, a ratatouille soup, a salmis of rabbit, noodles, roast garlic, saffron, lentils and so on. This he seems to do with great skill: the flavours are true and the accuracy is there. The format is a meal of four or five courses. There is choice on the main *cartes*; there is no choice if you have the pricier chef's gourmet special during the season. The pudding stage is well worth waiting for: hot pistachio soufflé (with some crème de menthe in the background) robed in chocolate, with a chocolate ice-cream, was outstanding. Hot apple croustade was proficient too. This is good cooking with some modern gusto joined to country-house style. The pity is the price: not so far adrift in Lake District terms, it does come dear to those who think the recession should have mitigated the margins to which the industry works. The wine list has many decent bottles on offer at £12 or under and half-bottles are in abundance. Classic areas are favoured, but our advice is not to ignore the more lively antipodean and Spanish sections. There is a hint of conservatism about the wine-buying here that may benefit from a more widely cast net. Nevertheless this remains a fine list. House wines are from £10.50. CELLARMAN'S CHOICE: Gewurtztraminer, Clos Gaensbroenel 1988, Alsace Willm, £15.90; St-Emilion, Ch. la Tour du Pin Figeac 1985, £2.50.

CHEF: Kevin Mangeolles   PROPRIETOR: Reg Gifford   OPEN: all week; 12.30 to 1, 7.15 to 8.45   MEALS: Set L £27.50, Set D £38 to £46   SERVICE: not inc   CARDS: Access, Amex, Diners, Visa   DETAILS: 55 seats. Private parties: 35 main room. Car park. No children under 12. Smart dress preferred. No smoking in dining-room. No music   ACCOMMODATION: 14 rooms, all with bath/shower. D,B&B £105 to £340. Deposit: £50. No children under 8. Garden. Swimming-pool. Sauna. Fishing. Golf. TV. Phone. Doors close at 11.30 or by arrangement. Fax: (053 94) 35765

▲ White Moss House 🍷 ✲✳

Rydal Water, Grasmere LA22 9SE
GRASMERE (053 94) 35295

COOKING 3*
COST £36

The mountains rise higher than the house; the setting is very fine. White Moss is small, though no cottage, and there is a sense of family in all customers sitting down at one time and being served the same menu (with no choice until pudding stage). There may even be a sense of shepherding, as in a large and disparate family, with Susan Dixon directing her young staff, and even making one feel it's time for beddybyes by 10.30. The form of the meal is immutable (and so are many of the dishes). Start with soup, then a soufflé or a fish dish, then meat (which is often roast) with five vegetables, before a choice of four puddings, one of which is going to be steamed traditional, and finally cheese and coffee. For the precision of the cooking, and the length of the meal, the price is fair. Some do find the tastes quite muted – 'a definite lack of seasoning' was one comment. To counter that is the enthusiasm for the use of herbs (marjoram in a mushroom and Marsala soup) and tastes which point up flavours (passion-fruit sauce with breast of goose is a favourite). Vegetables are enjoyed for their variety – beetroot with orange and ginger, leeks with Pernod, stir-fried plain baby carrots on one evening – though some have found the quantities inadequate for a larger party. Desserts are always a hit: 'Guardsman's pudding was traditional but elevated to a most untraditional finesse; sticky chocolate hazelnut cream slice was one of the best chocolate desserts since Hilaire in its heyday.' The cheeses are British, served with oat biscuits, and very well tended. This is a careful restaurant, and loved because of that. Wine is both good and cheap; the benefits of canny buying are not seen as opportunities for easy profit, so although some prices look high they are no more than a fair reflection of cost. White Moss House opts not for first growths, but for the Ch. Cissacs and Alsace co-op wines of this world. This is not to disparage the list of fine names from Burgundy, or the many excellent Rhônes. Bottles such as J-L. Colombo's Cornas suggest that a tendency to timidity, shown in the ranges from Spain and Italy, may be cracking. We would still welcome a clearer and more consistent listing of wines. House wine is £8.50.

CHEF: Peter Dixon   PROPRIETORS: Susan and Peter Dixon   OPEN: Mon to Sat, D only; 8 CLOSED: end Nov to mid-Mar   MEALS: Set D £25   SERVICE: not inc, card slips closed DETAILS: 18 seats. Private parties: 18 main room. Car park. Children welcome. No smoking in dining-room. Wheelchair access. No music   ACCOMMODATION: 7 rooms, all with bath/ shower. D,B&B £79 to £170. Children welcome. Baby facilities. Garden. Swimming-pool. Sauna. Fishing. TV. Phone. Doors close at 11. Confirm by 4 (*The Which? Hotel Guide*)

GRAYSHOTT Hampshire   map 2

Woods Place

Headley Road, Grayshott GU26 6LB   COOKING 1
HINDHEAD (0428) 605555   COST £21–£30

The restaurant occupies a former butcher's shop; the best room is the front one. Eric Norrgren cooks from a menu that develops slowly, simple though it may be. The Scandinavian dishes are the most interesting, and the quality of the kitchen lies in its uncluttered approach. Gravlax, Jansson's 'temptation'(sliced potatoes baked with cream and fish), oxfilé Johanna (marinated beef with horseradish and mustard), good cured herrings and Danish frigadeller were being prepared in the summer, and Baltic soft fruits – cloudberries and lingonberries – abounded. In simplicity may lie success. The wine list is pleasantly cheap, containing Len Evans' Hunter Valley Chardonnay and Shiraz alongside Fontaine-Gagnard's Chassagne-Montrachet 1987 and Mont-Redon Châteauneuf 1986 at very fair cost. House wine is £7.50.

CHEF: Eric Norrgren   PROPRIETORS: Eric and Dana Norrgren   OPEN: Tue to Sat; 12 to 3, 7 to 10.30   MEALS: alc   SERVICE: 10%, card slips closed   CARDS: Access, Amex, Diners, Visa (5% surcharge)   DETAILS: 35 seats. Private parties: 12 main room. Vegetarian meals. Children's helpings. Wheelchair access (also WC). Music

---

'When you have a room half full, and of such size as to hide a squadron of B52s, resplendent with kids on a sandwich course or something, plus a table full of fertiliser reps, its cold atmosphere isn't going to impress despite the wonderful room itself.'
On eating in Hertfordshire

GREAT DUNMOW Essex
map 3

▲ *The Starr* ♟

Market Place, Great Dunmow CM6 1AX
GREAT DUNMOW (0371) 874321

COOKING 1
COST £18–£44

'We hadn't dined at The Starr for some time and were pleasantly surprised,' write local supporters of this ancient black and white painted restaurant, with a beamed dining-room and modern bedrooms in the stable block. The bare bones of the menu are chalked on a blackboard, and staff explain dishes in detail. Fish is a feature and there is a noticeable fondness for fruity accompaniments, which can lead to palate-jarring combinations such as escalope of salmon with strawberry liqueur. Ingredients are good, fresh and well timed, as in parcels of crab in filo pastry, rack of new season's English lamb cooked exactly pink, and fillet of turbot with red wine and shallot sauce. The policy of undercooking vegetables can produce odd results ('crunchy aubergine is not pleasant'). Desserts such as spotted dick, caramel bavarois with caramel sauce, and a fruity mix of blackberries and raspberries with miniature coffee ice-cream have been enjoyable. Service is well paced and competent. Most reporters feel that prices are on the high side. Lay & Wheeler supply the wines on a list that maintains a fair and steady balance between the classics and antipodean upstarts. Prices at the lower end are notably fair with no slip in quality or interest. House wines are from £9.45. CELLARMAN'S CHOICE: St Helena, Pinot Blanc 1990, £12.45; Fleurie 1990, Paul Bernard, £16.30.

CHEF: Mark Fisher PROPRIETORS: Brian and Vanessa Jones OPEN: all week, exc Sat L and Sun D; 12 to 1.30, 7 to 10 CLOSED: 2 to 9 Jan MEALS: Set L £10 to £23, Set D £19 to £31 SERVICE: not inc (10% for 6 or more) CARDS: Access, Amex, Visa DETAILS: 60 seats. Private parties: 8 main room, 2 private room. Car park. Vegetarian meals. Children's helpings. Wheelchair access (also WC). Music ACCOMMODATION: 8 rooms, all with bath/shower. Rooms for disabled. B&B £60 to £110. Children welcome. TV. Phone. Doors close at midnight. Confirm by noon. Fax: (0371) 876337

GREAT GONERBY Lincolnshire
map 6

Harry's Place ⅙✳

17 High Street,
Great Gonerby NG31 8JS
GRANTHAM (0476) 61780

COOKING 3
COST £35–£58

Heady wafts from the kitchen as you enter this small house on the main road (opposite the Social Club) confirm that here is cookery. The name might imply cool-jivin' sophistication for the smart set of Grantham. You could not be more wrong. There are three tables set in a front room – warm pimento walls, an abundance of stripped pine – with seats for less than a dozen; one hostess-cum-waitress, Caroline; one chef, Harry; a short daily menu (in January a choice of two dishes in each course): a little shrine to gastronomy. No lobster is boiled, sauce started, or vegetables shredded until the command. There are no staff to dilute the intentions, no coach parties to compromise the purity. You can sense the poetic wholeness of the ambition. The cooking shows good training: sauces are impeccably made, meat and fish cooked the correct time; pastry is light and crisp; soufflés rise, don't fall. There is no provincial heaviness – here you won't find everything smothered with cream, or tastes ironed out but, in fact, a desire to heighten flavours that can sometimes get the better of discretion. Herbs get used in bunches, not sprigs, garlic in heads not cloves. This may result in a refined conception being coarsened. The repertoire develops slowly, but dishes that have come well-recommended include pancakes of scallops with leeks, mushrooms and basil; squab with madeira, bacon and tarragon; guinea-fowl with calvados, lemon thyme and grapes; lemon tart and hot soufflés. Most people end up in the kitchen having lessons in soufflé-whisking. From the little high-flavoured canapés to the 'very good' coffee, everything is done in pukka style. Do not expect to hurry through Harry's meals. Three hours is par. Moments there are when the waits seem overextended, especially if you collapse into wordlessness in a room populated by only two other people. However, Caroline usually keeps banter on the trot and her touching enthusiasm is infectious. Nor should you expect to dine cheaply. Prices are firm for south Lincolnshire. The wine list is short, badly balanced and generally expensive (though not profiteering), but evidently the product of similar enthusiasm – many of the bottles (there is only one half-bottle) are a personal find, like the Protos 1976 from Ribera del Duero, or Hermanos Barril's Priorato 1983.

CHEF: Harry Hallam   PROPRIETORS: Harry and Caroline Hallam   OPEN: Tue to Sat (Sun and Mon by arrangement); 12.30 to 2, 7 to 9.30   CLOSED: 25 Dec, bank hols   MEALS: alc
SERVICE: not inc   CARDS: Access, Visa   DETAILS: 10 seats. Private parties: 10 main room, 4 private room. Car park. Children's helpings on request. No smoking. No music

---

GREAT MILTON Oxfordshire   map 2

▲ Le Manoir aux Quat'Saisons ▼ ⁵⁄ₓ

Church Road, Great Milton OX9 7PD   COOKING 5
GREAT MILTON (0844) 278881   COST £44–£99

Le Petit Rapporteur is the quarterly newsletter for Le Manoir. In its 'Famous names' column for Spring 1992, it notes that Warren Beatty, Paul 'Gazza' Gascoigne and Matthew Corbett (Sooty and Sweep) have been customers. The menu (for which you will be charged £7 if you want one to take home, and it may not even be the menu that you had that day) carries the legend 'China and glassware by Villeroy & Boch'. The observant may take in that the marbling on the same menus is a hallmark of V&B. There's a lot more to running a restaurant than cooking the food. Le Manoir is a seventeenth-century honeyed-stone manor house. Stables have been converted to bedrooms, magnificent gardens surround every building, a kitchen garden has a positive team to maintain it, and the restaurant occupies the ground floor of the house itself and spreads into the garden with a large conservatory extension which is now the main dining-room. Its florid lime greens and pinks and the slight smell of stale food make it resemble an over-decorated motorway service station 'Country

Harvest' style of restaurant. It gets very hot by day, and is much appreciated by night. The long seasonal *carte* is reinforced by a cheaper lunch menu (with a pair of choices at each course), an eight-course gourmet menu (but some object that of the eight courses, one is a minute soup, one a sorbet and one petits fours), and some daily supplementary dishes. If you want to know Raymond Blanc's repertoire, the best thing is to read his books. Much of the menu figures among the recipes. A meal might take in amuse-bouches with aperitifs, but make sure that if you sit outside it has not rained in the previous day, for the cushions on the chairs are foam rubber and will soak your bottom. On offer may be tiny samosas of lamb's brains with curry – delicious; anchovy straws – delicious; and chicken liver mousse – delicious. The meal seems set fair. An appetiser is brought to your table: a coffee cup of smooth gazpacho, with all the flavours you might expect. Bread is rolls: a white leaven dough is excellent, a Viennese is crisp and exact. The first course of noodles with fresh-water crayfish (from the Windrush) and a shellfish sauce is heaven. The sauce is not too strong, but there is enough of it. The crayfish is delicate, but fresh and full of texture. The noodles are fine, but too buttery. The most exciting flavour comes from some diced tomato flesh and tarragon. This sings, the rest hums. Main course is a boned quail stuffed with a farce of liver and meat. The sauce is grapefruit. It is contained on the plate by a palisade of candied grapefruit peel that would not be out of place in a pudding. Many sauces are contained by some such ring-motif. The quail tastes well seasoned. It is wonderful for three mouthfuls, then the strong citrus content to the stuffing begins to overpower. The sauce is too strongly reduced (all the sauces on that day are too strongly reduced). There is not enough of it. A plate of vegetables comes with the quail. They are outstanding – runners, mange-tout, baby beet, potato and carrot – and are dressed with the right amount of beaten butter. They taste fresh and true. Cheese trundles up, from Philippe Olivier in Boulogne – no British ones here. The range is limited – no double creams, all strong, some old. Dessert is perhaps the finest course. A roasted peach sits on a slice of savarin. Eating the two in combination is a fine experience, the dough giving depth to the acid notes of the fruit. There is a scattering of wild strawberries and a pair of poached figs, filled with port ice-cream. There is a mild fig coulis and a syrup that tastes so light, alcoholic, and yet sweet. Coffee is strong arabica; petits fours are not as good as they have been. The coconut tuile is soft, the cream slice is not of the best, the tartlets are great, and everyone likes the truffles. This is very capable cooking. The things that come out best are the simplest. People have been more pleased this year than last. There has been great take-up of special offers in newspapers for bargain breaks at Le Manoir, including the eight-course dinner. People have felt they have had a bargain. Whether £100 a head, which may be roughly the cost of a normal meal and wine from the *carte*, is felt to be a bargain depends on your sense of priorities. There are a lot of staff to pay. The waiters have done a fair job this year; the young ladies on the front desk need to learn more about a sense of welcome – and how to say goodbye. Massive expenditure on the excellent wine list is possible but not essential. Care has gone into providing a good range of interesting French regional wines, some below £20. No one comes here to save money, but a modest jump to the £25 to £30 range will bring in view such worthwhile bottles as a Juillot Mercurey, Dom. de Trevallon, Sangioveto from Badia and decent bourgeois clarets with some age. Beyond that the world is your oyster, but do not expect anything as old-fashioned as value for money. Some half-bottles are provided, but as we noted last year, even these cannot cope adequately with the abrupt and frequent changes offered by a multi-course meal. The provision of wines by the glass should be possible at a place as large as this. House wines are from £22.

CHEF: Raymond Blanc   PROPRIETORS: Blanc Restaurants Ltd   OPEN: all week; 12.15 to 2.30, 7.15 to 10.30   MEALS: alc. Set L £29.50, Set D £59.50   SERVICE: net prices, card slips closed   CARDS: Access, Amex, Diners, Visa   DETAILS: 95 seats. 4 tables outside. Private parties: 45 private room. Car park. Vegetarian meals. Children's helpings. Smart dress preferred. No smoking in dining-room. Wheelchair access. Music   ACCOMMODATION: 19 rooms, all with bath/shower. Rooms for disabled. B&B £174.50 to £404. Deposit: £150. Children welcome. Baby facilities. Afternoon teas. Garden. Swimming-pool. Tennis. TV. Phone. Fax: (0844) 278847 (*The Which? Hotel Guide*)

GREAT MISSENDEN Buckinghamshire   map 3

La Petite Auberge

107 High Street,
Great Missenden HP16 0BB   COOKING 1*
GREAT MISSENDEN (024 06) 5370   COST £31–£38

This tiny restaurant is out of the way at the end of the village street. It manages to survive because it is a family business, although the pace can seem slow when the kitchen is under pressure. The Martels offer a staunchly Gallic menu, including vegetable terrine with tomato coulis, asparagus in puff pastry with chervil sauce, free-range chicken with morels, and breast of duck with green peppercorn sauce. Fish dishes tend to receive most endorsements: well-judged fish soup with garlicky rouille; sea bass on tomato slices with sherry vinegar; John Dory with vegetables and cream. There are also good reports of sweets such as hot apple slices with cinnamon ice-cream, lemon tart and chocolate gâteau with crème de menthe. The cooking is good in a refined way, avoiding extremes of flavouring, but sometimes lacking sufficient variety to sustain interest. There is no house wine, but a short French list provides some affordable drinking.

CHEF: H. Martel   PROPRIETORS: Mr and Mrs H. Martel   OPEN: Mon to Sat, D only; 7.30 to 10.30   CLOSED: 25 Dec, Easter, bank hols   MEALS: alc   SERVICE: not inc   CARDS: Access, Visa   DETAILS: 30 seats. Private parties: 35 main room. Children welcome. Smart dress preferred. Wheelchair access. Music

---

GREAT YARMOUTH Norfolk   map 6

Seafood Restaurant

85 North Quay, Great Yarmouth NR30 1JF   COOKING 2
GREAT YARMOUTH (0493) 856009   COST £22–£50

It was a little disconcerting for one reader who admired the great display of fish in the bar area but was never sure how much it all would cost until the moment the bill was presented. There is in fact a menu, but the two forms of choice were difficult to combine. Some of the general cooking may not scale the heights, but most people come here for the evidently fresh and enthusiastically served fish and seafood. Lobster swim in tanks and the converted pub is comfortable and plush. On the wine list there's a run of Drouhins and Latours in the white burgundies and you may want to try one of the half-dozen or more hocks or mosels. Prices are not high. House wine is from £8.70.

CHEFS: Mark Chrisostomou and Gary Crompton PROPRIETORS: Christopher and Miriam Kikis OPEN: Mon to Sat, exc Sat L; 12 to 2, 7 to 10.45 MEALS: alc SERVICE: not inc CARDS: Access, Amex, Diners, Visa DETAILS: 40 seats. Private parties: 40 main room. Children's helpings. Smart dress preferred. Music

---

GRIMSTON Norfolk   map 6

▲ Congham Hall ⁑✳

Lynn Road, Grimston PE32 1AH   COOKING 1*
HILLINGTON (0485) 600250   COST £18–£50

All around the Hall – a handsome Italianate villa dating from the early nineteenth century – are flat lawns. When you eat in the conservatory you can watch the teeming population of rabbits and pigeons (visitors were surprised, maybe relieved, not to find them on the menu). The house is comfortable, apart from the seats in the bar, and the welcome varies from good to stately among the captains, not so well-informed when you get to the foot-soldiers. This year sees the appointment of a new chef, a representative of Great Britain in the Prix International Pierre Taittinger. Perhaps prize-winners work too hard for their effects; certainly Murray Chapman's dishes are not the 'simpler approach', as the hotel claims. If sauté Jerusalem artichoke, wild mushrooms and celeriac between layers of pasta with a tomato vinaigrette, garnished with a tiny potato rösti and a filo purse of ratatouille is simple, then what is complex? According to an inspector, this dish suffered from flabby pasta, rubbery wild mushrooms and tomatoey sauce, drowned by the flavour of celeriac. Simpler things succeeded: brill with saffron sauce and mussels; some (but not all) of the cheeses; a double sandwich of lime and caramel ice-creams that went with a good pear soufflé; and an excellent madeira sauce with lamb that unfortunately overpowered the meat. There is good cooking here, but it needs pulling together. The wine list has a fair range, including some interesting South Africans and good French country bottles. House wines start at £10.50.

CHEF: Murray Chapman PROPRIETORS: Trevor and Christine Forecast OPEN: all week, exc Sat L; 1.30 to 2, 7.30 to 9.30 MEALS: Set L £15 to £17.50, Set D £30 to £36 SERVICE: not inc, card slips closed CARDS: Access, Amex, Diners, Visa DETAILS: 50 seats. Private parties: 8 main room, 12 private room. Car park. No children under 12. Jacket and tie. No smoking in dining-room. Wheelchair access. No music ACCOMMODATION: 14 rooms, all with bath/shower. B&B £65 to £170. Deposit: £20. No children under 12. Garden. Swimming-pool. Tennis. TV. Phone. Doors close at 11. Confirm by 6. Fax: (0485) 601191 (*The Which? Hotel Guide*)

Healthy eating options *in the details at the end of an entry signifies that a restaurant marks on its menu, in words and/or using symbols, low-fat dishes or other healthy eating choices.*

HALFORD Warwickshire map 2

Sykes House ✦

Queen Street, Halford CV36 5BT
STRATFORD-UPON-AVON (0789) 740976

COOKING 2
COST £40

Book at least 24 hours in advance; have explained to you a set menu of six courses with a welcoming appetiser and then coffee at the end; attend the sixteenth-century stone house between 7.30 and 8.15pm to eat. This is the formula of Sykes House, where David and Peggy Cunliffe live, garden and entertain paying customers. It may sound claustrophobic, but it is done with tact and style as well as professionalism. A spring meal began with chicken consommé and a slice of onion tart; then came a fish course of sweet-and-sour brill ('caveached'), before boiled beef and carrots. Cheese was roast goats' from Somerset, served with sorrel and salad leaves, before a rest with an orange sorbet and sloe gin. Finally, there were Sally Lunn pudding and coffee. Bought by the day, cooked for the customer – there is nothing pre-packed about the food. Nor yet about the bits and pieces: bread (perhaps apricot bread with Munster cheese, or buttermilk bread with haddock soup), appetisers, petits fours – all are made for the occasion. There have been moments when the balance of a particular menu has been questioned, but praise for skill, substance and invention outweighs such points. The wine list may be short (40 bins), but each choice has been thought about. 'From an area in Central Spain renowned for its awful wine-making' starts a comment introducing 'award-winning' Señorio de Los Llanos Gran Reserva 1978. The range is more than adequate. House wines are from £8.25.

CHEF: David Cunliffe PROPRIETORS: David and Peggy Cunliffe OPEN: Wed to Sat D (reservations only), Mon and Tue D and L by arrangement for 8 or more; 7.30 to 8.15
MEALS: Set D £28.50 SERVICE: not inc, card slips closed CARD: Visa DETAILS: 24 seats.
Private parties: 12 main room, 12 private room. Car park. Children welcome. Smart dress preferred. No smoking in dining-room. Wheelchair access (3 steps). No music

HAMBLETON Leicestershire map 6

▲ *Hambleton Hall* ▮

Hambleton LE15 8TH
OAKHAM (0572) 756991
off A606, 3m SE of Oakham

COOKING 4
COST £25–£55

A writer has called Hambleton Hall 'tweedy'. This the outside may be: hardly the international sophistication of classical palace architecture, more an outgrown piece of domesticity from the late Victorians. Tweeds abound round abouts – lots of huntin', don't you know – but inside, the house is 'sumptuous' rather than ostentatious, ever smart and never dowdy, brilliantly kept up to the mark by a serious owner who does not wish his original vision to be compromised. Tim Hart has always gone for home-grown cooking talent – first Nicholas Gill, then Brian Baker, and now Aaron Patterson. The last two have been internal promotions. Aaron Patterson has not lacked outside advice, however. Periods of attachment to Le Manoir aux Quat'Saisons, Tante Claire,

293

Anton Mosimann and Le Crocodile in Strasbourg have given him plenty of perspective. He has begun his stint with great success. Though these are early days, inspectors have been unanimous on this. There is, however, one reservation: 'If anybody writes to say it is elaborate, please believe them; there is a tendency to get too much on the plate, to distract attention.' Witness to the tendency is an assiette of sucking pig: loin, fillet, a square of crackling stuffed with prunes, minced pork with oriental spicing and soy in a deep-fried raviolo, a piece of roasted red apple on top of apple purée, then turnips, carrots, onions and morels, all ranged around the meat, in a deep-flavoured sauce. The last flourish was a small trotter, stuffed with morels and sweetbreads, which was neither rich nor fatty. It was all consumed with relish, and room left for cheese and praline parfait. The moral, therefore, is that the complexity can work. The same lesson was pointed up by a first course of ballottine, of duck foie gras, wrapped in leeks. There was a vinaigrette, with scattered shards of duck breast ham, some young green beans, and an outer circle of onion marmalade. 'Another chef's luxury dish perhaps, but the contrast of sweet and rich flavours against the sharp, refreshing acidity of the rest was impressive.' Vegetables have also come in for praise, each considered, each satisfactory, and all part of the main dish itself. Too much detail here would obscure the evident pursuit of high flavours – particularly from southern vegetables and sharp, light sauces – the intelligent use of seasoning, and the high quality of the ingredients. The slight country-house blandness seems to have been sent packing. Details have had all the thought you would expect – canapés, good to brilliant complementary soups as appetisers, petits fours (very good), breads, and breakfasts on the next day. Service can break down on very busy nights, but it is well-motivated and there is an ease of approach here that masks many hours of training. The wine list is serious, with age and pedigree given their due as much in Burgundy as in Western Australia. A price has to be paid for these pleasures, but what is good about this list is the unstuffy attitude that allows enthusiasm for a humble Pinot from Alsace or a Bordeaux petit château; here is a restaurateur who recognises that there is a time and a place and a pocket for each wine. 'Wines of the moment' start at £12.50.

CHEF: Aaron Patterson   PROPRIETORS: Timothy and Stefa Hart   OPEN: all week; 12 to 1.45, 7 to 9.30   MEALS: alc. Set L £18.50 to £27.50 (Sun), Set D £35 to £39   SERVICE: net prices, card slips closed   CARDS: Access, Visa   DETAILS: 60 seats. Private parties: 45 main room, 20 private room. Car park. Vegetarian meals. Children's helpings. Smart dress preferred. No cigars/pipes in dining-room. Wheelchair access (also WC). No music
ACCOMMODATION: 15 rooms, all with bath/shower. Rooms for disabled. Lift. B&B £110 to £240. Children welcome. Baby facilities. Pets welcome. Afternoon teas. Garden. Swimming-pool. Tennis. TV. Phone. Doors close at midnight. Fax: (0572) 724721
(*The Which? Hotel Guide*)

Dining-rooms where live and recorded music are never played are signalled by No music *in the details at the end of an entry.*

All details are as accurate as possible at the time of going to press, but chefs and owners often change, and it is wise to check by telephone before making a special journey. Many readers have been disappointed when set-price bargain meals are no longer available. Ask when booking.

HAMPTON WICK **Surrey** map 3

Dijonnais

NEW ENTRY

35 High Street, Hampton Wick,
Kingston upon Thames KT1 4DA
081-977 4895

COOKING 2
COST £17–£39

Mme Jolivet makes all the pastry here, and very good it is too. One reader discovered this when telephoning for a table, only to surprise Madame up to her elbows in flour. M. Jolivet cooks classic French, with grace notes. The financial grace notes, also French, are a cover charge and extra for vegetables, but this remains a fair-priced neighbourhood restaurant, of a standard beyond that reached in most London suburbs. Poached eggs in red wine, a tart of mussels with spinach and cheese, monkfish with prawns and vermouth, salmon with sorrel sauce and a gutsy civet of duck with apples and cream have impressed, as have the vegetables – particularly the dauphinois. Desserts too, where pastry comes top, are satisfactory. Mme Jolivet also acts the hostess in a charming room of pinks and steel blues which would respond to being as busy as the place deserves. The wine list is perfunctory. House Duboeuf is £8.25.

CHEF: Lionel Jolivet   PROPRIETORS: L. and J. Jolivet   OPEN: all week, exc Sat L and Sun D; 12 to 2.30 (3 Sun), 7 to 10   MEALS: alc. Set L £9, Set D £16. Cover £1   SERVICE: not inc CARDS: Access, Visa   DETAILS: 26 seats. 2 tables outside. Private parties: 24 main room. Vegetarian meals. Children's helpings. Wheelchair access (1 step). Music

---

HARROGATE **North Yorkshire** map 5

Drum and Monkey £

5 Montpellier Gardens, Harrogate HG1 2TF
HARROGATE (0423) 502650

COOKING 2
COST £13–£35

If you want lunch on spec, turn up at 11.30, advises one habitué. The place (once a pub) is on two floors: bar below and restaurant above. It serves fish, no meat (but what status snails?). The slate-topped tables are close-packed, it's no man's description of luxury, but the bustle generates enthusiasm and the welcome, once over a certain threshold of acceptance, is genuine. There is close concordance between lunch and dinner menus, though prices are a mite cheaper in the morning. First courses revolve around crustacea and bi-valves, with traditional fish cookery much in evidence: croustade of seafood Mornay, crab cocktail, avocado with prawns or crab. Main dishes, too, have ignored the chargrill revolution and tend to sauces – florentine, dieppoise and bonne femme offered with fillets of sole – rather than Mediterranean vegetables, olive oil or herbs as might be the case in other circles. The restaurant has a consistent following for a consistent product, causing distress only when so busy that delivery slows and the immediate relationship of stove to table slackens. The wine list is short and sharp; prices are keen. There are hardly any reds, but the Paillard champagne, Sauvion Muscadet or Saget Menetou-Salon should please. Four out of six white burgundies are alternate vintages. House wines are £5.95.

CHEF: Keith Penny PROPRIETOR: William Fuller OPEN: Mon to Sat; 12 to 2.30, 7 to 10.15
CLOSED: Christmas to New Year MEALS: alc SERVICE: not inc CARDS: Access, Visa
DETAILS: 48 seats. Private parties: 8 main room. Children's helpings. Wheelchair access
(3 steps). No music

Millers

COUNTY RESTAURANT OF THE YEAR

1 Montpellier Mews, Harrogate HG1 2TG   COOKING 3
HARROGATE (0423) 530708   COST £25–£40

Simon Gueller is a talented chef working in a small kitchen and fairly
rudimentary restaurant set among boutiques in a mews. Shelves behind the bar
half-filled with bottles of Kaliber do not encourage visions of serious cooking,
but maybe these are what keep Simon Gueller hard at it. When plates arrive at
table (and they may take a longish time), the work put into them is evident to
taste and sight. The menu has a tilt towards fish and shellfish but is not lop-
sided. The Mediterranean fish soup ('you could smell it in the street') is high-
grade, though one night it summarily disappeared, to be substituted by a
seafood consommé that was neither clear enough nor intense enough for the
disappointed diner. Yet the gratin of oysters was exactly timed, still tasting of
the sea, with a bed of spinach and the lightest of vermouth sauces. Ravioli of
langoustines with a thin jus has not always worked – overcooking reducing
the fish themselves to a pulp – but the quality of a lobster mosaic, studded with
carrots and beans and plenty of lobster flesh, was remarkable, and enhanced by
the strong mayonnaise that accompanied. This is not just a little country
kitchen, nor does it pander to Harrogate's lowest common denominators.
Witness the pig's trotter filled with sweetbreads and chicken, with a very fine
stock reduction for a sauce, given body by oyster and shiitake mushrooms, and
contrast by a liquid potato purée and morels. If plain food is more to your
liking, then no criticism could be levelled at lamb with a brioche and herb crust
or at a great piece of turbot with a vermouth sauce. Complexity with turbot –
wrapped round a smoked salmon mousse – has been equally well reported.
Desserts have been only adequate rather than extra, though a longing to repeat
the passion-fruit délice has been noted by one correspondent. The bread is
good. The service is affable and can be fine. The wines are less satisfactory. On
one occasion, too much was out of stock or of a different vintage, with no
attempt at explanation. The list itself is rudimentary. House wines are from
£8.50.

CHEF: Simon Gueller PROPRIETORS: Rena and Simon Gueller OPEN: Mon to Sat, exc
Mon D; 12 to 2, 7 to 10 MEALS: alc SERVICE: not inc CARDS: Access, Visa DETAILS: 30
seats (45 in summer). 6 tables outside. Vegetarian meals. Children's helpings. No children
under 13 D. Wheelchair access (1 step; also WC). Music

---

*County round-ups listing additional restaurants that may be worth a visit are at the back of
the Guide, after the Irish section. Reports on round-up entries are welcome.*

*The text of entries is based on unsolicited reports sent in by readers, backed up by
inspections conducted anonymously. The factual details under the text are from
questionnaires the Guide sends to all restaurants that feature in the book.*

HARROW Greater London   map 3

Country Club £

160 College Road,
Harrow-on-the-Hill HA1 1BH   COOKING 1
081-427 0729   COST £15–£23

'Peking Cuisine,' says the menu, and at first glance it seems little different from
scores of restaurants that deal in hot-and-sour soup, crispy duck and sizzling
king prawns. The façade, the décor, even the name give little indication of the
real delights that can be experienced in the small private room at the back of
the restaurant. Mr Chu is one of the few Chinese chefs in this country who
understands – and can deliver – an authentic version of Shanghai cuisine. It is
hardly worth going to this restaurant on spec, or turning up unannounced to
sample a meal from the regular menu. The trick is to telephone a couple of days
in advance, explain your interest in the food and discuss a possible feast. To
start, you may have deep-fried 'fingers' of yellow croaker, wheat gluten with
cloud-ear mushrooms, Shanghai spring rolls and lacquered tea-smoked frogs'
legs. To follow there might be anything from lobster with minced pork to
steamed eel with wolfberry. To finish, it is customary to have soup, perhaps
accompanied by steamed Shanghai dumplings. Drink jasmine tea. House
French is £7.

CHEF/PROPRIETOR: T.A. Chu   OPEN: all week, D only; 6 to 11   MEALS: alc. Set D £12 to
£20. Minimum £6   SERVICE: not inc   CARDS: Access, Visa   DETAILS: 55 seats. Private
parties: 50 main room, 14 private room. Children welcome. Music

HARVINGTON Hereford & Worcester   map 2

▲ Mill at Harvington ⅏✳   NEW ENTRY

Anchor Lane,
Harvington WR11 5NR   COOKING 2
EVESHAM (0386) 870688   COST £19–£33

The hotel is well away from the village, down by the River Avon, in the middle
of nowhere: turn off the B439 and follow the signs. Once a bread mill and also
used for hop-drying, the Georgian house has been sprucely converted into a
country hotel by Simon and Jane Greenhalgh. Meals are served in a quiet
dining-room, done out in shades of pink and grey, that has views of the lawns
and wooded parkland from the windows. The cooking is a mixture of old-style
classics, plus some more modern ideas; dishes avoid superfluous garnishes and
the results can be impressively accomplished. Dinners, priced according to the
main course, might take in beef en croûte and blanquette of veal as well as
warm bacon and potato salad and medallions of monkfish with Martini and
ginger sauce. Reporters have been won over by chicken and sweetbread terrine
with apricot and ginger purée ('surprisingly sophisticated, surprisingly
subtle'); 'beautifully supple' juicy roast Gressingham duck breast with red
wine sauce; and 'tart' summer pudding. Service is excellent, intelligent and
'comfortable'; young cheerful staff know about the food and the history of the

place. Wines are adequate but display no great flair. Prices though are reasonable. House wine is £8.

CHEFS: Jane Greenhalgh, Bill Downing and John Hunter   PROPRIETORS: Simon and Jane Greenhalgh   OPEN: all week; 11.45 to 1.45, 7 to 9   CLOSED: 24 to 27 Dec   MEALS: Set L £10.95 to £13.95, Set D £17.95 to £23   SERVICE: not inc, card slips closed   CARDS: Access, Amex, Visa   DETAILS: 45 seats. 8 tables outside. Private parties: 40 main room, 14 private room. Car park. Vegetarian meals. Children's helpings on request. No smoking in dining-room. Wheelchair access (1 step; also WC). No music   ACCOMMODATION: 15 rooms, all with bath/shower. Rooms for disabled. B&B £54 to £85. No children under 10. Garden. Swimming-pool. Tennis. Fishing. TV. Phone. Fax: (0386) 870688

HARWICH Essex   map 3

▲ *Pier at Harwich* ♥

The Quay, Harwich CO12 3HH   COOKING 1
HARWICH (0255) 241212   COST £16–£46

Its advantage is that it does serve fresh fish; its disadvantage is that prices can seem steep, and there are niggles about standards and organisation. Some reflection of the way things are going in the world of food is that salmon (farmed) now costs less than monkfish: shades of chicken in the 1950s – let's hope salmon doesn't go the whole way. The Pier is a big building, on two river fronts: bar, restaurant, accommodation with many verandahs (not for sitting on) and murals (not always thought the best of art). The menu changes slowly and reflects the need for catering control rather than the inspired reaction to what is in the market today that is usually the best aspect of seaside fish restaurants. Cooking is adequate and, many find, consistent; vegetables have been described as overcooked; portions are generous. An inspector felt this to be a borderline entry this year, but Harwich is a town of many visitors and the Pier is a necessary address. Any hesitation should be overcome by the wine list, strong in whites and showing a refreshingly wide spread at fair prices. There are good halves and an interesting 20-bottle house selection from £7.95.
CELLARMAN'S CHOICE: Sancerre, Dom. de la Mercy Dieu 1990, £16.95; Australia, Chardonnay 1991, Seaview, £11.25.

CHEF: C.E. Oakley   PROPRIETOR: G.M.W. Milsom   OPEN: all week; 12 to 2, 6 to 9.30 MEALS: alc. Set L £9 to £11.75, Set D £16   SERVICE: 10%, card slips closed   CARDS: Access, Visa   DETAILS: 80 seats. Private parties: 85 main room, 50 private room. Car park. Children's helpings. Wheelchair access (2 steps). Music   ACCOMMODATION: 6 rooms, all with bath/shower. B&B £45 to £72.50. TV. Phone. Fax: (0206) 322752 (*The Which? Hotel Guide*)

Restaurateurs justifiably resent no-shows. If you quote a credit card number when booking, you may be liable for the restaurant's lost profit margin if you don't turn up. Always phone to cancel.

Prices quoted in the Guide *are based on information supplied by restaurateurs. The prices quoted at the top of each entry represent a range, from the lowest meal price to the highest; the latter is inflated by 10 per cent to take account of likely price rises during the year of the* Guide.

HASLEMERE Surrey   map 3

Morels ♟ ✗

25–27 Lower Street,
Haslemere GU27 2NY   COOKING 4
HASLEMERE (0428) 651462   COST £24–£50

Set on a pavement high above the road, the three cottages that make up Morels
are easy to walk to, the devil to drive to. Three into one is the message of the
dining-room: changing levels, corners and turns, and quite low ceilings all
brought together by an insistent cool colour-scheme of blue and white from
curtains to coffee-cups. Cottage origins may account for a certain serried-ranks
problem when the restaurant fills up. Jean-Yves Morel's cooking maintains
sophistication and aplomb – and enough enthusiasm to fire customers with
longing as he came into the dining-room one day with a basket of fresh-picked
chanterelles. Although one old hand wondered if some of the edge had gone –
Morels has been here for more than a decade – most disagree. The appetisers of
miniature tortellini of crab and ginger – or, better, floating islands on a sea of
mushroom – endorse that the majority is correct. Note this impressive
catalogue: deliciously soft quail's eggs, endive, lambs' leaves, beans and
croûtons simply dressed with peppery olive oil and lemon; a picture-book tart
of crisp pastry with tomato and basil; breast of duck with mango and Grand
Marnier sauce; wild pigeon on an intense stock sauce with a lasagne made from
cornmeal; sea bass dipped in soy, dusted with flour then chargrilled, served
with potato mousseline and vinaigrette; noisettes of lamb served on a tian of
ratatouille with a fragrant thyme-scented gravy; a seriously popular *assiette du
chef* containing miniatures of every pudding; proper cheeses, good coffee. In
general, the cooking is light: 'The saffron sauce served with grey and red
mullets was neither oily nor creamy, yet full of flavour.' It deploys tastes well,
though never stridently, and uses very good ingredients. While not sounding
immensely exciting, the cooking seems to offer the right level of interest and
zip to make each dish memorable (for instance, that sea bass). That M. Morel
can manage upstanding flavour may be seen in his fish soup with rouille – a
good one. There are certain long-runners on the menus, but people don't seem
to mind. A place builds its own character. The pricing sometimes muddles. A
single price is quoted for the first two courses of the *carte*, so that there are those
who are then surprised to pay for pudding. The less expensive fixed-price
menu is not available on Saturday. Service from time to time suffers from those
mutual antagonisms of French- and English-speakers; usually, however, it is
cheerful and enjoyed. The wines are entirely French. The strength of the list lies
in impeccable sourcing and some fine clarets and burgundies. It is, therefore,
expensive. Not a lot of bother has gone into finding country or provincial
wines, but if you want mature clarets, this is a good place to start. House wines
are £11. CELLARMAN'S CHOICE: Chassagne-Montrachet premier cru 1988,
Lamy, £27; Tokay 1989, Gisselbrecht, £17.

'Ordered a meat balti, which was brought as usual sizzling to the table. Unfortunately the
meat was in clumps which were hot on the outside and cold in the middle. They don't
appear to be taking enough care with their defrosting.'   On eating in Birmingham

CHEF: Jean-Yves Morel PROPRIETORS: Jean-Yves and Mary Anne Morel OPEN: Tue to Sat, exc Sat L; 12.30 to 1.45, 7 to 10 CLOSED: 25 Dec, bank hols (exc Good Fri), 2 weeks end Feb, 2 weeks Sept/Oct MEALS: alc. Set L £19.50 (inc wine), Set Tue to Fri D £23.50 (inc wine) SERVICE: not inc CARDS: Access, Amex, Visa DETAILS: 45 seats. Private parties: 12 main room. Children's helpings. No smoking in dining-room. Wheelchair access (1 step). No music

---

HATCH BEAUCHAMP Somerset | map 2

Nightingales

Bath House Farm, Lower West Hatch,
nr Taunton TA3 5RH
HATCH BEAUCHAMP (0823) 480806   COOKING 1*
on A358, between Taunton and Ilminster   COST £26–£32

This place in the country pursues its chosen role with professionalism and success. A set-price menu offers lots of choice and does not leave the customer hungry. If any gaps remain, they will be filled by the substantial desserts. There is a delight in pastry and cake-work: a tartlet of crab for first course is followed by a feuilleté of wild mushrooms with a fillet steak, and scallops with star-anise and ginger under a flaky crust. Then there are those puddings: pecan, apple and maple syrup, lemon and almond roulade, chilled baked goats'-cheese torte with rhubarb. People speak well of the attention to detail: the table dressing, the salad dressing, the home-made ice-creams, the Taylors coffee. They also enjoy the gentle service from both the Barlows, and the fair-priced wine list. This takes in some Australasian, Spanish and Italian bottles to buttress the French selection and manages to offer two decent Somerset wines as well. Note the good-value Côtes du Rhône, Ch. St-Georges, the Cabernet Sauvignon from Tim Knappstein in Australia, the CVNE Rioja and the inexpensive champagnes. House wine from Avery's is £7.25.

CHEFS: Sally Edwards and Margaret Barlow PROPRIETORS: Jeremy and Margaret Barlow OPEN: Thur to Sat, D only (other times by arrangement); 7.30 to 10 MEALS: Set D £18.50 to £21.50 SERVICE: not inc, card slips closed CARDS: Access, Visa DETAILS: 40 seats. 2 tables outside. Private parties: 46 main room. Car park. Vegetarian meals. Children's helpings with prior notice. Wheelchair access (1 step; also WC). Music in bar

---

HAWKSHEAD Cumbria | map 7

▲ Tarn Hows Hotel ⚡✳   [NEW ENTRY]

Hawkshead Hill,
Hawkshead LA22 0PR   COOKING 2*
HAWKSHEAD (053 94) 36696   COST £33

The hotel is a Victorian Gothic building on a hilltop surrounded by 25 acres of grounds and woodland overlooking the valley of Esthwaite. New owners have created an inviting atmosphere, although the place may seem 'under-furnished'. Much is made of the new kitchen regime. Chef Kevin Cape earned his reputation at The Bell, Aston Clinton (see entry), and delivers an 'inspirational' menu bristling with modern ideas and artful invention. Fish shows up strongly. Presentation is sometimes at the expense of generosity, as in steamed cod on a crown of sliced potatoes in a lemon olive sauce topped with a salad of warm lettuce shaped like a rose. The idea was good and flavours were convincing, but the fish was 'probably less than a dessertspoonful'. Even so, this is a kitchen with high aspirations. Reporters have been impressed with many dishes from the regularly changing four-course menu. Flakes of braised lamb set in a mould with a clear gelée accompanied by crisp vegetables and tarragon, and a kebab of salmon, mullet and cod on a bed of wild rice have been excellent preliminaries. Main courses, such as fillet of red mullet with home-made noodles and a powerful lobster sauce 'that demanded to be mopped up with a piece of the excellent bread', and fillets of hare with their own quenelles on a bed of red cabbage, julienne of leek and sauce poivrade, have shown 'class and sophistication in real depth'. Desserts have been examples of artistic wizardry, although one reporter's summer pudding was 'rather stodgy'. Around 60 wines are well described and offer good drinking at fair prices. House French is £7.50.

CHEF: Kevin Cape   PROPRIETORS: Alan and Karen Campbell   OPEN: all week, D only; 7 to 9   MEALS: Set D £21.95   SERVICE: not inc, card slips closed   CARDS: Access, Amex, Diners, Visa   DETAILS: 60 seats. Private parties: 12 main room, 10 private room. Car park. Vegetarian meals. Children's helpings 7 to 8pm. Smart dress preferred. No smoking in dining-room. Wheelchair access (also WC). No music   ACCOMMODATION: 19 rooms, all with bath/shower. Rooms for disabled. B&B £59 to £88. Deposit: £50. Children welcome. Baby facilities. Pets welcome. Afternoon teas. Garden. Sauna. Fishing. TV. Phone. Fax: (053 94) 36766

HAWORTH West Yorkshire   map 5

▲ *Weavers* £

15 West Lane, Haworth BD22 8DU   COOKING 2
HAWORTH (0535) 643822   COST £18–£35

There is a mood of Yorkshire bonhomie about the Rushworths' relaxed restaurant in a set of converted cottages, and 'traditional Yorkshire' is one of the themes of the short, seasonal menu, which ranges from Yorkshire pudding to 'cow pie' and 'old school puds'. Many dishes are rightly accompanied by appropriate gravies, sauces, relishes and jellies: casserole of beef in a beer-flavoured sauce, and roast fillet of pork with herbs, apple sauce and scrumpy cider gravy have both been notable for the quality of meat, fresh flavours and spot-on timing. But there is also a modern Anglo-French thread, which shows in dishes such as crisp roast breast of Gressingham duck, fanned out and served with a puff-pastry parcel of rhubarb sauce. Main courses come with dishes of honest, fresh vegetables. Spinach pancakes with mushrooms and Lancashire cheese are a favourite starter, and there is always a vegetarian special, as well as a daily fish dish. 'Ask the dinner lady what she can offer,' states the menu when it comes to sweets. Well, it may be home-made ice-cream, dark-textured chocolate and coffee mousse, steamed syrup sponge with proper custard, or apple and almond tart. The 'early doors' menu (£12.95) written on a blackboard is a bargain for those who arrive between 6.30 and 7pm, Tuesday to

Friday. The short wine list is a well-spread selection offered at fair prices.
Seven house wines start at £7.95.

CHEFS/PROPRIETORS: Colin and Jane Rushworth OPEN: Tue to Sat, D only, and Sun L (Oct
to Easter); 12 to 1.30, 7 to 9 CLOSED: 2 weeks July, 2 weeks Christmas MEALS: alc. Set
Sun L £12.50, Set D £13.50 SERVICE: not inc CARDS: Access, Amex, Diners, Visa
DETAILS: 45 seats. Private parties: 14 main room, 14 private room. Vegetarian meals.
Children's helpings. Music. Air-conditioned ACCOMMODATION: 4 rooms, all with bath/
shower. B&B £45 to £65. Deposit: £20. Children welcome. Air-conditioned. TV. Phone.
Doors close at midnight. Confirm 1 day ahead (*The Which? Hotel Guide*)

HAYDON BRIDGE Northumberland   map 7

General Havelock Inn

Radcliffe Road, Haydon Bridge NE47 6ER   COOKING 2
HAYDON BRIDGE (0434) 684376   COST £16–£30

From the outside, General Havelock's uniform is no fancier than any North
Country roadside pub. The bar, and Ian Clyde's welcome, may give heart, as
may the sitting-room, but go through french doors for the double-storey
dining-room that opens on to a terrace and lawn running down to the Tyne. It
also has a view, lots of paintings ('for a change their quality was good'),
antique mirrors, bare stone walls and 'atmosphere'. 'We look for honest
cooking, cleanliness and friendly service. General Havelock has them all' was
the burden of one report; 'Money goes into the ingredients rather than frills,
but the peripherals are all so right as well' was another. The dinner menu is
short and at a fixed price with a couple of supplements. It reads like cook's
jottings: 'Fillet of pork Seville: pork, sliced, fried; onion; mushrooms; garlic;
orange; sliced apple; pepper; white wine; cream.' There are long-runners in the
repertoire: hot 'Shields' smokie, sirloin with horseradish, duck with
redcurrant. Cooking is direct and with flavour. Mushroom soup tasted of
mushrooms; crab tartlet was the brown meat bound with egg and greatly
enhanced by the use of cheese shortcrust; smoked salmon was wrapped round
a filling of crab, prawns and onion; salmon was poached and wild ('prime fish
cooked spot-on'); prawns were not overpowered by their garlic butter and
remained 'huge and fluffy'. Puddings will delay departure: pecan pie, apple
pie, pavlova, lemon tart. Reporters have been struck by the accuracy of the
cooking, the intelligent use of seasoning, the avoidance of unnecessary
embellishment, and the good value. The wines are a short list, rarely straying
above £12, with best value from the New World. House wines are from
Slovakia and cost £6.90.

CHEF: Angela Clyde PROPRIETORS: Ian and Angela Clyde OPEN: Wed to Sun, exc Sun D;
12 to 1.30, 7.30 to 9 CLOSED: first 2 weeks Jan, last week Aug, first week Sept, second
week Mar MEALS: alc L. Set L £10 to £13, Set D £17 to £20 SERVICE: not inc DETAILS:
28 seats. 4 tables outside. Private parties: 30 main room. Car park. Vegetarian meals.
Children's helpings. Wheelchair access (1 step; also WC). No music

---

The Guide *relies on feedback from its readers. Especially welcome are reports on new
restaurants appearing in the book for the first time.*

HAYFIELD Derbyshire

map 5

▲ *Bridge End* ✤

NEW ENTRY

7 Church Street,
Hayfield SK12 5JE
NEW MILLS (0663) 747321

COOKING 2
COST £21–£33

As you sit, surrounded by pine, you look through large shop-front windows on to inn and parish church: a classic village setting in a popular tourist trap. Here is an amusing contradiction of images – a guesthouse and restaurant at the foot of Kinder Scout, in famous walking country, serving, instead of the expected massively portioned robustly English-inspired food, an imaginative *carte*, modern in concept, light in approach, based on fresh local produce (especially game, lamb and cheeses), plus home-made bread, pasta, pastry and petits fours. Some may feel the style is more suited to Manchester or London, but have a care for walkers who think of their taste-buds. A summer meal began with perfectly cooked monkfish with Pernod and chives in puff pastry, with spring onions and star-anise, followed by roast Barbary duck breast sliced and interleaved with mango, on an orange and Drambuie sauce; then a passion-fruit and blackcurrant sorbet. Vegetables, although perfectly al dente, were a very small portion indeed, and cheeses too were thin slivers, the concept of lightness and balance taken as far as it could be. Cooking is assured, flavours are well handled, and incidentals show an overall attention to detail. Fixed-price gourmet dinners are provided twice a month. A sane approach to pricing means profit is lower for more costly wines, making them 'better' value. This gives the list an admirably restricted range of £24.30 for a Charmes-Chambertin 1983 from Vallet down to £8.40 for a Côtes de Thongue. The moral is: drink quality. House wines are £8.30.

CHEFS: Jonathan Holmes and Joanne Winch PROPRIETORS: Geoffrey and Barbara Tier OPEN: Tue to Sat, D only; 7.30 to 10 CLOSED: first week Jan MEALS: alc CARDS: Access, Amex, Visa SERVICE: not inc DETAILS: 50 seats. Private parties: 35 main room, 18 private room. Car park. Vegetarian meals. Children's helpings. No smoking in dining-room. Wheelchair access (1 step). Music ACCOMMODATION: 4 rooms, all with bath/shower. B&B £25 to £40. Deposit: 25%. Children welcome. Baby facilities. TV. Fax: (0663) 742121

HELFORD Cornwall

map 1

▲ *Riverside* ♥

Helford TR12 6JU
MANACCAN (0326) 231443

COOKING 2
COST £18–£40

Riverside is creekside; the Helford River flows a few hundred yards away, but the creek that splits the village – *molto* picturesque – is but a stone's throw distant. The enterprise is in a gathering of cottages, set on a vertiginous slope, with bedrooms in various outliers. The dining-room and terrace occupy the largest cottage. Fish is the thing, supplies are of the freshest. Lobster with a sabayon glaze, a fricassee of mussels, clams and oysters with chive butter sauce, or a salad of scallops with asparagus and shavings of Parmesan, can precede salmon with spinach, or monkfish with cabbage, sultanas and nutmeg. Reports of the last year have been complimentary about the standard of cooking, very keen about the breakfasts, and have only occasionally pointed to scant portions or irritated service. Prices have never been low, but an economy dinner menu has been introduced. The wine list is serious and extensive; French classics predominate but Alsace gets a better than usual showing; and, beyond that, selection is reassuringly very sound. Prices are fair throughout and decent under-£12 drinking is well provided for, as are half-bottles. House wines are £9.50. CELLARMAN'S CHOICE: Redwood Valley Sauvignon 1989, £12.70; Haut-Médoc, Ch. Caronne-Ste-Gemme 1985, £16.50.

CHEFS: Susan Darrell, Alyn Williams and Jason Hole   PROPRIETOR: Susan Darrell   OPEN: all week D, and Sat and Sun L; 12.30 to 2, 7.30 to 9.30   CLOSED: early Nov to mid-Feb   MEALS: Set L £11.75 to £13.25, Set D £18 to £28   SERVICE: net prices   DETAILS: 35 seats. 4 tables outside. Private parties: 30 main room. Car park. Vegetarian meals. No children under 12 D (high tea provided). No pipes in dining-room. Wheelchair access (2 steps). No music   ACCOMMODATION: 6 rooms, all with bath/shower. Rooms for disabled. B&B £65 to £95. Deposit: £75 to £100. Children welcome. Baby facilities. Garden. TV. Confirm by 6. Fax: (0326) 231443 (*The Which? Hotel Guide*)

HERSTMONCEUX East Sussex   map 3

Sundial 😊✸

| Gardner Street, Herstmonceux BN27 4LA | COOKING 2 |
| HERSTMONCEUX (0323) 832217 | COST £25–£56 |

More than 25 years at the helm has mellowed Giuseppe Bertoli, who is very much the host, even if his spotless whites denote executive control of the kitchen. The formula remains the same: a long *carte*, a series of set-price menus, a classic basis to the cooking, and an enormous centrepiece where the desserts are displayed. Some people who keep on coming over the years find the lack of change here vexing, but others respect the skills and the consistent intention. The wine list is impressive for its clarets and burgundies, and has some superior Rhônes and Rhines and a few Italians worth investigating. Its strengths are among the higher price levels, for example the 1970 clarets, but the mark-ups are not unreasonable. House wines are £10.95.

CHEF: Giuseppe Bertoli   PROPRIETORS: Laurette and Giuseppe Bertoli   OPEN: Tue to Sun, exc Sun D; 12.30 to 2 (2.30 Sun), 7.30 to 9.30 (10 Sat)   CLOSED: mid-Aug to Sept, 25 Dec to 20 Jan   MEALS: alc. Set L £15.50 to £19.50, Set D £19.50 to £24.50   SERVICE: 10%, card slips closed   CARDS: Access, Amex, Diners, Visa   DETAILS: 70 seats. 8 tables outside. Private parties: 50 main room, 22 private room. Car park. Vegetarian meals. Children's helpings. No smoking in dining-room. Wheelchair access (also WC). Music

---

'More signs of life in the spaniel which wandered in and out of the kitchen than in most of the staff.'   On eating in Gwynedd

'The ''tomato farce'' owed more to sandwich paste than Feydeau.'
On eating in London

'The service was friendly if a little laid-back. I suspect the waiters were drinking wine – it was a red fluid anyway.'   On eating in Scotland

---

HETTON North Yorkshire   map 5

Angel Inn ❙ ✳

Hetton BD23 6LT   COOKING 3
CRACOE (0756) 730263   COST £16–£30

It goes from strength to strength, this inn that still functions as a pub but which
is turned over more and more to food – whether in the beamed and dark-green
restaurant, or in the 'bar-brasserie'. And it's good; not always perfect, but the
heart is in the right places of freshness, value and invention. One of the
problems is popularity. This can make some customers feel processed, not
always helped by affability from every member of staff. Denis Watkins reflects
that the food gets more 'modern' every year: Mediterranean flavours,
chargrilling and Italian vegetables sit happily beside substantial (and sweet)
English puddings and farmhouse cheeses. Old favourites still have their
innings: 'little moneybags' stuffed with fish; salmon with cheese sauce,
wrapped in filo then served on a lobster sauce; duck two ways on red cabbage;
or fillet of beef – although the saucing for this has moved from béarnaise or
horseradish to a topping of rocket salsa verde with a shallot and red wine sauce
below. Most people find the cooking of high standard, in dishes such as
layered salmon, smoked haddock and spinach with a mussel cream sauce, or an
Italian salad of lamb, grilled aubergine, sun-dried tomatoes, pesto and
Parmesan. But harsher critics have reflected that sometimes a dish like guinea-
fowl done two ways (as if it were duck), sitting on lentils, onions and flageolet
beans, can miss the mark of flavour, as did the fish soup that day (needing a
decent rouille and a poke of garlic), even if the chicken, foie gras and truffle
essence parfait was excellent, and the young lamb served round a mound of
boulangère potatoes had the authentic flavour of grassy youth. On Fridays
there is a special fish menu. Value is maintained in the bar as well as in the
restaurant. We have had few reports this year of bar meals, but what we do hear
does not disturb. Finding good merchants is one matter, buying with
intelligent discrimination to assemble a coherent wine list is another. At the
Angel both services are offered in style, at knock-down prices. The antipodes
are explored gingerly, but that is a minor criticism of a list that many more
exalted restaurants could employ as a model. House wines are from £6.95.
CELLARMAN'S CHOICE: Bourgogne Blanc, 'Les Hauts d'Azenay' 1989, Georges
Blanc, £15.80; Ch. Musar 1983, £13.10.

CHEFS: Denis Watkins and John Topham   PROPRIETORS: Denis and Juliet Watkins, and
John Topham   OPEN: restaurant Mon to Sat, D only, and Sun L; 12.15 to 2, 7 to 9.30. Bar all
week; 12 to 2 (2.30 Sat and Sun), 6 to 10 (9.30 winter Suns)   CLOSED: 26 Dec, 1 Jan, 1 week
Jan   MEALS: bar alc. Restaurant Set Sun L £15, Set D £20.70   SERVICE: not inc, card slips
closed   CARDS: Access, Visa   DETAILS: restaurant 54 seats, bar 60 seats. 15 tables outside.
Private parties: 40 main room. Car park. Children's helpings on request. Smart dress
preferred in restaurant. No-smoking area in dining-room. No-smoking room in bar.
Wheelchair access (also female WC). No music. Fax: (0756) 730363

✳ indicates that smoking is either banned altogether or that a dining-room is maintained
for non-smokers. The symbol does not apply to restaurants that simply have no-smoking
areas.

Black House 🍴✳

Dipton Mill Road, Hexham NE46 1RZ
HEXHAM (0434) 604744

COOKING 2*
COST £24–£37

Gleaming oak table tops, a 'cloakroom' housed in an enormous mirrored
wardrobe, a 'bar' that was a Victorian sideboard, polished silver, brightstar
glassware, giant domes lifted to reveal the main dishes: so the list goes on of
things that people notice about this small country restaurant where Chris
Pittock does the greeting and Hazel Pittock, with Dawn Aston, the cooking.
The pace is leisurely by design, but who cares when aperitifs are accompanied
by such canapés? Meals are enjoyed for the small touches that finish a dish –
without overloading it to death – such as the slivers of almond on croûtons for
a curried parsnip soup, or the jug ('at least a pint') of cream left with the
flaming bananas. While first courses are kept straightforward, more elaboration
creeps in with the meat. North Country appetites are needed for a dish of pork
fillet with a Brie and hazelnut topping, finished with calvados and cream. Fish,
however, preserves its modesty: salmon layered with rösti, turbot with a
simple mustard and dill sauce. This can only be to preserve space for the
Beaumes de Venise cake with caramel sauce, or pear and ginger upside-down
pudding with butterscotch. The skill evinced in the cooking is fully matched
by the wine list. This may not be long, but it is long enough. The sources are
impeccable: note Thanisch's Graacher-Himmelreich 1983, Leflaive's Meursault
1988, two Chablis from Michel, Penfolds and Cape Mentelle from Australia,
and Simi from California. Light drinkers might wish for a greater choice of
halves – always a problem with short lists. House wines are £7.75.
CELLARMAN'S CHOICE: Rully Rabourcé 1989, Leflaive, £18.20; Chorey-lès-
Beaune 1986, Tollot-Beaut, £19.30.

CHEFS: Hazel Pittock and Dawn Aston PROPRIETORS: Chris and Hazel Pittock OPEN: Tue
to Sat, D only (L bookings only, for 6 or more); 7 to 9.30 MEALS: alc SERVICE: not inc,
card slips closed CARDS: Access, Visa DETAILS: 26 seats. Private parties: 26 main room.
Car park. Vegetarian meals. Smart dress preferred. No smoking in dining-room.
Wheelchair access

The Shoes

The Street, High Ongar CM5 9ND
BRENTWOOD (0277) 363 350

COOKING 1*
COST £23–£45

Beams and shoes are the theme. They are everywhere in this converted
coaching-inn once called the Three Horseshoes. Paul Spry's regularly changing
menu indulges in plenty of modern manners: pasta and noodles with many
dishes, wild mushrooms likewise, oil emulsion sauces as well as simple
reductions. Combinations are on the same lines: Parma ham with asparagus
and a pepper relish, oysters with cucumber spaghetti and sorrel sauce, duck
with cabbage, Stilton and caraway, or salmon with mashed potatoes and red
wine. Performance can be very successful, as in starters such as a parfait of calf's

liver, salmon and crab ravioli, or a slightly bland monkfish wrapped in spinach on a bed of carrot strips, followed by duck with red cabbage, salmon on a bed of onion and lentils, or chicken with mango stuffing on a bed of crisp noodles with a coriander sauce. Things can also be very uneven: good first course and vegetables; misbegotten main course, canapés and petits fours. Lunch is fair value. The wine list gives a voice to plenty of things other than France, thus allowing a decent price range. House wine is £8.75.

CHEF: Paul Spry   PROPRIETORS: Lyndon Wootton, Peter Gowan and Doreen Gowan
OPEN: all week, exc Sat L and Sun D; 12 to 2.30, 7.30 to 9.30   CLOSED: 1 week after
Christmas   MEALS: alc D. Set L £14.25 to £16.75, Set Tue vegetarian D £23   SERVICE: not
inc, card slips closed   CARDS: Access, Amex, Visa   DETAILS: 55 seats. Private parties: 40
main room, 20 private room. Vegetarian meals. Children welcome. Smart dress preferred.
Wheelchair access (1 step). Music

HINTLESHAM Suffolk   map 3

▲ Hintlesham Hall ♥ ⅚✳

Hintlesham IP8 3NS   COOKING 3
HINTLESHAM (047 387) 268 and 334   COST £30–£60

Old hands will regret the move of the hotel's front door from the original grand entrance to a smaller, more secluded opening. This detracts from the public gesture but may make the hotel function more efficiently. Somehow, though facilities have been added at a rate of knots, this place retains a real urge to please and a sense of hospitality. The public rooms are magnificent (Georgian and Caroline), the bedrooms are fine, and furnishings have character. There is continuity of staff at front-of-house and in the kitchen, where Alan Ford is an able chef. He can produce a mushroom and chicken consommé of great flavour, or a simple salad with characterful dressing at the other end of the spectrum of skill and complexity. The menu is blessed with colour-words: everything is 'interesting', 'light', 'rich' and 'tangy'. The eating is not so bad. Reports reflect that it may, in the cumulation, be quite heavy. A meal in the winter started with artichoke heart stuffed with tomatoes and olives, topped with poached quail's eggs, then a small course of scallops and salmon 'drizzled' with olive oil, before venison with caramelised aubergines and a tartlet of cranberries, finishing with a warm mille-feuille of bananas. Good stuff, but the aubergines overpowered the venison and collided with the cranberries. Come the spring, and people noted the excellence of the canapés and contrasted the richness of a fricassee of fish with a highly reduced cream velouté and light saffron noodles, to a refreshing feuilleté of monkfish with three colours of pimento and a sweet/ sour sauce. Noisettes of lamb were served with a creamed garlic sauce as well as a tart of roast garlic cloves. There is no wish to court simplicity for its own sake here – though carpaccio of salmon with capers, Parmesan and good olive oil is perfect of its kind – and high levels of performance are obtained in dishes such as andouillette of guinea-fowl on a bed of Puy lentils, with small onions and lardons and a sherry stock reduction. Desserts are as they should be: good pastry, lots of cooking. Coffee and ancillaries are fine. Food does not come cheap if you eat off the *carte*. The mid-week table d'hôte is affordable but not very interesting; the lunch menu is affordable and better constructed.

Breakfasts are excellent. The wine list is very fine, but enthusiasm is muted by high mark-ups and a method of presentation that defies logic, making selection difficult for the cautious as well as the curious. A pity, because there are many mid-range wines at fair prices tucked in between more extravagant bottles. But the 'House Recommendations' are helpful, 10 good wines are available by the glass and there are many interesting halves. A glass is awarded but with reservations. House wine is £12.95. CELLARMAN'S CHOICE: Quincy 1990, Mardon, £16.85; Tuscany, Rugo 1986, Fattoria dell'Ugo, £16.70.

CHEF: Alan Ford PROPRIETORS: Hintlesham Hall Ltd OPEN: all week, exc Sat L; 12.15 to 1.45, 7 to 9.45 MEALS: alc. Set weekday L £18.50, Set Sun L £19.50, Set Sun to Thur D £19.50 SERVICE: not inc, card slips closed CARDS: Access, Amex, Diners, Visa DETAILS: 100 seats. Private parties: 100 main room, 16, 40 and 80 private rooms. Car park. Vegetarian meals. Children's helpings. No children under 10 D. Smart dress preferred. No smoking in dining-room. Wheelchair access (also WC). Music ACCOMMODATION: 33 rooms, all with bath/shower. Rooms for disabled. B&B £85 to £300. Children welcome. Baby facilities. Pets welcome. Garden. Swimming-pool. Sauna. Tennis. Fishing. Golf. Snooker. TV. Phone. Doors close at midnight. Fax: (047 387) 463 (*The Which? Hotel Guide*)

HOCKLEY HEATH West Midlands   map 5

▲ *Nuthurst Grange*

Nuthurst Grange Lane,
Hockley Heath B94 5NL   COOKING 2
LAPWORTH (0564) 783972   COST £18–£53

The motorway box encloses this house and controls the route of access (except for those travelling by helicopter, for whom a helipad is available). However, the protection of gardens and grounds and an interior that is heavily padded allow the image of a country house *à l'anglaise* to rule. The cooking can be well padded too, perhaps to support its relatively high price at dinner. Just as the meal experience is fully topped and tailed with canapés, appetisers and petits fours, so there are usually a number of elements deployed on a single plate and people enjoy the artfulness of presentation and elaboration as much as the food itself. The style has undertones of current fashion, for instance in a vinaigrette sauce with brill, or home-made noodles with calf's liver, but also harks back to the glory days of modern British cooking with a Stilton mousse atop a fillet of beef, a chicken liver parfait with an onion marmalade, and scallop mousseline with a chervil sauce. Things are sometimes stuffed or processed more than they warrant. Lobster, often recommended in reports, is almost a permanent resident on the menu – and liable to a surcharge, even if one is paying nearly £40 as a set price for four courses and coffee. Vegetables are a full array. Puddings get the British treatment, so are hot as well as cold – just like our reports. The wine list is not overlong, but covers most angles (though nothing from Spain). Price range is given some consideration, even if the choice does not electrify. House wines start at £7.95.

Card slips closed *in the details at the end of an entry indicates that the total on the slips of credit cards is closed when handed over for signature.*

CHEFS: D.L. Randolph and S. Wilkes   PROPRIETORS: D.L. and D.A. Randolph   OPEN: all
week, exc Sat L; 12.30 to 2, 7 to 9.30   MEALS: Set L £12.50 to £17.90, Set D £17.90 to £39.50
SERVICE: not inc, card slips closed   CARDS: Access, Amex, Diners, Visa   DETAILS: 50 seats.
5 tables outside. Private parties: 60 main room. Car park. Vegetarian meals. Children's
helpings. Wheelchair access (also WC). No music   ACCOMMODATION: 15 rooms, all with
bath/shower. B&B £85 to £135. Children welcome. Baby facilities. Garden. TV. Phone.
Doors close at midnight. Fax: (0564) 783919

HOLDENBY Northamptonshire   map 3

▲ Lynton House ❊✳

| Holdenby NN6 8DJ | COOKING 2 |
| HOLDENBY (0604) 770777 | COST £18–£37 |

Some rectors must have had a good life in the old days for Holdenby's former
rectory is as big as they come. The dining-room feels comfortable, although
'green shades around orange bulbs certainly make you concentrate on the
food'. Carol Bertozzi's Anglo-Italian cooking avoids the clichés of high street
trattorias, has little truck with new-wave anything, and satisfies Shires
appetites for a square meal with proper meat or fish. On one occasion, however,
some items such as anchovies and olive oil on bread, and zampone (stuffed
pig's trotter) looked promising but did not live up to expectation. Other dishes
have been more successful. An April inspection reported first-rate tagliatelle
with lobster sauce, cannelloni stuffed with minced chicken and veal, fillet of
beef with dolcelatte and Parma ham, well-timed vegetables and tiramisù
which was 'a fine example of its kind'. Yet timing can sometimes go awry: sea
bass baked in a paper bag 'was welded to the paper' and a crème brûlée
topping was genuinely burnt. To sum up, 'it is basically sound cooking with
the occasional lapses'. An emphasis on Italian wines is reinforced with good
clarets. Prices are reasonable. House Italian is £9.75.

CHEF: Carol Bertozzi   PROPRIETORS: Carlo and Carol Bertozzi   OPEN: Mon to Sat, exc Mon
and Sat L; 12.15 to 1.45, 7.15 to 9.45   CLOSED: Christmas, 2 weeks summer   MEALS: alc.
Set L £12.75 to £16.75. Minimum £19.75 Sat D   SERVICE: net prices, card slips closed
CARDS: Access, Amex, Visa   DETAILS: 45 seats. Private parties: 55 main room, 20 private
room. Car park. Vegetarian meals. Children's helpings. No children under 6. Smart dress
preferred. No smoking in 1 dining-room. Wheelchair access. No music   ACCOMMODATION:
5 rooms, all with shower. B&B £49 to £55. No children under 6. Garden. TV. Phone. Doors
close at 12.30am. Confirm by 9am (*The Which? Hotel Guide*)

HOLT Norfolk   map 6

Yetman's

| 37 Norwich Road, Holt NR25 6SA | COOKING 2 |
| HOLT (0263) 713320 | COST £24–£35 |

'Cheerful', 'relaxed' and 'informal' are words that crop up frequently in reports
about this admirable little restaurant. The pale-lemon décor and abundance of
fresh flowers appeal, so does the spotless linen. Alison and Peter Yetman put
their faith in local produce, including fish from Lowestoft and beef and poultry

from nearby farms. 'It never ceases to be a delight when gardeners bring in just-picked fruit and vegetables,' enthuses Peter Yetman. The inspiration and philosophy of the set-up depend on fresh, seasonal ingredients and uncluttered flavours: 'Intimidating customers is not our style.' The menu is short – too limited for some – but there is always something to please: fillets of sardines with Greek stuffing; twice-cooked goats' cheese soufflé; brioche of chicken livers with bacon and sour cream; monkfish with pesto sauce on tagliatelle; sea trout with fennel. There have been several votes for roast new season's lamb stuffed with apricots. Vegetables are well-timed, cheeses are British and sweets are the likes of walnut and strawberry roulade, or hot rhubarb and orange meringue. Simple lunches are served on Saturday and Sunday. The wine list is distinguished not so much by length as by the quality of many of the growers and proprties. It is not just France, there is a lot by the half-bottle and glass and it is all fairly priced. Ten house wines are from £7.

CHEF: Alison Yetman   PROPRIETORS: Alison and Peter Yetman   OPEN: Wed to Sun (and bank hol Mons) D, Sat and Sun L; 12.30 to 2, 7.30 to 9   MEALS: alc. Surcharge on main course alone £3.75   SERVICE: not inc   DETAILS: 32 seats. Private parties: 20 main room. Vegetarian meals. Children's helpings. No smoking during meals. Wheelchair access (1 step). No music

HORNCASTLE Lincolnshire   map 6

Magpies £

73–75 East Street, Horncastle LN9 6AA   COOKING 1
HORNCASTLE (0507) 527004   COST £14–£33

The row of converted cottages on the way to Skegness is 'pinky but not sugary, comfortable but not exciting, much loved by regulars, warm with a cosy feel' – to collect all the epithets from one report. Matthew Lee cooks generously and is prepared to try more adventurous dishes than are the norm for Lincolnshire, even if details sometimes need attention. Next to deep-fried Camembert and melon with strawberries on the starter menu are king prawn tails stir-fried in chilli oil, and tagliatelle in a smoked salmon and mushroom sauce; as well as good steaks, there are osso buco or duck done two ways. The costs are as fair as the service is amiable. Puddings and cheese may be more of a mixed bag. The wines are not dear and include some acceptable Loires and Rhônes. The estimable Côtes de Gascogne from Plaimont costs less than the house wines, which are £7.60 a litre.

CHEF: Matthew Lee   PROPRIETORS: Joan, Matthew and Caroline Lee   OPEN: Tue to Sat, D only, and Sun L; 12.30 to 2, 7.30 to 9.30   CLOSED: 25 and 26 Dec, 2 weeks Sept or May   MEALS: alc. Set Sun L £8.50. Minimum £11.50   SERVICE: not inc   CARDS: Access, Visa   DETAILS: 45 seats. Private parties: 45 main room. Children's helpings Sun L. No children under 12, exc Sun. Smart dress preferred. Wheelchair access. Music

£ *indicates that it is possible to have a three-course meal, including coffee, a half-bottle of house wine and service, at any time the restaurant is open (i.e. at dinner as well as at lunch, unless a place is open only for dinner), for £20 or less per person.*

French Partridge ▮

Horton NN7 2AP   COOKING 3
NORTHAMPTON (0604) 870033   COST £25–£31

The Partridge family (no relation to the singing TV family) have been in the
Guide some 28 years. Continuity, not revolution, is the order of the day; a steady
system – a certain procedure to ordering, then proceeding to table, a form to the
meal itself – underlies the character of the place. This is a Georgian house
extending into contiguous barn, architectural virtues that are as honest and
plain-speaking as the culinary. Meals are four courses at a set price: soup or
cold starters succeeded by hot fish or egg dishes before game, poultry or meat,
then sweets or cheese – or savoury. Coffee is included in the price. The style
harks back sometimes to Partridge *père*'s love affair with France and French
cooking (a very 1950s syndrome), for the restaurant was intended to replicate
the virtues of a French country *auberge*. In the intervening years, more echoes of
English restaurant cooking, even a certain international eclecticism, have been
heard, but not to the extent of throwing everything out for the chargrill, or
reviving the homely stuff of a Northamptonshire grandmother. Examples have
been rillettes of pork; eggs en meurette; warm sole and mussel mousse; rabbit
with tomato, wild mushrooms and noodles; or breaded pork chops with a
cheese sauce. For some, the food is no more than a gentle accompaniment to the
wine. The list is remarkable for its range and good value; its preoccupation is
with the solid: bourgeois growths, good middle-range burgundies and Rhônes
and Germans of reasonable age. Details are sometimes partial, but this is a list
of honest, interesting and very fairly priced wines. Long may it continue.
House wines are from £8. CELLARMAN'S CHOICE: Mercurey, Champ Martin
1986, Juillot, £18; Pouilly Fuissé 1989, Forest, £20.

CHEFS: David Partridge and Justin Partridge   PROPRIETORS: David and Mary Partridge
OPEN: Tue to Sat, D only; 7.30 to 9   CLOSED: 2 weeks Christmas and Easter, 3 weeks July
to Aug   MEALS: Set D £21 to £22   SERVICE: net prices   DETAILS: 50 seats. Private parties:
10 main room. Car park. Children welcome. Wheelchair access. No music

▲ Lodge Hotel

48 Birkby Lodge Road, Birkby,
Huddersfield HD2 2BG   COOKING 1
HUDDERSFIELD (0484) 431001   COST £17–£30

The hotel aims for that 'country-house feel', achieving part of its goal by dint of
a bosky suburban setting, a lot of fabric and linen and some fine last-century art
nouveau decoration from the Manchester architect Edgar Wood. The cooking is
somewhat 'country-house' of the 1970s and 1980s: a lot of presentation,
sweetness and ingredients. Dishes such as 'scallop and smoked haddock
mousse wrapped in Japanese seaweed on a lime and watercress sauce with a
garnish of mussels' sound daunting, as might wild boar with banana and
mustard sauce or breast of chicken with a 'heart of wild mushrooms and a Brie

and vermouth sauce'. However, they taste less alarming, and reports of a substantial game casserole of wild boar, venison, rabbit and pheasant and decent soups show that not all the effort is wasted on wild mixtures. Traditional Sunday lunches, not wild at all, are also well liked. The service and conviviality are admirable. The wine list has a wide spread and its prices are very fair. There is a small 'connoisseur's section', but most people will be well suited by the main grouping. House wines are £7.95.

CHEF: Richard Hanson PROPRIETORS: Kevin and Garry Birley OPEN: all week, exc Sat L and Sun D; 12 to 2, 7.30 to 9.45 MEALS: Set L £10.95, Set D £19.95 SERVICE: not inc, card slips closed CARDS: Access, Amex, Visa DETAILS: 60 seats. 4 tables outside. Private parties: 24 main room, 20 and 24 private rooms. Car park. Vegetarian meals. Children's helpings. Smart dress preferred. No smoking in half of dining-room. Wheelchair access (1 step; also WC). Music ACCOMMODATION: 11 rooms, all with bath/shower. Rooms for disabled. B&B £56 to £65. Children welcome. Baby facilities. Pets welcome. Afternoon teas. Garden. Snooker. TV. Phone. Doors close at 2am. Confirm by noon. Fax: (0484) 421590

Paris II £

84 Fitzwilliam Street,	
Huddersfield HD1 5BD	COOKING 1
HUDDERSFIELD (0484) 516773	COST £17–£34

This is an offshoot of Paris in Leeds (see entry) and runs along identical lines, with an early-bird menu of three courses off the *carte* for £11.95 (plus some wine as well), a very good wine list, consumer-friendly pricing and lots of choice. Steak with leeks and Silton, venison in filo pastry with onion and garlic confit, calf's liver with bacon and onions, and oxtail with potato purée are some of the main dishes that put this one step forward from the bistros of our youth. Execution is slightly mixed, but the place gets the votes as a local resource that should be encouraged. The wines are very intelligently chosen and fairly priced. A lot could be learned, even by students on a grant, by careful study of what is on offer here. House wine is £6.95.

CHEFS: Michael Rowley and David Rose PROPRIETORS: Martin Spalding and Steven Kendell OPEN: Mon to Sat, exc Sat L; 12 to 2, 6 to 10.30 MEALS: alc. Set D £11.95 (inc wine, 6 to 7.30pm) SERVICE: not inc CARDS: Access, Amex, Visa DETAILS: 70 seats. Car park. Vegetarian meals. Children welcome. Music. Air- conditioned

---

HURSTBOURNE TARRANT Hampshire	map 2

▲ Esseborne Manor ▼

Hurstbourne Tarrant SP11 0ER	
HURSTBOURNE TARRANT (026 476) 444	
on the A343, 1½m N of	COOKING 2
Hurstbourne Tarrant	COST £23–£50

The Yeos are planning extensions to this handsome late-nineteenth-century manor, including new conservatories attached to the lounge and dining-room. Little else changes. Chef Mark Greenfield cooks to fixed-price menus of three courses, plus cheese as an extra; there is also the option of a two-course 'quickie' at lunch-time. The kitchen handles a mixed bag of ideas, from chicken curry and spotted dick to dill-marinated salmon with Jersey Royal potato vinaigrette and salad of green lentils and tomato with croûtons and shallots. Reporters have approved of warm duck salad with walnut oil dressing and – to finish – meringue nest with fresh strawberries. In between, there might be pan-fried salmon with tomato rice and saffron sauce; honey-glazed breast of duckling with oriental spices; and medallions of beef with duxelle and thyme sauce. Vegetables may be treated with a heavy hand, according to one observer. There is a good selection of British farmhouse cheeses. Wine-buying here is excellent, it is just the selling that does not excite; prices are high with very little on offer below £15. Burgundies are very strong and there is fair spread of bourgeois clarets, good Rhônes and antipodeans. House wine is £12. CELLARMAN'S CHOICE: Menetou-Salon 1990, Clément, £15.70; Médoc, Ch. Potensac 1985, £25.40.

CHEF: Mark Greenfield PROPRIETORS: Michael and Frieda Yeo OPEN: all week; 12.30 to 2, 7.30 to 9.30 MEALS: Set L £11.50 to £15, Set D £25 to £35 SERVICE: not inc, card slips closed CARDS: Access, Amex, Diners, Visa DETAILS: 36 seats. Private parties: 36 main room, 10 private room. Car park. No children under 12. Jacket and tie. No cigars/pipes in dining-room. Wheelchair access. No music ACCOMMODATION: 12 rooms, all with bath/shower. Rooms for disabled. B&B £84 to £125. No children under 12. Garden. Tennis. TV. Phone. Doors close at midnight. Confirm by 6. Fax: (0264) 76473 (*The Which? Hotel Guide*)

IPSWICH Suffolk   map 3

Kinsella's ⅝✳

19 St Peters Street, Ipswich IP1 1XF   COOKING 2
IPSWICH (0473) 259732   COST £27–£43

This is an enterprise with a mission. Vivienne Kinsella-Jaques and Craig Marchant are staunchly committed to organic, free-range and naturally reared produce, and everything – apart from pasta – is made on the premises. Their informal restaurant is also something of a showcase for wild foods: not only fish and fungi, but also wall lettuce, dandelion, chickweed and – from the East Coast shoreline – sea beet and marsh samphire. A short *carte* now supplements the five-course dinner menu. The owners describe their cooking as 'resolutely robust in stature and English/Irish in style', although the range and availability of authenticated produce has allowed them to expand their repertoire. Typical examples include bresaola with red cabbage and dried-fruit salad; cheddar cheese soufflé with lovage and Parmesan; monkfish and bacon with organically grown Paris Pink mushrooms; marinated sirloin of beef served with a nutmeg and brandy sauce; and bread-and-butter pudding. There is usually something for vegetarians. Deep-fried Camembert with cranberry sauce, stuffed fillet of lamb in puff pastry with port and redcurrant sauce, breast of chicken with cheese and Dijon mustard sauce, and roast pheasant with truffle and madeira sauce have all been recommended. Cheeses are traditionally British. Organic wines show up well on the wide-ranging list; there are also organic beers and fruit liqueurs. House vin de pays is £8.80.

313

CHEF: Vivienne Kinsella-Jaques PROPRIETORS: Craig Marchant and Vivienne Kinsella-Jaques OPEN: Tue to Sat, D only; 7 to 9.30 CLOSED: Maundy Thur to Easter Tue, 23 to 30 Dec, bank hols, Tue after bank hol Mon MEALS: alc. Set D £28.50. Minimum £16.50 SERVICE: not inc, card slips closed CARDS: Access, Visa DETAILS: 18 seats. Private parties: 13 main room, 6 private room. Vegetarian meals. No children under 12. Smart dress preferred. No smoking in dining-room. Music

Mortimer's on the Quay £

Wherry Quay, Ipswich IP4 1AS	COOKING 1
IPSWICH (0473) 230225	COST £17–£38

Wherry Quay is off Key Street, and Mortimer's is to the left of the old customs house. This converted warehouse is a popular lunchtime venue for business people. Inside it resembles its sister restaurant in Bury St Edmunds (see entry), with Thomas Mortimer watercolours on the white walls and oilcloths on the tables. The menu also follows similar lines, with fish as the main strength. Results can be mixed: excellent Loch Fyne oysters, home-made taramasalata and fillet of pollack flamande have been praised, although reporters have found the potted shrimps 'disappointing' and the steamed salmon overcooked. The lack of accompanying vegetables – apart from potatoes – also causes some irritation. To finish, smooth rich chocolate pot has been a memorable sweet. The short wine list favours whites. House French is £7.25.

CHEF: Kenneth Ambler PROPRIETORS: Kenneth Ambler and Michael Gooding OPEN: Mon to Sat, exc Sat L; 12 to 2, 7 to 9 (6.45 to 8.15 Mon) CLOSED: bank hols and day after, 24 Dec to 5 Jan, 2 weeks Aug MEALS: alc SERVICE: not inc CARDS: Access, Amex, Diners, Visa DETAILS: 60 seats. Private parties: 8 main room. Children's helpings on request. Smart dress preferred. No-smoking area. Wheelchair access (1 step). No music. Fax: (0284) 752561

Singing Chef

200 St Helen's Street, Ipswich IP4 2RH	COOKING 1
IPSWICH (0473) 255236	COST £21–£37

The graffiti dotting the menus may warn that an eccentric – 'lovable', people say – is at large. Kenneth Toyé is a man of long service, yet still has the heart to sing at the stove. He remains irrefragably Francophile, cooking his versions of French bourgeois cuisine such as soupe de poissons, tarte à l'oignon, pissaladière, côte de porc avesnoise, beef à la gardiane or navarin of lamb. To finish you would expect, and you get, petit pot au chocolat, crêpes and tarte alsacienne, even if pavlova appears from down under to keep them company. This is an honest place, not always perfect, not always as cheerful as it can be, in a less than posh bit of town. The joint stays jumping at regular jazz evenings. The wine list is short, short, short – French, of course. House wines are from £8.50.

Several sharp operators have tried to extort money from restaurateurs on the promise of an entry in a guidebook that has never appeared. The Good Food Guide *makes no charge for inclusion and does not offer certificates of any kind.*

CHEFS: Kenneth Toyé and Jeannine Toyé   PROPRIETORS: Cynthia and Kenneth Toyé
OPEN: Tue to Sat, D only (Sun and Mon D, and L all week, for 6 or more by arrangement);
7 to 11   MEALS: alc. Set D Tue to Fri £13.95   SERVICE: not inc, card slips closed   CARDS:
Access, Visa   DETAILS: 35 seats. 4 tables outside. Private parties: 20 private room.
Vegetarian meals. Children's helpings. No-smoking area. Wheelchair access (also WC).
Music

IXWORTH Suffolk   map 6

Theobalds ⁵⁄✳

| 68 High Street, Ixworth IP31 2HJ | COOKING 2 |
| PAKENHAM (0359) 31707 | COST £22–£40 |

'After 10 years, the premises is still pristine,' comments a Suffolk reporter.
'Simon still does all the cooking and Geraldine is as charming as ever. It
remains good enough to attract us at least once a week.' The modest beamed
dining-room is traditional English, yet the kitchen draws most of its
inspiration from France. Short, regularly changing menus are priced on the
main course – although regulars have noted little alteration in starters and
sweets over the years. Dishes such as fillet of halibut with mild mustard sauce,
hare served on croûtons with orange juice and port sauce, and roast partridge
with apples and calvados show the scope of the repertoire. Reporters have
approved of twice-baked cheese soufflé, baked scallops with spinach and
cream sauce, and fillet of lamb with rosemary and sherry sauce. Iced Grand
Marnier mousse with chocolate sauce has been a successful sweet. The wide-
ranging list of around 200 wines has a notable showing of halves.
Recommended French country wines are from £9.40.

CHEF: Simon Theobald   PROPRIETORS: Simon and Geraldine Theobald   OPEN: Tue to Sun,
exc Sat L and Sun D; 12.15 to 2, 7 to 9.30   MEALS: Set L £14.95, Set D £23.50 to £26.50
SERVICE: not inc   CARDS: Access, Visa   DETAILS: 36 seats. Private parties: 36 main room.
Children's helpings. No children under 8 D. No smoking in dining-room. No music

---

JEVINGTON East Sussex   map 3

Hungry Monk ⁵⁄✳

Jevington BN26 5QF	
POLEGATE (0323) 482178	COOKING 2
on B2105, between Polegate and Friston	COST £31

A tiny car park and compact garden, complete with peacocks, lead into a warm,
dark rabbit warren of a restaurant: some of the small linked rooms used as
lounges have no windows, and the furniture boasts no two pieces the same.
The dining-room is lit only by candles; beams are heavy and dark. The
blackboard menu, 'moved from lounge to lounge', offers at a set price a good
choice of about eight items per course, but supplements for a couple of dishes
continue to annoy. Modern elements do occasionally join the tried and trusted
English savoury-cum-fruit dishes of stuffed saddle of rabbit with plum and
madeira sauce, or quails en croûte with raisin sauce. Filo pastry encases
spinach and ricotta and is set on a sweet pepper sauce; leg of English lamb is

315

served with a garlic and red wine sauce; pink Barbary breast is set side by side with crisp Norfolk breast of duckling; baby vegetables appear with the fillet of Scotch beef. Fish still gets little attention; but 'such fish as they do get is of the freshest and best' is a comment from one who describes a first course of salmon and scallop terrine as 'brilliant'. Even the incidentals shine: home-made bread, good-quality butter, strong coffee, excellent amuse-gueules and petits fours. 'Altogether civilised' is the verdict. Taken to task for our 'unambitious' comment about the wine list in 1992, brief explanations may be in order. Wine-making and wine-buying have changed dramatically, and we expect to see some of that dynamism reflected in restaurant wine lists. The Hungry Monk wine list is good, neither too short nor over-long, catholic in range and priced reasonably (house wines from £8). But more adventurous and wider buying would remove the uneasy feeling that not every bottle ordered with equal assurance.

CHEFS: Claire Burgess and Thai La Roche   PROPRIETORS: Nigel and Susan Mackenzie   OPEN: all week, D only, and Sun L (other days by arrangement for parties of 10 to 16); 12.15 to 2, 7 to 10   MEALS: Set Sun L and D £19.50   SERVICE: not inc (12.5% for 8 or more)   DETAILS: 36 seats. Private parties: 36 main room, 10 and 16 private rooms. Car park. Vegetarian meals. Children's helpings. No children under 3. Smart dress preferred. No smoking in dining-room. Music. Fax: (0323) 483989

KENDAL Cumbria   map 7

Duffins £ | NEW ENTRY |

54 Stramongate,
Kendal LA9 4BD   COOKING 1
KENDAL (0539) 720387   COST £14–£26

'An open fire, a tiny bar, the linen and silver all seemed to convey that they meant business.' And congratulatory reports indicate that the brothers Duffin have found favour enough through adept cooking and smart service. The dinner *carte* offers six or seven choices per course; at lunch it's a three-course menu at a fixed low price. Andrew Duffin is a classicist with a light touch whose work has been characterised as accurate and honest. Concessions to fashionable health-consciousness don't apply: stock-based sauces are finished with cream, butter and fresh herbs, as in lemon sole with a white wine and chive cream sauce. 'All the money must go into ingredients,' surmised a happy couple after eating twice-baked soufflé of cheese ('incredibly light with a distinct Gruyère taste') and roast saddle of hare ('sitting on a forcemeat mixed with wild mushrooms and very good'). A pudding of iced white chocolate gingerbread was abetted by an 'intense' red plum and cinnamon sauce. Home-made truffles, fudge and 'nutty toffee cherry bits' arrive with strong, hot coffee. The wine list seems to match the food well. House wine is £7.25.

CHEFS: Andrew Duffin and Darren Ebden   PROPRIETORS: Steven and Andrew Duffin   OPEN: Tue to Sat, exc Sat L; 12 to 2, 7 to 9   CLOSED: Christmas   MEALS: alc. Set L £7.95   SERVICE: not inc   CARDS: Access, Amex, Visa   DETAILS: 36 seats. Private parties: 36 main room. Vegetarian meals. Children welcome. Wheelchair access. Music

Moon ✻ £

129 Highgate, Kendal LA9 4EN	COOKING 1
KENDAL (0539) 729254	COST £19–£23

'It's Saturday night and everyone is still going to the Moon,' wrote one who waited for a table (no bookings), then went on to mushrooms provençale (almost a meal in itself) and a vegetable curry containing courgettes, carrots, two sorts of pimento, cauliflower, onions and green beans, cooked nice and crisp but with the mildest of curry flavour. There is a foot in both meat and veg camps in this low-cost, partially no-smoking restaurant that avoids flim-flam and preserves informality. The cooking does not always work, but it still draws the crowds. The wine list is a dozen bottles all at the same price; there are also beers. House wine is £6.95 a litre.

CHEFS: Sharon Moreton and Val Macconnell PROPRIETOR: Val Macconnell OPEN: all week, D only; 6 to 10 (10.30 Fri and Sat) MEALS: alc SERVICE: not inc, card slips closed CARDS: Access, Visa DETAILS: 40 seats. Private parties: 38 main room. Vegetarian meals. Children's helpings. No smoking downstairs. Wheelchair access. Music

---

KENILWORTH Warwickshire   map 5

Restaurant Bosquet ▼

97A Warwick Road, Kenilworth CV8 1HP	COOKING 3
KENILWORTH (0926) 52463	COST £29–£45

This little house in a row of several has been redecorated. A deep red is the colour of the new-hung wallpaper. The cooking might be seen as a mighty triumph of substantive food over decorative style. Bernard Lignier works with classic French materials and believes in processing them. Hence a spring menu ran to three pâtés/terrines: quail, foie gras and sweetbread; lobster and smoked salmon with leeks and caviare; and red mullet and prawn. There was also a ravioli for good measure. An eloquent supporter denied the chef was into stuffing, but this same menu had braised loin of veal stuffed with vegetables, guinea-fowl stuffed with foie gras, and saddle of lamb stuffed with aubergines, onion and olives. Combinations may work: a celeriac cannelloni filled with asparagus and courgettes was brilliant, but a timbale of sauerkraut and salmon had too much cabbage, making the salmon taste like haddock. Too much chefing makes the sauces too strong; too much messing makes the vegetables seem mimsy. However, clarity can prevail, for instance in the fish cooking, and calf's liver in a lime sauce had non-offal eaters returning for more. There is no doubting Mr Lignier's capabilities. These continue to the sweet course, when a lemon tart and sorbet spiked with angelica was pronounced 'the best thing of the meal', closely pursued by an assiette au chocolat – three tuile baskets filled with chocolate mousse, chocolate ice-cream and fresh raspberries, the whole accompanied by a slice of rich chocolate marquise. Petits fours are good, even if coffee goes up and down. Service from Jane Lignier follows the kitchen's pace; this may be gentle. Do not be deceived by the handwritten wine list; this is French, serious, and very expensive at the upper reaches. The selection is sound throughout, including the reasonably priced Crozes-Hermitage from

Chave, a Zind-Humbrecht Alsace or one of the Vins Régionaux. Half-bottles are good but sparse. House wines are from £9.50.

CHEF: Bernard Lignier PROPRIETORS: Bernard and Jane Lignier OPEN: Tue to Sat, exc Sat L; 12 to 2, 7 to 10 CLOSED: last week July, first 2 weeks Aug MEALS: alc. Set L and D £19 (exc Sat) SERVICE: not inc CARDS: Access, Amex, Visa DETAILS: 28 seats. Private parties: 30 main room. Vegetarian meals. Children welcome. No music

---

KESWICK Cumbria   map 7

▲ Brundholme Country House Hotel 🍴✳

Brundholme Road, Keswick CA12 4NL
KESWICK (076 87) 74495
from A66 roundabout take Keswick   COOKING 2
road, then first left after garage   COST £21–£34

This house once belonged to the Calvert family, benefactors of Wordsworth. Then it was called Windy Brow, evoking its fine views and elevation. The Regency architecture, by George Basevi, is distinguished and the interiors developed by Ian Charlton do it fair justice. Kevin Burlison's cooking is both more direct and modern than his predecessor's. Rillettes of goose with horseradish cream, white fish soup with leeks and saffron, venison with shallot purée and pesto noodles, or salmon with wild mushrooms and soy are examples from a spring menu that have given satisfaction. A short run of desserts includes hot and substantial examples in the Lake District manner. Although general approval is recorded, reports also arrive of visits during periods of crisis or lassitude when things are not so sparkling. The wine list relies on the big-name shippers and négociants. House wines are £6.90.

CHEFS: Ian Charlton and Kevin Burlison PROPRIETOR: Ian Charlton OPEN: all week, D only (L by arrangement); 7.30 to 8.45 CLOSED: 23 Dec to 1 Feb MEALS: alc. Set D £19.50 to £22.50 SERVICE: not inc, card slips closed CARDS: Access, Visa DETAILS: 50 seats. Private parties: 55 main room, 55 private room. Car park. Vegetarian meals. Children's helpings with prior notice. No children under 12. Smart dress preferred. No smoking in dining-room. Wheelchair access (also WC). No music ACCOMMODATION: 12 rooms, all with bath/shower. D,B&B £57 to £154. Deposit: £20. No children under 12. Pets welcome. Garden. TV. Phone. Doors close at 11. Confirm by 6 (*The Which? Hotel Guide*)

▲ Swinside Lodge 🍴✳ | NEW ENTRY |

Grange Road, Newlands,
Keswick CA12 5UE   COOKING 2
KESWICK (076 87) 72948   COST £20–£22

The white house, with black window frames in Lakeland country style, sits beneath Catbells; Derwent Water is not far distant. Graham Taylor started Breamish House in Powburn (see entry) and has settled on the other side of the country after a gap of two years. Swinside is a comfortable hotel, cooking dinner for its residents from a daily set menu. Outsiders may be able to arrange a table, but only if the hotel is not full. Though there is one sitting (the menu is out on the sideboard from 5.30pm, aperitifs are served from 7.30), the place does not have the regimented touch of those where 'we all sit down together'. The cooking is understated and British; all agree it is skilful too. An asparagus mousse with an orange hollandaise kicked off a meal that continued with red pepper and tomato soup, roast fillet of beef with button onions and Yorkshire pudding, cauliflower cheese, pommes Anna, small scrubbed carrots and stir-fried cabbage with juniper berries, then finished with a choice of three puddings, including a lemon tart and a hot ginger, pear and walnut pudding, cheese (all North Country except for Stilton), and coffee with truffles. The details were exact, the cooking was tactful and true, and the choice interesting without worry. There is no licence, but part of the meal deal is a complimentary glass of sherry.

CHEFS: Irene Dent and Graham Taylor   PROPRIETOR: Graham Taylor   OPEN: all week, D only; 7.30   MEALS: Set D £18 to £20. Unlicensed, but bring your own: no corkage SERVICE: not inc   DETAILS: 18 seats. Private parties: 12 main room. Car park. Vegetarian meals with prior notice. No children under 12. No smoking in dining-room. No music ACCOMMODATION: 9 rooms, all with bath/shower. B&B £34 to £68. Deposit: £20. No children under 12. Garden. TV. Doors close at 11. Confirm by 4 (*The Which? Hotel Guide*)

KEYSTON Cambridgeshire   map 6

Pheasant Inn ♟

Keyston P18 0RE   COOKING 1
BYTHORN (080 14) 241   COST £22–£37

This thatched cottage pub-cum-restaurant has been in the care of Nick Steiger for almost two years and has gained in confidence. Its popularity was never in question. The restaurant runs a steadily changing menu that avoids clichés. Though adventure may take it as far as chicken stuffed with a salmon mousse on a sorrel sauce, the main repertoire is good up-to-the-minute stuff: gnocchi with wild mushrooms and bacon, red mullet with sweet peppers and aubergine, hake with celeriac and cabbage and a caraway sauce, chocolate terrine with a coffee sauce, or summer fruits with crème fraîche. The blackboard in the bar gives full rein to English staples. The Pheasant saw early steps in cooking from Somerset Moore, now at Painswick Hotel (see entry, Painswick), and his student or assistant was David Wilson of the Peat Inn (see entry, Peat inn, Scotland) – so this is a house with a heritage. A dozen modest but good house wines from £7.75 a bottle (all available by the glass) head the succinct and intelligent list. It is arranged by style of wine, so Washington State nudges shoulders with Chablis, while Chianti is neighbour to Margaux. There are good halves; the bin-ends are worth a look. Pricing is fair throughout.

CHEF: Nick Steiger   PROPRIETORS: Poste Hotels Ltd   OPEN: all week; 12 to 2, 7 to 10 CLOSED: D 25 and 26 Dec, 3 Jan   MEALS: alc. Set Sun L £15.95   SERVICE: not inc, card slips closed   CARDS: Access, Amex, Diners, Visa   DETAILS: 100 seats. 4 tables outside. Private parties: 30 main room, 30 private room. Car park. Vegetarian meals. Children's helpings. Music. Air-conditioned

---

♟ *denotes an outstanding wine cellar;* ♟ *denotes a good wine list, worth travelling for.*

KILN PIT HILL Northumberland   map 7

Manor House Inn *⅝* £

Carterway Heads,
Shotley Bridge DH8 9LX
EDMUNDBYERS (0207) 55268   COOKING 1
on A68, 2m S of Kiln Pit Hill   COST £17–£20

The wild location in the middle of the moors is impressive, especially in
midwinter, but it does not stop this house being full in bar and restaurant on
most days. Rearrangement and refurbishment have continued apace: 'This
gives it a much less formal and more French provincial atmosphere,' reported
one person calling in on his way to his holiday. Bar meals are as popular as
those from the short fixed-price menu in the restaurant. Small wonder, for there
is much invention in things like smoked ham and Brie croissant, beef satay,
cream cheese and mint tartlet, breast of chicken with lemon and olives, spiced
yam and vegetable ragoût, and lamb and aubergine casserole. Puddings are
always headed by sticky toffee, but lemon meringue ice-cream with home-
made shortbread, chocolate polenta pudding and chocolate and ricotta tart get
their yes-votes. It is all substantial and good value; moments of inattention are
rarely reported. The wine list offers 15 choices and changes often. House wines
are £6.20.

CHEFS: Jane and Elizabeth Pelly   PROPRIETORS: Anthony, Jane and Elizabeth Pelly
OPEN: all week; 12 to 2.30, 7 to 9.30 (9 Sun)   MEALS: alc. Set L and D £9.50 to £12.50
SERVICE: not inc, card slips closed   CARDS: Access, Visa   DETAILS: 90 seats. 6 tables
outside. Private parties: 60 main room. Car park. Vegetarian meals. Children's helpings.
No smoking in 1 dining-room. Wheelchair access (1 step; also female WC). Music

---

KINGSBRIDGE Devon   map 1

▲ Buckland-Tout-Saints Hotel,
Queen Anne *⅝* | NEW ENTRY |

Goveton, Kingsbridge TQ7 2DS   COOKING 2*
KINGSBRIDGE (0548) 853055   COST £20–£35

The house is secluded – first point in its favour; its gardens are fine, second; the
exterior is handsome Queen Anne, third; the inside is an English domestic mix,
up to the large Victorian panelled hall, fourth. Points against would be few.
The decoration might be more lively, so might the whole atmosphere, but the
house lacks nothing in terms of care and attention. Although the hotel went
through a blank year between closure and purchase by the Taylors, they were
fortunate to recover the help of Alastair Carter as chef. Returnees therefore find
it hard to see the join. The cooking is very sound indeed, though the menu is by
no means adventurous. Main courses of fillet steak, duck, rack of lamb and hot
smoked salmon need much fiddling to take them out of the ordinary.
Reliability, however, fulfils many requirements, so a dinner that encompassed
terrine of scallops and monkfish with a salsa verde, rack of lamb with onion
and garlic soubise, and poached pears with hot fudge sauce found no faults.
The wine list has a range of clarets as centrepiece, including some desirable

1970s. Prices are not impossible, though they have to be high. Other choices are sound, though those beyond France might be more interesting. Purchasing for the list has a Scottish tinge to it, even if Loddiswell, the hotel's local vineyard, is there in two colours. House wines are from £7.50.

CHEFS: Alastair Carter and Angela Mace   PROPRIETORS: John and Tove Taylor   OPEN: all week; 12.30 to 1.45, 7.30 to 9.30   CLOSED: Jan and Feb   MEALS: Set L £14.50, Set D £25   SERVICE: not inc, card slips closed   CARDS: Access, Amex, Visa   DETAILS: 30 seats. Private parties: 20 main room, 12 private room. Car park. Vegetarian meals. Children's helpings. No children under 8. No smoking in dining-room. No music   ACCOMMODATION: 12 rooms, all with bath/shower. B&B £55 to £145. No children under 8. Afternoon teas. Garden. TV. Phone. Doors close at midnight. Confirm by 6.30. Fax: (0548) 856261

KING'S LYNN Norfolk   map 6

Riverside

27 King Street,
King's Lynn PE30 1HA   COOKING 1
KING'S LYNN (0553) 773134   COST £15–£33

A man with knowledge of words wrote that the view from these handsome rooms, showing much brick and timber work, in a converted warehouse (shared with an arts centre) is lugubrious. 'A marvellous sight, with the moon, mudflats, harbour lights glinting off the water,' he continued. Inside, all is very cheerful and proper. 'Because it was next to an arts centre, I turned up looking casual,' wrote another, 'but the look of slight horror on the waitress' face told me of my mistake.' Not that intolerance has been identified here. 'They coped well with the children in the party' was a further comment. Avocado and coronation chicken mousse, melon and fruit cocktail, monkfish with green peppercorns, breast of duck with orange, or lamb with tarragon mousseline sauce are the sort of things cooked. A sweets trolley with tarts and mousses may attract or may not, 'but the strawberries were very good'. The cooking, however, while playing to middle-of-the-road tastes, is perfectly competent, and sometimes felt to be more than that. Watercress soup is spot on, smoked mackerel pâté ('not the two-week old lump that I feared') is light and flavourful, venison en croûte much enjoyed, and the salads are decent. The short wine list has some acceptable makers such as Lafarge from Mâcon and Fèvre from Chablis, though it is not exactly cheap. House wines are £7.75.

CHEF: Dennis Taylor   PROPRIETORS: Michael and Sylvia Savage   OPEN: Mon to Sat; 12 to 2, 7 to 10   MEALS: alc   SERVICE: not inc, card slips closed   CARDS: Access, Visa   DETAILS: 65 seats. 24 tables outside. Private parties: 75 main room. Car park. Vegetarian meals. Children's helpings. Music

---

If a restaurant is new to the Guide *this year (did not appear as a main entry in the last edition)* NEW ENTRY *appears opposite its name.*

Healthy eating options *in the details at the end of an entry signifies that a restaurant marks on its menu, in words and/or using symbols, low-fat dishes or other healthy eating choices.*

Rococo ♀

COUNTY OF THE YEAR RESTAURANT

NEW ENTRY

11 Saturday Market Place,
King's Lynn PE30 5DQ
KING'S LYNN (0553) 771483

COOKING 2
COST £19–£37

King's Lynn unfortunately lost a restaurant, Garbo's, in 1992, but luck has
supplied them with a replacement, Nick Anderson's Rococo. Nick comes to
Norfolk from the Canal Brasserie in West London, so there is a certain chic to
the yellow dining-room and to the dishes he is offering East Anglia. This is not
at the cost of friendliness: 'On a bleak weekday lunch in February, the
welcome as the door opened was warm and undiminished by the sight of a
four-year-old and a baby.' It is well-sited: on the market-place, next to the
town hall, opposite the church. This may explain why various revellers popped
in and out one night when a civic masked ball was in progress. Their
interruption may also have affected Nick Anderson's cooking, for good ideas
seemed spoiled by inattention to flavours or by technical faults. Sauces were
overheated, good meats overcooked, sorbet overfrozen, but vegetables were
under-boiled. The experience on this evening has been gainsaid by many other
reporters who have enjoyed, for example, a sausage of sweetbreads on a bed of
pulses; a hotpot of mussel and crab with a 'boldness of flavouring (he is not
afraid of chilli) and a fine use of herbs'; layered fillet of beef and garlic in puff
pastry; a tart of pecans, Roquefort and tomatoes; and a flan of hunza apricots
and goats' cheese. Let's hope King's Lynn gets on with Nick Anderson and that
he gets on with ironing out those few faults. The wine list is also full of big-city
ideas. Really good wines are classified by type and weight and are not
overpriced. The notes are not embarrassing. House wines are £8.95.
CELLARMAN'S CHOICE: Napa Valley, Chardonnay 1989, Cuvaison, £23;
Vinattieri Rosso II 1986, Castelli, £19.90.

CHEF: Nicholas Anderson   PROPRIETORS: Anne and Nicholas Anderson   OPEN: all week,
exc Mon L and Sun D; 12 to 2.30, 7 to 10   MEALS: light L menu. Set L £9 to £12, Set D
£18.75 to £23.75   SERVICE: not inc, card slips closed   CARDS: Access, Visa   DETAILS: 40
seats. Private parties: 40 main room. Vegetarian meals. Children's helpings. No cigars/
pipes in dining-room. Wheelchair access (also WC). Music

KING'S NORTON West Midlands   map 5

▲ Norton Place, Lombard Room ♀ ⁵⁄✳

180 Lifford Lane,
King's Norton B30 3NT
021-451 3991 and 3992

COOKING 1
COST £21–£55

It does seem surreal, a rich man's folly: a park containing a collection of historic
automobiles, and in walled gardens this luxurious small hotel and restaurant
entirely new-built, complete with resident pianist, indoor swimming-pool and
'fitness centre' (for residents only). Customers are expected to fit the image as
enthusiastically as the management pursues it – collar and tie here – but the
menu is sign that there is no wish to break with convention. Gravlax, apple and

Stilton soup with a puff pastry top, brill with fresh noodles and a chive and white wine sauce, venison with juniper, lamb with a rosemary gravy and roasted garlic, beef with potato and celeriac galette are all dishes that have been decently executed and fairly received. Whether duck with asparagus and crème de cacao and chocolate sauce is as successful has not been reported. The wine list is a great document. It covers classic material at length, and offers high-grade properties and makers from countries outside France as well. Bouchard, Latour, Drouhin and Leflaive bulk large among the burgundies; Lynch-Bages, Gruaud-Larose, La Lagune, Trotanoy and Haut-Brion are among the many aristocrats in clarets. David Hohnen's Cloudy Bays are offered in little runs of vintages. Half-bottles are in abundance, and, for all the expensive numbers, there is a fair range of prices. House wines are £11.50. CELLARMAN'S CHOICE: Chablis 1988, Albert Pic, £22; Côtes du Rhone 1986, Guigal, £16.50.

CHEF: Anthony Morgan PROPRIETOR: J.A. Patrick OPEN: all week, exc Sat L; 12 to 2, 7 to 10 MEALS: alc. Set L £13.50 to £14.95, Set D £18.50 SERVICE: not inc, card slips closed CARDS: Access, Amex, Diners, Visa DETAILS: 60 seats. 10 tables outside. Private parties: 120 main room, 20, 40 and 120 private rooms. Car park. Vegetarian meals. Children's helpings. Jacket and tie. No smoking in dining-room. Wheelchair access (also WC). Music. Air-conditioned ACCOMMODATION: 10 rooms, all with bath/shower. Rooms for disabled. B&B £90 to £250. No children under 10. Afternoon teas. Garden. Swimming-pool. TV. Phone. Confirm by 6. Fax: 021-433 3048

KINGSTON UPON THAMES Surrey   map 3

Ayudhya

14 Kingston Hill,
Kingston upon Thames KT2 7NH   COOKING 1*
081-549 5984 and 546 5878   COST £21–£37

There are three floors, and the lower-ground has a waterfall – the full experience is offered here and it is popular too. The range goes from a strong suit of seafood through to vegetarian curries and soups, with the added bonus of desserts such as coconut, pumpkin and palm-sugar custard, and bananas cooked in coconut milk. There have been nights below par, but people speak warmly of jungle curry with plenty of prawns, squid and chicken, as well as a dish of crisply fried pomfret with a tamarind sauce with chillies, garlic and spring onions. There are no complaints about the noodles or the soups. The wine list is not long, but the sources are good. New World makers such as Saintsbury and Collards and French names like Natter's Sancerre or Legland's Chablis give confidence, and the prices are never out of the way. House wine is £6.95.

CHEF/PROPRIETOR: Somjai Thanpo OPEN: all week, exc Sat L; 12 to 2.30, 6.30 to 11 (11.30 Fri and Sat) CLOSED: 25 and 26 Dec, 1 Jan, Easter Sun MEALS: alc SERVICE: not inc CARDS: Access, Amex, Diners, Visa DETAILS: 84 seats. Private parties: 30 main room, 28 and 20 private rooms. Children welcome. Wheelchair access. Music

---

CELLARMAN'S CHOICE: *Wines recommended by the restaurateur, normally more expensive than house wine.*

▲ Penrhos Court ✦

Kington HR5 3LH	COOKING 1*
KINGTON (0544) 230720	COST £23–£45

Martin Griffiths wrote last year: 'We started in the cow byre 15 years ago and have now got to the cruck hall (built in 1280).' This is a mammoth restoration of a remarkable group of buildings. Meanwhile, Daphne Lambert cooks, including banquets with a historical tilt (her special expertise lies in medieval cooking), weddings, demonstrations and the day-to-day menu for guests. The modern repertoire is a criss-cross of English and French influences: curried parsnip soup, a version of gravlax, mussels marinière, venison and steak pie, pheasant with calvados, apples and cream, French apple tart and hazelnut ice-cream, spiced pears, or meringue with fresh pineapple. This sounds quite simple but can seem, as one reporter described it, 'careful, conscientious yet sometimes verging on the precious'. People have applauded the home-made bread, the intelligent vegetables (honeyed carrots, garlicked French beans, new potatoes) and the excellent ice-creams. They have also liked the personal involvement of the owners, while regretting the inadequacy of the heating on really cold nights – 'best to go on a fine day'. Breakfast is communal and not brilliant, bedrooms are no-smoking and more modern-commercial in their fitting out than the location might imply. The wine list is short, some say to a fault, but the choices are nicely judged even if details of growers are at times scanty. House French is £10.50.

CHEF: Daphne Lambert   PROPRIETORS: Martin Griffiths and Daphne Lambert   OPEN: Mon to Sat, D only, and Sun L; 12.30 to 2, 7.30 to 10   CLOSED: 2 weeks Feb   MEALS: alc. Set Sun L £15.50 to £18.50   SERVICE: not inc, card slips closed   DETAILS: 20 seats. 10 tables outside. Private parties: 25 Elizabethan room, 80 medieval hall. Car park. No smoking in 1 dining-room. Children's helpings. No music   ACCOMMODATION: 19 rooms, all with bath/shower. Rooms for disabled. B&B £60 to £120. Deposit: 50%. Children welcome. Baby facilities. Garden. TV. Phone. Fax: (0544) 230754

▲ Dundas Arms 🍾

Station Road, Kintbury RG15 0UT	COOKING 1
KINTBURY (0488) 58263 and 58559	COST £21–£41

The pub stands on a green-lawned tongue of land between the river and the canal. There is water fore and aft. Tables are laid out along the river bank; inside there is a big bar for pub grub, plus a peaceful, flowery lounge and a long, narrow dining-room with views of the garden at one end. David Dalzell-Piper's cooking is straightforward and unadorned, with the emphasis on fish and game. Home-cured gravlax is a fixture, served with a decent dill and mustard mayonnaise. Well-judged, subtly flavoured sauces have impressed most reporters: tomato and fresh coriander with prawns and asparagus; jasmine tea and sultana with roast duckling; a simple white wine sauce with grilled monkfish. There is also a touch of class about the well-judged prune and armagnac ice-cream. Against this there have been signs of basic faults in the kitchen: poorly timed asparagus and duck, sea bass 'floating in its poaching liquor', 'tired' vegetables. But most serious criticisms relate to the service, which seems to suffer from bad organisation and understaffing. There are no such reservations about the wine list. Francophile in the main, it shows real strength in bourgeois clarets and is solid with fine Burgundian growers. Prices are fair, and there is a useful range of house wines. Half-bottles are sparse. House wines are from £7.

CHEF/PROPRIETOR: David Dalzell-Piper OPEN: Tue to Sat; 12.30 to 1.30, 7.30 to 9.30
CLOSED: Christmas to New Year MEALS: alc. Set L £16.50 to £18.50. Bar menu. Minimum
£16 SERVICE: not inc CARDS: Access, Amex, Visa DETAILS: 50 seats. 10 tables outside.
Private parties: 22 main room. Car park. Children's helpings. Smart dress preferred. No
cigars/pipes in dining-room. Wheelchair access (2 steps; also WC). No music
ACCOMMODATION: 5 rooms, all with bath/shower. Rooms for disabled. B&B £55 to £65.
Children welcome. Pets welcome. TV. Phone. Doors close at 11.30. Confirm by 6. Fax:
(0488) 58568 (*The Which? Hotel Guide*)

KIRKBY LONSDALE Cumbria   map 7

▲ *Lupton Tower* ⸙✳

Lupton, Kirkby Lonsdale LA6 2PR
CROOKLANDS (053 95) 67400   COOKING 1*
off A65, NW of Kirkby Lonsdale   COST £27

The approach is down a slightly tatty drive; there are animals about – a sheepdog and a hen called Henrietta have been mentioned – but smokers and meat-eaters are not really accommodated here. Get through the door and the place is fine – 'light and bright, a wood-burner kept the dining-room warm as toast, an enormous dresser holds the breakfast buffet, candlelight imparts evening charm'. Dorothy Smith is a self-taught cook and techniques are not what you might expect (pears poached in Ribena and syrup, for instance). The results are much enjoyed. Vegetarian cooking here is not a lump of stodge, as instanced in spinach soufflé with a hollandaise, courgette and rosemary soup, a filo packet of asparagus (not much) and nuts with a mushroom sauce; and there are excellent puddings from profiteroles to banana brown betty. Coffee is not up to a lot. The place is enthusiastic and fairly priced for the four-course menu, with coffee, that has no choice till dessert. House wine is £7 a litre.

CHEF: Dorothy Smith PROPRIETORS: Mr and Mrs G.J. Smith OPEN: all week, D only;
7.30 for 8 CLOSED: Mon and Tue winter if no room bookings MEALS: Set D £18
SERVICE: not inc DETAILS: 32 seats. 3 tables outside. Private parties: 28 main room, 12
private room. Car park. Vegetarian meals only. Children's helpings. No smoking in dining-
room. Wheelchair access (2 steps; also WC). Music ACCOMMODATION: 6 rooms, 4 with
bath/shower. B&B £18.50 to £37. Deposit: £10. Children welcome. Pets by arrangement.
Garden. Doors close at 1am. Confirm by 4

'The receptionist, on being given a cheque, announced shrilly that she would have to phone the bank to check that "you can afford it", and "Can't you pay by credit card?"'
On staying in Oxfordshire

KIRKHAM Lancashire | map 5

Cromwellian ♥

16 Poulton Street, Kirkham PR4 2AB
KIRKHAM (0772) 685680

COOKING 2
COST £27–£35

The Fawcetts' beamed house continues to exude cosiness, but there have been improvements of late. 'I was amazed,' writes a Midlands reporter. 'The restaurant has been upgraded, beginning at the front door and front windows, with new curtains and new prints and flowers on the walls.' Much work has been done in the garden, particularly with fruit and herbs: the results appear in the kitchen and as jars of preserves and bottled vinegars for sale. Josie Fawcett's monthly-changing fixed-price menus have generated enthusiastic reports: broccoli, mango and lime soup is frequently mentioned. Other good dishes have included koulibiac of salmon in filo pastry, flageolet bean salad with honey and orange vinaigrette, mille-feuille of salmon and mushrooms, sliced lamb on a bed of spinach with port sauce, and pork and sausage ragoût. A vegetarian option of chickpea and asparagus casserole almost converted one carnivorous reader. The range of desserts has been extended and has benefited from the Fawcetts' efforts in the garden: 'stunning' queen of puddings, rum sponge with pear in red wine sauce, and home-made meringues with strawberries have been mentioned. Good half-bottles and attractive range, at fair prices, contribute to a very adequate wine list. Presentation is much improved and notes, mercifully, are briefer. This is a good place for vinous experiment and gets a glass award this year. House wine is £7.95.
CELLARMAN'S CHOICE: Montagny premier cru 1989, Roy, £16.95; Victoria, Cabernet Sauvignon, Schinus Molle, 1990, £13.50.

CHEF: Josie Fawcett PROPRIETORS: Peter and Josie Fawcett OPEN: Tue to Sat, D only (L by arrangement); 7 to 9.30 MEALS: Set D £18.95 to £21.95 SERVICE: not inc, card slips closed CARDS: Access, Amex, Visa DETAILS: 30 seats. Private parties: 17 main room, 12 private room. Vegetarian meals. Children's helpings with prior notice. Wheelchair access. Music

KNUTSFORD Cheshire | map 5

▲ *La Belle Epoque*

60 King Street, Knutsford WA16 6DT
KNUTSFORD (0565) 633060 and 632661

COOKING 1
COST £29–£46

The first instruction is to go and look at the building, a remarkable piece of art nouveau, with more to come in the bars and ante-rooms. The dining-room's influence is Napoleon, however. There is a lot of silk, pleated and swathed, a lot of wood-panelling and a lot of 'atmosphere'; and the place can get so crowded that a licence is needed to drive the very good cheese trolley. The cooking goes up and down on a long menu. The character might be gauged as 'English' in that it is beyond classic, yet has not been swept up in the recent love affair with the south and with far-flung flavours. Fresh melon with a strawberry and goats' cheese sabayon, or pork with bacon and sage on a leek sauce, could only happen here. People have enjoyed spinach pancakes with goats' cheese and a tomato sauce, quail stuffed with peaches and smoked chicken on a sauce made with Pineau des Charentes, and ravioli of snails, garlic and mushrooms on a red wine sauce. Others have questioned poor appetisers, inapposite sauces – for instance, with salmon and spinach lasagne, as well as with a cheese and bacon tartlet – and failings in general technique. The restaurant does have a strong local following. Celebrations are a regular event, but the prices are quite celebratory as well. The wine list spreads round the world and has some sound enough drinking. House wines are from £9.50.

CHEFS: Graham Codd and David Mooney PROPRIETORS: Keith and Nerys Mooney
OPEN: Mon to Sat, D only; 7.30 to 10 CLOSED: first week Jan MEALS: alc SERVICE: 10%,
card slips closed CARDS: Access, Amex, Diners, Visa DETAILS: 70 seats. Private parties:
60 main room, 20, 60 and 80 private rooms. Vegetarian meals. No children under 10. No
pipes in dining-room. Music ACCOMMODATION: 7 rooms, all with bath/shower. B&B £35
to £50. No children under 10. Garden. TV. Doors close at midnight. Confirm by 2. Fax:
(0565) 634150

LANGAR Nottinghamshire   map 5

▲ Langar Hall

Langar NG13 9HG   COOKING 2
HARBY (0949) 60559   COST £15–£33

Tucked behind the church at Langar, this Regency house is plumb centre of the Vale of Belvoir, a stone's throw from the current source of England's best Stilton, and not a lot further from Bunny, once home of Sir Thomas Parkyn, the Wrestling Baronet. Eccentricity – just think of Nimrod's hunting characters – fills the air, and Imogen Skirving's hotel has its share. 'When I first stayed there, Mrs Skirving seemed to be doing everything, including cooking, but it has since developed into something more professional' was one early report. This has not worn the welcome or cramped the style of Crispin Harris, the Singing Butler ('He certainly soothed this savage breast, if not the duck's'), or stopped the staff leaving white wine in ice buckets under a guest's table: 'This seemed unusual but was quite handy in view of the scarcity of waiters.' Into this 'home from home' with its antiques, pictures, candlelight and comfortable bedrooms has been inserted a capable kitchen offering quite a long monthly menu. Performance is not invariably accurate, but ambition is there in dishes such as wild mushroom, pigeon and pork terrine with an onion marmalade, salmon mousseline with red caviare and leeks, venison sausages with white beans and juniper, and rabbit with bacon and thyme, served with Jerusalem artichokes. There has been a change of chefs, but the style has not altered; nor, it is hoped, has the standard varied. The wine list is less interesting than the food, but will provide something for everyone. The Butler has some bin-ends of fancy clarets. House wines are from £8.50.

The Guide *office can quickly spot when a restaurateur is encouraging customers to write recommending inclusion – and sadly, several restaurants have been doing this in 1992. Such reports do not further a restaurant's cause. Please tell us if a restaurateur invites you to write to the* Guide.

CHEFS: Jason Timms, Mark Osbourne and Gary Crozier PROPRIETOR: Imogen Skirving
OPEN: Mon to Sat, D only, and Sun L (Mon to Sat L by arrangement); 12 to 2.30, 7.30 to 9
MEALS: Set Sun L £9.50 to £21.50, Set D £21.50 to £23.50 SERVICE: net prices, card slips
closed CARDS: Access, Amex, Diners, Visa DETAILS: 30 seats. Private parties: 30 main
room, 4, 6, 8 and 10 private rooms. Car park. Vegetarian meals with prior notice. Children
restricted. Wheelchair access (1 step). Music ACCOMMODATION: 12 rooms, all with bath/
shower. B&B £50 to £98. Deposit: £20. Children welcome. Pets by arrangement. Garden.
TV. Phone. Confirm by 6. Fax: (0949) 61045 (*The Which? Hotel Guide*)

LANGHO Lancashire   map 5

▲ *Northcote Manor*

Northcote Road, Langho BB6 9BB
BLACKBURN (0254) 240555   COOKING 2*
On A59, 9m E of M6 exit 31   COST £18–£44

As we go to press, this Victorian red-brick house is in the final stages of a
transformation. New bedrooms have been built, a stone mullion conservatory
is being added on to the dining-room and a private dining suite is being
created with its own lounge. A helipad is promised. Nigel Haworth offers a
short *carte* backed up by a 'Market Menu' of more adventurous specialities with
fish as a strong suit. It moves comfortably from the classical richness of collops
of venison with calvados sauce or peppered fillet of beef flamed with brandy
and cream, to the simplicity of grilled Dover sole to the up-to-the-minute
stylishness of pavé of halibut on a fondue of mussels and root vegetables with
tarragon. In-vogue ingredients are exploited in dishes such as grilled monkfish
on spinach leaves and deep-fried onion rings with a sauce of sun-dried
tomatoes and lentils. Sweets range from Atholl brose to praline wafers with
praline cream and a passion-fruit and pink grapefruit coulis. Service is
attentive without being 'smothering'. The wine list has been re-vamped, with
fairer prices across the range and a decent showing of halves. House French
is £7.95.

CHEF: Nigel Haworth PROPRIETORS: Craig J. Bancroft and Nigel Haworth OPEN: all
week, exc Mon L; 12 to 1.30 (2 Sun), 7 to 9 (10 Sat) MEALS: alc. Set L £12.40 SERVICE:
10%, card slips closed CARDS: Access, Amex, Diners, Visa DETAILS: 90 seats. Private
parties: 90 main room, 40 private room. Car park. Children's helpings. Smart dress
preferred. Music ACCOMMODATION: 14 rooms, all with bath/shower. Rooms for disabled.
B&B £49 to £60. Children welcome. Baby facilities. Pets by arrangement. Afternoon teas.
Garden. TV. Phone. Doors close at 1am. Confirm by 6. Fax: (0254) 244568 (*The Which? Hotel
Guide*)

Net prices *in the details at the end of an entry indicates that the prices given on a menu
and on a bill are inclusive of VAT and service charge, and that this practice is clearly stated
on menu and bill.*

The 1994 Guide *will be published before Christmas 1993. Reports on meals are most
welcome at any time of the year, but are extremely valuable in the spring. Send them to*
The Good Food Guide, *FREEPOST, 2 Marylebone Road, London NW1 1YN. No stamp
is needed if posted in the UK.*

LANGLEY MARSH Somerset   map 2

▲ *Langley House Hotel* ♥ ✸

Langley Marsh TA4 2UF   COOKING 3
WIVELISCOMBE (0984) 23318   COST £34–£42

Langley House is neither large nor grand but the hospitality is considered and
of a high standard. Comfort, colour, flair and attention to minutiae make a stay
or a dinner here very enjoyable, although the size of the place lays an emphasis
on peace and quiet rather than rumbustious jollification. Dinner is bereft of
choice until dessert. On weekdays it is of four courses; on Saturday the hair is
let down and an extra starter is inserted in the running order. Peter Wilson's
repertoire may become familiar over the years, but its advantage stems from
exactness and discretion. Flamboyance may seem out of place.

Recommendation has been forthcoming for a warm salad of quail with walnut-
oil dressing; more walnut with a salad of pear and Stilton cream; fish such as
turbot and scallops with a leek sauce, or red mullet with a warm vinaigrette;
meat such as plain but flavourful lamb, or beef with a mint béarnaise;
vegetables that still come on a side plate; and desserts like syllabubs, chocolate
terrine or maybe a bread-and-butter pudding. Cheeses seem invariably British,
usually no more than one or two. The atmosphere is often called 'home from
home', and that is what many look for in a country weekend. The wine list
shows the same degree of intelligent care. Apart from muted enthusiasm for
Italy and Spain, it offers as good a spread geographically as it does in price –
exemplified by a decent Côtes du Rhône at about £10 up to a Guigal Hermitage
at £34.50. Buying is sound and prices throughout are fair. Some especially good
halves and bin-ends should make for varied interest. House wines are from
£7.75. CELLARMAN'S CHOICE: Petaluma Chardonnay 1987, £25.50; Meursault
Rouge 1987, Giraud, £22.75.

CHEF: Peter Wilson   PROPRIETORS: Peter and Anne Wilson   OPEN: all week, D only;
8 (8.30 Fri and Sat) to 9   MEALS: Set D £24.50 to £28.50   SERVICE: not inc, card slips
closed   CARDS: Access, Amex, Visa   DETAILS: 18 seats. Private parties: 35 main room, 18
private room. Car park. Vegetarian meals. Children's helpings. No children under 7. No
smoking in dining-room. Wheelchair access (also WC). No music   ACCOMMODATION: 8
rooms, all with bath/shower. B&B £59 to £105. Children under 7 by arrangement. Baby
facilities. Pets welcome (not in public rooms). Afternoon teas. Garden. TV. Phone. Doors
close at midnight. Confirm by 6. Fax: (0984) 24573 (*The Which? Hotel Guide*)

LAUNCESTON Cornwall   map 1

Randells | NEW ENTRY |

Prospect House, 11 Western Road,
Launceston PL15 7AS   COOKING 1
LAUNCESTON (0566) 776484   COST £21–£29

In the well-converted Victorian house next to the town hall, Patrick Randell
and Debbie Hutchings re-interpret our traditions. Duck with plum sauce,
salmon Wellington and beef with oyster sauce are offered on a menu that may
also include 'a real prototype' steak and pigeon pie with 'juniper and possibly
allspice', or a lamb Shrewsbury – three small cutlets coated with mustard,

herbs and breadcrumbs and served with port and redcurrant sauce. There is attention to detail in a mushroom soup with 'dark flecks of mushroom, deep chicken stock, judicious use of cream', though cream figured perhaps too much in a spinach roulade stuffed with prawns that fell short of zing and zip. Get to the puddings and there will probably be something with body (a treacle and lemon tart, perhaps) something fruity (pears poached with cinnamon), something creamy (crème brûlée), something sickly (pavlova) and something chocolatey (profiteroles). Ignore the foil-wrapped butter and hope the wine list improves. House wine is £7.20.

CHEFS/PROPRIETORS: Patrick Randell and Debbie Hutchings   OPEN: Tue to Sat, D only; 7 to 9 (9.30 Sat)   CLOSED: last 3 weeks Jan   MEALS: alc   SERVICE: not inc   CARDS: Access, Visa   DETAILS: 32 seats. Private parties: 20 main room. Vegetarian meals. Children's helpings. Smart dress preferred. Music

---

LAVENHAM Suffolk   map 3

▲ *Great House*

Market Place, Lavenham CO10 9QZ   COOKING 2
LAVENHAM (0787) 247431   COST £21–£48

While the town is celebrated for its architectural distillation of medieval England, the Great House is unashamedly French: French food, French staff, French language. The menus, a series of tables d'hôte at varying prices, are a French giveaway at the outset. The food, too, for a lunch that consisted of a fish terrine, simple lamb cutlets with herbs, excellent vegetables (the major non-French trait), deep apple tart and French cheeses in prime condition had few British overtones. The crisp linen, good bread, fair coffee and nice home-made chocolates rounded out a fair-value experience. It gets dearer on the *carte*, which may branch into dishes like lamb served with a soy and five-spice Chinese sauce, or a plate of salmon treated four ways, as well as dishing up calf's liver with wild mushroom sauce, or venison, sauce chasseur, but reporters do not begrudge it. The wine list is a mixture: a few fine old clarets, some decent Loires, Alsaces from Blanck, some useful bourgeois Médocs, and a quartet of Gaillacs from the Cros family. Prices vary – some dear, some fair. House Gaillac is £12.80.

CHEF: Regis Crépy   PROPRIETORS: John Spice and Regis Crépy   OPEN: Tue to Sun, exc Sun D; 12 to 2.30, 7 to 10.30   CLOSED: Jan   MEALS: alc. Set L £10.95 to £13.95, Set D £14.95   SERVICE: not inc   CARDS: Access, Amex, Visa   DETAILS: 65 seats. 7 tables outside. Private parties: 50 main room, 30 private room. Vegetarian meals. Children's helpings. No cigars/pipes in dining-room. Music   ACCOMMODATION: 4 rooms, all with bath/shower. B&B £50 to £78. Deposit: £20. Children welcome. Baby facilities. Pets welcome. Garden. TV. Phone. Doors close at 1am. Confirm by midday (*The Which? Hotel Guide*)

Prices quoted in the Guide are based on information supplied by restaurateurs. The prices quoted at the top of each entry represent a range, from the lowest meal price to the highest; the latter is inflated by 10 per cent to take account of likely price rises during the year of the Guide.

LEAMINGTON SPA Warwickshire   map 2

Les Plantagenêts

---

15 Dormer Place,
Leamington Spa CV32 5AA   COOKING 2
LEAMINGTON SPA (0926) 451792   COST £19–£45

As the name suggests, this old-style French restaurant in the basement of a
large terraced house has its heart and its root in Anjou. There is a deliberate
attempt to offer regional dishes, although the cumulative effect of butter and
cream can be too rich for palates – and digestions – weaned on jus and exotic
vinaigrettes. But, as one seasoned reporter observed, 'This sort of cooking has
been around for generations and people still love it.' The short *carte* and fixed-
price menus are notable for good fish: moules marinière, ragoût of monkfish
with saffron and Dijon mustard sauce, and turbot with a tomato-based sauce.
There have also been recommendations for chicken liver and bacon salad;
slivers of duck breast with Cassis and red wine sauce; and roast best end of
lamb. Vegetables are varied, minuscule and sometimes described as 'tasteless'.
The French cheeseboard is worth considered exploration. Délice de Marguerite
d'Anjou (home-made ice-cream with melon balls in a crunchy pastry tulip) has
won plaudits. The French wine list makes a feature of bottles from the Loire
and includes less familiar makers than the norm, for instance, Regis Minet in
Sancerre and Didier Champalou in Vouvray. The clarets also seem a fair list.

CHEF/PROPRIETOR: Remy Loth   OPEN: Mon to Sat, exc Sat L; 12.15 to 2.15, 7.15 to 10.15
MEALS: alc. Set L £12.50, Set D £17 to £30   SERVICE: not inc   CARDS: Access, Amex, Visa
DETAILS: 35 seats. Private parties: 45 main room. Children welcome. Smart dress preferred.
Music. Air-conditioned

LECK Lancashire   map 7

▲ *Cobwebs*

Leck, Cowan Bridge LA6 2HZ   COOKING 3
KIRKBY LONSDALE (052 42) 72141   COST £32

Visitors are struck by the unusual 'informal formality' of this delightful house
off the A65 near Kirkby Lonsdale. The kitchen works to the philosophy of the
new British cooking, which means a commitment to home-made items and
local ingredients: four kinds of bread are baked on the premises, while the
cheeseboard is a dazzling assortment of up to 14 varieties – all from the
neighbouring counties of Cumbria, Yorkshire and Lancashire. Dinner is
normally five courses – with a sorbet before the centrepiece. Yvonne
Thompson's trademark is the pairing and contrasting of ingredients and
themes. Surprising 'split' soups (two types in one bowl) are regularly praised:
carrot and pineapple paired with broccoli and walnut; curried parsnip and
Jerusalem artichoke; chilled smoked salmon and cucumber with hot
mushroom. The notion of multiples extends to other courses: a quartet of
grilled fishes with two sauces – one tomato, the other watercress; salmon and
halibut in a filo basket with lime and ginger sauce; chicken, duck, turkey and
spinach rolled together and served with shellfish and leek sauces. Vegetables

are generally a crunchy assortment. Of the sweets, fresh fruits marinated in Grand Marnier with yoghurt-based ice-cream, and the tart apple slice with sweet caramel sauce, have both been recommended. Wines remain kindly priced and liberally provided, with enthusiasms spread widely; Alsace is as strongly represented as Australia, but the classics are not left wanting. Customers need not feel intimidated, since there is little reason to stray beyond the carefully and considerately constructed house selection (from £9). CELLARMAN'S CHOICE: Graves, Ch. de Landiras 1989, £11.50; Victoria, Dromana Estate, Pinot Noir 1988, £16.

CHEF: Yvonne Thompson   PROPRIETORS: Paul Kelly and Yvonne Thompson   OPEN: Wed to Sat, D only; 7.30 for 8   CLOSED: end Dec to mid-Mar   MEALS: Set D £22   SERVICE: not inc, card slips closed   CARDS: Access, Visa   DETAILS: 20 seats. Private parties: 16 main room. Car park. No children under 12. Smart dress preferred. No smoking in dining-room. Music   ACCOMMODATION: 5 rooms, all with bath/shower. B&B £40 to £56. Deposit: 15%. No children under 12. Afternoon teas. Garden. TV. Phone. Confirm by 6. Fax: (052 42) 72141 (*The Which? Hotel Guide*)

LEDBURY Hereford & Worcester   map 2

▲ *Hope End* 🍷 ✶✗

Hope End, Ledbury HR8 1JQ
LEDBURY (0531) 3613
changes to (0531) 633613 early 1993
⅔m N of Ledbury, just beyond   COOKING 3
Wellington Heath   COST £37–£41

The setting is enough to make anyone poetic, let alone Elizabeth Barrett Browning whose childhood home this was. Minaret, walled garden, long low house, stables: enough remains of the original to fire the imagination, set in a miraculous landscape. Go through the door and imbibe more Englishness, yet do not expect unrelieved eighteenth-century grandeur: this is a conversion and rehabilitation. Patricia Hegarty's cooking has something of the house and setting about it. It aims to profit from revivalist gardening (the walled garden is sanctuary to many otherwise moribund varieties); it is English in inspiration, yet modern in application. Dinner offers no more than three choices at any stage. After the first and main courses, there is a pause for salad, then cheese, then dessert. The price includes coffee. It is clear that the garden rules. Where else could you get a sea kale, prawn and crème fraîche salad? Where else is going to offer 'estate-bottled peaches'? Herbs, fruit relishes and preserves dictate the flavours. Salts and sugars, as mere additives, are avoided, just as most materials are unrefined, as nature intended. There is always a vegetarian dish among the main courses; it should be tried, even by carnivores, at some time during a stay. The flavours can be strong, yet techniques are often direct, lifted by the addition of some piercing herb or spice: cinnamon in a tomato sauce, lovage in a soufflé. Some find a certain weight to the style. This marks it as Patricia Hegarty's own, just as John Hegarty puts his stamp on the running of the hotel and the construction of the pleasurable wine list. This is anchored firmly in the classic areas but provides a sensible range of price and vintage, where good bourgeois clarets jostle with the finest names of Burgundy. Real strength is also to be found in Australia and New Zealand with Henschke and Redwood Valley included. Alsace is disappointingly staid and Italy is still a no-go area for Mr Hegarty. Half-bottles, a fine range of spirits and decent unfussy typography more than compensate. House wine is £8. CELLARMAN'S CHOICE: Mâcon-Viré 1988, Bonhomme, £14; Médoc, Ch. les Grands Chênes 1986, £16.

CHEF: Patricia Hegarty   PROPRIETORS: John and Patricia Hegarty   OPEN: Wed to Sun, D only (Mon and Tue residents' supper only); 7.30 to 8.30   CLOSED: mid-Dec to mid-Feb   MEALS: Set D £30   SERVICE: not inc, card slips closed   CARDS: Access, Visa   DETAILS: 24 seats. Private parties: 6 main room. Car park. Vegetarian meals. No children under 12. Smart dress preferred. No smoking in dining-room. Wheelchair access (2 steps). No music   ACCOMMODATION: 9 rooms, all with bath/shower. B&B £85 to £135. Deposit: £60. No children under 12. Garden. Phone. Doors close at 11. Fax: (0531) 5697, changes to (0531) 636366 early 1993 (*The Which? Hotel Guide*)

LEEDS West Yorkshire   map 5

Brasserie Forty Four £ | NEW ENTRY |

44 The Calls, Leeds LS2 8AQ   COOKING 1*
LEEDS (0532) 343232   COST £18–£40

Leeds must like brasseries and fast, fair-value restaurants. This is new, occupying a former grain warehouse in a rapidly changing zone by the River Aire. Started by three restaurateurs (from Pool Court, Hodgsons and Wood Hall), it also has the former chef from Pool Court (see entry, Pool in Wharfedale). It should, therefore, be good and sure is stylish. 'Soho in New York,' say the proprietors; 'East Coast preppie,' says the press. It's large and maple-floored, and has cream walls set off with big splashes of student art. There's some humour in the swinging seats suspended from RSJs in the bar and in the robot piano-player ('Play it again, RAM'). The menu is what might be imagined: some American influence (ribs, burgers), some new-wave oriental (tempura, tartare of tuna, stir-fry of beef and broccoli), some Italian (chargrilled vegetables with linguine, bresaola) and some old English (puddings, salt-beef, Yorkshire puddings with gravy). Prices are not high, though vegetables and service come extra. Good things have been reported: onion soup, the stir-fry, aubergine and tomato ramekin, decent calf's liver; others have not done quite so well. There is a gap between expectation and reality of flavour, which may be bridged with practice. Art is usually avoided, but barbecued pineapple came with a strawberry and a sprig of mint, and 'of 101 uses of a pineapple skin, tying it in a fisherman's knot to decorate the plate must rate 102'. Seventy fine wines and a dozen beers are offered. There is fair geographic range and many decent wines below £12 (house wines are £8.75). Brevity in a brasserie wine list is a virtue; a little trimming here might be beneficial.

CHEF: Melvin Jordan   PROPRIETORS: Martin Hodgson, Jonathan Wix and Michael Gill   OPEN: Mon to Sat, exc Sat L; 12 to 2.30, 6.30 to 10.30   CLOSED: bank hols   MEALS: alc. Set L and D £10.95   SERVICE: 10%, card slips closed   CARDS: Access, Amex, Visa   DETAILS: 115 seats. 7 tables outside. Private parties: 55 main room, 55 private room. Vegetarian meals. Children's helpings. No cigars/pipes in dining-room. Wheelchair access (also WC). Music. Air-conditioned. Fax: (0532) 343332

La Grillade £   **NEW ENTRY**

Wellington Street, Leeds LS1 4HJ   COOKING 1
LEEDS (0532) 459707   COST £16–£37

This basement restaurant, in the cellars of the Wellesley Hotel, continues to make its mark as a 'very French' spot with all the outward signs of a bistro – rickety chairs, oilcloth tablecloths – and an unchanging menu that fits the bill too. Materials are good, and cooking is acceptable. It's the place for black pudding with apples and sauté potatoes, followed by grilled steak with simple butters. Chips will please if you are tired of fish-and-chip shop chips. Grilled fish is effectively done and presented on a wooden board, and there seems no doubt as to its freshness. The cheeseboard is a big selection for Francophiles. This place is popular for lunch, and the prices seem right. House wine is £6.30.

CHEF: Orenzo Padolino   PROPRIETORS: Meritlight Ltd   OPEN: Mon to Sat, exc Sat L; 12 to 2.30, 7.30 to 11   CLOSED: Christmas week and bank hols   MEALS: alc. Set L and D £10.80 SERVICE: 10%   CARDS: Access, Visa   DETAILS: 62 seats. Children welcome. No cigars/pipes in dining-room. No music. Air-conditioned

Olive Tree £   **NEW ENTRY**

Oaklands, Rodley Lane,
Leeds LS13 1NG   COOKING 1
LEEDS (0532) 569283   COST £19–£33

'We were having such a good time that I have forgotten what we had to eat,' speaks volumes for the quality of hospitality and service here. And comfort, too – even the loos have won the owners an award. People enjoy it, especially the bouzouki evenings. There is canny marketing at work here as well: George Psarias holds the world record for the longest kebab; he also appears on TV. The Olive Tree runs a standard Greek-Cypriot menu, but alongside there is a run of chef's specials, written on the blackboard, that highlights unfamiliar dishes from the islands, as well as a lot of fresh fish. This element had grown over the years. It is thus worth exploring for dishes such as bakaliaos (salt cod pan-fried in batter), pastitsada (a beef braise with pasta from Corfu), melizanes yemistes (stuffed aubergine with cumin and a yogurt sauce), chargrilled red mullet or octopus stewed in red wine. Some find that the cooking promises more than it delivers, others that it is better than they found in Cyprus! House wine is £7.95.

CHEFS: George Psarias and Andreas Iacovou   PROPRIETORS: George and Vasoulla Psarias OPEN: all week, exc Sat L; 12 to 2, 6.30 to 11.30   CLOSED: 1 Jan, bank hols   MEALS: alc. Set L and D £13.50   SERVICE: 10%, card slips closed   CARDS: Access, Amex, Visa   DETAILS: 120 seats. Private parties: 50 main room, 25 private rooms. Car park. Vegetarian meals. Children's helpings on request. Wheelchair access. Music. Air-conditioned

---

'Four round, bright pieces of meat the size and shape and colour of red rubber door-stops – they even had a hole in the middle to screw them to the floor – no screws supplied though.' On eating in the West Midlands

---

Paris £

36A Town Street, Horsforth,
Leeds LS18 4RJ
LEEDS (0532) 581885

COOKING 1
COST £14–£36

Everybody approves the principle behind this inexpensive restaurant that occupies the site once filled by Cranks. Bare boards and busy-ness provide the atmosphere, the cheap early-bird menu (6 to 7.30pm, with wine thrown in) and bargains in the wine list and the *carte* supply the satisfaction. A hard critic made comparisons with French originals when eating the onion soup and inspecting the crudités, but this may be thought nit-picking. In fact, the performance on dishes as disparate as deep-fried Brie with mango sauce, or roulade of salmon and leeks with a butter sauce, breast of chicken stuffed with Boursin or choucroute garnie is satisfactory, and for a place with so many seats (and two sittings every night) the response to the market is impressive. The wine list is good too, with a modern selection that is worth drinking around. The wine provided for the early birds is not quite so enticing. House wines are £6.95.

CHEF: Steven Kendell PROPRIETORS: Martin Spalding and Steven Kendell OPEN: all week, D only; 6 to 10.30 (11 Fri and Sat) MEALS: alc. Set D £11.95 (inc wine 6 to 7.30pm) SERVICE: not inc, card slips closed CARDS: Access, Amex, Visa DETAILS: 86 seats. Private parties: 16 main room. Vegetarian meals. Children welcome. Music

Sous le Nez en Ville ▼ £

NEW ENTRY

The Basement, Quebec House,
9 Quebec Street, Leeds LS1 2HA
LEEDS (0532) 440108

COOKING 1
COST £17–£36

John Ritchie and chef Andrew Carter have brought their successful formula from Ilkley to a basement in the centre of Leeds, not far from the railway station. The style is modern bistro. A regular, fortnightly menu is supplemented by a daily blackboard of mainly fresh fish specials; there are also tapas (actually world foods), plus a simple choice of bar snacks. The fixed-price 'menu du soir' is available from 6 to 7.30pm. Many dishes have received endorsements: goats' cheese in filo pastry, smoked duck breast with a sharp fruity sauce, pan-fried liver with bacon and onions, pork fillet in filo pastry 'splendidly accompanied' by Dijon mustard sauce, red snapper with salad vegetables, and fillet of plaice with lentil mousse and smoked prawn sauce. Sweets such as walnut crème brûlée have also been mentioned. Service is fast and sharp. Moderate prices make this place a 'distinct asset to the local eating scene,' comments a Yorkshire reporter. The cellar has intelligent range tilted towards bourgeois and modest bottles at affordable prices. Spain is well represented but enthusiasts for older claret will come to a halt with a clutch from 1978. There are decent half-bottles. House wines are from £6.95. CELLARMAN'S CHOICE: St-Véran 1991, Pacquet, £14.50; Coteaux du Languedoc, La Clape 1989, Boscary, £9.95.

CHEF: Andrew Carter PROPRIETORS: C.R.C.R. Partnership OPEN: Mon to Sat, exc Sat L;
12 to 2.30, 6 to 10.30 (11 Fri and Sat) CLOSED: 25 and 26 Dec, bank hol Mons MEALS:
alc. Set D £10.95 (6 to 7.30pm) SERVICE: not inc, card slips closed CARDS: Access, Visa
DETAILS: 70 seats. Private parties: 80 main room, 12 and 30 private rooms. Vegetarian
meals. Children welcome. No pipes in dining-room. Music D. Fax: (0532) 450240

LEICESTER Leicestershire
map 5

Bobby's £

154–156 Belgrave Road,
Leicester LE4 5AT   COOKING 1
LEICESTER (0533) 660106 and 662448   COST £9–£19

Bobby's is a restaurant that crosses the cultural divide. In the heart of
Leicester's Asian community, it now draws more and more English customers
by offering exemplary vegetarian café-food. The Lakhani family have been here
since 1976, and their culinary secret is to buy ingredients locally, grind and
blend their own spices and cook fresh each day. Authentic Gujarati recipes are
the mainstay, but the kitchen also delivers south Indian and Punjabi
specialities. The sheer range of the menu is daunting: a vast array of 'farsan'
savoury snacks ranging from samosas and excellent uthappam (rice-flour
pancakes with tomatoes and peppers) to rare specialities such as deep-fried
mogo (cassava chips) with tamarind sauce, and dhokla (steam-cooked sponge
garnished with mustard, sesame seeds and fresh coriander). The menu also
features thalis, vegetable curries, colourful sweetmeats, and a superb range of
breads including fried spicy thepla. Service is 'magic'. Alcohol is not served on
the premises, although the place is licensed, but customers can bring their own
wine without corkage.

CHEF: Mrs M.B. Lakhani PROPRIETOR: Mr B.A. Lakhani OPEN: Tue to Sun; 11.30 to
10.30 (11 Sat) MEALS: alc. Set L and D £6.50. Cover 40p. Bring your own: no corkage
SERVICE: not inc CARDS: Access, Amex, Visa DETAILS: 90 seats. Private parties: 50 main
room, 25 private room. Vegetarian meals. No-smoking area. Wheelchair access (1 step).
Music. Air-conditioned

Man Ho £

14–16 King Street, Leicester LE1 6RJ   COOKING 1
LEICESTER (0533) 557700   COST £13–£40

A new team has taken over this stylishly decorated Chinese restaurant in a
leafy walk off King Street, and chef Jeffery Chan is now one of the proprietors.
The décor is unchanged, but the menu has been revamped: there is more
emphasis on seafood and sizzling specialities, while the list of 'principal
independent dishes' has some fashionably up-market ideas, such as crispy
aromatic quail, grey mullet served in a fondue pot, and lettuce-wrapped
seafood. Otherwise, there is the now-familiar mix of Peking, Szechuan and
Cantonese specialities, ranging from paper-wrapped prawns and bang-bang
chicken to deep-fried oysters, shredded beef with chilli, and spicy bean curd
family-style. Set menus (including one for vegetarians) and four-course

weekday lunches are good value. Readers should note that the last Friday of each month is advertised as 'karaoke buffet evening'. House wines are from £7.50.

CHEF: Jeffery Chan   PROPRIETORS: Edward Tsang, Gerry McHugh and Jeffery Chan   OPEN: all week; 12 to 2, 6 to 11.30 (all day Sat and Sun)   CLOSED: 25 and 26 Dec   MEALS: alc. Set L £7.50 to £10, Set D £10 to £16   SERVICE: 10%, card slips closed   CARDS: Access, Amex, Diners, Visa   DETAILS: 100 seats. Private parties: 60 main room, 40 and 60 private rooms. Vegetarian meals. Children welcome. Music. Air-conditioned. Fax: (0533) 600523

Rise of the Raj £

6 Evington Road, Leicester LE2 1HF	COOKING 1
LEICESTER (0533) 553885	COST £15–£26

This smartly appointed restaurant is about 15 minutes' walk from the railway station on the fringes of Highfields – the neighbourhood that spawned Leicester's first generation of old-style curry houses. By contrast, it offers something closer to new-wave, with the emphasis on north Indian tandooris, vegetable dishes, thalis and jazzy cocktails. The Madras/vindaloo tendency is overshadowed by the likes of chicken tikka masala and lamb pasanda nawabi. Well-reported dishes have included murgh chaat, tandoori mixed grill, chicken dhansak, lamb bhuna, mushroom bhaji and sag masala. Accompaniments such as nan bread and pilau rice are up to the mark. Most visitors find the food consistent and vividly flavoured, although there can be occasional hiccups when dishes sink to blandness and are 'no more than average'. It is quiet at lunch-time, but can get very busy in the evenings (booking is suggested). Drink Kingfisher beer. House French is £5.95.

CHEF/PROPRIETOR: Abdul Bashir   OPEN: all week; 12 to 2, 6 to 11.45   MEALS: alc. Minimum £7.95   SERVICE: 10%   CARDS: Access, Amex, Diners, Visa   DETAILS: 70 seats. Private parties: 45 main room, 40 private room. Vegetarian meals. Children's helpings. No children under 5. Smart dress preferred. Wheelchair access (2 steps). Music. Air-conditioned

Welford Place

NEW ENTRY

9 Welford Place, Leicester LE1 6ZH	COOKING 1
LEICESTER (0533) 470758	COST £16–£34

'The Leicester end of the Wig & Mitre operation [see entry, Lincoln]' was how this new venture was described to the *Guide*. Without treading on impish toes, Lino Poli seems to have got this off to a good start and Leicester might be well pleased. He worked with Paul Vidic in Lincoln and has absorbed his instructions. The premises were once a gentlemen's club. It has preserved a sense of being a place to eat, meet, read and drink – a place of 'civilisation' in short. 'Let's hope it doesn't get taken over by the rowdy elements like barristers' was a more aspersive remark. Food is available through the day and evening. There are nods towards fads, but the cooking is underlined with a solidity that will please conservative eaters. Approval has been gained for dishes such as jellied oxtail with a tartarish sauce, twice-baked cheese soufflé with prawns, John Dory with balsamic vinegar and a potato purée, fillet of venison with oyster mushrooms, and elaborate sweets. You can eat sandwiches here – actually almost anything is possible in this obliging place. The wine list wanders around the world, but it is not exactly cheap. The house wines (£8.90) could be better.

CHEF: Lino Poli   PROPRIETORS: Michael Hope and Sarah Hope   OPEN: all week; 8am to 11pm   CLOSED: 25 Dec   MEALS: alc. Set L £8.75   SERVICE: not inc, card slips closed
CARDS: Access, Amex, Diners, Visa   DETAILS: 60 seats. Private parties: 16, 30, 40 and 150 private rooms. Vegetarian meals. Children's helpings. No music. Fax: (0533) 471843

LEWDOWN Devon   map 1

▲ *Lewtrenchard Manor* ♥ ⁵⁑

Lewdown EX20 4PN
LEWDOWN (056 683) 256 and 222
from A30 Okehampton to Launceston,   COOKING 2
turn left at Lewdown for ¾m   COST £22–£45

A grey-stone Elizabethan house that was restored in the last century and converted to its present use in the last decade. The heavy furniture tends to weigh the place down, but you are never far from a splendid open fire. 'The atmosphere is of solemn comfort,' notes an inspector. Patrick Salvadori is the latest recruit to the Murrays' kitchen. He is finding his stride and early reports are favourable. A French classical *carte* is in operation. Sometimes presentation wins over flavour: a chicken terrine served with beetroot and apple in sour cream was 'sadly bland and a trifle rubbery in texture'. But pig's trotters in aspic has garnered applause. Fillet steak in a crust presented with foie gras and truffles in a wine sauce was delicious: 'The tenderness of the steak set off by the crunchy exterior and the combination of the other flavours with the well-reduced sauce was altogether successful.' Puddings are competent if over-elaborate. A summer dinner ended with a trio of fruit tartlets: 'The pâté sucrée was crisp and the respective coulis complemented rather than overwhelmed the fruit.' Menetou-Salon by Pellé alongside a Guigal Hermitage on the wine list show a concern for the humble as much as the grand, reinforced this year by well-chosen New World wines. There is much respectable drinking below £12. Do not expect wines of great age here. House wines are from £7.50.
CELLARMAN'S CHOICE: Sancerre, Clos de Roches 1990, Vacheron, £17.50; Rioja Gran Reserva, Viña Real 1982, CVNE, £19.50.

CHEF: Patrick Salvadori   PROPRIETORS: James and Sue Murray   OPEN: all week, D only, and Sun L; 12 to 2.30, 7.15 to 9.30   MEALS: alc. Set Sun L £16, Set D £24.50   SERVICE: not inc, card slips closed   CARDS: Access, Amex, Diners, Visa   DETAILS: 40 seats. Private parties: 8 main room, 16 and 50 private rooms. Car park. No children under 8. Smart dress preferred. No smoking in dining-room. Wheelchair access. Music   ACCOMMODATION: 8 rooms, all with bath/shower. B&B £75 to £130. No children under 8. Pets by arrangement. Afternoon teas. Garden. Fishing. TV. Phone. Doors close at midnight. Confirm by 6. Fax: (056 683) 332 (*The Which? Hotel Guide*)

All letters to the Guide *are acknowledged with an update on latest sales, closures, chef changes and so on.*

LICHFIELD Staffordshire   map 5

▲ *Swinfen Hall Hotel* ⁵⁄⁎

Swinfen, nr Lichfield WS14 9RS   COOKING 1
LICHFIELD (0543) 481494   COST £19–£41

'The glorious things about Swinfen are the house (built by Benjamin Wyatt in 1755; ignore the modern conference function which overlays a grand piece of architecture) and the staff, who would gain an entry in *The Good Staff Guide*, were there one.' The food suffers from over-ambition and modest execution. The menu is full dress: from ravioli of wild mushrooms with spinach and herb sauce, to rack of lamb with herb and mustard crust on a port and redcurrant sauce, and lemon tart. It is best to eat simply. The wine list contains some good names. House wines are £9.50.

CHEF: Jerry Toth   PROPRIETORS: Mr V.J and Mrs H.L. Wiser   OPEN: all week, exc Sat L; 12.30 to 2, 7.30 to 9 (9.30 Sat)   CLOSED: 25 to 31 Dec   MEALS: alc. Set L £9.95 to £12.95, Set D £16.95   SERVICE: not inc, card slips closed   CARDS: Access, Amex, Visa   DETAILS: 60 seats. Private parties: 80 main room, 28 and 120 private rooms. Car park. Vegetarian meals. Children's helpings. Smart dress preferred. No smoking in dining-room. Wheelchair access. Music   ACCOMMODATION: 19 rooms, all with bath/shower. B&B £65 to £125. Children welcome. Baby facilities. Afternoon teas. Garden. TV. Phone. Confirm by 6. Fax: (0543) 480341

LIFTON Devon   map 1

▲ *Arundell Arms* ⁵⁄⁎ £

Lifton PL16 0AA
LIFTON (0566) 784666   COOKING 1*
on A30, 3m E of Launceston   COST £16–£43

Fishing and shooting are prime attractions of a stay at this former coaching-inn, which has 20 miles of fishing rights on the Tamar and four of its tributaries. Visitors have commented on the 'incredibly friendly welcome', charming staff and the elegance of the dining-room and lounge. The kitchen makes good use of local ingredients: fish is delivered daily from Looe and Plymouth; well-hung and organically produced meat is from pure Devon breeds; herbs and vegetables come from local market gardeners; cheeses are from West Country farms. This translates into a menu featuring dishes such as fricassee of turbot, scallops and sole; roast fillet of south Devon beef with rosemary crust and shallots; and fillet of Tamar salmon with herb mousseline, asparagus and dill butter sauce. Well-reported soups such as mushroom and mussel or celeriac and saffron come with home-baked breads; coffee is served with 'wonderful' truffles. Reporters have also been impressed with the quality of simpler dishes, such as filet mignon with chargrilled vegetables, served in the lounge bar. The wine list is solidly reliable, with fair prices, good names and a fair showing of halves. House wines are from £8.

See the back of the Guide *for an index of restaurants listed.*

CHEF: Philip Burgess   PROPRIETOR: Anne Voss-Bark   OPEN: all week; 12.30 to 2,
7.30 to 9   CLOSED: 4 days Christmas   MEALS: alc. Set L £14.50, Set D £23.75. Bar menu
SERVICE: not inc   CARDS: Access, Amex, Diners, Visa   DETAILS: 70 seats. Private parties:
80 main room, 30 private room. Car park. Vegetarian meals. Children's helpings. No
smoking in dining-room. Music   ACCOMMODATION: 29 rooms, all with bath/shower. B&B
£54 to £86. Children welcome. Baby facilities. Pets welcome. Afternoon teas. Garden.
Fishing. TV. Phone. Doors close at 11.30. Fax: (0566) 784494

LINCOLN Lincolnshire map 6

Jew's House

NEW ENTRY

15 The Strait, Lincoln LN2 1JD

LINCOLN (0522) 524851

COOKING 2

COST £22–£39

The restaurant is in one of the oldest buildings in Lincoln, dating back to the
twelfth century. It stands at the bottom of Steep Hill, the road leading up to the
cathedral. Inside, it tries to create a warm, relaxed atmosphere – the place is at
its best when it is busy. Richard Gibbs trained and worked for many years in
south-west France and has globe-trotted, picking up ideas and influences along
the way. More recently he was at the Seafood Restaurant, Padstow (see entry).
His menus are catholic and wide-ranging, but France is the main inspiration –
galette of oyster mushrooms with thyme, venison with madeira and mushroom
sauce, paella, confit of duck with lentils. Daily fresh fish specials are worth
exploring: poached hake with fennel, brochette of king prawns and scallops
with cucumber and ginger, and steamed turbot with leeks are all typical. There
is always something for vegetarians, such as niçoise vegetables in filo pastry
with Roquefort sauce, which 'looked wonderful' and was indeed 'very
appetising and good'. Other dishes have been spot-on, too: thick orange-
coloured fish soup, asparagus and tangy hollandaise, leek tart with red pepper
coulis, good-quality rack of lamb, magret of duck with kumquats. Everyone
mentions the excellent home-made walnut bread and the chocolates. But there
have been quibbles, such as dull vegetables and a pigeon tartlet that was 'a
good idea that failed on execution'. Lighter meals are available at lunch-time.
The well-chosen wine list favours France, although it is tilted towards serious
bottles, at serious prices. House wines are from £7.25.

CHEFS: Richard Gibbs and William Ginnelly   PROPRIETORS: Richard and Sally Gibbs
OPEN: Mon to Sat, exc Mon L; 12 to 1.30, 7 to 10.15   CLOSED: bank hol Mons   MEALS:
alc   SERVICE: not inc   CARDS: Access, Amex, Diners, Visa   DETAILS: 28 seats. Private
parties: 30 main room. Vegetarian meals. Children's helpings. Music

Wig & Mitre £

29 Steep Hill, Lincoln LN2 1LU

LINCOLN (0522) 535190 and 523705

COOKING 2

COST £17–£37

This is an enterprise that shows many faces: it is a pub, a restaurant and an all-
day eating-place; it serves breakfast fry-ups at tea-time, bar snacks and full
restaurant meals. Valerie and Michael Hope have turned this old building into
something of a showcase for good value and admirable intentions: fresh food,

regularly changing menus dictated by the markets, fair prices and excellent service. Meals can be cheap or expensive; the mood can be formal or informal. The kitchen is capable of delivering anything from smoked haddock with poached eggs on toast to bowls of chilli, fillet of sea bass with spinach mousseline baked in filo pastry, or breast of duckling with pasta and a balsamic vinegar sauce. The crop of recommended dishes says it all: squid with crisp salad; celery soup; marinated salmon; cheese soufflé with mushrooms; rack of lamb; steak and kidney pie; guinea-fowl. Sweets are the likes of chocolate and brandy terrine, bread-and-butter pudding and strawberry flan. The cheese platter sometimes seems more interesting than its accompanying biscuits. The place serves good beers, as well as a creditable list of affordable wines, with France, Spain and Italy to the fore. House French is £8.90.

CHEFS: Paul Vidic, Peter Dodd, Simon Shaw and Adam Rogers PROPRIETORS: Valerie and Michael Hope OPEN: all week; 8am to 11pm CLOSED: 25 Dec MEALS: alc SERVICE: not inc, card slips closed CARDS: Access, Amex, Diners, Visa DETAILS: 100 seats. 6 tables outside. Private parties: 38 main room. Vegetarian meals. Children's helpings. Wheelchair access (1 step). No music. Fax: (0522) 532402

LIPHOOK Hampshire   map 2

▲ *Old Thorns, Nippon Kan*

Longmoor Road,
Liphook GU30 7PE   COOKING 2
LIPHOOK (0428) 724555   COST £22–£56

Old Thorns is a golf course-cum-country club, conference centre and hotel with a Western restaurant and a Japanese restaurant (the subject of this entry). It is owned by a Japanese company and has many Japanese clients. The food is of high quality. Teppanyaki may be the most popular form, but the menu offers a large range of set menus and a short *carte*, and is highly recommended for sushi and sashimi. This is an unlikely spot, but for some people the mood is more authentic than in many London Japanese places. The wine list is replete with first growths, but the prices are not quite so worrying if Sancerre is your bag. House wine is £8.50.

CHEF: M. Hama PROPRIETORS: London Kosaido Co Ltd OPEN: all week; 12 to 2 (4.30 Sat and Sun), 6 to 9.30 MEALS: alc. Set L £14.50 to £19.50, Set D £21 to £40 SERVICE: not inc CARDS: Access, Amex, Diners, Visa DETAILS: 30 seats. Private parties: 50 main room. Car park. Vegetarian meals. Children welcome. Jacket and tie. Music ACCOMMODATION: 33 rooms, all with bath/shower. B&B £78 to £98. Children welcome. Baby facilities. Afternoon teas. Garden. Swimming-pool. Sauna. Tennis. Golf. TV. Phone. Fax: (0428) 725036

'Attentive service later changed to over-attentive when the waiter got us in his clutches in the dining-room. His assumption throughout the meal that the woman would have what he viewed as "feminine" food could have been very annoying for some. For three courses he persisted in trying to guess who had ordered what and got it wrong each time.'
On eating in Worcestershire

LIVERPOOL Merseyside   map 5

Armadillo ▼

20–22 Mathew Street, L2 6RE   COOKING 2*
051-236 4123   COST £15–£33

The owner, even when merry of an evening, keeps mum about how the
Armadillo got its name. In the old fruit-market quarter, in what was once
doubtless a warehouse not a step away from the Beatles' Cavern, the restaurant
gives front-row views of city life. 'It was like a set from *Absolute Beginners*; we
even saw someone arrested outside our window' was one breathless report. As
this is Liverpool, there is some emphasis on value with the lunch and early
supper menus. The *carte* comes into operation in the evening. 'Eclectic with
foundations in classical technique' is the shorthand description of Martin
Cooper's style, and this comes over in the excellent saucing to dishes such as
turbot with a vermouth and saffron cream, pork, venison and quail in a red
wine reduction, or noisettes of lamb with a garlic cream sauce. Good touches
are sweetbreads, 'crumbed' not with bread but groundnuts. That eclecticism
pops up in first courses especially: hummus, pasta, meatballs on a warm lentil
salad, or aubergines and mozzarella are markers to an affection for hot sun and
Mediterranean skies. Even with sound foundations, materials and skills are
occasionally not mobilised as they might be: hence a skinny fish fillet ended up
too bready, meats that should be tender were tough and badly butchered, and
lemon tart was soggy, its tang buried by ground almonds. As fair
counterweight, hot raisin pudding is often described as matchless. There is
frequent approbation, too, of friendly, informal service and a nice sense of
'hang-loose' to promote good digestion. Good value carries through to the
excellent wine list, that is particularly good on France, without getting over-
excited by famous names, and has some fine Italians and Australians to give
range. House wines are £6.65.

CHEFS: Martin Cooper and John Scotland   PROPRIETORS: Martin and Angela Cooper
OPEN: Tue to Sat; 12 to 2.45 (5 Sat), 5 to 6.30 (Tue to Fri daytime menu), 7.30 to 10.30
CLOSED: bank hols, few days after Christmas   MEALS: alc   SERVICE: not inc (10% for 10 or
more), card slips closed   CARDS: Access, Visa   DETAILS: 65 seats. Private parties: 65 main
room. Vegetarian meals. Children welcome. Music

LIVERSEDGE West Yorkshire   map 5

▲ Lillibet's

64 Leeds Road, Liversedge WF15 6HX   COOKING 1
HECKMONDWIKE (0924) 404911   COST £25–£35

Extension and refurbishment have transformed the bar and dining areas in this
comfortable stone house, but the place has lost none of its intimate atmosphere.
The clientele is a catholic mix of well-to-do-locals and businessmen, with
casual visitors in equally casual dress. Jeans are not frowned upon. 'This seems
a little at odds with the formality of the service – no personal touch,' observed
one reporter. Four-course dinners (including an intermediate soup or sorbet,
plus coffee) are priced on the main course, and the kitchen is keen on sauces

and elaboration: for example, diced salmon and monkfish in a filo basket with lemon hollandaise garnished with crisp fried leeks; and breast of guinea-fowl stuffed with mushrooms, spring onions and tarragon served with a cream grain mustard sauce. The repertoire changes monthly. Recommended dishes have included pan-fried smoked turkey with bacon and onions, sea bass with lobster sauce, and roast duckling. Desserts are the likes of strawberry mille-feuille and banana tartlet, although some reporters have found them 'sickly and rather unsuccessful'. The well-spread list of around 60 wines is boosted by a blackboard list of specials. House French is £8.95.

CHEF: Liz Roberts   PROPRIETORS: Martin and Liz Roberts   OPEN: Mon to Sat, D only (L by arrangement); 7 to 9.30   CLOSED: 1 week between Christmas and New Year, 2 weeks end Aug   MEALS: Set D £18.50 to £23.95   SERVICE: not inc   CARDS: Access, Amex, Visa   DETAILS: 70 seats. Private parties: 70 main room. Car park. Vegetarian meals. Children's helpings. Music   ACCOMMODATION: 13 rooms, all with bath/shower. Rooms for disabled. B&B £46 to £65. Garden. TV. Phone. Doors close at midnight. Fax: (0924) 404912 (*The Which? Hotel Guide*)

LONG MELFORD Suffolk   map 3

Scutchers Bistro £

NEW ENTRY

Westgate Street,
Long Melford CO10 9DP   COOKING 1*
SUDBURY (0787) 310200   COST £18–£27

Nicholas Barrett has moved from Glemsford to larger premises in a reconstructed beamed pub, and has taken on board a more flexible, affordable brasserie approach, which is currently attracting a lot of popular support. Décor is spot-on: light and fresh-looking, with interconnecting rooms on different levels, stripped pine tables and pretty watercolours on the walls. The menu is in tune with the times: lots of warm salads, chargrilled fish and poultry, plus oriental and Mediterranean influences. Successful blackboard specials boost the repertoire: warm wild mushroom and rabbit terrine with onion marmalade has been outstanding. Elsewhere, the results can be patchy: excellent fillet steak with béarnaise sauce, and well-reported stir-fried tiger prawns with spring onions, soy and ginger, but rather ordinary marinated salmon with crème fraîche and chives, steak, kidney and Guinness pie with superb flaky pastry, but 'tasteless meat' and 'wishy-washy gravy'. Main courses come with separate dishes of vegetables, plus chips, boiled potatoes or rice. Steamed chocolate sponge pudding with custard is a frequently mentioned sweet. Service is swift and bustling amid the hum of conversation. To drink there are imported beers, plus a decent list of around 80 wines including a strong showing of halves and selections by the glass. House French is £6.50.

CHEFS: Nicholas Barrett and Stephen Spooner   PROPRIETOR: Nicholas Barrett   OPEN: Mon to Sat; 12 to 2, 7 to 9.30   MEALS: alc   SERVICE: not inc, card slips closed   CARDS: Access, Visa   DETAILS: 75 seats. 6 tables outside. Private parties: 75 main room. Car park. Vegetarian meals. Children's helpings. No pipes in dining-room. Wheelchair access (also WC). Music. Fax: (0787) 310157

LONGRIDGE Lancashire   map 5

Heathcote's

104–106 Higher Road,
Longridge PR3 3SY   COOKING 3*
PRESTON (0772) 784969 and 785713   COST £26–£53

Longridge, in the eyes of one visitor from salubrious Manchester, 'is a largely
undistinguished straggle of Victorian artisan cottages and more recent semis'.
Paul Heathcote's restaurant is a conversion of three of the old cottages. It makes
for cosiness, enhanced by the floral carpet, but some have wondered if cooking
of this nature, and service so formal with it, can happily survive surroundings
so humble. Someone who had eaten Paul Heathcote's food before commented
that this year it was 'better, more mature; the decoration, although elaborate,
was less frivolous, the flavours always to the fore'. Don't bother with the bar –
there are only three seats – but go to the table for drinks and good nibbles.
There is a *carte* and a gourmet set-price menu. On Friday and Sunday lunch-
times there is a good-value set menu. They may also think menu-planning
sometimes wayward. Of six 'speciality starters', two are foie gras, two involve
smoked salmon, one is melon, and the other is a vegetable terrine with
langoustines. A gourmet menu in the spring began with pan-fried foie gras on
a herb and garlic crumpet with glazed button onions, herb dumplings and
madeira sauce. The main course was pan-fried lamb with buttered potatoes,
baked garlic, button onions and an olive and thyme sauce. Too much garlic, too
many onions, too much brown sauce. Ignore such points, and the cooking
achieves high standards. Ravioli of lobster is stuffed with a lobster mousse,
topped with a deep-fried julienne of vegetables surrounded by a shellfish sauce
containing mussels and broad beans (both shelled). A compressed terrine of
scallops, langoustines and baby leeks was the high point of one meal, with
great fresh flavours and counterbalancing strength from the leeks. It came with
a little pile of potato salad surmounted by wigwams of green beans that had
themselves been dressed in a high-quality vinaigrette. Confit of duck, bacon
and apple with red pepper chutney contrasted the sharp apple, sweet chutney
and smoky bacon with the luscious duck to good effect. Pheasant is served
jointed in a soup plate on a dark-brown jus with walnut pasta. Duck lies on a
bed of apple and rösti, with a sausage of the leg meat in the form of a mousse.
When it comes to dessert, bread-and-butter pudding figures a lot, so does
summer pudding in early spring. Hot soufflés are good: sultana with chocolate
sauce and almond ice-cream, for instance. Plenty of strong coffee and sticky
petits fours end a meal that may also have taken in excellent cheeses. All the
attributes of a serious chef are on display here, from buying to self-confidence.
He works within classical confines, there is very little of the bold gusto of the
new wave, but nor should there be apology for that. Tucked in between the
over-long notes of the wine list are some good choices, although they could be
more helpfully arranged. Antipodean bottles are particularly sound, but
Burgundy is less than convincing. Prices have crept up a little, and choice
below £15 is restricted. House wines are from £10.50.

CHEFS: Paul Heathcote and Andrew Barnes PROPRIETOR: Paul Heathcote OPEN: Tue to
Sun D, L Fri and Sun; 12 to 2 (2.30 Sun), 7 to 9.30 MEALS: alc D. Set Fri and Sun L £18, Set
gourmet D £30 SERVICE: not inc, card clips closed CARDS: Access, Visa DETAILS: 46
seats. Private parties: 50 main room. Car park. Vegetarian meals. Children welcome.
Wheelchair access. Music

LONGSTOCK Hampshire
map 2

Peat Spade Inn £
NEW ENTRY

Longstock, Stockbridge SO20 6DR
ANDOVER (0264) 810612

COOKING 1*
COST £17–£33

This little Victorian pub with a garden is in prime trout country. Most of the
surrounding land seems to be owned by the John Lewis Partnership, and Julie
Tuckett – head chef, waiter, barperson and part-owner – could easily match
that retailer's price pledge. She offers very fair value for very genuine cooking.
The set menu is not long – a pair of alternatives only – but there is a bar menu
which may be plundered if you want something else. The cooking is fresh,
daily and exact. One prospector's meal yielded smooth crab pâté and rough
rillettes with a salad of mixed leaves dressed with an orange juice vinaigrette,
followed by breasts of pigeon, nicely pink, with a cooked-out calvados jus, and
a wonderful potato gratin and plain vegetables, which left just enough room for
a sticky toffee pudding as light and good as any. There is always a fish dish, for
instance salmon with white truffle sauce, and there are always plain meats
from the chargrill. Coffee could be stronger. The wine list includes a couple of
bottles from Switzerland and has no high prices; there are a dozen wines by the
glass. House wines start at £8.25.

CHEF: Julie T. Tuckett PROPRIETORS: T.P.M. Inns Ltd OPEN: all week, exc Sun D; 12.15
to 2, 7.15 to 10 CLOSED: 25 Dec, 3 weeks Jan to Feb MEALS: alc. Set L £14.75, Set D
£14.75 to £16.75 SERVICE: not inc, card slips closed CARDS: Amex, Diners DETAILS: 30
seats. 6 tables outside. Private parties: 24 main room, 14 private room. Car park. Vegetarian
meals. Children's helpings L. Children in small dining-room only. Wheelchair access. No
music

LOUTH Lincolnshire
map 6

Alfred's

Upgate, Louth LN11 9EY
LOUTH (0507) 607431

COOKING 2
COST £21–£37

Rosemarie Dicker has changed the menu from a fixed price to individual tickets
for each dish. This has not affected the repertoire, or made the offering longer:
about five choices at each course. People are agreed that this is the place to eat
in Louth. Skill in balance and seasoning on display in a meal that took in
potted crab with lime, artichoke stuffed with mushrooms topped by a
hollandaise, lamb shank with flageolets, squab with cabbage and a garlic
sauce, walnut and banana cheesecake and pear frangipane was considerable.
Plain steaks are also dealt with properly. Old restaurant habits die hard in the
matter of vegetables. Why serve insufficient beans with the lamb and yet offer

the same side plate of chef's vegetables as every other table? The once slightly gloomy appearance of the restaurant has been improved. The wine list is ambitious and yet not over-priced. Some good material is there: Hollick's Chardonnay, Masi's Recioto della Valpolicella as well as Sauzet's Puligny-Montrachet 1986 or Ch. La Lagune 1981. The halves do not excite. House wines are £7.95.

CHEFS: Rosemarie Dicker and Diane Willoughby PROPRIETORS: Paul and Rosemarie Dicker OPEN: Tue to Sat, D only (also L and D bank hol weekends); 7 to 9.30 (10 Sat) CLOSED: 25 Dec D MEALS: alc SERVICE: not inc, card slips closed CARDS: Access, Visa DETAILS: 45 seats. Private parties: 50 main room. Vegetarian meals. Children's helpings. Wheelchair access (3 steps). Music

---

LOWER BEEDING West Sussex   map 3

Jeremy's at The Crabtree ⅞✳ | NEW ENTRY |

Brighton Road,
Lower Beeding RH13 6PT   COOKING 2*
LOWER BEEDING (0403) 8912576   COST £15–£33

'I had thought a pub tenancy might prove the best exit from the King's Head,' writes Jeremy Ashpool. He has now settled into The Crabtree, along with Nick Wege ('a natural landlord'). The building could do with a lick of paint, but the dining-rooms are simply furnished in keeping with the stone floors and exposed beams, without fuss or frills. The atmosphere is calmer than at the King's Head, Cuckfield – more civilised – and this is reflected in the cooking. 'I get the feeling Jeremy is happier,' comments a regular from the old days. The food is just as inventive, but more mature. Indeed, Jeremy's adventurousness as a cook invites the same quality from his diners. Pan-fried scallops with celeriac and a coriander sauce, grilled artichoke with basil tagliatelle and lemon butter sauce, excellent home-made bread, a selection of fresh fish with crab mousseline, tomato and basil, and roast loin of lamb with rosemary sauce were components of one meal heartily enjoyed, except for the overly plain vegetables and puddings, which have never been a strong point. The absence of a cheeseboard was sharply noted. The style is marvellously direct, so that when it works, it works very well indeed. The kitchen is sure to improve if determination does not lapse. Dinner is fixed-price for two courses, and not cheap for a country pub. Inexpensive bar lunches are available every day. The wine list does not match the food for quality, although prices are reasonable. House wine is £6.95.

CHEFS: Jeremy and Vera Ashpool, and Martin Dodds PROPRIETORS: Jeremy and Vera Ashpool, and Nick Wege OPEN: restaurant Tue to Sat, D only, and Sun L; bar all week, L only; 12.15 to 2, 7.30 to 9.45 MEALS: alc. Set Sun L £11.50, Set D £18.95 SERVICE: restaurant 10%, card slips closed CARDS: Access, Visa DETAILS: 35 seats. 10 tables outside. Private parties: 24 main room. Car park. Vegetarian meals with prior notice. Children's helpings Sun L. No smoking in 1 dining-room. Wheelchair access (3 steps; also female WC)

Report forms are at the back of the book; write a letter if you prefer.

▲ *South Lodge* ※

Brighton Road, Lower Beeding RH13 6PS	COOKING 3
LOWER BEEDING (0403) 891711	COST £26–£54

This Victorian house has super-Victorian touches like the William de Morgan tiles and a fine garden (that seems, though, in need of some refurbishment). The dining-room feels like 'a real room, not some space hollowed out of a cavernous country house,' writes one who enjoyed the views as well as the luxury. The lunch menu is good value, the no-choice 'signature menu' put on at dinner is also fair, but the *carte* could have its prices reduced. Tony Tobin is a good chef and his choice of dishes is tantalising: scallops on a potato cake with a fish cream, warm salad of tongue, bacon, onions and mushrooms with balsamic vinegar, or gnocchi with olive oil, tomatoes and basil are three first courses; liver with baby onions and bacon in a cassis sauce, John Dory with asparagus and chervil butter, or lamb with a basil mousse and tomato and basil sauce are three to follow. At an inspection, a red mullet soup with cayenne had a 'wonderfully earthy smell, though it could have delivered more to the palate'; those gnocchi were a 'clean, uncomplicated start'. A confit of duck with lentils and creamed potato showed Tobin's apprenticeship at Simply Nico (see entry, London), and was produced with aplomb. 'It could so easily have been richly cloying, but the dark-brown sauce lent piquancy and made this one of the best restaurant dishes I can remember.' The imagination shown here was let down by the unseasonal and over-turned vegetables. The desserts, though adequate, also carry less conviction. Coffee and petits fours were not up to scratch. The wine list seems designed for rather rich people. The range is there, though burgundies and French regionals could show a bit more excitement, and the New World is represented by big, reliable names. House wines are £12.

CHEF: Anthony Tobin   PROPRIETORS: Laura Hotels Ltd   OPEN: all week; 12.30 to 2.30, 7.30 to 10 (10.30 Fri and Sat)   MEALS: alc. Set L £15, Set D £25 to £32   SERVICE: not inc, card slips closed   CARDS: Access, Amex, Diners, Visa   DETAILS: 40 seats. Private parties: 8 main room, 14, 45 and 80 private rooms. Car park. Vegetarian meals. Children's helpings. Jacket and tie. No smoking in dining-room. Wheelchair access. No music
ACCOMMODATION: 39 rooms, all with bath/shower. Rooms for disabled. B&B £100 to £255. Children welcome. Baby facilities. Afternoon teas. Garden. Tennis. Fishing. Golf. TV. Phone. Confirm by 6. Fax: (0403) 891766

LOWER BRAILES Warwickshire   map 2

▲ *Feldon House* ▼

Lower Brailes OX15 5HW	COOKING 2
BRAILES (060 885) 580	COST £24–£32

In a quintessentially English setting hard by the village church ('The bells went through "Abide with me" a large number of times at 9pm – someone very clearly enjoying himself') is this red-brick Victorian house. Loving care goes into every detail, even to having a book ready on a table for a solitary diner. The cooking, from a no-choice set menu, is ambitious and full of good ideas, but may contain success and failure at one and the same meal; for instance, salmon had been unnecessarily breadcrumbed before being grilled, a little too long, and was accompanied by a thick, frothy sauce which tasted of nothing but butter, yet the accompaniment of sauté vegetables was excellent. A fillet of lamb was served with a dull, floury, white leek sauce, but a rhubarb and elderflower jam was finely balanced and full of flavour. A winter dinner was more on course: lentil and orange soup, a smoked mackerel pâté with rollmops, a quail's egg and home-made mayonnaise all on a finely cut mange-tout base, and pheasant with sherry sauce. Service remains excellent and the house is a delight to visit. The wine list is not long, but the notes make it feel longer. It shows the marks of an enthusiast with a wide-ranging choice of sound drinking within a small compass. There are sufficient half-bottles. Bin-ends add to the fun. House wines are £7.95. CELLARMAN'S CHOICE: Coleraine Cabernet Merlot 1988, Te Mata Estate, £25.75; Rioja 1985, Marqués de Murrieta, Reserva Blanca, £15.95.

CHEF: Allan Witherick PROPRIETORS: Allan and Maggie Witherick OPEN: all week, exc Sun D; 12.30 to 2, 7.30 to 8.30 MEALS: Set L £17.95, Set D £22.50 SERVICE: not inc, card slips closed CARDS: Access, Amex, Visa DETAILS: 14 seats. Private parties: 10 main room, 4 conservatory. Car park. Vegetarian meals. Children's helpings with prior notice. No music ACCOMMODATION: 4 rooms, all with bath/shower. B&B £30 to £56. No children under 12. Pets by arrangement. Garden. TV. Phone. Doors close at 11. Confirm 1 day ahead (*The Which? Hotel Guide*)

LYMINGTON Hampshire　　　　　　　　　　　　　　　　　　　map 2

▲ *Provence* ✹✸

Gordleton Mill Hotel, Silver Street,
Hordle, Lymington SO41 6DJ
LYMINGTON (0590) 682219

COOKING 3*
COST £32–£51

The redecoration is so complete and so convincing that many would believe lunch was about to be served in a many-starred French country restaurant. There is the exact degree of luxury and, on a good day, the same apparent luminosity – product of hard work and the glow of conviction. It is impressive stuff. Jean-Christophe Novelli has stayed the course since the re-opening in the spring of 1991. Indeed, he has moved from chef-manager to chef-patron in all publicity material, and his mark is on all the restaurant undertakes. He runs a long menu, with certain lines of continuity from season to season. The clearest is pork butchery and offal: for example, poached pig's knuckle with lentils; an assiette du boucher that includes trotter stuffed with mushrooms and foie gras, ox tongue and tail and lamb sweetbreads; and a spiced tête de porc. Another line is preserving and smoking: the salmon wrapping artichoke, crab and avocado or the carpaccio of duck breast 'ham'. A third is major-league complication of interleaving, wrapping, stuffing and layering: beef is rolled in chopped parsley and herbs, topped by soi-disant fish scales of apple, served with a filo parcel of wild mushrooms; lamb cutlets are 'souffléd' with a Stilton or a foie gras mousse; turbot is wrapped in a cabbage leaf; and scallops and prawns get a layer of pasta, soup a top of puff pastry. This can cause mild apoplexy, as hinted in the comment, 'tiny portions, arranged very artistically', but most people have found that there is a creative dynamic here that is not all derivative, even if some dishes may have been inspired by the current work of famous colleagues. There is a boldness in some of the sauces – anchovy with beef, chocolate with another beef fillet, vanilla with scallops or prawns – yet it does not detract from subtlety. There is a wish to cook expressively which avoids overstatement and yet is not drowned by the superstructure of 'fine cooking'. A meal as simple as tartare of salmon trout, beef fillet and clafoutis of cherries can be resoundingly brought off, while reserving the fireworks for the visitors anxious to be impressed. Service has gained mixed reports here and there, but the intentions are clear. The cellar develops, clarets doing better than burgundies. Prices are steep, and the urge is to go for the best (most expensive), even in California and Australia. House wines start at £10.

CHEF: Jean-Christophe Novelli   PROPRIETOR: William F. Stone   OPEN: Wed to Sun, exc Sun D; 12 to 2.30, 7 to 10   CLOSED: 1 to 3 Jan   MEALS: alc. Set L and D £28.50   SERVICE: not inc   CARDS: Access, Amex, Diners, Visa   DETAILS: 50 seats. 5 tables outside. Private parties: 50 main room, 14 private room. Car park. No children under 7. No smoking in dining-room. Wheelchair access (also WC). Music. Air-conditioned   ACCOMMODATION: 7 rooms, all with bath/shower. B&B £70 to £120. Deposit: £50. No children under 7. Pets welcome. Afternoon teas. Garden. TV. Phone. Confirm by noon. Fax: (0590) 683073

LYMPSTONE Devon   map 1

▲ *River House*

The Strand, Lympstone EX8 5EY   COOKING 2
EXMOUTH (0395) 265147   COST £21–£46

'We had the water on one side, the owners' allotment on the other. Both were used regularly.' 'During my estuarine holiday, we lived on very fresh fish.' Two comments on the aptly named River House (it is on the waterfront of the River Exe), where Michael and Shirley Wilkes do most of the work connected with their dining-room and the two guest bedrooms. For so small an operation, the menu is long, the cooking labour-intensive, and the prices are at the top end of the local scale (offset by a cheaper light-lunch menu): 'Every night we had at least six vegetables left on the table for us to help ourselves; every night they were different.' The style is straightforward enough: tomato, cucumber and pepper mousse with a prawn mayonnaise, prawns wrapped in bacon with fresh grapefruit and tomato ('great inspiration this'), rack of lamb with rosemary and oregano, lamb's liver with Dubonnet and orange, or salmon with sorrel. The use of herbs is as evident as the enjoyment of fresh fish. Michael Wilkes runs the dining-room forcefully. This can lead him into the byways of dispute, but 'where else', a happy reader asks, 'can you expect the proprietor to park *and* fetch your car for you?' 'Our wine was suggested (very firmly) by our host', but the thought proved correct and the wine list is indeed sufficient for most tastes, even if there are none too many halves. House wines are £7.85.

CHEF: Shirley Wilkes   PROPRIETORS: Mr and Mrs J.F.M. Wilkes   OPEN: Tue to Sun, exc Sun D; 12 to 1.45, 7 to 9.30 (10.30 Sat)   MEALS: alc L. Set L and D £22.50 to £34.50, Set Sun L £16 to £20. Minimum £9.25   SERVICE: not inc   CARDS: Access, Amex, Visa   DETAILS: 35 seats. Private parties: 25 main room, 14 private room. Vegetarian meals. Children's helpings. No children under 6. Smart dress preferred. No cigars/pipes in dining-room. No music   ACCOMMODATION: 2 rooms, both with bath/shower. B&B £41 to £69. No children under 6. TV

MAIDEN NEWTON Dorset   map 2

Le Petit Canard

Dorchester Road, Maiden Newton DT2 0BE   COOKING 2*
MAIDEN NEWTON (0300) 20536   COST £30

If you think you'll avoid ducks, think again. They turn up on most surfaces and on the menu too: confit perhaps, presented with bean sprouts and a honey and five-spice fumet, or with lentils cooked with tarragon. The good thing about the Chapmans' enterprise is that they have not jettisoned their modern approach in favour of Dorset favourites. There may even be no steak on the menu. 'Modern' does not mean zany, though combinations are arresting enough to provoke interest: grilled chicken with angel-hair pasta and satay dip, tiger prawns and ginger in filo parcels with crab sauce, lamb steak off the chargrill with roast red pepper and rosemary butter, or venison stir-fried with Chinese greens, mushrooms and peppercorns. The methods of cooking, as well as the recipes, show a wish to move with the times. Lin Chapman is cheerful and informed; the Chapmans may be out on their own in a bucolic wilderness, but they don't stop developing. Organically reared lamb, good fish-suppliers and new carpets have been on the agenda this year, and the restaurant glows with commitment. The wine list is kept short and it changes fast, but every bottle has been chosen – as the notes testify – with some point in view. Prices are sane, bottles are sound. House wines are from £8.

CHEF: Geoff Chapman   PROPRIETORS: Geoff and Lin Chapman   OPEN: Tue to Sat, D only; 7 to 9   MEALS: Set D £18.95   SERVICE: not inc   CARDS: Access, Visa   DETAILS: 28 seats. Private parties: 28 main room. Vegetarian meals. Children welcome. No cigars/pipes in dining-room. Music

---

MAIDSTONE Kent   map 3

Soufflé   NEW ENTRY

The Green, Bearsted,
Maidstone ME14 4DN   COOKING 2
MAIDSTONE (0622) 37065   COST £27–£43

The cottage sits on the green at Bearsted, all timber partitions and pretty-pretty clutter. The name has changed since last it was in the *Guide*, as have the chef and owner, but the menu shows strong signs of continuity, just as the prints by Graham Clarke go on and on. The cooking displays a love of pastry (tourte of pigeon and chicken, beef in pastry) but also a willingness to chance the arm on a casserole (oxtail or chicken legs), a strong memory of what it used to be like to do a mousse or two, and a capacity to cook a good soufflé. It made a surprise for a chance visitor to have duck giblets as a first course, as if he were back in the Dordogne; it also was a pleasant experience to eat rump of lamb with an impeccable madeira sauce and to follow it with an excellent raspberry soufflé. There is an awful lot of Muzak. The wine list seems arranged according to no logic, but will give some satisfaction among a mainly French selection. House wine is £8.90.

CHEF: Craig Broom   PROPRIETOR: Paul Sefer   OPEN: all week, exc Sat L and Sun D; 12 to 2.15 (2.30 Sun), 7 to 10   MEALS: Set L and D £18.90 to £28.90   SERVICE: 10%, card slips closed   CARDS: Access, Amex, Diners, Visa   DETAILS: 42 seats. 5 tables outside. Private parties: 55 main room, 30 private room. Car park. Vegetarian meals. Children welcome. Smart dress preferred. No-smoking area. Music

---

MALVERN WELLS Hereford & Worcester   map 2

Croque-en-Bouche ▮ ✳

221 Wells Road, Malvern Wells WR14 4HF   COOKING 4
MALVERN (0684) 565612   COST £43

The Joneses go it alone in a Victorian house. This is a self-sufficient restaurant: no other staff act as interface; the garden produces so much (and no ranks of gardeners); and Marion Jones cooks everything that is served at table by Robin Jones. The service may be abbreviated – soup in tureens, the main course on serving platters, wine opened but not poured – 'but Mr Jones carries it off with elan', though 'he has no time to chat until the end of the evening and by then he is too tired,' noted one couple revisiting after a long absence. The form of menu is unchanging. There are sushi appetisers, then a soup, a choice of three entrées, then of three main dishes, served with some sort of vegetable accompaniment built in and a gratin of potatoes, before a salad, cheese (British) and a range of desserts. The price for this is very fair, especially as it's so good. There are many recommended dishes, but the way in which the garden informs the cooking is a general trait always remarked on, as is the lightness of the cookery, the accuracy of flavouring, and the ability to meld various traditions such as Mediterranean, northern and oriental in a single, seamless repertoire. The salad course, using Chinese and Japanese condiments for the dressings, is an instance of this. The ability to do a single thing really well, yet build some sort of variety into it, is also remarkable. Thus gratin of potatoes may indeed be a fine dauphinois, but equally it could be a gratin of potatoes and Jerusalem artichokes. That self-sufficiency comes up again with home-smoking used for the salmon, as well as, for instance, lamb. The wide range of Marion Jones' palate is seen in the main courses offered early in the summer: rump of beef was roast and served with a mustard sauce and accompanied by Glamorgan sausages of leek and lovage; rabbit was braised with root vegetables after marinating with cumin and coriander, served with couscous and Moroccan pickled lemon; chicken breast was served with 'dark opal' basil, a pesto and grilled vegetables marinated in olive oil and balsamic. The cheeses are well-kept and sweet dishes win enthusiasm: toffee rice pudding, crème brûlée, apricot and almond tart served with prunelle de bourgogne, wonderful sorbets, and sticky creamy affairs like the frozen ginger meringue. This is an operation with edge. There are moments when the edge is too sharp – Robin Jones may discipline those he thinks wayward as to time, so be prompt. An unpompous approach to wine service ('We like to pour our own wine and hope you do'), matched by an enviable and quite extraordinary range make this lovely and generous cellar alone worth a journey. Prices are as remarkable as the geographical spread, with the reliable Sauvignon du Haut Poitou at £7.90, many top white burgundies at well under £30 and classy clarets offered at or near retail prices. If you have not had the opportunity to purchase the bedside reading list, then most, apart from the very knowledgeable, would be advised to set a price and leave the choice to Mr Jones. House wines are from £6.80. CELLARMAN'S CHOICE: Muscat, Moenchreben 1987, Rolly-Gassmann, £15.90; Rouge Homme Cabernet 1986, £14.40.

CHEF: Marion Jones PROPRIETORS: Robin and Marion Jones OPEN: Wed to Sat, D only; 7.30 to 9.30 CLOSED: Sun before Christmas to Wed after New Year, 1 week May and Sept MEALS: Set D £32.50 SERVICE: net prices, card slips closed CARDS: Access, Visa DETAILS: 24 seats. Private parties: 6 private room. No smoking in dining-room. Wheelchair access. No music

Planters £

191–193 Wells Road,
Malvern Wells WR14 9HB
MALVERN (0684) 575065

COOKING 2
COST £19–£30

Although Chandra de Alwis hails from Sri Lanka, his cooking takes in the whole of south-east Asia for ideas and inspiration. Thus a Thai feast was a special event in the spring, and an Indonesian rijstafel and a Malaysian meal have been the focus of other evenings. The advantage of this eclecticism is that no one quite knows what will be brought into the repertoire next, and Planters does not slip into the mindless typecasting of so many 'ethnic' restaurants. The food is fresh, and the spices sing. A blackboard alerts people to extras that day. Approval is gained for the satays, the nasi goreng, the stir-fried chilli prawns, and a burning hot dish of cashew-nuts cooked in coconut milk. Come the time for sweet dishes, the mood changes back to England. Sandra Pegg is informed about what's cooking and lively with it. There is an acceptable, short wine list that changes as often as the menu. House wines are from £6.75.

CHEF: Chandra de Alwis PROPRIETOR: Sandra Pegg OPEN: all week, exc Sun and Mon winter; 6.30 (7 winter) to 11 CLOSED: 1 week Jan MEALS: alc. Set D £17.95 SERVICE: 10%, card slips closed CARDS: Access, Visa DETAILS: 40 seats. Private parties: 40 main room. Vegetarian meals. Children welcome. No cigars/pipes in dining-room. Wheelchair access. No music

MANCHESTER Greater Manchester   map 5

▲ Granada Hotel, Armenian £

404 Wilmslow Road, Withington, M20 9BM
061-434 3480

COOKING 1
COST £13–£31

This basement beneath a small hotel is done out in taverna style and offers Middle Eastern food cooked with 'subtle spicing and fragrance' and served with 'a welcoming, caring, generous air'. Portions of dishes such as couscous or kofta, Tbilisi kebab (a mixture of minced and whole meat kebabs), and Yerevan kebabs (a mixture of five different sorts of kebabs) are enormous. The couscous is separate and fluffy, the rice and the salads, such as fasulya (white and red beans), prepared accurately. London visitors have wondered if it quite reaches the standard of the best couscous houses in the capital (see entries for

Laurent and Adams Café), but it makes an acceptable Manchester alternative to Chinese restaurants. Turkish delight is excellent, as is the coffee. The wine list is very short, with the odd Greek item as well as Ch. Musar (but no vintage). House wines are £7.95 a litre.

CHEFS: Mrs Minto and Mr Hovnanian   PROPRIETORS: Hanni Al-Taraboulsy and Mr Jajoo
OPEN: all week, D only; 6 to 10.30 (11 Fri and Sat)   MEALS: alc. Set D £6.95 (6 to 7.30 Mon to Thur)   SERVICE: not inc, card slips closed   CARDS: Access, Amex, Diners, Visa
DETAILS: 50 seats. Private parties: 65 main room. Vegetarian meals. Children's helpings.
Music   ACCOMMODATION: 11 rooms, all with bath/shower. B&B £35 to £50. Children welcome. Baby facilities. TV. Phone. Confirm by 5. Fax: 061-445 4902

Koreana £

Kings House,
40 King Street West, M3 2WY
061-832 4330

COOKING 1
COST £11–£35

'Manchester needs a place like this,' observes a local reporter. 'It's like nowhere else in the city – robust flavours combined with a light healthy philosophy.' The basement restaurant is close to the main shopping area, well away from Chinatown, and it continues to 'orientalise' with screens, an ever-increasing assortment of Korean artefacts on the walls, and waitresses in national costume. The repertoire has been expanded and many of the dishes are sensitively balanced, although regulars have noticed a slight decline in the precision of the cooking. Four set menus (including one for vegetarians) are a good introduction to the cuisine. Recommended dishes from the main menu have included dak muchim (sweet marinated chicken with garlic and mustard seeds), deep-fried seafood, dumpling soup, bindae tok (a bean-flour 'pizza' topped with vegetables), and cod hotpot with bean curd and slices of fish-cake. Shinsul-lo (a dish originally served in the Royal Courts of Korea) is an elaborate mixture of meat, fish and vegetables in a casserole arranged round a charcoal-burner which reduces the stock to progressively greater intensity. Korean rice-cake makes an unusual sweet. Ginseng tea and Korean saké are available. House French is £7.95.

CHEFS: Hyun K. Kim, H.S. Shin and C.S. Jeong   PROPRIETORS: Koreana Restaurant Ltd
OPEN: Mon to Sat; 12 to 2.30, 6.30 to 11 (11.30 Fri); noon to 11.30 Sat   MEALS: alc. Set L £4.75 to £7.30, Set D £14 (vegetarian) to £19.50   SERVICE: not inc (10% for 8 or more)
CARDS: Access, Amex, Diners, Visa   DETAILS: 80 seats. Private parties: 100 main room.
Vegetarian meals. Children welcome. Smart dress preferred. No music. Fax: 061-832 2293

Kosmos Taverna £

248 Wilmslow Road, M14 6LD
061-225 9106

COOKING 1
COST £14–£23

'Has definitely gone from strength to strength,' writes a reporter who first visited this admirable taverna not long after it opened a decade ago. Loulla Astin's effervescent personality has made her something of a local TV celebrity and she continues to deliver some of the most genuine Greek-Cypriot food in the North-West. Readers enthuse about the quality and range of the meze banquets (meat, fish and vegetarian): spanakopitakia (feta cheese and spinach pastries) and 'heavenly' baby squid have been singled out. Alongside this, there are traditional stews, casseroles and chargrilled meat and fish. It is also worth investigating the weekly specials: psari plaki is halibut cooked in ouzo and black olive sauce; stamna is an Athenian dish of rump steak baked in an individual earthenware pot with baby potatoes, tomatoes and wine. To drink there is a good crop of Greek-Cypriot wines, although the house wine is Italian (£6.95 a litre).

CHEF: Loulla Astin   PROPRIETORS: Stewart and Loulla Astin   OPEN: all week, D only, and Sun L; 6.30 (1 Sun) to 11.30 (12.30 Fri and Sat)   CLOSED: 25 and 26 Dec, 1 Jan   MEALS: alc. Set D £10 to £12.50   SERVICE: not inc   CARDS: Access, Visa   DETAILS: 80 seats. Private parties: 40 main room. Vegetarian meals. Children's helpings. Wheelchair access (also WC). Music. Air-conditioned

Lime Tree £

8 Lapwing Lane,
West Didsbury, M20 8WS   COOKING 1
061-445 1217   COST £16–£30

'There is an element of creeping self-satisfaction that prevents it rising above its current standard,' remarks an inspector. The current standard is inconsistent, but moderate prices and some flair continue to ensure widespread Mancunian support. The setting is bistro: cramped tables, paper and basic tableware. The cooking can be accomplished. Recommended dishes span salmon and monkfish terrine with a lemon and dill dressing, baked goats' cheese coated with honey and poppy seeds, salmon grilled with a basil and almond crust and roast guinea-fowl with a sultana mousse served on a fennel sauce. Puddings such as steamed chocolate with butterscotch sauce redress the balance in the kitchen's favour. Service is 'perfunctory', but the effect of an evening is likely to be 'congenial'. Wines are carefully selected, fairly priced and exclusively French. House wines are £7.95.

CHEFS: Patrick Hannity and Alison Eason   PROPRIETORS: Patrick Hannity and Robert Williams   OPEN: all week, D only, and Sun L; 12 to 2.30, 6.30 to 10.30   MEALS: alc. Set Sun L £10.50   SERVICE: not inc   CARDS: Access, Visa   DETAILS: 80 seats. Private parties: 40 main room, 40 private room. Vegetarian meals. Children's helpings Sun L. Wheelchair access. Music

Market Restaurant

Edge Street/104 High Street, M4 1HQ   COOKING 2
061-834-3743   COST £22–£34

'Overall this has been a year when we have concentrated on trying to do what we do well,' writes Peter O'Grady. Opinions are divided on whether this has been a success. Some have had inadequate meals, especially at the price; others have found everything perfect – good food, wine and service. Eclectic menus are changed each month. Representative examples have included a provençal dish of pumpkin in deep-fried olive oil pastry parcels; breast of chicken marinated in fresh ginger, soy and sherry; noisettes of lamb with little leek pies; and date, almond and apricot macaroon cake with chocolate sauce. Vegetarians are offered an inventive choice: twice-baked courgette soufflé with goats' cheese sauce; summer vegetables with fresh parsley pasta and warm tomato vinaigrette; hazelnut noodles with a light mushroom sauce and intriguingly named 'Parsnips Molly Parkin'. Diners continue to contribute to the culinary creative process at the popular Pudding Club and Starters Society; these meet two nights every alternate month. Peter O'Grady – a CAMRA enthusiast – has a newly extended and fascinating list of beers that is strong on Belgian and German examples. The decent wine list is sensibly priced, with much genuine choice under £15. House French is £4.25 a half-litre.

CHEFS: Mary-Rose Edgecombe, Paul Mertz and Dawn Wellens PROPRIETORS: Peter O'Grady, Anne O'Grady and Mary-Rose Edgecombe OPEN: Tue to Sat, D only; 6 (7 Sat) to 9.30 CLOSED: 1 week spring, 1 week Christmas, Aug MEALS: alc SERVICE: not inc, card slips closed CARDS: Access, Amex, Diners, Visa DETAILS: 40 seats. Private parties: 40 main room, 25 private room. Vegetarian meals. Children welcome. Wheelchair access. Music

Mr Kuks £

55A Mosley Street, M2 3HY	COOKING 1
061-236 0659	COST £15–£40

This basement continues in business, even if every hindrance to easy access seems to have dogged its existence in the past year: sewage works, Metrolink supertram works, and so on. The new chef is Hong Kong-trained and there is less of a Peking tilt to the specials, but recommendations still come for the dim-sum, the Peking duck and the Peking fillet steak, as well as the banquet menus for two or more. Lunchtime noodle dishes are excellent. House French is £6.50.

CHEF: Mr Tsang PROPRIETOR: Stephen Kuk OPEN: Mon to Sat (Sun before bank hol Mons); 12 to 2.30, 6 to 11.30 (midday to 11.45 Sat) CLOSED: Sun and Mon after bank hols MEALS: alc. Set L and D (2 or more persons) £11 to £20 SERVICE: 10%, card slips closed CARDS: Access, Amex, Diners, Visa DETAILS: 95 seats. Private parties: 95 main room. Vegetarian meals. Children's helpings. Music. Air-conditioned

▲ Moss Nook

Ringway Road, M22 5NA	
061-437 4778	
on B5166, 1m from Manchester	COOKING 3
Airport, M56 exit 5	COST £23–£57

With the Harrisons having opened their hotel in the Lakes (see entry, Applethwaite, Underscar Manor), taking Robert Thornton to supervise the cooking, the team left in charge at Moss Nook is the sous-chef and maître d' of last year. 'The good news is that nothing has changed,' writes a local follower; 'The bad news is that nothing has changed,' he concludes. He qualifies his paradox by observing, 'The nouvelle cuisine style with fruity sauces, lots of dome-lifting, mousses and the like may be looking rather dated, but it is done well. Flavours are sound, materials good, the technique is flawless, but the repertoire changes very slowly. Visitors from London may find it a refreshing change from the tyranny of Mediterranean/Californian clichés that are *de rigueur.*' The menu is long and expensive. It chimes perfectly with the restaurant itself. The waiting is elaborate, but the manner is Mancunian-direct and very welcoming. Cream of chicken soup was light years from its canned equivalent; appetisers are almost a meal in themselves (and good with it); vegetables are thought about and full of flavour; first courses such as chicken marinated in yoghurt, coriander and turmeric served on a salad with exotic fruit sound alarming but have good strong tastes in their constituent parts. Meat, too, though often all prime cuts, is carefully butchered and accurately timed. It's not a place for stews, and foie gras seems to find its way on to many a dish. Desserts complete the illusion of the glory years of our youth. Enjoy it for what it is, and take out a loan. The wine list is acceptable, the margins not so high as to cause seizure. House wines start at £8.90.

CHEF: Kevin Lofthouse   PROPRIETORS: Pauline and Derek Harrison   OPEN: Tue to Sat, exc Sat L; 12 to 2, 7 to 9.30 (10 Sat)   CLOSED: 24 Dec for 2 weeks   MEALS: alc. Set L £16.50, Set D £26   SERVICE: not inc, card slips closed   CARDS: Access, Amex, Visa   DETAILS: 50 seats. 8 tables outside. Private parties: 10 main room. Car park. Vegetarian meals. No children under 12. Smart dress preferred. No cigars/pipes in dining-room. No music. Air-conditioned   ACCOMMODATION: 1 room, with bath/shower. D,B&B £140. No children under 12. Garden. TV. Phone. Fax: 061-498 8089

Pleasure £   NEW ENTRY

58-60 George Street, M1 4HF   COOKING 2
061-236 0191 and 237 9272   COST £17-£45

The newest arrival in Manchester Chinatown has décor that outshines most of its immediate competitors, with 'pretensions to smartness' in the rust and pink colour schemes. A pagoda crowns the bar area; a fountain splashes by the entrance to the dining-room; motifs of Chinese deities appear on the windows. Raymond Wong (formerly of Pearl City) is in charge of the front-of-house and oversees the brigade of helpful waitresses. The list of dim-sum features around 40 items cooked to a high standard: deep-fried yam croquettes, beef dumplings with ginger and spring onion, and crabmeat and shark's-fin dumplings have all been recommended. Steamed ox-tripe with ginger and spring onion had 'a much better flavour than the recollection of tripe from my youth,' recalls one Mancunian devotee. The massive 200-dish Cantonese menu has a number of specialities seldom found in Manchester and early samplings have been impressive: fish maw soup with crabmeat, stir-fried monkfish with asparagus and Chinese mushrooms, and duck with orange have been noticeably fresh in flavour and finely executed. 'The Manchester Cantonese scene has stagnated a little of late,' observes a reporter with keen knowledge of the genre, 'and a competitor with this much promise must be beneficial.' Whether it will maintain quality once the honeymoon period is over, remains to be seen. House French is £6.95.

The text of entries is based on unsolicited reports sent in by readers, backed up by inspections conducted anonymously. The factual details under the text are from questionnaires the Guide *sends to all restaurants that feature in the book.*

CHEF: Mr Kan Lin Chung PROPRIETORS: Mr Kan Lin Chung, Mr Lee Koon Yuen, Mr Li Yat Si and Mr Kan Ling Hung OPEN: all week; noon to 11.30 CLOSED: 25 Dec MEALS: alc. Set D £13 to £25 SERVICE: 10% CARDS: Access, Amex, Diners, Visa DETAILS: 180 seats. 33 tables outside. Private parties: 120 main room, 60 private room. Vegetarian meals. Children welcome. Wheelchair access (also WC). Music. Air-conditioned. Fax: 061-237 9282

Quan Ju De £

44 Princess Street, M1 6DE
061-236 5236

COOKING 1*
COST £10–£30

The cool modernity of this restaurant is in sharp contrast to most of its neighbours in Manchester Chinatown. A great deal has been spent on décor and design, although visitors often find the atmosphere rather cold and soulless – unless it happens to be an evening when the pianist is playing. The menu is firmly rooted in Peking, and the roast duck generally meets with approval. Most reporters single out the hot starters and appetisers as high points: the mixed platter of fried seaweed, spare ribs, crispy smoked chicken and sesame prawn toasts. There is a feeling that some dishes – such as shredded duck wrapped in lettuce and sizzling Teppan beef – are bland and insipid, and that more forthright spicing and flavouring would lift the cooking. There are also complaints about the lack of fresh fish specialities and the limited choice of Westernised ices and sorbets to finish. The waiters seem interested and keen to please. Hot-buffet business lunches are a new feature. House French is £7.60.

CHEF: Jian Ping Ma PROPRIETOR: Hoo Man Lau OPEN: all week; 12 to 2.30, 6 to 11 CLOSED: bank hols MEALS: alc. Set L £4.80 to £9.50, Set D £15.50 to £19.50 SERVICE: 10% CARDS: Access, Amex, Visa DETAILS: 120 seats. Private parties: 90 main room, 30 private room. Vegetarian meals. Children welcome. Smart dress preferred. Music. Air-conditioned

Sanam £

145–151 Wilmslow Road,
Rusholme, M14 5AW
061-224 1008 and 8824

COOKING 1
COST £7–£20

'The secret of Sanam's success,' observes an inspector, 'is that it manages to cook on a gigantic scale and get it right.' Prices are low, turnover is high and the food is generally fresh. This is one of three related outlets on the colourful 'Curry Alley' extending southwards from the university. Two floors of paper-clothed tables are invariably packed with customers; the cheerful, jolly mood is helped along by courteous waiters with a good feel for the informality of the place. The menu features curry-house stalwarts and special karahi dishes, plus unexpected items such as 'humos', lamb and liver tikka and spiced lamb's brains. Most successful have been dahi bahallay (gram flour pieces with spiced yoghurt and chickpeas), aloo tikka, makhani chicken and aloo sag. Accompaniments, such as fresh-tasting pickles and chutneys, pilau rice and nan bread, are good. Pistachio kulfi and rasmalai are refreshing sweets. Take-aways are available.

CHEFS: Sultan Mahmood and M. Saleem PROPRIETORS: Abdul Ghafoor Akhtar and Sons OPEN: all week; noon to midnight (1am Fri and Sat) MEALS: alc. Set L £4.50 to £5.50, Set D £5 to £7.50. Unlicensed SERVICE: not inc CARDS: Access, Visa DETAILS: 350 seats. Private parties: 200 main room, 60 private room. Vegetarian meals. Children's helpings. Wheelchair access (also WC). Music. Air-conditioned

Siam Orchid £

54 Portland Street, M1 4QU   COOKING 1
061-236 1388 and 9757   COST £10–£37

Manchester's best-known Thai restaurant continues to thrive despite fierce competition from its Cantonese neighbours. What it offers is an accessible assortment of soups, salads, curries, noodles, rice and vegetables, backed up by weekly specials. Some dishes clearly work better than others and one reader's advice is to order carefully from the main menu, rather than opt for a set meal. Recent successes have included spicy Thai fish-cakes with sweet-and-sour cucumber relish, satays, mild Muslim curry, stir-fried beef with chillies, and 'superb' noodles. Banana in hot coconut cream is a suitably refreshing sweet and Singha Thai beer is the preferred drink. House French is £7.

CHEF: C. Sirisompan PROPRIETORS: C. Sirisompan and K. Sirisambhand OPEN: all week, exc Sat and Sun L; 11.30 to 2.30, 6.30 to 11.30 (6 to 11.30 Fri and Sat, 5 to 11 Sun) MEALS: alc. Set L £5 to £27, Set D £16 to £27 SERVICE: 10% CARDS: Access, Amex, Visa DETAILS: 55 seats. Private parties: 55 main room. Children welcome. Music. Air-conditioned. Fax: 061-236 8830

That Café

1031 Stockport Road,
Levenshulme, M19 2TB   COOKING 1
061-432 4672   COST £19–£31

A motley collection of furniture and miscellaneous ornaments sets the scene for Joe Quinn's lively restaurant. The atmosphere gets as many endorsements as the food. 'An excellent night out' was one comment. The value-for-money cooking revolves around a tried and tested repertoire, such as deep-fried Brie, orange hummus, minted lamb casserole and stuffed chicken with apricots. Reports have praised salmon kedgeree, salmon mousse wrapped in strips of plaice and served with a lemon sauce, and chicken cooked in yoghurt and spices. Vegetarians have equal choice on the short menu with vegetable and chestnut strudel, spicy vegetable brochettes and courgette roulade showing the range. A 'generous portion' of passion-fruit cheesecake and date and banana pudding in rum sauce make good finishes. House French is £6.95.

CHEF: Joe Quinn PROPRIETORS: Joe Quinn and Stephen King OPEN: Mon to Sat, D only, and Sun L; 12 to 2.30, 7 to 10.30 MEALS: alc. Set D Mon to Thur £12.95 SERVICE: not inc (10% for 8 or more) CARDS: Access, Amex, Visa DETAILS: 75 seats. Private parties: 50 main room, 25 private room. Vegetarian meals. Children's helpings. Music

The Guide *always appreciates hearing about changes of chef or owner.*

Woodlands

33 Shepley Road,
Audenshaw, M34 5DJ
061-336 4241

COOKING 2*
COST £23−£40

This red-brick suburban villa on the outskirts of Manchester is a favourite for business entertaining and pleasure. Visitors approve of the charming 'very English atmosphere' and the quality of the food. The menu − written in French and English − is Gallic by persuasion and follows the seasons. Typically there might be lobster terrine with herb mayonnaise; Dover sole baked in brandy and Noilly Prat with wild mushrooms; and venison steak with burgundy sauce and glazed onions. The cooking is classical and thoroughly professional. Reporters have approved of sizzling fresh whitebait; loin of pork with an orange and port sauce that was sweet without being cloying; and an 'incredible' orange and lemon soufflé in a brandy-snap basket. Sticky toffee pudding was old-fashioned but 'with a lightness that nursery puddings never enjoyed,' according to one reporter. The professional approach extends to service, which is faultless and caring. A short list of around 40 wines centres on France and Germany. House French is £8.25.

CHEF: William Mark Jackson PROPRIETORS: Mr and Mrs D. Crank OPEN: Tue to Sat, exc Sat L; 12 to 2, 7 to 9.30 (10 Sat) CLOSED: first week Jan, 1 week after Easter, 2 weeks Aug MEALS: alc. Set L £14.65, Set D £16.65 SERVICE: not inc, card slips closed CARDS: Access, Visa DETAILS: 36 seats. Private parties: 22 main room, 14 private room. Car park. Children's helpings. Smart dress preferred. No cigars/pipes in dining-room. Wheelchair access (3 steps). Music. Air-conditioned

Yang Sing £

34 Princess Street, M1 4JY
061-236 2200

COOKING 2*
COST £15−£27

The Yang Sing bandwagon rolls on: the latest scheme is a new ground-floor restaurant with its own kitchen due to open before the end of 1992. Most reporters agree that when this place is on form it has few rivals in Manchester Chinatown. Even run-of-the-mill dishes, such as duck with pineapple and ginger, are lifted by spot-on timing and high-quality ingredients. The full menu is a 250-dish Cantonese monster, dominated by highly rated dim-sum, roast meats, one-plate rice and noodle dishes, hotpots and casseroles. Juicy steamed scallops, stir-fried lobster with ginger and spring onion, strips of Dover sole with asparagus, special fried rice with belly pork and prawns, and fried vermicelli noodles Amoy-style have all been excellent. It is worth asking what is fresh − particularly fish and shellfish. Daily specials are also worth investigation. One reporter was dazzled by two vast casseroles: crisply battered eel with seaweed, then a mélange of scallops, slimy green seaweed, pork tendons, ginger and green leaves that was 'rich but not gloopy − one of the best Chinese dishes I've ever had'. But all is not rosy: there are question marks about the consistency of the cooking, the freshness of some ingredients and the service. House wines are from £6.85.

CHEF: Harry Yeung   PROPRIETORS: Yang Sing Restaurant Ltd   OPEN: all week; noon to 11
CLOSED: 25 Dec   MEALS: alc. Set L and D £12.25   SERVICE: 10%   CARDS: Access, Amex,
Visa   DETAILS: 140 seats. Private parties: 220 main room, 30 and 70 private rooms.
Children welcome. Wheelchair access. Music. Air-conditioned. Fax: 061-236 5934

MANNINGTREE Essex

map 3

Stour Bay Cafe £

39–43 High Street,
Manningtree CO11 1AH
COLCHESTER (0206) 396687

COUNTY OF THE YEAR RESTAURANT

COOKING 1*
COST £18–£30

Sherri Singleton is American and cooks it – new-style, too, not Chicken
Maryland. The house is quintessentially English, done out sparely, doing good
business – where many a fancy joint in this part of the world has gone down
Carey Street – with a seasonal menu supplemented by lots of daily fish. The
American side to it means, in Essex terms, that nothing is what was expected:
skate is with ginger brown butter, not beurre noisette, grouper comes with a
salsa of paw-paw and coriander, sea trout with roasted red pepper butter.
Flavours get better, as does performance. It is a refreshing place. The value
of the wine list is good and most of the New World is stocked. House wine
is £7.95.

CHEF: Sherri Singleton   PROPRIETORS: David McKay and Sherri Singleton   OPEN: Tue to
Sat; 12 to 2.45, 7 to 9.30 (10 Sat)   CLOSED: first 2 weeks Jan, last 2 weeks Sept   MEALS:
alc   SERVICE: not inc   CARDS: Access, Visa   DETAILS: 75 seats. Private parties: 60 main
room, 15 private room. Vegetarian meals. Children's helpings. No smoking in 1 dining-
room. Wheelchair access. Music

MARSTON MORETAINE Bedfordshire

map 3

Moreteyne Manor

NEW ENTRY

Woburn Road,
Marston Moretaine MK43 0NG
BEDFORD (0234) 767003

COOKING 2*
COST £26–£62

The chef-patron is Jeremy Blake O'Connor, last seen at Pebbles in Aylesbury.
He is a man of character who seems to attract one form of disaster or another.
The latest is a fire and, as we go to press, he is out of order for the time being
(except for banquets and parties) as some of the premises is rebuilt. The house
is encircled by a moat and is half-timbered, with plenty of woodwork in the
dining-room as well. The bar was designed by 'joiners rather than interior
designers; the furniture is not expensive and gives some sense of money
running out when the final stages were reached' was one slightly dismissive
comment from a man who then maintained that all was redeemed by the food.
Jeremy Blake O'Connor's cooking may have gained directness since relocation.
He was ever one to load the plate with gewgaws – quite possibly a few
pound's worth of foie gras – before sending it to the diner. Nowadays, the
plates are still loaded, but it's what the menu said would come that comes.
Roast beef and 'three large Yorkshire puddings' was one delighted account.

Direct and massive tastes – sometimes entirely misdirected – are a pleasure to many people: calf's liver with onion marmalade, pheasant with cider and calvados, fillet of beef with a garlic confit, jambonette of chicken with noodles and mushrooms – the menu starts to read like a caricature of French provincial cookery. This is a place for trenchermen – with patience on some nights and perhaps earplugs, for the kitchen conversations are audible and made for interest on one quieter night. Clarets are the thing on the wine list. House wines start at around £9.

CHEF/PROPRIETOR: Jeremy Blake O'Connor   OPEN: all week, exc Sun D; 12.15 to 2, 7.15 to 10   CLOSED: first week Jan for a few days   MEALS: Set L £12 to £46, Set D £23 (Mon to Thurs only) to £46   SERVICE: not inc, card slips closed   CARDS: Access, Amex, Visa   DETAILS: 27 seats. Private parties: 24 main room, 20 and 75 private rooms. Car park. Vegetarian meals. Children's helpings. Smart dress preferred. No cigars/pipes in dining-room. Wheelchair access (1 step; also WC). No music. Fax: (0234) 765382

MARY TAVY Devon   map 1

▲ *Stannary* 🔆✳

Mary Tavy PL19 9QB   COOKING 1
TAVISTOCK (0822) 810897   COST £23–£35

This charming Victorian guesthouse must rate as one of the 'greenest' eating-places in the South-West. Not only is it luxuriantly adorned with plants, but Michael Cook and Alison Fife are fully committed to organic and free-range produce. The cooking is totally vegetarian and despite the strictures – minimal use of salt and sugar, no alcohol or animal fats – the approach is never puritanical. Dishes are vivid and imaginative, with fruit and vegetables paired in unusual ways. 'Sunrise soup' is a mix of mangoes and other fruits with golden vegetables; palm hearts are cooked with rose petals and pink peppercorns. Food from the wild is much in evidence: parcels of laver seaweed filled with sweetcorn; elderflower fritters; young nettles puréed and layered with red onion in nettle pancakes; even sloes are used to flavour yoghurt. Readers have mentioned lemon and herb broth, olive and peanut pâté, wild mushroom loaf, bean stew with bright green herb dumplings, and a ginger pillow with cinnamon custard. Michael Cook is also a bee-keeper who produces his own honey and mead. The short wine list has a strong organic contingent. House French (organic) is £7.90.

CHEF: Alison Fife   PROPRIETORS: Michael Cook and Alison Fife   OPEN: Tue to Sat, D only (by arrangement winter for non-residents); 7 to 9.30   MEALS: alc. Minimum £11   SERVICE: net prices, card slips closed   CARDS: Access, Visa (4% surcharge)   DETAILS: 32 seats. Private parties: 25 main room. Car park. Vegetarian meals only. Healthy eating options. No smoking in dining-room. Music   ACCOMMODATION: 3 rooms, 1 with shower. B&B £20 to £50. Deposit: 20%. No children under 12. Garden. TV. Fax: (0822) 810898

All details are as accurate as possible at the time of going to press, but chefs and owners often change, and it is wise to check by telephone before making a special journey. Many readers have been disappointed when set-price bargain meals are no longer available. Ask when booking.

Floodlite £

7 Silver Street,
Masham HG4 4DX
RIPON (0765) 689000

COOKING 3
COST £13–£38

A casual passer-by might be excused from recognising the Floodlite as a
serious restaurant. It does not exactly look the part – 'subdued décor and dim
lighting might have stopped us going there had we not been told otherwise'
was confirmation of this. To miss it would be a pity: the table settings are *comme
il faut*, Christine Flood (once the children are in bed) is a model hostess, Charles
Flood is a proper chef who has decided to cook real food at reasonable prices.
The combination of no short-cuts and fair value is a winner. The menu is
surprisingly long for so small a place, but canny buying and sound knowledge
keep the food fresh. The dishes most favoured are classic, but they have none of
the sad hallmarks of tired cooking; the flavours stand up, everything is pukka.
Fillet steak with a mushroom purée and a hollandaise is always popular, so is
lobster thermidor when available. Hare is something of a speciality, and
venison – for instance, with mustard seeds and red wine sauce – is also
recommended. The repertoire changes slowly, a reflection of a one-man kitchen
and a preference for keeping a certain routine that may derive from Charles
Flood's own experience in large hotel kitchens. Don't forget the dessert course:
a blackberry and apple bread-and-butter pudding, a banana mousse with
toffee sauce, even the crème caramel, are well reported. Wine prices are as
reasonable as those for food, and the list gives ample choice with plenty of
recognisable and sound offerings such as the Villa di Capezzana Carmignano,
CVNE Riojas, or some Jurançons from Clos Guirouilh. House wines are £6.95.

CHEF: Charles Flood   PROPRIETORS: Charles and Christine Flood   OPEN: Tue to Sun D, Fri
to Sun L (other days by arrangement); 12 to 1.45, 7 to 9.30   CLOSED: 3 weeks Jan   MEALS:
alc. Set L £8.50   SERVICE: not inc, card slips closed   CARDS: Access, Visa   DETAILS: 36
seats. Private parties: 28 main room, 12 private room. Vegetarian meals with prior notice.
Children's helpings. No-smoking area. Wheelchair access (2 steps). Music

▲ Riber Hall

Matlock DE4 5JU
MATLOCK (0629) 582795
1m off A615 at Tansley

COOKING 2
COST £24–£43

The house is striking, so too the setting. The approach is steep as the hotel is
perched on a sheer scarp above Matlock, but the climb is worth it: for the
welcome, the terraced garden and the cooking. Jeremy Brazelle continues to
work in a country-house style: a sweetness edging dishes such as smoked fish
salad with honey vegetable vinaigrette, or fricassee of fish with grapes,
asparagus and sherry cream sauce; a certain elaboration; a plethora of
vegetables; and a concern for presentation. Pastry work is often praised, but so
too is the combination of flavours: for example, in venison with a red wine jus

and poached pear, or fillet of brill with a lobster mousse wrapped in spinach – 'immaculately steamed, with a champagne butter sauce'. The fun doesn't end with the main courses for there is a good range of puddings as well as home-made ice-creams that make you wish for cones. Effort is made for vegetarians, including a specific vegetarian menu. The dining-rooms come with 'lots of old oak, polished tables, cut glass and flowered china', not forgetting 'a *most* pleasant head waiter'. He will take you through a wine list that travels effortlessly from Frascati to Ch. Latour at prices that are fair but never give-away. Some good makers – Deiss in Alsace, Millérioux in Sancerre, Oak Knoll in Oregon and Cloudy Bay from New Zealand – give confidence in the choice. House wine is £9.75.

CHEF: Jeremy Brazelle   PROPRIETOR: Alex Biggin   OPEN: all week; 12 to 1.30, 7 to 9.30   MEALS: alc. Set L £14.50 to £19.50   SERVICE: not inc, card slips closed   CARDS: Access, Amex, Diners, Visa   DETAILS: 42 seats. Private parties: 34 main room, 14 private room. Car park. Vegetarian meals. Children's helpings. No children under 12. Smart dress preferred. No music   ACCOMMODATION: 11 rooms, all with bath/shower. B&B £78 to £92. Deposit: £35. No children under 12. Afternoon teas. Garden. Tennis. TV. Phone. Fax: (0629) 580475 (*The Which? Hotel Guide*)

MAWGAN Cornwall   map 1

Yard Bistro £ | NEW ENTRY |

Trelowarren, Mawgan TR12 6AF   COOKING 1
MAWGAN (032 622) 595   COST £12–£29

In the stables of Trelowarren, a house belonging to the Vyvyan family for more centuries than most of us like to recall, is this little bistro that functions as a café by day. The surroundings are pretty and restful. There is a short blackboard menu that hops through hoops of change at regular intervals and offers quite ambitious-sounding food such as rillettes of quail with a feuilleté of wild mushrooms or rendezvous of brill, bass and scallops in a vermouth and chive fish essence. Other things may be simpler: a plate of charcuterie, a tortelloni of spinach and cream cheese, a soup, straightforward steaks or poached salmon. Apple strudel and crèmes brûlées have been reported, though not enthused over. With its friendly welcome, this place makes a useful stop for those marooned so far from home. House wine is £6.50.

CHEF: Trevor Bayfield   PROPRIETOR: Ferrers Vyvyan   OPEN: all week, exc D Sun and Tue (Mon Oct to Whitsun); 12 to 2, 7 to 9 (9.30 Sat July and Aug)   CLOSED: 13 Dec to last week Mar   MEALS: alc. Set Sun L £7   SERVICE: not inc   CARDS: Access, Diners, Visa   DETAILS: 46 seats. 6 tables outside. Private parties: 100 main room. Car park. Vegetarian meals. Children's helpings D. Wheelchair access (also WC). Music

---

All entries in the Guide *are rewritten every year, not least because restaurant standards fluctuate. Don't trust an out-of-date* Guide.

Restaurateurs justifiably resent no-shows. If you quote a credit card number when booking, you may be liable for the restaurant's lost profit margin if you don't turn up. Always phone to cancel.

▲ *Nansidwell Country House*

Mawnan Smith TR11 5HU COOKING 2
FALMOUTH (0326) 250340 COST £23–£44

Barnaby, the black labrador, greets you at the door; service is 'amiable, amateur antipodean'; everything is 'relaxed country house, lots of books, magazines, cosy chairs'; 'the whole evening was more than expected'. These are some of the comments about the Robertsons' home/hotel by the sea. The hospitality works. Tony Allcott does the cooking, offering a *carte* and a set-price short menu. He likes the edge given by citrus and the extra dimension from the sweetness of fruit. Main courses at the beginning of the year were accompanied by grapefruit (sole and scallops), oranges (rabbit stuffed with duck liver), redcurrants (loin of lamb), and pears (Gressingham duck, with sage as well). The cooking is satisfactory, with some attention given to variety ('"Chef's hors d'oeuvre" consisted of avocado mousse, smoked duck, fish terrine, and game pâté') and to presentation (the loin of lamb is wrapped in leeks, with a port and redcurrant sauce). The home-smoker is mobilised, bread and bits and pieces are all home-produced, and the cheeseboard (local in the main) is endorsed. The best things to look for on the wine list are from Spain. Clarets rise steeply in price, and burgundies are from larger houses. The excellent house wines are from £9.50.

CHEF: Anthony Allcott PROPRIETORS: Jamie and Felicity Robertson OPEN: all week; 12.30 to 2, 7 to 9 MEALS: alc. Set L £14.75, Set D £22 SERVICE: not inc CARDS: Access, Visa DETAILS: 32 seats. Private parties: 10 main room. Car park. Vegetarian meals. Children's helpings L. No children under 7 D (6pm supper). No cigars/pipes in dining-room. Wheelchair access. No music ACCOMMODATION: 12 rooms, all with bath/shower. Rooms for disabled. D,B&B £60 to £170. Deposit: £100. Children welcome. Baby facilities. Pets welcome. Garden. Tennis. Fishing. TV. Phone. Fax: (0326) 250440 (*The Which? Hotel Guide*)

▲ *Toxique* NEW ENTRY

187 Woodrow Road,
Melksham SN12 7AY COOKING 1*
MELKSHAM (0225) 702129 COST £20–£31

The name may act as warning. 'Not a place for those who don't like laid-back informality,' said one; 'The owner is charmingly laconic and unhurried,' said another. He (the owner) was seen wine-waiting, waiting, cooking and washing up. It is a place that has opened on a budget in what must have been a farmhouse, with views of fields beyond and of a pleasant garden, complete with weeping ash – a balmy spot for a sip of wine. The food is serious, and the decoration (taking in plastic garden chairs covered with stapled drapes) is 'wackily stylish'. Some of the dishes sampled in early summer were marinated duck breast in a salad with spinach leaves, spring onions and rösti potatoes; chilled tomato and herb soup; lemon sole fillets with coriander and lime; spinach, oyster mushrooms and mozzarella strudel (somewhat flabby); summer pudding; and mixed sorbets. This should liven Melksham up a bit. The decent, simple wine list has house wines at £8.85.

CHEF: Helen Bartlett   PROPRIETORS: Peter Jewkes and Helen Bartlett   OPEN: Mon to Sat, D only and Sun L (weekday L by arrangement); 12.30 to 2.30, 7.30 to 10   MEALS: Set Sun L £14, Set D £21   SERVICE: not inc, card slips closed   CARDS: Access, Amex, Diners, Visa DETAILS: 20 seats. 4 tables outside. Private parties: 24 main room. Car park. Vegetarian meals. Children's helpings. No-smoking area. Wheelchair access (also WC). Music ACCOMMODATION: 4 rooms, all with bath/shower. D,B&B £55 to £100. Children welcome. Baby facilities. Garden (*The Which? Hotel Guide*)

MELMERBY Cumbria   map 7

Village Bakery ✾✕ £

Melmerby CA10 1HE   COOKING 1
LANGWATHBY (0768) 881515   COST £14–£19

This business is an ecosystem in itself: smallholding, large wood-fired bread oven flanked by a greenhouse to take the surplus heat, all organic foods, producing for the restaurant and craft gallery, for the shop and for other small businesses in need of good bread. The bakery's fame may have spread most for the two minor meals of the day, breakfast and tea, but they are anything but minor in scale. Lunch is a useful stop too: seriously substantial soups, breads and cheese, beef casserole, or a vegetarian dish. We are not dealing with ethereal mousses here, but the food also rises above mere honest solidity. Wines and beers are as organic as the grub. House wine is £6.50.

CHEF: Diane Richter   PROPRIETORS: Andrew and Lis Whitley   OPEN: all week, daytime only; 8.30am (9.30 Sun and bank hols) to 5pm   CLOSED: Sun Jan and Feb   MEALS: alc SERVICE: not inc, card slips closed   CARDS: Access, Diners, Visa   DETAILS: 40 seats. Private parties: 25 main room. Car park. Vegetarian meals. Children's helpings. No smoking. Wheelchair access (1 step). No music. Fax: (0768) 881848

MIDDLE WALLOP Hampshire   map 2

▲ Fifehead Manor

Middle Wallop SO20 8EG   COOKING 3
ANDOVER (0264) 781565   COST £24–£44

If an alternative festival at Stonehenge is your goal, consider refuelling here for the inevitable battles. The house is handsome (with a succession of additions from the Middle Ages onwards), the service amiable, and the cooking to the point. What is more, prices have certainly stabilised. Mark Robertson's cooking has gained in assurance and range. There seems a tilt towards the Mediterranean, even on the wind-blasted Salisbury Plain, with things such as a bourride of chicken, beef with a garlic and shallot confit, or pigeon wrapped in Parma ham served with grapes and a honey sauce. A certain conventional line, that may offer calf's liver with Dubonnet, chicken liver parfait or grilled goats' cheese, solves the problem of non-garlic-eaters. The kitchen has become more responsive to the markets: fish is no longer pre-ordained on a printed menu, but bought and sold each day according to a daily menu. An autumn encounter with red pepper mousse, marinated beef gravlax-style, salmon with cucumber spaghetti and a light cream sauce, monkfish with mussel liquor and mustard, and good thick-cut potatoes laid over a mound of spinach, followed by a moistly nutty hazelnut tart with light and true pastry, and a cardamom and orange ice-cream, was adjudged a great success. British cheeses have been enjoyed, as have the ancillaries. The wine list's chief attraction is that it steers clear of the impossibly expensive, even if it hardly srays from France. It is not adventurous, but sound enough: Ch. Hanteillan 1986, Ch. Chambert-Marbuzet 1986, Santenay 1985 from Clerget, or Sancerre from Vacheron all show judgement. House wines are £8.50.

CHEF: Mark Robertson   PROPRIETOR: Margaret van Veelen   OPEN: all week; 12 to 2.30, 7.30 to 9.30   CLOSED: 1 week Christmas   MEALS: alc. Set L £17.50, Set D £25   SERVICE: not inc   CARDS: Access, Amex, Diners, Visa   DETAILS: 40 seats. Private parties: 16 main room, 14 private room. Car park. Children's helpings. Wheelchair access (also WC). No music   ACCOMMODATION: 16 rooms, all with bath/shower. Rooms for disabled. B&B £50 to £95. Children welcome. Baby facilities. Pets welcome. Afternoon teas. Garden. TV. Phone. Doors close at midnight. Confirm by 6. Fax: (0264) 781400 (*The Which? Hotel Guide*)

MIDHURST West Sussex   map 3

▲ *Angel Hotel* ♥ £

NEW ENTRY

North Street, Midhurst GU29 9DN   COOKING 1
MIDHURST (0730) 812421   COST £19–£39

Peter Crawford-Rolt has returned from a stint in the West Indies to take up the cudgels of hotel-keeping once again. He had some success at a country place at Beanacre, near Melksham. The style was a bit upper-crust and very laid-back, so it was loved by people who wanted a relaxed weekend. He could cook as well, which was lucky. The new venture is in a small town – taking an old lag of a hotel and converting it with speed and aplomb. He has not gone so far as 'country house' but it has all the design tricks that make those places enjoyable to sit about in. He has started with restaurant and brasserie. The brasserie is tiny but offers good shellfish and grills. The restaurant is trying altogether harder and will succeed more if it rids itself of memories of country living and converts more to the short-order direct cooking styles that Peter Crawford-Rolt picked up in the Caribbean – the chargrill is there, dead centre-stage, waiting for the action to begin. The wine list is very up to the minute, arranged by grape and with plenty of stuff from beyond France. Prices are fair. House wines start at around £8.50.

CHEFS: Michael Taylor and Peter Crawford-Rolt   PROPRIETORS: Peter Crawford-Rolt and Nicholas Davies   OPEN: all week; 12 to 2.30, 7 to 9.30 (6.30 to 10 brasserie)   MEALS: alc. Set Sun L restaurant £13.50   SERVICE: not inc, card slips closed   CARDS: Access, Amex, Visa   DETAILS: restaurant 45 seats, brasserie 50 seats. 6 tables outside. Private parties: 60 main room, 36 and 78 private rooms. Car park. Vegetarian meals. Children's helpings. No cigars/pipes in restaurant. Wheelchair access (also WC). Music (brasserie)   ACCOMMODATION: 17 rooms, all with bath/shower. B&B £45 to £90. Deposit: £50. Children welcome. Baby facilities. Afternoon teas. Garden. TV. Phone. Confirm 1 day ahead. Fax: (0730) 815928

Maxine's £

Red Lion Street, Midhurst GU29 9PB
MIDHURST (073 081) 6271

COOKING 2
COST £16–£31

'You may gather that with 31 visits in the last 12 months we like this place,'
write devotees of the de Jagers' unassuming restaurant in a half-timbered
house slotted into central Midhurst. Their attendance record is by no means
unique. Part of the attraction is the value for money, especially in the set
menus: 'Where else can you get three good home-cooked courses for £10.95 on
a Friday evening?' asks another habitué. The main tilt of the cooking seldom
changes, although there are always daily fish dishes and specials such as rabbit
casserole. This year's crop of recommendations has included mushrooms in
garlic and leek sauce, terrine with ginger preserve, beef bourguignonne,
kidneys and sweetbreads in red wine, and chicken with wine and tarragon
sauce. Vegetables are perfectly presented. Sweets have included good Dutch
apple pie and lemon and yoghurt ice-cream. Traditional Sunday roasts are
greatly liked. Consistency is the keynote of Robert de Jager's cooking, while
his wife is a welcoming, thoughtful and attentive hostess. House French
is £7.95.

CHEF: Robert de Jager PROPRIETORS: Robert and Marti de Jager OPEN: Wed to Sat, Sun
L, bank hol weekends; 12 to 2, 7 to 10 MEALS: alc. Set L and D £10.95 SERVICE: net
prices, card slips closed CARD: Access, Visa DETAILS: 27 seats. Private parties: 30 main
room. Vegetarian meals. Children's helpings. No music

MILFORD ON SEA Hampshire   map 2

Rocher's

69–71 High Street,
Milford on Sea SO41 0QG
LYMINGTON (0590) 642340

COOKING 3
COST £18–£37

'All dishes very tasty and not at all fussy' was the pith of a recommendation of
Alain Rocher's classical, yet not hidebound, French cooking. Rocher's is none
too fancy: a converted shop on the High Street done out pleasantly enough, the
posters of Loire châteaux reminding everyone of Alain Rocher's origins.
Rebecca Rocher's handling of customers is invariably remarked upon as a
happy balance of informality and efficiency, reinforced by the professionalism
of her staff. The prices, albeit sharply increased since last year, are one cause of
full houses. The standards are another: 'sauces especially good', 'consistency',
'simple yet accurate' are typical readers' comments. The menu offers half a
dozen choices for the main stages, plus four fish. One or two dishes are long-
stay residents: feuilleté of spinach with shallots, and a crème brûlée 'of the
day', for example. There is 'not a lotta stuffing goin' on'; in the main the chief
ingredient is presented with a sauce and plainish vegetables. First courses
include some made dishes: mousse of ratatouille, pike terrine, parfait of
chicken livers. 'Alain Rocher's forte must be duck breast,' says one reporter,
only to be contradicted by another who espouses the excellence of the lamb.
The wine list is all French and the Loire selection is worth exploring. The
prices for the classic regions are not low, so if it's not the Loire, look at the

Rhône or the Mâconnais. House wines are £8.50. CELLARMAN'S CHOICE: Quincy, Denis Jaumier 1990, £13.60; Chinon Rouge, Ch. de Ligré 1985, £12.50.

CHEF: Alain Rocher   PROPRIETORS: Alain and Rebecca Rocher   OPEN: Wed to Sun; 12.15 to 1.30, 7 to 10   CLOSED: 2 weeks winter, 2 weeks summer   MEALS: alc. Set L £12.50, Set D £15.30   SERVICE: not inc, card slips closed   CARDS: Access, Visa   DETAILS: 30 seats. Private parties: 30 main room. No children under 14. Smart dress preferred. No cigars/pipes in dining-room. Wheelchair access. Music

---

MINSTER LOVELL Oxfordshire   map 2

▲ Old Swan   NEW ENTRY

Minster Lovell OX8 5RN   COOKING 2
WITNEY (0993) 774441   COST £20–£42

The conjunction of meadows, the River Windrush, the ruins of Minster Lovell Hall, cricket pitch, Cotswold stone, peace, trees and an old pub is part of everyone's vision of good old England. Qualifications creep in when the Mill Conference Centre hoves in view and the pub is a little too 'couth', but what to do in the 1990s? 'The Old Swan has always been couth,' says one who was there the night Kennedy was shot *and* had his first wedding reception in the restaurant. Over the last 18 months new owners have made it hang together better. Admire the old stone walls and the high beams of the dining-hall and settle down to read the fixed-price *carte*. It is dear, too dear if you are going to offer grey mullet as your prime fish – 'the fish was dull, but the cooking and accompaniments were excellent' – but you can console yourself with a cheaper table d'hôte. If you ignore the dangers of pretension, Clive Dixon's cooking has hope. A langoustine soup with coriander, rouille, Gruyère and croûtons had guts; confit of duck layered with too-crisp filo on a plum sauce both looked impressive and tasted rich; mullet was done with tagliatelle and ratatouille and should have been red mullet only to stand up to the flavours; lamb with a pesto crust came with potatoes topped with mozzarella and tomato, as well as carrots seasoned with a strong prune juice; baked figs with crème pâtissière and blackcurrant sauce left the eater trembling with delight; while crème brûlée with sauté bananas and a butterscotch sauce showed Clive Dixon to be utterly insouciant to richness, over-egging the pudding or putting everything into one pot in case something misses. Service is tremendously keen. The wine list is a start, expensive as well. The best place to research is Spain. The burgundies are mixed, the clarets dear. House wines are from £9.75.

CHEF: Clive Dixon   PROPRIETORS: Minster Lovell Mill Ltd   OPEN: all week; 12 to 2, 7 to 10   MEALS: Set L £13.50, Set D £19.50 to £30   SERVICE: not inc   CARDS: Access, Amex, Diners, Visa   DETAILS: 35 seats. 5 tables outside. Private parties: 14, 30 and 40 private rooms. Car park. Vegetarian meals. Children's helpings. Smart dress preferred. Wheelchair access (2 steps). No music   ACCOMMODATION: 16 rooms, all with bath/shower. B&B £85 to £165. Children welcome. Baby facilities. Pets welcome. Afternoon teas. Garden. Tennis. Fishing. TV. Phone. Confirm by 6. Fax: (0993) 702002

The Guide is totally independent, accepts no free hospitality, and survives on the number of copies sold each year.

MOLLINGTON Cheshire map 5

▲ *Crabwall Manor*

Parkgate Road,
Mollington CH1 6NE COOKING 2
GREAT MOLLINGTON (0244) 851666 COST £21–£55

This is a giant of a place. It started small and historic, then gained many wings
(and car parks), as well as a conservatory dining-room. Our comments in last
year's edition have resulted in non-co-operation this year. The management
has, however, become sharper and more on the ball, resulting in much-
improved welcome and service. But complaints have been received about poor
bread, dull vegetables costing over £3 per portion, and weak but plentiful
coffee. Michael Truelove can certainly cook well. The menu is not too long, so
materials are not left hanging around; there is a level of skill, for instance, in a
ravioli filled with scallop mousse and served with a crab sauce, that would
disgrace no one. Desserts show the skills in even greater evidence. The wine
list is long and good with interesting bottles from around the world. House
wine is £9.75.

CHEF: Michael Truelove PROPRIETOR: Carl Lewis OPEN: all week; 12 to 2, 7 to 9.30
MEALS: alc. Set L £14.50, Set D £25.50 SERVICE: not inc, card slips closed CARDS: Access,
Amex, Diners, Visa DETAILS: 120 seats. Private parties: 85 main room, 45 and 100 private
rooms. Car park. Vegetarian meals. Children's helpings. Jacket and tie. No cigars/pipes in
dining-room. Wheelchair access (also WC). Music. Air-conditioned ACCOMMODATION:
48 rooms, all with bath/shower. Rooms for disabled. B&B £94.70 to £120.70. Children
welcome. Baby facilities. Afternoon teas. Garden. Snooker. TV. Phone (*The Which? Hotel
Guide*)

MONTACUTE Somerset map 2

▲ *Milk House* ✸

The Borough, Montacute TA15 6XB COOKING 1
YEOVIL (0935) 823823 COST £16–£32

This converted fifteenth-century milk house is now a 'natural food restaurant
with rooms'. In summer there is also a sun terrace and courtyard garden, much
appreciated by visitors. Elizabeth Dufton cooks to a fixed-price menu with six
choices at each stage – at least two of these being vegetarian and vegan. This is
thorough-going, homely cooking with plenty of honest flavour and an
allegiance to organic and additive-free ingredients. Spiced mushrooms with
nut topping, home-made gravlax, guinea-fowl with herb sauce, pork steaks
with cider brandy sauce, and lentil loaf with mint sauce show the style. Soups
and fish dishes change daily; vegetables are plentiful and timed to perfection.
Puddings follow the same theme: crêpes with brandied apple served with
smetana ('a much more interesting contrast than cream'); date, rum and honey
pudding; home-made brown sugar meringues with fresh fruit. Sunday lunch
has been a enjoyable experience enhanced by William Dufton's friendly,
unhurried service. The modest, affordable wine list has a strong showing of
organics. House wines are from £7.50.

CHEF: Elizabeth Dufton PROPRIETORS: Elizabeth and William Dufton OPEN: Wed to Sat,
D only, and Sun L (Wed to Sat L by arrangement for 6 or more); 12.30 to 2, 7.30 to 9.30
MEALS: Set Sun L £12.50 to £15.50, Set D £19.80 to £24 SERVICE: net prices, card slips
closed CARDS: Access, Visa DETAILS: 24 seats. 3 tables outside. Private parties: 24 main
room, 24 private room. Vegetarian meals. Children welcome (if well-behaved). Smart dress
preferred. No smoking in dining-room. Wheelchair access ACCOMMODATION: 2 rooms,
both with bath/shower. D,B&B £60 to £98. Deposit: £20. No children under 12. Garden.
Doors close at midnight. Confirm by 4

MORETON-IN-MARSH Gloucestershire — map 2

Annie's

NEW ENTRY

3 Oxford Street,
Moreton-in-Marsh GL56 0LA
MORETON-IN-MARSH (0608) 51981

COOKING 1*
COST £21–£44

The name (Annie's) painted on the window of an old Cotswold-stone cottage
complete with hanging baskets, dried-flower arrangements and chintz says it
all. This is an old-fashioned, personally run restaurant, that tries very hard to
be accommodating to all. David Ellis cooks, his wife, the eponymous Annie,
commands front-of-house. The food, a mixture of English and French country
cooking, involves a lot of pan-frying and is reassuringly familiar. One meal
started with fresh, breadcrumbed monkfish tails, pan-fried well beyond *à point*,
with garlic and herb butter, served with a pleasant red pepper sauce; then
venison, with a decently made sauce of brandy and pink peppercorns, with a
poached pear and cranberry garnish, and accompanied by good fresh-tasting
vegetables; before toffee pudding with well-made butterscotch and pecan
sauce. For some this is the 'Chanel suit of Gloucestershire eateries'; for others,
the bread, butter, ice-cream, petits fours and background music will qualify the
judgement. The wine list does an adequate job and is not overpriced. House
wines are £8.75.

CHEFS: David Ellis and Mandy Kent PROPRIETORS: David and Anne Ellis OPEN: Mon to
Sat D, and Sun L; 12 to 2, 7 to 10 CLOSED: last week Jan, first week Feb MEALS: alc. Set
Sun L £15, Set Mon to Fri D £17.50 SERVICE: not inc, card slips closed CARDS: Access,
Amex, Diners, Visa DETAILS: 30 seats. Private parties: 30 main room. Vegetarian meals.
Children's helpings. No cigars/pipes in dining-room. Wheelchair access. Music

Marsh Goose

High Street,
Moreton-in-Marsh GL56 0AX
MORETON-IN-MARSH (0608) 52111

COOKING 3
COST £20–£35

An inspector who had come from what he reckoned the claustrophobic
atmosphere of a small English country guesthouse/restaurant was bowled over
by the Marsh Goose. 'Beautiful, full of personal and interesting touches in its
inter-connecting rooms; warm; welcoming; brightly served by staff in brighter
waistcoats and bow-ties who managed to be swift, intelligent and
unpretentious.' The cooking gets more eulogy: 'Distinct, fresh tastes; beautiful
but not ostentatious; technically sound sauces; authentic flavours.' There is a

short and cheap *carte* at lunch, a longer set-price menu at dinner. The repertoire is large, and recommendations occur for many things: a light eggy binding to a salmon and herb tart; chestnut and spinach soufflé; curried parsnip soup; lamb with tomato, garlic and basil; mixed fish with noodles; calf's liver with mash and bacon; venison with orange and ginger; and even good vegetables 'with none of that English country-house hotel thing of a crescent plate and little piles of tastelessness'. Desserts will include something British and hot and, if lucky, may repeat apple fritters with blackcurrant sauce and vanilla ice-cream: one man's idea of ecstasy. The Marsh Goose has dragged Cotswold eating into the '90s and the Cotswolds seem to have taken it to their hearts. If you like the food, buy some of it from the shop next door. Wines are what you might expect: not overpowered by France, not too expensive, not a bad selection, though nothing to amaze. House wine from Navarra is £8.05.

CHEF: Sonya Kidney   PROPRIETORS: Sonya Kidney, Leo Brooke-Little and Gordon Campbell-Gray   OPEN: Tue to Sun, exc Sun D; 12.15 to 2.30, 7.30 to 9.45   MEALS: alc. Set Sun L £14.50, Set D £19.90 to £25   SERVICE: not inc   CARD: Access, Visa   DETAILS: 60 seats. Private parties: 20 main room, 14 private room. Vegetarian meals. Children's helpings. Smart dress preferred D. Wheelchair access (also WC). No music

---

MORSTON Norfolk   map 6

▲ *Morston Hall* | NEW ENTRY |

Morston, nr Holt NR25 7AA
CLEY (0263) 741041
on A149, 2m W of Blakeney,   COOKING 1
opposite Morston Quay   COST £18–£33

There is a lot for the Blackistons to do at Morston Hall, a comfortable (rather than grand) flint-built house with gardens. They have already spent a fortune on fabrics, and doubtless on sharpening lawnmower blades as well. They come to the venture from Miller Howe, Windermere (see entry): this is the first Tovey satellite so far from the Lake District. Many parts of the formula have been transplanted, most importantly the single sitting for a no-choice meal at set price. It is early days yet and there will doubtless be improvement, but first comments from seasoned hotel-triers are that they need to relax a bit and smarten up the cooking beyond 'superior dinner-party level' (especially since Loyd Grossman got his vowels around dinnering in Britain). When choice is restricted, the cooking really does have to be top-hole. A meal in the early summer yielded Melon Utter Bliss: a fan of under-ripe melon with a fruit and wine purée and a blob of cream – feasible as a dessert, fairly worrying as a starter. Fresh (but dry) pasta with 'hazelnut and basil dressing' (in fact, hazelnut oil mayonnaise and chopped basil sprinkled over) and some fillets of smoked trout came next, before roast breast of chicken with orange and thyme, on a calvados purée (apple puréed to resemble baby food, flavoured with the spirit) with a brown sauce (slightly over-caramelised). The end, a rhubarb and apple farmhouse pie, might have been an entry for a village show competition. The location is very useful. The wine list has a sensibly unfettered approach to buying throughout the world. It is very serviceable. House wines are from £9.

CHEF: Galton Blackiston   PROPRIETORS: Tracy and Galton Blackiston, and Justin Fraser
OPEN: all week D, Sun L; 12.30 for 1, 7.30 for 8   CLOSED: 1 Jan to late Feb   MEALS: Set Sun
L £12, Set D £19.50   SERVICE: not inc, card slips closed   CARDS: Access, Amex, Visa
DETAILS: 30 seats. Private parties: 50 main room. Car park. Vegetarian meals. Children's
helpings Sun L. Smart dress preferred. No smoking during meals. Wheelchair access (also
WC). No music   ACCOMMODATION: 4 rooms, all with bath/shower. B&B £60 to £120.
Children welcome. Dogs by arrangement. Afternoon teas. Garden. TV. Phone. Confirm by
6. Fax: (0263) 741041 *(The Which? Hotel Guide)*

MOULSFORD Oxfordshire   map 2

▲ *Beetle & Wedge* ▮

Moulsford OX10 9JF	COOKING 3
CHOLSEY (0491) 651381	COST £28–£60

The Smiths' great adventure continues. This is a giant, old pub-hotel, with the
Thames its front garden. You can come by boat or by car. The owners' energy is
demonic: not just a restaurant (the Dining Room), but also the Boathouse bar-
restaurant with its own giant menu, and a fine-weather al fresco arrangement
in the garden – again with its separate menu. This wish to be available to as
many different sorts of people, and appetites, as possible is of course
reminiscent of the Smiths' previous enterprise, the Royal Oak at Yattendon (see
entry). The menus are so large that every sort of cookery propensity can be
covered: old-fashioned calves' tongues with ravigote sauce in the Boathouse, or
kidneys and black pudding with mustard and herb sauce in the Dining Room;
spinach soufflé with a shrimp sauce; and a lot of grilled foods, especially in the
Boathouse, where you can watch the process under way. The palate tends
towards classical flavours and traditional tastes, rather than the Mediterranean
Italianate tendency to put garlic and olives (or basil and Parmesan) with
everything. Although much effort has been put into evening out the rushes and
scurries of business – Kate Smith stresses how essential it is to book a table –
reports can still reflect a certain muddle, especially in the Boathouse. One diner
also commented that whereas the product of the kitchen was fine (a salad of
avocado and scallops), the grilled sole 'seemed to be cooked by one or more of
the waiting staff' and was not so good. For reliability, the Dining Room fares
much better – but then, it is much dearer, though Sunday lunch at a set price is
universally approved. For simple accuracy, a meal that included avocado and
tomato salad with a basil vinaigrette, fresh asparagus soup, roast leg of lamb
boulangère, duck with apples and calvados, chocolate rum truffle cake, and
blueberry and blackberry cheesecake could not be bettered. The wine list here
got off to a good start last year. Kate Smith knows her bottles and has
preferences that come out in excellent Alsaces and cheaper clarets, for example,
although mark-ups generally are rather fierce. There is a shorter list for those
who cannot face the choosing. A reader commented that the cellar seemed 'in
flux', but the probability is that any movement is to our benefit in the long run.
House wines are £9.75 and good.

▮ *denotes an outstanding wine cellar;* ▼ *denotes a good wine list, worth travelling for.*

CHEF: Richard Smith PROPRIETORS: Richard and Kate Smith OPEN: Dining Room Tue to
Sun, exc Sun D; Boathouse all week; 12.30 to 2, 7.30 to 10 MEALS: Dining Room alc and
Set Sun L £24.50. Boathouse alc SERVICE: not inc CARDS: Access, Amex, Diners, Visa
DETAILS: Dining Room 35 seats, Boathouse 65 seats. 5 tables outside Boathouse. Private
parties: 25 and 40 main rooms, 40 private room. Car park. Vegetarian meals. Children's
helpings on request. Smart dress preferred in Dining Room. No cigars/pipes in Dining
Room. Wheelchair access (also WC) ACCOMMODATION: 10 rooms, all with bath/shower.
Rooms for disabled. B&B £75 to £125. Children welcome. Baby facilities. Pets by
arrangement. Afternoon teas (must book). Garden. TV. Phone. Fax: (0491) 651376
(*The Which? Hotel Guide*)

MOULTON North Yorkshire

map 7

Black Bull

Moulton DL10 6QJ
DARLINGTON (0325) 377289   COOKING 2*
1m SE of Scotch Corner, 1m from A1   COST £18–£48

'Basically still the best food in the area by far,' enthuses one regular. 'A pub/
restaurant freed of the dead hand of the big brewers can provide at a
reasonable price precisely what the customer wants,' writes another. The Bull offers a
number of eating areas: a seafood bar, 'Hazel' – the renovated Pullman carriage
from the Brighton Belle – and a conservatory. The cooking is honest,
comforting and served in massive portions: fish soup in a bowl 'large enough to
bath a baby'; tagliatelle of seafood in a cream-cheese sauce ('a meal in itself');
scallops Walewska ('an enormous plateful of scallops with generous pieces of
lobster'). Main courses are served with great platefuls of perfectly cooked
vegetables, and puddings include a 'magnificent crêpe suzette'. All the reports
in this year's postbag comment exclusively on the seafood bar, where there is a
no-booking policy; the Pullman, which offers fish and meat – chateaubriand
béarnaise, rack of lamb, fillet of beef with mushrooms and pastry – requires
prior booking. The owners are also wine merchants, and offer an almost
exclusively French list with a fair selection of half-bottles and very reasonable
prices. House Duboeuf is £7.25.

CHEF: Stuart Birkett PROPRIETORS: G.H. Pagendam and Mrs A.M.C. Pagendam
OPEN: Mon to Sat; 12 to 2, 6.45 to 10.15 CLOSED: 23 to 31 Dec MEALS: alc. Set L £11.75
SERVICE: not inc, card slips closed CARDS: Access, Amex, Visa DETAILS: 100 seats.
4 tables outside. Private parties: 30 main room, 10 and 30 private rooms. Car park. No
children under 7. Wheelchair access. No music. Fax: (0325) 377422

NAYLAND Suffolk

map 3

Martha's Vineyard ❢ £

18 High Street, Nayland CO6 4JF   COOKING 3
COLCHESTER (0206) 262888   COST £20–£26

An old-world shop premises, now carpeted, houses emphatically New World
cooking and wines. Larkin Warren bakes good bread every day, and red-hot
calzones (folded pizzas) stuffed with mushrooms and cheese. (Baking is

increasingly a marker of someone switched on to current fashion.) This place is popular for its prices, its happy informality and its fresh approach. Smoked chicken salad with cranberry chutney and spiced pecans, chilli pasta with mussels and bacon, lemon gravlax with mustard and horseradish on rye blinis, turkey with quince sauce, venison with chocolate, juniper and orange, almond butter cake with pineapple compote, or chocolate bread-and-butter pudding with Tia Maria sauce – none of these is run-of-the-mill. They betray Larkin Warren's native America, but without tendentious emphasis. Regulars enjoy the variations on a theme: breads will change daily, bread-and-butter pudding may be lemon- (as well as chocolate-) flavoured, risottos may be seafood or have three sorts of wild mushrooms and pigeon breast. Braised dishes and casseroles vie with fried or sauté things for popularity: a day may see cassoulet (with home-made sausage), haddock with mash and short ribs of beef with peppers and onions sharing the stage with turkey breast and a pizza. 'Cheerful' is a word from a report that may give some hint as to the brave and enterprising cooking as well as accurately describe the service and approach. The wine list can only be said to be short and just as interesting as the cooking. There is no reliance on France here, but lots of choice from everywhere without breaking through the £20 barrier on more than a handful of occasions. Christopher Warren knows what he has bought, and you may need guidance before choosing: for instance, between Chardonnays from South Africa, New Zealand, California, Italy and Burgundy. It is not the place to look for a range of clarets, but you could try three Martha's Vineyard Cabernet Sauvignon from Joseph Heitz if you have the odd £50-plus. House wines start at £7.25. CELLARMAN'S CHOICE: New Zealand, Oyster Bay, Sauvignon 1991, £11.50; California, Clos Dubois, Merlot 1988, £15.95.

CHEF: Larkin Warren PROPRIETORS: Christopher and Larkin Warren OPEN: Tue to Sat, D only; 6.45 to 9 (9.30 Fri and Sat) CLOSED: 2 weeks summer, 2 weeks Christmas, 2 days Easter MEALS: alc SERVICE: not inc (10% for 6 or more) CARDS: Access, Visa DETAILS: 45 seats. Private parties: 8 main room. Vegetarian meals. Children's helpings. No smoking while others are eating. Wheelchair access. No music

---

NEWARK Nottinghamshire   map 5

Gannets Bistrot

35 Castlegate, Newark NG24 1AZ   COOKING 1*
NEWARK (0636) 702066 and 610018   COST £16–£24

'Would that Newark were nearer,' wrote a Lincolnshire wanderer who lit first on the café overlooking the Trent, then progressed to the quieter first-floor restaurant – mahogany bar, blackboard menus, airy, lots of greenery, that authentic bistro feel – for a good lunch that took in beef bourguignonne, venison and vegetable pie with wholemeal crust, plenty of vegetables, then banoffi pie ('not banoffi, but jolly good as a banana and cream pie') and redcurrant tart with plenty of crème pâtissière. The menu upstairs has a constant base, with a superstructure of daily specials. Materials are given their proper due, and shopping is no chore: thus local organic pork sausages, local smoked salmon, wild salmon not farmed, free-range chicken. The materials may be cooked bistro-style, in casseroles and stews, or come from the chargrill (a method the Bowers are anxious to promote) if they are poussin, guinea-fowl or swordfish. Spices are enjoyed here, as are classic bistro dishes like stuffed mushrooms, seafood pancakes, potted crab and lasagne. Salads are a major accompaniment, and potatoes are often new ones, roasted in their skins. Puddings are large, sticky and sweet – 'The sticky toffee pudding was the stickiest and toffiest,' wrote one expert. The wine list is short with few bottles over £10. The sources, however, are reliable: Gisselbrecht Alsaces, Guigal's Côtes du Rhône, Hunter from Australia, Guntrum's Niersteiner. A sweet fan looked for sweet wine but couldn't find one. House wine is £7.50 a litre.

CHEFS: Hilary Bower and Paul Godfrey PROPRIETORS: Hilary and David Bower OPEN: Wed to Sat; 12 to 2, 6.30 to 9.30 CLOSED: 25 and 26 Dec, 1 Jan MEALS: alc. Set L £7.95 to £9.95 SERVICE: 10%, card slips closed CARDS: Access, Visa DETAILS: 38 seats. Private parties: 38 main room. Vegetarian meals. Children welcome. Music. Air-conditioned

---

NEWCASTLE UPON TYNE Tyne & Wear   map 7

Courtney's

5–7 The Side, NE1 3JE   COOKING 2*
091-232-5537   COST £20–£33

New to the *Guide* last year, Courtney's goes from strength to strength. Sensibly, prices have lifted but little and the original informality allied to quality has not been overlaid by ambition of the wrong sort. An ingenious conversion of an old property in the Quayside area, the place makes no concessions to Olde English restaurant decoration. The printed brasserie menu has developed over 12 months, but has not altered radically. Popular dishes remain, such as a variation on eggs Benedict with avocado and smoked salmon, Caesar salad, mushrooms with boursin, beef fillet with pickled walnut sauce, and chicken with red wine, mushrooms, onions and bacon. Every day there are extras to satisfy the need for change: a scallop mousse, salmon coated with sesame seeds, crab-cake with a tomato sauce, and venison with juniper sauce are some of those that have been enjoyed. Cooking is generally accurate and flavours are lively. Desserts may seem to get less attention but are not skimped: pecan pie, mango and brandy fool, floating islands and Northumbrian cheeses are examples. A crème caramel that cloyed was not so successful. Service is bright and professional, though occasionally anxious to lecture. The wine list is short and fast changing. Prices are kept down and some interesting alternatives are offered to the daily run. House recommendation (dearer than the house wine) is Moyston Semillon or Shiraz Cabernet at £8.95.

CHEF: Michael Carr PROPRIETORS: Michael and Kerensa Carr OPEN: Mon to Sat, exc Sat L; 12 to 2.30, 7 to 10.30 (10.45 Sat) CLOSED: bank hols, exc Good Fri D MEALS: alc. Set L £11.95 to £13.95 SERVICE: not inc (10% for 6 or more) CARDS: Access, Amex, Visa DETAILS: 27 seats. Private parties: 27 main room. Vegetarian meals. Children welcome. Children's helpings on request. No cigars/pipes in dining-room. Music

---

'On arriving, it took a full half hour to get one round of drinks, which included mineral water being filled up with tap water before our eyes.' On dining in Birmingham

---

Fisherman's Lodge ✸

Jesmond Dene, NE7 7BQ   COOKING 3
091-281 3281   COST £23–£58

The Lodge stands alone in its own grounds at the end of the road through
Jesmond Dene Park. Turn off the coast road (A1058) at Benton Bank and follow
the track past Millfield House and Pet's Corner. The substantial building with
its solid stonework and high-pitched roofs was once entry to the home of Lord
Armstrong – inventor, engineer and one of Newcastle's famous benefactors.
Regular visitors have noted a transformation in the décor of late. Victorian
patterns translated into modern colours and materials create a much more
relaxed mood than the original style. Like the décor, the cooking evolves. Fish
from North Shields is still the mainstay, although meat shows up more
strongly, and there is now a full vegetarian menu. A classic *carte* is backed up
by daily specials. The kitchen moves confidently between surf'n'turf, sole
Waleswka and grilled lobster with garlic butter to more modern inventions
such as steamed salmon with basil and tomato vinaigrette. Game is handled
simply; lamb is local. The cooking is generous and accurate, ingredients are
spot-on and dishes look good on the plate. This is a smooth, well-oiled set-up;
it may seem slightly conservative at times, but it knows its market. Recent
successes have included tomato and green pepper tart garnished with
medallions of sauté monkfish; succulent pan-fried scallops with linguine and
deep-fried pastry parcels each concealing a clove of garlic; lemon sole soufflé;
halibut grilled with garden herbs; and best end of Northumbrian lamb stuffed
with spinach. Meals end on a high note: the 'melting chocolate dessert' and
Bourbon parfait with caramelised mango have been superb. Occasional
hiccups, such as 'prosaic' vegetables and grey stringy bean sprouts used as a
bed for salmon and scallops, can mar the overall effect – particularly as prices
are far from cheap. Service is smooth and professional. The wine list is long and
fairly priced, but errs on the side of safety. House French is £9 a litre.

CHEF: Steven Jobson   PROPRIETORS: Franco and Pamela Cetoloni   OPEN: Mon to Sat, exc
Sat L; 12 to 2, 7 to 11   CLOSED: 25 to 28 Dec   MEALS: alc. Set L £16 to £17   SERVICE: not
inc   CARDS: Access, Amex, Diners, Visa   DETAILS: 70 seats. 3 tables outside. Private
parties: 14 main room, 10 and 40 private rooms. Vegetarian meals. Car park. Children's
helpings. No children under 6. Smart dress preferred. No smoking in dining-room.
Wheelchair access. No music. Fax: 091-281 6410

Leela's £

20 Dean Street, NE1 1PG   COOKING 2
091-230-1261   COST £13–£36

This is a far cry from the majority of provincial Indian restaurants. It is decently
decorated – 'the feeling of a home dining-room' – service is excellent and
willing, and the menu of predominantly Keralan and Tamil Nadu recipes is
short and properly described ('new wave' in the best of senses). Given the
food's origins, there's no surprise that half the menu is vegetarian. The dosas,
vadas and pooris are 'as good as any I have eaten in London's Drummond
Street'. The appam and vegetable pappas, a main course of 'lightly raised soft

pancakes served with vegetables', do not get quite the same praise as stir-fried broccoli, green beans with garlic, mushrooms with coconut, or spinach and potatoes with onions. Well-mobilised flavours such as tamarind and coconut are enjoyed, as are the talent for presentation and the ability to spice mildly and herb generously. Prices are not low and portions are not enormous. Lunch-time sees a shorter fixed-price menu – much dearer than last year's. Two desserts, kulfi and halva, show Indian skills, the rest are sorbets and gâteaux. The wine list is considered, even if short. Leela is an enthusiast for matching Indian food to wine. It would help decision if the list gave more information as to growers, but Leela is herself not shy of giving advice.

CHEF: Kuriakose Paul PROPRIETORS: Kuriakose and Leela Paul OPEN: Mon to Sat; 12 to 2.30, 5.30 to 11.30 MEALS: alc. Set L £7.95 to £9.95, Set D £9.50 to £12.90 SERVICE: not inc CARDS: Access, Amex, Visa DETAILS: 54 seats. Private parties: 25 main room. Vegetarian meals. Children welcome. Music

21 Queen Street ♥

21 Queen Street,
Princes Wharf, Quayside, NE1 3UG   COOKING 3*
091-222 0755   COST £22–£56

Almost underneath, but just east of, the Tyne bridges, 21 Queen Street has a brass plate outside stating, 'A Restaurant'. Inside, it has comfort aplenty, a feel of the '30s, and a lot of waiters. Terence Laybourne is unquestionably a fine chef. He offers a long menu, with many things forming part of a stable repertoire, and with a fast-changing galaxy of fish dishes. He cooks with an eye to the wider world, yet is not besotted by fashion. He can produce light and appetising food, though some people have detected too heavy a hand with the butter on some evenings. He should achieve higher ratings still, were it not for some one thing going wrong in many meals reported this year. 'The quality of the main course overshadowed the rest of the meal, particularly the dessert' was one reflection; 'We very much enjoyed the meal as a whole, in spite of these criticisms' was another. A summer dinner revealed unmemorable appetisers (sometimes they are excellent) and a mixed bag of breads – raisin and walnut was better than the tomato. A salad of cured, moist and fresh-tasting salmon with griddled scallops came with little mounds of diced vegetables in a brilliant, sharp yet sweet liquor, that was ideal foil to the fish in texture and taste. The salad itself contained lemon peel and coriander among the mixed leaves. This was a great dish. Grilled calf's liver would have been more successful had the liver been better trimmed and perhaps more thinly cut. An onion marmalade was not satisfactory, and a very fine sour-sweet sauce was vitiated by too many whole mustard seeds. The diner involved had no more vegetables than carrots, beans and dauphinois – a mixture he maintained went to every table in the place – and not very good ones at that. Others have found the vegetables better and more tailored to each dish. If the main course foundered, form returned with a semolina bavarois with hazelnut cream and caramel oranges, which again showed ability to balance sharp and sweet, and to get the textures right. Cheeses are good, but cheese biscuits and home-made oatcakes are less so. Portions are very large, and doggy-bags are freely given. Fish is worth the visit. Coffee will do. Whatever the errors, few people come away dissatisfied. Prices are high for Newcastle, but that's not the Laybournes' fault. The wine remit has extended slightly to encompass a few antipodeans, but Italy has yet to qualify. Selection is careful and there are good half-bottles, but this remains a list that has no qualms about old-fashioned mark-ups. House wine is £9.60. CELLARMAN'S CHOICE: Montagny premier cru, les Vignes sur le Clou 1990, Roy, £17.40; Washington State, Merlot Ch. Ste Michelle 1988, £16.50.

CHEF: Terence Laybourne PROPRIETORS: Susan and Terence Laybourne OPEN: Mon to Sat, exc Sat L; 12 to 2, 7 to 11 CLOSED: 25 and 26 Dec, 1 Jan, bank hols MEALS: alc. Set L £15.50 SERVICE: not inc CARDS: Access, Amex, Diners, Visa DETAILS: 50 seats. Private parties: 50 main room. Children's helpings. Smart dress preferred. No pipes in dining-room. No music. Fax: 091-230 5837

NEW MILTON Hampshire   map 2

▲ *Chewton Glen Hotel, Marryat Room* ❢

Christchurch Road,
New Milton BH25 6QS   COOKING 3*
HIGHCLIFFE (0425) 275341   COST £28–£61

Conservatories have become popular places to eat in and Chewton Glen's is no exception. It, like the rest of the hotel, is elegant and manicured. It's all a bit too good to be true for some, but a place of pilgrimage for the international set who mean service when they say it, and expect hotels to provide everything. The swimming-pool and health facilities have continued to be much used. There is also some conference business: hotels have to expand their horizons to survive. The cooking by Pierre Chevillard has never wavered in its ability to keep up with the times yet present a fairly staid exterior. It deals, therefore, in materials that are familiar to jet-setters: foie gras, truffles, lobster and langoustines. But it dresses the langoustine open ravioli with warm olive oil, the crab soup with pesto, and serves a fritter of marinated sardines with tomato, courgette and aubergine, and a basil vinaigrette. The *carte* is long, makes generous provision for vegetarians and light eaters, and is supplemented by an expensive table d'hôte at dinner – with rather plainer, less interesting food. Lunch is a short menu at a fixed price. Performance shows a high level of competence, sufficient to impress visiting chefs with the balance of the dressings, the preparation of offal such as calf's kidney, the ability to extract flavour from a slow-braised shin of beef, and even to make a good old standard like lemon meringue pie. Other recommended dishes include a carpaccio of tuna with exotic fruits, plaice with potato 'scales' and chicken jus, salmon with tomato and asparagus and a chervil butter sauce (most sauces tend to the light side), liver with lentils and parsley and a sherry vinegar sauce, and quail cutlets with potato galette and an armagnac sauce. It is possible to eat boringly but correctly here, and sometimes flavours are too muted to be worth pursuing, as in a foie gras mousse flavoured with old madeira which was liverish but not foie gras in flavour, and had madeira in the jelly – but who could tell if it was old, or if there was very much of it? A dessert of crème brûlée with honeyed pear was burnt but not crunchy, but was very good all the same; hot chocolate fondant was heavyish but made a variation on soufflé. Petits fours go up and down. Service is by bevies, usually of prime efficiency. Entire pages of the wine list are given over to first-growth clarets and the offerings of Dom. Romanée-Conti; prices are high and vintages are excellent. Geographical spread is remarkable, taking in the good Barbaresco la Spinono, Pipers Brook Pinot Noir from Tasmania and many good Alsaces. Imagination falters in some areas – the Mâconnais and Beaujolais and a few Rhônes look under par. Halves are few but good; dessert wines apart, nothing is apparently offered by the glass. House wines are from £11.75. CELLARMAN'S CHOICE: Marlborough, Nobilo Sauvignon Blanc 1990, £18.10; Tempranillo Navana 1988, Bodegas Ochoa, £18.25.

CHEF: Pierre Chevillard   PROPRIETOR: Martin Skan   OPEN: all week; 12.30 to 2, 7.30 to 9.30   MEALS: alc. Set L £22.50, Set D £39   SERVICE: net prices, card slips closed   CARDS: Access, Amex, Diners, Visa   DETAILS: 120 seats. 6 tables outside. Private parties: 20 main room, 6 and 80 private rooms. Car park. Vegetarian meals. Healthy eating options. Children's helpings. No children under 7. Jacket and tie. No cigars/pipes in dining-room. No music   ACCOMMODATION: 58 rooms, all with bath/shower. Rooms for disabled. B&B £178 to £365. Deposit: 1 night. No children under 7. Afternoon teas. Garden. Swimming-pool. Sauna. Tennis. Golf. Snooker. TV. Phone. Fax: (0425) 272310 (*The Which? Hotel Guide*)

NORTH HUISH Devon   map 1

▲ *Brookdale House* ▮ ✸✖

North Huish TQ10 9NR   COOKING 3
GARA BRIDGE (054 882) 402 and 415   COST £40

The house would be an apt setting for a Trollope novel – no Omnium Castle, not even a squire's old hall, but a solid residence of a worthy gentleman. The hotel-keeping is in this vein. No flash, no false snobbery, but things are done properly in their context. Come the dining-room, that context is a fair quantity of late-Victorian plasterwork and reliable cooking. Though Terry Rich has left, Carol Trevor-Roper remains in control of the kitchens as always. First courses may sometimes be miniatures of a main dish, different only in that they are packaged in pastry; hence lambs' tongues with wild mushrooms and a tarragon sauce, steamed brill with leeks and green peppercorn sauce, or venison and hazelnut pie with red wine and shallots were preliminaries one night to beef with a herb butter sauce, pork with ratatouille and pimento sauce, or skate with lime butter. Quantities are well-judged, to avoid that bursting feeling. Fireworks, however, are not to be expected. Cheeses are British and come as a trio. Desserts do not always have the sureness of aim demonstrated by what came before. If you are lucky, you can hear strains of old pop coming from Charles Trevor-Roper's study while you drink aperitifs, with good nibbles, or take coffee, with crisp petits fours, in the large sitting-room. Dive on further and you will reach the bar, and the owner's own barrel of beer. The wine list may give you pause before the hop. Our enthusiasm for this wine list is undimmed. Additional support from Richard Sandford, a welcome boost in the provision of half-bottles and the further strengthened selection of 'Recommended Wines' mean that anyone venturing here will be well pleased. Prices are modest and fairly judged. House wines are from £9.40.

CELLARMAN'S CHOICE: Kathryn Lake, Sauvignon/Semillon 1991, £11.65; Ridge Zinfandel 1987, Paso Robles, £22.20.

CHEFS: Carol Trevor-Roper and Richard Sandford PROPRIETORS: Charles and Carol Trevor-Roper, and Richard Sandford OPEN: all week, D only; 7.30 to 9 MEALS: Set D £28 SERVICE: not inc CARDS: Access, Visa DETAILS: 35 seats. Private parties: 24 main room. Car park. No children under 10. No smoking in dining-room. No music
ACCOMMODATION: 8 rooms, all with bath/shower. B&B £60 to £110. No children under 10. Garden. TV. Phone. Doors close at midnight. Confirm by 6 (*The Which? Hotel Guide*)

NORTHLEACH Gloucestershire   map 2

Old Woolhouse

The Square,
Northleach GL54 3EE   COOKING 3
COTSWOLD (0451) 860366   COST £54

The Astics do not make a show of their restaurant: 'I found it hard to see whether it was open, or where the front door was.' Nor does M. Astic think his achievement warrants great surprise: 'I cook because my father cooked before me,' he confesses; 'In France if your family is in this business, you never think of any other career.' The family portrait is there for all to see. In truth, he married a Cornishwoman, so he pursued his vocation in England. The product is still endlessly French: 'You can eat like this anywhere in France,' he says. Not so, as many of us will have experienced. The Old Woolhouse is a small gem, each facet carefully polished, from the Hungarian porcelain coffee-service, to the drawn-thread linen table-mats, to the daily repetition of a menu format that must sometimes cause ennui to executants and consumers alike. It does mean that everything can be done by the Astics themselves. M. Astic cooks a classical repertoire. Brill is served with bacon and mushrooms on a red wine sauce extended with cream. Sole and crab tart comes with the lightest pastry and a sauce that seems cream-based again, but with greater zip to its flavour. Veal is served with its kidney and a light Cassis sauce; the meat is dense, too dense. Poulet au vinaigre is a big portion, the sauce made with cream, espagnole and vinegar. 'The spare elegance in the flavouring makes it memorable.' Served with it were little individual casseroles of dauphinois potatoes. These were not so brilliant. A salad, with a sharp dressing to ruin the wine, came at this point too. Then the dessert, made by Mme Astic, along classic lines again: an almond tart, or a strawberry shortcake. This was fine stuff, but not light. Very strong coffee came with a good chocolate praline but a stodgy almond biscuit. Thus one meal. Others will be of that ilk. The set price is not always easy to discover, as the menu is recited. People enjoy the considered calm and some become addicted. The consistency is remarkable. The wine list is expensive.

CHEF: Jacques Astic PROPRIETORS: Jacques and Jenny Astic OPEN: Tue to Sat, D only (L and Sun and Mon D by arrangement); from 8.15 CLOSED: Christmas MEALS: Set D £35
SERVICE: not inc DETAILS: 18 seats. Children welcome. No music

---

The Good Food Guide *is a registered trade mark of Consumers' Association Ltd.*

Wickens ♟ ⅝✳

Market Place, Northleach GL54 3EJ	COOKING 3
COTSWOLD (0451) 860421	COST £14–£31

An English restaurant: perhaps it acts as a counterpoint to the Astics' Old Woolhouse (see previous entry). This is not to say that the only thing served is bangers and mash, but that Christopher Wickens deals in more robust ways with a wider range of ingredients than the seductive classicism of Jacques Astic. Sprats are baked with garlic, parsley, butter and breadcrumbs; partridge, grouse and veal terrine is served with a zinging pickle; chicken and celery are layered with a herb sauce, topped with cheese; lamb may be casseroled and well spiced. Lots of flavours, lots of body, but some have said the cooking lacks that type of sophistication beloved of 'gourmets'. Lunch is a social service – one city-dweller who visited on Christmas Eve delighted in the carrot and orange soup, the game casserole with lashings of vegetables, the crème brûlée, and conversation with the entire Wickens family. The set-price dinner is more elaborate than lunch, when you may have no more than a giant open sandwich, but both meals share an intense concern for origins and condition of the mainly local ingredients and for the honesty of their presentation and cooking. It is not surprising that there is good beer here. This Cotswold cottage with a conservatory resounds to debate and opinion; much loved by those who agree. Maintain an opposite viewpoint and be seduced by Joanna Wickens' puddings and sweet things. Conversion, too, in the wine list, which has a helpful grouping of wines in price blocks; the curiosity is that the French, and they are several and good, are excluded and consigned to separate listings at the end. The Australian selections are especially fine and prices are fair across the board. House wine is £8.50. CELLARMAN'S CHOICE: Hawke's Bay, Esk Valley Sauvignon Blanc 1989, £12.95; Western Australia, Mount Barker Shiraz 1988, Plantagenet, £12.95.

CHEFS/PROPRIETORS: Christopher and Joanna Wickens OPEN: Tue to Sat (L Easter to Oct only); 12.15 to 1.45, 7.20 to 9 MEALS: alc L. Set D £21.50 to £23.75 SERVICE: net prices, card slips closed CARDS: Access, Amex, Visa (5% surcharge) DETAILS: 36 seats. Private parties: 22 main room. Children welcome. No smoking in dining-room. Music

---

NORTHWICH Cheshire   map 5

▲ *Nunsmere Hall* ⅝✳

Tarporley Road, Sandiway,	
nr Northwich CW8 2ES	
NORTHWICH (0606) 889100	COOKING 3*
off A49, 4m SW of Northwich	COST £21–£64

Country-house hotels all too often produce food that is over-decorated, over-complex and under-flavoured. Nunsmere is an exception. Paul Kitching is capable of high-flavoured dishes, even though they may sometimes suffer from too many elements. Nunsmere's immediate attraction is the site: it stands on a promontory jutting into a large lake bounded by forest. The house is turn-of-the-century and not beautiful by anyone's reckoning. The McHardys have done wonders inside, however, producing a wedding-cake paint job in the lounge, a strongly provençal and floral character to the dining-room, and bedrooms of 'full rich material, but with a modern feel'. Service is enthusiastic and able, an uncommon combination. The problem is that the hotel has caught the Cheshire disease and is too expensive. Menu prices are in excess of the West End, and they should not be. Reports have been consistent through the year: the cooking has character and is capable. Dishes such as breast of woodpigeon set on black pudding with root vegetables and a truffled madeira game sauce, beef consommé with smoked chicken, thyme and saffron fettuccine, and scallops and oysters with cucumber and a chervil and tomato butter sauce edged with vinegar have been outstanding for taste. Lamb with the fat on, ringed by girolles, yellow courgettes, carrot, peas and potato, was served with an intensely tarragon gravy; duck was also served with its fat on, poached figs the accompaniment, on a port and sage sauce, with the leg braised to moist dissolution in port and figs. Deep-fried cabbage underlying the duck hindered rather than helped: one thing too much, and it was burnt anyway. Paul Kitching obviously likes fat on things – for flavour, perhaps – but the quantities give digestion problems. Desserts are few: a grand selection and cheese leave a choice of four, one a hot soufflé. If he hangs on to the tastes, he will refine his execution; in the meantime, starve for a day before you go to eat there. The wine list relies on big shippers for many French items and preserves price range by offering plenty from new countries. House wines are £10.25. 'We occasionally saw the chef darting back and forth from kitchen to restaurant. He always looks so tired. Why do these chefs choose to work this way?' So closed one ecstatic report. The answer lies in the ecstasy.

CHEF: Paul Kitching   PROPRIETORS: Malcolm and Julie McHardy   OPEN: all week; 12 to 2, 7 to 9.30 (10.30 Sat)   MEALS: alc. Set L £14.25 to £18.75, Set D £28.50 to £40   CARDS: Access, Amex, Visa   SERVICE: not inc, card slips closed   DETAILS: 48 seats. 6 tables outside. Private parties: 60 main room, 24, 30 and 42 private rooms. Car park. Vegetarian meals. Children restricted. Jacket and tie. No smoking in dining-room. Wheelchair access (3 steps; also WC). Music   ACCOMMODATION: 32 rooms, all with bath/shower. Rooms for disabled. Children welcome. B&B £95 to £150. Deposit: £50. Afternoon teas. Garden. Snooker. TV. Phone. Confirm by 6. Fax: (0606) 889055

NORTON Shropshire   map 5

▲ *Hundred House Hotel* £

[NEW ENTRY]

Norton, nr Shifnal TF11 9EE
NORTON (095 271) 353
on A442, midway between
Bridgnorth and Telford

COOKING 1
COST £18–£35

It is the garden that is the first delight: old roses on pergolas, 'romantic, yet formal, yet cottagey,' wrote one who saw it in its June trappings. Inside the inn, colours are more autumnal, warm and with a prospect of cosiness. It is run by the Phillips family: father, mother and two sons, the youngest of whom has seen the big wide world (including Kensington Place, London, see entry) and cooks. Thus elements of fashionable brasserie eating and some real skill have been grafted on to a pub. It is not always possible to disentangle the two streams: poor butter and bread, not very good coffee, plenty of gammon and pineapple, but almost everything is home-made, herbs come straight from the garden, and here is a menu that has bruschetta (albeit with the wrong bread), polenta with Gorgonzola, black pudding, risotto, rack of lamb persillade (good, this), and fillet steak with madeira and chicory coulis. Fish is fresh and might be chargrilled trout or brill with a chive beurre blanc. You are asked if you want chips and these, too, are home-made. Desserts tried were not so successful. There is scope and hope here. No wonder most people love it. There are some good wines, some not so good, no halves (except Sauternes), but seven house wines by the litre, half-litre, quarter-litre and glass. They cost from £10.50 a litre.

CHEF: Stuart Phillips   PROPRIETORS: the Phillips family   OPEN: all week; 12 to 2.30, 6 to 10 (9 Sun)   MEALS: alc. Set Sun L £10.95. Bar menu   SERVICE: not inc   CARDS: Access, Visa   DETAILS: 60 seats. 10 tables outside. Private parties: 30 main room. Car park. Vegetarian meals. Children's helpings. No music   ACCOMMODATION: 9 rooms, all with bath/shower. B&B £59 to £79. Deposit: £30. Children welcome. Baby facilities. Pets by arrangement. Afternoon teas. Garden. TV. Phone. Doors close at 11.30. Confirm by 9am. Fax: (095 271) 355 (*The Which? Hotel Guide*)

NORWICH Norfolk   map 6

Adlard's 🍸

79 Upper St Giles Street,
Norwich NR2 1AB   COOKING 4
NORWICH (0603) 633522   COST £28–£47

'Overall an excellent regional restaurant,' a report concludes. 'Usually, you associate this type of cooking with dead-smooth restaurants, and reverence all around. This place had nice atmosphere, good pictures, a pleasant staff,' comments another. 'I like the room, very green,' adds a third. Green it certainly is, inside and out. The room is ground-floor and mezzanine, with the kitchen at the back. Tables are well spaced, though the coffee machine, as it whooshes milk for cappuccino froth, interjects (when it works) reality between those exchanges of sweet nothings. David Adlard is not a demonstrative cook. Though a lone voice or two may be heard saying his food is messed about, it is generally discreet and almost conservative. What people enjoy is that it also hits taste nails on the head. A danger with discretion is that marks missed may lead to food that is intensely prosaic. The menu is short and changes as things come and go. Regulars will find the repertoire repeated. Came the spring, a London couple ate appetisers of wild mushrooms, bacon and cheese, with some pâté croûtons. Their first courses were seized scallops and Dover sole with a little spinach and a creamy sauce with all the sharp depth of citrus fruit, and puff pastry pillows of poached oysters with a basil and Parmesan sauce which tamed the potential aggression of each ingredient, melding to a perfect whole. Rack of lamb was crusted with herbs and crushed hazelnuts – again, discretion kept the thyme flavour to an exact minimum as well as judging the correct crunch from the nuts; good pommes Anna accompanied. A fillet steak in pastry was boring as a choice but justified by the strong flavours in the mushroom duxelles, by the lightness of the pastry, and by the richness of a red wine and shallot sauce that never cloyed. A warm caramelised apple tart with crisp nougat wafers, a pronouncedly armagnac sabayon, and an apple sorbet of great depth of flavour were a resounding conclusion. Quibbles that have surfaced include a suggestion that 'seafood' should be more shellfish than white fish in a fricassee, just as the ragoûts are not always ragoûts, venison sometimes has been felt to lack flavour, and wild mushrooms might include a greater range of fungus; and a few people fall out with the waiting staff – not often, though. To list dishes may be invidious, but special mention might be made of escalope of lamb, in the manner of veal; fricassee of chicken with vinegar and vermicelli; duck with celeriac pancakes of confit of duck plus a stir-fry of lightly spiced vegetables (now *there* was a good variation on Peking duck); a bavarois of rhubarb; very good crèmes brûlées; and lemon tart 'second only to Harveys'. Intelligent buying from some of the country's best merchants underpins the wine list. A dozen or so carefully selected wines available by the glass render a journey into the main list unnecessary for all but the enthusiast. For these the choice almost overwhelms, in range and quality; fair prices allow experiment. House wines are £9. CELLARMAN'S CHOICE: Reuilly 1990, Lafond, £14; Argentina, Cabernet Sauvignon 1983, Mendoza, £17.50.

CHEF: David Adlard PROPRIETORS: David and Mary Adlard OPEN: Tue to Sat, exc Sat L; 12.30 to 1.45, 7.30 to 9 MEALS: Set L £16.50 to £19, Set D £29 to £32 SERVICE: not inc, card slips closed CARDS: Access, Amex, Diners, Visa DETAILS: 40 seats. Private parties: 40 main room. Children's helpings. Wheelchair access (also WC). No music

Brasted's

8–10 St Andrews Hill,
Norwich NR2 1AD
NORWICH (0603) 625949

COOKING 2
COST £22–£42

'John Brasted is clearly an aficionado of the Middle East,' observed one reporter who was struck by 'the bedouin effect' of metres of terracotta- and white-striped material lining the walls and ceiling of this tented dining-room. New chef Shaun Smith-Roberts worked with Ian McAndrew at Flitwick Manor (see entry, Flitwick), and there are echoes of the Flitwick menu in his repertoire: carrot consommé with coriander, spring salad of asparagus and baby leeks with yoghurt dressing, and roast duck with a rillette of its leg all feature. But he is developing his own style. The short *carte* is modern, with hints of peasant revivalism: terrine of cauliflower with smoked salmon sauce, and mille-feuille of salt-cod and crab, share the bill with more traditional ideas such as parfait of chicken livers in filo pastry bourride, and navarin of lamb with flageolet beans. A good deal of preparation goes into some dishes, such as an impressive ballottine of boned oxtail, chunky in the centre and finely minced round the outside and wrapped in caul. Reporters have also been impressed by warm cheese parcels with apple and thyme jelly, gâteau of smoked haddock with dill and yoghurt sauce, and slices of pink Challans duck breast with a crisp tartlet of wild mushrooms. Excellent sweets have included warm brioche filled with morello cherry compote, and a crisp toffee-coated peach set on a sweet almond parfait with butterscotch sauce. 'Wonderful,' drooled one reporter. Service 'works like clockwork – a joy to see'. There are 60 carefully chosen wines with reasonable mark-ups. House Chardonnay is £9.50.

CHEF: Shaun Smith-Roberts PROPRIETOR: John Brasted OPEN: Mon to Sat, exc Sat L; 12 to 2, 7 to 10 MEALS: alc. Set L £13 to £16, Set D £18 to £22 SERVICE: not inc CARDS: Access, Amex, Diners, Visa DETAILS: 22 seats. Private parties: 20 main room, 6 private room. Vegetarian meals with prior notice. Children welcome. Music. Fax: (0603) 766445

Green's Seafood

82 Upper St Giles Street,
Norwich NR2 1LT
NORWICH (0603) 623733

COOKING 1
COST £20–£38

East Anglian reporters point out that this restaurant has recently undergone 'a major upheaval': the entrance is now directly off the street and there is a new bar in the dining-room, which allows drinks to be brought to each table. However, Dennis Crompton's repertoire and style of cooking is unchanged. The emphasis is firmly on fresh fish, and most reports suggest that standards are being maintained. Seafood platter has been 'as good as in the old days', and lemon sole has been recommended. Daily specials are worth exploring: sea bass – simply grilled, or served with white wine sauce and prawns – has met with approval. There are steaks and a handful of other options for meat-eaters. Salad of crottin de Chavignol (soft cheese and home-cured salmon on toast) has been a fine starter; home-made ice-creams and pear savarin have been well-reported sweets. Presentation is 'picturesque' and most agree that portions are generous. The short wine list favours whites. House French is from £7.60.

CHEF/PROPRIETOR: Dennis Crompton OPEN: Tue to Sat, exc Sat L; 12.15 to 2, 7.15 to 10.45 CLOSED: 1 week Christmas, bank hols MEALS: alc. Set L £14, Set D £26 SERVICE: not inc, card slips closed CARDS: Access, Visa DETAILS: 48 seats. Private parties: 30 main room. Vegetarian meals. No children under 8. No cigars/pipes in dining-room. Music. Air-conditioned

Marco's ▯ ✳✦

17 Pottergate, Norwich NR2 1DS
NORWICH (0603) 624044

COOKING 1*
COST £26–£50

The décor – a homage to the colour yellow – is offset by the classical Italian menu. 'I do admire a cook who still produces such genuine food after 22 years in one and the same restaurant so far from his native Italy,' enthuses one reader. In all this time Marco Vessalio has not pandered to popular taste; nor has he moved with the times. On the other hand, his temerity in continuing to produce pot-roasted game, stews and offal dishes is perhaps a positive facet of his old-fashioned approach. A spring inspection meal commenced with fresh, home-made black fettucine served with fresh Norfolk crab sauce, a dish only available for about two months of the year; then the clear flavours of spring lamb, sautéed with chopped fresh artichokes, garlic, parsley and white wine, which came with a huge pile of well-timed, fresh-tasting vegetables (charged extra). Zabaglione classico, preceded by classical sounds of hand-whisking from the kitchen, was perhaps spoiled by too heavy a hand with the Marsala. Ancillaries were in need of greater attention. The food is served without unnecessary elaboration in large portions. If you like Italian tenors, you will like the music. Champagne and an English Müller-Thurgau apart, the wine list is rightly all Italian. Quality and detail may occasionally be found wanting, but generally this is a fair-priced list that invites experiment – even a Super-Tuscan Sassicaia from 1968 can be had for £180, and a good Barbera d'Asti 1987 for £12.50. House wines are £8.50. CELLARMAN'S CHOICE: Barbera d'Alba 1988, Conterno, £13.50; Ghemme 1983, Berletti, £16.

CHEF/PROPRIETOR: Marco Vessalio   OPEN: Tue to Sat; 12.30 to 2, 7.30 to 9.30   CLOSED: 20 Sept to 20 Oct   MEALS: alc. Set L £18   SERVICE: not inc, card slips closed   CARDS: Access, Amex, Diners, Visa   DETAILS: 20 seats. Private parties: 12 main room. Vegetarian meals. Children's helpings. No smoking in dining-room. Wheelchair access. Music

St Benedicts Grill   £ |NEW ENTRY|

9 St Benedicts Street,
Norwich NR2 4PE   COOKING 2
NORWICH (0603) 765377   COST £17–£29

Nigel and Jayne Raffles – he cooks, she waits – with partners Robert and Johanna Mabey of Mabey's Brasserie (see entry, Sudbury), are the inspiration behind this simple bistro. Tongue and groove feature on almost all walls; what isn't wood and bare is painted beige. To sit on there are church pews with cushions and hard spindly chairs – no lolling here. Two giant blackboards display the regular menu, two smaller ones the daily specials, which always include the fish dishes. The choices are straightforward. Although St Benedicts is not above garlic bread, chips and (marvellous) mashed potatoes, at the same time it is modern enough for tempura. The place fills a gap in Norwich, serving decent and ambitiously prepared food. The cooking is robust, portions are generous. Dishes enjoyed have included a tartlet of salmon lightly flavoured with ginger, a dish of tempura prawns, chicken breast stuffed with Gruyère, grilled venison with red cabbage, black peppercorn sauce and the superb creamy mashed potato (the latter also accompanying 'stunning' home-made garlic and white wine sausage), a green salad of strong, country flavours and iced praline parfait. A short, straightforward wine list, with some half-bottles, offers inexpensive drinking. House wines are from £5.95.

CHEF: Nigel Raffles   PROPRIETORS: Nigel and Jayne Raffles, Robert and Johanna Mabey OPEN: Tue to Sat; 12 to 2, 7 to 10 (10.30 Fri and Sat); pre- and post-theatre D by arrangement   CLOSED: L 25 to 31 Dec   MEALS: alc   SERVICE: not inc   CARDS: Access, Visa   DETAILS: 42 seats. Private parties: 42 main room, 20 private room. Vegetarian meals. Children's helpings. No cigars/pipes in dining-room. Wheelchair access. No music

If a restaurant is new to the Guide _this year (did not appear as a main entry in the last edition)_ NEW ENTRY _appears opposite its name._

£ _indicates that it is possible to have a three-course meal, including coffee, a half-bottle of house wine and service, at any time the restaurant is open (i.e. at dinner as well as at lunch, unless a place is open only for dinner), for £20 or less per person._

map 5

Saagar £

473 Mansfield Road, Sherwood,
Nottingham NG5 2DR   COOKING 1
NOTTINGHAM (0602) 622014 and 692860   COST £11–£28

Nottingham's most favourably reported Indian restaurant is away from the city
centre in the suburb of Sherwood. The décor may appear Regency in style, but
the kitchen is firmly rooted in north Indian cuisine with a strong showing of
familiar kormas, bhunas and birianis. It also spreads its net further afield for
south Indian kaallan specialities (prepared with mangos, yoghurt and
coconut), Kashmiri baltis and dishes such as aubergine paneer and nizami
masala chicken pointed up with sesame seeds. Prawn puri and sizzling
tandoori lamb are regular favourites. Portions are generous and the price of
most main dishes includes rice, poppadum and chutney. The atmosphere and
service draw mixed reports: some readers have found the mood complacent and
impersonal, although the quality of the food is compensation. House wine is £7
a litre, otherwise drink lager.

CHEF: Amjaid Habib PROPRIETOR: Mohammed Khizer OPEN: all week; 12 to 2.30, 5.30
to 12.30am CLOSED: 25 Dec MEALS: alc. Set L £6, Set D £11 to £16 SERVICE: not inc
CARDS: Access, Amex, Visa DETAILS: 45 seats. Private parties: 45 main room. Car park.
Vegetarian meals. Children's helpings. No pipes in dining-room. Music. Air-conditioned

Sonny's £

3 Carlton Street, Hockley,
Nottingham NG1 1NL   COOKING 1*
NOTTINGHAM (0602) 473041   COST £18–£33

The provincial offshoot of Sonny's in Barnes (see London entry) is on the
fringes of the new Lace Market development in Nottingham. The décor is pure
brasserie – a monochromatic mix of white paintwork, lampshades and curtains
with bare black floorboards. The cooking suits the setting and is in tune with
the current world view, its trends and its fashions. Chargrilling is the main
feature, backed up by dishes with a Mediterranean flavour: carpaccio of beef
with extra virgin olive oil and shaved Parmesan, breast of chicken stuffed with
roast red peppers, baked aubergine with pesto, and chargrilled salmon with
salsa verde are typical. There are always fish and pasta specials of the day. The
ambience is 'congenial', but the informal service can be too laid-back for some
people. Prices are reasonable, although some reporters have questioned the
value for money. Two dozen wines from around the world provide plenty of
affordable drinking. House wine is £7.25.

CHEF: Iain Broadbent PROPRIETORS: Rebecca Mascarenhas and Vernon Mascarenhas
OPEN: Mon to Sun, exc Sun D; 12 to 2.30 (3 Sat), 7 to 11 CLOSED: 25 Dec, bank hols
MEALS: alc. Set L £9.50 to £12.50, Set D £12.50 SERVICE: not inc CARDS: Access, Visa
DETAILS: 70 seats. Private parties: 70 main room. Vegetarian meals. Children's helpings.
Wheelchair access. Music

Truffles

NEW ENTRY

43 Broad Street, Nottingham NG1 3AP
NOTTINGHAM (0602) 472857

COUNTY OF THE YEAR RESTAURANT

COOKING 2
COST £21–£31

Anthony and Firooze Scott moved from Manchester in 1990 to open this converted shop in the centre of Nottingham. The décor is low-key and neutral, with sewing-machine tables, a few prints, quiet background jazz and dim lighting. The menu changes daily, depending on the market, and Anthony Scott brings a no-nonsense approach to planning it. The main influence is modern Anglo-French, but the cooking soaks up influences from elsewhere. Ingredients are fresh and local – although Manchester and Birmingham markets are used for raw materials such as offal. Food is cooked with restraint and conviction, and flavours are generally vigorous, yet a reporter found one of the vegetarian dishes 'pretty bland'. One impressive meal featured slices of game sausage with mango sauce and celeriac; baked goats' cheese topped with a round of filo pastry plus sweet pepper marmalade; guinea-fowl with grain mustard and tarragon sauce; and highly flavoured woodpigeon breasts with port sauce and grapes. Main dishes come with ample helpings of carefully cooked vegetables. Sweets are a speciality: the sticky toffee pudding is a winner. Pleasant, efficient staff 'behave like normal human beings doing a good job'. The wine list is workmanlike, adequate and reasonably priced. House French is from £7.25.

CHEF: Anthony Scott PROPRIETORS: Anthony and Firooze Scott OPEN: Tue to Sat, D only; 7 (6.30 Sat) to 11 CLOSED: first 2 weeks Jan MEALS: alc SERVICE: not inc CARDS: Access, Amex, Diners, Visa DETAILS: 45 seats. Private parties: 45 main room. Car park. Vegetarian meals with prior notice. Children welcome. Wheelchair access (1 step; also WC). Music

---

OAKHILL Somerset

map 2

▲ Oakhill House ⁙

Bath Road, Oakhill BA3 5AQ
OAKHILL (0749) 840180

COOKING 2*
COST £21–£29

In the months since they moved in, the Coopers have been building, painting and furnishing Oakhill House. The top-lit galleried hall is now a clear yellow, the bar is billiard-green, and the kitchen is new. Paul Cooper gains confidence with the customers and Marion Cooper continues to cook proper food for a short daily menu (but with plenty of range). Salmon and cod sausages with fennel sauce, asparagus with butter and shaved Parmesan, duck with onion confit, lamb with leek pithiviers and a herb sauce, cajun-blackened cod with tomato sauce, and chicken with Savoy cabbage and Parma ham are dishes that show happy hours of reading recipes and a wish to present upstanding flavours. Vegetables, such as one evening's ratatouille, celeriac purée and mange-tout, are worth the pause and there is always a vegetarian choice among the three main dishes. Insist on several puddings. These are good; so is pastry and baking; so is the price in a generally overcharged area. The wine list may be short, but much is available by the glass. House wine is £7.50.

CHEF: Marion Cooper PROPRIETORS: Paul and Marion Cooper OPEN: Tue to Sat, D only (Sun and Mon D, and L by arrangement); 7.30 to 9.30 MEALS: Set D £15 to £20 SERVICE: net prices, card slips closed CARDS: Access, Visa DETAILS: 20 seats. Private parties: 50 main room, 20 and 60 private rooms. Car park. Vegetarian meals. Children's helpings. No smoking in dining-room. Wheelchair access. No music ACCOMMODATION: 6 rooms, all with bath/shower. B&B £25 to £80. Children welcome. Baby facilities. Garden. Snooker. TV. Phone. Doors close at midnight. Confirm by 6. Fax: (0749) 840180 (*The Which? Hotel Guide*)

OLD BURGHCLERE Hampshire   map 2

Dew Pond 🍴✸

Old Burghclere RG15 9LH
BURGHCLERE (063 527) 408   COOKING 3*
off A34, 3m W of Kingsclere   COST £24–£35

Reworking of the main road to Newbury makes a dip in the Dew Pond (drought permitting) complicated. Frustrated map-readers say that the restaurant may only be reached from the old road. It is worth the effort. Keith Marshall is a wizard with sauces: 'Of the three wonderful sauces I enjoyed, that with the feuilleté of scallops (tasting lightly of the chargrill) and asparagus was possibly the best.' That was a herb butter sauce, the second was a chive and Roquefort butter emulsion with beef fillets sandwiched between a purée of leeks and a bird's-nest of deep-fried shredded leek. The third was a creamy toffee sauce that went with a sticky toffee pudding and was better than both the pudding and the caramel ice-cream that was a third element. Good cooking, good materials and attention to details such as pastry and petits fours combine to the customer's benefit. Each set-price menu may run for about a month, and there are perhaps eight options at each course. Recipes are modern yet classical: twice-baked soufflé with wild mushrooms, venison with tartlets of apples and oyster mushrooms and a sage and red wine sauce, and a lemon tart with a lime sorbet are examples from another meal. Come the spring, a dish of brill and salmon with vermouth, basil and tomato sauce on a bed of root vegetables, chicken with langoustine, garlic and a saffron sauce, and duck with Cassis sauce are items that have proved successful. Desserts may include interesting sorbets such as a terrine composed in layers, or intriguing flavours like blackcurrant and kiwi with a lime syrup. The restaurant is run by various members of the Marshall family and has retained that sense of collective activity. They have certainly done wonders with the wine list. A greater range (much taken from Berry Bros & Rudd) has given it the depth that the food deserved. There are many New World choices to keep the prices in balance and an adequate number of halves. There is a useful house selection under £15 as well as the house Duboeuf at £8. CELLARMAN'S CHOICE: Ch. Thieuley, Sauvignon Blanc 1990, £11.55; Côtes du Rhône, Guigal 1986, £13.50.

CHEF: Keith Marshall PROPRIETORS: Keith and Julie Marshall OPEN: Tue to Sat, exc Sat L; 12 to 2, 7 to 10 CLOSED: first 2 weeks Jan, 2 weeks mid-Aug MEALS: Set L £16 to £19.50, Set D £23 SERVICE: not inc CARDS: Access, Visa DETAILS: 40 seats. Private parties: 50 main room, 25 private room. Car park. Vegetarian meals. No children under 12. Smart dress preferred. No smoking in dining-room. Wheelchair access (also WC). No music

OLDBURY West Midlands   map 5

▲ *Jonathans* ⚑✱

16–20 Wolverhampton Road,
Oldbury B68 0LH   COOKING 1
021-429 3757   COST £19–£51

At first glance, this looks like a modern, purpose-built hotel in pristine brick.
But inside, according to one visitor, it is 'delightful, fun, different and
adventurous'. Everything about the décor harks back to Victorian and
Edwardian times, although the place is very deliberate in its intentions.
Coloured wooden arrows, each representing a different railway line, guide
people around the network of rooms, shop-fronts and displays; some prices are
marked up in old money. The kitchen looks to the past also, drawing on
everyone from Parson Woodforde to Mrs Beeton for inspiration. There is great
emphasis on sauces and relishes and a conscious attempt to recreate the
flavours of history: chicken terrine with pickled lemons, spatchcocked trout,
jugged pheasant and Charles II syllabub are typical of the repertoire. Herb
bread is baked twice daily on the premises. Farmhouse cheeses are from British
producers. If you like a fairground approach to eating out, and don't set too
much store by subtlety, this place is for you. The wine list favours France, Italy
and the New World. House French is £9.80.

CHEFS: Jonathan Bedford and Graham Bradley   PROPRIETORS: Jonathan Bedford and
Jonathan Baker   OPEN: all week; 12 to 2 (4 Sun), 7 to 10.30   MEALS: alc. Set L £12.50, Set
D £24.50   SERVICE: not inc, card slips closed   CARDS: Access, Amex, Visa   DETAILS: 160
seats. 10 tables outside. Private parties: 100 main room, 10, 18 and 30 private rooms. Car
park. Vegetarian meals. Children's helpings Sun L. No smoking in 1 dining-room.
Wheelchair access (also WC). Music   ACCOMMODATION: 26 rooms, all with bath/shower.
Rooms for disabled. B&B £69 to £118. Deposit: 10%. Children welcome. Baby facilities.
Pets welcome. Afternoon teas. Garden. TV. Phone. Confirm 1 day ahead. Fax: 021-434 3107
(*The Which? Hotel Guide*)

ORFORD Suffolk   map 3

Butley-Orford Oysterage £

Market Hill, Orford IP12 2LH   COOKING 1
ORFORD (0394) 450277   COST £15–£28

The oysterage is a long-standing fixture of the Suffolk scene, particularly
during high summer and the festival season. The attraction is the range of
prime smoked fish from the Pinney family's own smokery, plus fresh oysters
from the Butley Creek beds and an assortment of locally caught seafood. These
items draw regular praise. Visitors are generally less enamoured with cooked
dishes, which can be treated with a heavy hand and served with
'disappointing' sauces. Rum cake has been a 'delicious' dessert. Service is by
local girls: it may seem amateurish, but it is generally 'quite sweet'. To drink,
there is Guinness and a short list of well-chosen white wines from £6.60
(served in tumblers) with plenty of halves.

CHEF: Mathilde Pinney   PROPRIETORS: Mathilde and William Pinney   OPEN: all week
May to Oct; L all week and Fri and Sat D Nov to Apr; 12 to 2.15, 6 to 8.30   MEALS: alc
SERVICE: not inc   DETAILS: 82 seats. Private parties: 25 main room. Car park. Children
welcome. Wheelchair access (also WC). No music

OXFORD Oxfordshire   map 2

Al-Shami £

25 Walton Crescent, Oxford OX1 2JG   COOKING 1
OXFORD (0865) 310066   COST £14–£26

Long opening hours are an attraction at this popular Lebanese restaurant
unexpectedly located in a residential street. A harvest festival of raw vegetables
– crisp lettuce, giant tomato, green pepper and cucumber – and a dish of olives
are left on each table as a healthy distraction. The strength of the menu lies in
the long list of three dozen hot and cold starters, which ranges from tabouleh
and moussaqa'at badhinjan (fried aubergine with chickpeas and tomatoes) to
falafel and fatayer (spinach-filled pastries). Main courses from the chargrill are
generally fresh and well spiced. Occasionally a bad experience may cause
devotees to lose faith, but the overriding impression is one of authentic food,
good value and friendly, considerate service – even at peak times. Lebanese
Ch. Musar, Ksara and Araks dominate the short wine list. House French is from
£6.50.

CHEF/PROPRIETOR: Mimo Mahfouz   OPEN: all week; noon to midnight   MEALS: alc. Set L
£8 to £15, Set D £12 to £15. Cover £1   SERVICE: not inc (10% for 6 or more)   DETAILS: 40
seats. Private parties: 60 main room. Vegetarian meals. Children welcome. Wheelchair
access (also WC). Music. Fax: (0865) 311242

▲ Bath Place Hotel ⁑✳

4–5 Bath Place, Oxford OX1 3SU   COOKING 2*
OXFORD (0865) 791812   COST £23–£43

The message about this diminutive building now functioning as a hotel and
restaurant is clear. People like the location: down an alley, away from the
traffic. People enjoy the decoration: a neat finish to small rooms with lots of
doors. The food's all right too; but there are some grumbles about service – as,
for example, when a hotel guest finds that there's no room in the restaurant
until well after 10pm – although these are outweighed by plaudits. The menu
gives half a dozen choices, and you pay according to how many courses you
consume. The cooking is fashionable. A warm hake terrine wrapped in a
spinach leaf with a tomato butter sauce preceded one man's fillet of pork with
bacon, mushrooms and spinach and a light cream sauce; he finished with a
sharp lemon tart the slight stodginess of which was cut by a garnish of citrus
segments. Several meals here have hit the target precisely. Pasta with wild
mushrooms, tartare of salmon, duck with black olives, brill and red mullet
with a cinnamon and red wine sauce are some things remarked on; oysters
with pasta and a lime sauce, red pepper terrine with chicken livers, oxtail and
onion ragoût, a casserole of pheasant, and rabbit with tagliatelle and an

armagnac sauce are others. Everyone has warmed to the apple and almond pithiviers with a cinnamon ice-cream. Portions are adequate without overload. If the service were smartened up, things might be good. The wine list is soundly based, with the range pitched to value by recruiting bottles from the New World. House wines are £10.50.

CHEF: Peter Cherrill   PROPRIETORS: the Fawsitt family   OPEN: Tue to Sun, exc Tue L and Sun D; 12 to 2, 7 to 10 (10.30 Fri and Sat)   MEALS: Set L £14.50 to £17.50 (Sun), Set D £21.95 to £28.50   SERVICE: not inc (10% for 6 or more)   CARDS: Access, Amex, Visa DETAILS: 34 seats. 4 tables outside. Private parties: 40 main room. Car park. Vegetarian meals on request. Children welcome. Smart dress preferred. No smoking in dining-room. Music   ACCOMMODATION: 10 rooms, all with bath/shower. B&B £70 to £125. Deposit: £25. Children welcome. TV. Phone. Doors close at 10. Confirm 1 day ahead. Fax: (0865) 791834 (*The Which? Hotel Guide*)

Cherwell Boathouse ♥ £

Bardwell Road, Oxford OX2 6SR   COOKING 1
OXFORD (0865) 52746   COST £20–£24

The name conjures up the setting, and for many this is an idyllic spot for lunch, or dinner on a fine evening. Gerard Crowley's short, weekly set menus are attractive both in price and choice. Cooking is accurate and influenced mainly by France and Britain, with touches from Greece and Italy. A meal that began with mussels, white wine and cream, continued with baby chicken and shallot and rosemary sauce and finished with sticky toffee pudding presented fair ingredients in a more than adequate light. Readers have praised the breast of pigeon with a shallot, basil and tomato sauce, tagliatelle with pepper and fennel in a cashew-nut sauce, the mountainous piles of vegetables, and the home-made bread and ice-cream. 'It's not the Waterside Inn, but far friendlier.' Friendliness extends to the wine list which is both reasonably priced and generously provided, with as much attention devoted to the modest as to the fine. The only lapse is a relative paucity of half-bottles. House wine is £6. CELLARMAN'S CHOICE: Meursault, Goutte d'Or 1982, Comte Lafon, £29; Ch. Beaucastel 1987, £15.

CHEF: Gerard Crowley   PROPRIETOR: Anthony Verdin   OPEN: Tue to Sun, exc Tue L and Sun D; 12 to 2, 6.30 to 10.30   MEALS: alc L. Set L and D £15.50   SERVICE: not inc CARDS: Access, Amex, Diners, Visa   DETAILS: 50 seats. Private parties: 50 main room, 120 boathouse. Car park. Vegetarian meals. Children's helpings. Wheelchair access (1 step; also WC). No music

15 North Parade

15 North Parade Avenue, Oxford OX2 6LX   COOKING 1*
OXFORD (0865) 513773   COST £20–£40

The address requires some clarification: North Parade Avenue is a tiny one-way street off the Banbury Road, considerably further south than South Parade. Inside, this is small but roomy, with bright, fresh décor and wicker chairs. The restaurant offers a variety of flexible menus – a full *carte*, fixed-price lunches, dinners, theatre meals, Sunday lunches and special menus for special occasions. Although the Mediterranean looms large, chef Stanley Matthews plunders the globe for inspiration: bortsch and confit of duck with orange marmalade sauce share the stage with caramelised pepper and mozzarella tartlet, and calf's liver with sage and lemon. Wild mushrooms seem to be a current trend: they appear as an authentic-tasting soup, as part of a creamy fricassee with chicken, and as a dark sauce for stuffed guinea-fowl. Reporters have also enjoyed smoked-chicken salad, roast fillet of pork with basil and honey sauce, and pumpkin pie peppered with nutmeg. Breads and ice-creams are made on the premises. Service is excellent. The short, wide-ranging wine list has house wine at £9.50.

CHEF: Stanley Matthews   PROPRIETOR: Georgina Wood   OPEN: all week, exc Sun D; 12 to 2, 6.30 to 10.30 (theatre menu 6.30 to 7.15 and 9.30 to 10.30)   MEALS: alc. Set L £14.75 to £15.75, Set D £15.75. Theatre menu £11.75   SERVICE: not inc   CARD: Access, Visa
DETAILS: 55 seats. Private parties: 55 main room. Vegetarian meals. Children's helpings. Wheelchair access (also WC). Music. Air-conditioned

Gee's Brasserie £

> **NEW ENTRY**

61 Banbury Road,
Oxford OX2 6PE
OXFORD (0865) 53540

COOKING 1
COST £20–£32

A cleric's throw from St Giles church, Gee's inhabits a large white conservatory, once a flower shop. Alistair Campbell has created a convivial greenhouse for town and gown; hothouse dons and undergraduates break ciabatta with local business folk and culture-sated travellers. 'The food is Cal-Ital and you can eat long or short,' remarks a fan. Sometimes the food promises more than it delivers: bruschetta can be 'oily' and roasted plump red peppers may not yield full flavour. With so many popular Mediterranean-style dishes collated on a single *carte* results are bound to be uneven. But a coil of spicy Italian sausage with roasted and braised shallots and breast of duck with a honey and peppercorn glaze are recommended, as is weekend brunch. Desserts fail to inspire; service is slick. The wine list is perfunctory but stays cheap. House wine is from the Bocuse label at £7.50.

CHEF: Paul Petrillo   PROPRIETORS: Alistair Campbell and Paul Petrillo   OPEN: all week D, Sat and Sun L; noon to 11.30 (Sat and Sun), 6 to 11.30 (Mon to Fri D)   MEALS: alc
SERVICE: not inc (10% for 5 or more, card slips closed)   CARDS: Access, Amex, Visa
DETAILS: 80 seats. Private parties: 100 main room. Car park. Vegetarian meals. Children's helpings. Wheelchair access. Music. Air-conditioned

Liaison £

29 Castle Street, Oxford OX1 1LJ
OXFORD (0865) 242944

COOKING 1
COST £18–£38

This elegant Chinese restaurant is on two floors, near the Westgate Centre. The menu is a familiar provincial assemblage of Cantonese, Pekinese and Szechuan dishes ranging from sesame prawn toasts and hot-and-sour soup to duck with plum sauce and shredded beef with chilli. There are also one or two curiosities, such as 'baked trio of heavenly seafood in Portuguese style' and ho pang –

described as a 'delicious omelette oyster cooked with spring onion'. Recommendations have included steamed scallops, deep-fried paper-wrapped prawns, Peking duck and sizzling chicken. Strangely, desserts feature home-made ice-creams and chocolate mousse as well as exotic rambutans. Lunches are good value, although visitors on one occasion found the quality of the cooking 'not particularly high' – possibly because the dining-room was in the process of major renovation. House wine is £6.95.

CHEF: Kok Leung Lam   PROPRIETOR: Timmy Tsang   OPEN: all week; 12 to 3 (4 Sun), 6.30 to 11.30 (12 Fri and Sat)   CLOSED: 3 days Christmas   MEALS: alc. Set D £14.50 to £22.50 SERVICE: not inc (10% for 5 or more)   CARDS: Access, Amex, Visa   DETAILS: 90 seats. Private parties: 60 main room, 18 private room. Vegetarian meals. Children's helpings. Wheelchair access (2 steps). Music

Munchy Munchy £

6 Park End Street, Oxford OX1 1HH	COOKING 1
OXFORD (0865) 245710	COST £15–£24

Ethel Ow's Malaysian café has been a fixture of the Oxford scene for many years, although some regulars feel that it has lost much of its original zing. Meals are served in a room that has been likened to a canteen – unfussy, practical and almost clinical with its regimented tables. The short menu makes enticing reading: duck with oregano, cinnamon, passion-fruit juice, nutmeg, cloves and white wine; king prawns with juniper berries, star-anise, scented screw-pine leaves and coconut milk. Often, this barrage of ingredients can produce excellent, distinctive results, but sometimes the flavours merely cancel each other out. Reporters have praised 'incredibly tender' well-marinated meat and poultry, a vegetarian dish full of 'healthy' Eastern spinach and Eastern chives in a subtly spiced oily sauce, and chicken with Indonesian pickle. Others have lamented 'rather muddy flavours', cold satays, and 'lukewarm fatty lamb with very poor spiciness'. Service can be as variable as the cooking. To drink there are unusual oriental teas and the restaurant is now licensed. House French is £6.95.

CHEF: Ethel Ow   PROPRIETORS: Tony and Ethel Ow   OPEN: Tue to Sat; 12 to 2, 5.30 to 10 CLOSED: 2 weeks Aug, 2 weeks Dec   MEALS: alc   SERVICE: not inc (10% for 5 or more) DETAILS: 60 seats. Private parties: 10 main room. No children under 6 Fri and Sat D. No-smoking area. Wheelchair access. No music

Restaurant Elizabeth ▼

82 St Aldate's, Oxford OX1 1RA	COOKING 1*
OXFORD (0865) 242230	COST £24–£40

This suite of rooms dates from the seventeenth century and is situated over Littlemore Court, which is fifteenth-century. Plasterwork and panelling are worth the tourist visit, and the view across St Aldate's to Christ Church is a visual dividend. Señor Lopez runs a conservative restaurant. Care is solicitous: 'In that aching gap between ordering and the first bite, when there isn't a great deal for a lone diner to do other than contemplatively sip your sherry and curse yourself for not having brought the paper, I was given a selection of magazines to thumb through. As a result I know rather a lot about swimming-pool installation.' The menu does not change much and includes first courses like avocado with prawns, baked mussels, or quenelles of salmon with sauce Nantua, followed by breast of chicken with brandy and cream, steak with green peppercorns or duck with orange. These are often done well. Daily offerings are more interesting, particularly if they include game. Sorbets are not brilliant, but crème brûlée is. Coffee could be stronger. This place has faults, and the plainer cooking which is done best begins to seem expensive. Lunch is better value. Cover charge is still levied, and there is a space labelled 'gratuity' on the credit card slip even though service has already been included. Conservatism is one thing but it must be some years since Alsace could have appeared under the 'Vins d'Allemagne' heading. This apart, the wine list shows quiet enthusiasm and knowledge, leading with some fine Spanish bottles and lingering over French classics chosen with care. Prices are highish but some economy is possible with decent half-bottles. House wine is £8.25. CELLARMAN'S CHOICE: Chardonnay 1990, Latour, £12.90; Côtes du Rhône 1989, Parallèle 45, Jaboulet, £12.90.

CHEF: Salvador Rodriguez   PROPRIETOR: Antonio Lopez   OPEN: Tue to Sun; 12.30 to 2.30, 6.30 to 11 (7 to 10.30 Sun)   CLOSED: 24 to 30 Dec, Good Fri   MEALS: alc. Set L Tue to Fri £14.25 (weekdays only). Cover £1. Minimum £12   SERVICE: net prices   CARDS: Access, Amex, Diners, Visa   DETAILS: 40 seats. Private parties: 40 main room, 20 private room. Vegetarian meals. Children welcome. No music

---

PADSTOW Cornwall   map 1

▲ *Seafood Restaurant* ▮

Riverside, Padstow PL28 8BY   COOKING 4
PADSTOW (0841) 532485   COST £26–£61

Rick Stein Inc. grows and grows. The shop and bakery (round the corner in downtown Padstow) have been refurbished and extended, there is talk of a coffee-shop, a new book is due, and the restaurant is now open for lunch every day. To achieve these ends, the brigade has been strengthened, and Rick Stein hopes consistency is improved. The Seafood shows that real restaurants – busy, good, bright and humming with every sort of life – can exist in Britain, and can make money. It is inevitable that this place gets differing ratings from readers – it serves so many of them. Right by the riverside, the view is more important to the bedrooms upstairs (comfortable, brightly furnished and a bargain off-season) than to the dining-room. This has a conservatory at the front then a pair of large rooms with 'very white walls interrupted by colourful posters, large Victorian mirrors, hanging baskets of vines and standing tubs of same, cane chairs with patterned cushions, and prettily laid tables with fresh flowers, crisp linen, simple cutlery and china and a jug of water'. This is many people's idea of perfection: no candles, no table lamps, no frills, just colour and brightness. The menu is fish, with one meat main dish and a couple of others for the first course (foie gras and corn pancakes is a regular). The grill is the dominant cooking appliance: grilled langoustines with garlic and chives, tuna with olives, lemon and sorrel, silver bream and John Dory with tomato and tarragon and potato purée. Sauces become salsa, or are oil dressings or just juices. There are butter emulsions, like beurre blanc and cucumber and coriander with brill, but this is a long way from fish restaurants and white sauce. Materials are of tip-top origin. It is difficult to begin description of all that has pleased. It may range from chargrilled monkfish that reminded a reader of bonfires on Catalan beaches in the '60s, to simple grilled sea trout, to vast plates of shellfish, or lobster stewed with plenty of saffron and herbs. It may extend to the vegetables – everyone gets the same, on a side plate – which are often exact, but which perhaps attract more criticism that any other component of the meal. It may touch on the occasional forays to the East, as in the dish of raw fish (scallops, salmon, turbot, sole and monkfish) with wasabi, soy dipping sauce and two sorts of pickled ginger. It may even include the strong coffee. Desserts get mixed mentions: good ice-creams, a good feuilleté of plums and apples, but not such good pears (often undercooked). The service is usually proficient, with no more than the expected number of slips. On the wine list, six Alsace Gewurztraminers to two Rieslings is a curious distribution, but quality is consistently very fine, and prices start low and rise slowly to reflect quality very fairly. 'Our Selection' is a succinctly edited and helpful list of 10 bottles; would that the same approach were followed throughout. CELLARMAN'S CHOICE: Pouilly Fumé, Cuvée d'Eve 1989, Dagueneau, £24; Meursault, La Pièce sous le Bois 1984, Ampeau, £39.90.

CHEF: Richard Stein   PROPRIETORS: Richard and Jill Stein   OPEN: Mon to Sat; 12.30 to 2.15, 7.30 to 9.30 (10 Sat)   MEALS: alc. Set L £17.50, Set D £25.50   SERVICE: not inc CARDS: Access, Visa   DETAILS: 75 seats. Private parties: 24 main room. Children's helpings. Music. Air-conditioned   ACCOMMODATION: 10 rooms, all with bath/shower. B&B £32 to £99. Children welcome. Baby facilities. Pets welcome. TV. Phone. Fax: (0841) 533344 (*The Which? Hotel Guide*)

PAINSWICK Gloucestershire   map 2

Country Elephant | NEW ENTRY |

New Street, Painswick GL6 6XH   COOKING 3
PAINSWICK (0452) 813564   COST £18–£38

Painswick houses have a habit of imposing their own character on a place: good. The elephant, mostly sporting if you look at the sign, may be 'country' in general terms, but the traffic lights near the front door bring a spot of town, and Mark Anton Edwards' cooking has more assurance than any bumpkin's. After spells at Popjoy's in Bath and at Lucknam Park (see entry, Colerne), he has come here to work in the restaurant of his parents-in-law. The menu is of ample length, offering a proper range and exhibiting many flavour types. Garlic bread accompanied by a salad, pesto and tapénade sits next to a dish of poached eggs on a bed of mushrooms and asparagus, with a madeira sauce. New-wave meets the classic, perhaps. Diners have been impressed by the exact cooking and the clarity of tastes. A hotpot of fish included mackerel along with brill and monkfish: most had been either grilled or fried, giving added flavour. Texture came from a nest of fried shredded leek, the sauce (rather than a stew-like liquid) was fresh, lemony and apposite. A breast of chicken had a strong sauce emboldened by black olives and an accompaniment of ratatouille elements (but no aubergine) to add some moist juices to the whole, as well as some whole roast cloves of garlic. The simplicity never lapsed into crudeness; each element contributed its tithe to the harmony. A pear in fanned slices came with a parfait of honey and almond and a wonderful tuile. Again, what impressed were the clear flavours. Service varies but has country character and observant efficiency. Coffee has not been thought up to the mark of the food. As yet the wine list is simple, the interest coming from the various bin-ends. House wine is £8.50.

CHEFS: Mark Anton Edwards and Marril Gibson PROPRIETORS: Kenneth and Marril Gibson OPEN: Tue to Sun, exc Sun D; 12 (12.30 Sun) to 2, 7 to 10 CLOSED: L Nov to Apr MEALS: alc. Set Sun L £10.50 to £12.50 SERVICE: alc 10%, Set L not inc, card slips closed CARDS: Access, Diners, Visa DETAILS: 36 seats. 4 tables outside. Private parties: 40 main room. Vegetarian meals. Children's helpings. No cigars/pipes in dining-room. Wheelchair access (2 steps). Music

---

▲ Painswick Hotel

NEW ENTRY

Kemps Lane, Painswick GL6 6YB
PAINSWICK (0452) 812160

COOKING 2
COST £24–£43

Rectory? Some rectory. It has been converted with ease into a 20-bedroomed hotel and restaurant. Not only did the rector of Painswick manage 99 yews in his churchyard but he had a palace for a house. The public rooms are a pleasure to enter and have not been over-decorated. Somerset Moore came here from Flitwick Manor (see entry, Flitwick) and a long career of cooking and catering before that. He has landed on his feet. He has always enjoyed cooking fish, so it is small surprise that he installed a seawater tank here and makes a thing of shellfish, particularly oysters, lobster and langoustines. There is a normal menu as well, though fish and lobster outnumber meat in a summer listing. The cooking shows some enthusiasm in good bread, decent sauces and nice ideas such as the pile of garlic cloves served with pork fillet in a lemon sauce. However, it may also show lapses of technique: damp pastry underneath a lemon tart, the cheese taste that drowned the lobster in a first-course ravioli, and the lackadaisical vegetables. The style is modern mainstream: it avoids fruits and relishes, and espouses pasta, wild mushrooms and savoury flavours. Stir-fry of beef with black-bean sauce, salmon with cucumber sauce, skate with capers and tomato in beurre noisette or a first course of prawn mousse with red pimentos and olive oil are notes of the character now pursued. Desserts may be strawberry shortcake, crème brûlée or an aniseed parfait. There are good British cheeses, coffee is fair and there are three sorts of fudge. A mighty pleasant place to visit. The wine list will aid merriment. There is a set of 'house selections' arranged in price bands, another set of 'classics' that are simply more expensive, and some half-bottles. The range is drawn from round the world, the prices are fair, and the sources are good. House wines start at £10.50.

'Our glasses were refilled after almost every sip. This was hardly relaxing, so I asked if I could pour it myself. The wine waiter said he would prefer it if we asked him. The head waiter then explained that there might be writers of guidebooks in the restaurant and they would receive a bad impression.' On dining in Hampshire

---

CHEF: Shaun Cook PROPRIETORS: Somerset and Hélène Moore OPEN: all week; 12.30 to 2, 7.30 to 9.30 MEALS: seafood alc. Set L and D £18.50 to £27 SERVICE: net prices, card slips closed CARDS: Access, Amex, Visa DETAILS: 65 seats, 4 tables outside. Private parties: 65 main room, 12 and 12 private rooms. Car park. Vegetarian meals. Children's helpings. No-smoking room on request. Music ACCOMMODATION: 20 rooms, all with bath/shower. B&B £60 to £125. Deposit: 50%. Children welcome. Baby facilities. Dogs welcome. Garden. TV. Phone. Doors close at midnight. Confirm by 6. Fax: (0452) 814059 (*The Which? Hotel Guide*)

PAULERSPURY Northamptonshire   map 2

▲ *Vine House* | NEW ENTRY |

100 High Street,
Paulerspury NN12 7NA   COOKING 2
PAULERSPURY (032 733) 267   COST £21–£36

New owners often need time to settle. After taking over this converted Northamptonshire farmhouse in June 1991, Marcus and Julie Springett have overcome early traumas and are now beginning to find a sense of direction. They are a hard-working couple, and their cooking is gaining in confidence. Menus change daily and almost everything is produced in-house. This is a kitchen full of ideas, and the style is new-wave traditional British: hot oxtail sausage with mustard sauce; baked lamb, smoked bacon and rosemary suet roll with truffle sauce; apple charlotte with vanilla pod custard. The results can be impressive and technically sharp: duck and butter-bean broth and salmon and smoked salmon bubble and 'squeek' have been excellent. Occasionally the kitchen veers off course; in particular, the notion of seasonality (a talisman of new British cooking) seems to be ignored or badly thought out: a springtime dish of good-quality new season's shoulder of lamb was given a dark, autumnal stuffing of wild mushrooms and garlic and a dark, reduced rosemary sauce which seemed to lack 'any sense of appropriateness'. Apple and marmalade crumble with 'properly made' custard has been a good sweet. To start there are home-made crusty brown bread rolls; to finish there are unpasteurised British cheeses with home-made oatmeal biscuits. A decent list of around 80 wines has a good choice of halves. House French is £7.95.

CHEF: Marcus Springett PROPRIETORS: Marcus and Julie Springett OPEN: all week, exc L Mon and Sat, and Sun D; 12 to 2.30, 7.30 to 10 MEALS: Set L £13.95, Set D Mon to Thur £19.50, Set D Fri and Sat £23.50 SERVICE: not inc CARDS: Access, Visa DETAILS: 46 seats. Private parties: 40 main room, 12 private room. Car park. Vegetarian meals with prior notice. Children's helpings. Smart dress preferred. No cigars/pipes in dining-room. No music ACCOMMODATION: 6 rooms, all with bath/shower. B&B £39 to £61. Children welcome. Baby facilities. Garden. TV. Phone. Doors close at midnight. Confirm by 7.30. Fax: (032 733) 309 (*The Which? Hotel Guide*)

The Guide *relies on feedback from its readers. Especially welcome are reports on new restaurants appearing in the book for the first time.*

County round-ups listing additional restaurants that may be worth a visit are at the back of the Guide, *after the Irish section. Reports on round-up entries are welcome.*

PINNER Greater London   map 3

La Giralda £

66 Pinner Green,
Pinner HA5 2AB   COOKING 1
081-868 3429   COST £15−£21

'What incredibly good value for money' is a view often echoed about this long-standing Continental restaurant, which celebrated two decades of trading in 1992. A new feature is all-day opening on Sundays, when a menu of 'market seasonal dishes' is available. There is a noticeable Spanish undercurrent to the menu, although recommended dishes show that the kitchen casts its net further afield for inspiration: smoked salmon and prawn parcels, spatchcocked poussin with grapes, chicken breasts stuffed with pâté, and chestnut pear with toffee sauce have all been enjoyed. There are also daily specials, such as skewered pork with avocado dip. The repertoire seldom changes and most attributes of La Giralda belong to the days of the '60s and '70s. The place is invariable busy, but the waiters get full marks for their smiles and swift, excellent service. The wine list is a monumental tome devoted to fine Spanish bottles. House Rioja is £7.60.

CHEFS: David Brown and Derek Knight PROPRIETOR: David Brown OPEN: Tue to Sun; 12 to 2.30, 6.30 to 10.30 (12 to 8 Sun) MEALS: Set L £6 to £11, Set D £10 to £15 SERVICE: 10% (net prices Sun L) CARDS: Access, Amex, Visa DETAILS: 120 seats. Private parties: 50 main room, 16 and 35 private rooms. Vegetarian meals. Children's helpings. Wheelchair access. No music. Air-conditioned. Fax: 081-868 1218

PITTON Wiltshire   map 2

Silver Plough

Pitton SP5 1DZ   COOKING 1
FARLEY (072 272) 266   COST £21−£27

This is a village pub in perfect walking country – a barrow for breakfast, tuna for lunch – with a restaurant extension as well as a bar for food. While most pubs concentrate on lasagne, chilli and steak and kidney, the Silver Plough can rustle up pizzette, tapénade croûtons, lamb grilled with olive oil and sage, or mussels grilled with cucumber and cumin butter. Sometimes it does it well, other times approximately, but full marks for trying. While beams (real and imitation) are so thick on walls and ceilings to give barely any space for intervening plaster, the place gets praise for comfort and the owners and staff are applauded for willingness. The restaurant has a set-price menu of a half-dozen choices at each course; there is also the blackboard in the bar. Steaks are still a popular item, for instance with garlic butter, and the chips get paeans, as do the ice-creams (even if portions seem scant) and other puddings, such as a hot ginger, orange and chocolate affair with brandy custard. Bread and various small incidentals could be improved. The wine list gives fair range, and takes in plenty from overseas as well as a central core from France. There are eight house wines to choose from, starting at £8.75.

CHEF: Miss J. Dockerty   PROPRIETORS: Michael Beckett, P.K. Parnell and C.I. Mantkelow   OPEN: all week; 12 to 2, 7 to 10 (9.30 Sun and Mon)   CLOSED: 25 Dec, Sun D Jan and Feb   MEALS: alc. Set L £9.95 to £12.95, Set D £12.95 to £15.95   SERVICE: not inc, card slips closed   CARDS: Access, Amex, Diners, Visa   DETAILS: 100 seats. 14 tables outside. Private parties: 40 main room, 40 private room. Car park. Vegetarian meals. Children's helpings L. Music

---

PLUMTREE Nottinghamshire   map 5

Perkins Bar Bistro £

Old Railway Station, Plumtree NG12 5NA	COOKING 2*
PLUMTREE (0602) 373695	COST £16–£31

This admirable enterprise recently celebrated its tenth anniversary, and Tony Perkins' philosophy of consistency, high quality and value for money remains unchanged. For some visitors, a trip to the intriguingly converted railway station is 'a break in the country, only a couple of miles from Nottingham'. Tony Perkins' gastronomic roots are in traditional French cuisine, and his snack and evening menus have a strong Gallic accent: eggs Bénédictine; poached salmon Dugléré; ballottine of tarragon chicken béarnaise; crêpes suzette. The repertoire changes every few weeks and the blackboards are always boosted by daily specials. One popular lunch featured braised woodpigeon breasts in orange sauce and herb-crusted loin of lamb soubise with vegetables 'cooked just right', followed by chocolate roulade and banana rum and raisin tart. Others have enjoyed the simple pleasures of a half-pint of fresh prawns with dip. Service is generally excellent. Tony Perkins plans to trim a few of the least attractive bottles from the affordable 50-strong wine list. House French is £6.67.

CHEFS: Tony Perkins and Kevin Pole   PROPRIETORS: Tony and Wendy Perkins   OPEN: Tue to Sat; 12 to 2, 7 to 9.45   CLOSED: 1 week Christmas   MEALS: alc   SERVICE: not inc   CARDS: Access, Amex, Visa   DETAILS: 90 seats. 6 tables outside. Private parties: 24 main room. Car park. Vegetarian meals. Children welcome. Wheelchair access (1 step). Music

---

PLYMOUTH Devon   map 1

Chez Nous ▼

13 Frankfort Gate, Plymouth PL1 1QA	COOKING 3*
PLYMOUTH (0752) 266793	COST £34–£62

Chez Nous retains its cosy bistro feel and that blackboard menu (totally illegible without 20/20 vision). It occupies a shop premises in the small pedestrian square of Plymouth's post-war reconstruction, a hop and skip away from a multi-storey car park. Trees are in leaf, pigeons abound, and fish and chip papers swirl, but go through the door and cross to a memory of France. Jacques Marchal cooks modern realities – there is no nostalgia at the stove. His menu is large (for a one-man band), and the repertoire does not change radically from year to year, even if dishes come and go from day to day as supplies are marshalled. The style is light. One seasoned cook reflected that the sauces needed greater concentration to bring out the flavours. Fish and shellfish are especial strengths: scallops with ginger lodged strong in the consciousness of one visitor; steamed fillets of brill showed accuracy of cooking even when under pressure. Offal, too, is worth a second look: in a dish of calves' sweetbreads and kidneys, the latter were done to a precise turn of pink in the centre (not bloody raw), with a light stock adequately supporting them. Vegetables may be the same for everyone, but these get full marks for freshness and condition. One small kitchen, yet M. Marchal is capable of delivering perfect tuiles and shortbread (even if the bread is not his own, alas) or summoning up a nice appetiser, or cooking a plain steak as well as rolling and stuffing ravioli. Suzanne Marchal keeps everything ship-shape front-of-house. It is a pleasure to eat here; there is a true sense of 'chez nous'. A predominantly French wine list is reinforced by a modest selection of 'Vins d'autres pays', but this remains a serious list conceding little beyond the classic areas. Prices at the lower reaches are fair with much decent drinking below £15; thereafter the mark-ups can be steep, compensated by reasonable provision of half-bottles. House wines are from £9.50. CELLARMAN'S CHOICE: Montagny premier cru 1989, £15; Ch. Fourcas-Dupré 1985, £17.

CHEF: Jacques Marchal   PROPRIETORS: Suzanne and Jacques Marchal   OPEN: Tue to Sat; 12.30 to 2, 7 to 10.30   CLOSED: first 3 weeks Feb and Sept, bank hols   MEALS: alc. Set L and D £24.50   SERVICE: not inc   CARDS: Access, Amex, Diners, Visa   DETAILS: 30 seats. Private parties: 30 main room. Children welcome. Wheelchair access (also WC). Music. Air-conditioned

Yang Cheng £

30A Western Approach, Plymouth PL1 1TQ   COOKING 1
PLYMOUTH (0752) 660170   COST £12–£33

This is one of the few genuine Cantonese eating-places in the South-West. The menu has its share of dim-sum, roast meats and one-plate rice and noodle dishes; the chef will also cook unadvertised specialities, and special banquets can be booked in advance. This year's crop of recommended dishes includes deep-fried wun-tun, Cantonese chicken, sizzling beef fillet with black pepper sauce, aromatic crispy duck, and sliced pork with ginger and spring onion. Vegetables are crisp and fresh. Business is brisk and the smart waiters cope hospitably with the crowds. Drink tea, saké or wine. House French is £6.30.

CHEF: K.Y Wong   PROPRIETORS: K.Y. Wong and K.S.L. Wong   OPEN: Tue to Sun; 12 to 2.30 (3 Sun), 6 (6.30 Sun) to 11   MEALS: alc. Set L £6.50 to £8.40, Set D £12.80 to £16.50 SERVICE: not inc   CARDS: Access, Visa   DETAILS: 70 seats. Private parties: 70 main room. Vegetarian meals. Children welcome. Music. Air-conditioned

---

Several sharp operators have tried to extort money from restaurateurs on the promise of an entry in a guidebook that has never appeared. The Good Food Guide *makes no charge for inclusion and does not offer certificates of any kind.*

£ *indicates that it is possible to have a three-course meal, including coffee, a half-bottle of house wine and service, at any time the restaurant is open (i.e. at dinner as well as at lunch, unless a place is open only for dinner), for £20 or less per person.*

POLPERRO Cornwall   map 1

Kitchen

The Coombes, Polperro PL13 2RQ   COOKING 1
POLPERRO (0503) 72780   COST £22–£42

If the number of dishes on offer is added together, the total is impressive – a
great achievement, given the size of the kitchen itself in the pink and pine
cottage restaurant on the road to the harbour. Yet people do not impugn the
freshness of the lobster served, even if it does come out of the shell and is either
wrapped in filo with a tomato basil sauce or served hot with a sauce made from
elderflower wine. 'The value is excellent, the restaurant well run, with pride in
the produce and fine-tasting lobster in filo preceded by a seafood salad. Bread-
and-butter pudding was enjoyed as much as the ice-creams.' So ran a report of
one summer visitor; others echo praise for a menu that ranges from seafood to
local garlic and cider sausage, hummus, lamb passanda and duck with
blueberry and Drambuie sauce. The repertoire does not change greatly from
year to year. The wine list stays short and generally cheap. House wine is £7.90.

CHEFS/PROPRIETORS: Ian and Vanessa Bateson   OPEN: Wed to Mon, D only; Fri and Sat
only in winter; 6.30 to 9.30 summer (winter by arrangement)   MEALS: alc. Minimum
£8.50   SERVICE: not inc, card slips closed   CARDS: Access, Visa   DETAILS: 24 seats.
Vegetarian meals. No children under 7. No cigars/pipes in dining-room. Wheelchair access.
Music

POOL IN WHARFEDALE West Yorkshire   map 5

▲ *Pool Court* ▮ £

Pool Bank,
Pool in Wharfedale LS21 1EH   COOKING 3*
LEEDS (0532) 842288   COST £18–£51

This plush operation still offers its £10 three-course menu: for instance, parsnip
soup with almonds, ramekin of pheasant and rabbit with gingered pears and
polenta, finishing with cheese. This should disarm those, and there are some,
who find it pretentious, fussy in service, or expensive. Most people eat from the
full menu – four courses, priced by the main dish, with set reductions should
you want fewer than four. The double-fronted house is close to the main road;
you start with the hall and bar – 'dark oak panelling, rich deep greens and reds
give it a real country-house feel' – then on to a series of rooms for dining where
light greys and pinks and brighter lights give a major shift in mood. A winter
meal showed many skills, from the good nibbles at the start, through
interesting breads, to petits fours distinguished by the crispness of the tuiles.
Ravioli of salmon with ginger and coriander and a fish broth were light and
arresting, while scallops served with excellent spaghetti, the corals in tiny filo
purses, and scattered with roasted garlic, were robust yet fresh. Twice-baked
soufflés were of salmon and seafood, with a sprinkling of cheese, and were
light enough to ensure the middle course did not leave you gasping. Duck was
not cooked pink, but the skin was crisp. The leg came as a juicy confit wrapped
in a cabbage parcel. The stock reduction was a mite sticky. The richness of bone

marrow was evident in the osso buco, served with macaroni rather than rice, and the veal was both tender and glutinous. Vegetables did not excite, but Wensleydale and fruit-cake did. Some people find the flavours obscured by presentation and fuss; others find the really simple things like good game the best: 'The food, from bacon sandwich to smoked haddock soufflé, always delights.' There is sufficient variety and gusto in the cooking for 'country-house' to be an inadequate description. Lovers of older wines may be disappointed by the relatively small range on offer. This apart, the wine list is magnificent, well-structured and nicely idiosyncratic; prices reflect quality very fairly, starting with a careful selection of 'everyday wines' all at £8.95. There is evidence of well-considered and widespread buying from the country's best merchants. CELLARMAN'S CHOICE: Hautes Côtes de Nuits Blanc 1988, Fribourg, £18.80; Châteauneuf-du-Pape, 'Cèdres' 1985, Jaboulet, £25.95.

CHEF: David Watson PROPRIETOR: Michael W.K. Gill OPEN: Tue to Sat, D only (L by arrangement for 10 or more); 7 to 10 CLOSED: 2 weeks Christmas MEALS: Set D £10 to £32 SERVICE: not inc CARDS: Access, Amex, Diners, Visa DETAILS: 65 seats. Private parties: 85 main room, 30 private room. Car park. Vegetarian meals. Healthy eating options. Children's helpings. No cigars/pipes in dining-room. Wheelchair access. No music. Air-conditioned ACCOMMODATION: 6 rooms, all with bath/shower. B&B £70 to £120. Children welcome. Garden. Air-conditioned. TV. Phone. Confirm by 6. Fax: (0532) 843115 (*The Which? Hotel Guide*)

PORTHOUSTOCK Cornwall   map 1

Café Volnay £

Porthoustock TR12 6QW	COOKING 2
HELSTON (0326) 280183	COST £17–£26

Porthoustock is a seaside hamlet, a gathering of cottages, of which Café Volnay is one: but even a Phoenician tin trader could find this 'café at the end of the world'. Expect no luxury, but get good food and cheerful attention from a pair of London exiles who cook an enterprising menu – first and last courses sometimes thought more fun than mains – that may bake crab in a tart, serve chicken salad with a pesto dressing, put hottish cajun sauce with chicken, or Muscadet and white grapes with confit of duck before fruit or walnut and honey tarts, or gooey meringue cakes filled with strawberries. As one Surrey man communicated: 'On a beach; you have to book; all interesting, as well as delicious.' Prices are not a lot and brunch is served on winter Sundays. Wines start at £6.25 and do not rise above £13.75 other than for champagne.

CHEFS/PROPRIETORS: S.A. Chapman and C.N. Rye OPEN: Tue to Sun, D only, and Sun brunch winter; 7.30 to 9 CLOSED: day after bank hols MEALS: alc SERVICE: not inc DETAILS: 24 seats. Private parties: 20 main room. Children's helpings with prior notice. Wheelchair access (2 steps; also WC). Music

'I ordered an '84 Châteauneuf-du-Pape which I wanted to try, having recently had an '83; I was offered an '86 without explanation or apology. I pointed out politely that it was not what I had ordered, to be greeted by a somewhat disgruntled "Oh is that a problem?" as if my remark was unreasonable or querulous.' On eating in Oxfordshire

POUGHILL Cornwall

map 1

▲ Reeds ⁵⁄※

Poughill EX23 9EL
BUDE (0288) 352841

COOKING 2
COST £28

'The essence of the place is consistency. Nothing looks worn out or ill-used. Everything is always spotless, flowers are always fresh, Margaret Jackson is always bright and cheerful,' enthuses one regular. Another writes, 'The standard of cooking, welcome, excellent housekeeping and general feeling of a lady who really does enjoy her guests remain unchanged.' Margaret Jackson's cooking is straightforward yet assured. Simple cooking lets materials stand on their own. No choice is offered to guests but discussion of the menu, and even a demand for the return of a favoured dish eaten the night before, are cheerfully accommodated. Thus local plaice on the bone poached in white wine with a prawn sauce could be followed the next day by suprême of chicken in a fragrant red wine sauce; vegetables are 'light and crisp', seconds are encouraged. Puddings include home-made ice-cream, treacle tart and pears cooked in lemon syrup with fresh ginger. There is a short but decent wine list with a good selection of half-bottles. House Duboeuf is £6.75.

CHEF/PROPRIETOR: Margaret Jackson   OPEN: Fri to Mon, D only; 8   CLOSED: 25 Dec
MEALS: Set D £19.50   SERVICE: not inc   DETAILS: 10 seats. Private parties: 10 main room.
Car park. No children under 16. Smart dress preferred. No smoking in dining-room. No
music   ACCOMMODATION: 3 rooms, all with bath/shower. B&B £37.50 to £65. Deposit:
£10. No children under 16. Garden. Doors close at midnight. Confirm by noon (*The Which?
Hotel Guide*)

POULTON-LE-FYLDE Lancashire

map 5

▲ River House ♟

Skippool Creek,
Thornton-le-Fylde FY5 5LF
POULTON-LE-FYLDE (0253) 883497

COOKING 2
COST £37–£61

The general placing is pretty good: a stretch of water, views of seabirds through masts, keels and lanyards of waiting yachts. The house has character as well, but once through the door there are people who find this overstated. Some are not too keen on dogs and (blind) cats, others find the housekeeping basic. The cooking may go some way to reconciling you to all this – it can be good. There is substantial meat cookery, for instance a dish of venison both fried with a port sauce and braised in a civet with vegetables, and there is a melding of Western and oriental in dishes such as beef served Japanese-style, including a cup of saké, or maybe other fish served teriyaki-style. Some appreciation of London fashion is also shown: hence a breast of chicken with cabbage and air-dried ham. This is good; it really is substantial, genuine and enjoyable. The wine list continues to impress, particularly for its clarets and Germans. The burgundies may be good, if the list told us more about them; there is a nice little flight of Bandols, and the Italian selection is up to the minute. House wine is about £12.50.

CHEFS/PROPRIETORS: Bill and Carole Scott   OPEN: Mon to Sat, exc Sat; 12 to 2, 7.30 to
9.30   MEALS: alc   SERVICE: not inc   CARDS: Access, Visa   DETAILS: 40 seats. Private
parties: 40 main room. Car park. Vegetarian meals. Children's helpings. Music
ACCOMMODATION: 4 rooms, all with bath/shower. B&B £55 to £120. Children welcome.
Baby facilities. Pets welcome. Garden. TV. Phone. Fax: (0253) 892083 (*The Which? Hotel
Guide*)

POWBURN Northumberland   map 7

▲ *Breamish House* ⁵⅟✳

| Powburn NE66 4LL | COOKING 1 |
| POWBURN (066 578) 266 | COST £18–£31 |

This former farmhouse and hunting-lodge is not grand, but it is comfortable.
Meals are served at a single sitting, with a set-price menu offering a short
choice, with a soup course (cream of parsnip and ginger, for instance) in the
middle, and cheese and coffee at the end included. The style is self-
proclaimedly not over-rich, nor over-balanced by complication. First courses
may include a mousse of smoked wild salmon or apple stuffed with walnut
and herbs and coated in a tarragon cream, followed by sauté monkfish and
salmon in hazelnut oil with a chive sauce, or venison with a red wine sauce and
a gooseberry jelly. The wine list is made up of some excellent names: Dom. de
Nalys' Châteauneuf, Javillier's Chassagne-Montrachet, Penfolds in Australia,
Selaks from New Zealand, and Ch. Musar from the Lebanon. Prices are fair and
the range is well judged. House wines are £10.90 a litre.

CHEFS/PROPRIETORS: Doreen and Alan Johnson   OPEN: all week, D only, and Sun L; 12.30
to 1, 7.30 to 8   MEALS: Set L £10.95, Set D £19.95   SERVICE: not inc   DETAILS: 30 seats.
Private parties: 22 main room. Car park. No children under 12. Smart dress preferred. No
smoking in dining-room. Wheelchair access (also WC). No music   ACCOMMODATION: 11
rooms, all with bath/shower. D,B&B £54 to £133. Deposit: £25. Children under 12 by
arrangement. Pets welcome. Afternoon teas. Garden. TV. Phone. Doors close at 11. Confirm
by 5. Fax: (066 578) 500 (*The Which? Hotel Guide*)

POWERSTOCK Dorset   map 2

▲ *Three Horseshoes* ⁵⅟✳ £

| Powerstock DT6 3TF | COOKING 1 |
| POWERSTOCK (030 885) 328 and 229 | COST £17–£44 |

It is not much help, if you are sitting in the restaurant, to have to go over to the
bar to read and memorise the menu for the day. This, and the drawbacks of
service, make the bar a much better place to try the fish at this handsome Dorset
pub. This can be of a high standard, fresh and properly cooked. Skate with
black butter, and a zarzuela of lobster have been favourably reported on;
scallops, soles and sea bass are often available. Some first courses are
nourishing and substantial – for instance, the spinach pancakes, or even the
macaroni cheese. Some of the desserts, such as the chocolate cake have been
outstanding (as is the cream). The wine list is not dear and includes some gems

like the Côtes du Rhône from Dom. de la Renjardière, the Campo Viejo Rioja, or Vincent's St Véran. House wines are £7.50.

CHEF: Pat Ferguson PROPRIETORS: Pat and Diana Ferguson OPEN: all week; 12 to 2 (3 Sun), 7 to 10 MEALS: alc. Set Sun L £10.50 to £12.50, Set D £12.50 to £16.50 SERVICE: not inc, card slips closed CARDS: Access, Amex, Diners, Visa DETAILS: 50 seats. Private parties: 50 main room, 20 and 24 private rooms. Car park. Vegetarian meals. Children's helpings. Smart dress preferred. No smoking in dining-room. Wheelchair access (also WC). Music ACCOMMODATION: 4 rooms, 2 with bath/shower. B&B £25 to £55. Deposit: 1 night. Children welcome. Baby facilities. Pets welcome. Garden. TV. Doors close at midnight. Confirm by 6.30 (*The Which? Hotel Guide*)

PRESTBURY Cheshire

map 5

▲ *White House*

New Road, The Village,
Prestbury SK10 4DG
PRESTBURY (0625) 829376

COOKING 1*
COST £17–£49

Once a farmhouse and manor house, White House is now a restaurant with linked accommodation in the house. Visitors sometimes exclaim at the array of motors parked outside – 'A Cheshire village! You would think it was Mayfair.' This is a measure, therefore, of Ryland Wakeham's popularity, and of the fair value for set menus at lunch-time, though cost may escalate come the *carte* at dinner. The cooking here keeps abreast of trends: a flan of tomatoes, goats' cheese and basil oil, baked peach stuffed with cream cheese herb pâté and served with pesto crostini, lobster with mango and sesame vinaigrette. Simplish cooking as in a set of very fresh fillets of plaice with crisp asparagus and a chervil sauce has also been well reported. There is a continued policy of cooking some things with people's weight and diet in mind – here called 'spa cuisine' – though many are happy to abandon such causes when faced with a grand combination of sweet things, or a chocolate fudge cake that got full marks for size, if not for taste. The best section of the wine list is perhaps that for the New World, which offers fair value and decent makers. House wine is Cordier at £9 a litre.

CHEF: Ryland Wakeham PROPRIETORS: Ryland and Judith Wakeham OPEN: Tue to Sun; 12 to 2, 7 to 10 CLOSED: first week Jan and Aug MEALS: alc. Set L £9.95, Set D £16.95 SERVICE: not inc, card slips closed CARDS: Access, Amex, Diners, Visa DETAILS: 75 seats. 2 tables outside. Private parties: 70 main room, 20 and 40 private rooms. Car park. Vegetarian meals. Healthy eating options. Children's helpings. Wheelchair access (also WC). Music ACCOMMODATION: 8 rooms, all with bath/shower. Rooms for disabled. B&B £70 to £105. No children under 12. Pets by arrangement. Garden. Sauna. TV. Phone. Doors close at midnight. Confirm by midday. Fax: (0625) 828627

Not inc *in the details at the end of an entry indicates that no service charge is made and any tipping is at the discretion of the customer.*

Net prices *in the details at the end of an entry indicates that the prices given on a menu and on a bill are inclusive of VAT and service charge, and that this practice is clearly stated on menu and bill.*

PRESTON Lancashire   map 5

Auctioneer £

ADT Auction Centre, Walton Summit,
Bamber Bridge, Preston PR5 8AA   COOKING 1
PRESTON (0772) 324870   COST £15–£27

It looks out on to a car auction-ring; the menu is divided into lots; the crowds
are drawn by the fair value, healthy portions and robust tastes. There may be
scampi in a basket at the bar, but Nigel Brookes is a man with a mission and
cooks rabbit with onions, mushrooms and cream, venison with red wine, and a
score of different steak combinations to encourage adventure beyond the
cocktails, melons and fruit juices. Do not expect sophistication or linen table
napkins, but enjoy a warm welcome. The wine list gives less information than
most auctioneers' sale catalogues – high on opinion, low on names and
numbers. House wine is £7.50 a litre.

CHEF: Nigel Brookes   PROPRIETORS: Nigel and Elizabeth Brookes   OPEN: Mon, Wed, Thur
and Sun L, and Fri and Sat D; 12 to 2.30, 7 to 10   MEALS: alc. Set L £9.95 and bar snacks
SERVICE: not inc, card slips closed   CARDS: Access, Visa   DETAILS: 100 seats. Private
parties: 100 main room. Car park. Vegetarian meals. Children's helpings. Music.
Air-conditioned

PULBOROUGH West Sussex   map 3

Stane Street Hollow ⁵⁄✱

Codmore Hill, Pulborough RH20 1BG   COOKING 3
PULBOROUGH (0798) 872819   COST £17–£37

'I used to visit Geneva annually, but I can't recall restaurants there being
anything like so Hansel-and-Gretely as this one' was the comment of one who
found the folksy accordion music in the bar hard to bear. Otherwise, moderate
coffee and an unannounced changed vintage of Chardonnay notwithstanding,
the reporter was impressed by the cooking, the vegetables and the 'pleasant
people looking after us'. The Hollow is a personal venture. Lots of gardening,
lots of poultry, lots of home smoking and a Swiss tilt to the menu make it
unmistakably the Kaisers'. The smoker is used for salmon, ham, haddock and
various fowl for first courses. Classical training gives technique, evinced for
instance in pastry work, meringues or ice-creams; a sense of current trends
makes for variety, as in dishes such as poached egg on chickpea purée with a
yoghurt mayonnaise, bresaola, or chicken with horseradish and sour cream,
and a sensitive palate gives flavour where flavour is needed. Lunch is a bargain.
The wine list is distinguished by its fair prices as well as decent bottles (and
plenty of halves in proportion). Look carefully at the red burgundies and
Rhônes. House wines are £10.

CHEF: René Kaiser   PROPRIETORS: René and Ann Kaiser   OPEN: Wed to Sat, exc Sat L;
12.30 to 1.15, 7.30 to 9.15   CLOSED: 2 weeks May, 24 to 26 Oct, 31 Dec to 5 Jan   MEALS:
alc. Set L £8.50   SERVICE: not inc   DETAILS: 35 seats. Private parties: 24 main room, 16
private room. Car park. Children's helpings. No smoking in dining-room. No music

Village Restaurant ▮ ⅝✳

16 Market Place, Ramsbottom BL0 9HT	COOKING 3
RAMSBOTTOM (070 682) 5070	COST £39–£49

One should reiterate: old Lancashire, cobbled streets, stone cottages, in one of which a small restaurant offers a set meal, with wine chosen for you if you want, at a set price at a set time. 'It said 8 for 8.30 and did not finish until 12.15. Chris Johnson is careful to ensure that every guest understands what is in a dish, which may be sad for those who want to discover by taste.' This is a unique and much-loved experience. Some people travel far to study the details: 'The music included Jim Reeves' Christmas album as well as Lloyd Webber cello arrangements (just like last time). Chris Johnson waxed lyrical about single-estate chocolate for the rather too heavy and intense chocolate mousse. I noticed that both the proprietors were wearing exactly the same clothes as last year.' Ros Hunter's cooking is much enjoyed. The materials are good, lovingly sought out and carefully produced. The format is constant: cold beginning, soup, fish, meat (with two sauces or 'prepared two ways'), five vegetables, cheese, a choice of three or four puddings, coffee and Valrhona chocolates. Lamb is done as a hotpot (for the front end) and the leg is roasted pink – all on the same plate. If you go too often, you may find repeats: sea urchin mousseline sauce was popular with all sorts of fish at the beginning of 1992. The care and attention are so great that almost every meal contains some outstanding success: a terrine of foie gras for one, simple smoked salmon for another, firm brill for a third. Crèmes brûlées are fine. For many years, there was an intention to open a wine bar next door. When the ambition seemed finally achieved, it was stopped at the last furlong by the withdrawal of business partners. A delicatessen is now planned instead. The wine list stays the same as last year. This means it is a giant, with immense reserves from a thousand bins (not all full, however). Our endorsement of Mr Johnson's vinous enthusiasm is thus unchanged. Value is guaranteed throughout.

CHEF: Ros Hunter   PROPRIETORS: Ros Hunter and Chris Johnson (The Ramsbottom Victuallers Co. Ltd)   OPEN: Wed to Sat, D only (Tue by arrangement); 8 for 8.30   MEALS: Set D £25 (vegetarian) to £30   SERVICE: not inc, card slips closed   CARDS: Access, Visa DETAILS: 20 seats. Private parties: 12 main room. Children restricted. No smoking in dining-room. Music

▲ *Langley Wood*

Hamptworth Road, Redlynch SP5 2PB	COOKING 2
ROMSEY (0794) 390348	COST £16–£33

'Rather like being in a friend's home,' comments one reader; others have reported the Rosens' lack of pretension as breathtaking. The setting for such cordiality is a substantial manor fringed by the New Forest. Generosity extends to the plate: after ordering pheasant – with button mushrooms and madeira sauce – an unaccustomed couple were provided with half a bird each. Cooking is calibrated as 'largely a demonstration of simple things done very well'. Fillet steak with garlic butter was 'charred outside and juicy pink inside. Not quite the stuff of fantasies but pretty good all the same.' Sylvia Rosen also turns out creditable roasts and ensures at least one vegetarian option per menu. Whatever happens, vegetables are reported to be varied and unflawed. David Rosen serves single-handedly and with aplomb. Accommodation is adequate and keenly priced, as is the wine list. House wine is £5.75.

CHEF: Sylvia Rosen   PROPRIETORS: David and Sylvia Rosen   OPEN: Wed to Sat, D only, and Sun L; 12.45 to 2, 7.30 to 11   MEALS: alc. Set Sun L £11.75   SERVICE: not inc   CARDS: Access, Amex, Diners, Visa   DETAILS: 30 seats. Private parties: 65 main room. Car park. Vegetarian meals. Children's helpings. No cigars/pipes in dining-room. Wheelchair access (also WC). Music   ACCOMMODATION: 3 rooms. B&B £16 to £32. Deposit: £10. Children welcome. Pets welcome. Afternoon teas. Garden

---

RICHMOND North Yorkshire   map 7

▲ Howe Villa ✸✳

Whitcliffe Mill,
Richmond DL10 4TJ   COOKING 2*
RICHMOND (0748) 850055   COST £20–£23

'This is a wonderful peaceful house with the atmosphere of a bygone time,' writes a devotee of the Berrys' much-loved North Country retreat off the Leyburn and Leeth Road. Visitors are fulsome in their praise for the owners' sense of humour, welcome and, above all, for Anita Berry's cooking. It is a tribute to her skill and homely invention that her menus are always interesting and seldom repetitive, even for visitors who stay longer than one week. The place is unlicensed, but the Berrys will buy wine for you and include an aperitif ('your favourite drink') in the price of dinner. The menu is four courses, plus cheese and coffee, but with no choice in the main course. To start, there might be poached sole, prawns and scallops in a filo basket, followed by lettuce and courgette soup or a sorbet. The prosaically described centrepiece often belies Anita's sharp technique and flair: 'breast of guinea-fowl with vegetables' actually has a moussseline of the leg meat stuffed under the skin and is served with a reduction of madeira and stock. Sweets such as rhubarb and lemon cream flan or chocolate parfait with Tia Maria precede local Wensleydale and Coverdale cheeses served with walnut and sultana bread. The food 'is served with great style'. Breakfasts are superb. Credit cards are not accepted.

CHEF: Anita Berry   PROPRIETORS: Tom and Anita Berry   OPEN: all week, D only; 7.30   CLOSED: Dec and Jan   MEALS: Set D £18 to £19. Unlicensed, but bring your own: no corkage   SERVICE: not inc   DETAILS: 12 seats. Private parties: 12 main room. Car park. Vegetarian meals. Children's helpings with prior notice. No children under 12. No smoking in dining-room. Music   ACCOMMODATION: 5 rooms, all with bath/shower. D,B&B £92. Deposit: £20. No children under 12. Garden. TV. Doors close at 11.30. Confirm by 6 (*The Which? Hotel Guide*)

▲ *This symbol means accommodation is available.*

RIDGEWAY Derbyshire

map 5

Old Vicarage 🍾 ✱

Ridgeway Moor,
Ridgeway S12 3XW
SHEFFIELD (0742) 475814
off A616, on B6054 nearly opposite
village church, 5m SE of Sheffield

COOKING 4
COST £27–£43

'The food can sound and look ordinary, but what lifts it above the competition is the way in which unexpected flavours pop up throughout the meal – the hint of chilli in the ratatouille, the cardamom in the salad dressing, caraway in the cabbage, ginger in the soup,' wrote a couple happy to drive across the Pennines to eat in this very Trollopean house, made cheerful by decoration and colour, and given gusto by Tessa Bramley's cooking. The cheeriest spot, the couple also said, is the conservatory. The Old Vicarage's achievement is to move with the times. That is not the same as slavishly following fashion, but tastes change and pockets shrink, and realism always was a Northern virtue. Cooking here has been described as a hybrid of two traditions: English and classical French. The Mediterranean world has been recruited as a third element. Gone are luxury ingredients such as caviare and foie gras, left out are butter and much cream; now in favour are vinaigrettes and oil emulsions, and hello to a touch of vibrancy as seen in a vegetarian trio of courgette and cinnamon rissoles, red pepper and coriander timbale and pancakes stuffed with spiced carrot purée. Tessa Bramley is a wizard with flavourings and a magician in the garden – hence those fine salads, vegetables and discreet yet unmistakable touches with blossoms, flowers and unidentifiable leaves in salads and trimmings. The British tradition is not ignored if you can eat roast beef with thyme and a steak and kidney pie at one sitting, or order the grilled cheese savoury which consists of three croûtons with a fluffy cheese topping, anchovies and olives. Cookery skill is not lacking from a kitchen that can deliver ratatouille with the taste of each vegetable distinct yet combining to a greater whole, or produce rhubarb, vanilla, mango and passion-fruit ice-creams that lose nothing of their fruit originals, or offer a first course of 'cannelloni' filled with leeks and mushrooms, with a parsnip soufflé and a thyme cream sauce that had balance and brilliance. Once the place seemed a touch ponderous in service – no more, according to latest comments. Wine-buying here has stretched beyond France but shows no let-up in quality. An intelligent pricing policy provides many decent bottles at £12 or under, while the profligate are well-cared-for with a string of 1970 and older clarets. Alsace is a favourite, but a larger party would do well to turn to the Almecenista sherries offered by the bottle; moderately priced and wonderful for a first course. House wines are £11. CELLARMAN'S CHOICE: Gewurztraminer, Médaille d'Or 1989, Rolly-Gassmann, £18.50; Penedès, Cabernet Sauvignon 1979, Jean Leon, £26.

CHEF: Tessa Bramley   PROPRIETORS: Tessa and Andrew Bramley   OPEN: Tue to Sun, exc Sun D (Sat L by arrangement); 12.15 to 2.30, 7 to 10   MEALS: Set L and D £18.50 to £27.50   SERVICE: not inc, card slips closed   DETAILS: 50 seats. Private parties: 40 main room, 12, 26 and 40 private rooms. Car park. Children welcome. No smoking in 1 dining-room. Music. Fax: (0742) 477079

RIPLEY Surrey   map 3

Michels' ♀

13 High Street, Ripley GU23 6AQ   COOKING 3
GUILDFORD (0483) 224777 and 222940   COST £26–£49

A Georgian front, Queen Anne back and modern middle, with the bar in a pit
at a lower level than the restaurant, was one shorthand description of the Clock
House, where Erik Michel pursues an individual line at his stoves. The
pleasant garden, the generous swags of fabric, lots of flowers and tasteful
ornaments (elephants and cockerels) might have also been included. The
cooking here still has overtones of nouvelle cuisine: it is often complex and
more than carefully presented. However, many recipes show the move of
fashion, for instance, salmon roasted and served with seaweed and cockles,
duck cassoulet (with cabbage and polenta), pollack with Parmesan sauce, a
bouillabaisse, rouille and couscous. The liberal interpretation of cassoulet is
measure of the kitchen's approach. When bread-and-butter pudding is
converted into a soufflé, with brandy currants and an apricot sauce, invention
comes up trumps, as it does with a kedgeree that turns out to be a classic risotto
with curry flavour, haddock and poached quail's eggs. Lovers of surprises will
find secret menus offered at most meals; haters of traditional roasts will find
Sunday lunch refreshingly different. There are occasional hints at cross-
currents that make welcome and reception less easy than they should be. The
wine list is short and French, with four Spanish and four Australian bottles to
help out. The list is longest in clarets, the choices of growers and properties are
very accurate (Goyard, Guigal, Dezat, Camus, Jayer, Dauzac and Chauvin, to
name but a few) and prices are not too greedy. House wines are £9.
CELLARMAN'S CHOICE: Margaret River, Chardonnay 1989, Cullens, £24.95;
Médoc, Ch. La Cardonne 1982, £19.65.

CHEF: Erik Michel   PROPRIETORS: Erik and Karen Michel   OPEN: Tue to Sun, exc Sat L
and Sun D; 12.30 to 2, 7.30 to 9.15 (7 to 9.45 Sat)   MEALS: alc. Set L £17.50, Set D £27
SERVICE: not inc   CARDS: Access, Amex, Visa   DETAILS: 45 seats. Children welcome.
Music

RIPLEY North Yorkshire   map 7

▲ Boar's Head | NEW ENTRY |

Ripley HG3 3AY   COOKING 3
HARROGATE (0423) 771888   COST £19–£35

The Ingilby family, owners of nearby Ripley Castle, have transformed this one-
time coaching-inn opposite the village stocks into a pedigree hotel. The place
now boasts an attractive outdoor lawned area, and two comfortable lounges
with family portraits on the walls; even the public bar is air-conditioned.
Everywhere there is minute attention to detail, yet the hotel maintains a
relaxed, informal atmosphere. Meals are served in an elegant dining-room
classically decorated in burgundy and olive green. Chef David Box worked at
the Savoy and Claridges and his sheer professional skill shows in the
seasonally changing menus. Dinner is fixed-price for four courses (plus cheese

411

at a £3 supplement) and coffee. The quality of the raw materials is outstanding: much of the fruit, vegetables and herbs is grown in the hotel's cottage garden; venison, pheasant and rabbit are from the Ingilby Estate. Timing is immaculate, and dishes are accompanied by 'the most skilfully prepared, intensely flavoured sauces'. One test meal drew many superlatives. Gratin of Dublin Bay prawns contained first-rate fresh shellfish, contrasting magnificently with sharp pan-fried spinach; chicken and wild mushroom terrine with spring salad was superbly presented and deeply flavoured; noisettes of pink, tender spring lamb with vegetable spaghetti on a light thyme sauce were 'absolutely superb'. Other reporters have been impressed by ragoût of wild mushrooms, chicken mousse with blackcurrant coulis, lobster with grain mustard sauce, and fillet of beef with caramelised shallots. Unusual soups and sorbets are also well reported. Pan-fried bananas in rum with cinnamon toast and sour cream has been excellent. Details, such as the 'wonderfully fresh' bread, cheese with home-made biscuits and coffee with petits fours, are those of a serious enterprise. Service is courteous, unfailingly helpful and keen to please. The wine list is good value, with decent half-bottles that encourage further experiment. Selection is even-handed, showing as much enthusiasm for Spain as for New Zealand, although evidence of special fondness for dessert wines (these are handsome) is clear. House wine is £8.50.

CHEF: David Box   PROPRIETOR: Sir Thomas Ingilby   OPEN: all week; 12 to 2, 7 to 9.45
MEALS: Set L £9.95 to £12.95, Set D £24.50   SERVICE: not inc   CARDS: Access, Amex,
Visa   DETAILS: 50 seats. Private parties: 60 main room, 15 private room. Car park.
Vegetarian meals. Children's helpings. No cigars/pipes in dining-room. Wheelchair access
(also WC). Music   ACCOMMODATION: 25 rooms, all with bath/shower. Rooms for
disabled. B&B £80 to £98. Children welcome. Baby facilities. Pets welcome. Afternoon teas.
Garden. Tennis. Fishing. TV. Phone. Fax: (0423) 771509 (*The Which? Hotel Guide*)

ROADE Northamptonshire   map 3

Roadhouse Restaurant

16–18 High Street, Roade NN7 2NW   COOKING 3
ROADE (0604) 863372   COST £20–£33

'Frequent visits here have confirmed the steady excellence and inventiveness of Mr Kewley,' pronounced one reader. This adjudication is echoed in other reports although some criticism of staff demeanour is also repeated. Dinky table lamps reflect off dusty-pink walls and white napery, Mrs Kewley is 'welcoming as usual', and the *carte* is succinct and deceptively plain; an unfussy attitude is, however, the style of this restaurant. Quenelles of salmon and crab with breadcrumbs and well-ground hazelnuts, their coating crisped under the grill, caused a reporter to comment, 'Fish-cakes, but what fish-cakes!' Sauté fillet of pork was tender and 'perfectly matched with its prunes and its light cream sauce – cream is no panacea for Roadhouse sauces, reductions being the general rule'. Excellent ingredients build in quality, but good flavour-matching technique is the hallmark of Chris Kewley's kitchen: roast breast of pheasant with a herb dressing under the crisp skin had 'its relative freshness (as pheasant) ingeniously foiled with the most delicious, strong game sausage'. The set-price Sunday lunch menu offers exceptional value. Treacle tart – 'not quite the school sticky treat I remember' – has pastry 10 times better than a school's, and another big pud, apple and plum crumble, shows an ability to handle this style of dessert. 'Chris Kewley's portions are always generous,' observes one who went on to mince pies with coffee – 'We managed them, though.' Strawberry strudel and profiteroles get the yes-vote while other sweet items are received with a touch of moderation. Wines are good. The list is not long but growers are more than sound. Penfolds and Knappstein in Australia, Bianchi from Montepulciano, and Roty and Mongeard-Mugneret in Burgundy are not priced extortionately, nor are Ch. Lynch-Bages and Ch. Ducru-Beaucaillou 1981. House wines are £8.25.

CHEF: Christopher Kewley PROPRIETORS: Christopher and Susan Kewley OPEN: Tue to Sun, exc Sat L and Sun D; 12.30 to 1.45, 7 to 10 MEALS: alc. Set L £14, Set Sun L £15 SERVICE: net prices, card slips closed CARDS: Access, Visa DETAILS: 32 seats. Private parties: 40 main room. Car park. Children's helpings. Smart dress preferred. No music

---

ROMSEY Hampshire   map 2

Old Manor House 🍷

21 Palmerston Street, Romsey SO51 8GF   COOKING 4
ROMSEY (0794) 517353   COST £23–£51

A wealth of beams and leaded lights in hallowed rooms (and redecorated bar) earn the manor house its epithet, though visitors would level no criticism at the sparkling table settings, nor call the open welcome worn by time. Mauro Bregoli displays many talents in a broad repertoire. Classic techniques, suitably sharp and up to date, feature when he puts fillet of brill with Sauternes, cream and a subtle interplay of celery and celeriac, or chicken breast with truffle and chive butter and a watercress sauce. Yet he can also produce Italian dishes with gusto: home-made cotechino sausage with lentils (almost too salty, one person remarked), tagliatelle with Parma ham and dandelion leaves, or saddle of rabbit with thyme and polenta. This dual approach gives the kitchen particular force, derived from sophistication and a willingness to grapple with earthy, direct flavours. The staff also know the value of 'production': the pastry basket to hold the vegetables, the flourish of the glass when serving the wine, the silver domes (these mourned in their passing at lunch-time). 'Service here is of the best, yet avoids the stuffy' was one person's appraisal. Dinner may not be cheap, but some hold on reality is kept in daylight hours with three choices of menu at lunch. Even the cheapest will allow you a good risotto before venison with a red wine sauce, then dessert. It seems natural that Mauro Bregoli's strengths are for pasta, game of all sorts, wild mushrooms, and home-cured meats such as bresaola – one thinks immediately of Franco Taruschio at the Walnut Tree Inn (see entry, Llandewi Skirrid, Wales). But this should not obscure the praise heaped on dishes such as parcels of crab with ginger, mussels in a pastry case with mushrooms and a light butter sauce, monkfish with apples, port and pink peppercorns, leg of duck stuffed with mushrooms and herbs, or duck stuffed this time with brandied raisins, a 'roll' of chicken with prunes, casserole of rabbit with Riesling and herbs. Desserts, too, may cause swooning when as accurate as a mille-feuille glacé – six scoops of sorbet, including mango, redcurrant, lemon and elderberry, in a triple-decker of puff pastry. Coffee is strong espresso. Breads, canapés and petits fours are high-grade. Arrive early to get the most from the wine list – 30 pages of unalloyed bliss for the wine-lover. Fine Alsaces, excellent Australians and magnificent Italians more than match the best of France. None of this comes cheap, although there is much to be recommended at well below the £20 mark. Concession to the thrifty and the less knowledgeable is provided in a considerate and intelligent page of 'Choice of the House' wines from £9.50. CELLARMAN'S CHOICE: Bordeaux Blanc, Ch. Thieuley 1989, £15; Cahors, Ch. La Caminade 1989, £14.50.

CHEF/PROPRIETOR: Mauro Bregoli   OPEN: Tue to Sun, exc Sun D; 12 to 2, 7 to 9.30
CLOSED: 24 Dec to 1 Jan   MEALS: Set L £14.50 to £25, Set D £35   SERVICE: not inc
CARDS: Access, Amex, Visa   DETAILS: 45 seats. 6 tables outside. Private parties: 12 main room, 24 private room. Car park. Children welcome. Smart dress preferred. No cigars/pipes in dining-room. No music

---

ROWDE Wiltshire   map 2

George & Dragon

High Street, Rowde SN10 2PN   COOKING 3
DEVIZES (0380) 723053   COST £16–£35

In a village pub, perched high above the apex of a bend in downtown Rowde, Tim and Helen Withers have kept the drinkers happy but let rip on the food side, allowing the provision of meals to become the principal activity of the house. Pork and goose rillettes, brill and salmon terrine, roast beef and Yorkshire, bourride of turbot, mullet and mussels, brown sugar meringues and sticky toffee pudding make glorious pub food (even if the rillettes were too cold, hence solid, and curly kale and parsnip seemed odd veg for the bourride). This is great stuff, cooked fresh as a daisy. Menus change all the time and length may depend on supplies and demand – there are moments when the choice seems restricted, others when up to 10 things may be on offer for the principal dish. Excellent fish soup, salmon fish-cakes, cheese soufflés, home-made noodles or lambs' kidneys with mustard sauce may be first courses. Follow them with mallard, cod roasted in olive oil, salmon in pastry with ginger and currants, plain steaks ('good meat') or sweetbreads with capers and black butter. For a place that is so far inland, fish, particularly lobster, is worth a mention. Prices are keen and service is cheerful, knowledgeable and adequate. From some of the dishes mentioned, a time of pupillage with Joyce Molyneux at the Carved Angel, Dartmouth (see entry) may be inferred. There is something of the same unforced attitude to the art of cooking, and a willingness to change because customers like you to. The wine list is short and sharp, influenced by the brewery, and prices are consumer-friendly. House wines are from £7.25. CELLARMAN'S CHOICE: Mâcon Villages, Dom. d'Azenay 1988, £12.15; Chinon, Dom. de la Bellonnière 1987, £8.75.

CHEF: Tim Withers   PROPRIETORS: Wadworth & Co   OPEN: Tue to Sun, exc Sun D; 12 to 1.45, 7 to 10   CLOSED: 25 and 26 Dec, 1 Jan   MEALS: alc. Set L £9.50   SERVICE: not inc
CARDS: Access, Visa   DETAILS: 35 seats. 6 tables outside. Private parties: 20 main room. Car park. Vegetarian meals with prior notice. Children's helpings. No children after 9pm. Wheelchair access (1 step; also WC). No music

RYE East Sussex   map 3

Landgate Bistro ♥ £

5–6 Landgate, Rye TN31 7LH   COOKING 2*
RYE (0797) 222829   COST £17–£26

The atmosphere is that of a bistro – happy, sometimes noisy, yet unfussy in
style. There is also a forthright immediacy about Toni Ferguson-Lees' cooking:
flavours matter more than photogenic presentation, although this is 'correct and
comfortable'. The quality of the raw materials stands out: fish from the local
boats, excellent meat and vegetables, an extraordinary array of salad leaves
from rocket to peppery landcress. A fixed-price menu is now available
(Tuesday to Thursday) in addition to the main *carte*. Some reporters return
again and again for their 'old loves': crab terrine, chicken quenelles, wild duck
with port and orange. But new dishes are also mentioned: deep-filled onion
and feta cheese tart, salmon fish-cakes with home-made tomato ketchup, calf's
liver with sage and apple juice, and perfectly timed scallops and brill with
orange and vermouth sauce. The walnut and treacle tart is described in acute,
loving detail by one devotee: 'The pastry has a layer of treacle curd, rich like
lemon curd and also lemony; on top are cheek-to-cheek solid walnuts. It's rich
and unusual and one doesn't feel the need for cream (which isn't offered
anyway).' A sure hand and a generous heart keep the wine list up in quality
and down in price (house wine is £6.90). Uncertainties about suppliers hit by
the recession have suggested caution over continuity, so we omit a cellarman's
choice this year. If changes are in the air, might we expect more exciting house
wines?

CHEF: Toni Ferguson-Lees   PROPRIETORS: Nick Parkin and Toni Ferguson-Lees   OPEN:
Tue to Sat, D only; 7 to 9.30   MEALS: alc. Set D £13.50 (Tue to Thur)   SERVICE: net prices,
card slips closed   CARDS: Access, Amex, Diners, Visa   DETAILS: 34 seats. Vegetarian
meals. Children's helpings. Music

SAFFRON WALDEN Essex   map 3

Old Hoops

15 King Street, Saffron Walden CB10 1HE   COOKING 1
SAFFRON WALDEN (0799) 522813   COST £17–£34

'An old favourite,' writes a devotee, 'an oasis in the North Essex desert', and
this much-liked local restaurant has slightly upgraded its image of late. Gone
are the model aeroplanes hanging from the ceiling: instead there is a ceiling fan
and a large potted fern. The thrust of the menu seldom changes, although there
are encouraging signs that the cooking has acquired a little more imagination,
and the bread has improved. The kitchen still works to a classically based
repertoire tilted towards France. Everyone approves of the 'musselcress' soup
(watercress, potatoes, mussels and cream), which is 'better than ever' according
to one report. Other good dishes have included salmon fillet in sauce Dugléré;
chicken in filo pastry with creamy tarragon sauce; veal chop portugaise; and
fillet of lamb wrapped in spinach and bacon with Dijon mustard sauce. Sweets
such as baked chocolate sponge have drawn mixed reports. Service is generally

cheerful and attentive. The modest wine list would benefit from more half-bottles. House French is £6.95.

CHEF: Ray Morrison PROPRIETORS: Don Irwin and Ray Morrison OPEN: Tue to Sat; 12 to 2.15, 7 to 10 CLOSED: bank hols MEALS: alc SERVICE: not inc CARDS: Access, Amex, Diners, Visa DETAILS: 40 seats. Private parties: 40 main room. Children's helpings. Music

---

ST IVES Cornwall   map 1

Pig'n'Fish

NEW ENTRY

Norway Lane, St Ives TR26 1LZ   COOKING 2
PENZANCE (0736) 794204   COST £22–£48

Above the craft centre behind the Sloop Inn is a former net loft, all bare brick walls, stripped pine, beamed attic ceiling, Terry Frost ceramic plates and a view over the rooftops to the bay. There is a certain mixed message here: the feel is less serious than the food. Paul Sellars' last posting was with the Seafood Restaurant at Padstow (see entry), and he has brought with him the message of good modern fish cookery. There are token meat dishes, but the Pig is less in evidence than the Fish. The style may be gauged from a list that includes roast monkfish with pancetta, plaice with celeriac, flat-leaved parsley and a mustard beurre blanc, cod with a clam chowder, or a bouillabaisse sauce with mullet, gurnard, John Dory, mussels and cuttlefish. First courses do not leave out the garlic – fish soup with rouille, salt-cod fish-cakes with aïoli, smoked aubergines with stir-fried pork, chilli and garlic. Plain shellfish lovers will have all they want here too – at a price. Early menus have shown a similarity in some sauces and a ringing of changes on the fish as the boats come in. Execution can vary, but it is consistently strong flavours that are being dispensed. Smoked aubergines were too smoky by half, but the cuttlefish in its own ink with home-made noodles – 'a visual masterpiece' – was 'ideally garlicky'. Desserts do not let the side down: excellent crème brûlée; strawberries with a spiced red wine and mascarpone 'looked wonderful, tasted pretty good'; a light rhubarb steamed pudding came with cinnamon custard. Coffee is poor, but bread is a moist, dense and delicious wholemeal. St Ives has not been blessed with good spots at which to eat, so this one needs encouragement for bravery and enterprise. Debby Wilkins' service is exemplary. The wine list is a beginning; house wines from René Barbier are £7.50.

CHEF: Paul Sellars PROPRIETORS: Paul Sellars and Debby Wilkins OPEN: Wed to Mon, D only; 7 to 9 (may vary according to season) CLOSED: Christmas, Jan and Feb MEALS: alc SERVICE: not inc CARDS: Access, Visa DETAILS: 30 seats. 5 tables outside. Private parties: 30 main room. Vegetarian meals with prior notice. Children welcome. No pipes in dining-room. Music

---

The Guide *office can quickly spot when a restaurateur is encouraging customers to write recommending inclusion – and sadly, several restaurants have been doing this in 1992. Such reports do not further a restaurant's cause. Please tell us if a restaurateur invites you to write to the* Guide.

▲ *Well House*

St Keyne PL14 4RN
LISKEARD (0579) 342001
on B3254, 3m S of Liskeard

COOKING **3**
COST £28–£36

'When we heard the coffee grinder, we felt on to a good thing,' reported one
satisfied visitor. Others have found Nicholas Wainford's apparent insistence on
reading or reciting the menu, then not letting the forgetful among us see the
script, rather eccentric, if not picayune. His kingdom is a small country house
beyond Liskeard, close to St Keyne's well, good for eye complaints. The
interior is easy on the eye, while the exterior improves each season. This place
is comfortable and sophisticated, but avoids grandeur. David Woolfall's
cooking is restrained yet apposite. Materials are thought about ('They have
taken to serving smoked sea trout rather than salmon, as they don't like the oily
texture') and methods are not rich. Sauces vary. They are not all deep
reductions, but ring the changes between a port sauce with bacon and lentils
for venison, a nicely light jus with lamb and ratatouille, or a tarragon cream
with guinea-fowl. A menu may include choice from five dishes in each course,
the main dishes being for once more interesting than the starters (once soup
and at least one terrine, confit or parfait have been taken care of, the remainder
seem rarely to involve hot things cooked to order). Shellfish also seems an
infrequent item. Pleasure seems to derive from the accuracy of the cooking, its
lack of over-elaboration, and the attention to detail. Usually, the desserts and
the cheeses are appreciated. If cooking is kept to a minimum at the start, the last
course sees well-reported Bakewell tart, flaming bananas and sticky toffee
pudding, as well as a mean marquise and good ice-creams. The wine list has
taken in a welcome supply of halves. It is still restricted to Europe and the
clarets are a special strength. For the rest, Germany shines, but makers and
négociants are sound rather than exciting; to retain the glass award more
adventure might have been hoped for. House wines are £8.50.

CHEF: David Woolfall   PROPRIETOR: Nicholas Wainford   OPEN: all week; 12.30 to 2, 7.30
to 9   MEALS: Set L £21, Set D £25   SERVICE: not inc, card slips closed   CARDS: Access,
Amex, Visa   DETAILS: 36 seats. 5 tables outside. Private parties: 40 main room. Car park.
Vegetarian meals. No children under 8. Smart dress preferred. Wheelchair access (1 step).
No music   ACCOMMODATION: 7 rooms, all with bath/shower. B&B £60 to £105. Deposit:
£25. Children welcome. Baby facilities. Pets welcome. Afternoon teas. Garden. Swimming-
pool. Sauna. Tennis. TV. Phone. Doors close at midnight (*The Which? Hotel Guide*)

Prices quoted in the Guide *are based on information supplied by restaurateurs. The prices
quoted at the top of each entry represent a range, from the lowest meal price to the highest;
the latter is inflated by 10 per cent to take account of likely price rises during the year of
the* Guide.

*All details are as accurate as possible at the time of going to press, but chefs and owners
often change, and it is wise to check by telephone before making a special journey. Many
readers have been disappointed when set-price bargain meals are no longer available.
Ask when booking.*

ST LEONARDS East Sussex   map 3

Röser's 🍾

64 Eversfield Place,
St Leonards TN37 6DB   COOKING **3***
HASTINGS (0424) 712218   COST £23–£45

You might not come for the setting, although piers and sea-fronts have a certain
je ne sais quoi, even in towns as moribund at St Leonards. But you might come
for Gerald Röser's cooking. This runs on luxurious lines: a warm salad of foie
gras with smoked salmon and avocado pear and a balsamic dressing seems to
hit two bull's-eyes at once, and, if you want to vary the smoked salmon theme,
try the blinis with caviare and smoked salmon. The repertoire develops slowly;
Gerald Röser is not anxious to change things he knows well. Thus
recommendations from last year resurface this: guinea-fowl with wild
mushrooms and shallots, lamb coated with herbs and served with a red wine
and tarragon sauce, or home-made wild boar sausages with choucroute. Care is
evident, both from the way food is presented (perhaps with excess of artistry
for some people) and in its preparation. Wild boar chops are marinated for
three weeks, and much time is spent in gathering herbs and wild things, and in
buying the best produce. This comes through in the menu, which is kept
deliberately short to avoid over-stocking. Desserts continue the themes of skill
and intelligence. A mille-feuille of apple consists of poached slices of apple
separating a calvados-flavoured crème pâtissière, served with a butterscotch
sauce; a chocolate mousse with coffee sauce reveals the point of paying as much
as possible for cooking-chocolate. The kitchen is largely a one-man band,
delays have therefore been noted when tables come in a single rush, especially
as ancillaries fore and aft of the meal take time and so much trouble. Quiet
times may also lead to sepulchritude, and busy ones to too much smoking.
Maintaining a wine list of such magnitude and quality in a recession and in St
Leonards must say something for the Rösers' fortitude. It is beginning to have a
slightly old-fashioned look, eschewing as it does smaller growers in Alsace
and treading lightly in Italy. New World and a few Spanish bottles are good,
and with fair range of bourgeois clarets there is much below £20. Otherwise,
prices are high but reflect quality fairly in the classic regions. House wine is
£8.95. CELLARMAN'S CHOICE: Riesling Réserve Personelle 1983, Hugel,
£22.95; California, Firestone Vineyard, Cabernet Sauvignon 1987, £15.95.

CHEF: Gerald Röser   PROPRIETORS: Gerald and Jenny Röser   OPEN: Tue to Sat; 12 to 2,
7 to 10   MEALS: alc. Set L £15.95   SERVICE: net prices, card slips closed   CARDS: Access,
Amex, Diners, Visa   DETAILS: 40 seats. Private parties: 20 main room, 40 private room.
Vegetarian meals. Children welcome. No pipes in dining-room. Wheelchair access (2
steps). No music

All entries in the Guide *are rewritten every year, not least because restaurant standards
fluctuate. Don't trust an out-of-date* Guide.

All letters to the Guide *are acknowledged with an update on latest sales, closures,
chef changes and so on.*

ST MARGARET'S AT CLIFFE Kent   map 3

▲ *Wallett's Court* ✻

West Cliffe,
St Margaret's at Cliffe CT15 6EW   COOKING 2
DOVER (0304) 852424   COST £23–£32

The Oakleys must get tired of recounting the story of their purchase and
restoration of this remarkable old house. The fact remains that they did it all up
themselves and that old beams and structures dominate the interior landscape.
The initial intention was a B&B, and this has somehow developed into a
restaurant. A series of set-price menus offers food described by one American
visitor as 'capable but provincial, not so much sophisticated as generous and
earnest, and charming and willing because of it'. Chris Oakley's highly
professional background (first English chef at Le Poulbot, the Roux brothers'
City outpost, and so on) means that misses are few. The intended clientele and
the style of the house determine the rest. Meat and fish are served with
substantial sauces: salmon with cucumber and dill, lemon sole with asparagus
and cream, pork with claret and oyster mushrooms, beef with paprika, or
perhaps beer and onions, but both with cream. Pâtés, terrines and soups are
strong points here. 'Presentation superb; flavours wonderful; had the Saturday-
night gourmet meal and crawled to bed' was the message of one happy pilgrim
from Essex. The wine list is very reasonably priced while the sources are not
always familiar. It keeps to France save for a quartet from Australia including
two from Coldstream Hills. House wines are £8.

CHEF: Chris Oakley   PROPRIETORS: Chris and Lea Oakley   OPEN: Tue to Sat, D only (Mon
D for residents); 7 to 9   MEALS: Set D £18.50 to £25   SERVICE: net prices, card slips
closed   CARDS: Access, Visa   DETAILS: 50 seats. Private parties: 50 main room, 20 private
room. Car park. Vegetarian meals. Children's helpings. No smoking in dining-room. No
music   ACCOMMODATION: 8 rooms, all with bath/shower. B&B £40 to £60. Rooms for
disabled. Children welcome. Baby facilities. Garden. Tennis. Snooker. TV. Phone. Doors
close at midnight. Confirm by 5. Fax: (0304) 853430 (*The Which? Hotel Guide*)

ST MICHAEL'S ON WYRE Lancashire   map 5

Mallards

Garstang Road,
St Michael's on Wyre PR3 0TE   COOKING 1*
ST MICHAEL'S (099 58) 661   COST £15–£33

The 'slightly mixed-up décor' and the rooms knocked into one on the ground
floor of a village cottage put Mallards into a recognisable category. John Steel's
cooking – copious and good – puts it into another. The recipes are not complex
and have a slightly sweet edge to the sauces: salmon with cucumber and
Riesling cream sauce, duck with cassis, lamb with a Beaujolais and onion
gravy, beef with whisky and mustard, and venison with green peppercorn and
port. They certainly satisfy. Soups have been flavoured effectively, and first-
course fresh pasta with cheese, bacon and chicken was 'rich, creamy and tasty'.
Vegetables are a good and generous show, fresh-baked brown flatbread is

welcome, cheeses go on and on, and desserts include a winner of a trifle as well as tip-top meringues. Sunday lunch is bargain time, though press of people can cause delay. One hesitates to call places unpretentious, but the Steels seem to have got the measure of what they want to do. The wine list is a very decent range at competitive prices.

CHEF: John Steel PROPRIETORS: John and Ann Steel OPEN: Mon to Sat, D only, and Sun L; 12 to 2.30, 7 to 9.30 (10 Sat) CLOSED: 2 weeks Aug, 1 week Jan MEALS: alc. Set Sun L £9.95 SERVICE: not inc, card slips closed CARDS: Access, Visa DETAILS: 24 seats. Private parties: 36 main room. Car park. Children's helpings. Wheelchair access. Music

---

SALISBURY Wiltshire   map 2

Harper's £

7 Ox Row, The Market Square,	
Salisbury SP1 1EU	COOKING 1
SALISBURY (0722) 333118	COST £13–£26

'Great traditional eating and good value for money' is how one visitor recommended Adrian and Ann Harper's modest first-floor dining-room. Wholesome, unpretentious food reigns: coronation chicken, beef casseroled with herb dumplings and grilled mild-cure pork loin with cider, apple, onion and calvados sauce are indications of the style. Local produce is acquired whenever possible: Poole mussels added to a cream and dill soup, and New Forest venison baked in a pie. Vegetables are approved – 'buttered cabbage was perfectly cooked and not many restaurants can do that'. Puddings such as 'luxury' bread-and-butter and treacle tart complete the picture of sufficiency. The wine list is rather good for range and value. House wines are £7.50.

CHEF: Adrian Harper PROPRIETORS: Adrian and Ann Harper OPEN: Mon to Sat; 12 to 2, 6.30 to 10 (10.30 Sat) CLOSED: 25 and 26 Dec MEALS: alc. Set L £6.90, Set D £13.50 SERVICE: not inc CARDS: Access, Diners, Visa DETAILS: 60 seats. Private parties: 60 main room. Car park. Vegetarian meals. Children's helpings. Music. Air-conditioned

---

SCARBOROUGH North Yorkshire   map 6A

Lanterna

33 Queen Street,	
Scarborough YO11 1HQ	COOKING 1*
SCARBOROUGH (0723) 363616	COST £21–£29

Old-style trattorias have gone out of fashion but continue to do good business. This place runs and runs; its decoration is a mite 'gloomy but reassuring', serves many local people and cooks sound food. Over and above the too-familiar menu there are daily specials. Eat queenies provençale or a frittata of local sole, even asparagus with a mousseline sauce when the season is upon us – evidence of more than just caricature cooking. Desserts get boring, but crème caramel is ace and there may be a special like poached peaches in zabaglione custard. There are a few Italian bottles on the skeletal wine list. House wines are £8.50 a litre.

CHEF: G. Arecco   PROPRIETORS: Mr and Mrs G. Arecco   OPEN: Tue to Sat, D only; 7 to 9.30
MEALS: alc   SERVICE: not inc, card slips closed   CARDS: Access, Visa   DETAILS: 36 seats.
Private parties: 36 main room. Vegetarian meals. No children under 2. Wheelchair access.
Music

SEAFORD East Sussex	map 3

Quincy's

42 High Street, Seaford BN25 1PL	COOKING 1
SEAFORD (0323) 895490	COST £26–£34

Ian and Dawn Dowding have lasted long enough in their bow-fronted
restaurant to be part of the Seaford scene. Although urban cowboys from the
Fulham Road are not a common sight, Ian's cooking is more than just the meat-
and-two-veg that once was Seaford. Lamb gets coriander as well as mint in its
sauce; fillet steak has pesto, not horseradish; duck has sweet peppers and
madeira, not orange. The daring may try ginger and garlic with squid and
crayfish, hot goulash soup or five-mushroom Stroganoff. The intentions work
for the readers who have reported this year, and get especial support once the
labour-intensive sweets are commented upon. Prices do not run away from
you, even on the wine list that has been improved with some 'new additions'.
House wines are £8.25.

CHEF: Ian Dowding   PROPRIETORS: Ian and Dawn Dowding   OPEN: Tue to Sat, D only,
and Sun L; 12 to 2, 7.15 to 10   MEALS: Set Sun L and Tue to Sat D £15.95 to £21.95
SERVICE: not inc   CARDS: Access, Amex, Visa   DETAILS: 32 seats. Private parties: 20 main
room. Vegetarian meals. Children's helpings on request. No cigars/pipes in dining-room.
Music

SHAFTESBURY Dorset	map 2

La Fleur de Lys ▼ ⅍ | NEW ENTRY |

25 Salisbury Street,	
Shaftesbury SP7 8EL	COOKING 3
SHAFTESBURY (0747) 53717	COST £20–£38

Satisfaction abounded in Shaftesbury when, in the summer of 1991, David
Shepherd upped sticks from Lewtrenchard Manor in Lewdown, North Devon
(see entry) and opened on his own account here at La Fleur de Lys. He is a
capable chef, well supported by Mary Griffin front-of-house and Marc Preston
in the kitchen. They set about offering fair value and ambitious cooking in a
first-floor dining-room, reached by narrow and winding stairs from a cobbled
court flanked by the kitchens and a small vestibule with a large dresser. The
cooking has not gone down one notch as a result of moving out of a country-
house setting: plenty of good materials, lots of stuffings and elaboration. 'The
salmon dish may sound "over-egged" but in fact it worked very well' was the
comment of one person who viewed the menu with mild distrust. Lamb
wrapped in a wild-mushroom mousseline, salmon and turbot in a scallop
mousseline in filo, planked beef filled with Stilton and wrapped in bacon,
asparagus mousse and a Roquefort puff: these are dishes from a single evening.

If proof of the pudding is sought: 'Honey-roast duck with rosemary sauce and apples, celeriac and courgettes was fine, and the beef was as good as any I have tasted, not overpowered by Stilton or bacon, given a faint tang by the oak plank.' For this man, the last course was even better: more parcels, this time of bananas, with banana ice-cream; coffee beignets with Tia Maria sabayon and hazelnut ice-cream. Good presentation, good service, good flavours, decent rolls, nice hot canapés served after you have ordered, plenty of coffee and adequate petits fours complete the picture. Ignore the Mouton Cadet and the Mateus and look in the wine list for Australian and New World offerings such as Corbans from New Zealand or Inglenook from California. Closer to home, an Umani Ronchi Verdicchio or Carlo Santi Pinot Grigio also give first-rate value, and prices for the classic French regions are by no means out of order. There is a useful set of 1982 and 1983 clarets for the bigger spenders who want to try out their progress. House wines are from £6.95.

CHEFS: David Shepherd and Marc Preston   PROPRIETORS: David Shepherd, Mary Griffin and Marc Preston   OPEN: all week, exc Mon L; 12 to 3, 7 to 10   CLOSED: last 2 weeks Jan (may vary)   MEALS: alc. Set D £17.95   SERVICE: not inc   CARDS: Access, Visa   DETAILS: 30 seats. Private parties: 32 main room. Vegetarian meals. Children's helpings. Smart dress preferred. No smoking in conservatory. Music. Air-conditioned

---

SHEFFIELD South Yorkshire   map 5

Greenhead House ✸✷

84 Burncross Road, Chapeltown,
Sheffield S30 4SF   COOKING 2*
SHEFFIELD (0742) 469004   COST £31–£40

'The accent is on comfort and relaxation,' remarks a reader. This amid stylish, flower-adorned rooms within a square stone cottage. The unhurried approach, despite playing to a full house most evenings, is one indication of professionalism. Another is the constant calibre of Neil Allen's and Christine Roberts' menu: four courses, each comprising four or five options, changed monthly, with coffee and petits fours included in the price. 'Ingredients are fresh and the season's best,' rates a regular. Treatment is modern with French undertones, and invention is accompanied by technique: a spring dinner began with tuna in a tapénade marinade served with asparagus, followed by tomato, orange and basil soup, then a roulade of turkey with morels and monkfish and home-made brioche and strawberry pudding. 'Flavours and textures were balanced, offering interest and variety,' reported the recipient who related a solemn verdict of 'attention to detail without affectation'. Chante Cigale's white Châteauneuf, Corsin's Pouilly-Fuissé and 1982 Ch. d'Issan are three off a reliable list that has a long tail of bin-ends for those who like to rummage. House wines are £9.

CHEFS: Neil Allen and Christine Roberts   PROPRIETORS: Neil and Anne Allen   OPEN: Tue to Sat, D only; 7.15 to 9   CLOSED: first 2 weeks Apr, first 2 weeks Aug, 24 to 31 Dec   MEALS: Set D £23.95 to £28.50   SERVICE: not inc, card slips closed   CARDS: Access, Visa   DETAILS: 32 seats. Private parties: 32 main room. Car park. Children welcome. No smoking in dining-room. Wheelchair access. No music

Blostin's

29 Waterloo Road,
Shepton Mallet BA4 5HH   COOKING 2
SHEPTON MALLET (0749) 343648   COST £16–£30

Local residents describe this as a simple bistro-looking restaurant, but kept in proper condition so that it demands a second look, when, most likely, you'll find it full of other locals taking advantage of the fair prices on the table d'hôte, the sound yet sometimes adventurous cooking by Nick Reed, and the energetic service of Lynne Reed and her band. 'Piping hot (this matters in Somerset), generous portions, good service' were three points singled out by a supporter. Any place that can deliver moules marinière, grilled goats' cheese, duck braised in red wine with mushrooms and bacon, rack of lamb in a herb crust, four vegetables, walnut and treacle tart, sticky toffee pudding and chocolate and Grand Marnier parfait without complaint shows that it has some steady essentials worked out. If fillet of sea bream with a pesto sauce, sea bass with saffron sauce and asparagus, squid with garlic butter and leeks or veal with Marsala and wild mushrooms are as good, then another constituency will have voted for the operation. The wine list will break no banks and offers an acceptable range. One reporter thought Nick Reed might be 'coasting', but how do you coast if you've got it right? And note that the reporter was delighted to be back there. House wines are £7.25.

CHEF: Nick Reed   PROPRIETORS: Nick and Lynne Reed   OPEN: Tue to Sat, D only (L Tue to Fri by arrangement); 12 to 2, 7 to 9.30 (10 Sat)   MEALS: alc. Set L £10, Set D £13.50 to £14.50   SERVICE: not inc, card slips closed   CARDS: Access, Visa   DETAILS: 32 seats. Private parties: 30 main room. Vegetarian meals. Children's helpings. Wheelchair access. Music

▲ Bowlish House ♥

Wells Road, Shepton Mallet BA4 5JD   COOKING 1
SHEPTON MALLET (0749) 342022   COST £31

Formerly a wool merchant's house, Bowlish has lots of pediments, honeyed stone and passing traffic on the Wells Road; yet peace for residents is assured (not at rush-hour) by the tender ministrations of the Morleys. Assurance too is found in the greater self-sufficiency and elaboration of the kitchen's product for diners and residents alike – a complimentary appetiser and a greater range of fish dishes are two new features mentioned. Dinner at Bowlish House is an event – the entertainment of the evening, not its accompaniment. The set-price menu, running to half a dozen choices at each stage, is not of the 'new brutalist' school. Hot beetroot mousse dressed with orange zest and coriander vinaigrette, and a warm salad of turkey, ginger, spring onions, coriander and sesame are two elegant first courses, though a plate of air-dried ham, shaved Parmesan, black olives, basil and virgin olive oil shows other influences. These latter may reappear in main dishes like a vegetarian sauté of mushrooms with cumin, pink peppercorns and polenta, while pork with apples, calvados and cream harks back to English country restaurant cooking. Desserts, one reader avers, never 'lack oomph' (*GFG '92*) but rather set his tastebuds tingling. Chocolate mousse on raspberry sauce with a brandy-snap, filo parcels of apple and banana with butterscotch, and good local cheeses set up the happy jangles. Coffee and home-made sweeties calm them down again. Bob Morley is 'attentive while never over-zealous'. The choice of halves on the wine list has expanded since last year. Fair space is given to the main producing countries, and there is a good house selection at very keen prices. The clarets and the Spanish reds are perhaps the most interesting sections to explore, though Italy is excellent too. House wines are all £7.95. CELLARMAN'S CHOICE: Rioja 1987, Carta d'Oro, Berberana, £7.95; Marsanne, Côtes de Thongue 1990, Dom. Mont-Auriol, £7.95.

CHEF: Linda Morley PROPRIETORS: Bob and Linda Morley OPEN: all week, D only (L by arrangement); 7 to 9.30 (9 Sun) CLOSED: 1 week Feb, 1 week Oct MEALS: Set D £21.50 SERVICE: not inc, card slips closed CARDS: Access, Visa DETAILS: 24 seats. Private parties: 36 main room. Car park. Vegetarian meals. Children welcome. No smoking while others are eating. No music ACCOMMODATION: 3 rooms, all with bath/shower. B&B £48. Children welcome. Baby facilities. Pets welcome. Garden. TV. Doors close at midnight. Confirm by 6 (*The Which? Hotel Guide*)

SHINFIELD Berkshire   map 2

L'Ortolan ♥

The Old Vicarage, Church Lane,
Shinfield RG2 9BY   COOKING 5
READING (0734) 883783   COST £44–£75

This bird's cage is a castellated, red-brick rectory in nominal countryside, but with a looming sense of encroaching settlement and motorway beyond. The house is balanced by a pair of conservatories: one for liquids, the other for solids. Between them is hall, bar and original dining-room. Decoration is mercifully tactful – there is little of the French three-star desire to go over the top. The view, in some people's eyes, would be improved if the front door were free of motor vehicles. There are defined steps up the financial ladder here with two set-price menus, each with ample choice. John Burton-Race is not a chef who loves simplicity. For many, the subtlety is beyond description or unnoticed, for some it is misplaced, but there is a strong contingent that finds it satisfying. The reliance on truffles and foie gras has disappeared from at least half the repertoire, but it surfaces, as the prices rise, in dishes such as a ravioli filled with chicken and foie gras mousseline spiked with truffles, that comes with glazed leeks and a madeira sauce, an asparagus mousse with truffle cream, John Dory with mushrooms and potatoes that has a cream mushroom sauce 'scented with truffle', or squab studded with truffle on a madeira sauce with a potato galette wrapped round a pigeon liver gâteau. Mousses have not been abandoned in this repertoire – one reason for a sense of richness in many meals, and for accusations of over-subtlety. Take for instance a lasagne of lobster, the tower held together with a tarragon lobster mousse, given moisture by a truffle oil, or the dish of lamb with a crab mousse, wrapped in green leaves, sharing the plate with a curried crab quenelle, and split by two sauces, one meat, one crab. Desserts continue the labour; witness the plate of chocolate sweets, but not the gratin of fruits described as lacking alcohol or taste. However, all is recovered with pear soufflé tart Rosamunde, served with raspberries, pear sorbet and raspberry sauce. For some people this course is the best. Ancillaries, which may include canapés of anchovy sticks, a tart filled with ratatouille or a tiny lamb samosa (cf. Le Manoir aux Quat'Saisons, Great Milton, see entry), and all the pukka stuff are not criticised, and the cheese gets a vote of confidence. At around £14 to £19 the 'Choix de l'Ortolan' will be the wine choice of many customers. If not, the bill could soar. Quality and range are good, half-bottles are provided liberally, but nothing can compensate for a modest St-Véran being offered at £28.50 or a 1985 Savigny from Bize for £62.50. Only dessert wines are offered by the glass. CELLARMAN'S CHOICE: Tursan, Ch. de Bachen 1989, £18.90; Chinon, Clos de l'Olive 1982, Couly-Dutheil, £34.50.

CHEF: John Burton-Race   PROPRIETORS: John and Christine Burton-Race   OPEN: Tue to Sun, exc Sun D; 12.15 to 2.15, 7.15 to 10.30   CLOSED: last 2 weeks Feb, last 2 weeks Aug MEALS: Set L and D £29.50 to £48   SERVICE: not inc   CARDS: Access, Amex, Diners, Visa DETAILS: 60 seats. Private parties: 40 main room, 32 private room. Car park. Children's helpings. Wheelchair access (2 steps). No music. Fax: (0734) 885391

SHIPTON GORGE Dorset   map 2

▲ *Innsacre* ♥ ⅚✳

Shipton Gorge DT6 4LJ   COOKING 2
BRIDPORT (0308) 56137   COST £18–£32

'I ate outside on an evening when the rest of the world stayed in. Amazing! The view spread out over the neighbouring hillside; there were pigs chuntering to the left, a manic parrot to the right,' reported a local man who had visited this converted farmhouse which improves all the while. There are two lunch menus (plus one for Sunday lunch) and one dinner menu (plus a short *carte* and vegetarian menus), which stretch to wider horizons than pastoral Dorset when they offer prawns with a garlic sauce, chargrilled ratatouille vegetables wrapped in a parcel of spinach, or Yorkshire pudding with onion gravy topped with a slice of foie gras, before chicken pot-roasted with mussels, saffron, basil and white wine, or pigeon breast wrapped with Parma ham and served with calvados sauce and browned apples. It is a place not afraid to mix and match its inspirations – neo-Italian creations sit happily next to curried banana soup and fish-cakes with crab sauce; roast duck is served with its liver on a bed of black beans and bean shoots with a ginger and honey sauce. Serious hot puddings include beignets in a 'tangy and zesty' lemon sauce. The wine list shows the same serious intent as do the ancillaries and details of the cooking. It is no slouch: Au Bon Climat, Altesino, Dom. du Vieux Télégraphe, Henri Jayer, Bernard Defaix, Bruno Paillard and Mudgee are names to conjure with, from a wide range of sources. The half-bottles list gives plenty of choice, including some from the New World and Italy for a change. House wines start at £8.50.

Dining-rooms where live and recorded music are never played are signalled by No music *in the details at the end of an entry.*

CHEF: Anthony Sutch PROPRIETORS: Sydney and Lesley Davies OPEN: all week, exc
Mon L and Sun D (exc bank hols); 12 to 1.45, 7 to 9.45 CLOSED: 1 week Nov, 25 and 26
Dec MEALS: alc. Set L £9.80 to £12, Set Sun L £13.50, Set D £19.80 SERVICE: not inc, card
slips closed CARDS: Access, Visa DETAILS: 42 seats. 8 tables outside. Private parties: 60
main room. Car park. Vegetarian meals. Children's helpings. No smoking in dining-room.
Wheelchair access (also WC). Music ACCOMMODATION: 6 rooms, all with bath/shower.
B&B £45 to £66. Deposit: £25. Children welcome. Baby facilities. Pets welcome. Garden.
TV. Doors close at midnight. Confirm by 6. Fax: (0308) 27277 (*The Which? Hotel Guide*)

SHURDINGTON Gloucestershire   map 2

▲ *Greenway*

Shurdington GL51 5UG
CHELTENHAM (0242) 862352   COOKING 2
on A46, 2m S of Cheltenham   COST £21–£48

This is tip-top Cotswold stuff, just the thing to show off England's heritage:
great views, smashing gardens, a fine old house, well-established decoration,
and a handsome dining-room looking on to the lily pond and formal garden.
'They whack it on for pre-meal drinks, but the rest is good value in a nice
setting,' wrote one set of local residents. Visitors tend to ignore the 'whacking
on' and reflect that the kitchen is improving and the operation is well founded.
Value is most evident at lunch-time; the evening *carte* is well up to city prices,
indeed beyond. Edward Stephens came here from Le Caprice in London (see
entry) and has continued to offer smart food rather than become a stick-in-the-
mud. Skate with a tomato sauce, resting on seaweed, hot red mullet mousse
with chive butter sauce, venison with wild mushrooms and a sharp plum
sauce, salad of quail with truffle oil, good home-made pasta, and courgette and
carrot salad with couscous and a hazelnut dressing all work for the main part.
So, too, do the desserts, referred to with enthusiasm for such things as a tart of
fresh figs with honey sabayon or banana brûlée with vanilla ice-cream. There
are hangovers from the days of country-house cooking – complicated
vegetables, complementary dishes – and an expectation that gentlemen shall
wear jackets in the hotel from 7pm. The wine list offers a long choice,
especially of clarets. You do not have to pay a lot – some care is taken with the
selection below £20 and house wines are £10.25.

CHEF: Edward Stephens PROPRIETOR: Tony Elliott OPEN: all week, exc Sat L; 12 to 2,
7 to 9.30 (8.30 Sun) CLOSED: 3 to 8 Jan, L bank hols MEALS: alc D. Set L £14 to £16, Set
D £23.50 SERVICE: not inc, card slips closed CARDS: Access, Amex, Diners, Visa
DETAILS: 50 seats. 4 tables outside. Private parties: 14 main room, 12 and 26 private rooms.
Car park. Vegetarian meals. No children under 7. Smart dress preferred. No cigars/pipes in
dining-room. Wheelchair access (1 step; also WC). Music ACCOMMODATION: 19 rooms,
all with bath/shower. Rooms for disabled. B&B £85 to £175. No children under 7. Garden.
TV. Phone. Doors close at 11.30. Fax: (0242) 862780 (*The Which? Hotel Guide*)

▲ *This symbol means accommodation is available.*

Card slips closed *in the details at the end of an entry indicates that the total on the slips
of credit cards is closed when handed over for signature.*

SISSINGHURST Kent   map 3

Rankins'

The Street, Sissinghurst TN17 2JA   COOKING 2
CRANBROOK (0580) 713964   COST £27–£41

Hugh and Leonora Rankin have added a postscript to this year's menu:
'Untreated double cream and fresh whole eggs in our cooking.' Fans of the
beamed dining-room have found convincing enough evidence on their plates.
Indeed, output has been praised as 'interesting but not over-complicated'.
Others have finished dinner unpersuaded, but cite quantity, not quality, as
meagre. Duck breast, dry-fried, served with pan juices and a smoked sausage,
ratatouille and lentil compote was 'excellent but on the small side'. Ingredients
have been judged as 'splendid' and may be combined with imagination.
Schizophrenic chicken is presented with a drumstick maple syrup-glazed as
well as a thigh fricasseed with tarragon cream sauce. Roasts are added to the
Sunday lunch *carte*. Service is 'friendly and correctly paced'. An abridged wine
list of French, Australian and New Zealand bottles includes a fairly priced
selection of halves. House French is £7.80.

CHEF: Hugh Rankin   PROPRIETORS: Hugh and Leonora Rankin   OPEN: Wed to Sat, D only,
and Sun L; Sun L 12.30 to 1.30, 7.30 to 9   MEALS: alc   SERVICE: not inc   CARDS: Access,
Visa   DETAILS: 30 seats. Private parties: 10 main room, 24 private room. Children's
helpings Sun L. No children under 8. Tidy dress preferred. Smoking only after 2pm and
after 10pm. No music

SLAIDBURN Lancashire   map 5

▲ Parrock Head ⅙✳ £

Slaidburn BB7 3AH
SLAIDBURN (020 06) 614   COOKING 1
1m NW of Slaidburn   COST £19–£31

Visitors appreciate the cosiness, comfort and friendliness of this congenial
country house set in remote moorland with Pendle Hill clearly visible a few
miles away. The upstairs lounge, in particular, is a most appealing retreat –
stylish, but with no pretensions to grandeur. Vicky Umbers' cooking is based
on local ingredients, is pitched at the right level and displays flair and
imagination, without overreaching itself. The short menu changes daily. One
well-reported meal began with farmhouse vegetable soup (boosted with ham),
before roast rack of Bowland lamb with redcurrant glaze, and medallions of
pork with different stuffings (mushroom, spinach and paw-paw). To finish,
there was cold cinnamon tart chosen from an array of desserts on the sideboard
in the dining-room. The Umbers go out of their way to treat vegetarians fairly
and deal happily with special requests; one guest was surprised to receive a
gift-wrapped box of chocolates at the end of his birthday meal. The well-spread
wine list has affordable drinking from the Old World and New World. House
wines are from £7.

CHEFS: Vicky Umbers and Lorraine Chapman   PROPRIETORS: Vicky and Richard Umbers
OPEN: all week, D only, and Sun L; 1 to 2, 7 to 8.30   MEALS: alc   SERVICE: not inc, card
slips closed   CARDS: Access, Amex, Visa   DETAILS: 32 seats. Car park. Vegetarian meals.
Children's helpings. No smoking in dining-room. Wheelchair access. No music
ACCOMMODATION: 9 rooms, all with bath/shower. Rooms for disabled. B&B £36 to £60.
Deposit: £10. Children welcome. Baby facilities. Pets welcome. Afternoon teas. Garden. TV.
Phone. Doors close at 11.30 (*The Which? Hotel Guide*)

SOUTHALL Greater London   map 3

Madhu's Brilliant £ | NEW ENTRY |

39 South Road, Southall UB1 1SW   COOKING 1*
081-574 1897 and 571 6380   COST £11–£27

This is arguably the best example of neighbourhood Indian cooking in
Southall. The Anand family have strong connections in the area: Madhu
(himself) set up the original Brilliant restaurant in Western Road; his sons have
inherited the tradition and run this spacious venue on two floors connected
by a spiral staircase. The kitchen delivers an outstanding version of
predominantly Punjabi cooking that can excite even experts. 'Our menu is
simple and small,' say the owners, which means that dishes are likely to be
prepared to order. Butter chicken and jeera chicken with cumin seeds and black
pepper are renowned specialities. Aloo chat, crisp vegetable samosas,
exemplary matar paneer and aloo chollay have been highly recommended.
Thick, dark chicken tikka masala was 'an absolute delight' according to one
aficionado of the genre. Breads, rice and chutneys are well above average
and the home-made kulfi is in a class of its own. Drink lassi or lager. House
wine is £7.

CHEFS: Sanjeev Anand and Jagdish Kumar Anand   PROPRIETORS: Jagdish Kumar Anand,
Krishna Kumari Anand, Sanjay Anand and Sanjeev Anand   OPEN: Wed to Mon, exc L Sat
and Sun; 12.30 to 3, 6 to 11.30 (12 Fri and Sat)   MEALS: alc. Set L £6 to £15, Set D £8 to
£15   SERVICE: 10%, card slips closed   CARDS: Access, Amex, Diners, Visa   DETAILS: 104
seats. Private parties: 60 main room, 60 private room. Vegetarian meals. Children welcome.
Wheelchair access. Music. Air-conditioned. Fax: 081-813 8639

SOUTH MOLTON Devon   map 1

▲ *Whitechapel Manor* ♥ ⅝✕

South Molton EX36 3EG   COOKING 3*
SOUTH MOLTON (0769) 573377   COST £23–£53

A country-lover's dream, architecture-buff's nirvana, Whitechapel is tucked
away on the lowest slopes of Exmoor. Not a lot has gone on hereabouts since
heavy horses were traded in for tractors. Get through the door, admiring the
terracing on the way, and witness a fine conversion, leaving all the woodwork
and decorative painting intact (seventeenth- and early eighteenth-century) yet
providing an eminently usable set of rooms. The Shaplands have a gentle
touch, but unerring: 'The hotel is carried by the lovely personalities of the host
and hostess.' They manage to run an expensive hotel as naturally as if it were a

hospitable Devon farmhouse. What does impress is their thoroughness. Having done the house and gardens properly, they realised the restaurant should be up to the mark. So they hired, and have kept, Thierry Leprêtre-Granet almost since the opening. His food flirts with country-house forms but avoids their pitfalls of tedium and elaboration. He courts simplicity with sophistication, using few elements in each dish but making them work hard. Scallops with asparagus, crab with avocado and mango, asparagus soup with wild mushrooms, sweetbreads with lentils and port, salmon with sorrel sauce, fillet of beef with green peppercorns or with a mustard sauce are some of the dishes that deceive by innocence yet convince by accuracy and discretion. Menus are offered at two prices and two lengths. They are not cheap. Most people find them fair value for the standard achieved. There is thoroughness also in the breads, sorbets and ice-creams. If, however, you think you will get flamboyance, you are in the wrong place. The wine list, self-effacing but intelligently constructed, is reassuring. Catholic range is matched by fair pricing and sound selection. House wines are from £12.50. CELLARMAN'S CHOICE: Vernaccia di San Gimignano 1989, Teruzzi & Puthod, £27.50; Mercurey, Ch. de Chamirey 1988, £19.50.

CHEF: Thierry Leprêtre-Granet   PROPRIETORS: John and Patricia Shapland   OPEN: all week; 12 to 2, 7 to 8.45   MEALS: Set L £15 to £26, Set D £26 to £37   SERVICE: not inc, card slips closed   CARDS: Access, Amex, Diners, Visa   DETAILS: 20 seats. Car park. Children welcome. No smoking in dining-room. No music   ACCOMMODATION: 10 rooms, all with bath/shower. B&B £65 to £170. Deposit: 25%. Children welcome. Afternoon teas. Garden. TV. Phone. Doors close at 11.30. Fax: (0769) 573797 (*The Which? Hotel Guide*)

SOUTHSEA Hampshire   map 2

Bistro Montparnasse

103 Palmerston Road,
Southsea PO5 3PS   COOKING 1
PORTSMOUTH (0705) 816754   COST £25–£33

Gillian Scott's move into the kitchen of this likeable establishment has been a change for the better. She works to a monthly-changing fixed-price menu that offers some accessible but enterprising dishes along the lines of tagliatelle with pancetta and artichoke; oak-smoked fillet of beef; and roast guinea-fowl with corn bread stuffing and onion sauce. Influences from the Mediterranean and the Orient loom large. Reporters have approved of filo pastry parcels of crab and ginger with lemon grass, and game sausage on a purée of white vegetables with a slightly fruity jus. Daily fish dishes, such as perfectly poached brill with a 'scrumptiously intense' dark orange shellfish sauce, have been impressively good. To finish, steamed banana sponge pudding with custard was 'a perfect example of its kind', although a beautifully created chocolate dessert looked more impressive than it tasted. Prices are admirably affordable. Around 100 wines include a contingent from England as well as the New World. House French is £8.

See inside the front cover for an explanation of the symbols used at the tops of entries.

CHEF: Gillian Scott   PROPRIETORS: Peter and Gillian Scott   OPEN: Tue to Sat, D only;
7 to 10   CLOSED: bank hols   MEALS: Set D £18.90 to £22.90   SERVICE: not inc   CARDS:
Access, Amex, Visa   DETAILS: 40 seats. Private parties: 40 main room. Vegetarian meals.
Children's helpings on request. No pipes in dining-room. Wheelchair access. Music

---

SOUTHWOLD Suffolk   map 6

▲ *Crown* ❘ ⁵✕ £

90 High Street,
Southwold IP18 6DP   COOKING 2
SOUTHWOLD (0502) 722275   COST £17–£28

The Crown and the Swan are twin pillars of Adnams, brewer and wine
merchant. The Crown has the racier image but both have nourished or
lubricated many a day at the seaside. Racy may mean modern, in the style of the
cooking for bar and restaurant – vegetable curry, grilled sardines, cassoulet of
duck, skate with Pernod butter – but it can also mean slapdash. Value is high,
though, particularly in the bar, and service is willing. The restaurant, which
offers its menu at a set price (two or three courses), may serve duck breast
while the bar offers a cassoulet, or quenelles of haddock rather than kedgeree,
but the manner is similar. Some have found the duck breast soggy and the
curry under-spiced, but all applaud the quality of the vegetables and the
substance of the puddings and pies – dainty sweets are not in favour. Cheer the
wine list too. Succinctness replaces the more high-flown Loftus language of
Adnams' retail list; but this is a peach of a selection. Fine Italians, Volpaia and
Antinori vie with careful listings of burgundies and clarets, grand and
bourgeois. The fair prices reflect quality accurately, and there are many
interesting wines below £12. Half-bottles are few, except in the dessert
department. For New World exploration, this list would make a good
base camp.

CHEF: Andrew Mulliss   PROPRIETORS: Adnams plc   OPEN: all week; 12.30 to 1.30 (1.45
bar), 7.30 to 9.45   CLOSED: second week Jan   MEALS: bar menu. Set L £12.75 to £14.75,
Set D £16.25 to £18.50   SERVICE: not inc, card slips closed   CARDS: Access, Amex, Visa
DETAILS: 25 seats. 4 tables outside. Private parties: 18 main room, 25 and 45 private rooms.
Car park. Vegetarian meals. Children's helpings. No smoking in dining-room. Air-
conditioned. No music   ACCOMMODATION: 12 rooms, all with bath/shower. B&B £35 to
£55. Children welcome. Baby facilities. Air-conditioned. TV. Phone. Doors close at 11.30.
Fax: (0502) 724805 (*The Which? Hotel Guide*)

▲ *Swan Hotel* ❢ ⁵✕

Market Place, Southwold IP18 6EG   COOKING 1
SOUTHWOLD (0502) 722186   COST £16–£40

The hotel is dead-centre: on the market-place and minutes from the beaches. It
is as Southwold as can be: genteel, 'gentle', 'pleasantly formal'. People like the
conservatism laced with a little enterprise that comes over in the decoration
and the general welcome. If you go in jeans and sneakers to Adnams' other
place, the Crown, you should wear a collar and tie here. There is care to offer a

service to all levels of clientele. Bar meals are not dear, nor is lunch in the restaurant, and at night there are three set-price menus of rising length and elaboration. Cooking can be sound, but sometimes lacks pzazz. Of eight first courses on one evening, five involved some form of processing – terrines, parfaits, 'loaves' or 'cheese'. These may not always pack a punch: a fish mousse was thought too modest, a 'mixed fowl terrine' not good enough, yet a broccoli and wild salmon terrine was excellent. On another occasion, a dinner of spinach and bacon salad, guinea-fowl on a bed of straw potatoes with white wine sauce, then raspberries and cream was pleasantly unadventurous and decently executed. The wine list here is very good – a fine range, with well-balanced selections from the antipodes, Italy and the classic French regions all fairly priced, as at the Crown. There is a page of good house wines, all offered by the glass, but the Swan is pipped again by its better-endowed sister. CELLARMAN'S CHOICE: Chablis 1990, J. Brocard, £13.45; Dalwood's Shiraz/Cabernet 1989, Penfolds, £7.95.

CHEFS: David Goode and Kevan Ryland   PROPRIETORS: Sole Bay Hotels Ltd   OPEN: all week; 12.15 to 1.45, 7 to 9.30   CLOSED: restaurant Mon to Fri from 4 Jan to Thur before Easter   MEALS: Set L £10.50 to £17.50, Set D £16.50 to £27.50. Bar meals L   SERVICE: not inc, card slips closed   CARDS: Access, Amex, Visa   DETAILS: 90 seats. Private parties: 90 main room, 36 and 44 private rooms. Car park. Vegetarian meals. Children's helpings. No children under 5 after 7pm. Smart dress preferred. No smoking in dining-room. Wheelchair access (also WC)   ACCOMMODATION: 45 rooms, all with bath/shower. Rooms for disabled. Lift. B&B £42 to £140. Deposit: £10. Children welcome. Pets in garden-rooms only. Afternoon teas. TV. Phone. Confirm by 6. Fax: (0502) 724800 (*The Which? Hotel Guide*)

SPARK BRIDGE Cumbria   map 7

▲ *Bridgefield House* 🍷 ⁕

Spark Bridge, Ulverston LA12 8DA
LOWICK BRIDGE (022 985) 239
4m N of Ulverston, off A5084 on back   COOKING 2*
road to Coniston   COST £27–£34

Times may be quiet but the Glisters have not dimmed their stoves, nor the customers their appreciation of all the efforts that have gone into turning this Victorian house into a place of comfort and delight. Returnees are frequent. Rosemary Glister's meals conform to a pattern: six courses – a choice of three beginnings, soup, main course, sorbet, one of three puddings, then cheese or hot savoury, and coffee. Soup usually comes with something to chew – perhaps a bannock, a cheese palmier or brioche. Main courses are accompanied by enterprising vegetables: on one night there were carrots with poppy seeds, pan-fried fennel, honey-roast small potatoes, glazed red onions with pine-kernels, and leeks with yoghurt and cheese. The cheese course is one named sort (British), a piece of fruit, some nuts and a few leaves of salad. People have stressed the care that is taken with all this – and the rewarding effort of David Glister's service – and that often the tastes are precisely what they were advertised to be. For example, lambs' sweetbreads and oyster mushrooms were distinct in taste and texture, just as the carrot and parsnip in the soup gave two levels of flavour as well as combining to great effect. There was perhaps less

431

attack in the ginger, vermouth and cream sauce that accompanied the well-judged salmon, but this was compensated for when the Bramley and marzipan lattice flan was served with its calvados cream. Coffee was strong and came with chocolate thimbles filled with rum-flavoured ganache. Prices are not high. There are high mark-ups on the better bottles on the wine list, but it is intelligent and wide-ranging, with much enjoyable drinking below £12. Half-bottles are abundant. In hard economic times, might it not be wise to edit such a long list as this? Vigorous pruning would still leave much pleasure and interest. CELLARMAN'S CHOICE: Waipara Springs, Chardonnay 1991, £16.35; Koombahla, Cabernet Sauvignon 1988, Brown Brothers, £15.95.

CHEF: Rosemary Glister   PROPRIETORS: David and Rosemary Glister   OPEN: all week, D only; 7.30 for 8   MEALS: Set D £21 (residents) to £24 (non-residents)   SERVICE: not inc, card slips closed   CARDS: Access, Visa   DETAILS: 20 seats. Private parties: 24 main room. Car park. Vegetarian meals. Children's helpings. Smart dress preferred. No smoking in dining-room. No music   ACCOMMODATION: 5 rooms, all with bath/shower. B&B £35 to £70. Deposit: £20. Children welcome. Baby facilities. Pets welcome. Afternoon teas. Garden. Phone. Doors close at 1am. Confirm by 3. Fax: (022 985) 379

STADDLEBRIDGE North Yorkshire   map 7

▲ McCoy's

The Tontine, Staddlebridge DL6 3JB   COOKING 3*
EAST HARLSEY (060 982) 671   COST £28–£65

It's called the Tontine (a form of lottery) because that's how the original building, a staging post halfway between Newcastle and York, was financed. This original use explains why the place is islanded by roads, and why the stables are so big. The house itself is a fine piece of classical building. The McCoy family, who run it, are not so interested in classical architecture; the '30s and '40s are more their scene, with a large dash of idiosyncracy. So the public rooms are a remarkable mix of old sofas, furniture that might be the star attraction in a second-hand dealer's, dim, atmospheric lighting, and even parasols over tables in the main dining-room. It has humour and affection and most people are seduced, though some are shocked, due, perhaps, to the relaxed good nature of most people working here. Actually, the staff are often well trained and effective, but there are readers who only see the dark side of potential sloppiness. The menu runs on steady lines from year to year and remains expensive. This is partly to finance more purchase of foie gras and truffles, without which the place seems unable to function. It also seems unable to produce many first courses without whisking up a mousse: for example, three-herb chicken mousse pasta, pasta filled with a langoustine mousse, scallop mousse with a sliver of foie gras, or smoked salmon with a mousse of celery, cucumber and truffle juices. The mousses were undeniably good – the stated flavour is right there, they are light, and they can also be rich. There is no keeness for new-wave vinaigrettes, or for large-scale bulk foods other than pasta. Main dishes combine good meats and exceptional sauces, not over-reduced or light on flavour. Veal with madeira sauce, lamb with tomato, parsley and truffle sauce, pigeon with port glaze (and cream, leeks, and more truffle), and beef with deep red wine sauce are examples. Desserts are definitive: rich chocolate fondant, great crêpes, layers of chocolate with a mousse, an orange ice-cream and orange sauce, mille-feuille of strawberries. When game is in season, eat game; when the fish delivery is a good one, eat fish. The repertoire has been thought out with care, and long practice has made performance very consistent. The wine list has as much character as the rest of the operation. There are good wines, chosen with care, interesting wines, not found everywhere, and high prices for the top ones. The notes are useful. House wines are from £13.95. Downstairs, there is the bistro, where everything is cheaper, more cheerful, and still good. Tables may be bare of cloths, accoutrements basic, but a dinner that included snails in garlic, herbs and cream, seafood croustade with lots of scallops, prawns and squid, rack of lamb, chicken 'Jojo' with vermouth cream sauce, duck with port, lamb with a mint béarnaise, sticky toffee pudding, bakewell tart and chocolate fudge cake was pronounced excellent value and done with care and skill.

CHEF: Tom and Eugene McCoy PROPRIETORS: Peter, Tom and Eugene McCoy OPEN: restaurant Wed to Sat, D only; 7 to 10; bistro all week; 12 to 2, 7 to 10 CLOSED: 25 and 26 Dec MEALS: alc SERVICE: not inc, card slips closed CARDS: Access, Amex, Diners, Visa DETAILS: 45 seats. Private parties: 60 main room, 25 private room. Car park. Vegetarian meals. Children's helpings. Music. Air-conditioned ACCOMMODATION: 6 rooms, all with bath/shower. B&B £89 to £109. Children welcome. Pets welcome. Afternoon teas. Garden. Air-conditioned. TV. Phone. Confirm by lunch-time. Fax: (060 982) 660

STAITHES North Yorkshire   map 6A

▲ *Endeavour* £ | NEW ENTRY |

1 High Street, Staithes TS13 5BH   COOKING 1
WHITBY (0947) 840825   COST £18–£34

The restaurant was once a village shop. It is a tall building of local stone in the centre of a long, narrow street leading down to the sea. Parking is at the top of the very steep hill, which can be a problem. Lisa Chapman has created a charming, informal dining-room with wood-panelled walls, vases of flowers and attractive striped tablecloths; with drinks served in a cramped bar. The mainstay is fish, direct from the boats to the kitchen: octopus is paired with avocado; sea trout baked with orange and thyme; turbot gets a lime hollandaise; monkfish is roasted with garlic and fennel. Technique and presentation are high for such a modest set-up: two curls of lemon sole stuffed with smoked salmon arrive laid on a pool of orangey-pink lobster sauce, adorned with pretty vegetables. From her tiny kitchen, Lisa Chapman can also deliver anything from lamb kebabs with rice or pork fillet with fresh cherry sauce to vegetarian enchiladas. 'Outstanding' crème brûlée is the bestselling sweet. Thirty wines are fairly priced. House French is from £6.75.

CHEF/PROPRIETOR: Lisa Chapman OPEN: Mon to Sat, exc Sat L (Sun D July to Sept and bank hol weekends); 12 to 2, 7 to 9.30 (later in high summer) CLOSED: early Jan to early Mar MEALS: alc SERVICE: not inc DETAILS: 45 seats. Private parties: 25 main room, 14 and 20 private rooms. Vegetarian meals. Children welcome. Music ACCOMMODATION: 3 rooms, 1 with bath/shower. B&B £16.50 to £35. Children welcome

STAMFORD Lincolnshire   map 6

▲ *George* ▮

71 St Martins, Stamford PE9 2LB   COOKING 1
STAMFORD (0780) 55171   COST £22–£50

Elizabethan property developer and first minister Lord Burghley
commissioned this stalwart hotel. It is handy still as a staging post for nearby
Burghley House. Where highwaymen returned with booty, tourists now rest
after plundering Stamford shops. The oak-panelled restaurant's established
repertoire is uncluttered by fashion and generally well executed: artichoke
hearts, wood mushrooms and pine-kernels to start; scallops, sea bream, red
snapper, parrot fish and crayfish pan-fried with a red wine sauce to follow.
Otherwise, there are beef and lamb from the silver carving wagons. The Garden
Lounge offers good value at lunch. Service is attentive and amicable. Residents
have the benefit of a wine list in their room; a nice touch and here a worthwhile
one since the quality and range is provided by intelligent buying from
excellent merchants. Italy is strong, half-bottles are plentiful and price and
range are very fair. The sensible 'House list' starts from £8.45. CELLARMAN'S
CHOICE: Tuscany, Parrina 1990, £9.95; Vin de Pays du Var, Dom. de Triennes
1990, £10.65.

CHEFS: Chris Pitman and Matthew Carroll   PROPRIETORS: Poste Hotels Ltd   OPEN: all
week; 12.30 to 2.30, 7.30 to 10.30   MEALS: alc. Set L Mon to Sat (restaurant) £15.50
SERVICE: not inc, card slips closed   CARDS: Access, Amex, Diners, Visa   DETAILS:
restaurant 90 seats, Garden Lounge 80 seats. 20 tables outside. Private parties: 90 main
room, 22, 35 and 40 private rooms. Car park. Vegetarian meals. Children's helpings. Jacket
and tie in restaurant. Wheelchair access (also WC). No music   ACCOMMODATION: 47
rooms, all with bath/shower. B&B £66 to £154. Children welcome. Baby facilities. Pets
welcome. Afternoon teas. Garden. TV. Phone. Confirm by 6. Fax: (0780) 57070 and 66104
(*The Which? Hotel Guide*)

STANDON Hertfordshire   map 3

No.28 ▮✳

28 High Street,
Standon SG11 1LA   COOKING 1
WARE (0920) 821035   COST £20–£38

There has not been much news from the Balls' handsome restaurant set in an
Edwardian house next to their successful catering company; but what there is,
is encouraging. The menu is kept short so that waste is at a minimum, and
freshness is kept at its proper premium. For once, it is not the usual Home
Counties mix of Marie Rose sauce and a variety of steaks. A day's offering may
include marinated Arctic char with celery and cucumber, gâteau of mushrooms
and fennel with home-made brioche, monkfish with an orange and coriander
black-butter sauce, guinea-fowl stuffed with pigeon mousseline, hot soufflés,
or a confection of bananas and blueberries with a marmalade ice-cream. More
adventure than Hertfordshire knows how to deal with. There is adventure, too,
if you choose the Dom Pérignon 1983 from the short and adequate wine list. It
is passed on at very small profit. House wines start at £8.

CHEFS: Adam Baldwin and Miranda Ball   PROPRIETORS: Miranda and Trevor Ball, and
Adam Baldwin   OPEN: Tue to Sat; 12 to 2.30, 7 to 9.30   MEALS: Set L £14.50 to £27.50, Set
D £27.50   SERVICE: not inc, card slips closed   CARDS: Access, Amex, Visa   DETAILS: 18
seats. Private parties: 26 main room. Vegetarian meals. Children welcome. No smoking in
dining-room. Wheelchair access (1 step). Music. Fax: (0920) 822630

STAPLE CROSS East Sussex   map 3

Olivers

Cripp's Corner, Staple Cross TN32 5RY   COOKING 2
STAPLECROSS (0580) 830387   COST £18–£23

'A restaurant on stilts' was how one report described this building tucked
away on a sleepy, sloping hillside with lovely views down the valley. Inside, it
is sprucely done out, with well-cared-for plants, ruched curtains and pretty
patterned wallpaper. There is now a choice of only two fixed-price dinner
menus, but the care, enthusiasm and hard work that go into the cooking remain
undiminished. An inspection meal began on a high note with Roquefort and
pine-nut bavarois, artfully presented with a salad of unusual leaves and crisp
bacon; then there was well-timed juicy loin of lamb baked in pastry with
whole tarragon leaves. Vegetables were interesting but 'notable more for
intention and effort than for anything else'. To finish, a very nouvelle-looking
honey and almond parfait with an intensely flavoured chocolate sauce was
impressive. Some details and techniques seem uneven: no dressing for the
salad starter; some vegetables not as fresh as they should be. Even so, Gary
Oliver deserves support for continuing to offer excellent value for money
despite pressure from the recession. The three-dozen wines are equally good
value. House French is £7.50.

CHEF: Gary Oliver   PROPRIETORS: Albert and Gary Oliver   OPEN: Wed to Sun, D only, and
Sun L; 12 to 1.30, 7 to 9.30   CLOSED: first 3 weeks Jan   MEALS: Set Sun L £10.95, Set D
£15.50 to £19.50   SERVICE: not inc   CARDS: Access, Visa   DETAILS: 36 seats. Private
parties: 45 main room, 18 private room. Car park. No children under 5. Music

---

STAPLEFORD Leicestershire   map 5

▲ Stapleford Park ▼ ⁵⚹

Stapleford, nr Melton Mowbray LE14 2EF   COOKING 2*
WYMONDHAM (057 284) 522   COST £31–£59

One disadvantage of working to a high profile is that you wear your problems
on your sleeve. So when Bob Payton decided to put this wonderful house-
turned-hotel on the market, it hit the headlines. Not that things were
impossible, just that the industry was sluggish and money seemed tight. So far
no sale, and the hotel sails on. The house is great: a mixture of periods, some
Gothic revival of the seventeenth century, some baroque carving (the dining-
room), some rather gloomy Victorian (used as a main lounge), some cosy
country-house (the library bar), some plain interesting (the columned old
kitchen used for breakfast and lunch). Bedrooms are a mix of named designer
and the more orthodox, not always hot, but often with good features such as

baths deep enough for a swim. The American chefs who finally got the place off to a run, culinarily speaking, have left and Mark Barker carries their torch. He has not changed the approach. This is more fashionable than orthodox English country-house, though the menu may read more lively than the food may be in the eating. Bouillabaisse, lamb carpaccio, Caesar salad, salmon with couscous, lots of salsas, and chocolate pecan pie are the sort of dishes that might crop up in California (a bit conservative there) or London (way-out), but not in So-and-So Hall in Cumbria. It is a pity that the flavours are less stand-up, but some meals have given much pleasure: rigatoni with prawns, excellent beef, good kebabs of fish with lemon butter sauce, nicely chargrilled strips of vegetables. Light lunches (from £4.50) are also available. Service is generally well thought of: Mr Payton's training has had effect, and there is no lack of enthusiasm. Gentle persuasion to risk a bottle from California rather than Burgundy is exerted by listing wine by style rather than country. Although there is little below £15, wines are priced fairly and reflect quality. There are good half-bottles. House wines are from £11.75. CELLARMAN'S CHOICE: Dry Creek, Chenin Blanc 1990, £15.50; Monticello, Cabernet Sauvignon 1986, £21.

CHEF: Mark Barker   PROPRIETORS: Bob and Wendy Payton   OPEN: all week; 12 to 2.30, 7 to 9 (10.30 Fri and Sat)   MEALS: alc. Set Sun L and Sun to Thur Set D £19.92   SERVICE: not inc, card slips closed   CARDS: Access, Amex, Diners, Visa   DETAILS: 150 seats. 11 tables outside. Private parties: 70 main room, 16, 30, 40 and 150 private rooms. Car park. Vegetarian meals. Children's helpings. No children under 10 unless accompanied by nanny. Smart dress preferred. No smoking in dining-room. Wheelchair access (also WC). Music   ACCOMMODATION: 35 rooms, all with bath/shower. Rooms for disabled. Lift. B&B £125 to £285. Deposit: £50. No children under 10 unless accompanied by nanny. Pets welcome. Afternoon teas. Garden. Tennis. Fishing. TV. Phone. Fax: (057 284) 651 (*The Which? Hotel Guide*)

STOKE-BY-NAYLAND Suffolk   map 3

▲ *Angel Inn*

Stoke-by-Nayland CO6 4SA   COOKING 1
COLCHESTER (0206) 263245   COST £19–£35

'A super, comfortable old inn' is one reader's description of this renovated pub on the main road through the village. Eating is the main business here and space in the dining area and garden is at a premium, especially in the evenings and at weekends. The bar menus (written on blackboards) draw most enthusiastic votes: carrot and cumin soup, pot-roast pork with apple and brandy sauce, blackcurrant bavarois and home-made strawberry soufflé have been recommended. Reporters using the restaurant have mentioned the quality of the smoked duck, oriental seafood parcels, venison steak and plentiful fresh vegetables. Griddled fresh fish and a daily vegetarian dish are always available. The sheer popularity of the pub can occasionally disrupt the smooth running of the place, but most visitors agree that the service is pleasant and helpful. Local beers are on draught; house wine is £7.

London round-ups listing additional restaurants that may be worth a visit can be found after the main London section.

CHEF: Mark Johnson PROPRIETORS: Richard Wright and Peter Smith OPEN: Tue to Sun, exc Tue L and Sun D (all week bar meals); 12 to 2, 6.30 to 9 CLOSED: 25 and 26 Dec MEALS: alc. Set Sun L £12 SERVICE: not inc CARDS: Access, Amex, Diners, Visa DETAILS: 40 seats. Private parties: 26 main room. Car park. Vegetarian meals. Children restricted. Wheelchair access (also WC). Music ACCOMMODATION: 6 rooms, all with bath/shower. B&B £42 to £55. No children under 8. TV. Phone. Doors close at 11.30 (*The Which? Hotel Guide*)

STOKE-ON-TRENT Staffordshire   map 5

Ria £   NEW ENTRY

61–67 Piccadilly, Hanley,
Stoke-on-Trent ST1 1HR   COOKING 1
STOKE-ON-TRENT (0782) 264411   COST £9–£28

This converted shop rates as one of the few creditable Thai restaurants in the Midlands. The frontage may look unassuming, but a lot of thought and care has gone into the decoration – mirrored panels on the walls, Thai frescos and a black carpet printed with an 'R' monogram. Dishes are attractively presented and served on blue and white crockery. The 130-choice menu covers all the major components of the Thai repertoire, from curries to salads and noodles. Vegetables are a strong point and there is a separate mini-menu highlighting vegetarian specialities. An inspector found the flavours clear and refreshing, although dishes may sometimes be unassertive and timidly spiced. Starters such as chicken satay, salmon fish-cakes, stuffed chicken wings and excellent vermicelli salad come with appropriate vividly flavoured dips. Other good items have included 'green' curry of beef with coconut milk, bamboo shoots, pea aubergines and basil; crispy roast duck served on a bed of cabbage with sharp plum sauce; aubergines in yellow bean sauce; and spicy rice with prawns. Singha Thai beer suits the food. House French is £6.95.

CHEF: Mrs Anong Sangpreechakul PROPRIETOR: Mr Charoon Sangpreechakul OPEN: all week, exc L Mon and Sun; 12 to 2, 6.30 (7.30 Sun) to 11.30 (10.30 bank hols) MEALS: alc. Set L £5 to £6.95, Set D £10 to £13.75 SERVICE: 10%, card slips closed CARDS: Access, Amex, Diners, Visa DETAILS: 65 seats. Private parties: 75 main room, 50 private room. Vegetarian meals. Children welcome. Wheelchair access (also WC). Music. Air-conditioned

---

STOKESLEY North Yorkshire   map 7

▲ Chapters £

27 High Street,
Stokesley TS9 5AD   COOKING 2*
STOKESLEY (0642) 711888   COST £17–£37

Alan Thompson's handsome coaching-inn is one of the few providers of good food in the district. It should be encouraged. That people like what they find is clear from the fact that the restaurant has been supplemented by a 40-seat bistro with a cheaper menu. The success of this and, for instance, McCoys of Staddlebridge (see entry) must be some pointer that the area could support better places than it does at present. The longest paragraph in the chapter is reserved for fish. There is a lot of it on the daily menu and lobster alone makes a visit worthwhile. A summary of a year's eating from one supporter admitted that production could sometimes be variable but 'at its best it's unbeatable'. A catalogue of success includes lobster stuffed with prawns on a bed of noodles; a ragoût of scallops, red mullet and salmon; an amazing seafood pancake; brioche stuffed with crab and prawns; and mushrooms stuffed with crab, in filo pastry, with a Malibu sauce. The last is an example of '90s invention in full flow, but traditionalists may respond better to a good paella. Desserts, too, get cheers: strawberries in a meringue, banana and hazelnut pie with toffee sauce, and good pancakes. The approach is thoroughgoing (good bread, daily marketing, practical innovations such as a barbecue) and enthusiastic. Some choices on the wine list are good – Paillard champagne, Laporte Sancerre – but there is not much attention to non-French bottles and the range is not great. Prices are competitive. House Duboeuf is £8.50 per litre.

CHEFS: David Brownless and Alan Thompson PROPRIETOR: Alan Thompson OPEN: all week; 12 to 3 (restaurant bookings only), 7 (6.30 bistro) to 10 CLOSED: 25 Dec and 1 Jan MEALS: alc and bistro menu SERVICE: not inc CARDS: Access, Amex, Diners, Visa DETAILS: 64 seats. 8 tables outside. Private parties: 50 main room. Vegetarian meals with prior notice. Children's helpings with prior notice. Smart dress preferred. Wheelchair access (2 steps). Music ACCOMMODATION: 13 rooms, all with bath/shower. B&B £42 to £57. Children in larger rooms only. Baby facilities. Pets by arrangement. Afternoon teas. TV. Phone. Fax: (0642) 711888

STON EASTON Somerset   map 2

▲ Ston Easton Park 🍷 ⅙✳

Ston Easton BA3 4DF   COOKING 3
CHEWTON MENDIP (0761) 241631   COST £31–£47

'The establishment oozes quality. It is summed up by saying that a member of staff came out of the front door to greet us as we drew up. We had telephoned from the wayside but half an hour before.' The message remains constant from year to year: the Smedleys and their staff are accomplished hosts and the locale is unmatched. 'We stayed for the afternoon and played three games of croquet, all for the price of two cups of tea.' Gardens, park, vegetable plot, views and prospects are outside; plasterwork, magnificence, and a succession of glorious state rooms humanised by unaffected care and attention are within. Against this backdrop, Mark Harrington offers set-price *cartes* in the dining-room or a more informal menu for daytime eating on the terrace. None is cheap, though luncheon is more affordable. The style is deceptively simple, and materials are prime. A terrine of foie gras, asparagus in puff pastry with an orange hollandaise, braised confit of duck with ginger and soy, beef with potato galette and girolles are examples of a luxurious plainness. The defence is that they work. (There is a supplementary menu of melon and grilled sole for those who like their food plainer still.) A haddock and spinach roulade with quail's eggs and caviare was 'very open, giving the effect that it breathed', roast duck was expertly carved off the bone and magically reconstructed, an exquisite chocolate mousse was served in a swan pastry case and a plate of sorbets included one of champagne and mint of unusually deep flavour. The price for dinner is only possible in a country like Britain, and some justification may be the setting, the care with which details are attended to and the quiet skill of the buying and cooking. 'The five of us had different things from the menu and we all agreed that by comparison with the best, this *was* the best.' The wine list gives fine support. Around the base price of £15 there is plenty of choice, reinforced this year by extra supplies from the New World. The range of halves has also been extended. It is a long, classic list that gets better year by year with special commendation for Beaujolais. House wines are £14.50. CELLARMAN'S CHOICE: New Zealand, Wairau River, Sauvignon Blanc 1991, £18; Australia, Cabernet Sauvignon 1983, Wolf Blass, £22.

CHEF: Mark Harrington   PROPRIETORS: Peter and Christine Smedley   OPEN: all week; 12.30 to 2, 7.30 to 9.30 (10 Fri and Sat)   MEALS: 'Terrace Menu' L. Set L £24, Set D £35 SERVICE: net prices, card slips closed   CARDS: Access, Amex, Diners, Visa   DETAILS: 40 seats. 8 tables outside. Private parties: 40 main room, 14 and 22 private rooms. Car park. Vegetarian meals. Children's helpings. No children under 7. Jacket and tie. No smoking in dining-room. No music   ACCOMMODATION: 21 rooms, all with bath/shower. B&B £95 to £320. Babies and children under 7 by arrangement. Pets by arrangement. Afternoon teas. Garden. Tennis. Snooker. TV. Phone. Doors close at midnight. Confirm by 6. Fax: (0761) 241377 (*The Which? Hotel Guide*)

STONHAM Suffolk   map 3

Mr Underhill's ▼

Stonham IP14 5DW
STOWMARKET (0449) 711206   COOKING 3
on A140, 300 yards S of junction with A1120   COST £26–£45

The Bradleys opened their restaurant 11 years ago; now they have a shop as well, in case you need a pint of extra-virgin. Mr Underhill's has operated hitherto with intending diners agreeing on a menu for their table before arrival: no choice until dessert. There has been some modification of this, with a short slate now offered for Sunday lunch and a variety of set-price menus (mix-and-match permitted) on every day save Saturday. There has been no change, however, in Chris Bradley's way of cooking: Italy and the Mediterranean show their influence in things like compote of red pepper and anchovy, confit of Barbary duck with mustard lentils, lamb shank with leek polenta, or Italian-style bread-and-butter pudding. Modern tastes from the north come out in a plate of smoked salmon with dill and ginger and a potato salad, twice-cooked soufflés, or pears with blackberry sauce. The cooking is accurate, sophisticated and enjoyable, made more so by Judy Bradley's guidance through the meal, as well as the setting of strong colours and bold furnishings. New Zealand wines continue their hold on the Bradleys' enthusiasm with a fine range. A useful and intelligent selection of white and red precedes the main list and decent named house wines are listed at the end with generous provision of halves. The Bradleys go to good merchants, buy with discretion and their mark-ups are not greedy. House wines are from £8.95. CELLARMAN'S CHOICE: Mâcon-Viré 1990, Gillet, £16.95; Moulin-à-Vent 1988, Berrod, £16.95.

▲ *This symbol means accommodation is available.*

CHEF: Christopher Bradley PROPRIETORS: Christopher and Judy Bradley OPEN: Tue to
Sat, D only, and Sun L (L Tue to Fri by arrangement); 12.30 to 1.45, 7.30 to 8.45 MEALS:
Set Sun L £15 to £19.95, Set Tue to Fri L and D £18.95 to £29.50, Set Sat D £29.95
SERVICE: not inc CARDS: Access, Visa DETAILS: 30 seats. 6 tables outside. Private parties:
30 main room, 16 private room. Car park. Vegetarian meals. Children's helpings with prior
notice. No smoking during meals. No music

STONOR Oxfordshire   map 2

▲ Stonor Arms

Stonor RG9 6HE   COOKING 2
TURVILLE HEATH (049 163) 345   COST £22–£44

Two restaurants in one refurbished Thames Valley hotel – both have
conservatories appended, with views on to an admirable summer garden. In
winter, when both glass-houses are too chilly, diners covet tables near the fire.
The easy-going flagstoned bar-restaurant, Blades, sports prints of varsity
oarsmen and a comprehensive lunch and supper menu. Portions of gravlax –
'supple and marinated in fresh dill' – are said to be generous. Good reports also
cover marinated anchovies and dill-cured herring, poached smoked haddock
with poached eggs, and field mushrooms baked with mozzarella served on
assorted salad leaves. Readers continue to approve items such as hot rabbit pâté
with roast garlic, and the venison casseroled with blueberries and port to be
had in the Stonor Restaurant, the more formal dining-room, on a fixed-price
three-course *carte*. For pudding choose 'splendid' poached fresh figs served
between caramelised biscuits with Pernod and fig ice-cream, or perhaps
chocolate truffle cake with orange sauce. Unfortunately, service in both
restaurants has sometimes, this year, been deemed abrupt. The wine list is a
claret and burgundy special, though the vins de pays are an appealing group.
House wines are £8.75.

CHEF: Stephen Frost PROPRIETORS: Stonor Hotels Ltd OPEN: Stonor Restaurant Mon to
Sat, D only, and Sun L; Blades all week; 12 to 1.45, 7 to 9.30 MEALS: Blades alc. Stonor
Restaurant Set Sun L £19.95 to £24.50, Set D £27.50 to £32 SERVICE: not inc CARDS:
Access, Amex, Visa DETAILS: Stonor Restaurant 38 seats, Blades 38 seats. 6 tables outside.
Private parties: 22 main room. Car park. Children's helpings. Smart dress preferred in
Stonor Restaurant. No cigars/pipes in Stonor Restaurant. Wheelchair access (also WC).
Music ACCOMMODATION: 9 rooms, all with bath/shower. Room for disabled. B&B £82.50
to £92.50. Children welcome. Baby facilities. Garden. TV. Phone. Doors close at 11. Fax:
(0491) 638863 (*The Which? Hotel Guide*)

'We were delighted when our party was shown to a round table which would facilitate the
good conversation so essential to an occasion of this sort, and we noted in passing the nearby
harp as a perhaps overly quaint touch of Celtic decoration. We were therefore absolutely
astonished when a few minutes later, a woman began to play the harp vigorously no more
than three feet from where we sat, rendering any further conversation utterly impossible.
We immediately made our views politely but quite unambiguously clear to the head waiter,
who made no response whatsoever. He did speak briefly to the harpist but for what purpose
I do not know, as the playing continued with only short breaks throughout the rest of our
enforced solitary and unsociable meal.'   On eating in Gwent

STORRINGTON West Sussex   map 3

▲ *Abingworth Hall*

Thakeham Road,
Storrington RH20 3EF   COOKING 2
WEST CHILTINGTON (0798) 813636   COST £19–£42

A lake, lawns, wistaria, conservatory, panelled drawing-room, three linked
dining-rooms: so might an estate agent describe this ideal small country hotel,
in a house built before the First World War. Steady consistency is the Bulmans'
pride, and a certain sense of not over-reaching themselves while conforming to
every propriety. Peter Cannon's cooking is in the same mode. A table d'hôte
and *carte* run in parallel and stay conservative, yet avoid boredom or utter
convention. The best sort of tradition pops up with a duck main course that has
onion sauce for once, not green peppercorns, orange, citrus, or honey and port.
First courses rely on cold food, though borrowing from the second course of the
longer set menu may ensure hot fish such as salmon quenelles or even some
baked mushrooms with goats' cheese. Presentation is as careful as the cooking.
The wine list will cause no heart-searching, or too much delving into the
pocket-book. House wines are £8.

CHEF: Peter Cannon PROPRIETORS: Philip and Pauline Bulman OPEN: all week; 12.30 to
2, 7.15 to 9 MEALS: alc. Set L £10.50 to £17.50, Set D £28 SERVICE: not inc, card slips
closed CARDS: Access, Visa DETAILS: 54 seats. Private parties: 54 main room. Car park.
Children welcome. Smart dress preferred. Jacket and tie D. No music ACCOMMODATION:
21 rooms, all with bath/shower. B&B £70 to £96. Deposit: £20. No children under 10.
Garden. Swimming-pool. Tennis. Fishing. TV. Phone. Doors close at 11. Fax: (0798)
813914

▲ *Manleys*

Manleys Hill, Storrington RH20 4BT   COOKING 3
STORRINGTON (0903) 742331   COST £28–£50

The house sits to one side of the long hill leading south out of Storrington, its
dining-rooms and bar leading back down the hill again after you have gone
through the front door. At the bottom, a deep inglenook houses a good log-
effect fire. Certainly comfortable, with tables that are properly appointed,
Manleys is a full-dress restaurant in rather a half-dress setting. The formality of
the service (sometimes too professional for its own good) is matched by the
serious intentions of the menu: modern classical cuisine allied to
interpretations of Austrian specialities. Some dishes suffer from a lack of clarity
– thus a pile of pasta with smoked ham bound together with egg and then
gratinated with cheese, although an Austrian familiar, reminded one person of
nothing more than school dinners, reinforced by the ring of slaw and carrot
ranged around the central tower. Contrast this to the expertly chosen and
cooked pigeon breast fanned over a bed of buttered cabbage with smoked ham,
with a natural yet deep-flavoured gravy. A beginning that was vitiated by an
added pile of fried potato purée, which spoiled the balance of the dish. A lack
of forethought may explain the intrusion of deep-fried cabbage (once crisp but
rendered soggy by the sauce) on a fine piece of sea bass. The cabbage tasted

badly of fat. Technique may thus sometimes nod, for many are the reports of refined (though rich) and accurate cooking: Mediterranean fish soup; a gâteau of four sorts of fish with a chive sauce; pork with prunes and a redcurrant cream sauce; squid with onion and red peppers; or celeriac pancake in the Chinese style. Desserts are a forte (and pastry can be first-rate, even if petits fours have on occasion been stale), none more so than the Salzburger Nockerln – an oval dish of foaming wonder, deeply flavoured with lemon and orange. All the skills are here and they often fire on all cylinders, though sometimes the plugs have needed a clean. A classic French wine list matches the style of the cooking; mark-ups are not unfair, but emphasis on Bordeaux and Burgundy means the price range is on the high side. Consider drinking a hock or Mosel while here: good and not dear. House wines are £12.80.

CHEF/PROPRIETOR: Karl Löderer OPEN: Tue to Sun, exc Sun D; 12 to 2, 7 to 9.15 (10 Sat) CLOSED: first 2 weeks Jan MEALS: alc. Set L £18.60, Set Sun L £24.50 SERVICE: not inc CARDS: Access, Amex, Diners, Visa DETAILS: 48 seats. Private parties: 36 main room, 22 private room. Car park. Children's helpings on request. No children under 7. Smart dress preferred. No cigars/pipes in dining-room. Wheelchair access (also WC). Music on request ACCOMMODATION: 1 double room, with bath/shower. B&B £50 to £87. No children under 12. TV. Phone

Old Forge

NEW ENTRY

6A Church Street, Storrington RH20 4LA COOKING 1*
STORRINGTON (0903) 743402 COST £19–£37

The old forge has gone, but beams remain and are padded to save unwary heads in the inglenook. This is a cottage restaurant, though prices can rise to urban levels. The welcome and attention, however, are far from streetwise cool. Enthusiasm for chutneys, spices and sharp seasoning (as well as nuts) often seems to inform Clive Roberts' cooking: a curried chicken and apple strudel with a spiced crab apple chutney, a breast of chicken with onion confit and red wine sauce, pork with honey and soy and a ginger wine sauce are examples. It is a repertoire that harks back to the glory days of 'modern British'. The details are good: bread, tiny cheese tartlets with aperitifs, chocolate truffles afterwards; but coffee is not so special. Ideas are often apposite: a warm salad of ox tongue and lentils with a mustard dressing and a chicken terrine with a spiced quince preserve were two excellent beginnings to a spring lunch. Space should be left for the sweet course, where Cathy Roberts reigns: layers of hazelnut meringue and caramel mousse served with an amaretto cream prompted ecstasy; banana and lemon parfait in a spun-sugar basket ran it a close second. The wine list is short and admirable. Every country is pillaged, to good effect and at very fair prices. There seems to be a lack of half-bottles. House wines are £6.50.

CHEF: Clive Roberts PROPRIETORS: Cathy and Clive Roberts OPEN: Tue to Sun, exc L Tue and Sat and Sun D; 12.30 to 1.30, 7.30 to 9 CLOSED: 1 week spring, 3 weeks autumn MEALS: alc. Set L £14, Set D £19 SERVICE: not inc, card slips closed CARDS: Access, Amex, Diners, Visa DETAILS: 24 seats. Private parties: 14 main room. Vegetarian meals. Children's helpings. Music. Fax: (0903) 743805

Report forms are at the back of the book; write a letter if you prefer.

STOW-ON-THE-WOLD Gloucestershire map 2

▲ *Wyck Hill House* ⚡✳

Burford Road,
Stow-on-the-Wold, GL54 1HY
COTSWOLD (0451) 831936
on A424, 2m SE of Stow-on-the-Wold

COOKING 2
COST £26–£60

The appeal of this 'delightful dining-room with wonderful views' is reaffirmed in reports. Visitors to the large early-eighteenth-century Cotswold mansion are handled with the same care that is lavished on the terraced lawns visible from the comfortable scenic salon. Ian Smith works with fine ingredients and has consolidated a *carte* defined by one reader as 'traditional but different'. A spring Sunday lunch began with pressed terrine of leeks, king prawns and tomato surrounded by a beetroot dressing, and a salad of oak-smoked chicken breast bound in a light tarragon yoghurt dressing with crisp potato wafers topped with marinated French beans. This was followed by a pavé of Cornish monkfish with mange-tout and asparagus tips in a saffron sauce, and a casserole of wild rabbit cooked in a watercress sauce and with stuffed cabbage. Vegetarians are provided with a mini-menu of less convincing alternatives. Puddings – including a crème brûlée mousse with apple and blackcurrant compote – have pleased, as have British cheeses served with home-baked chive and onion bread. The wine list is long, and prices are high; we hope that £33.40 is a record for Cloudy Bay Sauvignon. House wines are £11.75.

CHEF: Ian Smith PROPRIETORS: Lyric Hotels OPEN: all week; 12.30 to 2, 7.30 to 9.30 (10 Sat) MEALS: alc. Set L £16.95 (Mon to Sat) to £17.50 (Sun) SERVICE: not inc CARDS: Access, Amex, Diners, Visa DETAILS: 60 seats. Private parties: 80 main room, 40 private room. Car park. Vegetarian meals. Children's helpings. Jacket and tie. No smoking in dining-room. Wheelchair access (also WC). Music. Air-conditioned ACCOMMODATION: 29 rooms, all with bath/shower. Rooms for disabled. Lift. B&B £70 to £170. Children welcome. Baby facilities. Pets welcome. Afternoon teas. Garden. Air-conditioned. TV. Phone. Confirm by 7. Fax: (0451) 32243 (*The Which? Hotel Guide*)

STRATFORD-UPON-AVON Warwickshire map 2

Sir Toby's £

8 Church Street,
Stratford-upon-Avon CV37 6HB
STRATFORD-UPON-AVON (0789) 268822

COOKING 1
COST £19–£33

'The atmosphere, especially in the front room, is very much like a private home,' observes a reporter about the Watkins' diminutive restaurant in a seventeenth-century house. Most visitors take advantage of pre-theatre meals (although some mourn the early closing times), and the owners have perfected an efficient operation to ensure that no one is late for curtain-up. The menu reflects a good deal of in-house activity: home-cured bresaola, fish ravioli with prawn sauce, home-made ice-creams (whisky and ginger, blackcurrant, orange and yoghurt sorbet) – 'some of the best I've had,' enthuses one reader. Stir-fried scallops and salmon with ginger, spring onions and home-made egg noodles is a favourite. Other recommended dishes have included smoked quail with walnut mayonnaise; chicken livers with bacon and orange croûtons; spinach, sorrel and smoked haddock roulade; and wild mushrooms with garlic and lemon juice. The repertoire is 'inventive and intriguing', although some of the more original ideas, such as plaice stuffed with crab, prawns and grapes, do not convince everyone. House Bulgarian is £6.40.

CHEF: Joanna Watkins PROPRIETORS: Carl and Joanna Watkins OPEN: Tue to Sat, D only; 5.30 to 9.30 MEALS: alc SERVICE: not inc, card slips closed CARDS: Access, Amex, Visa DETAILS: 40 seats. Private parties: 36 main room, 16 private room. Vegetarian meals. Children's helpings. No pipes in dining-room. Wheelchair access (1 step). No music. Air-conditioned

---

STRETE Devon   map 1

Laughing Monk £ | NEW ENTRY |

Strete TQ6 0RN   COOKING 1
STOKE FLEMING (0803) 770639   COST £19–£29

The restaurant is an old schoolhouse next to the village church. Inside, it is cheerfully done out with pine tables and high-backed settles; hanging baskets of ferns are suspended from the ceiling. David Rothwell offers an honest blackboard menu. Fish shows up well in dishes such as pan-fried scallops with Pernod and chive sauce, and John Dory stuffed with mushrooms, onion and orange. Menu descriptions do not always match the results on the plate, but ingredients are fresh, portions are generous, and prices are sensible. Reporters have enjoyed smoked salmon cheesecake with yoghurt and cucumber sauce, crisp-skinned duck with plum and ginger glaze, and monkfish with provençal sauce in a pastry case. Vegetables show some enterprising touches. The sweets trolley provides 'a plethora of rich and sticky delights', including chocolate roulade with chocolate sauce and clotted cream, and slightly tart summer pudding. Service is friendly, efficient and unfussy, with Mrs Rothwell lending a hand in proceedings. The short wine list has plenty of decent drinking for around £10. House French is £6.50.

CHEF: David Rothwell PROPRIETORS: Mr and Mrs David Rothwell OPEN: Tue to Sat, D only, exc Tue D Nov to Feb; 7 to 10 (9.30 in winter) MEALS: alc SERVICE: not inc, card slips closed CARDS: Access, Visa DETAILS: 50 seats. Private parties: 40 main room. Car park. Vegetarian meals with prior notice. Children's helpings until 8pm. Smart dress preferred. No cigars in dining-room. Wheelchair access (2 steps; also female WC). Music

---

STROUD Gloucestershire   map 2

Oakes

169 Slad Road, Stroud GL5 1RG
STROUD (0453) 759950   COOKING 4
on B4070, ½m from Stroud   COST £24–£48

Behind the stone façade is a warm interior: perhaps the glow from one of the carefully restored fireplaces, the flames reflected from a polished wood floor, or a warmth of spirit engendered by Caroline Oakes' discretion, attention and unflappability. Christopher Oakes is regarded as similarly confident; his cooking is straight to the point, attractive and accurate. The *carte* offers either three or four courses at fixed prices and boasts, on its cover, a résumé of suppliers: meat from Jesse Smith and Co., Tetbury, dairy produce from Brookfield Farm, Prestbury, and so on. Readers have noted, with admiration, a high standard of raw material, and meals are identified as 'well balanced, beautifully presented but not over-elaborate'. Examples are abundant: 'gorgeous' shellfish bisque flavoured with brandy and finished with cream, 'superb' chicken liver terrine with home-made chutney and toasted brioche, and particularly good chicken breast stuffed with spinach and tarragon and served with a lemon sauce. Also recommended have been venison sausage on a bed of mixed lettuces with bacon and a red wine and shallot dressing, and sliced breast of pigeon served with braised haricot beans and an onion sauce. The cheeseboard is a fine option, but puddings have delighted more: 'exquisite' iced chocolate terrine in an orange and cream sauce or chocolate mousse 'to dream about'. The wine list continues to satisfy all except those in search of the wildly expensive. Selection is sound, prices are modest and good range is provided within the 70 bins. Ch. Cissac 1983 for £22.75 and Gigondas Pallières for £17.70 show wisdom and fair value. House wines are from £7.40.

CHEF: Christopher Oakes   PROPRIETORS: Christopher and Caroline Oakes, and Nowell and Jean Scott   OPEN: Tue to Sun, exc Sun D; 12.30 to 1.45, 7.30 to 9.30   MEALS: Set L Tue to Sat £18, Set Sun L £23, Set D £35   SERVICE: not inc, card slips closed   CARDS: Access, Visa   DETAILS: 40 seats. Private parties: 30 main room, 10 private room. Car park. Children's helpings. Wheelchair access. No music

---

STUCKTON Hampshire   map 2

Three Lions ▮

Stuckton Road, Stuckton SP6 2HF
FORDINGBRIDGE (0425) 652489   COOKING 3
1m off A338 at Fordingbridge   COST £21–£43

'We'd rather not have people in wellies, trunks, or with bare chests,' writes June Wadsack of her pub-restaurant near the New Forest – the cause, no doubt, of such sartorial variation. That she should even think of it may indicate the sort of place it is: no stuffiness, no ceremony, open to all comers. 'It is so good to be able to drink real ale (Wadworth's 6X) before one's meal' is the response of someone glad to have a rest from the bottled farragos of restaurant-restaurants. The hustle and bustle put a premium on calm service, languorous meals and endless room in which to stretch out the aching limbs. 'Impersonal' or 'non-existent' have been irritated descriptions of the quality of service on bad nights, and there may be more than one sitting at weekends. The pub gleams from cleaning, the rooms have a strong character, and the blackboard menus give everybody a chance to savour excellent cooking from a trained hand. Grilled tuna with pink peppercorns, pork with wild mushroom mousse and brandy sauce, tender breasts of pigeon with game sauce and cabbage, hock of ham, baked cod with spring onion and red wine sauce are the sort of main dishes that show Karl Hermann Wadsack has not nodded while taste changes in the South-East. His classical background gives him the techniques, and agility of mind imparts the rest. First courses are inventive: marinated herring, seafood jambalaya, spinach and Edam strudels, game soup, rabbit parfait. You can eat as much or as little as you require. Game and pastry work are strong points, but fish is worth exploring too. Prices are higher than for a usual pub lunch (the food is better), yet lower than those of most good restaurants in the area, although ancillaries can push up the total. Choice on the enthusiast's wine list is catholic but invariably accurate, and prices reflect quality fairly. Any structure to the list remains elusive; with so much available the customer should be offered a helping hand. There are some half-bottles, and more are promised. House wines are £8.50. CELLARMAN'S CHOICE: Tokay d'Alsace 1989, G. Lorentz, £12.50; Médoc, Ch. Fourcas-Hosten 1975, £28.

CHEF: Karl Hermann Wadsack   PROPRIETORS: Karl Hermann and June Wadsack   OPEN: Tue to Sun, exc Sun D; 12.15 to 1.30, 7.15 to 9 (9.30 Sat)   CLOSED: 2 weeks July to Aug, 1 week late autumn, 25 to 28 Dec, 1 Jan   MEALS: alc   SERVICE: not inc (10% for 6 or more)   CARDS: Access, Visa   DETAILS: 55 seats. Private parties: 40 main room. Car park. Vegetarian meals with prior notice. No children under 14. Wheelchair access (1 step). No music. Air-conditioned. Fax: (0425) 652489

STURMINSTER NEWTON Dorset   map 2

▲ *Plumber Manor* ♥

Sturminster Newton DT10 2AF
STURMINSTER NEWTON (0258) 72507
2m SW of Sturminster Newton,   COOKING 2
off A357 on Hazelbury Bryan Road   COST £22–£35

The house lies low in the middle distance, barns, stables, greensward around it, a bridge curves over a river, and trees soften the outlines: a very English scene. The Manor is a favourite resort for a country weekend: riding, shooting, fishing, tennis, and then a bit of dinner and some wine. The dining-room accommodates this need with two concurrent menus at differing prices that are most valued for their meats, such as venison, beef and lamb. These are well bought and not too fancifully cooked, yet offer elaboration in a dish such as veal with spinach and chicken mousse and Parma ham all wrapped in a filo parcel. Sweet things come from a trolley and underline the British style. The wine list is full of good names, particularly from Burgundy. Clarets are not ignored and there is a usefully high proportion of half-bottles. House wines are £9.

CHEFS: Brian Prideaux-Brune and Mrs S. Baker   PROPRIETORS: Richard, Alison and Brian Prideaux-Brune   OPEN: all week, D only, and Sun L; 12.30 to 1.45, 7.30 to 9.30   MEALS: Set Sun L £17.50, Set D £19.50 to £26.50   SERVICE: net prices, card slips closed   DETAILS: 60 seats. Private parties: 40 main room, 12 and 22 private rooms. Car park. Vegetarian meals. Children welcome. Smart dress preferred. No cigars/pipes in dining-room. Wheelchair access. No music   ACCOMMODATION: 16 rooms, all with bath/shower. Rooms for disabled. B&B £57.50 to £120. No children under 10. Garden. Tennis. TV. Phone. Fax: (0258) 73370 (*The Which? Hotel Guide*)

London round-ups listing additional restaurants that may be worth a visit can be found after the main London section.

SUDBURY Suffolk   map 3

Mabey's Brasserie £

47 Gainsborough Street,
Sudbury CO10 7SS   COOKING 2*
SUDBURY (0787) 74298   COST £20–£28

'Although the restaurant is fairly small,' writes Johanna Mabey, 'there is a lot
of atmosphere and buzz as the cooking takes place in front of the customers.' A
reader reports on a side-effect: 'Cooking front-of-house as it were, they have
not powerful enough extractors. You do come out ponging a bit, and it takes a
walk in the fresh air to clear the smell.' The blackboard menu, updated daily,
offers a fair amount of frying by way of hand-cut chips, fritters, tempura and
fried courgettes. However, most reports show that Robert Mabey's cooking and
the laid-back atmosphere are much enjoyed. The food is prepared without
nonsensical elaboration, and in most reported meals the tastes are noticed and
appreciated. Dishes such as vegetable tempura, plaice on brown lentils, fillets
of salmon in a dill sauce on a bed of wild rice, grilled breast of chicken in
madeira sauce, chocolate and walnut pudding with butterscotch sauce, and
hazelnut and crunchy praline ice-cream have all pleased. There is no stinting
on quantities, even if you do have to pay for extras like chips and vegetables. It
is worrying that the Mabeys foresee a possible change in running the place:
retaining ownership but leaving others to do the nitty-gritty. With the success
of their venture in Norwich (see entry under St Benedicts Grill), perhaps they
can achieve the magic recipe that enables them to stand back and yet retain
quality. The wine list is a model, helped by the model wine merchants Lay &
Wheeler: not too dear, not too long, and some interesting things to try like the
Marqués de Cáceres Riojas, Luquet's St-Véran, or Killawarra's sparkling pink
from Australia. House wines are £6.75.

CHEFS: Robert Mabey and Lawrence Clifford   PROPRIETORS: Robert and Johanna Mabey
OPEN: Tue to Sat; 12 to 2, 7 to 10   CLOSED: Christmas, some bank hols   MEALS: alc
SERVICE: not inc   CARDS: Access, Visa   DETAILS: 35 seats. Private parties: 40 main room.
Vegetarian meals. Children's helpings. Wheelchair access (2 steps). Air-conditioned. No
music

SURBITON Surrey   map 3

Chez Max

85 Maple Road, Surbiton KT6 4AW   COOKING 2*
081-399 2365   COST £27–£34

The broad street that sweeps past the front of this restaurant carries a tide of
humanity to and fro from town, and a few who realise that Surbiton itself holds
the key to any eating-out problems. Go through the door and discover a muted,
clean-angled and modern interior that plunges deep into the building.
Everything appears just-so – the tables are well-spaced, the lighting and music
are not strident, and the service is willing and effective. Max Markarian is a
chef with a classical background, which shows in his cooking and gradually
evolving repertoire. Gravlax, spiced duck in pastry with an apricot sauce,

roulade of haddock and salmon, duck with celery and almond sauce, monkfish with chive sauce and beef with pink and green peppercorns are some current examples. Winter offerings that gave pleasure included leeks with feta cheese ('small pieces of pungency buried beneath the bubbling hot cheese'), monkfish with lobster sauce ('tender and well seasoned, with a rich sauce that yet did not overpower'), fillet of beef with celeriac sauce, and hazelnut meringue with strawberries that proved to be 'a pyramid of fruit with a little bit of meringue, undeniably delicious'. Reported failings have been rolls that are too pale for a crust, meat with little flavour (but rescued by sauces) and lacklustre vegetables, terrines or mousses that have lost immediacy and strong taste. Coffee is good. The wine list is longest in claret and does not bother with much beyond France. Its chief fault is the range of prices. It looks long enough, but if you want to spend less than £20, the options reduce alarmingly. Details are not generous about makers or shippers. House white is £11.

CHEF: Max Markarian   PROPRIETORS: Mr and Mrs Max Markarian   OPEN: Tue to Sat, exc Sat L; 12.30 to 2, 7.30 to 10   MEALS: Set L £18.50, Set D Tue to Fri £15.95, Set D Sat £16.50   SERVICE: 12.5%, card slips closed   CARDS: Access, Amex, Diners, Visa   DETAILS: 45 seats. Private parties: 45 main room. No children under 7. No pipes in dining-room. No music L

SUTTON COLDFIELD West Midlands
map 5

▲ *New Hall* ⁵⁺✗ | NEW ENTRY |

Walmley Road,
Sutton Coldfield B76 8QX
021-378 2442

COOKING 2*
COST £31–£54

Reputedly the oldest-surviving moated manor house in England, New Hall now functions as a country hotel with its bedrock business set deep in the industrial culture. Despite modern extensions, the place covets its history, with old beams, panelling and mullioned windows in the dining areas. Since Glenn Purcell's arrival in 1990, the cooking has improved: portions are more generous, and prices are more realistic. A regular *carte* and daily-changing set menus offer plenty of choice and variety, blending traditional hotel classics, peasant-inspired creations and fashionable modern dishes with French and Mediterranean overtones: grilled Dover sole, roast quail on Savoy cabbage with truffle jus, and steamed délice of brill on Italian vegetable broth are typical. Salmon is oak-smoked on the premises. One impressive inspection meal produced salad of smoked chicken, avocado and sun-dried tomatoes; ravioli of spinach and goats' cheese with a 'highly original' thick, warm pine-nut vinaigrette; roast guinea-fowl ('moist and slightly gamey') with rich sage jus; and pink rack of lamb with morels. Main dishes come with generous vegetables; salads are available as an alternative. To finish, iced raspberry parfait was 'extremely attractive and skilfully flavoured,' according to a reporter. Service is well paced and attentive. The 300-strong wine list plunders the globe and mark-ups are reasonable; there are plenty of halves, plus a decent choice of vintage ports. House wines are £10.95.

See the back of the Guide *for an index of restaurants listed.*

CHEF: Glenn Purcell   PROPRIETORS: Thistle Country House Hotels   OPEN: all week, exc
Sat L; 12.30 to 2, 7 to 9.45 (9 Sun)   MEALS: alc. Set L £20.70, Set D £24.95 to £27.20
SERVICE: not inc, card slips closed   CARDS: Access, Amex, Diners, Visa   DETAILS: 60 seats.
6 tables outside. Private parties: 8 main room, 8, 15 and 40 private rooms. Car park.
Vegetarian meals. Children's helpings. Smart dress preferred. No smoking in dining-room.
Wheelchair access (1 step; also WC). No music   ACCOMMODATION: 60 rooms, all with
bath/shower. Rooms for disabled. B&B £102.45 to £128.90. No children under 8. Afternoon
teas. Garden. TV. Phone. Fax: 021-378 4637 (*The Which? Hotel Guide*)

SUTTON COURTENAY Oxfordshire

map 2

Fish at Sutton Courtenay ✝✳

Appleford Road,
Sutton Courtenay OX14 4NQ
ABINGDON (0235) 848242

COOKING 2
COST £25–£37

One reporter blessed the night his favourite restaurant was fully booked as it
gave him reason to try this unassuming village pub (but 'we are planning to lay
a marble floor in the dining-room'). 'What a surprise,' he commented. 'Clearly
here is a talented chef who should have more recognition.' Bruce Buchan belies
the name of his place by offering equal numbers of fish and meat dishes on his
nightly blackboard menu. Many still feel that the fish is the thing, be it a warm
salad of scallops, a ragoût of Brixham fish, steamed turbot with a black-bean
dressing, salmon with a pike soufflé, or home-marinated herring fillets with
sour cream and chives. 'Crisp and juicy' vegetables come on a side plate. Bruce
Buchan is a professional chef turned publican, rather than the other way round;
this explains the tilt of his menu, but does not determine his commitment to
fair value, fresh materials and direct methods of cooking, all of which are
admirable. Do not expect a grand setting, or even a very picturesque one, but
join with the others who find a visit rewarding. The wine list is short but high
on value and interest. House wines are £8.25.

CHEF: Bruce Buchan   PROPRIETORS: Bruce and Kay Buchan   OPEN: all week, exc Tue D;
12 to 2.15, 7 to 9.30 (10 Fri and Sat)   CLOSED: 4 days between Christmas and New Year
MEALS: alc   SERVICE: not inc, card slips closed   CARDS: Access, Amex, Diners, Visa
DETAILS: 45 seats. Private parties: 12 main room, 18 and 30 private rooms. Car park.
Vegetarian meals. Children's helpings. Smart dress preferred. No smoking in dining-room.
Wheelchair access. Music. Fax: (0235) 848242

SWANAGE Dorset

map 2

Galley

9 High Street, Swanage BH19 2LN
SWANAGE (0929) 427299

COOKING 1
COST £21–£30

As should befit the location, fish is the more interesting item. Meat dishes
develop only slowly over the months, and the constant presence of pheasant in
early summer over two years of Galley-watching makes one wonder where the
pheasants fly. Much more variation is seen in the recipes for fish, from turbot
with onions, mushrooms and smoked bacon, grilled sole with a tomato and dill

vinaigrette and sea bass with sorrel sauce, to griddled fresh tuna, simple mussels and monkfish mayonnaise. The Storers get full marks for trying, for growing herbs on their own allotment, dealing with plenty of local boats, and for offering a week-long service through the season. The three-dozen wines are just right to match the food and keep clear of silly prices. House wines start at £6.75.

CHEF: Nick Storer PROPRIETORS: N.D and M.G. Storer OPEN: all week, D only; 6.30 to 9.30 (10 Sat) CLOSED: 1 Jan to 1 Apr MEALS: alc SERVICE: net prices, card slips closed
CARDS: Access, Amex, Diners, Visa DETAILS: 30 seats. Private parties: 30 main room.
Vegetarian meals. Children welcome. Music. Air-conditioned

TAUNTON Somerset   map 2

▲ *Castle Hotel* ♟

Castle Green, Taunton TA1 1NF   COUNTY OF THE YEAR RESTAURANT

TAUNTON (0823) 272671   COOKING 3
                                                             COST £20–£61

'The dining-room, like every other dining-room in Britain, is pink,' remarked one seasoned traveller who lit upon this large, old, central, well-established and professionally run hotel in Taunton, capital of Somerset but an unlikely spot for a place of such evident ambition. The Castle really was a castle, though the stonework is so covered by wistaria you would be forgiven for not noticing. The cooking here is new wine in old vessels, while the service can remind visitors of very old vessels indeed – lots of it, just like hotels of yesteryear. Phil Vickery cooks with an English tilt, which makes his menus different to many in this particular sector of country-house hotels, though obviously in a line of development from the days when Kit Chapman, the prime mover here, and Gary Rhodes (now chef at the Greenhouse, London, see entry) were first working on better British dishes. Technique, over a series of short menus, some of which are very fair value, though the *carte* makes no bones about cheapness, is impeccable. Materials, too, are of first quality. People are particularly impressed by lunch: all the good things and not too much money. The quality of materials showed in a main course of duck with lentils, bacon and apples. The bird was roasted past the usual semi-raw state and had great succulence. The additions did not quite come together to make a complete dish, but it was extremely able. If that uses British ingredients – none of the Mediterranean here, though lobster sausage with couscous does indicate a preparedness to travel a bit – the first course of asparagus and lamb's sweetbreads in a modern salad was more mainstream. Again, it was professionally done. A strawberry tart confirmed that pastry is made properly here, that restraint may be the order of the tasting day, and that peach sorbet as an accompaniment to the tart is neutral to the point of vanishing. It is good that Phil Vickery has settled in so quickly. The menus are not long, therefore the immediacy of the cooking is not in doubt, and intending visitors should expect to meet very solid professionalism in dishes such as broth of smoked haddock and oysters, potted pigeon and wild rabbit with a Cumberland sauce, roast chicken with spinach, rösti and truffles, or braised shoulder of lamb with thyme and garlic. A page of good sherries offered by the glass and some cannily chosen house wines, including Jaboulet's Parallèle 45 and Hill-Smith Riesling, encourage.

Thereafter a conservative cast to the buying ignores the many readily available smaller growers in Alsace and Beaujolais and emphasises classified clarets at the cost of bypassing good petits châteaux. However, this remains a reliable list with a generous spread of price that will neither alarm the thrifty nor disappoint the prodigal. House wines are from £6.95. CELLARMAN'S CHOICE: Chambolle Musigny premier cru 1980, Loeb, £40.40; Pouilly-Fumé, La Moynerie 1990, £19.50.

CHEF: Phil Vickery PROPRIETORS: the Chapman family OPEN: all week; 12.30 to 2, 7.30 to 9 (9.30 Fri and Sat) MEALS: a1c. Set L £13.50 to £14.90, Set D £22.50 SERVICE: not inc, card slips closed CARDS: Access, Amex, Diners, Visa DETAILS: 110 seats. Private parties: 65 main room, 50 and 110 private rooms. Car park. Vegetarian meals. Children's helpings with prior notice. No cigars/pipes in dining-room. Smart dress preferred. Wheelchair access (also WC). No music ACCOMMODATION: 35 rooms, all with bath/shower. Rooms for disabled. Lift. B&B £75 to £180. Children welcome. Baby facilities. Pets welcome (in bedrooms only). Afternoon teas. Garden. TV. Phone. Doors close at midnight. Confirm by 6. Fax: (0823) 336066 (*The Which? Hotel Guide*)

TAVISTOCK Devon   map 1

▲ *Horn of Plenty*

Gulworthy, Tavistock PL19 8JD   COOKING 3
TAVISTOCK (0822) 832528   COST £21–£48

Brush, brush, hammer, hammer, have gone the Gatehouses as they repaint, refurbish and renew. More rooms for residents, excellent decoration and gleaming paintwork greet the newcomer. 'A hotel that treats you like invited house guests' was one enthusiastic response, although an occasional report of more acerbic dealings has come our way. One family was impressed by the easy welcome, and gentle charges, made in respect of very junior members on a Sunday lunch, as well as the willingness to accommodate various dietary demands. The house was once a mine captain's; the former workings are on the opposite slope, across the steep, wooded valley that forms a perfect backdrop to summer evening dining. Peter Gorton's cooking is light and generally accurate. Some would say it is too light: 'Not nouvelle, but not "plenty" either.' Sauces are kept simple and usually avoid overpowering the main ingredient. Dishes such as mussels on a bed of leeks and fennel with pasta and a Pernod sauce, or pigeon with noodles and a spiced mushroom sauce may be partnered by main courses of salmon with ginger and black pepper on a tomato and coriander sauce, or oriental duck confit with spiced lentils. Spices seem to get more favour than herbs. Good old-fashioned cooking as in a breast of pheasant with brandy and cream may also appear, and be more successful than wafer-thin escalopes of salmon almost lost in a monotonous cream and wine sauce. The pheasant was exceptional for its flavour and texture. Desserts have also received good notices: pancakes with oranges and apples and a caramel sauce, a heavy chocolate truffle cake, or perhaps fruit-filled meringues. The end result is of a sound standard, improved by nice touches such as the spicy samosas and Glamorgan sausages that come at the very beginning, or the acceptable coffee and petits fours to finish. The wine list improves. A very solid choice of clarets and burgundies is given extra range from Italy (Avignonesi and others),

California and Australasia. Prices are acceptable, though no bargain. House wines are £9.50 and include a Chianti Ruffino as well as a Chardonnay de Haut Poitou.

CHEFS: Peter Gorton and Karen Jones   PROPRIETORS: Elaine and Ian Gatehouse   OPEN: all week, exc Mon L; 12 to 2, 7 to 9.30   CLOSED: 25 Dec   MEALS: alc. Set L £14.50 to £17.50, Set D £23.50   SERVICE: not inc   CARDS: Access, Amex, Visa   DETAILS: 45 seats. 6 tables outside. Private parties: 40 main room, 20 private room. Vegetarian meals. Children's helpings L. Wheelchair access (also WC)   ACCOMMODATION: 7 rooms, all with bath/shower. Rooms for disabled. B&B £41 to £78. Children under 13 by arrangement. Pets welcome. Garden. TV. Phone. Doors close at midnight. Fax: (0822) 832528 (*The Which? Hotel Guide*)

Neil's   `NEW ENTRY`

27 King Street,
Tavistock PL19 0DG   COOKING 2
TAVISTOCK (0822) 615550   COST £23–£32

Once upon a time this was a farmhouse, but the town has closed in and the fields have retreated – so now it is a restaurant. Low ceilings, beams and simple dark oak furniture hark back to origins, and the Neils' willingness smacks of an open-hearted countryside we like to think once existed. 'If you want to eat on Sunday, we'll open on Sunday' was their accommodating reply to an enquiry from travellers. Janet Neil is a careful and generous cook. Her puddings would delight many a returning ploughman, soothed to an evening's rest by orange parfait (a marbled orange ice-cream) or caramel parfait ('almost like eating a melted Mars Bar – rich, dark, golden brown, topped with fresh cream and toasted almonds'). Her savoury palate is sure as well, and not afraid of strong flavour when put to making a red wine sauce for venison with crushed peppercorns and a rösti. Fish cookery can be classic (salmon steak served with a fennel hollandaise), imaginative (sea bream with lemon, thyme and coriander or monkfish with gazpacho and ratatouille), or accurate for poaching a soft lemon sole to the nearest 10 seconds. There is a *carte*, but also an excellent-value monthly set-price menu with alternatives at each course. A pity the butter is in packets, but forget that while trying the soufflé suissesse. Murray Neil looks after the drinks (a fondness for malt whisky in the bar) and has developed a short, fair-priced wine list that has some sure bets in the Viña Real Riojas and the Glen Ellen Chardonnay. House wine is £8.75.

CHEF: Janet Neil   PROPRIETORS: Murray and Janet Neil   OPEN: Tue to Sat, D only (L and Sun D by arrangement); 7 to 10   CLOSED: 25 Dec   MEALS: alc. Set D £15. Minimum £11.25   SERVICE: not inc   CARDS: Access, Visa   DETAILS: 24 seats. Private parties: 20 main room. Vegetarian meals. Children welcome. Music

---

If a restaurant is new to the Guide *this year (did not appear as a main entry in the last edition)* NEW ENTRY *appears opposite its name.*

An asterisk (*) after the 1 to 5 cooking mark at the top of an entry signifies that the Guide *and its readers think that the restaurant is a particularly fine example within its rating.*

TEFFONT EVIAS Wiltshire   map 2

▲ *Howard's House Hotel*

Teffont Evias SP3 5RJ   COOKING 2*
SALISBURY (0722) 716392   COST £24–£39

The sweep of lawn, the herbaceous border, field and woods beyond all fit
everybody's picture of a small English country house. 'Went there last year,
when we had the enjoyment of the garden. This year, rain of course, so we
sampled the comfortable insides.' These are certainly up to scratch and
reminiscent, too, of the garden beyond, with bold floral designs and a wealth of
green. Paul Firmin's cooking is up to date: scallops with lentils and coriander,
warm smoked salmon with chervil butter sauce and quail egg tartlet, home-
made pasta, and a roulade of lobster and leeks are some of the first courses.
Chinese duck with spring roll, lamb on a bed of steamed spinach with an
infusion of rosemary and redcurrants, or peppered pigeon breasts with
buckwheat noodles and roast red peppers are offered as principal dishes. They
are well executed and usually light in touch, though some details go awry: a
lobster roulade with too much leek and little of the shellfish, an excellent
Chinese-style roast duck, but vaguely anonymous and uncrisp spring rolls.
Desserts get full marks: a crème brûlée with oranges beneath, macerated in
Grand Marnier, light apple strudel, rising soufflés. Cheeses are French, fair and
unpasteurised. Wines are French too, but there is decent representation from
Italy, Spain and the New World. Prices are not wayward and the only trouble
might come from the limited choice of half-bottles. House wines start at £9.25.

CHEFS: Paul Firmin, Claire Ford and Michael Fox   PROPRIETORS: Paul Firmin and
Jonathan Ford   OPEN: all week, D only, and Sun L; 12.30 to 2, 7.30 to 10   MEALS: Set Sun
L £17, Set D £27.50   SERVICE: not inc, card slips closed   CARDS: Access, Amex, Visa
DETAILS: 40 seats. 4 tables outside. Private parties: 40 main room, 20 private room. Car
park. Vegetarian meals. Children's helpings Sun L. No cigars/pipes in dining-room.
Wheelchair access. Music   ACCOMMODATION: 9 rooms, all with bath/shower. Rooms for
disabled. B&B £60 to £85. Children welcome. Baby facilities. Pets welcome. Garden. TV.
Phone. Doors close at 1am. Confirm by 6. Fax: (0722) 716820 *(The Which? Hotel Guide)*

TETBURY Gloucestershire   map 2

▲ *Calcot Manor* ♀ ⁵✕

Beverston, Tetbury GL8 8YJ   COOKING 2*
LEIGHTERTON (0666) 890391   COST £21–£47

Beverston is a hamlet, yet complete with castle and church, some miles west of
Tetbury. Calcot was more a farm than manor, comfortable rather than grand.
What were cow-sheds are now cottages, byres are turned into beds. The Ball
family are much in evidence as hosts, with a large team of servitors – some
more effective than others, if tales of delays are to be believed. Yet the
graciousness of the surroundings, allied to overall politeness, reconciles many
people to any slight delay between courses. The chef of many years' standing,
Ramon Farthing, has left Calcot in the hands of Ben Davies, whose formative
time has been spent at Hambleton Hall, Hambleton (see entry). It's very early
days, so our mark may be seen as provisional, but an inspection revealed good

453

and bad things. There seems an affection for sandwiches: filo pastry, red mullet and fennel – moderate; potato and celeriac rösti, confit of duck leg and diced leeks in cream – very good. Vegetables are country-house boring, and a dessert of expert hot cherry soufflé was spoiled by joining it to blots of badly made vanilla sorbet. Coffee is weak but petits fours are generous. As matters settle, this will doubtless reassert itself as a kitchen of careful modernity, often with overtones of elaboration, but serious and well-intentioned. The wine list is a sensible, not overlong collection, that shows good range; the antipodes still await admission but the limited selections from Italy and the USA, as well as good classics from Burgundy, are reassuring. A choice of French country wines looks reasonable value and could provide interest. Prices are on the high side with such as the perfectly adequate Sancerre of André Dezat pitched at £25.60. There are carefully chosen halves and house wine is £12.95. CELLARMAN'S CHOICE: Collioure, Dom. de Mas Blanc 1988, £25.80; Quincy 1990, Jaumier, £18.75.

CHEF: Ben Davies   PROPRIETORS: the Ball family   OPEN: all week, exc Sun D (residents only); 12.30 to 2, 7.30 to 9.30   MEALS: Set L £13.50 to £17.50, Set D £26 to £32. Light L menu   SERVICE: not inc, card slips closed   CARDS: Access, Amex, Diners, Visa   DETAILS: 45 seats. 3 tables outside. Private parties: 40 main room, 12 private room. Car park. Vegetarian meals. Children's helpings L. Jacket and tie. No smoking. Wheelchair access (also WC). No music   ACCOMMODATION: 15 rooms, all with bath/shower. Rooms for disabled. B&B £85 to £145. Children by arrangement. Afternoon teas. Garden. Swimming-pool. TV. Phone. Doors close at midnight. Fax: (0666) 890394 (*The Which? Hotel Guide*)

THORNBURY Avon   map 2

▲ *Thornbury Castle* ♟ ⅝✕

Castle Street, Thornbury BS12 1HH   COOKING 2*
THORNBURY (0454) 281182   COST £26–£42

It is perhaps fitting that the Taylors, ex-owners of this unique ruined castle turned into a hotel, have succeeded to the barony of Portlethen. A truly baronial pile, where the humble prole can park the car, stay in medieval surroundings in four-poster beds, albeit with gas log-effect fires, and dine in an octagonal tower room, though the chairs are too high, some tables are too small and 'the knees fight for their bit of space beneath'. Cooking here is fairly straightforward country-house, so do not expect surprises. There are dishes such as a 'symphony of seafish with shallots in a white wine and herb sauce presented in a crisp filo pastry nest', 'fillet of salmon poached with white wine and dill, nestled on a crab and cognac sauce', and hot butterscotch pudding. Performance has been satisfactory, though there was a change of regime in the kitchen in the very recent past and reports are scanty. Service is thought to be relaxed. On the wine list look beyond France for happy and reasonably priced drinking; Spain is especially well represented with good reservas. This remains a good list throughout, although some burgundies may excite curiosity with lack of detail while the provenance of others looks less than reassuring; better to seek advice, or keep the expenditure modest to avoid an expensive lottery. House wines are from £11.

CHEF: Peter Brazill PROPRIETORS: the Baron and Baroness of Portlethen OPEN: all week; 12 to 2, 7 to 9.30 (9 Sun, 10 Fri and Sat) MEALS: Set L £17.75, Set D £25.50 to £29.50 SERVICE: net prices, card slips closed CARDS: Access, Amex, Diners, Visa DETAILS: 60 seats. Private parties: 25 main room, 12 private room. Car park. Vegetarian meals. No children under 12. No smoking in dining-room. Jacket and tie. Music ACCOMMODATION: 18 rooms, all with bath/shower. B&B £80 to £190. No children under 12. Afternoon teas. Garden. TV. Phone. Fax: (0454) 416188 (*The Which? Hotel Guide*)

THORNTON-CLEVELEYS Lancashire   map 5

▲ *Victorian House*

Trunnah Road,
Thornton-Cleveleys FY5 4HF   COOKING 1
CLEVELEYS (0253) 860619   COST £15–£28

The name reflects the prevailing mood and style of this former convent opposite the church. Inside, it is full of pretty Victoriana and bric-à-brac, particularly in the orangery. Service is by 'cheerful maidens in Victorian dress from the *Upstairs Downstairs* wardrobe,' observed one visitor. By contrast, the cooking is traditional French, with occasional oriental flourishes in dishes such as roast loin of lamb brushed with hoisin sauce. The four-course fixed-price menu changes monthly and readers have praised the value for money. Enjoyable dishes have included Parma ham decorated with exotic fruit, 'beautifully pink' lamb in pastry, halibut steak with tomato béarnaise sauce, suprême of chicken on a bed of fennel in filo pastry, and roast duck breast with port sauce. Vegetables are crisp and generous. Sweets are pretty, but one party noted the same fruit coulis with three separate items. The kitchen is generally on target. The 70-strong wine list is French and fairly priced. House wine is £8.30.

CHEF: Didier Guérin PROPRIETORS: Louise and Didier Guérin OPEN: Mon to Sat, exc Mon L; 12 to 2, 7 to 9.30 CLOSED: last week Jan, first week Feb MEALS: alc L. Set D £18.95 SERVICE: not inc, card slips closed CARDS: Access, Visa DETAILS: 65 seats. 4 tables outside. Private parties: 40 main room. Car park. Vegetarian meals. No children under 6. Smart dress preferred. Wheelchair access (3 steps). Music ACCOMMODATION: 3 rooms, all with bath/shower. B&B £49.50 to £69.50. Deposit: £10. No children under 6. Pets welcome. Garden. TV. Phone. Confirm by 6. Fax: (0253) 865350 (*The Which? Hotel Guide*)

THUNDRIDGE Hertfordshire   map 3

▲ *Hanbury Manor*

Thundridge SG12 0SD   COOKING 3
WARE (0920) 487722   COST £28–£87

Tea here comes in bags, and is as strong as the railway's. Not a good start to a stay; just as the sliced bread and wrapped pat of butter were no send-off worthy of the price. Hanbury Manor is large, very large. Walking through all of it seems like going back to school, or visiting a Ministry relocated in wartime. Its *raison d'être* seems to be golf, company presentations and swimming. There are two restaurants: one for golfers (the Vardon Grill) which is cheerful and acceptable at lunch; one for après-golf. This last – very expensive – is masterminded by Albert Roux of Le Gavroche (see entry, London), is comfortable and formal, and is in a room of Edwardian Tudorbethan plasterwork signifying the zodiac. Rory Kennedy does the actual cooking and must get a trifle bored: the à la carte does not seem to change much from month to month. Cooking is partly a clone of Le Gavroche (soufflés suissesses here too), partly just grand luxury. Its beginnings were bright, but it seems to have settled to some inconsistency. A winter meal, even with M. Roux in evidence, produced failed suissesses, over-reduced sauces, indeterminate flavours and out-of-season delicacies such as raspberries. Some things were good: pigeon with star-anise was good meat, just as was rabbit stuffed with its own liver on a wickedly strong rosemary sauce. Mullet with bone marrow and spinach was a clever balancing act between meat and fish, two sorts of richness. Cheese was fine, but a small selection. Service is keen, but not always knowledgeable and not always accurate. The wine list is a classy assembly that may shock by the price of its Sancerre, but offers plenty of choice in the lower register as well as some uncommon bottles such as Ch. Simone from Palette in Provence or some good Chardonnays from California. House wines start at £13.

CHEF: Rory Kennedy PROPRIETORS: Poles Ltd OPEN: Mon to Sat, D only, and Sun L; 12 to 3, 7 to 11 MEALS: alc. Set Sun L £19.50, Set D £25 SERVICE: net prices, card slips closed CARDS: Access, Amex, Diners, Visa DETAILS: 42 seats. 12 tables outside. Private parties: 120 main room, 32, 48 and 120 private rooms. Car park. Vegetarian meals. Jacket and tie. No cigars/pipes in dining-room. Wheelchair access (1 step; also WC). Music ACCOMMODATION: 98 rooms, all with bath/shower. Rooms for disabled. Lift. B&B £130 to £330. Deposit: 100%. Children welcome. Baby facilities. Pets welcome. Afternoon teas. Garden. Swimming-pool. Sauna. Tennis. Golf. Snooker. Air-conditioned. TV. Phone. Confirm 2 weeks ahead. Fax: (0920) 487692 (*The Which? Hotel Guide*)

TIVERTON Devon   map 1

Lowman £

45 Gold Street, Tiverton EX16 6QB   COOKING 2
TIVERTON (0884) 257311   COST £16–£31

The Lowman is the river by which the restaurant ('Pretty, lots of pink,' comments a visitor) sits. The cooking offers intelligent variety: simple mushroom salad with croûtons is balanced by more interesting buckwheat pancakes with devilled herring roes; conventional salmon may be avoided for a 'khichhari' (a spiced mixture of lentils, rice, lemon and tomato) or braised tongue with madeira sauce. Execution may occasionally slip, but the intentions are clear: that a restaurant should rely on local, fresh ingredients, and should provide its own incidentals such as bread and petits fours. Service is jollied along by Mr Filmer-Bennett, variously described as 'communicative' and 'a character'. His bi-monthly news-sheet is one side of his communicativeness; his claim to have created 262 new dishes in his first year of operation reflects his energy. The wine list begins with seven Devon bottles. No one will be shocked by the prices, and most will be satisfied by the range: a serviceable list for a small restaurant. House wines start at £6.80.

CHEF: Jeremy Filmer-Bennett   PROPRIETORS: Jeremy and Elaine Filmer-Bennett   OPEN:
Tue to Sat; 12 to 2, 7 to 9 (9.30 Fri and Sat)   CLOSED: Christmas to New Year   MEALS: alc.
Set D £14 to £17   SERVICE: not inc, card slips closed   CARDS: Access, Visa   DETAILS: 40
seats. Private parties: 40 main room, 20 private room. Vegetarian meals. Children's
helpings. No-smoking area. Music on request

TORQUAY Devon   map 1

Capers

7 Lisburne Square, Torquay TQ1 2PT   COOKING 1
TORQUAY (0803) 291177   COST £33–£40

Ian Cawley cooks in a little restaurant opposite Torquay's purveyor of luxury
cars for the retired classes. The view, therefore, has not much resonance of the
seaside. The enterprise, however, does echo to the chef's enthusiasm. Local
suppliers, local cheeses, local markets and the state of his own allotment will
start any conversation and inform the contents of the menu. This may be why
fish outnumbers meat in a short list that has kissed a long goodbye to cream
sauces and heaviness. Grilled goats' cheese on an olive brioche, duck with a
walnut salad, salmon in pastry with sorrel and hollandaise, and chicken
wrapped in greens and cured ham are dishes showing the relative simplicity of
intent, with prime materials hogging the limelight from either presentation or
fanciful development. One quiet evening, it did seem that simplicity had got
the better of everything, especially as charges in South Devon are never low;
but people are impressed by Ian Cawley's willingness to tackle everything
himself, from breads and chutneys, to hot appetisers with the drinks, and
biscuits with the cheeses, as well as earthing up the potatoes or killing the
blackfly. The wine list is short but sound. House Gascogne from Plaimont
is £8.50.

CHEF/PROPRIETOR: Ian Cawley   OPEN: Tue to Sat, D only (L by arrangement); 7 to 9.30 (10
Sat)   MEALS: alc   SERVICE: not inc, card slips closed   CARDS: Access, Visa   DETAILS: 24
seats. Private parties: 6 main room. Vegetarian meals with prior notice. Children's
helpings. Music

▲ Mulberry Room £

1 Scarborough Road, Torquay TQ2 5UJ   COOKING 2*
TORQUAY (0803) 213639   COST £14–£26

The Room is part of a guesthouse slap-bang in the middle of Torquay hotel
zone, but nothing could be less like the British tourist industry. There is a feel
of a tea-shop to the pair of pretty rooms, but a tea-shop with a difference: look
at the pottery, the pictures and the array of cakes and puddings laid out on a
great side-table – no toasted tea-cakes here. Lesley Cooper cooks lunch, and
charges little for what she gives. She also serves dinner on Friday and
Saturday. The choice is unexpected for Torquay: start with nibbles of fried nuts
and seeds; then take a duck and chicken liver pâté seasoned with brandy, mace
and ginger, or a minestrone thick enough to stand the spoon in, with fresh
Parmesan. Chicken with ginger, sesame, spring onion and soy has been a trifle

monotone, the ginger too light, but it was put in the shade by fresh-fried Torbay sole with a chunky tartare. Ham and chicory gratinated under a fierce grill was classic Elizabeth David, the vegetables – good mash, spring greens, carrot and beetroot – were generous and spot-on, and hot lemon pudding (Jane Grigson's influence this time), was cooked just as the recipe intended. Not everything works: pressure of time and numbers, for instance, on Sunday lunch, may make the slip show; sometimes the helpers are too callow to help. But this is some tea-room. Health-freaks will be well-served here. The wine list gets no longer, but it does get better, it's still cheap, and house wine is £7.

CHEF/PROPRIETOR: Lesley Cooper   OPEN: Wed to Sun L, Fri and Sat D; 12.15 to 2.30, 7.30 to 9.30   MEALS: alc. Set L £7.50 to £9, Set D £16.50 to £18.50   SERVICE: not inc   DETAILS: 30 seats. 2 tables outside. Private parties: 40 main room. Vegetarian meals. Healthy eating options. Children's helpings. Wheelchair access (also WC). Music   ACCOMMODATION: 3 rooms, all rooms with bath/shower. B&B £12.50 to £33. Deposit: 10%. Afternoon teas. TV. Doors close at dusk. Confirm by dusk

▲ Osborne Hotel, Langtry's ⁵✕   NEW ENTRY

Hesketh Crescent, Meadfoot,
Torquay TQ1 2LL
TORQUAY (0803) 213311

COOKING 2
COST £24–£29

The Osborne Hotel and its ramifications (conference centre, time-share, restaurants, apartments, you name it), occupy the whole of Hesketh Crescent, a classical nineteenth-century development in the grand manner, looking out to Brixham across the bay, with ne'er a tripper in sight. A putative visitor was encouraged when he was met by a chef bearing bunches of fresh herbs and a name-tag identifying him as Colin Liddy. Everyone has a name-tag, even waitresses called 'Trainee', but smiles may exist, though sometimes the strain of trying to be posh in Torbay gets on top of the staff. The cooking is posh too, perhaps too posh. A doctor who stayed for three weeks – 'studying', don't you know – was impressed by the overall performance. A casual visitor one summer's day found good pork and prune terrine, not so good watery prawns on a sea of yoghurt with gritty curry powder, very fresh plaice with light tomato and basil sauce, sharp lime sauce with calf's liver, decent pigeon with 'gamma-grade' pastry, and fair enough vegetables. A trio of pears – poached, sorbet and ice-cream – on a blackcurrant coulis is a winner among desserts. The wine list is drawn from the cellars of Eldridge Pope, so there are no quibbles about quality. The most expensive bottles, for example, the Bâtard-Montrachet 1988 from Dom. Prieur Brunet, seem to be offered at less than cost price; others have more expected mark-ups. House wines are £8.80.

CHEF: Colin Liddy   PROPRIETORS: Caparo   OPEN: all week, D only; 7 to 10   CLOSED: Sun D Dec to Feb   MEALS: Set D £19.50 to £21.50. Minimum £19.50   SERVICE: net prices, card slips closed   CARDS: Access, Visa   DETAILS: 60 seats. Private parties: 20 main room, 24, 66 and 110 private rooms. Car park. Vegetarian meals. Children's helpings early D. Smart dress preferred. No smoking in dining-room. Wheelchair access (3 steps; also WC). Music   ACCOMMODATION: 23 rooms, all with bath/shower. Rooms for disabled. Lift. B&B £55 to £172. Children welcome. Baby facilities. Afternoon teas. Garden. Swimming-pool. Sauna. Tennis. Snooker. TV. Phone. Fax: (0803) 296788

Table

135 Babbacombe Road,
Babbacombe, Torquay TQ1 3SR
TORQUAY (0803) 324292

COOKING 3*
COST £33–£39

A front-parlour restaurant, and you ring the bell for eating. Jane Corrigan keeps the place as clean as a new pin: 'She was sweeping the step and the pavement when I arrived one January night.' Trevor Brooks is the kitchen. There are no short-cuts; it's thorough cooking, the size of the place notwithstanding. Hence you may sometimes have to wait, and there can be a sense of strenuous effort if the kitchen is wrong-footed by events. But no matter – 'We came for a family reunion, and ended with a gastronomic celebration.' Trevor Brooks has a way with food. His short set-price menu contains few compromises; he is prepared to work with foie gras, fungi and the other essentials of the ambitious chef. Success accompanies his efforts. Fish soup vibrates, not merely falters, with saffron – a golden liquid embracing a pile of mullet, sole, monkfish and tomato. Breast of pheasant is bounced into flavour by air-dried ham poked in strips along diagonal slashes: breast on top of the pile, the layers below reading pineapple chutney (not too sweet), lentils and dark meat from the thigh of the bird. Vegetables still live on side plates here. First courses such as crépinette of pig's trotter with potatoes and soy sauce have shifted firmly from the sweet/sour combos of the last decade; sauces, a fumet of shallots and ceps with venison, or an oxtail and tarragon jus with beef fillet, are light and true; desserts do not deal in out-of-season soft fruit or the tropical delights of last year's tired pâtissiers. 'The two ladies declined a first course, to their ultimate regret, but with the main dishes the murmurs of pleasure were immediately audible. Do people in the area know what they have in their midst?' The wine list has gained halves and maintains a range of French regions, bolstered from beyond in a very few areas. It is no longer than the scale of business demands, but prices are fair indeed and, with few exceptions, the sources are reliable. House wines are £9. CELLARMAN'S CHOICE: Sancerre, Clos du Roy 1990, Paul Millérioux, £13.50; Hautes Côtes de Nuits 1986, Gros, £15.

CHEF: Trevor Brooks   PROPRIETORS: Trevor Brooks and Jane Corrigan   OPEN: Tue to Sun, D only; 7.30 to 9.30   MEALS: Set D £24 to £26   SERVICE: not inc, card slips closed   CARDS: Access, Visa   DETAILS: 20 seats. Private parties: 21 main room. No children under 10. Music

---

TRESCO Isles of Scilly   map 1

▲ Island Hotel

Tresco TR24 0PU
SCILLONIA (0720) 22883

COOKING 1
COST £30–£51

It is all change at the Island, with new managers and a new chef who has hot-footed it from New York's Westbury Hotel, where he was Executive Chef, intending to improve things. Regular visitors have always liked the place for the position, the big windows illuminating the low-key building articulated mainly by its timber pillars and rafters, and the sense of adventure that comes from a semi-tropical environment a short hop from Penzance. The availability of supplies – most things are brought in by sea – must govern the standard of cooking here, and they have not been beyond criticism in earlier years. Whether Christopher Wyburn-Risdale gets his head round this problem remains to be seen. The menu shows little sign of immense metropolitan chic, if dishes such as beef with brandy and green peppercorns, lamb with redcurrants and sauce paloise, and veal with noodles and rosemary are any guide. First reports, however, indicate some dexterity in execution. Bar lunches are said to have improved. The prices of the *carte* may be adjusted upwards so as to pay for all that marine transport; they surely are not cheap. More reports, please. The wine list is serviceable, with some decent growers from Burgundy, as well as the excellent Lake's Folly Cabernet Sauvignon from the Hunter Valley. House wines are £9.50.

CHEF: Christopher Wyburn-Risdale   PROPRIETOR: Robert Dorrien Smith   OPEN: all week; 12 to 2, 7 to 9.30   MEALS: alc. Set D £22.50. Minimum £20   SERVICE: not inc, card slips closed   CARDS: Access, Amex, Visa   DETAILS: 130 seats. 10 tables outside. Private parties: 40 main room. Vegetarian meals. Children's helpings. Smart dress preferred. Music ACCOMMODATION: 40 rooms, all with bath/shower. D,B&B £80 to £220. Deposit: 20%. Children welcome. Baby facilities. Afternoon teas. Garden. Swimming-pool. Tennis. Fishing. TV. Phone. Fax: (0720) 23008

TRURO Cornwall   map 1

▲ *Alverton Manor* ⚡✳

Tregolls Road, Truro TR1 1XQ   COOKING 1
TRURO (0872) 76633   COST £14–£48

It is one of the sad facts about the current recession that various places, especially in the country, are being run by receivers whose duty is to keep the ship on course until it can be docked with new owners. Alverton Manor is one of these, but it is being operated professionally and people are still drawn to it. It is a comfortable house, the Gothic arches reminding the visitor of its former life as a bishop's palace, then a convent, though none of the furnishings bears a hint of austerity. The staff may be willing, but are apparently serving a catering novitiate. The menu, which treads some familiar corridors, is competently executed. What is more, the daily table d'hôte has gained many favours for execution with economy. John Dory with mussel and tomato sauce, beef with peppercorn sauce and oven-glazed salmon with rosemary and white wine are three main courses that have been recommended, as have desserts such as peach parfait, blackberry soufflé or choux buns with praline ice-cream. The wine list contains some bottles at fair prices, an acceptable range, and lacks details (like the maker or shipper) that may matter to many people. House wines are £8.75.

The Guide *always appreciates hearing about changes of chef or owner.*

⚡✳ *indicates that smoking is either banned altogether or that a dining-room is maintained for non-smokers. The symbol does not apply to restaurants that simply have no-smoking areas.*

CHEF: Mike Smith   OPEN: all week; 12.15 to 2, 7.15 to 9.45   MEALS: alc. Set L £8 to £12, Set D £15 to £25   SERVICE: not inc, card slips closed   CARDS: Access, Amex, Diners, Visa DETAILS: 70 seats. 4 tables outside. Private parties: 140 main room, 20, 60 and 60 private rooms. Car park. Vegetarian meals. Children's helpings. Smart dress preferred. Jacket and tie. No smoking in dining-room. Wheelchair access (1 step; also WC). Music ACCOMMODATION: 25 rooms, all with bath/shower. Rooms for disabled. Lift. B&B £55 to £75. Children welcome. Afternoon teas. Garden. Snooker. TV. Phone. Confirm by 6. Fax: (0873) 222989 (*The Which? Hotel Guide*)

TUNBRIDGE WELLS Kent   map 3

Cheevers

56 High Street, Tunbridge Wells TN1 1XF	COOKING 3
TUNBRIDGE WELLS (0892) 545524	COST £22–£32

This restaurant is so sparing of irrelevant decorator items that, on a good day, it might be said to resemble a Japanese room: 'The pale grey carpet and walls must be a nightmare to keep clean.' On a bad day, it is a shop conversion on a shoestring. For one reporter, a delicate mousseline of brill was so dramatically presented on a black octagonal plate with no garnish but a light butter and cream chive/dill sauce that he ate it 'quite reverently'. Tim Cheevers' assured style is based on a menu of firm favourites. It gives regulars the chance to see a dish develop: 'One of us had the rack of lamb with a mint and almond crust years ago. It has refined a little.' Praise continued for the duck with spring onions and ginger, a form of Peking duck with a rich, fruity sauce and good handling of star-anise. There have been recommendations, too, for a rich, creamy crab mousse, guinea-fowl stuffed with fennel and walnut and ginger pudding. Properly cooked vegetables, which in the past were embarrassingly over-generous, are now recession-trimmed to a more manageable plate; but there is still a tendency to 'front-end load' – plentiful crudités, fresh mayonnaise, 'grissini-sized cheese straws', hot tartlets and 'Tim's big, filling, muesli-style rolls'. Discipline is essential in order to reach the pudding stage. High spenders will be disappointed with the wine list. Tim Cheevers keeps his prices fair, and sensibly puts a limit on grandeur; Ch. Durfort-Vivens 1983 at £29.50 is the greatest indulgence. There are many decent wines around the £12 mark and the half-bottle list has been expanded. Buying gets better by the year. House wines from Lamblin are £7.50.

CHEF: Tim Cheevers   PROPRIETORS: Tim Cheevers, M.J. Miles and P.D. Tambini   OPEN: Tue to Sat; 12.30 to 2, 7.30 to 10.30   MEALS: alc. Set D £22.50   SERVICE: not inc, card slips closed   CARDS: Access, Visa   DETAILS: 36 seats. Private parties: 16 main room. Children welcome. No cigars/pipes in dining-room. Wheelchair access. No music. Fax: (0892) 535956

County round-ups listing additional restaurants that may be worth a visit are at the back of the Guide, *after the Irish section. Reports on round-up entries are welcome.*

Restaurateurs justifiably resent no-shows. If you quote a credit card number when booking, you may be liable for the restaurant's lost profit margin if you don't turn up. Always phone to cancel.

Thackeray's House ♟

85 London Road,
Tunbridge Wells TN1 1EA   COOKING 3*
TUNBRIDGE WELLS (0892) 511921   COST £20–£52

It's not easy keeping head above water in provincial England and, to do so,
Bruce Wass tries to be all things to all men. In consequence, Thackeray's House
(which *was* Thackeray's house) plays host to the restaurant, subject of this
entry; downstairs in the servants' hall and kitchen is a bistro addition, the food
cheaper and less elaborate but no less enjoyable; and now, reached via an
entrance from the garden, comes the wine bar. How the house survives so many
uses is a mystery, but it does, giving a warm air of occupation, with pictures
cramming the walls and no sense of set-in-aspic conservation on the one hand
or mindless 'improvement' on the other. Bruce Wass ploughs his own furrow of
food with flavour, employing proper classical techniques, and using the best
resources to hand – local where possible. He offers a series of menus, some set-
price, some not. There is no truck with blandness: seasoning is high and taste is
sought from expressive ingredients. Examples of this might be duck with
Szechuan pepper and kumquats, salty preserved duck and pine-kernels, skate
and scallop salad with black-bean sauce and sesame vinaigrette, zampone with
Puy lentils, or fillet of hake with spiced lentils. Yet he is also able to handle
more classic, milder tastes such as vichyssoise, hot sea bass pâté with asparagus
sauce, salmon with avocado sauce, or John Dory with little vegetables. The
thoroughgoingness is everywhere: in the bread (even if one reporter
encountered a bullet-hard roll amongst the new), appetisers, ice-creams, petits
fours, home curing and salting. Pastry work is excellent (so too is sticky-
pudding-making), and this is one of few small restaurants prepared to put cold
food on as a main course. Some will find it expensive, but Bruce Wass
preserves his individuality and does give you the choice. Comments about high
prices for wine should be muted by the intelligently constructed and fairly
priced house selection. The main list, with many halves, includes a fine Italian
range, very reliable burgundies and an enthusiastic page from California.
House wine is £9.75. CELLARMAN'S CHOICE: Mâcon-Peronne 1990, Dom. du
Bicheron, £16.90; Veneto, La Grola 1988, Allegrini, £19.50.

CHEF/PROPRIETOR: Bruce Wass OPEN: Tue to Sun, exc Sun D; 12.30 to 2, 7 to 10 CLOSED:
1 week Christmas MEALS: alc. Set L £11.90 to £22.75, Set D £19.85 to £39 SERVICE: net
prices, card slips closed CARDS: Access, Visa DETAILS: 35 seats. Private parties: 40 main
room. Children's helpings. No cigars/pipes in dining-room. No music

---

TWICKENHAM Greater London   map 3

McClements

12 The Green,
Twickenham TW2 5AA   COOKING 3
081-755 0176   COST £23–£46

This diminutive restaurant has some of the charms of well-set jewellery – it
glows in the sun on a bright day. The chef does everything in the kitchen and
one waiter keeps the front tidy and in order. Such small-scale enterprise may

have its drawbacks – things running out, or not enough time to catch up – but it makes for a country intimacy in the midst of town. John McClement is no mean chef. The advantage of eating here is that things taste. The range is not large, but the flavours are classic. He still lists black pudding among his first courses, and he is rightly famed for it. However, the pudding itself has undergone some changes as he is no longer able to make it in-house. It would be difficult to mark out lobster with Dublin bay prawns roasted in spices and served in an open ravioli, velouté of wild mushrooms with truffle, venison with black pudding, or sweetbreads with wild mushrooms and truffle as being better than any of the dozen other items he continues to cook. Reconstruction has made improvement to the setting and the ancillaries. The wine list is classically dear and largely French. House wines are £9.

CHEF/PROPRIETOR: John McClement   OPEN: Mon to Sat, exc Sat L out of rugby season; 12 to 2.30, 7 to 10.30   CLOSED: Christmas week   MEALS: alc. Set L and D £18.50 to £28.50   SERVICE: 10% (net prices L), card slips closed   CARDS: Access, Visa   DETAILS: 24 seats. Private parties: 20 main room, 15 private room. Vegetarian meals. Children's helpings. Smart dress preferred. Wheelchair access. Music. Fax: 081-890 1372

UCKFIELD East Sussex   map 3

▲ *Horsted Place* ⁵⛌

Little Horsted TN22 5TS
UCKFIELD (0825) 750581   COOKING 3
2m S of Uckfield, on A26   COST £37–£53

Puck, puck, puck ... the sound of golf balls driven to the blue yonder. Horsted Place sits amidst a golf course, yet is not dominated by the game – even if it does help pay the bills. The house is worth a visit; the Pugin staircase (done for the Great Exhibition) is a wow. Light floods the rooms and makes the High Victorian Gothic glow. Views, the other way, are a pastoral idyll. King, though, is the chef Allan Garth. Three dishes have dominated this year's reports: artichoke baked in a pastry lattice with spinach, mushrooms, garlic and/or cream; a terrine of Mediterranean vegetables layered with mozzarella, with a balsamic vinegar dressing; and a dessert – almond charlotte – which reminded one observer of nothing more than the sweets at the Ritz in the days of Michael Quinn. Not that Allan Garth is incapable of other successes, chosen from a fixed-price menu of perhaps half a dozen items per course. Plain, classic, fresh lobster, veal with leeks and lentils and a madeira sauce, lamb wrapped in pancetta and pastry, and sea bass on spinach with a red pepper coulis are praised, as are rolls, vegetables and incidentals. Service is enjoyed for its fresh enthusiasm – 'relaxing, not stiff; friendly, not ingratiating'. Don't expect a bargain, but enjoy the luxury if you are having to pay. The wine list is a marked improvement on the last two years in range and choice, though price may give pause. There are halves aplenty. House wines are from £12.

Card slips closed *in the details at the end of an entry indicates that the total on the slips of credit cards is closed when handed over for signature.*

CHEF: Allan Garth PROPRIETORS: Granfel Hotels OPEN: all week, exc Sat L; 12.30 to 2, 7.30 to 9.15 CLOSED: 1 to 10 Jan MEALS: Set L £25, Set D £35 SERVICE: not inc, card slips closed CARDS: Access, Amex, Diners, Visa DETAILS: 36 seats. 10 tables outside. Private parties: 36 main room, 18 and 24 private rooms. Car park. Vegetarian meals. No children under 7. Smart dress preferred. No smoking in dining-room. Wheelchair access (also WC). No music ACCOMMODATION: 17 rooms, all with bath/shower. Rooms for disabled. Lift. B&B £120 to £310. No children under 7. Afternoon teas. Garden. Swimming-pool. Tennis. Golf. TV. Phone. Doors close at 11. Confirm by 9. Fax: (0825) 750459 (*The Which? Hotel Guide*)

ULLSWATER Cumbria   map 7

▲ *Sharrow Bay* ⁵⅄✷

Howtown Road, Ullswater CA10 2LZ
POOLEY BRIDGE (076 84) 86301 and 86483
2m from Pooley Bridge on E side of lake,   COOKING 4
signposted Howtown and Martindale   COST £30–£53

Repetition is tedious. Most things have been said at least once about this hotel: 44 years and still going strong. Here are two comments: 'In our suite, my wife discovered a jar containing soap flakes in case we wanted to hand-wash our clothes'; 'We returned after a gap of 10 years and were so impressed by the housekeeping and attention – effortless, solicitous, interested, always there.' The Italianate villa is as close to the water as it could be. Surrounded by gardens, with tear-jerking views from the windows, it is as good for the sounds at dead of night – while lying digesting your dinner – as for the obvious delights to the eye. As well as the main building, there is a lodge (a glorious satellite a mile down the lake) and a cottage still further away for the overflow. Decoration is busy and soft. Some of the bedrooms are very fine indeed as an extreme statement of a certain taste. 'You learn to pace yourself at Sharrow. The first night you eat up, then breakfast. The second night you slow down, and the third you have melon and finish with fruit salad.' In other words, food is a big deal here. All four of the British stops in the day are treated with the respect they deserve. Dinner is six courses long. Sometimes heretics (who may not want sorbet or wish for cheese before dessert) find they have upset a routine of longstanding. The food is not light, though dessert is the lightest and 'most modern' of the courses. This can weigh heavy on some people, so starve beforehand, or go for a vigorous stroll. The menu is traditional in form as well as in content. Eat game if you can, and roasts as well. There are fixed points. You choose your three major courses, while the fish, the sorbet and cheese are single items. The fish always comes with a soufflé suissesse on the side – yet more delectable heaviness. The sorbet has received criticism. There are reservations too for the vegetables with the main course: not really good enough in some people's eyes. Rösti potatoes come later on, when you think your plate is full enough. Although much food is simply cooked, there will be additions that make the whole seem complex. Thus roast lamb has a mousse of leek and courgette, a tartlet with soubise sauce and a fine gravy with port. Desserts and pastry work are good here, so are breads, so are the petits fours taken with your sherry in the ante-rooms. These can get a trifle anticipatory, as the flock awaits its marching orders, and is shepherded past the sweets on the way to the dining-rooms. It is a great experience, one most people wish to repeat, and are willing to pay for. The wine list shows improvements, even if screw-top quarter-bottles are served when you order a glass of champagne. House wines are £11.50.

CHEFS: Johnnie Martin, Colin Akrigg and Chris Bond   PROPRIETORS: Francis Coulson and Brian Sack   OPEN: all week; 1 to 1.45, 8 to 8.45   CLOSED: Dec, Jan, Feb   MEALS: Set L £24.50 to £29.50, Set D £38.50 to £39.50   SERVICE: net prices   DETAILS: 65 seats. Private parties: 10 main room. Car park. Vegetarian meals. No children under 13. Jacket and tie. No smoking in dining-room. Wheelchair access. No music   ACCOMMODATION: 29 rooms, 24 with bath/shower. Rooms for disabled. D,B&B £84 to £280. No children under 13. Afternoon teas. Garden. TV. Phone. Doors close at midnight. Confirm by 10am. Fax: (076 84) 86349 (*The Which? Hotel Guide*)

ULVERSTON Cumbria   map 7

▲ *Bay Horse Inn* ❦ ✳

Canal Foot, Ulverston LA12 9EL   COOKING 3
ULVERSTON (0229) 53972   COST £17–£33

The views across the Leven estuary are sensational and the inn is well designed to take advantage of them, from the terrace or the new bedrooms that have given one more excuse for people to make the hazardous drive from Ulverston – 'the road goes through a factory' was one visitor's warning. Never fear, the welcome at the end is informed and professional, the food excellent. 'We would come here for a bar meal so regularly if we lived nearer – salmon at around £6' was the comment of an envious resident of Lancaster. There is also the restaurant menu – often doubling up dishes though a fraction dearer – and the involvement of John Tovey is evident from things such as kidneys with chestnuts and shallots, smoked bacon and a madeira sauce, or duck with honey and calvados on a cranberry and apple purée with a fresh sage and onion stuffing, pickled kumquat and gravy flavoured with rosemary. Many ingredients are intelligently disposed to make a harmony for most people. The lunchtime bar food is very different from most encountered in Britain, combining refinement with plenty in such dishes as layers of mushrooms, courgette and fettuccine infused with garlic and sage, or flaked haddock and sultanas with cheese and mustard sauce in a puff pastry case. Soups are excellent, as is the brown bread that comes with them, be they fennel and pear, or pea, pear and watercress, or tomato, apple and celery, to name three. Vegetables are not in multiples of 10, but there are plenty, plainly cooked on the whole, 'and flavoursome'. Desserts can be as multi-layered as anything else, and the good hot puddings are worth a try, though one person felt the savoury food was more interesting than the sweet, perhaps because the choice of the latter is kept quite short. The wine list is longer, the most useful part being the selection, made by Robert Lyons, of mainly Australasian wines. He describes their flavours as 'clean and strong', an intent perhaps found in the food as well. There is a choice of these bins printed on each menu – understandably, people often plump for it.

CHEF: Robert Lyons   PROPRIETORS: Robert Lyons and John J. Tovey   OPEN: Mon to Sat, exc Mon L; 12 to 1.30, 7.30 for 8   CLOSED: Jan and Feb   MEALS: alc. Set £13.50. Minimum £10   SERVICE: 10%, card slips closed   CARDS: Access, Visa   DETAILS: 50 seats. No children under 12. Smart dress preferred. No smoking in dining-room. Wheelchair access (1 step; also WC). Music. Air-conditioned   ACCOMMODATION: 6 rooms, all with bath/shower. D,B&B £75 to £130. No children under 12. Pets welcome. Afternoon teas. Air-conditioned. TV. Phone. Doors close at midnight. Confirm by noon. Fax: (0229) 580502

UNDERBARROW Cumbria   map 7

Tullythwaite House ᵎ✳

Underbarrow LA8 8BB
CROSTHWAITE (044 88) 397, changes to   COOKING 2
(053 395) 68397 in October 1992   COST £20–£37

Janet Greenwood says that every one of her dishes reflects her philosophy of 'making food which combines a modern approach and a respect for tradition with a love of nature'. Tullythwaite is an industrious domestic enterprise: vegetables and herbs are grown in the garden, breads and biscuits are baked on the premises, jellies and relishes are made from local ingredients. This activity translates into a daily-changing five-course dinner menu with no choice. The centrepiece is invariably a roast, often with unusual stuffings: free-range chicken with couscous and apricot; loin of local lamb with bacon, kidneys and walnuts, served with polenta and plum sauce. One typically successful meal began with poached salmon on a square of pasta with a herb sauce, followed by fennel soup. The main dish of tender, young fallow deer with cranberry and orange sauce was supported by spot-on fresh vegetables. Cheese is always a fine assortment of local and Scottish types laid out on a magnificent sideboard. To finish, there may be chocolate mousse with a fan of sliced pears, then good coffee with home-made fudge. House wines are from £6.75.

CHEF: Janet Greenwood   PROPRIETORS: Michael and Janet Greenwood   OPEN: Wed to Sat, D only, and Sun L; 12.30 for 1, 7 for 7.30 or 7.30 for 8   CLOSED: Feb   MEALS: Set Sun L £14.95 to £18, Set D £23.95 to £27   SERVICE: not inc, card slips closed   CARDS: Access, Visa   DETAILS: 16 seats. Private parties: 16 main room. Car park. No children under 12. Smart dress preferred. No smoking in dining-room. No music

---

UPPER SLAUGHTER Gloucestershire   map 2

▲ Lords of the Manor | NEW ENTRY |

Upper Slaughter GL54 2JD   COOKING 2
COTSWOLD (0451) 820243   COST £26–£54

The Slaughters are something else; the seventeenth-century Manor (a former rectory) is high-grade too, and 'at last they have found a chef who matches up to the setting'. 'Flunkies everywhere' was the despairing remark of one visitor, while another thought a bit more staff training was needed; but if the food comes up trumps these may matter little. The cost, however, is high; so Jenny Coaker has to perform for her living. Her script is an expensive *carte*, a table d'hôte dinner, a cheaper set-price lunch and some good (and not too dear) free-range lunch dishes (bubble and squeak with an egg) unattached to the trappings of a whole meal. That vegetables one night were a wedge of potato-cake, celeriac mousse, skinned broad beans with béarnaise, and a courgette stuffed with ratatouille is indication that no trouble is too much. Whether technique matches invention may be answered by a mille-feuille of scallops and cucumber spaghetti with a cucumber vinaigrette that combined dull flavour with greasy texture. At the same meal, however, matters recovered with a loin of hare plus red cabbage that had good taste and was not over-worked, even if a little overcooked. There was plenty of taste in a hot rhubarb soufflé – now that *is* clever, as rhubarb is the most evanescent of things. Petits fours, though cast all over the table by a tiro flunky, were better than the muddy cafetière coffee. The Lords of the Manor may come good, as the commentator says. One reader observes that the 'wine list is extremely prosy', which may intimidate some. Quality is assured, but it is a pity that with such a catholic selection many will be further dissuaded to experiment by the prices, which are dauntingly high. House wine is £9.75.

CHEF: Jenny Coaker PROPRIETOR: James Gulliver OPEN: all week; 12.30 to 2, 7.30 to 9.30 MEALS: alc D. Set L £12.50 to £15.95, Set D £28 to £33.25. Light 1-course L from £6.50. SERVICE: 10% D, not inc L, card slips closed CARDS: Access, Amex, Diners, Visa DETAILS: 60 seats. 4 tables outside. Private parties: 60 main room, 30 and 30 private rooms. Car park. Vegetarian meals. Children's helpings. Jacket and tie preferred D. No cigars/ pipes in dining-room. Wheelchair access (also WC). No music ACCOMMODATION: 29 rooms, all with bath/shower. B&B £75 to £160. Deposit: £50. Children welcome. Baby facilities. Afternoon teas. Garden. Fishing. TV. Phone. Confirm by noon. Fax: (0451) 820696

VOWCHURCH Hereford & Worcester   map 4

Poston Mill ✿✗ £ | NEW ENTRY |

Vowchurch HR2 0SF   COOKING 2
GOLDEN VALLEY (0981) 550151   COST £17–£33

Ignore the campsite; you won't have to pitch tent to eat at this prettily converted watermill in the Golden Valley where John Daniels has set up his plate. 'He is clearly aiming at more than feeding hungry farmers out for a wedding anniversary,' states one who tried it for the first time since it opened. Whether butter shaped like a rose is a good or bad sign depends on your taste, but no one has objected to the taste of the breadcrumbed cheese gnocchi, poached then fried and laid on a bed of salad leaves, or the lobster and fish mousse baked in pastry with a chive butter sauce, the pheasant with rosemary and peppercorns, and the generous and well-hung fillets of beef that he uses. The cooking, though sometimes smacking of country-house twirls, does seem very keen, as is Philippa Lydford's charming service. The materials are also approved – no hint of yesterday's fish to the mousse and chunks of lobster gratefully received. There are pleasant touches, such as a rabbit pâté with ginger and onion marmalade, and the trio of chocolate puddings which makes a fine end to a meal. Three menus are offered at differing prices, and at lunch there is a choice of lighter food if you do not care to take the plunge. The wine list may extend and deepen. House wines are from £7.50.

CHEF: John Daniels   PROPRIETORS: John Daniels and Philippa Lydford   OPEN: Tue to Sun, exc Sun D; 12 to 2, 7 to 9.30   CLOSED: 25 Dec for 3 weeks   MEALS: L snack menu. Set L and D £13.50 to £23   SERVICE: not inc, card slips closed   CARDS: Access, Amex, Visa   DETAILS: 20 seats. 2 tables outside L. Private parties: 20 main room. Car park. Vegetarian meals. Children's helpings. No smoking in dining-room. No music

---

WADHURST East Sussex

map 3

▲ *Spindlewood Hotel*

Wallcrouch, Wadhurst TN5 7JG
TICEHURST (0580) 200430
on B2099, between Wadhurst and
Ticehurst

COOKING 1
COST £20–£33

'A wonderful spot to recharge one's batteries on a weekend stay,' comments one visitor to this solid, late-Victorian house that exudes peace and old-fashioned comfort. The dining-room, with its attractive, well-spaced tables, has an air of quiet relaxation, but the set-up seems to require the presence and full attention of the proprietors to ensure that it maintains momentum and cheerfulness. Three-course fixed-price menus change regularly and there is always a decent showing of fish from the market. 'Acceptable, but not particularly inspiring' is one expert view of the food. Creditable cream of watercress soup with spring vegetables, Chinese-style steamed crab and prawn dumplings with ginger cream sauce, and salmon with ginger and spring onion sauce have been praised. Vegetarian dishes might be as hackneyed as pasta with vegetables and tomato sauce. Home-made sorbets are smooth and English cheeses pass with full marks. The wines, including a good showing of half-bottles, are fair-priced. House French is £7.10.

CHEF: Harvey Lee Aram   PROPRIETOR: R.V. Fitzsimmons   OPEN: all week; 12.15 to 1.30, 7.15 to 9   CLOSED: 4 days Christmas, L bank hols   MEALS: Set Sun L £14.95, Set D £23.80   SERVICE: not inc, card slips closed   CARDS: Access, Visa   DETAILS: 40 seats. Private parties: 50 main room, 22 private room. Car park. Vegetarian meals. Children's helpings. No cigars/pipes in dining-room. Music   ACCOMMODATION: 9 rooms, all with bath/shower. B&B £50 to £82.50. Children welcome. Baby facilities. Garden. TV. Phone. Doors close at midnight. Confirm by 6. Fax: (0580) 201132

WALTON-ON-THAMES Surrey

map 3

Le Pêcheur at the Anglers

NEW ENTRY

Thameside,
Walton-on-Thames KT12 2PG
WALTON-ON-THAMES (0932) 227423

COOKING 1
COST £18–£28

Agreeable vistas of Thameside suburbia from window-side tables boost attendance here in fine weather. Timid refurbishment of the dining-room above the Anglers pub exposes evidence of its previous incarnation as a Forte-style carvery. Three-course set-price menus are supplemented by daily seafood and fish specials: perhaps Whitstable oysters or John Dory in a basil crust. Stephen Read's cooking is attractive, although a spring inspection revealed that 'too little was seasoned so too much was bland'. Reports, however, indicate ample enjoyment of grilled salmon with sorrel and chives and steamed red mullet with tomato and tarragon. The highlight dessert is an old-fashioned chocolate marquise with an orange and Grand Marnier sauce. Service is prompt and capable. The brief wine list has a few expensive indulgences at the end. It is exclusively French, but has no particular slant to white wines – odd, given the nature of the menu; selection is sound and prices are fair. Half-bottles are notably absent. House wines are £8.95.

CHEF: Stephen Read   PROPRIETOR: Jean-Jacques Fontaine   OPEN: all week, exc D Sun and Mon; 12 to 2.15, 7.15 to 10.15   MEALS: Set L £11.95 to £13.95, Set D £16.50 to £18.95   SERVICE: net prices, card slips closed   CARDS: Access, Visa   DETAILS: 50 seats. Private parties: 60 main room. Vegetarian meals. Children's helpings Sun L. Music

---

WAREHAM Dorset   map 2

▲ *Priory Hotel* ❦

Church Green, Wareham BH20 4ND   COOKING 1
WAREHAM (0929) 551666 and 552772   COST £22–£56

You can arrive here by boat or yacht, tying up at the boathouse (a converted sixteenth-century barn). Upstairs – fine views from the Greenwood Dining-Room – or down below in the Abbots Cellar Restaurant, the hotel has atmosphere, history and location. There's history too in the very long *carte*, the guéridon for preparing scampi or flaming bananas at your table, and the trolley that runs around with desserts. More recent developments are seen in the daily *prix fixe* offering Dorset air-dried ham, a spiced pear chutney with a parfait of duck liver, or salmon rolled in Japanese seaweed with a saffron and shallot sauce. Performance is measured; progress through a Saturday night menu takes in five courses and coffee; people who go often observe some fluctuation in standards, but applaud the welcome and the hospitality. Inconsistency, remarked upon in earlier years, remains a trademark of the wine list. Some of the selection, the Beaujolais in particular, looks downright boring – strange, when there is clear evidence that someone here knows his bottles. The unwary will not be stung, as prices are all very fair, and our glass award will serve to guide the more knowledgeable to a list that contains many fine things. CELLARMAN'S CHOICE: St-Véran, Les Grandes Bruyères 1990, £15.50; Médoc, Ch. la Tour St-Bonnet 1985, £17.50.

CHEF: Michael Rust   PROPRIETORS: Stuart and John Turner   OPEN: all week; 12.30 to 2, 7.30 to 10   MEALS: alc. Set L £11.95 to £13.95, Set Sun L £16.95, Set D £22.50 to £26.50 (Sat)   SERVICE: not inc, card slips closed   CARDS: Access, Amex, Diners, Visa   DETAILS: 66 seats. 10 tables outside. Private parties: 44 main room, 22 private room. Car park. Vegetarian meals. Children welcome. Smart dress preferred. Wheelchair access Greenwood (also WC). Music   ACCOMMODATION: 19 rooms, all with bath/shower. Rooms for disabled. B&B £70 to £175. Children welcome. Afternoon teas. Garden. Fishing. TV. Phone. Fax: (0929) 554519 (*The Which? Hotel Guide*)

Not inc *in the details at the end of an entry indicates that no service charge is made and any tipping is at the discretion of the customer.*

▲ Old Beams

Waterhouses ST10 3HW   COOKING 3
WATERHOUSES (0538) 308254   COST £26–£45

Alton Towers has a purpose: leave the children there and come to Old Beams
for lunch; 'it saved the day' was one verdict. The Wallises have achieved a
resounding success. The old inn offers light and airy space (and very heavy
chairs) in the conservatory, or you can keep under cover in the original
building. If you stay the night, there are rooms in an annexe across the road –
this road-crossing is a drawback. 'We shall return, which we might not if either
the rooms or the food were less good, but the combination is irresistible.' The
restaurant is very busy, particularly for weekend meals, and this can jaundice
the newcomer. Ann Wallis' sense of hospitality is always applauded, but her
young staff are sometimes less than suave. While lunch may seem
competitively priced, dinner may appear expensive. Nigel Wallis certainly
makes the effort to get in good produce, and he is happy to splatter the luxuries
on to customers' plates: lobster, fillet, foie gras and caviare at relatively small
surcharges are regulars on the menu. The style of the kitchen is quite
conservative, and may even be understated: good for eating, more questionable
if you are paying a great deal. Dinners have begun with simple but good Parma
ham on mixed leaves with fine olive oil; turbot mousse with a truffle sauce that
complemented without swamping; hot smoked haddock soufflé with a curry
sauce to pour into its middle; and a terrine of leeks and wild mushrooms. This
last elicited the comment 'wonderful, beautiful presentation, excellent taste,
one of the best starters I have ever had', which might be a clarion call in favour
of deceptive simplicity. Later in the meal, a casserole of seafood with samphire,
lobster with garlic butter, duck with blackcurrant, cassoulet of duck, or even
fillet steak with black peppercorns have been deemed satisfactory, even if the
last course, the good cheese or the sweet, gets the loudest songs of praise.
Reports say plum pudding, cabinet pudding, summer pudding, hot chocolate
soufflé and lime tart are great. The wine list here improves by the year with its
careful, intelligent selection throughout, generous provision of half-bottles and
even-handed enthusiasm that gives Alsace the same space as Burgundy.
Everything is priced accurately and fairly. House wines are from £12.65.
CELLARMAN'S CHOICE: Pinot Grigio 1989, Jermann, £23.50; Stag's Leap,
Merlot 1983, £23.35.

CHEF: Nigel Wallis   PROPRIETORS: Nigel and Ann Wallis   OPEN: Tue to Sun, exc Sat L and
Sun D; 12 to 2, 7 to 10   MEALS: Set L £17, Set D £30   SERVICE: not inc, card slips closed
CARDS: Access, Amex, Diners, Visa   DETAILS: 50 seats. Car park. Children welcome. No
smoking in dining-room. Wheelchair access (also WC). Music   ACCOMMODATION: 6
rooms, all with bath/shower. Rooms for disabled. B&B £52.50 to £90. Children welcome.
Baby facilities. Garden. Fishing. TV. Phone. Fax: (0538) 308157 (*The Which? Hotel Guide*)

---

*indicates that smoking is either banned altogether or that a dining-room is maintained
for non-smokers. The symbol does not apply to restaurants that simply have no-smoking
areas.*

WATERMILLOCK Cumbria map 7

▲ *Rampsbeck Country House Hotel* ⚡✱

Watermillock CA11 0LP
POOLEY BRIDGE (076 84) 86442 and 86688
on A592 Penrith to Windermere

COOKING 2*
COST £22–£42

The white-painted Italianate villa commands the shores of Ullswater with much grace and a little whimsy. Handsome, well-proportioned public rooms complete the picture. The dinner menu is large and long-winded. To a multiplicity of choice is added a surfeit of ingredients. Fortunately the majority of combinations are handled with equal capability. These may include sauté calves' sweetbreads and woodland mushrooms in a tartlet topped with pan-fried foie gras and a madeira and truffle wine sauce to start, or roasted squab wrapped in Cumbrian dried ham in a jus flavoured with morels and with Savoy cabbage to follow. In addition, expect a minimum selection of seven fresh 'beautifully cooked' vegetables. Desserts are multifarious but mellifluent. The expurgated bar lunch menu is well plotted and better value. The wine list is sound enough and gives a fair range, though no one will be surprised by novelty. Various bottles are suggested to go best with your main course. Six house wines are £8.75.

CHEF: Andrew McGeorge PROPRIETORS: T.I. and M.M. Gibb, and M.J. MacDowall
OPEN: all week; 12 to 1.30, 7 to 8.45 CLOSED: early Jan to mid-Feb MEALS: bar L. Set L
£17.95 to £27, Set D £23 to £30 SERVICE: not inc, card slips closed CARDS: Access, Visa
DETAILS: 40 seats. Private parties: 60 main room, 20 private room. Car park. Vegetarian
meals. Children's helpings L and early evening D. No children under 5 D. Smart dress
preferred. No smoking in dining-room. Wheelchair access (2 steps) ACCOMMODATION: 21
rooms, all with bath/shower. B&B £48 to £140. Deposit: £15. Children welcome. Pets
welcome. Afternoon teas. Garden. Fishing. TV. Phone. Doors close at 11. Confirm by 5.
Fax: (076 84) 86442 (*The Which? Hotel Guide*)

WATH-IN-NIDDERDALE North Yorkshire map 7

▲ *Sportsman's Arms*

Wath-in-Nidderdale HG3 5PP
HARROGATE (0423) 711306

COOKING 2*
COST £18–£41

Despite its name, this old stone inn near Pateley Bridge functions first and foremost as a restaurant (with accommodation), although there is a bar for drinks and snacks. 'A visit here is a memorable occasion' is a view shared by most reporters. À la carte and fixed-price menus are available, and the kitchen puts its faith in local produce: black pudding, Nidderdale trout, Dales lamb, Yorkshire venison. The choice of fish depends on the catch from the East Coast boats. One impressive meal began with well-timed al dente asparagus with orange hollandaise and smoked salmon omelette, and was followed by pan-fried Scarborough woof (a fish) with almonds and lemon, supported by a dish of good fresh vegetables. To finish, an individual summer pudding bursting with nicely tart blackcurrants in their juice 'would be reason enough to visit this restaurant', reported an inspector. The cheeseboard includes several Yorkshire locals. Occasionally there are mishaps, such as overcooked roast beef with 'less than competent Yorkshire pudding' for Sunday lunch. One reporter also mentioned a lack of imagination in the menu. Care has gone into the wine list; a catholic range with some pedigree – Rioja Contino, Chapoutier Côte Rôtie and Cape Mentelle included – offers satisfaction and moderate mark-ups. There is a house selection of seven decent wines well under £9 for the less knowledgeable. CELLARMAN'S CHOICE: Cloudy Bay Chardonnay 1989, £22.50; Ch. Brane-Cantenac 1970, £45.20.

CHEF/PROPRIETOR: J.R. Carter   OPEN: all week; 12 to 2, 7 to 10   MEALS: alc. Set L £12.50 to £15, Set D £18.50 to £30   SERVICE: not inc, card slips closed   CARDS: Access, Visa DETAILS: 45 seats. 6 tables outside. Private parties: 60 main room. Car park. Vegetarian meals with prior notice. Children's helpings. Wheelchair access (also WC). No music ACCOMMODATION: 7 rooms, 2 with bath/shower. B&B £27 to £50. Children welcome. Pets welcome. Afternoon teas. Garden. Fishing. TV (*The Which? Hotel Guide*)

WATLINGTON Oxfordshire   map 2

▲ *Well House*

34–40 High Street, Watlington OX9 5PY	COOKING 1
WATLINGTON (049 161) 3333	COST £24–£39

Sixteen years at the winding wheel – the well is in the bar – is a goodly stint, and still the Crawfords elicit praise, not just for the careful cooking of a menu that evolves steadily rather than by giant seasonal leaps, but also for the immense solicitude meted out to customers. Prices have advanced little, and the style characterised by dishes such as a gratin of Arbroath smokies, stir-fried smoked chicken with ginger and spring onion, avocado with walnut butter wrapped in bacon, veal kidneys with mustard sauce, quail with grapes and hazelnuts, and venison with cherry sauce remains not too ambitious, yet satisfactory to many people. Desserts get substantial and show an enjoyment of baking, be they gâteaux or roulades. The most unexpected aspect of the wine list is a run of a dozen German bottles, including a couple of reds from the Nahe. The collection as a whole is sound and offers a fair price range, including the Rocca delle Macie Chianti Riserva and Berberana Riojas as well as French standards. House wines are £7.

CHEFS: Patricia Crawford and Linda Membride   PROPRIETORS: Patricia and Alan Crawford   OPEN: Tue to Sun, exc Sat L and Sun D; 12.30 to 2, 7 to 9.15 (9.30 Sat)   MEALS: alc. Set L and D £12.90 to £16.40   SERVICE: not inc, card slips closed   CARDS: Access, Amex, Diners, Visa   DETAILS: 40 seats. 4 tables outside. Private parties: 45 main room. Car park. Vegetarian meals. Children's helpings. Smart dress preferred. Wheelchair access (3 steps). No music   ACCOMMODATION: 10 rooms, all with bath/shower. Rooms for disabled. B&B £40 to £80. Children welcome. Baby facilities. Afternoon teas. TV. Phone. Doors close at 11.30. Confirm by 6. Fax: (0491) 612025

See the inside of the front cover for an explanation of the 1 to 5 rating system for cooking standards.

WELLS Somerset　　　　　　　　　　　　　　　　　　　　map 2

Ritcher's £

5 Sadler Street, Wells BA5 2RR　　　　　　　　　　　　COOKING 1
WELLS (0749) 679085　　　　　　　　　　　　　　　　COST £16–£29

All things to all persons – restaurant, bistro, snackery and lunchtime bite – but
pretty with it, Ritcher's is well sited for the cathedral and the original centre of
town, even if parking in the day may give trouble. The bistro is downstairs, the
restaurant up. Neither is large, neither is dear. Nicholas Hart is a capable chef,
willing to blend his style into the culinary undergrowth of the district in dishes
like prawn and avocado cocktail or prawns with garlic butter and orange,
while creative dishes such as salmon rolled round a chicken and asparagus
mousse, pork with Stilton, or guinea-fowl en croute with smoked salmon have
the mark of someone working in 'modern British' mode. Which culinary sub-
group claims sticky toffee pudding with Bailey's ice-cream is a moot question.
Wines are not overpriced; a handful from Spain may offer the most interest.
House wines start at £7.45.

CHEF: Nicholas Hart　PROPRIETORS: Nicholas Hart and Kate Ritcher　OPEN: Mon to Sat; 12
to 2 (11.30 to 2.30 bistro), 7 (6.30 bistro) to 9.30　CLOSED: bank hols　MEALS: alc bistro.
Set L £12.50 to £14.50, Set D £14.50 to £19.50　SERVICE: not inc, card slips closed　CARDS:
Access, Visa　DETAILS: 14 seats restaurant, 18 seats bistro. 3 tables outside. Private parties:
24 main room. Vegetarian meals. Children's helpings (L only). No children under 10
restaurant D. Wheelchair access. No music

WELLS-NEXT-THE-SEA Norfolk　　　　　　　　　　　　map 6

Moorings 🍴

6 Freeman Street,
Wells-next-the Sea NR23 1BA　　　　　　　　　　　COOKING 3
FAKENHAM (0328) 710949　　　　　　　　　　　　　COST £19–£26

'You have never mentioned Bernard Phillips' taste for wild shirts,' began a
report on a meal at this small seaside restaurant (fish a speciality) that began
with oriental fish soup, then went on to gratin of sea trout and lobster ('good
chunks, strong orange flavouring, rich') with copious vegetables. Wild shirts
may not have a lot to do with cooking, but this indicates at least that the
Moorings is a personal restaurant. There is no likelihood of ignoring the
owners, and quite a lot of people obviously come here for their company. The
cooking is firmly based on the locality: venison from Holkham goes into a rich
pie; fish is bought from many boats, each an individual study; smoked salmon,
pigeon, oysters – you name it – all come from *somewhere*. Many dishes are
recommended: Norfolk brawn served with a pickle – maybe onions, maybe
pumpkin – home-cured herring or salmon, and Russian salad for first courses;
cod 'stockfish' style, with potatoes, garlic, walnut oil and cream, pigeon with
port and cream, venison wrapped in cabbage leaves, fairly plain Dover sole,
and Greek-style plaice or bream for mains. Desserts do not knock people out
in the same way: almond torte said by some to be heavy, pear poached in
Sauternes with a blackberry sauce that lacked presence. But a rice and custard

473

pudding was an evident hit. Bread should be better than that served during the winter; vegetables are often enjoyed, though there have been nights when lack of texture and flavour contrasts have reduced their impression to near-zero. This place is busy in the season, and its pricing and committed approach should cause it to be full all the while. The wine list shows the same impress of personality – 'Here at least is the cellar of someone who drinks'. There are as many wines from Portugal as red burgundies. It is wise to ask advice, but note the Mercurey from Leflaive, the Alsaces from Runner, the reds from south-west France and the cheapies from Italy. House wines start at £6.50.

CHEFS: Carla Phillips and Jane Lee PROPRIETORS: Bernard and Carla Phillips OPEN: Thur to Mon, exc Thur L; 12.30 to 2, 7.30 to 9 CLOSED: 7 to 25 June, 28 Nov to 17 Dec MEALS: alc. Set L and D £15.60 to £17.10 SERVICE: not inc (10% for 8 or more) DETAILS: 40 seats. Private parties: 40 main room. Vegetarian meals. Children's helpings. No smoking. Wheelchair access. No music

---

WEST BAY Dorset   map 2

Riverside Restaurant and Café

West Bay, Bridport DT6 4EZ   COOKING 2*
BRIDPORT (0308) 22011   COST £15–£34

People's views of what constitutes a restaurant vary. This café/restaurant/sub-post office is not exactly silver service – you take your drinks out of the fridge, people drink cups of tea and have a bun next door to a merry band of lobster eaters: these things unsettle those who have donned a suit, can't lift a bottle, and care more for ritual than reality. Arthur and Janet Watson have their own aims in view: serve fish cheap, cook it fresh, and run that relaxed sort of place that is home to a multitude of people. The café seems to be on an island: you reach it by footbridge and pedalos pass gently by in the water below. How you are served (self- or table-service) depends on what you eat, but everyone is cheerful. This is a good thing, because the place can get busy and service may get slow. The main eating area is full of light from giant windows, but not overburdened with comfort: no place for upholstery. There is a fixed menu of the obvious things (the fried or grilled soles or plaice, the prawns and mussels), but the list to go for is the daily *carte*: halibut, turbot, skate, black bream, sea bass, giant Pacific oysters from Abbotsbury, clams, mussels, lobster and crab. Methods of cooking are both simple (steamed turbot with watercress sauce) and more conventional (sole fillets deauvillaise). Janet Watson can do good things with garlic and tomato, be it gazpacho or brill in the Greek style with garlic, herbs, onions and olive oil. For first courses there are calamari with decent batter, plenty of bi-valves, oysters stuffed with spinach, spiced herrings, gravlax and others. Trimmings such as side salads tend to the unsophisticated. Desserts are fine, and ice-cream is local farmhouse. Children are happy with the burgers, the Watsons are happy with children. This is a model for all seaside towns. After a week in France at fancy restaurants, one family was convinced this was the best, most natural, least processed, and cheapest meal of the whole holiday. The wine list is short but never overpriced. House wines don't exist, but the cheapest bottle is only £6.95.

CHEFS: Janet Watson and Natalie Ansell Green   PROPRIETORS: Janet and Arthur Watson
OPEN: Tue to Sun, plus bank hol Mons; 10.30 to 3.30, 6.30 to 8.30 (10.30 to 6 Sun)
CLOSED: Dec to end Feb   MEALS: alc   SERVICE: not inc, card slips closed   CARDS: Access,
Visa   DETAILS: 80 seats. 10 tables outside. Private parties: 70 main room. Vegetarian meals.
Children's helpings. Wheelchair access (also WC). Music

WEST BEXINGTON Dorset

map 2

▲ *Manor Hotel*

Beach Road, West Bexington DT2 9DF
BURTON BRADSTOCK (0308) 897616

COOKING 1
COST £19–£28

It is a measure of the value and welcome of this hotel that it can be nigh-on full
even in the darkest nights of winter. The February view is as good as July's, if
the fog lifts, and Chesil Beach is an alluring prospect for getting rid of spiritual
cobwebs. The food – lots of it and robustly cooked, in restaurant and in bar – is
designed to feed up fainting townies. The restaurant serves menus of two
lengths and prices. It is always worth trying the fish – oysters or scallops,
plaice, salmon or sole – and pies and hearty stews, of game, or steak, kidney
and oyster, for example. Elaborate sauces are not so good. Substance continues
when the sweets trolley is in view: pavlova, gâteaux, deep mousses (though
not always deep-flavoured) and summer puddings are greedily reported. The
common leitmotif of people's accounts is the cheerfulness of the staff. The wine
list makes an effort with its halves. It draws on France to the virtual exclusion
of the rest of the world, but the choices – largely from Eldridge Pope – are very
sound. Prices are not adrift, but it would help if a little more detail as to the
maker were included. House wines are £6.65.

CHEF: Clive Jobson   PROPRIETORS: Richard and Jayne Childs   OPEN: all week; 12 to 2,
7 to 10 (10.30 Sat)   MEALS: Set L £12.95 to £14.95, Set D £14.95 to £18.95   SERVICE: not
inc, card slips closed   CARDS: Access, Amex, Diners, Visa   DETAILS: 65 seats. 18 tables
outside. Private parties: 65 main room, 20 and 50 private rooms. Car park. Vegetarian
meals. Children's helpings. Music   ACCOMMODATION: 13 rooms, all with bath/shower.
B&B £40 to £68. Deposit: £10. Children welcome. Baby facilities. Afternoon teas. Garden.
TV. Phone. Doors close at midnight. Confirm by 6. Fax: (0308) 897035 (*The Which? Hotel
Guide*)

WESTLINGTON Buckinghamshire

map 2

La Chouette

| NEW ENTRY |

Westlington Green,
Dinton HP17 8UW
AYLESBURY (0296) 747422
off A415, 4m SW of Aylesbury

COOKING 1*
COST £19–£53

This former public house, the origins barely overlaid by owls everywhere to
lend credence to the name, is the kingdom of Frédéric Desmette, sole chef,
bottle-washer and keen ornithologist and gardener. A single-handed kitchen
and nigh-on single-handed service (the English is not too fluent, either) make
for long meals, longer if the place is busy. A range of set menus is offered, some

good value (including wine) and some on the steep side. Then, there is a *carte* which adds a few more dishes to the range. M. Desmette is Belgian, and his origins show in the plenty, the robust classicism and some of the recipes – asparagus flamande has parsley and hard-boiled egg, but uses green, not white, spears. Englisness comes out when the vegetables – at least half a dozen sorts – are arranged round a duck breast with morels, though gratin dauphinois coloured with turmeric is an unorthodox turn. Prices may surprise, but then morels on toast with a cream sauce may surprise as well when served in a former pub in Bucks. People speak well of substantial and old-fashioned dishes like sole and lobster in champagne sauce or kidneys with mustard sauce, but feel the desserts – variations on a theme of ice-cream – may be neglected in favour of what comes before. The wine list will remind you of France: hot on clarets, hot on price, good properties. House wines are £10. Belgian beers and lots of jazz keep spirits high.

CHEF/PROPRIETOR: Frédéric Desmette   OPEN: Mon to Sat, exc Sat L; 12 to 2, 6.30 to 9
MEALS: alc. Set L £15 (inc wine) to £35, Set D £19.80 (inc wine) to £35   SERVICE: 12.5%,
card slips closed   CARDS: Access, Visa   DETAILS: 40 seats. 4 tables outside. Private parties:
48 main room, 14 private room. Car park. Vegetarian meals. Children's helpings. Smart
dress preferred. No cigars in dining-room. Wheelchair access. Music

---

WEST MERSEA Essex   map 3

▲ *Blackwater Hotel,* *Le Champenois*

20–22 Church Road,
West Mersea CO5 8QH   COOKING 2
COLCHESTER (0206) 383338 and 383038   COST £20–£38

A Victorian coaching-inn, camouflaged in ivy, harbours a dining-room dressed in French gingham. 'Time seems to stand still: the red check curtains, tablecloths and napkins, the wine list (a book of labels), every horizontal nook and cranny bearing an ornament; and the cooking and welcome remain of the same high standard,' remarked one who also felt, satisfied though he was, that time stood still on the service front as well – 'leisurely rather than remiss'. Mainstays such as moules marinière, onion soup and snails are recommended. *Plats du jour* like spiced turbot in red wine and star-anise sauce, and skate wing with beurre noir, relay virtuosity. Mersea oysters feature when available. But the slowly changing *carte*, fleshed out by daily fish and seasonal specials, is in the business of well-defined Anglo-French restaurant or bistro cooking. The prices are not so bistro, however. That wine list is indeed a volume – labels and years give it bulk and serve as visual reminders. The range is as French as the intentions of the food. House wines are £7.50.

The 1994 Guide will be published before Christmas 1993. Reports on meals are most welcome at any time of the year, but are extremely valuable in the spring. Send them to The Good Food Guide, *FREEPOST, 2 Marylebone Road, London NW1 1YN. No stamp is needed if posted in the UK.*

CHEF: R. Roudesli   PROPRIETOR: Monique Chapleo   OPEN: all week, exc Tue L and Sun D; 12 to 2, 7 to 10   CLOSED: last 3 weeks Jan   MEALS: alc. Set L £12.85 to £17, Set D £17   SERVICE: not inc, card slips closed   CARDS: Access, Amex, Visa   DETAILS: 46 seats. 3 tables outside. Private parties: 55 main room, 25 private room. Car park. Vegetarian meals. Children's helpings. Smart dress preferred. No cigars/pipes in dining-room. Wheelchair access (1 step; also WC). No music   ACCOMMODATION: 7 rooms, 4 with bath/shower. B&B £29 to £65. Deposit: £10. Chidren welcome. Baby facilities. Pets by arrangement. Afternoon teas. Garden. TV. Doors close at 1am. Confirm by 9pm (*The Which? Hotel Guide*)

WETHERAL Cumbria

map 7

Fantails

The Green, Wetheral CA4 8ET
CARLISLE (0228) 560239

COOKING 2
COST £22–£38

A suite of rooms has extended the boundaries of this former hayloft on the village green. Rusticity still prevails, antiques and oddments sit prettily against whitewashed walls, and the kitchen is no less removed from its pastoral surroundings – 'The sight of the chef visiting his herb garden heightened initial good impressions,' noted a reader. The herbs duly appeared, with fruit, in an 'intensely flavoured' chicken breast stuffing, and with tomato in a sauce for peanut and spinach roast (vegetarians are accorded at best three main course choices); otherwise they might join with garlic to coat a roast best end of lamb. If one local was shocked at our suggesting this as a motorway stop (near junction 42 on the M6), another correspondent, coming from Perth, thanked us heartily. 'We last ate there in our courting days, and this visit was with three results of that courting, aged 9, 7 and 2 (including the middleweight eating champion of Perthshire).' The Bowmans could not have been more accommodating. The wine list is a reliable if unexciting French selection; the most interest and value comes from the New World. House wines are £7.95.

CHEF: Cameron Clarke   PROPRIETORS: Jennifer and Bob Bowman   OPEN: Mon to Sat; 12 to 2, 7 to 10   MEALS: alc. Set L and D £16.95   SERVICE: not inc, card slips closed   CARDS: Access, Visa   DETAILS: 75 seats. Private parties: 50 main room, 12 and 25 private rooms. Car park. Vegetarian meals. Children's helpings. Smart dress preferred. No-smoking area. Music

---

WETHERSFIELD Essex

map 3

Dicken's ♥

The Green, Wethersfield CM7 4BS
GREAT DUNMOW (0371) 850723

COOKING 3
COST £21–£39

John Dicken is a 'hot chef', one of those elected by television to instruct the waiting nation at some early morning hour in the art of cooking. His restaurant, with his wife supplying 'attentive but not starchy' service, carries on regardless. Drink in the bar surrounded by cookery books, old copper and brass; continue through to a pair of dining-rooms, the first with curtains and wallpaper, the second with beams, age, and a minstrels' gallery. Reports have been very favourable this year for food such as mussel and scallop salad in a sauce vierge, tempura of fish, or parsnip soup with chives at the beginning; then fillet of lamb marinated with provençal herbs and served with wild mushrooms and leeks, salmon with sorrel and vermouth sauce, chicken with oriental spices and ginger, lobster à la nage, or confit of duck with glazed summer turnips as main courses. 'Being a Scot, I thought I had experienced every possible method of cooking salmon, but the thin slices of wild salmon were of maximum flavour and soft (almost fruit-like) texture,' wrote one man impressed by John Dicken's ability to rework old favourites (salmon, for instance, may come with a pimento and coriander vinaigrette), even if that fish has also been taxed here with lack of flavour in several manifestations in a single meal. Pastry work has come in for much praise: 'The apricot and almond tart was the high point of the meal' was one opinion; 'hot apple tart with a calvados sauce was greatly enjoyed' was another. Tarte Tatin, chocolate dishes with pear (or peanut mousse with pear and a hot chocolate sauce, for a change), or walnut and caramel in a biscuit tulip are other recommended items. A meal in the dead days of February did reveal an unnerving desire to serve sprouts (strong ones, at that) with salmon, as well as wishy-washy coffee. The set-price meals are consistently applauded for their value. Wines are nicely balanced over the price range, with as much care in selection of the cheaper as of the dearer bottles. The core is French, but other areas help to extend the choice below £20. Growers and sources are impeccable, with Lay & Wheeler providing the majority of bottles. House wines begin at £7.95. CELLARMAN'S CHOICE: Chardonnay, Brokenback Vineyard 1990, Rothbury Estate, £12.95; Napa Valley, Cabernet Sauvignon 1986, Clos du Val, £19.95.

CHEF: John Dicken PROPRIETORS: John and Maria Dicken OPEN: Wed to Sun, exc Sat L and Sun D; 12.30 to 2, 7.30 to 9.30 CLOSED: 2 weeks Feb MEALS: alc. Set L £15.50, Set D £17 SERVICE: not inc CARDS: Access, Visa DETAILS: 45 seats. Private parties: 35 main room, 20 private room. Car park. Vegetarian meals. Children's helpings. Smart dress preferred. Wheelchair access (2 steps; also WC). No music

---

WHIMPLE Devon   map 1

▲ Woodhayes

Whimple EX5 2TD   COOKING 2
WHIMPLE (0404) 822237   COST £33

The house is a large country rectory rather than a grand mansion; the decoration is ruched chintz, log fires, starched linen, flowers and plants. The Rendles care for you. Dinner is a no-choice affair through six courses to coffee, with some options available in sweet things. Well-vented dislikes are easily coped with, the owners say. Steady cooking deals with classics of the modern sort: smoked salmon mousse with king prawn, pear and apple soup, salmon hollandaise, beef fillet with red wine sauce, crème brûlée or hazelnut and raspberry roulade, cheddar or Stilton cheese was the running-order for one winter visitor. The range is wide enough not to tire people staying a week, though the vein from which it is drawn is consistent. Comfort and quiet may be the watchwords. A short, general wine list, largely from merchant Christopher Piper, offers plenty of halves and restrains extravagance and greed. The dozen or so house selections are good value at £9.20.

CHEFS: Katherine Rendle and Michael Rendle   PROPRIETORS: Katherine and Frank Rendle   OPEN: all week, D only (L residents only); 7.30 to 10   MEALS: Set D £25   SERVICE: net prices, card slips closed   CARDS: Access, Amex, Diners, Visa   DETAILS: 18 seats. Private parties: 18 main room. Car park. Vegetarian meals. No children under 12. Smart dress preferred. No cigars/pipes in dining-room. Music   ACCOMMODATION: 6 rooms, all with bath/shower. B&B £60 to £80. No children under 12. Garden. Tennis. TV. Phone (*The Which? Hotel Guide*)

WHITBY North Yorkshire   map 6A

Magpie Café £

14 Pier Road, Whitby YO21 3PU   COOKING 2
WHITBY (0947) 602058   COST £12–£30

'It turned out to be the last day they were open for the season and we shared a table with four others. A pot of tea (no bags), bread and butter, and chips with wonderful fish in batter I realised I hadn't tasted the like of since childhood.' Another reporter had first mentioned the Café to the *Guide* in 1980, and believed that the place continued to improve. There are few dissentient voices to this sort of comment. There are still queues, shared tables, strong tea, great fried fish, excellent cod with fresh tarragon and cream, haddock with cheese and prawns, tables in the window with views across to the abbey and parish church, dressed crab, and the endless amenability of staff and owners to families (there's even a separate children's changing-room). The desserts, all home-made, are also to be supported, whether the hazelnut meringue or the rum and Bailey's Jamaican fudge slice. Weight-watchers are also catered for. There is a short wine list, though many stick to tea. House wines are £5.95.

CHEFS: Ian Robson and Alison McKenzie-Robson   PROPRIETORS: Sheila and Ian McKenzie, Ian Robson and Alison McKenzie-Robson   OPEN: all week, L only; 11.30 to 6.30   CLOSED: late Nov to Mar   MEALS: alc. Set meals £7.25 to £10.95   SERVICE: not inc   DETAILS: 100 seats. Private parties: 50 main room. Vegetarian meals. Healthy eating options. Children's helpings. Air-conditioned. No music

Trenchers £

New Quay Road, Whitby YO21 1DH   COOKING 1
WHITBY (0947) 603212   COST £15–£25

Terry Foster and his two sisters are the driving forces behind this highly successful set-up, with its smart green décor, ceiling fans, Tiffany lamps and eye-catching open-plan frying range. Daily supplies of exemplary fresh fish from Whitby are the mainstays, backed up by sandwiches, salads, home-made pies and casseroles. Terry Foster says that he may be removing chargrilled steaks from the menu, due to the popularity of his seafood. Most reports agree that the place is run with super-efficiency, although there are occasional quibbles about 'careless' cooking. Sweets are huge. There are good facilities for children. House wine is £9.75 a litre.

See inside the front cover for an explanation of the symbols used at the tops of entries.

CHEFS: Timothy Lawrence, Gary Moutrey and Barry Brecon   PROPRIETOR: Terry Foster
OPEN: all week; 11 to 9   CLOSED: Christmas to mid-Mar   MEALS: alc   SERVICE: not inc
DETAILS: 150 seats. Private parties: 150 main room. Vegetarian meals. Children's helpings.
Baby facilities. Wheelchair access. Music

WHITLEY BAY Tyne & Wear   map 7

Le Provençale

179–183 Park View,
Whitley Bay NE26 3RE   COOKING 1
091-251 3567   COST £12–£38

Some find brown a depressing colour, others relish it for its comfort and calm.
Le Provençale is brown. It is also popular. 'Would that other restaurants might
follow its sensible pricing' was one comment. There is a long *carte* at dinner,
though on two evenings a week (Monday and Thursday) it is substituted by a
set-price menu with a particular theme – perhaps as broad as 'French'. The
repertoire is substantially classical; the *carte* indulges many variations of steak,
as well as a fair range of fish and seafood. Sauces are much in evidence in first
courses like mussels with a soubise of mushrooms, coated with a Mornay
sauce, or a tart of duck and smoked chicken with green peppercorns, a demi-
glace and cranberry sauce, and in main dishes such as langoustines Magenta,
tournedos Henri IV, or tournedos Rossini. At lunch the menu is shorter,
cheaper and much less full-dress. A winter lunchtime visit to eat sole
meunière, scallops cooked with smoked salmon, pear Belle Hélène and crème
caramel drew praise for value, a passing regret at unnecessary frills of
decoration and ornament, and approval of the fish cookery. A short,
mainstream wine list is as reasonably priced as the food, and includes some
excellent bottles such as Ryckwaert's Ch. du Grand Moulas and a 1986 Ch.
Lyonnat. House wines are £7.25 a litre.

CHEF: Michel Guijarro   PROPRIETORS: Mr and Mrs M. Guijarro   OPEN: Mon to Sat D, Wed
to Fri L; 12 to 2, 7.30 to 9.45 (7 to 10 Sat)   CLOSED: 2 weeks summer   MEALS: alc. Set D
Mon and Thur £15.95   SERVICE: not inc   CARDS: Access, Amex, Diners, Visa   DETAILS:
52 seats. Private parties: 52 main room. Children's helpings L. No children under 7. Music

---

WHITSTABLE Kent   map 3

Whitstable Oyster
Fishery Co £ | NEW ENTRY |

Royal Native Oyster Stores,
Horse Bridge Beach,
Whitstable CT5 1BU   COOKING 1
WHITSTABLE (0227) 276856   COST £20–£30

A pebble's throw from the shore is the Whitstable Royal Native Oyster Stores –
a bare-boarded, timbered warehouse with rough brick walls, seafaring prints
and white-painted wooden beams. The secret of its success lies beneath the
restaurant, where live shellfish are held in tanks and monitored by a state-of-

the-art purification system that uses ultra-violet light to kill bacteria and hold bi-valves in 'a totally safe environment'. No meat is served here. As one reporter remarked, 'This is a place for fish- and seafood-lovers only. The ambience is very French – good food, no frills, no pretence.' Everything hinges on procuring fresh supplies and handling them with as little culinary interference as possible. Whitstable oysters are wild and therefore seasonal; farmed giant Pacifics are available all year from the Isle of Skye; mussels are rope-grown in the Hebrides; salmon is brought from Scotland and smoked on the premises; lobsters and crabs are boiled in purified seawater. Other ingredients are from local boats and Billingsgate. Starters such as angels on horseback, steamed clams with tomatoes and parsley, and marinated chargrilled cuttlefish come with a bowl of salad. More substantial dishes – poached grey mullet stuffed with celery and onion, skate with black butter, grilled lobster – are served with new potatoes and vegetables. Service is as casual as the atmosphere. The short wine list is from Yapp Brothers. House French is £7.85.

CHEFS: Phil Colthop and Nikki Billington   PROPRIETORS: Whitstable Oyster Fishery Co
OPEN: Tue to Sun, exc Sun D; 12 to 2.30, 7 to 9.30   MEALS: alc   SERVICE: not inc, card slips closed   CARDS: Access, Amex, Diners, Visa   DETAILS: 85 seats. 10 tables outside. Private parties: 80 main room, 200 private room. Car park. Vegetarian meals. Children's helpings. Wheelchair access (1 step; also WC). No music. Fax: (0227) 770666

WICKHAM Hampshire   map 2

▲ *Old House*

The Square, Wickham PO17 5JG   COOKING 2
WICKHAM (0329) 833049   COST £26–£33

There have been few changes at the Old House. Nicholas Harman continues to offer a short French *carte* – short in number of dishes, lengthy in description – now at a set price with vegetables included. On paper the cooking appears to lack culinary integrity: Mediterranean flavours of olive oil, saffron, fennel and tomato mingle with the butter and cream of more northern climes, while spicing reflects English tastes. The results, however, please. A spring inspection produced a fine terrine of maize-fed chicken and 'pink and very livery' chicken livers, well complemented by a raw apple salad flavoured with lime pickle; fillet steak with a tarragon sauce; monkfish topped with an aubergine caviare and served with a tomato and olive oil sauce; and tarte Tatin. House wines are £10.

CHEF: Nicholas Harman   PROPRIETORS: Richard and Annie Skipwith   OPEN: Mon to Sat, exc L Mon and Sat; 12 to 1.45, 7 to 9.30   CLOSED: 10 days Christmas, 2 weeks July to Aug   MEALS: Set L and D £19 to £23   SERVICE: net prices, card slips closed   CARDS: Access, Amex, Diners, Visa   DETAILS: 40 seats. Private parties: 35 main room, 14 private room. Car park. Children's helpings. No cigars/pipes in dining-room. Wheelchair access. No music   ACCOMMODATION: 12 rooms, all with bath/shower. B&B £70 to £85. Children welcome. Baby facilities. Garden. TV. Phone. Doors close at midnight. Confirm by noon. Fax: (0329) 833672 (*The Which? Hotel Guide*)

WILLINGTON Co Durham   map 7

Stile ✳✕ £

97 High Street, Willington DL15 0PE   COOKING 1
BISHOP AUCKLAND (0388) 746615   COST £19–£30

Mike Boustred announces his gourmet events (almost weekly there is a
different theme night) in a newsletter that simply effervesces. Buying game
from his local dealer, enjoying happy colour contrasts in woods at Wallington
Hall, trundling across the Cheviots in an old Riley and adding wines to his
cellar are all grist to an enthusiastic mill. The mood is one good reason for
visiting Stile, a collection of cottages, conservatories, greenery and pinery. The
food is another: robust, with 'no pretensions to nouvelle cuisine', it allows
choice to vegetarians, and shows a fondness for steak, venison and Barbary
duck. The steak may be wrapped in pastry – Wellington, or a rump steak pie
with red wine, are examples; the venison boned and rolled haunch with
apricot stuffing; the duck perhaps with honey and green peppercorns. Desserts
do not disappoint: some 'soft-centred and rich' like the chocolate terrine, or
'fresh and fruity' as the the trio of sorbets. The wine list is a measure of the
place: not expensive, with Bruno Paillard champagne at a smidgeon over, and
Condrieu from Vernay a tad under, £20; more red Rhônes than burgundies are
on offer, and there is a willingness to roam far for value and good drinking.
House wines are from £5.95.

CHEF: Jenny James PROPRIETORS: Mike Boustred and Jenny James OPEN: Tue to Sat,
D only; 7 to 9.45 MEALS: alc. Set D £15.50 to £16.95 SERVICE: not inc, card slips closed
CARDS: Access, Visa DETAILS: 50 seats. Private parties: 34 main room, 18 private room.
Car park. Vegetarian meals. Children's helpings on request. No smoking in dining-room.
Wheelchair access (2 steps). Music

WILLITON Somerset   map 2

▲ White House Hotel 🍴

Williton TA4 4QW   COOKING 2*
WILLITON (0984) 632306 and 632777   COST £35

Supporters of this estimable hotel on the main road through the village criticise
the *Guide* for giving undue weight to culinary fashion, so dismissing the
Smiths' achievement. 'I have eaten here every month for the past four or five
years. Splendid ingredients are matched with sauces that really do their job of
enhancing the flavour without drowning it. There is a simple honesty to the
whole procedure that is so refreshing. You go in, Dick greets you in his shirt-
sleeves and offers you a glass of wine. Let him choose, you are never
disappointed.' Dick Smith had a serious accident in 1992, and as a consequence
the menu has been reduced in range and length. The silver lining is that the
price has been reduced as well. Kay Smith is a careful cook with an eye on
simplicity and seemliness rather than elaboration or display. Her repertoire
includes soufflé suissesse, gravlax, ragoût of oyster and shiitake mushrooms,
monkfish with fresh herbs, loin of pork stuffed with olives and pine-nuts, loin
of lamb with a tarragon and potato crust, excellent crèmes brûlées, nicely

turned sweet pancakes and decent sorbets. These are supported by proper soups, good local cheeses and strong coffee. It is a relaxed and gentle place at which to stay. 'I thought it close to my ideal,' said one impressed by the unobtrusive service, the taste of the food and the palpable value of the 'slightly rustic' rooms. The value extends to the wine list, which is wonderful. The range of clarets, Rhônes and half-bottles is enviable. The reinforcement to the French selection from Italy (small), Spain (larger) and the New World (growing) is well chosen. The enthusiasm and intelligence informing the whole are impressive. House wines start at £9. CELLARMAN'S CHOICE: Jurançon, Petit Manseng, Dom. Castera 1988, £21; Barbaresco, La Spinona 1985, Berutti, £13.

CHEFS/PROPRIETORS: Dick and Kay Smith   OPEN: all week, D only; 7.30 to 8.30   CLOSED: early Nov to mid-May   MEALS: Set D £22.50   SERVICE: not inc   DETAILS: 26 seats. Private parties: 12 main room. Car park. Children's helpings. No smoking during meals. Wheelchair access. No music   ACCOMMODATION: 12 rooms, 10 with bath/shower. Rooms for disabled. B&B £30 to £68. Deposit: £25. Children welcome. Baby facilities. Pets welcome. TV. Phone. Doors close at 11.30. Confirm by 6

WINDERMERE Cumbria   map 7

▲ *Gilpin Lodge* ♥ ⁵⁄✳

Crook Road, Windermere LA23 3NE   COOKING 2
WINDERMERE (053 94) 88818   COST £17–£27

This turn-of-the-century lakeland lodge is set in some 20 acres. Three of the ground-floor rooms, 'beautifully laid out, furnished and decorated', are converted for dining. Christine Cunliffe offers modern country-house-style dishes from a daily fixed-price dinner menu running to five courses. Reports mention good feuilleté of lambs' kidneys in a grain mustard sauce; baked goats' cheese and dressed salad with walnuts; calf's liver with confit of sweet-and-sour-onions; and blanquette of pheasant, chestnuts and Brussels sprouts in a cream sauce. A winter Sunday lunch, with the rain lashing down outside, produced enthusiasm for a duck liver parfait with filo pastry and sliced kumquats; suprême of chicken with wild mushrooms in a cream sauce; and a crème caramel with fruit compote. Less enthusiasm has been expressed for vegetables not quite up to the mark and disappointing soup. Service is polite and professional. The wine list's reasonable prices and catholic range have led to a glass award this year. There are strengths throughout. Tough buying could spread itself wider and be even more selective. House wines start at £8.50. CELLARMAN'S CHOICE: Sancerre, Les Perrières 1990, Vatan, £14.75; Givry, Clos Marceau 1988, Juillot, £16.50.

CHEFS: Christine Cunliffe and Chris Davies   PROPRIETORS: John and Christine Cunliffe   OPEN: all week, D only, and Sun L; 12.30 to 1.45, 7 to 8.45   MEALS: Set Sun L £12.75, Set D £23   SERVICE: not inc   CARDS: Access, Amex, Diners, Visa   DETAILS: 45 seats. Private parties: 22 main room, 12 and 14 private rooms. Car park. Vegetarian meals. No children under 9. Smart dress preferred. No smoking in dining-room. No music   ACCOMMODATION: 9 rooms, all with bath/shower. B&B £50 to £110. No children under 9. Garden. TV. Phone. Fax: (053 94) 88058

▲ *Miller Howe* ♟ ⁵⁄⁂

Rayrigg Road, Windermere LA23 1EY
WINDERMERE (053 94) 42536
on A592, between Windermere   COOKING 3
and Bowness   COST £48

If you were lucky enough to be staying in the spring, you might have had a
chance to try the Victorian breakfast in this hotel-restaurant that 'seems to
perch over the very water itself, with the fells and hills clustered round the
head of the lake'. Grapefruit in crème de menthe, porridge with whisky and
butter, kidneys with a glass of Cabernet Sauvignon were followed by the
lakeland platter, then toast and marmalade, 'Oh, and don't forget the Buck's
Fizz to start with'. This may set the tone of the cooking here. A black-glazed
floral plate totally laden with food constitutes a main course, served in a no-
choice dinner that will have already had an hors d'oeuvre, soup and fish course
or entrée. One summer night the plate held salmon, with a coating of
hollandaise and spears of asparagus laid across the top. Around the fish were
disposed a caviare tartlet, glazed carrots with chives, deep-fried leeks, purée of
celeriac with pine-kernels, spring cabbage with black pepper butter, bean
sprouts in soy sauce, french beans and new potatoes – a plateful indeed. Miller
Howe has reached its majority, in the sole care of its founder John Tovey. The
style he developed in earlier stints at the Windermere Hydro, and after working
at Sharrow Bay (see entry, Ullswater), is substantially unchanged. It is the
highest expression of an arguably British cuisine and now seems either
wonderful or strangely dated. Miller Howe may be overstated, but usually the
technical parts of the cooking are well performed. Not many criticise it for
sloppiness. The range of invention is breathtaking. There is a strong vein of
sweetness, as in a fish course of fillet of sole wrapped round a banana, baked
with single cream and flaked coconut ('cloying' was the verdict); there is an
urge to give lots of texture (nuts are a useful vehicle) as in tomato, apple and
celery soup (soups are very, very thick) with toasted cashews and a tartlet of
parsley and savoury; and there is a wish to vary flavours, almost to the extent of
muddle. The meals take place in uniform progression – everyone sits down at
once. The new(ish) conservatory has taken the heat off the press of public;
canapés ease the strain of waiting. Reports are gladdened by the better health
of John Tovey this year. Many are also high in praise of the staff and its
attitude, though perhaps very busy periods see a certain brusqueness to some
delicate souls. It is still a remarkable achievement. Four hundred and fifty
corks later, Mr Tovey and his staff have narrowed down the range of
exclusively New World wines on offer. Prices are not low or high, for a
collection that must be second to none; two wines are offered by the glass each
evening. A glass is awarded this year for interest, audacity and good value.
House wines are from £11.50.

---

*The text of entries is based on unsolicited reports sent in by readers, backed up by
inspections conducted anonymously. The factual details under the text are from
questionnaires the* Guide *sends to all restaurants that feature in the book.*

CHEFS: Ian Dutton and Chris Blaydes PROPRIETOR: John J. Tovey OPEN: all week, D only; 8 for 8.30 CLOSED: Dec to Feb MEALS: Set D £32 SERVICE: 12.5%, card slips closed CARDS: Access, Amex, Diners, Visa DETAILS: 70 seats. Private parties: 30 main room. Car park. Vegetarian meals. No children under 12. Smart dress preferred. No smoking in dining-room. Music. Air-conditioned ACCOMMODATION: 13 rooms, all with bath/shower. B&B £95 to £240. No children under 12. Pets welcome. Afternoon teas. Garden. Air-conditioned. TV. Phone. Doors close at 11. Confirm by noon. Fax: (053 94) 45664 (*The Which? Hotel Guide*)

Miller Howe Café 🏃✶ £

Lakeland Plastics Ltd,
Alexandra Buildings, Station Precinct,
Windermere LA23 1BQ
WINDERMERE (053 94) 46732

COOKING 1
COST £13–£19

Don't expect an intimate setting for a lunchtime tryst. You may have to queue for the very decent food cooked by Ian Dutton and Bill Tully, chefs with long years of service at Miller Howe itself. The short printed menu is but a base, the blackboard is the icing. A lunch that might start with a good and proper salad, then take in devilled mushrooms, macaroni with smoked bacon or Cumberland sausage with apple sauce and date chutney, finishes with a flourish on sticky toffee pudding or perhaps a blackcurrant mousse. Teas are something else. There are occasional signs that life is too hectic, but the food is remarkably genuine and fresh-flavoured. Prices are democratic. House wine is £5.90 a litre.

CHEFS: Ian Dutton and William Tully PROPRIETORS: John J. Tovey and Ian Dutton
OPEN: Mon to Sat; 9am to 5pm (4.30 Sat) MEALS: alc SERVICE: not inc CARDS: Access, Amex, Visa DETAILS: 40 seats. 4 tables outside. Private parties: 40 main room. Car park. Vegetarian meals. Children welcome. No smoking. Wheelchair access (also WC). Music

Roger's

4 High Street, Windermere LA23 1AF
WINDERMERE (053 94) 44954

COOKING 3
COST £22–£39

Two floors that are 'dark and elegant' for some, a little cheek-by-jowl for others, with smokers not helping. On the other hand, proximity may breed fraternisation. Alena Pergl-Wilson has a fine way with customers, and the cooking is serious. 'It seems hardly to have changed at all, and with food this good, why should it?' Classical technique, an enjoyment of fish, a willingness to try out various aspects of French regional cookery (gourmet evenings), and very good pastry, meat purchasing and vegetable cookery all contribute their tithe. Monkfish and scallops with pungent chilli sauce, breast of chicken stuffed with 'wonderfully moist' ceps, spinach topped with goats' cheese with tangy tomato sauce, rack of lamb with smooth and full-flavoured madeira sauce are items that have pleased. Over-rare grouse has done the opposite. Desserts like an amaretto and almond sponge, walnut tart, treacle tart or a light two-tone chocolate terrine get full marks. Consistency is impressive; a poor meal was charitably put down to the end of a long season, but such lapses are rare. The wine list is growing in size and range, with welcome help from the New World. Rhônes and Loires have some good growers; burgundies have a roll-call of famous houses rather than single domaines. It is all fair value with house Cordier at £9.25.

CHEF: Roger Pergl-Wilson   PROPRIETORS: Roger and Alena Pergl-Wilson   OPEN: Mon to Sat (Sun bank hols), D only (L by arrangement); 7 to 10   MEALS: alc. Set D £14.95 to £16.50   SERVICE: not inc, card slips closed   CARDS: Access, Amex, Diners, Visa   DETAILS: 42 seats. Private parties: 28 main room, 18 private room. Children's helpings. Wheelchair access. Music

---

WINKLEIGH Devon   map 1

Pophams ⅛✶ £

Castle Street, Winkleigh EX19 8HQ   COOKING 2*
WINKLEIGH (0837) 83767   COST £10–£14

Melvyn Popham's and Dennis Hawkes' village shop, coffee-bar and café combination offers no pretence: 'Looks like a corner shop/delicatessen, which it is.' Open for morning coffee and light lunches, it should serve as an inspiration for every village. Even with some ingenious positioning of tables, 10 people is the maximum that can be accommodated (it's a good idea to telephone first). Such close proximity encourages chatting with neighbours. 'I usually do not like being conspicuous, where every guest is necessarily involved in conversation with the chef/proprietor. It was, however, a very enjoyable experience.' Everything on the menu is home-made. The popular steak and kidney pudding (available for four people only) is highly praised. A winter lunch of potato and watercress soup, chicken stuffed with leeks and grapes, red cabbage with orange, and chocolate marquise with coffee bean sauce was pronounced 'excellent'. Other choices include locally smoked venison; pan-fried duck breast with madeira sauce; local rainbow trout poached and served on salad greens with lime mayonnaise and new potatoes; rum, date and stem ginger tart; and sticky toffee pudding. The value for money is as striking as the quality of the cooking.

CHEF: Melvyn Popham   PROPRIETORS: Melvyn Popham and Dennis Hawkes   OPEN: Mon to Sat; 11.30 to 3   MEALS: alc. Unlicensed, but bring your own: no corkage   SERVICE: not inc, card slips closed   CARDS: Access, Visa   DETAILS: 10 seats. Private parties: 8 main room. Vegetarian meals. No children under 14. No smoking in dining-room. Music. Air-conditioned

---

WINTERINGHAM Humberside   map 6

▲ Winteringham Fields ⑂ ⅛✶

Winteringham DN15 9PF   COOKING 4
SCUNTHORPE (0724) 733096   COST £22–£49

'It is, frankly, an ugly village' was one person's opinion, but the house is an oasis in a wasteland of industry 'like the face of the moon', and 'literally stuffed with Victoriana which somehow avoids being overpowering'. This is an old farmhouse transformed by decoration and by the presence of Germain and

Annie Schwab. 'They were so pleased to see us again after our visit a year before' was indication of the waves of hospitality that flow from the Schwabs. Visitors try to impress by statistics: 'There were 31 cheeses on the board'; 'There were 10 different sorts of fish on offer that day.' They find the value, especially at lunch, out of the ordinary: 'We knew, as we entered, that we were in for something a little bit special. We left with a warm glow from our expectations being confirmed.' Germain Schwab takes no short-cuts to a full-dress experience. The appetisers may even come in threes: oxtail soup, crespolini of foie gras, quail's egg florentine. Technique is never forgotten, nor presentation; you have only to hear about desserts such as the three mousses in a chocolate box, or the fine hot soufflés, or the delivery of trout with a 'crown' of citrus-flavoured sour cream. There is a wish to experiment with sweetness, as in turbot with vanilla sauce or hare with a crème de cacao sauce, but it does not become cloying. Indeed, the main comment is about the depth of flavour, yet perfect balance, that is achieved in the cooking. Dishes that have been recommended this year, from lunch menus as well as those at dinner, have included a koulibiac of salmon, fillet of lamb with honey and carrot sauce, and blinis of foie gras and chestnuts. The fish is so fresh that 'you can smell the brine', as in sea bass with sauce maltaise, brill with ratatouille, and surprising mixtures that work to everyone's delight such as the oysters double-wrapped, first in smoked duck, then in filo pastry before being deep-fried. Vegetables gain special mention. The ambitious nature of the food needs decent service, which it does not lack. Wines, too, benefit from the advice of a capable sommelier. The list is noteworthy for fair pricing and the offer of great choice below £20. The Swiss and Beaujolais sections stand out, but the clarets are not as inspiring. House wines are from £9.50. CELLARMAN'S CHOICE: Marlborough, Sauvignon/Semillon 1990, Selaks, £16; Ticino 1988, Collivo Azienda Agricola, £18.50.

CHEF: Germain Schwab PROPRIETORS: Annie and Germain Schwab OPEN: Mon to Sat, exc L Mon and Sat; 12 to 1.30, 7.30 to 9.30 CLOSED: first 2 weeks Jan, first week Aug MEALS: alc. Set L £13.75, Set D £32 to £36 SERVICE: not inc, card clips closed CARDS: Access, Visa DETAILS: 40 seats. Private parties: 14 main room, 10 private room. Car park. Children welcome. Smart dress preferred. No smoking in dining-room. Wheelchair access (1 step; also WC). Music. Air-conditioned. Fax: (0724) 733898 ACCOMMODATION: 7 rooms, all with bath/shower. Rooms for disabled. B&B £60 to £95. No children under 10. Afternoon teas. Air-conditioned. TV. Phone. Doors close at midnight. Confirm by 6. Fax: (0724) 733898 (*The Which? Hotel Guide*)

WITHERSLACK Cumbria   map 7

▲ *Old Vicarage* ▮ ⚡✳

Witherslack LA11 6RS
WITHERSLACK (044 852) 381
changes to (053 95) 52381 spring 1993

COOKING 3
COST £23–£36

This Victorian house takes on extra bits and pieces as the years go by: another two bedrooms in 1992. 'We stayed in one of the new rooms in the Orchard House and it was well worth it,' reports a regular who comes to see if and how improvements have affected the tenor of the whole. Two pairs of partners run this as a hotel, splitting the shifts between them. Argument sometimes develops as to which is the better time to visit: the jury is always out, which may imply that the formula works even-handedly. Certainly there is a formula. The large breakfasts, the lakeland teas, and the set meal at dinner time which allows choice at the last course but at no other, although 'the appearance of choice at pudding stage is illusory; they give you both and expect you to eat them'. The first chink in the armour has appeared this year. It is now possible to eat an abbreviated (three-course) dinner at a more realistic price. The style of the cooking is British, with a satisfactory vengeance. This pleases many people: the main course is almost always roast meat; the cheeses are a good British selection; the puddings are usually a hot and a cold, one of which is traditional Brit, the other some airier confection such as pavlova or roulade. At the first course, other influences may creep in: linguine pasta, a fish mousseline, or a smoked fish pancake; but the Lake District will have its say even here, with offerings like Cumberland ham. The arrangement has its advantages and drawbacks. Much care is taken by the partners and their staff to ensure that everyone is happy. Most find this lightly done, a few balk at the intrusion. The good points are, unanimously, the vegetables ('varied, and nicely seasoned'); the soups ('clear and intense flavours'); the cheeses; and the use of herbs, ('we particularly liked the purée of cauliflower with parsley'). This is often careful cooking, accurately executed. Attentive to quality, the wine list is not intended to astound in quantity; wines from good growers such as Burgundian Chopin-Groffier and Baumard on the Loire, and antipodean wines of equal stature guarantee an interesting pre-prandial read. There are decent wines by the glass and half-bottle, but economy is not an issue since the price range is generously broad. House wines are from £13.50. CELLARMAN'S CHOICE: Adelaide Hills Chardonnay 1990, David Wynn, £12.50; Eden Valley Shiraz 1990, David Wynn, £12.50.

CHEFS/PROPRIETORS: Roger and Jill Burrington-Brown, Irene and Stanley Reeve OPEN: all week, D only, and Sun L; 12.30 to 2, 7.30 for 8 MEALS: Set Sun L £15, Set D £19.50 SERVICE: not inc, card slips closed CARDS: Access, Amex, Diners, Visa DETAILS: 35 seats. Private parties: 18 main room. Car park. Vegetarian meals. Children welcome. No smoking in dining-room. Music ACCOMMODATION: 15 rooms, all with bath/shower. Rooms for disabled. B&B £45 to £118. Children welcome. Pets welcome. Afternoon teas. Garden. Tennis. TV. Phone. Doors close at 11.30. Confirm by 6. Fax: (044 852) 373, changes to (053 95) 52373 spring 1993 (*The Which? Hotel Guide*)

WOBURN Bedfordshire   map 3

Paris House

COUNTY OF THE YEAR RESTAURANT

Woburn Park, Woburn MK17 9QP
WOBURN (0525) 290692
A4012, 1½m E of Woburn   COOKING 3
in Abbey grounds   COST £27–£50

'Fortunately, we did not enter the safari park, though we kept stumbling across deer and other wild life,' wrote a relieved arrival at this half-timbered pavilion that was removed from the Paris Exhibition of 1878 and reconstructed in the great park at Woburn. Peter Chandler describes his cooking as 'rustic classical' and there are certainly elements of the classical – coming, perhaps, from his long apprenticeship in the kitchens of the Roux brothers – and of rusticity, evidenced by dishes such as blanquette of lamb or hefty braises for winter lunchtime eating. He is an enthusiastic host. 'He mingled with the masses and, unlike some, managed to do it with some style. His keenness comes across and it was more than just the token "Is everything all right?" which is so tedious.' Some dishes are the old classics stripped of inessentials. Technique, however, remains – for instance in soufflés, always approved save in one instance where the raspberry flavour was held to be at vanishing point. A mille-feuille of mushrooms with sweet-and-sour leeks had good flavours, even if the pastry was heavy, but the confit of duck with orange that came as a first course had all the succulence that is demanded of such meat. Rib of beef with red wine and onions is just one of those dishes that appeals to the present following – the meat properly cooked and generous, the sauce good, the vegetables plain and profuse. Petits fours come in pretty profuse numbers, too. Soufflés are all the rage here, but a tarte Tatin was so laden with alcohol as to make it a drink as well. Altogether a good and friendly restaurant, though the French waiting staff sometimes need better English. People regret the presence of too much smoke in the dining-room and wonder at the price for dinner. The wine list is fairly upper-crust. House wines are £9.50.

CHEF/PROPRIETOR: Peter Chandler   OPEN: Tue to Sun, exc Sun D; 12 to 2, 7 to 10   MEALS: Set L £19.50, Set D £32 to £36   SERVICE: not inc   CARDS: Access, Amex, Diners, Visa   DETAILS: 60 seats. Private parties: 45 main room, 15 private room. Car park. Vegetarian meals. Children's helpings L. Smart dress preferred. No music. Fax: (0525) 290471

WOODSTOCK Oxfordshire   map 2

▲ *Feathers Hotel*

Market Street,
Woodstock OX20 1SX   COOKING 3
WOODSTOCK (0993) 812291   COST £26–£50

The building is a rabbit-warren of interconnecting rooms, with a dining-room done out in cool, greyish blue and yellow. The mood is informal – children are welcome, and jeans are not frowned upon even on a Saturday evening. It helps to create a suitably relaxed country impression, enhanced by thoroughly English service that is well trained, but tends towards the jovial. After a period when the kitchen seemed to lose its way and some of its originality, David Lewis and his brigade are back on form. A blend of sheer gutsiness and sophistication shows across the repertoire, from the little pastry tarts with sliced chorizo and pesto offered as a nibble to the 'heavily creamy' chocolate truffles served with potent cafetière coffee. Sampled dishes prove the high-flying intentions of the place. Consider this: a wooden skewer of beautifully timed, fragrant chargrilled scallops and tuna on an 'extraordinary' balsamic vinaigrette that was 'rich, greasy, acid, fruity, really quite amazing'. Or, roast fillet of mature Angus beef topped with rough slices of barely cooked oyster mushrooms and a strong gravy perfumed with tarragon, plus some whole roasted shallots and cloves of garlic in their skins. 'This was food that really made you sit up and smell,' enthused an inspector. Vegetables are part of each dish, but they are impeccably cooked: sliced runner beans, skinned broad beans and mange-tout added greeness to dark beef. To finish, sablé biscuits with coffee mousse and cappuccino sauce have been full of intense flavours, although the contrasts were less vivid than in other dishes. The practice of adding a 'suggested 15 per cent gratuity' persists. It still causes disgruntlement among readers and marred many dazzling meals. High mark-ups are maintained on the wine – a pity because quality is good throughout. A few wines by the glass and decent half-bottles soften the blow, but the 'house selection', an adequate gathering from the French provinces, will remain the choice for most sensible customers. House wines are from £9.85.

CHEF: David Lewis   PROPRIETORS: Andrew Leeman, Simon Lowe and Howard Malin
OPEN: all week; 12.30 to 2.30, 7.30 to 9.30   MEALS: alc. Set L £17.50 to £17.95, Set D £19.95
to £29.95 (Sat)   SERVICE: 15%, card slips closed   CARDS: Access, Amex, Diners, Visa
DETAILS: 60 seats. 14 tables outside. Private parties: 60 main room, 28 and 30 private rooms.
Vegetarian meals with prior notice. Children's helpings. Wheelchair access. Music. Air-
conditioned   ACCOMMODATION: 17 rooms, all with bath/shower. B&B £75 to £125.
Children welcome. Baby facilities. Dogs welcome. Afternoon teas. TV. Phone. Doors close
at 11. Fax: (0993) 813158 (*The Which? Hotel Guide*)

WOOTTON Isle of Wight   map 2

▲ *Lugleys*

Staplers Road,
Wootton Common PO33 4RW   COOKING 2*
NEWPORT (0983) 882202   COST £21–£33

'Premises modest,' points out a reader who was amused by the view through the window of 'all insect life at work – death, pairing, procreation and separation.' 'The conservatory badly needs an overhaul,' commented another, 'but it did not put us off our peach champagne.' Angela Hewitt's house is not a soigné restaurant. Not a lot matches, but that is part of the appeal. Her food, though, is all of a piece. A short menu, no more than three choices, will give rise to a long meal as extra courses of sorbet or maybe tomatoes in cream are slipped in without warning (or payment). The cooking has nothing to do with Isle of Wight standard fare. Lobster jelly with coral cream and red pepper sauce, ravioli of lamb with creamed ratatouille and Parmesan, noisettes of lamb with soubise mousse and rosemary glaze, and duck with baby beetroot and red wine and orange sauce, are more her line. This can be spectacularly successful. 'Quail with wild mushrooms, and goats' cheese soufflé in filo pastry with a sweet, possibly honey, sauce were ecstatic; but lobster fricassee had a sauce so salty it was uneatable. A cheddar cheese sauce with smoked haddock mousse showed that unlikely combinations could be made to work; simple sorbets like pink grapefruit or melon were really fine.' These were the terms of a mixed report, which also reflected that the food had little concern for balance over a whole meal, leaving you panting by the end. This is cooking of character, by a natural enthusiast. Where faults occur, it may come down to a lack of assistance to even out the work load. The wine list is very short indeed, and may not always be exact. House wines are from £7.95.

CHEF/PROPRIETOR: Angela E. Hewitt   OPEN: Tue to Sat, D only (Sun and Mon D and L by arrangement); 7 to 9.30 (varies in winter)   CLOSED: 4 weeks winter   MEALS: alc. Set L £15, Set D £20.45 to £22. Minimum £12.95   SERVICE: not inc   DETAILS: 16 seats. 5 tables outside. Private parties: 16 main room. Car park. No children under 12. No cigars in dining-room. No music   ACCOMMODATION: Self-contained flat for 1 to 3, £30 a night, with bath/shower. Deposit: 50%. No children under 12. Garden. TV

WORCESTER Hereford & Worcester   map 2

Brown's

The Old Cornmill, South Quay,	
Worcester WR1 2JJ	COOKING 2
WORCESTER (0905) 26263	COST £20–£38

This fine warehouse conversion provides a modern, spacious restaurant on several levels, including a mezzanine bar with views on to the River Severn. The food is of a piece with the fashionably modern décor, as seen in dishes such as pasta with ricotta, Parmesan and walnuts; roast Barbary duck with ginger and lime and the leg as a confit; and spatchcock of grilled quail on a bed of herb risotto. Lunch – noticeably cheaper than dinner – is the subject of most readers' recommendations: hot, fresh crab-cakes with basil sauce, warm salad of chicken livers, chicken with crab stuffing, brill with a butter sauce, pear and apricot flan, and an 'excellent cheeseboard' have all pleased. The dinner menu offers a wide choice for each course: to start, perhaps, warm scallops with a cold hazelnut sauce or grilled fillet of fresh herring with a cold mustard sauce; then, roast carré of lamb with a couscous of apricots and almonds or chargrilled fillet of beef (at a supplement). Desserts may include marquise of two chocolates, pear and apricot flan, and rhubarb crumble. The 200-strong wine list has a strong contingent from France. House wines are £9.50.

CHEF: W.R. Tansley   PROPRIETORS: W.R. and P.M. Tansley   OPEN: all week, exc Sat L and Sun D; 12.30 to 1.45 (2 Sun), 7.30 to 9.30   CLOSED: bank hols, 1 week Christmas   MEALS: Set L £15, Set Sun L £20, Set D £30   SERVICE: net prices, card slips closed   CARDS: Access, Amex, Diners, Visa   DETAILS: 80 seats. Private parties: 80 main room. Vegetarian meals. No children under 10. Wheelchair access (also WC). No music

---

Il Pescatore £

34 Sidbury, Worcester WR1 2HZ	COOKING 1
WORCESTER (0905) 21444	COST £15–£41

Once a tea-room, this is now a popular Italian restaurant proclaiming that fish is the thing. Look at the menu, and meat would seem as important; and 'Italian' may mean no more than avocado filled with crab and prawns, gratinated with Parmesan, then called *pera avocado farcita*. But daily specials are a better guide: home-made pasta, a range of fish from John Dory to shark, and some exact cookery with a tendency to cream sauces that has been much enjoyed. Squid has a light batter, mussels are served in profusion, and the flavours in scallops with cream and basil, or monkfish with cream and saffron, have impressed. Desserts are an Italian mixture. There are no surprises on the wine list, but no price shocks either. When there is a decent deli round the corner, what a pity, one visitor remarked, that the bread should be so 'disappointingly bland'. House wine is £6.45.

CHEF: Adrian Clement PROPRIETOR: Giuliano Ponzi OPEN: Tue to Sat; 12 to 2, 6.45 to 10 CLOSED: first 2 weeks Aug MEALS: alc. Set L £9.50, Set D £14.50 SERVICE: not inc CARDS: Access, Visa DETAILS: 40 seats. Private parties: 40 main room. Vegetarian meals. Children's helpings. Smart dress preferred. Wheelchair access (1 step). Music

---

WORLESTON Cheshire   map 5

▲ *Rookery Hall* ♟ ✳

Worleston, nr Nantwich CW5 6DQ
NANTWICH (0270) 610016   COOKING **3**
on B5074, off A51   COST £26–£65

In gently rolling country to the north of Nantwich lies this odd collection of buildings. The giant stable block has conference rooms and bedrooms; the Regency house is the core, though Baron von Schroder's Victorian alterations give it a strangely truncated air; and now there is a new bedroom wing 'which may blend in in 30 years or so'. Although the owners, Select Country Hotels, are in receivership, the team here remains the same and maintains continuity: 'It eschews expensive ingredients and concentrates on quality British produce,' writes an inspector. 'Vegetables are nothing out of the supermarket ordinary, but fowl and meat are of impeccable provenance. The cooking is competent in technique, showing French influences on local produce. Menus change slowly, so consistency is a virtue rewarded. Of many country-house hotels offering modern British cooking, it seems one of the more individual.' This cooking is provided in the form of a fair-priced lunch menu and a rather dearer dinner affair. Each offers ample choice. After generous appetisers, a winter meal started with a croquette of smoked haddock and Cheshire cheese with diced apple and apple purée, and steamed mussels with orange butter sauce and gutsy croûtons topped with rouille. The main dish of best end of lamb saw the meat coated with an assertive pesto and placed on a bed of leeks. The sauce of stock reduction had a lip-coating stickiness that was apt for the weather as well as for the dish. Steamed chocolate and hazelnut pudding came with a good custard and redundant piece of orange and half a strawberry. Perhaps the cheeseboard was the better bet that day. Continuity is evident: some dishes have been there for three years or more, but the size of the menu disarms complaint. There has also been a visible shift towards modern methods (braising, for example) and materials. Christopher Phillips puts some of this down to an extended visit to the highly regarded Caen restaurant, La Bourride. The dining-room is a handsome panelled affair (alas for the carpeting of the polished boards here), and the drawing-room is ornately and classically decorative. The wine list is a fine one, vitiated by its high prices, and the range is reasonably drawn. House wine is from £13.75. CELLARMAN'S CHOICE: St-Véran, Gruber, 1989, £24.50; Fleurie, Louis Dornier, 1989, £26.

🍶 *denotes an outstanding wine cellar;* ♟ *denotes a good wine list, worth travelling for.*

CHEF: Christopher Phillips PROPRIETORS: Select Country Hotels OPEN: all week; 12.15 to 2.15, 7 to 9.30 MEALS: alc. Set L £16.50, Set D £17.50 SERVICE: not inc, card slips closed CARDS: Access, Amex, Diners, Visa DETAILS: 60 seats. Private parties: 40 main room, 20 private room. Car park. Children welcome. Jacket and tie. No smoking in dining-room. Wheelchair access (also WC) ACCOMMODATION: 45 rooms, all with bath/shower. Room for disabled. Lift. B&B £91.50 to £255. Children welcome. Baby facilities. Afternoon teas. Garden. Tennis. Fishing. TV. Phone. Fax: (0270) 626027 (*The Which? Hotel Guide*)

WRIGHTINGTON Lancashire   map 5

High Moor

Highmoor Lane, Wrightington WN6 9QA   COOKING 2*
APPLEY BRIDGE (0257) 252364   COST £18–£44

High Moor sits serenely amid the bleaker stretches of Lancashire moorland. The interior is a mixture of cluttered, 'comfy' lounges and a more classically discreet dining-room with tables that, though not seeming closely packed, can present logistical difficulties for service. There is a discernibly talented hand at work in the kitchen, although over-elaboration can reduce impact. A salmon and lobster terrine was 'bracingly fresh' but overwhelmed with salad, smoked salmon and strong vinaigrette; another salad – of scallops and smoked bacon – also had layers of leaves, in which lurked unexpected items like radish roses and hard-boiled quail's eggs. Against these a large bowl of tomato and fennel soup was refreshingly straightforward. Main-course choices are weighted more in favour of meat than fish. A thick-cut loin of veal stuffed with mushrooms, shallots and ginger and served with a cream, wine, mushroom and mustard sauce ('a shade ungentle, but the meat just coped with it'), and a 'sensitively pink' loin of lamb sauced with a rich port, have both been strongly endorsed. Come the sweet course, artistry is let rip. White chocolate parfait sits on rounds of meringue, garnished with a yellow tomato and half a passion-fruit, with a pool of strawberry coulis feathered with crème anglaise into the outlines of a musical stave. High Moor deserves continued support: it is capable of serving sound, satisfying food at sensible prices. The wine list carries some pricey clarets and burgundies, but by restricting choice to the New World, for instance, the budget-conscious should be happy. House wines are from £8.40.

CHEF: Stephen Sloan PROPRIETOR: John Nelson OPEN: all week, D only, and Sun L; 12 to 2, 7 to 9 MEALS: alc. Set Sun L £11.95, Set D Sun to Tue £15.95 SERVICE: 10% CARDS: Access, Amex, Diners, Visa DETAILS: 95 seats. Private parties: 80 main room. Car park. Vegetarian meals. Children welcome. Wheelchair access. Music. Air-conditioned

---

WYE Kent   map 3

Wife of Bath

4 Upper Bridge Street, Wye TN25 5AW   COOKING 1
WYE (0233) 812540 and 812232   COST £17–£34

If you want to be Chaucerian, you can have the Pilgrim's Lunch every weekday. It's not a lot of money, and has a fair set of dishes. The menu gets longer, and dearer, at night, but people speak kindly of John Morgan's and

Robert Hymers' efforts in this well-remembered restaurant. There is enough variation in the cooking to arrest attention: grilled sardines with Dijon mustard and deep-fried spinach, or a salad of chicken breast with sweet pepper dressing and quail's eggs for first courses; and, at the main course, chicken again, but stuffed with smoked salmon and made more smoky still by a bacon and parsley sauce, or duck with honey and lavender – each had something unexpected, and pleasing, about it. The spinach 'was reason enough for the resurrection of our deep-fryer'. The duck was tender and had 'an amazing and very agreeable flavour'. Sticky treacle and walnut tart, a tulip filled with fruit and a raspberry mousse, and brown bread ice-cream are acceptable desserts. The wine list will not amaze, or shock. House wines are £7.95, or you can have a different glass of selected wines at each course for £8.

CHEF: Robert Hymers PROPRIETOR: John Morgan OPEN: Tue to Sun, exc Sun D; 12 to 2.30, 7 to 10 (10.30 with a reservation) CLOSED: 1 week Christmas to New Year MEALS: alc. Set L £10.75 (Tue to Sat), Set Sun L £12.75, Set D £19.75 SERVICE: not inc CARDS: Access, Visa DETAILS: 50 seats. Private parties: 60 main room, 20 private room. Car park. Children's helpings L. No pipes in dining-room. Wheelchair access. Music. Fax: (0233) 813454

WYLAM Northumberland   map 7

▲ *Laburnum House*

Wylam NE41 8AJ   COOKING 1
WYLAM (0661) 852185   COST £30–£38

The setting is a lovely old house – once a shop – in a pretty village beside the River Tyne. It now serves as an out-of-town restaurant-with-rooms, offering pleasant accommodation and sound, if rather conservative, cooking. Some items on the blackboard menu are fairly static, although fish and game do respond to the market. The seasonality is sometimes off-key: one meal at the end of January featured raspberries in no less than three dishes across the menu. Even so, reporters have praised king prawns with garlic and ginger; 'superb' bouillabaisse; poached scallops; and a 'scintillating' home-made bitter orange and horseradish sauce with smoked trout. Execution and presentation are well up to the mark. A short, one-page wine list provides affordable drinking across the range. House French is £9.

CHEF: Kenn Elliott PROPRIETORS: Rowan Mahon and Kenn Elliott OPEN: Mon to Sat, D only (L by arrangement; Sun D residents only); 6.30 to 10 MEALS: alc SERVICE: not inc CARDS: Access, Amex, Diners, Visa DETAILS: 40 seats. Private parties: 40 main room. Children's helpings. Wheelchair access (1 step; also WC). Music ACCOMMODATION: 4 rooms, all with bath/shower. B&B £40 to £50. Children welcome. Pets welcome. TV. Doors close at midnight

---

The Guide *is totally independent, accepts no free hospitality, and survives on the number of copies sold each year.*

London round-ups listing additional restaurants that may be worth a visit can be found after the main London section.

YATTENDON Berkshire   map 2

▲ *Royal Oak* ♈

The Square, Yattendon RG16 0UF   COOKING 2*
HERMITAGE (0635) 201325   COST £24–£52

The bar 'has not been substantially altered since Oliver Cromwell dined there on the eve of the battle of Newbury' states the publicity. Perhaps there have been a few replacements to the curtains, chairs, carpet and miscellanea, but the place is certainly redolent of age. Not so the restaurant, which has been prettily refurnished and equipped with a bigger, better kitchen. The Royal Oak gives equal importance to the food in bar and restaurant; that is one of its major charms. A doubt whether this has been as good as it could have been this year is due perhaps to the endless building works. We would be grateful for more reports on how the new arrangements settle down. Dishes interchange between the two menus, though the bar list runs to more things than does the restaurant *carte*. Price differentials may be explained by the simpler service and less elaborate presentation in the bar; quantity is not in question. An inspection meal did not run smoothly. Pâté en croûte of hare and venison with madeira aspic was heavy, over-chilled and stale in taste; grilled tuna was overcooked and the butter sauce of basil, garlic and red pepper, though good, was not light enough for the fish; vegetables were first-rate, even if heavy on the butter; hot plum and peach tart was decidedly burnt; and coffee was weak and muddy. Not all reports have been so unfortunate and the crowds do still press for decidedly superior and imaginative cooking. The restaurant affords a more gentle environment, at a price. Service is without affectation. The scope of the wine list has broadened hesitantly, with good Australians and Californians but timid selections from Spain and Italy. Burgundy, though, is fairly strong and Rhônes are excellent. High prices are offset by an interesting set of regional wines and the remarkable offer to open any bottle of wine and charge half, to compensate for the absence of half-bottles. House wine is £9.75.

CHEF: Dominique Orizet PROPRIETOR: Julie Huff OPEN: all week (Sun D bar meals only); 12 to 2, 7.30 to 10 MEALS: alc. Set L £18.50 SERVICE: not inc CARDS: Access, Amex, Diners, Visa DETAILS: 30 seats. 10 tables outside. Private parties: 30 main room, 8 private room. Car park. Children's helpings. No cigars/pipes in dining-room. Wheelchair access. Music ACCOMMODATION: 5 rooms, all with bath/shower. B&B £60 to £80. Children welcome. Baby facilities. Pets welcome by arrangement. Afternoon teas. Garden. TV. Phone. Doors close at 12.30am. Confirm by 6. Fax: (0635) 201926 (*The Which? Hotel Guide*)

Healthy eating options *in the details at the end of an entry signifies that a restaurant marks on its menu, in words and/or using symbols, low-fat dishes or other healthy eating choices.*

The Guide *office can quickly spot when a restaurateur is encouraging customers to write recommending inclusion – and sadly, several restaurants have been doing this in 1992. Such reports do not further a restaurant's cause. Please tell us if a restaurateur invites you to write to the* Guide.

▲ *Grange Hotel, Ivy Restaurant*

Clifton, York YO3 6AA COOKING 2
YORK (0904) 644744 COST £17–£36

'Not exactly cheerful' was a comment on the team that dishes out food in the Grange. The setting is not exactly cheerful either. The dining-room looks and feels formal, which has made unevenness in performance the more difficult to bear over past months. However, news from the North is more encouraging, as if things have settled down. Cara Baird's serious training at Le Gavroche (see entry, London) is used as a selling tool; it results in serious sauces and some good cooking for a menu that has no truck with *faux naiveté* but concentrates on prime ingredients cooked classically and with an eye to any conservatism in the custom. Hence steak with green peppercorns and lamb with mushrooms and madeira; these are heightened, however, by the presence of monkfish with Cumberland ham and a sorrel sauce, or crisp leaves of potato surrounding oysters on an overstrong watercress and lemon sauce. A starter of lambs' kidneys with wild mushrooms and leaves of puff pastry with a red wine sauce showed that skill lurks behind the kitchen door, as did a breast of guinea-fowl with asparagus and basil and another fine reduction sauce. Desserts on this spring evening had less to recommend them – cool, stodgy pancakes with lemon and lychee sauce were relieved by a better mille-feuille of chocolate sandwiching a chestnut mousse. One might conclude that this is high-class food with potential, but it is sometimes unpredictable. There is a brasserie which shares the Ivy's kitchen for simpler, cheaper things. It can be satisfactory. The wine list is sound. House wines are £9.

CHEF: Cara Baird PROPRIETOR: Jeremy Cassel OPEN: all week, exc Sat L; 12.30 to 2.30, 7 to 10.15 MEALS: alc. Set L £12.50, Set D £21 SERVICE: not inc, card slips closed
CARDS: Access, Amex, Diners, Visa DETAILS: 60 seats. Private parties: 60 main room, 30 private rooms. Car park. Vegetarian meals. Children's helpings. No pipes in dining-room. Wheelchair access (3 steps; also WC). Music ACCOMMODATION: 29 rooms, all with bath/ shower. Rooms for disabled. B&B £85 to £135. Children welcome. Baby facilities. Pets welcome. Afternoon teas. TV. Phone. Confirm by 6 previous day. Fax: (0904) 612453

Kites £

13 Grape Lane, York YO1 2HU COOKING 1
YORK (0904) 641750 COST £17–£30

Redecoration has smartened it up, but the stairs to Kites are still vertiginous and the food remains a 'hippy gourmet' or 'interestingly eclectic' mixture, according to taste. The success of it all may sometimes be approximate: 'My asparagus and chicken mousseline was light-flavoured indeed, but my braised lamb shank, a mighty hunk of protein on the bone, may not have had much red wine to it but was tender and had plenty of flavour.' The side dish of caramelised chicory was not so successful. More charitably, reporters observe that desserts have improved this year – for example, the rose-petal ice-cream and the goats' cheese and hazelnut soufflé – and people either love or hate the laid-back character of it all. Wines are sensibly priced and come from as many places as do Boo Orman's recipes. House wines are £7.50.

CHEFS: Belinda Elderfield and Pauline Hornby PROPRIETOR: Boo Orman OPEN: Mon to Sat, D only, and Sun L; 12 to 1.45, 6.30 to 10.30 (6 to 11 Sat) MEALS: alc SERVICE: not inc (10% for 10 or more) CARDS: Access, Visa (2.1% surcharge) DETAILS: 48 seats. Private parties: 30 main room. Vegetarian meals. Children's helpings. No-smoking area. Music

Melton's

7 Scarcroft Road, York YO2 1ND   COOKING 3*
YORK (0904) 634341   COST £20–£31

Is complimentary mineral water the mark of a Roux brothers graduate? Michael Hjort worked for the Roux and the mineral water and coffee are free in the evenings at his restaurant. Melton's does not aspire to the mentors' level of plush: it was 'formerly a central-heating supplier next to a sex shop', in a Victorian terrace 10 minutes from the Minster. A touch of light colour – blues, pinks and greys – bare tables, and pictures from local artists on the walls contribute atmosphere, as does the see-through door into the kitchen if you like watching men at work. Melton's is a rarity: a place that transparently sets out to please. Beer? 'Of course we're happy to serve it with your meal' – six worthwhile examples are offered. Vegetarian? Thursday is special vegetarian time, but every day Melton's makes an effort. Lucy Hjort must take credit for this. The quarterly menu is not long and is buttressed by daily specials – often fish (especially on Tuesday), but game and other things are found here. The lessons imbibed from the Roux come out in technique but do not extend to elaboration or grandeur. The food is well-judged for value and local tastes; simplicity and accuracy may be watchwords. First courses of (huge) pigeon breast with orange poached in ginger, squid braised with olive oil and basil served on a tomato salad, and pressed leek terrine with wild mushrooms have tasted fresh and true. So, too, have main dishes such as goose with pears (not fatty), venison with a dariole of wild mushrooms, red mullet on a bed of saffron noodles with a saffron sauce, and a nage of sole fillets cooked in vegetable stock of fennel, celery, parsley, carrot and onion, finished off with segments of orange. Vegetables are excellent and depend on the dish served (not merely 'one, two or three veg'). Skill remains in hand to finish the meal: roast figs with nuts, an immense meringue filled with red fruit, poached pear and cinnamon ice-cream. Breads and petits fours, such as the strips of crystallised orange peel or almond praline, show the same thoroughgoing enthusiasm. The wine list is fairly priced. A strong choice of wines under £15 ranges the world; a 'vintage selection' sticks mainly to France, but realism keeps extravagance in check.

CHEF: Michael Hjort PROPRIETORS: Michael and Lucy Hjort OPEN: Tue to Sat; 12.30 to 2, 7 (5.30 by arrangement) to 10 CLOSED: 3 weeks from 24 Dec, 1 week from Aug bank hol MEALS: alc SERVICE: net prices, card slips closed CARDS: Access, Visa DETAILS: 40 seats. Private parties: 30 main room, 12 private room. Vegetarian meals. Children welcome. Wheelchair access (1 step). Music. Fax: (0904) 629233

The Good Food Guide *is a registered trade mark of Consumers' Association Ltd.*

▲ *Middlethorpe Hall* 🍷

Bishopthorpe Road, York YO2 1QB   COOKING 2
YORK (0904) 641241   COST £17–£57

This stunningly restored William III house is a bastion of civilised leisure. 'It
has real velvety, seductive class,' observes a reporter. Aperitifs are served in the
drawing-room or out on the terrace overlooking the immaculately tended
grounds. Chef Kevin Francksen delivers a lavish version of modern Anglo-
French cooking, with fashionable touches and occasional nods towards
tradition – with sometimes unexpected results. Locally cured York ham is
served with a Bloody Mary sorbet; confit of duck and walnuts comes with an
amaretto vinaigrette; and fillet of turbot is steamed on a bed of braised lentils.
Soups such as pea and mint and chilled spinach are favourably reported. Other
successful dishes have included bouillabaisse of North Sea fish, grilled lambs'
kidneys with grain mustard sauce, and pan-fried fillet of salmon with scallops
and fennel on a dill sauce. Baked Alaska and nougat glace with apricot coulis
have been recommended sweets. Occasionally there are disappointments:
chicken Maryland with a 'tired' batter coating; breast of duck 'overpowered' by
its honey and wine marinade. Less elaborate meals are served in the Grill
Room, and Sunday lunch of 'fabulous' roast sirloin of beef was a glorious
experience for one reporter. Service is smooth. Most criticism concerns the
steep prices at dinner. A minimal commitment to economy is shown in the
cellar by canny selection of bottles offered below £15. Halves also get a
reasonable showing. A glass is awarded, but with a warning to those without
unlimited funds. House wine is £11. CELLARMAN'S CHOICE: Macon Uchizy
1990, Talmard, £20; Vacqueyras, Côtes du Rhône Villages 1987, £18.

CHEF: Kevin Francksen   PROPRIETORS: Historic House Hotels Ltd   OPEN: all week; 12.30
to 1.45, 7.30 to 9.45   PRICES: alc. Set L £14.90 to £16.90 (inc wine), Set D £29.95   SERVICE:
net prices, card slips closed   CARDS: Access, Amex, Diners, Visa   DETAILS: 60 seats.
Private parties: 50 main room, 14, 20 and 50 private rooms. Car park. No children under 8.
Jacket and tie. No cigars/pipes in dining-room. No music   ACCOMMODATION: 29 rooms,
all with bath/shower. Lift. B&B £92.95 to £208.50. Deposit: 1 night. No children under 8.
Afternoon teas. Garden. TV. Phone. Confirm by 6. Fax: (0904) 620176 (*The Which? Hotel
Guide*)

19 Grape Lane

19 Grape Lane, York YO1 2HU   COOKING 2
YORK (0904) 636366   COST £26–£41

Watch your head, the ceilings are low; mind how you stretch, space is at a
premium. Nevertheless, the restaurant, rebuilt after a crippling fire a few years
ago, draws people back to enjoy Michael Fraser's cooking and Gordon
Alexander's 'very efficient service'. Alas, there is no longer a cheaper lunch
menu and the price of the rather long-lived *carte* is not low, but the mainstream
style gets repeat business. First courses such as fettuccine with salmon and
broccoli impress by generosity, and a warm salad of duck breast with bacon
and a walnut dressing shows an adept hand at enlivening old favourites by
accurate seasoning. Fish may be a good bet: salmon with pasta and a red wine
sauce or baked in filo with a chive sauce, or cod with a lime butter sauce are

examples. Lamb, done in melting shortcrust, with a mint béarnaise and guinea-fowl wrapped once more in pastry, this time with lime sauce (stronger than that with the cod), are meat dishes that come up to standard. Standard also describes the vegetables: one regular notes they remain the same varieties for days on end. Long service appears also to be a mark of the desserts: a choice of Bakewell tart, treacle tart or Eve's pudding remains on offer from year to year. The wine list is a good one. It has strengthened its New World selection, but includes good makers from France and a useful set of clarets. House Duboeuf is £8.75.

CHEFS: Michael Fraser and Wendy Murray   PROPRIETORS: Gordon and Carolyn Alexander   OPEN: Tue to Sat; 12.30 to 1.45, 7.30 to 10.30   CLOSED: 2 weeks Feb, last 2 weeks Sept   MEALS: alc. Set D £18.95   SERVICE: not inc   DETAILS: 34 seats. Private parties: 20 main room. Children welcome. No cigars/pipes in dining-room. Wheelchair access (1 step). Music

Scotland

Faraday's

2 Kirk Brae, Cults, Aberdeen AB1 9SQ   COOKING 1
ABERDEEN (0224) 869666   COST £18–£34

The atmospheric room – in a building that was once a hydroelectricity sub-
station (hence the name) – wins over many people: 'intimate, quiet (but
classical music on tape), candlelit, a colour scheme of restful plums and
purples'. John Inches offers a cheap but adventurous lunchtime menu, a short
carte priced by the course for dinner from Monday to Thursday, and a weekend
dinner at a set price. He likes curry: where else in Aberdeen would you find
Malaysian pork and fruit curry with condiments on a weekday lunch, or rogan
josh at dinner? This gives a pleasantly exotic tilt to the meals. Materials are not
left to speak for themselves, and stews and casseroles are favoured: pork is
served with a bitter orange sauce, cinnamon and Bramley apples, and a
forcemeat of prunes and walnuts; lamb is stewed in an Italian ragù; chicken is
stuffed with cream cheese. The simple – for instance, smoked salmon with
scrambled egg – is done well. There have been times when the promise of the
setting has been let down by the standard of the cooking, even on expensive
weekend nights. The wine list is short, with firm prices. House wine is £12.90
per litre.

CHEF/PROPRIETOR: John Inches   OPEN: Mon to Sat, exc Mon L; 12.15 to 2, 7 to 9.30
MEALS: alc. Set D Fri and Sat £24.90   SERVICE: net prices, card slips closed   CARDS:
Access, Visa   DETAILS: 42 seats. Private parties: 32 main room. Car park. Vegetarian meals
with prior notice. Children's helpings. Wheelchair access (also WC). Music. Air-
conditioned

Silver Darling

Pocra Quay, Footdee, Aberdeen AB2 1DQ   COOKING 2
ABERDEEN (0224) 576229   COST £31–£40

'It's down by the riverside, in the attractive part of Aberdeen,' one reader
reported with relief. The quayside setting between river and sea gives close-
ups of the fishing boats that form the chief lines of supply to a kitchen that
specialises in the use of the barbecue. It is not always sea fish that is cooked;
one item on a summer menu was a civet of river fish with red wine. Nor does
the restaurant – incredibly busy, noisy and increasingly expensive – cook only

plain things. Most have been prettified – stuffed perhaps, done as a bouillabaisse, or modified in some other fashion. Didier Dejean is Provençal and the inspiration remains, even if he has gone off to run the stoves at Owlies. The vein of elaboration may extend to the vegetables. Tomatoes stuffed with mushroom, lyonnaise potatoes, and stir-fried Savoy cabbage with asparagus seem unlikely accompaniments to fish. The well-reported appearance of sushi on the menu is another sign of an open mind that extends beyond the grill. The wine list is French, with little to excite. House wines are £8.50. Didier Dejean's new venture at Owlies – Unit C, Littlejohn Street, Tel: (0224) 649267 – is a cheaper brasserie occupying three storeys of the former university department of engineering. Lifts and hoists have been religiously preserved. Reports so far are mixed, as well they might be if all 150 seats are taken. We await developments, but in the meantime it is a useful daytime resort.

CHEF: Philippe Clement PROPRIETORS: Didier Dejean, Norman Faulks and Catherine Wood OPEN: Mon to Sat, exc Sat L, and Sun D mid-Apr to mid-Oct; 12 to 2, 7 to 10 CLOSED: 2 weeks from Christmas MEALS: alc SERVICE: not inc, card slips closed CARDS: Access, Amex, Visa DETAILS: 35 seats. Private parties: 35 main room. Car park. Children welcome. Wheelchair access (1 step; also WC). Music. Fax: (0224) 626558

ABERFELDY Tayside   map 8

▲ *Atkins at Farleyer House* 🍴✳

Aberfeldy PH15 2JE
ABERFELDY (0887) 820332
from Aberfeldy take B846 to   COOKING 3*
Kinloch Rannoch for 2m   COST £18–£45

After a few years in the Perthshire countryside Frances Atkins has put down roots. This is shown in the gardens at this slightly austere (but how many small Scottish country houses are not?), white-painted house on the side of the Tay valley: herbaceous borders, herbs and vegetables improve season by season. She has taken the materials of her adopted country to heart: lots of venison and game, wild mushrooms, soft fruit, good cheeses and more figure on her menus. The house itself is comfortable, as too is the solicitude of the staff for the customers. The economic conditions of the last year or two have caused a rethink in the camp, and the appeal of the hotel has been broadened by the opening of a bistro that seems to play to packed houses. Value here is clear, more so than it is for the high-priced, but very good cooking in the main restaurant. By giving herself more room for creativity, Frances Atkins has become more understated and classical in her cooking for the restaurant. This is no bad thing. Gone the medley of meats and flavourings; in favour are venison with caramelised apples and a port jus, beef with mustard sauce, partridge with green peppercorns, or turbot with lobster cannelloni and a tomato and basil vinaigrette. An old affection for sweetness comes out in the bistro menu: chicken curry with banana, chicken sausages with pineapple are examples. The cooking does get rhapsodic comments: 'The stimulating and eclectic cookery left this conservative palate feeling pleasantly diversified'; 'Imaginative and exciting, yet the freshest of ingredients are not obscured by over-saucing.' 'Service is impeccable and the ambience of the dining-room with its gleaming brass and silver and polished woods and warming fire cannot be surpassed.' There is little choice on the dinner menu: two beginnings, a single soup in the middle, a pair of main courses, cheese, then a choice of three desserts, one of which is almost guaranteed hot – the soufflés come well recommended. Details, canapés, petits fours and coffee, are well thought of too. Accidents and disappointments are few. The wine list is well endowed with clarets and also has some fine names in other sections, such as Guigal, Comte Lafon, Leflaive, Vincent, and Durup. There is range enough under £20, though Italy or Spain could supply more and the Californian section be strengthened, even if Australasia does fairly well already. House wines are £9.50.

CHEF: Frances Atkins   PROPRIETORS: Derek and Janice Reid   OPEN: all week; 12 to 2, 7.30 to 8.30   MEALS: alc bistro. Set D £32.50   SERVICE: not inc, card slips closed   CARDS: Access, Amex, Diners, Visa   DETAILS: 30 seats (restaurant), 45 seats (bistro). Private parties: 30 main room, 12 private room. Car park. Children welcome. Smart dress preferred in restaurant. No smoking in dining-room. Wheelchair access (also WC). Music ACCOMMODATION: 11 rooms, all with bath/shower. Rooms for disabled. B&B £30 to £90. Deposit: £25. Children welcome. Afternoon teas. Garden. Fishing. Golf. TV. Phone. Doors close at midnight. Confirm by 10.30am. Fax: (0887) 29430 (*The Which? Hotel Guide*)

ABERFOYLE Central   map 8

Braeval Old Mill ▮

By Aberfoyle, Stirling FK8 3UY
ABERFOYLE (087 72) 711   COOKING 3*
on A81, 1m from Aberfoyle   COST £25–£39

A constant visitor observes: 'The Nairns continue to improve their welcome and their cooking in this sparse but homely mill conversion.' The conversion, it should be added, was achieved through their efforts alone, and made the more handsome by bold use of colour to set off the natural tones of the building itself. Nick Nairn is a self-taught chef and the learning process is continuous. People have also noticed that presentation and even the substance of dishes have been simplified in an effort to keep prices realistic. Tastes, however, have not suffered. The 'daring' of smoked salmon with an avocado mousse, or another first course of salmon with an avocado and tomato compote and basil butter sauce, is set off by the masculine flavours of a plate of mixed game – pheasant, mallard, and pigeon – with red cabbage and a game sauce. Occasionally tastes do not come out, as in the mussel and coriander ravioli that sat atop otherwise exactly cooked ragoût of monkfish and salmon, or the cinnamon in a sauce that went with a 'marvellously intense and elegant' marquise au chocolat. Nick Nairn is not afraid to handle boldness: a lasagne of monkfish and mussels with a velouté of coriander and curry, turbot with cabbage and mussel sauce, fig chutney (one of this year's fashionable favourites) with a game terrine, cod with squat lobsters and mussels. Nor does he shy away from intensity. Vegetable cooking has been criticised ('lukewarm and overbuttered for my tastes'), but desserts that may include hot caramel soufflé with a caramel parfait, or a tulip of ice-cream to plunge in the centre of that high-floating cloud, get much applause. Wine-buying is concentrated on a few of the best merchants. Good bourgeois clarets are carefully balanced with top growths and impeccable selection from the antipodes. The fair-priced 'House Selection' of a dozen or so wines from £11 will serve most customers handsomely. CELLARMAN'S CHOICE: Barossa Valley, Stewart Point, Semillon/Chardonnay 1990, £13; Navarra, Tempranillo 1988, Bodegas Ochoa, £13.

CHEF: Nick Nairn   PROPRIETORS: Nick and Fiona Nairn   OPEN: Tue to Sat, D only, and Sun L (midweek L by arrangement); 12 to 1.30, 7 to 9.30   CLOSED: 2 weeks Feb, 1 week May to June, 2 weeks Nov   MEALS: Set Sun L £17.50, Set D £26   SERVICE: not inc, card slips closed   CARDS: Access, Visa   DETAILS: 34 seats. Private parties: 34 main room. Car park. No children under 10. Smart dress preferred. No cigars/pipes in dining-room. Wheelchair access (1 step; also WC). No music

---

ACHILTIBUIE Highland   map 8

▲ *Summer Isles Hotel* ▮ ✳✱

Achiltibuie IV26 2YG   COOKING 2*
ACHILTIBUIE (085 482) 282   COST £42

Their eyes set on the far horizons of the Summer Isles encircling blue water (in sunlight, that is), customers may falter in describing the front doorstep. Once the food hits the deck, amnesia slips away. The hotel occupies an old inn but the years have seen additions, Scandinavian-style, to accommodate residents, restaurant, kitchens and more. The near-dogmatic isolation of earlier years has fallen to the installation of a television (one) and better telephone facilities (but credit cards are not accepted). A visit from one who last saw it eight years ago elicited this: 'While less idiosyncratic than it used to be, most changes are for the better. The cooking is less spontaneous, but more professional, perhaps in line with changing tastes.' What the cooking does is present you with a set meal of five courses and coffee at a single price. Southerners reckon this high, though not out of step with much of the Highlands. (Competition is different here, as is the pattern of trade and the effort of shopping.) Soup precedes fish, before meat, cheese, and then pudding. After taking five meals in sequence, one reader's thought was that strong meat (for example, pigeon breast with morels) at second place threw the meal out of balance. Do not think dinner over before cheese: 'The cheeseboard and the sweets trolley, accompanied by Mark and Geraldine Irvine respectively, are usually the high points,' said one. Do not dismiss Chris Firth-Bernard's cooking: excellent soups, fresh as fresh shellfish, good lamb, venison and beef. He likes wild mushrooms (chanterelles with monkfish, a mushroom and mustard soup), makes his own bread (saffron herb loaves have been enjoyed) and has the sense to avoid overdressing the meats. He also makes good puddings: strawberry and bramble flan, lemon and fruit roulade, apple and cinnamon tart. Vegetables, still grown in Irvine senior's hydroponicum, are often first-rate. The wine list will encourage anyone to stay a week. The half-bottle list is strong, and the attempt to give a range, particularly of clarets, is estimable. The Italian and Spanish sections are sound, and there is not much truck with places further afield like America, though Hunter Valley in New South Wales gets a showing. If you can't afford the red burgundies, try the Rhônes. CELLARMAN'S CHOICE: Gewurztraminer, Réserve Personelle 1985, Kuentz-Bas, £20; Fronsac, Ch. de la Rivière 1979, £17.

CHEF: Chris Firth-Bernard PROPRIETORS: Mark and Geraldine Irvine OPEN: all week, D only; 8 CLOSED: mid-Oct to Easter MEALS: Set D £29 SERVICE: not inc DETAILS: 28 seats. Private parties: 8 main room. Car park. Vegetarian meals. No children under 8. No smoking in dining-room ACCOMMODATION: 11 rooms, all with bath/shower. B&B £41 to £83. Deposit: £50. No children under 8. Pets welcome. Afternoon teas. Fishing. Doors close at 11. Confirm by 6. Fax: (085 482) 251 (*The Which? Hotel Guide*)

ANSTRUTHER Fife   map 8

Cellar ▮ ✗

24 East Green, Anstruther KY10 3AA   COOKING 3
ANSTRUTHER (0333) 310378   COST £16–£38

The building that houses the Cellar was once a store for herring barrels. It has not been so prettified as to lose that original simplicity, and the same can be said of the cooking. 'I'm delighted,' writes Peter Jukes, 'that the simple style we have delivered for eight years seems at last to be back in vogue.' Not for him heavy cloying sauces; rather let the fish (for it is mostly fish) sing its own song. The method may be as minimalist as grilling, though there are plenty of sauces too: reductions, last-minute confections, complements rather than blankets. There is absolute endorsement for the materials, and for dishes such as fish soup ('a dense bisque, very fishy, rich, outstanding'), monkfish with tomato and basil sauce and a tomato and garlic butter, turbot with scallops and Chardonnay, grilled halibut, dressed crab, a mixture of turbot, mussels, salmon and monkfish with a fine velouté and a gravlax done on the premises. Peter Jukes did not come to fish cookery through lack of acquaintance with the rest of the art. Vegetables are good (though simple), and desserts may rise to a sublime parcel of apple with cinnamon ice-cream or pure vanilla ice-cream with butterscotch sauce, or a terrine of three different chocolate mousses. It is all very accomplished. Coffee has not always been strong, bread has not always been perfect, and fudge has even been gritty. Tables are still old sewing-machine treadles, so long-legs beware. The wine list is tilted in favour of whites; a page of excellent Alsaces, 10 grand cru Chablis and almost as many Puligny-Montrachets give a hint of what to expect. The US and the antipodes are well represented. Prices are high but so is the quality, and there is adequate choice below £15 and several wines are offered by the glass. Half-bottles are relatively sparse. House wines are from £9.50. CELLARMAN'S CHOICE: Riesling Réserve 1985, Dopff au Moulin, £15; St Aubin premier cru Les Champlots 1986, Bachelet, £21.50.

CHEF: Peter Jukes PROPRIETORS: Peter and Vivien Jukes OPEN: Mon to Sat D, and Fri and Sat L (closed Mon out of season); 12.30 to 1.30, 7 to 9.30 CLOSED: 2 weeks Christmas and New Year, 1 week May MEALS: alc L. Set D £25 SERVICE: not inc CARDS: Access, Amex, Visa DETAILS: 32 seats. Private parties: 32 main room. No children under 5. No smoking in dining-room. Wheelchair access (also WC). Music

---

'*Rack of lamb with peppery wild mushroom sauce: since when have sliced button mushrooms from the local shop been wild? I tried growling at them a couple of times but couldn't get them even vaguely annoyed.*'   On inspecting in Nottinghamshire

---

ARISAIG Highland   map 8

▲ *Arisaig House* ⁵✳

Beasdale, By Arisaig PH39 4NR
ARISAIG (068 75) 622   COOKING 2
on A830, 3m E of Arisaig village   COST £24–£54

The setting always takes the breath away: formal gardens, hills beyond, woods,
forests, water. The house may come as an anti-climax, but has dour Scottish
presence outside, formality and comfort within. The hotel is part of the Relais &
Châteaux grouping; this shows in the prices, which are (for food) as high as
those of many of the best London restaurants. Matthew Burns keeps up with
trends inasmuch as lentils, vinaigrettes and confits find their place on his
menu, yet some of his sauces seem to follow older fashions in their reduction.
The style needs to accommodate many preferences, so will include the
simplistic plate of smoked salmon or an avocado and grapefruit salad as well as
the more expressive turbot with green lentils and a sherry vinegar jus.
Adventure is held back in favour of country-house refinement. The Smithers
are ever enthusiastic. Bar lunches are also available. The wine list is
conventional in the way it ignores the New World and has nearly three pages of
claret, only two bottles of which are under £25. House wines are from £15.

CHEF: Matthew Burns   PROPRIETORS: Ruth, John and Andrew Smither   OPEN: all week;
12.30 to 2, 7.30 to 8.30   CLOSED: early Nov to early Mar   MEALS: alc. Set D £29.50
SERVICE: not inc, card slips closed   CARDS: Access, Visa   DETAILS: 34 seats. 5 tables
outside. Private parties: 8 main room. Car park. Vegetarian meals. No children under 10.
Smart dress preferred. No smoking in dining-room. Wheelchair access (1 step). No music
ACCOMMODATION: 15 rooms, all with bath/shower. B&B £49.50 to £195. Deposit: £50. No
children under 10. Afternoon teas. Garden. Snooker. TV. Phone. Doors close at midnight.
Confirm by 4.30. Fax: (068 75) 626 (*The Which? Hotel Guide*)

AUCHMITHIE Tayside   map 8

But 'n' Ben ⁵✳ £

Auchmithie DD11 5SQ   COOKING 1
ARBROATH (0241) 77223   COST £11–£23

When smoked salmon is £3 and lobsters don't climb far into double figures, a
small cottage in a small village just north of Arbroath – try the smokies too – is
bound to be a place of pilgrimage. It runs all day, serving high tea between
lunch and dinner; the food is not messed about, vegetables are fresh, just like
the fish, and when the shooting starts there is game to contend with too. You
can't do better. There is a short wine list that seems to have dropped all its half-
bottles. House wines are £6.25.

CHEFS: Margaret and Angus Horn   PROPRIETORS: Margaret, Iain and Angus Horn   OPEN:
all week, exc Tue, and Sun D; 12 to 9.30   CLOSED: 26 Dec to 3 Jan   MEALS: alc   SERVICE:
not inc, card slips closed   CARDS: Access, Visa   DETAILS: 34 seats. 2 tables outside. Private
parties: 40 main room. Car park. Vegetarian meals. Children's helpings. No smoking in
dining-room. Wheelchair access (also WC). No music

map 8

▲ *Craigendarroch Hotel, The Oaks* ⁵⁄×

Braemar Road, Ballater AB3 5XA
BALLATER (033 97) 55858   COOKING 3
on A93, 1m W of Ballater   COST £27–£40

Craigendarroch is a giant venture that encompasses every form of sport and
leisured pursuit in very late-twentieth-century style. The Oaks goes for the
country-house experience. Single-mindedness and firm management mean
that however self-conscious this restaurant may be (just read the menu), it is
very successful – a job well done. There has been much chopping and changing
of chefs since Bill Gibb's days (when last Craigendarroch was in the *Guide*) and
there may still be an interregnum as we go to press. But the power-vacuum is
hardly noticed by perceptive readers who comment favourably on the food, the
very pukka service, and the ability (for once) of a bar to deliver a vodka-
Martini to specification. The current menu will raise no eyebrows for
adventure, but it is exactly what the formula requires: there are two prices, two
lengths of menu, but no tipping and no extras. Positive comments have been
made about a sauté of foie gras on caramelised apple and shallots; a jellied
compote of prawns and scallops with Mediterranean vegetables and green
peppercorns; venison served with red and green cabbage plus a cherry brandy
sauce and more peppercorns – pink this time; and cannon of lamb with three
vegetable purées, roast garlic and dauphinois potatoes. Desserts get major
sugar constructions as adornment.

CHEF: Joe Queen   PROPRIETORS: Craigendarroch Ltd   OPEN: all week, D only; 7 to 10
MEALS: Set D £22.50   SERVICE: net prices, card slips closed   CARDS: Access, Amex,
Diners, Visa   DETAILS: 54 seats. Private parties: 12 main room, 120 private room. Car park.
Vegetarian meals. Jacket and tie. No smoking in dining-room. Wheelchair access (also
WC). Music. Air-conditioned   ACCOMMODATION: 50 rooms, all with bath/shower. Rooms
for disabled. Lift. B&B £99 to £125. Children welcome. Baby facilities. Afternoon teas.
Garden. Swimming-pool. Sauna. Tennis. Snooker. Air-conditioned. TV. Phone.
Fax: (033 97) 55447

▲ *Tullich Lodge* ⁵⁄×

Ballater AB35 5SB
BALLATER (033 97) 55406   COOKING 2
on A93, 1m E of Ballater   COST £12–£34

Built in 1897, bought by the present owners in 1968, in the *Guide* for many
years, with a long record of particular hospitality, Tullich Lodge is an
institution. 'We can't dream up any more changes, except that we grow
mellower, older and greyer,' Neil Bannister writes. Setting and atmosphere are
here in abundance, and universally enjoyed. The house is not grandiose, but
substantial and imaginatively furnished. While an abbreviated menu is served
in the bar during lunch, dinner takes the form of a no-choice, set-price menu of
four courses and coffee. Cooking is not elaborate, nor is it artless. Meats may be

roasted or plain-cooked and served with a sauce (not stuffed with a mousse, for sure), but gratins (mussels, eggs), soups with trimmings (game consommé with herb pancake, halibut consommé with lobster quenelle and a quail's egg), or terrines (venison, smoked salmon) may take their place alongside smoked eel salad, marinated venison, chanterelles and cream, or straightforward avocado with a tomato vinaigrette as preliminary courses. 'Real food, not de-fatted, de-tasted or over-embellished,' wrote one fan. The danger lies in the occasional slip-up: no layers of complexity will mask the error. The owners have great character; they set their faces against the idea of 'the hotel-in-the-country' and set store by 'the home which is a hotel'. The wine list is no giant for length, but the sources are impeccable and prices fair. Half-bottles are well represented. House wines are £8 or £12.

CHEF: Neil Bannister   PROPRIETORS: Hector Macdonald and Neil Bannister   OPEN: all week; 1, 7.30 to 8.30   CLOSED: mid-Dec to end Mar   MEALS: Set L £6.50, Set D £24 SERVICE: not inc, card slips closed   CARDS: Access, Amex, Diners, Visa   DETAILS: 26 seats. Private parties: 10 main room. Car park. Vegetarian meals. Children's helpings L. Jacket and tie. No smoking in dining-room. Wheelchair access (also WC). No music ACCOMMODATION: 10 rooms, all with bath/shower. D,B&B £90 to £190. Children welcome. Baby facilities. Pets welcome. Garden. TV. Phone. Fax: (033 97) 55397 (*The Which? Hotel Guide*)

BIGGAR Strathclyde   map 8

▲ *Shieldhill Hotel* ⁵✳

| Quothquan, Biggar ML12 6NA | COOKING 1 |
| BIGGAR (0899) 20035 | COST £28–£40 |

It is not often a hotel like Shieldhill can boast foundation in 1199 (it has in fact only been a hotel since the 1960s), though perhaps the fact that it is twinned with an establishment in Santa Barbara makes the claim a more potent marketing tool. The place is now decked out with the strongest colours of carpet imaginable, and rolls of Laura Ashley everywhere. Main-course examples from a daily menu that charges enough to keep the house going for another few centuries are pigeon with red cabbage and a mustard sauce, scallops and sole with a champagne, chive and tomato cream, magret of duck with kumquat marmalade, and fillet of beef with lentils and a sherry vinegar gravy. Desserts have included crème brûlée and banana and rum ice-cream with caramel sauce. Reports are mixed. A regular visitor from Edinburgh reckons it is successful; a casual passer-by from Galloway found dry chicken, sauce that was meant to be raspberry and rosemary but ended up tasting only of raspberry, and lemon tart that was too sugary. The wine list is realistic; there are some good Californians. House wines are £8.90.

CHEF: David Clunas   PROPRIETORS: Jack Greenwald and Christine Dunstan   OPEN: all week D, Sat and Sun L; 12 to 2, 7 to 9   MEALS: alc. Set D £22.50 to £24.50   SERVICE: not inc, card slips closed   CARDS: Access, Amex, Diners, Visa   DETAILS: 30 seats. Private parties: 32 main room, 12 private room. Car park. Vegetarian meals. Children's helpings. Smart dress preferred. No smoking in dining-room. Wheelchair access. Music ACCOMMODATION: 11 rooms, all with bath/shower. B&B £90 to £140. Deposit: 1 night. No children under 12. Baby facilities. Garden. TV. Phone. Doors close at midnight. Confirm by 6. Fax: (0899) 21092

BLAIRGOWRIE Tayside   map 8

▲ *Kinloch House Hotel* ♀ ⚒⚒

Blairgowrie PH10 6SG
ESSENDY (0250) 884237   COOKING 2
on A923, 3m W of Blairgowrie   COST £18–£35

This pile stands amid far-reaching grounds and within sight of purple heather-clad hills. Reconnaissance confirms the dour formality that is promoted by kilt-clad laird, David Shentall; guests are expected to bring their tartans with them, or at the least jackets and ties. Highland cattle are to be found nibbling pasture close by, while Aberdeen Angus sirloin steaks, pan-fried and topped with pine-kernels or with a mushroom, Drambuie and cream sauce, wander on to the *carte*. Fussy items, like West Coast lobster served in its shell with brandy, white wine, mushrooms, mustard and a cream cheese sauce, have not fared so well in reports. The advantage of access to fine Scottish ingredients is demonstrated by more simple treatment of fish and seafood dishes. Dinners starting with quenelles of smoked haddock and spinach and ending with the home-made meringues have pleased. The four-course table d'hôte menu has supplements which can increase the cost considerably. The impressive wine list includes many clarets, some very superior burgundies and enough from the rest of the world to keep costs down. Half-bottles are given very fair treatment. House wines start at £8.95.

CHEF: Bill McNicoll   PROPRIETORS: David and Sarah Shentall   OPEN: all week; 12.30 to 2, 7 to 9.15   MEALS: Set L £13.95, Set D £21.90   SERVICE: not inc, card slips closed   CARDS: Access, Amex, Diners, Visa   DETAILS: 60 seats. Private parties: 30 main room, 25 and 30 private rooms. Car park. No children under 7. Jacket and tie. No smoking in dining-room. Wheelchair access (also WC). No music   ACCOMMODATION: 21 rooms, all with bath/shower. Rooms for disabled. D,B&B £69.75 to £138. Children welcome. Baby facilities. Pets welcome (some rooms). Garden. Fishing. TV. Phone. Doors close at midnight. Fax: (0250) 884333

CAIRNDOW Strathclyde   map 8

Loch Fyne Oyster Bar £

Clachan Farm, Cairndow PA26 8BH   COOKING 2
CAIRNDOW (049 96) 217 and 264   COST £13–£30

'I didn't realise it was a place to eat at until I entered what I thought was a first-rate fish shop – a clever layout which both whetted my appetite and ensured I did not leave empty-handed,' writes one who nearly despaired of finding simple, unpretentious, *good* food in these parts. The site is all, at the head of the loch, the trappings are basic, and the shop gives you the chance to stock up on smoked and fresh produce. Most reports are emphatic that this is a gem; those which take the other tack reveal that the gem has flaws. Eat the shellfish for its freshness and its flavour; there are hot dishes too, such as a mussel stew, baked oysters or hot smoked salmon served with boiled potatoes and mange-tout. Details, like the fresh brown bread, or the purple onion used before anyone else has supplies, are enjoyed. The place is mighty popular, serving all day – 'There were people eating oysters at 10am' was the surprised comment of one traveller. Popularity and a need to keep down costs seem to have had a consequence on the staff. Almost every report has regretted their lack of training and off-handedness. The company chairman John Noble reports that measures are in hand to improve speed at peak times. The short wine list is not dear, and kicks off with excellent sherry and champagne. The Rizzardi white wine from the Veneto makes a nice alternative to lashings of Gros Plant or Muscadet. Coffee is espresso. House white is £7.95.

CHEF: Greta Cameron   PROPRIETORS: Loch Fyne Oysters Ltd   OPEN: all week; 9am to 9pm   MEALS: alc   SERVICE: not inc   CARDS: Access, Amex, Visa   DETAILS: 90 seats. 10 tables outside. Private parties: 55 main room. Car park. Vegetarian meals. Children's helpings on request. Wheelchair access (also WC). Music. Fax: (049 96) 234

CANONBIE Dumfries & Galloway   map 8

▲ *Riverside Inn* ▾ ⅝✳ £

Canonbie DG14 0UX   COOKING 2
CANONBIE (038 73) 71512 and 71295   COST £15–£31

The seventeenth-century slate-roofed inn by the River Esk remains a personable retreat and the Phillipses take their cue from an abundance of patriotically Scottish ingredients (Loch Fyne oysters, wild salmon, sea trout, Aberdeen Angus steaks, venison). They buy wisely: cheeses come from a supplier in Penrith, organic breads from the Village Bakery at Melmerby in Cumbria (see entry). And there is some industrious cottage economy at work, which yields home-made pasta, terrines, ice-creams and marmalade. The meals draw a good deal of praise for the freshness and unfussy presentation. The menu changes daily and has included wholesome soups made from good stocks, ramekin of scallops and sole, mussels with garlic, chargrilled steaks, and pigeon with green peppercorn sauce. Grilled Dover sole has been enormous and perfectly judged, with firm, sweet, tender flesh. Dishes are supported by a cluster of good fresh vegetables. Lemon posset, border tart and rhubarb fool are well-reported sweets. The cheeseboard is an impressive Anglo-Scottish selection served with 'fabulous' oatcakes. Simpler food is available in the bar (at lunch and supper), where the mainstays are pâtés, soups, roasts and salads. The wine list is an eclectic and distinctive selection. With Adnams apparently holding the monopoly, quality and a safe quirkiness can be assured. House French is £7.80. Other prices are equally fair.
CELLARMAN'S CHOICE: Ch. Thieuley, Sauvignon 1989, £10; Brouilly, Ch. Thivin 1990, £12.95.

CHEFS/PROPRIETORS: Robert and Susan Phillips   OPEN: Mon to Sat; 12 to 2, 7.30 to 8.30 (bar suppers all week 7 to 9, exc Sun Nov to Mar)   CLOSED: 2 weeks Feb and Nov   MEALS: alc. Set D £22   SERVICE: not inc, card slips closed   CARDS: Access, Visa   DETAILS: 28 seats. 4 tables outside. Private parties: 28 main room. Car park. Children's helpings. No smoking in dining-room. Wheelchair access (also WC). No music   ACCOMMODATION: 6 rooms, all with bath/shower. Room for disabled. B&B £25 to £80. Deposit: £15. No children under 6. Garden. Air-conditioned. TV. Doors close at midnight. Confirm by 5 (*The Which? Hotel Guide*)

CRINAN Strathclyde map 8

▲ *Crinan Hotel,*
Lock 16 Seafood Restaurant

Crinan PA31 8SR
CRINAN (054 683) 261

COOKING 1
COST £51

The menu of the top-floor studio restaurant gives a weather forecast as well as the running order. The forecast changes more often than the food, a consistent offering of clams, oysters, prawns and lobster at an all-in price. If the view is cut to nil and there have been no landings, the *raison d'être* goes out of the window. The consistency of the cooking is impressive, and so is the shellfish. Oysters come plain, clams in their half-shell, prawns with an array of tropical fruit, and lobster is just split. A plate of smoked salmon appears as a second course; dessert, then Stilton, bring up the rear. Sitting watching the sunset flood the room with rosy light, waiting for a whole lobster landed at tea-time that day, is an enviable experience. The hotel which supports this effort is enjoyed by some, less by others. The wine list is full of very superior choices – from France, Italy, Australia and the USA, plus others. It is a pity that some of the vintages are too young to merit the very high prices asked for them. House wine is £9.95. There is another restaurant, the Westward, open for set dinners and bar lunches all year.

CHEF: Andrew Yuill   PROPRIETORS: Nick and Frances Ryan   OPEN: Tue to Sat, D only; 8
CLOSED: Nov to end Apr   MEALS: Set D £37.50   SERVICE: not inc, card slips closed
CARDS: Access, Visa   DETAILS: 20 seats. Car park. Vegetarian meals. Children welcome.
Jacket and tie. Wheelchair access (also WC). Music   ACCOMMODATION: 22 rooms, all with
bath/shower. Rooms for disabled. Lift. B&B £75 to £120. Deposit: £50. Children welcome.
Baby facilities. Pets welcome. Afternoon teas. Garden. Fishing. TV. Phone. Doors close at
midnight. Confirm by 6. Fax: (054 683) 292 (*The Which? Hotel Guide*)

CROMARTY Highland map 8

Thistles ⚡✳ £

20 Church Street, Cromarty IV11 8XA
CROMARTY (038 17) 471

COOKING 2
COST £16–£32

The Scottish Museum of the Year 1991 is housed in the Cromarty Courthouse. Visitors to this, and tourists in general, provide the subsoil on which Thistles can grow; nutriment is also drawn from 'a small core of loyal Ross-shire regulars and others from beyond Inverness'. 'Although it is a journey of around 100 miles, we make it as often as possible, usually at lunch-time' was the testimony of one of those regulars who finds Alison Wilkinson's reception welcoming and David Wilkinson's cooking imaginative. Lunch is normally a shorter and cheaper menu – chicken casserole with cardamom at £5.50 is a bargain anywhere, when cooked decently it is even more so. Other daytime offerings include a tart of kidneys with mustard, tagliatelle with mussels and salmon from Loch Nevis with a white wine sauce. It is even possible to have a filled roll and a slice of Dundee cake. The cooking is refreshing for this part of the world – neither reactionary nor over-elaborate. Simple and light sauces accompany accurately cooked principal ingredients: calf's sweetbreads in a brioche with a chanterelle-flavoured sauce; duck with green peppercorns, fresh cranberries and brandy sauce; turbot, shark and mussels with a shellfish and Pernod sauce. A sense of restraint is evident in the desserts too: strawberry sablé, crème brûlée, 'slightly warm, fresh fruit soup in a rich syrup'. Incidentals are nicely thought out and the wine list has some interesting items and unexpected lines – for instance, Alsaces from Kuentz-Bas and Siffert among others, St-Romain white burgundy from Buisson, and a quartet of châteaux from Pomerol, including a Vray Croix de Gay 1959 at £35. House wines are £8.50.

CHEF: David Wilkinson PROPRIETORS: Alison and David Wilkinson OPEN: Tue to Sat D and Sun L; all week L Easter to Oct (Nov to Easter Tue to Sat L by arrangement); 12 to 2, 7.30 to 9 MEALS: alc. Set D £10.50 SERVICE: not inc, card slips closed CARDS: Access, Visa DETAILS: 26 seats. Private parties: 30 main room. Vegetarian meals. Children's helpings. No smoking. Music

---

CUPAR Fife   map 8

Ostlers Close

25 Bonnygate, Cupar KY15 4BU   COOKING 3
CUPAR (0334) 55574   COST £17–£37

This is a small restaurant, occupied by enthusiasts who also have skill. 'It's a cottage up a close which must feel cramped when it's full and is done out in that endearing French country fashion of a kind of Anaglypta in cream on the walls, smallish tables, strings of garlic, but fresh flowers and well-shaped thin glasses.' The food is more sophisticated, and may run from a special Italian evening to coincide with St Andrews Festival, to a fine exposition of what is best on the East Coast – from fish to game. Attention to detail – the bread, the chutneys, the jellies, the gathering of this, the growing of that – is impressive. Even more so is seafood soup 'based on strong, clean fish stock with chunks of firm fish, prawns, mussels and just the right amount of cream'. Venison cooked with red wine and thyme has an intense sauce helped to a decadent sweetness by a bowl of redcurrant jelly, completed by a pile of dark, strong fungi. The clarity of flavouring comes out in an autumn meal that included sole in a cream sauce with bundles of fresh herbs, and a first course of autumn fruits in a Muscat sauce. There was also a fish stew that included whatever you fancied: prawns, lobster, cod and monkfish were all there, in a rich langoustine sauce. Pigeon breasts were the carnivore's choice, with red wine and wild mushrooms. Vegetables are bewildering in number but are not overbearing or silly, say most people: lightly curried parsnip purée, potato with a soufflé topping, spinach tart and fried cabbage are some mentioned. Carry on to dessert, usually made by Amanda Graham: a ricotta torte with a Marsala sauce was faultless, apricot tart was melt-in-mouth, sticky toffee pudding was light but lovely, strawberries Romanoff will be requested again, and more. There are times when faults appear, but generally they are rare. The wine list is good, as decently priced as the food. The small section of Italian and Spanish reds, the clarets (again not many, but well selected) and the Loire whites may be the things to look at. For a place that is so good at fish, the white burgundies might range wider. House wine is £9.95.

CHEF: James Graham   PROPRIETORS: Amanda and James Graham   OPEN: Tue to Sat; 12.15 to 2, 7 to 9.30 (10 Fri and Sat)   CLOSED: 1 week June, 1 week Nov   MEALS: alc   SERVICE: not inc, card slips closed   CARDS: Access, Visa   DETAILS: 28 seats. Private parties: 22 main room. Children's helpings. No children under 6 D. No smoking during meals. Wheelchair access (1 step). No music

---

DRUMNADROCHIT Highland   map 8

▲ Polmaily House ⅚✳

Drumnadrochit IV3 6XT   COOKING 2*
DRUMNADROCHIT (045 62) 343   COST £26–£40

'It seems a refined yet conservative establishment that does not attempt to deceive its guests by unnecessary recommendation' was the immediate response of an Oxford wanderer who might have regretted the Tarmac driveway, but found the beech hedge made 'the approaching diner curious'. He then went on to be surprised by the vibrancy of the cooking 'which gave a wonderful contrast to the surroundings. Veal stew, although it did have a bit of fat in it, was superb and exotic; the vanilla ice-cream in a caramel shell surrounded by a peach arrangement must not be missed.' Another traveller commented that of the eight places he stayed in on a tour of the Highlands, this was the only one where the morning tea came as leaf, with a strainer. Alison Parsons certainly can cook. Some of the dishes in her four-course dinners are conservative (haddock in oatmeal, home-made tartare sauce), others are more modern (scallops with vermouth, cream and coriander). People are struck by the flavours and the freshness. Wines are arranged in price bands and are not just the standard French selection. They include some interesting Ribera del Dueros from Spain, a pair of Stag's Leap from California, as well as Dujac, Bonneau du Martray and Javillier from Burgundy if expense is no problem. House wines are £7.

CHEFS: Alison Parsons and Barbara Drury   PROPRIETORS: Alison and Nick Parsons   OPEN: all week, D only; 7.30 to 9.30   CLOSED: end Oct to end Mar   MEALS: Set D £20 to £25. Minimum £20   SERVICE: not inc, card slips closed   CARDS: Access, Visa   DETAILS: 30 seats. Private parties: 12 main room. Car park. Vegetarian meals with prior notice. Children's helpings on request. No smoking in dining-room. Wheelchair access. No music   ACCOMMODATION: 9 rooms, 7 with bath. B&B £45 to £100. Deposit: £25. Children welcome. Baby facilities. Pets welcome. Afternoon teas. Garden. Swimming-pool. Sauna. Tennis. Doors close at midnight. Confirm by 4. Fax: (045 62) 813 (*The Which? Hotel Guide*)

'When I was asked by the proprietor if we had enjoyed our meal, I said that we were very disappointed. That caused him to behave in a way that would shame Basil Fawlty. He started swearing at us and called his partner from the kitchen who behaved in an equally bizarre fashion saying that he wished to fight with my husband outside! Both men are obviously unhinged and quite ill-suited to run any eating establishment.'
On eating in Northumberland

DRYBRIDGE Grampian map 8

Old Monastery ⁵⚡

Drybridge AB5 2JB
BUCKIE (0542) 32660 COOKING 1
2m S of junction of A98 and A924 COST £21–£36

The world agrees on the setting: here is landscape that would calm the retreat of any number of monks (for whom it was built in the nineteenth century), and which soothes many a tired brow from the fast lane of life. There is less unanimity about the comfort and atmosphere inside, but wood-burners keep the chill at bay and the tall, beamed dining-room elicits better response than the cloistered bar. The Grays themselves, however, do much to set the mind at rest ('thoroughly professional', 'could not have been nicer'), even if the staff sometimes fall down through inexperience. Douglas Gray does the cooking. He does not break far from conservative country-restaurant style but readers have enjoyed the crab claws with tarragon and lemon, the chunky soups, the venison with a bramble and mead sauce, and a hot-cold first course of pasta and a green salad. Desserts have not been so extolled: meringues seemed below par. Vegetables by contrast have been thoroughly well received. Winter may mean the tempests cause no white fish to be offered, regrettable in a region which produces the best. The wine list is more than adequate, in price and range. The notes, too, will assist the hesitant. House wines start at £9.25.

CHEF: Douglas Gray   PROPRIETORS: Douglas and Maureen Gray   OPEN: Tue to Sat; 12 to 1.45, 7 to 9.30 (10 Sat)   CLOSED: 2 weeks Nov, 3 weeks Jan   MEALS: alc   SERVICE: not inc, card slips closed   CARDS: Access, Amex, Visa   DETAILS: 45 seats. 2 tables outside. Private parties: 45 main room. Car park. Children's helpings. No children under 8. No smoking in dining-room. Wheelchair access (1 step). Music

---

DUNKELD Tayside map 8

▲ Kinnaird ⁵⚡

Kinnaird Estate,
By Dunkeld PH8 0LB COOKING 4
BALLINLUIG (0796) 482440 COST £25–£50

Every bedroom in the house has an open fire, stoked by eager staff. Such things are rare, even in Scotland, and contribute to this mansion's special appeal. The public rooms help some more: large, fine views, a new colour scheme of yellow and gold setting off the quasi-Fragonard paintings. In a word, sybaritic; even the loos qualified for a paragraph of close-written rapture in one report. This does not make the place forbiddingly grand. True, gents must wear collar and tie; true, Mrs Ward's forceful hospitality will make an impression, but the staff are properly trained and handle guests with effortless correctness warmed by a desire to oblige. John Webber still rules the kitchens. A couple who were bowled over by the quality of some of the cooking – 'our second dinner touched on the sublime' – did criticise a fondness for brown demi-glace sauces, an apparent enjoyment of cream and richness, and a quirky repetition of bacon in three details through a meal. There are still direct links of presentation and content with country-house cooking of a few years past. Vegetables come tied in little bundles; there are freebies everywhere – some people, perhaps not used to them in careful Scotland, find that the excellent unheralded appetisers at the start of a meal unbalance their progress through the rest. But this does not mean that everything is overfussy or indulgent. Plain cooking such as asparagus hollandaise is accurate enough to warrant ignoring any more elaborate dish. A modern classic such as red pepper mousse with vinaigrette and avocado showed perfect balance of sweet and sour. The elements brought out here may recur. A spring menu toys with sharp sweetness in sweetbreads with caramelised shallots and balsamic vinegar, or even in salmon tartare with tomato butter sauce. Mousses pop up – one of parsnip is the centrepiece to lamb with thyme jus. The browns of classic cooking are seen with a wild mushroom sauce on quail, or red wine and port with beef. The repertoire is not mould-breaking, but its skill impresses. The bits and pieces make up a whole: 'I foreswore my pudding and rested content with the petits fours.' The hot soufflés are spot-on. Prices for the four-course menu at dinner are high, though lunch is more affordable. The wine list is as serious as the rest of it, and holds on to economic reality by dint of fair lashings from the New World. The most exciting sections are claret and burgundy – age is no problem with the clarets – though the group of Alsaces is worth a second look. The choice of makers outside France is sound but predictable. Have fun with the bin-ends. House wines are £11. CELLARMAN'S CHOICE: Gewurztraminer 1987, Dietrich, £22; Cahors 1985, Pelvillain, £12.50.

CHEF: John Webber PROPRIETOR: Mrs C.C. Ward OPEN: all week; 12.30 to 2, 7.30 to 9.15 CLOSED: Feb MEALS: Set L £19.50 to £24, Set D £38 SERVICE: net prices, card slips closed DETAILS: 35 seats. Private parties: 25 main room, 25 private room. Car park. No children under 12. Jacket and tie. No smoking in dining-room. Wheelchair access (also WC). No music ACCOMMODATION: 9 rooms, all with bath/shower. Rooms for disabled. Lift. B&B £95 to £230. No children under 12. Pets in kennels only. Garden. Tennis. Fishing. Billiards. TV. Phone. Doors close at midnight. Confirm by 6. Fax: (0796) 482289

DUNVEGAN Highland   map 8

▲ Harlosh Hotel ⁵✳

By Dunvegan, Isle of Skye IV55 8ZG
DUNVEGAN (047 022) 367   COOKING 1
off A863, 3m S of Dunvegan   COST £23–£43

One reporter thought this white, very Scottish moorland building was 'more off the beaten track than much of Skye' but 'cosy' inside, with swirly carpets, beams on walls and ceilings, and a homely, unforced welcome. Surrounded by sheep, members of the clan Macleod, the odd otter, buzzard, eagle and seal, Peter Elford beats a culinary path far removed from Scottish ethnic. First courses include smoked venison with quail's eggs, a pepper salad and mayonnaise, squid fried with garlic and peanut oil, and moules marinière. Fish might be whole langoustines marinated with ginger and coriander, or halibut with a lemon cream sauce and shallots. Meat ranges from lamb wrapped in spinach with a mushroom stuffing, on a madeira and tarragon sauce, to duck with fried apple and pink peppercorn sauce. These are the products of someone in the mainstream of the northern kitchen. Peter Elford's restraint in decoration and complexity is admirable; his anxiety for the materials to speak their loudest is evident. The menu keeps changing nightly to avoid tedium for holiday visitors. Once at the end, ice-creams and sorbets are good, as can be the hot creations. The wine list is a small French collection with a set of German, Australian and Californian bottles to impart variety. You will not pay too much. House wines are £6.90.

CHEF: Peter Elford PROPRIETORS: Peter and Lindsey Elford OPEN: Tue to Sun, D only (residents only Mon); 7 to 8.30 CLOSED: end Oct to Easter MEALS: alc SERVICE: not inc CARDS: Access, Visa DETAILS: 18 seats. Private parties: 18 main room. Car park. Children's helpings. No smoking in dining-room. Wheelchair access (1 step). Music ACCOMMODATION: 6 rooms, 5 with bath/shower. B&B £32 to £64. Deposit: £20. Children welcome. Baby facilities. Afternoon teas. Garden. Doors close at midnight. Confirm by 5

Three Chimneys ♦ ✳

Colbost, Dunvegan,
Isle of Skye IV55 8ZT
GLENDALE (047 081) 258   COOKING 2
on B884, 4m W of Dunvegan   COST £17–£42

'Thank goodness we booked, as there is nothing else for miles,' wrote one traveller, who found this short row of cottages, just back from the foreshore, with restaurant and whisky shop, all bare stone, polished tables and low ceilings. Shirley Spear does not waver in her intention to serve the best of Skye produce (shellfish, in particular). The lunch and dinner menus still offer lobster, crab, scallops, langoustines and oysters. Meat is not ignored: lamb (loin, kidney and liver) with redcurrant and red wine sauce, venison with chocolate and chestnut sauce, steak with smoked salmon or with mustard and whisky. The sauces show her affection for sweet/sour combinations, as does lobster with raspberry vinaigrette. Lunch dishes of partan pie (crab baked in the shell), prawns and salmon kedgeree are simpler presentations of local tastes. The kitchen is self-supporting: perhaps a slice of quiche with mayonnaise as an appetiser, nicely baked breads, agreeable petits fours. Some would enjoy a leaner style: the lobster was served cold on 'acres of salad, coleslaw and all', and sometimes the venison with chocolate and chestnut sauce needs to work hard to gain converts. Puddings are warming and comforting. Service may be slow, sometimes strangely disassociated: 'We were the last there and we had to knock on the kitchen door for service.' The wine list is excellent and not overpriced. Modern makers jostle with classic names: Mâcon's Goyard next to Corton-Charlemagne's Bonneau du Martray; the Rhônes are few in number, tops for style; the choice from America and Australia (Bonny Doon, Seville Estate) is enviable. A glass is awarded this year for a consistently good list. House wines are from £9.45. CELLARMAN'S CHOICE: Rully Blanc 1989, 'Marrissou', Jacques Dury, £17.25; Rioja Crianza 1987, Bodegas Amezola, £12.95.

CHEF: Shirley Spear PROPRIETORS: Eddie and Shirley Spear OPEN: Mon to Sat; 12.30 to 2, 7 to 9 CLOSED: Nov to end Mar MEALS: alc. Minimum £2.50 L, £15.70 D SERVICE: not inc CARDS: Access, Visa DETAILS: 35 seats. 2 tables outside. Private parties: 24 main room. Car park. Vegetarian meals. Children welcome. No smoking. Music

L'Auberge ♥

56 St Mary Street, EH1 1SX	COOKING 2
031-556 5888	COST £16–£57

'The place has a slightly dated feel,' says one reporter. There is more charm in the *carte* tainted with school-book French, but sub-titled with convincing flavour combinations. At best this Auld Alliance marriage of Francophilic technique and Scottish produce yields pleasing results. A summer inspection reported a main course of duck breast 'perfectly cooked with a rich pinkness and crisp fat on a stock sauce with a hint of caramel. It was served with a pleasant poached pear and turned parsnips.' At worst a divorce between skill and ingredients produced an apple tart with 'undercooked pastry'. A local inhabitant considered the restaurant overpriced by contrast with the opposition, and took exception to being charged for vegetables that were not ordered. Coffee is good. The wine list is serious French; those from the New World are only admitted if made from French grape varieties. It is impressive for its range of clarets, not ignoring the bourgeois, for its Chablis, and for its useful bonus of country wines. There are too many alternate vintages. Prices are firm, rather like those for the food. House Duboeuf is £7.85.

CHEF: Fabrice Bresulier   PROPRIETOR: Daniel Wencker   OPEN: all week; 12.15 to 2, 6.30 to 9.30 (10 Sat)   MEALS: alc. Set L £10.95 to £13.95, Set D £19.85 to £26.80   SERVICE: not inc   CARDS: Access, Amex, Diners, Visa   DETAILS: 50 seats. Private parties: 30 main room, 25 private room. Vegetarian meals. Children's helpings. Smart dress preferred. No smoking during meals. Wheelchair access (1 step). Music. Air-conditioned

Chinese Home Cooking £

21 Argyle Place, EH9 1JJ	COOKING 1
031-229 4404	COST £7–£14

'There is not a lot to distinguish this from a thousand other Chinese restaurants, except the customers – jolly, carousing students with their six-packs – and excellent service' was one person's comment. Value is one reason for so many students, and you need to book or get there early of an evening. This is basic Anglo-Cantonese cooking, with an emphasis on rapid production and immediacy. It is unlicensed.

CHEF/PROPRIETOR: Steven Chan   OPEN: all week, D only; 5.30 to 11   MEALS: alc. Set D from £5. Minimum £3.50. Unlicensed, but bring your own: no corkage   SERVICE: not inc   DETAILS: 40 seats. Private parties: 30 main room. Children welcome. No music

Denzler's 121

121 Constitution Street, Leith EH6 7AE	COOKING 1
031-554 3268	COST £14–£30

The impressive façade and entrance of this Victorian classical building yield to an interior at once simpler, lighter and brighter in tone. Were analogies drawn, the cooking would be likened more to the outside view: it has roots in tradition, the menu shows relatively small change from season to season, and the decorative details on the plate are as predictable as the glyphs on a classical frieze. An 'exquisite' crab soup, salmon pâté, succulent lamb chops with a béarnaise sauce (popped into a hollowed tomato), potatoes berrichonne (another regular accompaniment), and a choux-pastry puff filled with rum-soaked bananas, topped with chocolate sauce have all been satisfactory. The cooking can also be more approximate. There are Swiss specialities (Sämi Denzler is Swiss) such as veal Valaisanne (mushrooms, cream, Gruyère, asparagus and tomato), veal Zürichoise (mushrooms and cream), venison with black cherries, and air-dried Swiss beef and ham. A cheaper and simpler lunch menu offers such things as sauerkraut, kalbsbratwurst and strudel. The wine list lacks a few details, but it does run to a trio of Swiss bottles and there are various offers which are worth pursuing. In the spring, for example, there was a fairly priced Ch. de Fuissé and a Cabernet Sauvignon from the highly rated Australian maker Geoff Merrill. House wines are £9.60 a litre.

CHEFS: Sämi Denzler and Ian Gordon   PROPRIETORS: Sämi and Pat Denzler   OPEN: Tue to Sat, exc Sat L; 12 to 2, 6.30 to 10   CLOSED: 2 weeks July, 1 week Jan   MEALS: alc. Set L £9.25 to £13.30, Set D £16.50 to £22.50   SERVICE: net prices, card slips closed   CARDS: Access, Visa   DETAILS: 65 seats. Private parties: 65 main room. Vegetarian meals with prior notice. Children welcome. No music

Kalpna ⅗✳ £

2–3 St Patrick Square, EH8 9EZ	COOKING 1*
031-667 9890	COST £9–£25

This Gujarati vegetarian restaurant has opened a carnivorous branch (Spices) at West Bow – otherwise, you could say, steady as she goes. That it is not invariably so is a reflection on the nature of some Indian cooking: 'bhel poori like Rice Crispies with minimal tamarind and coriander', cold and solid chapatis, a pre-preparation of even stir-fried dishes late one evening are some of the groans. To balance them is much acclaim for the usually willing, informative and intelligent service; the good balance of the short menu; the immediacy of the flavours; and the excellence of starters like the kachoris, main courses of Kalpna's own invention like shahi sabzi (vegetables with spinach, cream and coriander) and from traditional recipes like baigan bharta (aubergines and cashews with yoghurt, garlic, tomatoes and coriander) or ringna bhaji (aubergines with spinach, fenugreek and asafoetida). Rice is satisfactory, halva is enjoyed, and kulfi is consistently popular. Wines from Paris Wines are interesting too. House wines are £6.75.

CHEF: Ajay Bharatdwaj   PROPRIETORS: M.E. Jogee, Mrs Mehta, E. Barton and Ajay Bharatdwaj   OPEN: Mon to Sat, exc Sat L; 12 to 2.30, 5.30 to 11.30   MEALS: alc. Set L £3.50 to £5.50, Set D £7 to £9.50   SERVICE: 10%, card slips closed   CARDS: Access, Visa   DETAILS: 60 seats. Private parties: 40 main room, 30 private room. Children's helpings. No smoking in dining-room. Wheelchair access. Music

The Guide is totally independent, accepts no free hospitality, and survives on the number of copies sold each year.

Kelly's

46 West Richmond Street, EH8 9DZ	COOKING 1*
031-668 3847	COST £26–£34

'We have been converted to Kelly's' are the words of one Edinburgh reader. A second reflects that 'it proved a pleasant, civilised place for a relaxed meal. Although the room is small, tables are placed so conversation may be uninterrupted, and are pretty with their pink napery and small vases of interesting flowers.' Jacquie Kelly's short menu offers a considered amalgam of French and modern British cooking in dishes such as salmon in pastry, parsnip and coriander soup, prawn and salmon terrine, fillet of brill in a pepper sauce, breast of duck with bramble and port sauce, or loin of lamb together with breast of pigeon with cranberries in a port sauce. The highlight of the dessert menu seems to be the heavily endorsed chocolate mille-feuille. This is a personal place; it takes trouble to do what it does well; and Jeff Kelly complements his wife's cooking with solicitous service and advice on the fairly priced yet wide-ranging wine list. House wine is £7.50.

CHEF: Jacquie Kelly   PROPRIETORS: Jacquie Kelly and Jeff Kelly   OPEN: Tue to Sat, D only (L by arrangement); 6.45 to 9.45   CLOSED: first 3 weeks Oct   MEALS: Set D £20 to £24   SERVICE: not inc, card slips closed   CARDS: Access, Amex, Visa   DETAILS: 32 seats. Private parties: 28 main room. Vegetarian meals. Children's helpings. No smoking before 9pm. Wheelchair access (1 step; also WC). Music

Le Marché Noir

2–4 Eyre Place, EH3 5EP	COOKING 1*
031-558 1608	COST £12–£32

They still cook sauce Nantua at Le Marché Noir, evidence that this restaurant remains sturdily French while the world around it switches style to neo-Italian, East-meets-West or what-you-will cooking. A converted pair of shops, café curtains, lots of pictures, deeply French-language menus and a good wine list make for a popular spot on the edge of New Town. 'We go back regularly and have some good dishes like the duck breast with sharp citrus sauce, or a juicy (if small) Dover sole,' remarks one aficionado who identifies a trademark in the affection for fruits with meat (guinea-fowl with redcurrants and lime, game with raspberries, chicken with mango). A London visitor found there to be a sense of 'consolidating what they set out to do at a decent level for the clientele they attract', and although sad derelictions from good practice have been observed, the overall effect is sound. The wine list has a costly section devoted to Doudet-Naudin's old-style burgundies, a range of clarets that deserves attention and is not too dear, and an interesting selection of bottles from beyond France. There are barely any halves. House wines are from £7.50.

CHEFS: Neil Ross and Stephen Simpson   PROPRIETOR: Malcolm Duck   OPEN: all week, exc Sat and Sun L; 12 to 2.30, 7 (6.30 Sun) to 10 (10.30 Fri and Sat, 9.30 Sun)   MEALS: Set L £7 to £16.50, Set D £16.50 to £22.50   SERVICE: not inc   CARDS: Access, Visa   DETAILS: 45 seats. Private parties: 45 main room. Vegetarian meals. Children's helpings. No cigars/pipes in dining-room. Wheelchair access (1 step). Music

Martins ▼ ⁵⁄*

70 Rose Street North Lane,
EH2 3DX   COOKING 3
031-225 3106   COST £21–£44

The planners of Edinburgh New Town must have thought back lanes haven
only for menials, not smart restaurants. This is small consolation as you get lost
finding Rose Street North Lane, which opens off Rose Street Precinct, which
runs between Frederick and Castle streets – convenient for Princes Street.
Once you are through the door, calm and solicitude will soothe your ruffled
spirits. Cooking does have an even standard (high) that delivers food of quiet
rather than flash imagination. To say that it has affinity with the tasteful
modernity of the restaurant itself would be facile, but somewhat truthful. One
meal included tomato and sage soup, with slight edge provided by curry spice,
'beautifully cooked, firm, fresh salmon just seared at the edge, with a
watercress sauce', and noisettes of lamb with wild mushrooms as its
centrepiece. Vegetables were deeply seasonal – they included curly kale – and
to finish there was a grand little chocolate pot, that might have benefited from
alcohol, and a matchless set of Irish and Scottish cheeses (Tobermory and
Dunsyre Blue especially remembered). Coffee was espresso. The daily menu is
short, though supplemented at lunch by a short set-price menu. If steak is your
bag, don't bother without asking first, but lovers of turbot with chilli, garlic
and red pepper, halibut with sorrel butter, quail stuffed with aubergine and
orange, or venison haunch grilled and served with red cabbage and lentils will
be happy enough. There is occasional comment that prices are high, especially
if the 'modern tastefulness' wins out over zesty flavours. The not overlong but
intelligently chosen wine list is fairly priced, with much good drinking at £15
and well under. Good Burgundy growers Droin and Lignier are carefully
balanced with Rolly-Gassmann Alsaces and several bottles from Moss Wood
and Cape Mentelle. There are some carefully selected halves. House wine is
£8.95. CELLARMAN'S CHOICE: Jurançon Sec, Dom. Castera 1990, £13.95; Rioja
Crianza, Viña Amezola 1987, £13.20.

CHEFS: Forbes Stott and Christopher Colverson   PROPRIETORS: Martin and Gay Irons
OPEN: Tue to Sat, exc Sat L; 12 to 2, 7 to 10   CLOSED: 4 weeks from 25 Dec   MEALS: alc. Set
L £10.50 to £15   SERVICE: not inc (10% for 6 or more, card slips closed)   CARDS: Access,
Amex, Diners, Visa   DETAILS: 28 seats. Private parties: 34 main room, 8 private room. No
children under 7. No smoking in dining-room. Wheelchair access (2 steps). No music

Pierre Victoire £

10 Victoria Street, EH1 2HG   COOKING 1
031-225 1721   COST £9–£22

'There should be one in every town in Britain,' wrote someone who had just
paid the bill – so low, so low. Pierre Levicky evidently agrees. With three
branches in Edinburgh, one in Inverness and grandiose plans for franchising,
he may get there. This is a cumulative entry because it is difficult to unravel
qualities particular to any one branch. Everyone agrees about the low price and
lots find it good value too, but that will depend upon the performance. In

simple terms, the quantities of prime fish – for instance halibut, turbot and salmon – are impressive; what may go wrong is the cooking of them. Or the mayhem and muddle of the bistros themselves may be too much for enjoyment. But a visitor wrote, 'What an experience; it's the kind of place where you get chatting to the potwasher, the waiters, everyone. They even suggest you answer the phone for them, they're so busy: "Just say we're full tonight". The informality is reflected by the cardboard boxes in the restaurant, and the wonderfully healthy lack of deference in the waiters.' Many people enjoy this demystification of eating out. When business overtakes the kitchens, then some culinary shortcuts, for all the generosity of intent, become too strong: the bits of cinnamon stick 'that attacked my upper palate', too much cream in sauces, insipid tastes through lack of concentration. But a rousing cheer is due none the less for real effort. Chocolate fudge cake gets reported, but usually the sweet things are not picked out. 'Meringue filled with chocolate and orange mousse and a lemon tart with crispest pastry' are exceptions that deserve honourable mention from the Union Street branch. Wines are invariably French and don't offer much in halves. House wine is £5.70. The other two Edinburgh branches are at 38 Grassmarket, EH1 2TU, Tel: 031-226 2442, and 8 Union Street, EH8 9LU, Tel: 031-557 8451.

CHEF/PROPRIETOR: Pierre Levicky   OPEN: Mon to Sat; 12 to 3 (4 during Festival), 6 to 11 CLOSED: 2 days Christmas, 2 days New Year   MEALS: alc D. Set L £4.90   SERVICE: not inc, card slips closed   CARD: Access   DETAILS: 65 seats. Private parties: 65 main room. Vegetarian meals. Children's helpings. Wheelchair access (1 step). Music. Fax: 031-557 5216

Shamiana

| 14 Brougham Street, EH3 9JH | COOKING 1 |
| 031-228 2265 and 229 5578 | COST £16–£32 |

New owners have not, say the regulars, caused decline; possibly the opposite. After all, there has been a management buy-out, which usually results in good things for morale and ambition. The menu is encouragingly short, mostly an exploration of north Indian and Kashmiri dishes: for instance Hyderabadi murgh – chicken with lemon and a nut sauce and flavouring from fennel seed – or Kashmiri Chashni tikka, which takes no shortcuts. The anticipation derived from descriptions is sometimes not fulfilled, as in a baigan bhurta – aubergine grilled on a skewer then mashed with mango and mint sauce – which was more mango than mint and tasted pleasant rather than exotic. The same comment was made of the Parsee wedding lamb, where apricots were less in evidence than they might have been, yet reputation was restored with convincing sag dhal, excellent nans, enjoyable fresh carrot halva, good chutneys and competent rice. The wine list makes a point of suggesting wines for the food, and not run-of-the-mill ones either. House wine is £6.25.

CHEFS: M.A. Butt and Mahmood Khan   PROPRIETORS: M.A. Butt and A.N. Butt   OPEN: all week, exc Sat L and Sun L; 12 to 2, 6 to 11   MEALS: alc   SERVICE: 12.5%, card slips closed   CARDS: Access, Amex, Diners, Visa   DETAILS: 43 seats. Private parties: 32 main room. Vegetarian meals. Children's helpings. No-smoking area. Wheelchair access (1 step). Music. Air-conditioned

Shore 🍴 £

3 The Shore, Leith, EH6 6QW   COOKING 1
031-553 5080   COST £15–£32

Local reporters reckon that this up-and-coming bar/restaurant is 'arguably the best-value bistro cooking in the Lothian region'. The blackboard menu changes every two weeks and fish is the strong suit. Mussel chowder, monkfish with asparagus and saffron sauce, wolf fish with pepper sauce, and halibut with beurre blanc and coriander have all pleased. Other dishes praised include a variety of soups, tangy game terrine and vegetarian pasta with pesto sauce. Main courses come with fresh but 'haphazard' vegetables. Regulars also note that desserts are beginning to improve: lime tart, for example, has been 'good and generous'. Two-course weekday lunches are outstanding value. Service is in tune with the informal atmosphere of the place. To drink there is excellent draught beer and some creditable wines from a short, well-chosen list. House French is £7.40.

CHEF: Andrew Kerr   PROPRIETORS: Phillipa Crookshank and Simon Edington   OPEN: all week; 12 (12.30 Sun) to 2.30, 6.30 to 10   MEALS: alc. Set L £6. Minimum £5 L, £10 D in dining-room   SERVICE: not inc (10% for 10 or more), card slips closed   CARDS: Access, Visa   DETAILS: 38 seats. Private parties: 40 main room. Vegetarian meals. Children welcome. No smoking in dining-room. Wheelchair access (1 step; also WC). Music

Vintners Rooms 🍷 🍴

87 Giles Street, Leith, EH6 6BZ   COOKING 3
031-554 6767   COST £27–£39

The rooms occupy the ground floor of an eighteenth-century bonded warehouse that dates from the days when Leith was the gateway to claret and port for the drinking classes of Edinburgh. While casual callers may take a glass and a course, or a whole meal, in the high-ceilinged bar (warm plaster, stone and wood give varied natural tones) more formal affairs are conducted in the auction room where the clarets and ports were once put up for sale. This is smaller, ornately plastered and of great interest. The food at either end is the same. Tim Cumming cooks naturally, with little time for the stuffings and layerings of haute cuisine, yet with every bit as much concern for raw materials. Sauces may be gutsy, sometimes too strong, and may delight in the old forms of hollandaise or mayonnaise. Nor are chutneys and fruits ignored: a rhubarb butter with scallops, spiced oranges with terrines, mango mayonnaise with a seafood salad. When this style is on song, it is magic, as instanced in a summer meal for two of smoked salmon and rabbit terrine with lime pickle, followed by loin of pork with mustard sauce and turbot with a crab sauce, finishing with bi-coloured chocolate parfait with bitter mocha sauce and a warm cherry tart. Fine materials are set off by simple artistry. However, sometimes the execution does not match the invention. One report wondered if the 'Pierre Victoire effect' of offering too much food at never-increasing and low prices has had deleterious consequences on the whole of Edinburgh's eating scene: materials have to be skimped in order to preserve costs. This may be debated, but reporters have found that the Cumming style does not respond to indifferent materials. A tight reign is kept on the wine list; buying is restricted to good sources and prices reflect quality and value accurately. A good range of modestly priced house wines is finely balanced with great burgundies and Rhônes; more flair in Alsace and Italy would be appreciated. CELLARMAN'S CHOICE: Pouilly-Fuissé 1989, Dom. la Soufrandise, £21; Margaux, Ch. Notton 1987, £15.

CHEF: Tim Cumming   PROPRIETORS: Tim and Sue Cumming   OPEN: Mon to Sat; 12 to 2.30, 6.30 to 10.30   CLOSED: 2 weeks Christmas   MEALS: alc   SERVICE: not inc, card slips closed   CARDS: Access, Amex, Visa   DETAILS: 65 seats. Private parties: 40 main room. Car park. Vegetarian meals. Children's helpings. No smoking. Wheelchair access (2 steps). No music. Air-conditioned. Fax: 031-554 8423

Waterfront Wine Bar £

1C Dock Place, Leith, EH6 6LU   COOKING 1*
031-554 7427   COST £14–£22

'Gentrification' is the comment of one who used to like going to this wine bar scruffily dressed and not being shown up. Alternatively, all that extra space in the conservatory – for diners, not beer drinkers – makes the whole affair less frazzled, and most approve. Cooking has been on good form lately and good healthy soups, fresh fish, hearty casseroles (oxtail with ceps, vegetarian, clam, crayfish and squid chowder) and modern methods (chargrilled vegetables, home-smoked cod's roe, and spinach and mushroom croustade with a tomato and sorrel coulis), as well as satisfactory cheeses and a flan or two, are well worth the low prices asked for them. The wine list is very fair value also, as should be the case in a wine bar and so often is not. The choices are not all at the cutting-edge of interest. Ropiteau, Jaboulet-Vercherre and Mommessin are all right as big Burgundy négociants, but it might be preferable to have more and smaller growers as well. However, there is lots of interest from Portugal and Italy, and from the New World – for instance, Russian River Gewurztraminer and Sauvignon from the USA or Gramp's Chardonnay from Australia. Plenty comes by the glass, not so much by the half-bottle. House wines are £6.80.

CHEFS: Melanie Korte, Robin Bowie, Jenny McCrea and Heather McKendrick
PROPRIETORS: Helen and Ian Ruthven, Sarah Reid and Robin Bowie   OPEN: all week; 12 (12.30 Sun) to 2.30 (3.30 Fri, 3 Sat and Sun), 6 to 9.30 (10 Fri and Sat, 9 Sun)   MEALS: alc. Minimum £5 in conservatory   SERVICE: not inc (10% for 6 or more)   DETAILS: 110 seats. 19 tables outside. Private parties: 100 main room. Vegetarian meals. No children under 5. Wheelchair access (1 step; also WC). Music

See the inside of the front cover for an explanation of the 1 to 5 rating system for cooking standards.

The 1994 Guide *will be published before Christmas 1993. Reports on meals are most welcome at any time of the year, but are extremely valuable in the spring. Send them to* The Good Food Guide, *FREEPOST, 2 Marylebone Road, London NW1 1YN. No stamp is needed if posted in the UK.*

ELRICK Grampian

map 8

Courtyard

NEW ENTRY

Broadstraik Inn, Elrick AB32 6TL
ABERDEEN (0224) 742540
on A944, 6m W of Aberdeen

COOKING 1*
COST £18–£35

It is war up in Scotland: 'We will not compromise with the well-done sizzle steak and prawn cocktail brigade,' writes Tony Heath of his new venture that has opened at the back of the Broadstraik Inn, some miles west of Aberdeen. 'If only you could get decent fish in Aberdeen' is another of his comments – which may explain why a ragoût of sea fish had too much smoked haddock to let the tastes of turbot, monkfish and scallops have their outing. The locale – a 'slightly baronial' hall – and the menu have many attractions which certainly do not include prawn cocktail. Perhaps, instead, a puff pastry casket of prawns and skate with a shellfish sauce will satisfy. Menus have been short, perhaps four choices at each stage. They borrow on Tony Heath's experience at his own restaurant in Perth, and as chef-partner at Atkins at Farleyer House, Aberfeldy (see entry). They also take note of current fads: there is usually a pasta dish, smoked salmon comes with olive oil and sun-dried tomatoes, and layers of aubergine and polenta are served with sweet pepper and tomato sauce. Execution may have small failings like a cold warm salad or a cool rack of lamb, but these may be forgotten in desserts such as galette (hazelnut meringue, actually) of strawberries or apricot and almond flan. Coffee would be good if it were stronger. The wine list stays short but two sound choices are Brac de la Perrière's Beaujolais Blanc or Jaboulet's white Hermitage. House wines are £8.50. Let battle commence.

CHEFS: Katy Barr, Neil Simpson and Tony Heath   PROPRIETORS: Magnum Inns Ltd
OPEN: Wed to Sun D, and Sun L (L other days by arrangement); 12 to 2, 6.30 to 9.30
MEALS: alc. Set Sun L £12.50   SERVICE: not inc, card slips closed   CARDS: Access, Amex,
Visa   DETAILS: 36 seats. Private parties: 36 main room. Car park. Vegetarian meals.
Children's helpings. Wheelchair access. Music. Fax: (0224) 742796

ERISKA Strathclyde

map 8

▲ Isle of Eriska Hotel

Eriska PA37 1SD
LEDAIG (063 172) 371
off A828, 12m N of Oban

COOKING 2
COST £44

'You can watch the badgers eating bread and milk at the library door. There's probably nothing else left in the kitchen because we've eaten it all.' So said one contented visitor, whose 10 nights assaying Sheena Buchanan-Smith's cooking drew the verdict that although not much was on offer each evening on a five- or six-course menu with no more than two choices at any stage, over a period the depth of repertoire stood revealed. The dangers of a short menu are that on bad nights things can be really bad. At the very high price (no matter how long the meal) the food should, of course, be perfect. Though the centrepiece will tend to the traditional roast, there is scope for more enterprising things: hence a risotto laced with strawberries that was none the less much enjoyed, a plate of scallops with saffron, or, at the other end, some desserts light of sugar to suit every palate. The place itself and the Victorian house are red-hot for scenery, nature, peace and quiet, sport, history – the lot. The wine list shows a very solid cellar: Latour burgundies, a middling set of clarets, a few from the New World and Chile, and a run of vintage port.

CHEFS: Sheena Buchanan-Smith and Lindsay Little   PROPRIETORS: Robin and Sheena Buchanan-Smith   OPEN: all week, D only (L for residents); 7.30 to 9   CLOSED: Dec to Mar   MEALS: Set D £35   SERVICE: net prices, card slips closed   DETAILS: 40 seats. Private parties: 10 main room, 12 private room. Car park. Children's helpings. Children under 10 high tea only. Jacket and tie. Wheelchair access (also WC). No music   ACCOMMODATION: 17 rooms, all with bath/shower. Rooms for disabled. B&B £73 to £150. Deposit: £50. Children welcome. Baby facilities. Pets welcome (not in public rooms). Garden. Tennis. Fishing. TV. Phone. Confirm by noon. Fax: (063 172) 531 (*The Which? Hotel Guide*)

FORT WILLIAM Highland   map 8

Crannog ⁵⋇

Town Pier,
Fort William PH33 7NG   COOKING 2*
FORT WILLIAM (0397) 705589   COST £15–£33

'The seafood is so fresh it fairly leaps at you.' The site is on the bleak side: rather a lot of Tarmac before the beauties of Loch Linnhe. The building has a Scandinavian air. Be a non-smoker, take a table by the picture window and turn your back on roadworks to embrace 'green, rugged hills, sailing boats and small boys fishing from the pier'. 'We doubt that anywhere in Britain can match it for seafood,' wrote one refulgent Scot. It is not just plain seafood, though providentially it is not messed about too much. The menu remains fairly constant, but regulars will seek variety from the blackboard listing daily catches. Relax, and hear what one meal brought: bouillabaisse with vegetables, smoked mussel, lots of bits of fish, a langoustine and a croûton spread with garlic mayonnaise; Crannog's own gravlax, gelatinous and moist, with a vigorous dill mustard sauce; delicate and true pickled herring with sour cream and chives; a dozen langoustines in garlic butter, sweetly flavoured, cooked instantly after catching, and served with a row of small new waxy potatoes and a row of floury ones too; a mixed salad with upstanding vinaigrette. Cranachan – whipped cream, whisky, oatmeal and raspberries – was one dessert, not very smooth sorbets was the other. Service seems to be by students on vacation, but is by no means slack. Much of the wine list comes from Justerini and prices for bottles are as reasonable as they are for the shellfish. House wines are from £7.50. A second branch is at 28 Cheapside, Glasgow, Tel: 041-221 1727.

CHEF: Susan Trowbridge   PROPRIETORS: Crannog Ltd   OPEN: all week (restricted in winter); 12 to 2.30, 6 to 10 (9 winter)   MEALS: alc   SERVICE: not inc, card slips closed CARDS: Access, Visa   DETAILS: 50 seats. Private parties: 50 main room, 25 private rooms. Car park. Children's helpings. No-smoking in dining-room. Wheelchair access (also WC). Music. Fax: (0397) 705026

Amber Regent

50 West Regent Street, G2 2QZ	COOKING 1
041-331 1655 and 1677	COST £15–£40

One of a trio of restaurants in the region, it is lavishly appointed, the service is ultra-rapid and decoration comes not only in the curtains and carpets but also on the plate: 'They specialise in cutting onions, radishes and carrots into roses, whorls and spirals, then setting them at preposterous angles.' Stir-frying and the batters on fried foods are well thought-of, and there is an undeniable freshness to many of the ingredients. The menu will not surprise by arcane dishes – no fish lips here – but the aromatic crispy lamb served Peking duck-style and the beef with mandarin sauce come well recommended. High on convivial atmosphere. The wine list is very decent and fairly priced into the bargain. House wines are £8.90.

CHEF: Tommy Ho   PROPRIETOR: Andy Chung   OPEN: Mon to Sat; 12 to 2.30, 6 to 11.30 (midnight Thur to Sat)   MEALS: alc. Set L £6.95, Set D £21 to £28   SERVICE: not inc CARDS: Access, Amex, Diners, Visa   DETAILS: 90 seats. Private parties: 100 main room, 15 private room. Vegetarian meals. No children under 10. Smart dress preferred. Music. Air-conditioned. Fax: 041-353 3398

Buttery

652 Argyle Street G3 8UF	COOKING 3
041-221 8188	COST £19–£39

'We had heard that Glasgow fizzed. The Buttery reinforced the assessment; there was not much sign of recession here' was the remark of a visitor from depressed parts. Ecclesiastical overtones in the benches and dark mahogany of the bar area have been characterised as 'bizarre, a cross between art nouveau with stained glass and Ye Olde Tea Shoppe', but that is not true of the cooking or the effective, helpful service. Modern would be a better epithet for the cooking, though nothing too outrageous takes its place on the evening *carte* or the mid-priced lunch menu. Herb polenta filled with finnan haddock, fillet of salmon with spinach and tomato and queen scallop sauce, or navarin of lamb with rosemary dumplings is about as up to date as it gets. One happy customer enjoyed 'a terrine of sweetbreads and duck livers with a raisin and orange marmalade, the bitter sweetness of the latter enhancing, not killing, the delicacy of the terrine; the main course of lightly fried venison and pigeon breasts with a five-spice jus and roast parsnips was a brilliant mix and was served with potatoes à la lyonnaise made with garlic rather than onions.' The general performance has been approved for steady attention, as well as the effort made to provide vegetarians with their own menu, and tea drinkers with a real slate from which to choose. A fair wine list gives range, though not grand economy. House wines are £8.95.

All entries in the Guide *are rewritten every year, not least because restaurant standards fluctuate. Don't trust an out-of-date* Guide.

CHEF: Stephen Johnson   PROPRIETORS: Alloa Brewery Co Ltd   OPEN: Mon to Sat, exc Sat L; 12 to 2.30, 7 to 10.30   MEALS: alc. Set L £14.25   SERVICE: 10% (net prices Set L), card slips closed   CARDS: Access, Amex, Diners, Visa   DETAILS: 50 seats. Private parties: 45 main room, 8 private room. Car park. Vegetarian meals. Children welcome. Smart dress preferred. Wheelchair access. Music. Air-conditioned. Fax: 041-204 4639

Café Gandolfi £

64 Albion Street, G1 1NY
041-552 6813

COOKING 1
COST £15–£24

The décor of this former Victorian pub in the revived Merchant City is 'a wonderful mixture, ranging from a flock of fishes in stained glass to a flight of white plastic Scotties tacked on to a wall below'. This is a popular venue for the casually dressed under-forties (there are frequent queues), where interest centres on what is consumed rather than smartness or trimmings. The eclectic café-menu continues to evolve, with more emphasis on delicate starters and vegetarian dishes. Lunchtime-eaters tend to opt for soups and salads, but many items are recommended: smoked pheasant with onion tartlet; smoked venison with gratin dauphinois; gravlax with dill and mustard sauce; poached salmon with lemon butter. There is also praise for daily specials such as cheese gougère filled with ham, mushrooms and celery, and subtly spiced fish curry with coconut milk. The home-made ice-creams are rated as 'better than any Italian ice-cream in the city', although French apple tart has been less successful. Drinks range from German wheat beer and home-made lemonade to a short, sharp list of wines including some organics. House French is £7.95.

CHEFS: Maggie Clarence and Rona Tait   PROPRIETORS: Iain M. Mackenzie and Seumas MacInnes   OPEN: Mon to Sat; 9.30am to 11.30pm   CLOSED: bank hols   MEALS: alc SERVICE: not inc (10% for 6 or more)   DETAILS: 60 seats. Private parties: 12 main room. Vegetarian meals. Children's helpings. Wheelchair access (2 steps). Music

October

128 Drymen Road, Bearsden, G61 3RB
041-942 7272

COOKING 3
COST £15–£48

Ferrier Richardson's restaurant in Bearsden – a district for people of substance – stands out among its Glasgow peers as the most consistent devotee of modern cooking. You may be almost sure of this by simple inspection of the premises: a fine shop-front, then a reception area before the clean lines of the dining-room, slabs of colour from modern Scottish paintings, depth of tone from dark-blue carpet and upholstery. 'It sparkles,' said one visitor. 'Clean and crisp,' said another. The menu – short, fast-changing, a small set-price affair at lunch-time, a *carte* at dinner – wears a certain eclecticism on its sleeve: lamb satay, chicken with chilli-hot stir-fried vegetables, a casserole of fish with light curry sauce. It has a conventional line too: steak with parsley and peppercorn butter, salmon in filo with orange and watercress sauce, mussels with white wine, smoked salmon and avocado salad with dill vinaigrette. The intention to serve only the freshest, as and when available, is clear, though not to the extent of abandoning a recognisable repertoire. Ferrier Richardson is not one of those chefs who indulge in too much experiment at the expense of customers. A winter meal that included a filo parcel of mozzarella, tomato and basil (a variation on one of his consistent vegetarian dishes), quail and venison terrine, a trio of salmon (marinated, smoked and tartare), lemon sole with ginger and vermouth, rack of lamb with a rosemary crust and mushrooms, and monkfish and leek parcels with vegetable spaghetti and a curry sauce, ended with crème brûlée with passion-fruit, a trio of orange (tart, soufflé and sorbet) and a mocha mille-feuille. Presentation is good; details such as choice of potatoes and accurate vegetable cooking are also up to the mark (even if bread is sometimes cooked in too cool an oven). The criticism that surfaces most regularly is that flavours are not as strong as the description on the menu may imply. Service is 'smiling and welcoming'. The wine list is short, the wines are young, the style is modern. The price range is charitable, though nothing is given away. There is a spread across some of the newer producers, though no reds from America or Spain. House wines are from £8.25. As we go to press, the daily newspapers report Ferrier Richardson's appointment as chef at the still-to-be-finished Glasgow Hilton. The present position (summer 1992) is that October will continue with Derek Blair in sole charge of the kitchen. However, this entry pertains to the position before, not after, any move.

CHEFS: Ferrier Richardson and Derek Blair   PROPRIETORS: Premiere Cuisine Ltd   OPEN: Mon to Sat; 12 to 2, 7 to 10   CLOSED: 1 week Easter, first 2 weeks Aug   MEALS: alc. Set L £9.95 to £11.95   SERVICE: not inc   CARDS: Access, Visa   DETAILS: 48 seats. Private parties: 52 main room. Children welcome. No cigars/pipes in dining-room. Wheelchair access (also WC). Music. Air-conditioned. Fax: 041-942 9650

October Café £

The Rooftop, Princes Square,
Buchanan Street, G1 3JX   COOKING 2
041-221 0303   COST £15–£34

This is modern life. Take the dedicated lift to the top, sit on the long bar and peek out over the atrium of this wild shopping-centre, or retreat to the restaurant section where 'the seats are hidden behind a wall so depriving you of an outlook – designer madness'. Bar and restaurant offer different menus, though this time the view is the same: fair value, speed, intelligent plundering of the world's culinary styles ('"East-meets-West" is a good description'), plenty of fun and up-front flavours. A summer meal succeeded in many respects: 'The waiter seemed to read our thoughts; value for money was great; simple dishes scored highly for raw materials and sensible lack of over-ambition.' Dishes served were mussels with white wine, garlic and herbs ('so fresh and tender, the stock so light and tasty, and so many that I had to share'); beef with brandy, cream and mushroom sauce; chicken stuffed with broccoli and cream cheese on a chive sauce; French fries that could not be matched anywhere; vegetables that were crisp and plentiful; chocolate terrine with an espresso sauce. Other dishes such as squid with chilli, teriyaki beef and wasabi, lamb satay or stir-fried chicken, prawns, bamboo shoots and noodles with a chilli sauce show that the East outruns Italy for once. Even chopsticks come as a matter of course with some dishes. Close testing against October, the café's older sister, has not invariably put the cheaper place in a poorer light, though the experiment seems to have revealed a greater intensity to the sauces at October when dishes could be thus compared. The wine list is very short and house wines are £7.95.

CHEF: George Craig   PROPRIETORS: Premiere Cuisine Ltd   OPEN: Mon to Sat; 12 to 2.30, 7 to 11 (café noon to midnight)   MEALS: alc   SERVICE: not inc   CARDS: Access, Visa
DETAILS: restaurant 50 seats, café 120 seats. Private parties: 200 main room. Vegetarian meals. Children welcome. Wheelchair access. Music. Air-conditioned

---

▲ One Devonshire Gardens ♟

1 Devonshire Gardens, G12 0UX   COOKING 3
041-339 2001 and 334 9494   COST £30−£48

The setting is a tree-lined Victorian terrace to the west of the city, some 15 minutes from the centre. Inside all is smooth luxury. 'The aim is to recreate an unobtrusive, courteous Victorian ambience,' according to one visitor. Everywhere there are heavy drapes and rich wallpapers, dim lights, gilt mirrors and pale colour schemes. New chef Andrew Fleming has class and assurance, and cooks to a short fixed-price menu that runs to four courses (including soup) at dinner. Centrepiece dishes have been good. Consider this: thick succulent tournedos of Scotch beef fillet with light, wild mushroom dumplings and a rich, dark Brouilly wine jus flecked with slivers of truffle; or delectable thin slices of saddle of deer, cooked rare, curled over fried shallots in a superb fumet with just a hint of cinnamon. Desserts show that this is a kitchen with a feel for artistry as well as taste: white peach sponge with peach mousse and citrus syrup has been delicately judged, while the assiette of chocolate has been described as 'a splendidly accomplished trio of contrasting and complementary flavours'. The kitchen also has a high-class vegetarian repertoire. Feuilleté of artichoke and asparagus with basil and pesto sauce, and creamy ragoût of wild mushrooms with rosemary-flavoured noodles, have been handled with real expertise and serious intent. One or two details have marred the overall effect: pedestrian nibbles, 'uninteresting' vegetables, 'disappointing' coffee. Service is impeccable. Wine service and buying are matchless. Enthusiasm must be dulled by the prices, which are high by any standards; but oenophiles will be well pleased with the wide and very careful selection in evidence right across the range. House wine is £16.

CHEF: Andrew Fleming   PROPRIETOR: Ken McCulloch   OPEN: all week, exc Sat L; 12 to 2.30, 7 to 11   MEALS: Set L £19, Set D £32   SERVICE: not inc, card slips closed   CARDS: Access, Amex, Diners, Visa   DETAILS: 54 seats. Private parties: 10, 14 and 30 private rooms. Vegetarian meals. Children's helpings. Smart dress preferred. No-smoking area. Music
ACCOMMODATION: 27 rooms, all with bath/shower. B&B £115 to £160. Deposit: 1 night. Children welcome. Baby facilities. Pets welcome. Afternoon teas. Garden. TV. Phone. Fax: 041-337 1663 (*The Which? Hotel Guide*)

£ *indicates that it is possible to have a three-course meal, including coffee, a half-bottle of house wine and service, at any time the restaurant is open (i.e. at dinner as well as at lunch, unless a place is open only for dinner), for £20 or less per person.*

Rogano

11 Exchange Place, G1 3AN   COOKING 2
041-248 4055   COST £15–£41

Everyone should go to Rogano for the steamship deco, the '40s music and the service. People are as one on that and agree the price is high and may be side-stepped by using the café downstairs, which offers 'splendid soup, sandwiches and coffee', a cheap theatre menu and a lot of happy hurry. The restaurant is altogether more sedate, but well-served. The long *carte* offers plenty of fish with meat reinforcements for those who cannot face a meal *sans* flesh. The cooking can be accurate and the materials good, but prices rise inexorably. Plain fish is offered in the form of oysters, sashimi, grilled lobster or langoustines, and grilled sole. More complex ways of cooking are kept in check so the materials may shine through: salmon with coriander and redcurrants, brill with lobster and cognac cream sauce, or, at the most complicated, monkfish and scallops with ginger and spring onions en papillote. 'The brill was meaty and perfectly cooked, with a loose tarragon butter sauce' and 'the sole was properly cooked' are comments indicating that standards are currently sound. Vegetables have been absorbed into the price of the main dish this year. The wine list is worth exploring for Loires and Alsaces. The burgundies tend towards the larger houses, and there is a long choice of champagnes. House wines from Remy-Pannier in the Loire, the label designed by Archie Forrest, are £8.50.

CHEF: James Kerr   PROPRIETORS: Alloa Brewery   OPEN: all week, exc Sun L; 12 to 2.30, 6.30 (5 theatre D) to 10.30   MEALS: alc. Set L £15, Set theatre D £8.95   SERVICE: 10%, card slips closed   CARDS: Access, Amex, Diners, Visa   DETAILS: 100 seats. Private parties: 25 main room, 14 private room. Children welcome. Music. Air-conditioned. Fax: 041-248 2608

Ubiquitous Chip ▮ £

12 Ashton Lane, G12 8SJ   COOKING 2
041-334 5007   COST £16–£47

'It's rather like straying into part of Kew Gardens, or visiting a new-wave women's health spa' was the reaction of a Londoner used to finding such a profusion of plants and overhead glazing near a swimming-pool, not a restaurant. It is generally a happy place with a sense of relaxation that goes with good food and wine served at a proper pace. The Chip has a line in Scottish recipes and materials, and is perhaps best for shellfish from the West Coast and game cookery. However, not everyone has found a plate of shellfish as good as expected. The interest comes from a melding of influences in dishes such as cod on a bed of clapshot with roasted peppers and chilli oil, or venison with baked porridge cakes and Cumberland sauce. The drawback is that some dishes work on some days, but not on others. There is also a regret that the menu does not change enough. What appear to be fair prices rise quickly when you add on the vegetables. The menu itself is very long; that for the bistro upstairs seems almost longer, and one wonders if this is the root of the problem of inconsistency. Upstairs has had very mixed reports. Coffee is strong and generous, and comes with tablet and cake ('rather like bread pudding'); puddings may include an excellent chocolate marquise with orange sauce, but Caledonian ice-cream with oatmeal seemed strangely undersweetened. Cheeses are Scottish and worth trying. For reliability, concentrate on the wine and spirit list. Malt whiskies by the page are more than complemented by a long list of wines. Quality is remarkable throughout every region and country, and a generous spread of price will satisfy most pockets. Bargains and bin-ends can be searched out, but half-bottles seem less abundant than they were in previous years.

CHEF/PROPRIETOR: Ron Clydesdale   OPEN: all week; downstairs 12 to 2.30 (12.30 to 4 Sun), 5.30 (6.30 Sun) to 11; upstairs 12 to 11   MEALS: alc   SERVICE: not inc   CARDS: Access, Amex, Diners, Visa   DETAILS: 100 seats. 12 tables outside. Private parties: 60 main room, 40 private room. Vegetarian meals. Children's helpings. Wheelchair access (also WC). No music. Fax: 041-337 1302

GULLANE Lothian   map 8

La Potinière 🍾

Main Street, Gullane EH31 2AA   COOKING 3*
GULLANE (0620) 843214   COST £23–£37

It could be the nineteenth hole to the Muirfield course, so near is it, but there are other attractions to this small school-room/chalet building. 'Its front garden was rather overgrown, so it is easy to miss.' Hack your way through the undergrowth and you will achieve the 'pretty pink and flowery dining-room, with dried herbs hanging from the rafters'. Tables are quite close-packed, and dining happens in one sitting at 8pm (or 1pm at lunch). There is but one copy of the wine list, a mega-tome, so unless you have left your choice in the hands of David Brown, or fixed on something beforehand, you may have to wait a while. Waits may also occur as the courses unfold and perhaps as each table seeks out David Brown to pay the bill. La Potinière's very special recipe remains unchanged. David Brown does the serving, Hilary Brown the cooking. People love it. The cooking is fine, often with edge and excitement to the tastes, the value is still fair and the wines are sensational. The meal has a constant form. Soup is followed by a middle course of fish or vegetable, then there is poultry or some bird, with a sauce and a round of dauphinois potato (one of the really good ones in the UK), salad, then a wheel of Brie (perfectly ripened in the eyes of many, not ripe enough for a few who like it running away), and a finish of dessert, more often than not a parfait or cream confection, often with a liqueur poured over it. Critics complain that the repertoire remains too fixed: 'I have been four times and had the same fish course twice, the same main course three times and the same pudding every time.' They also protest that the textures can be too uniform. A thickish soup, in this instance pimento, served with a sweet walnut bread, 'was the stuff to line stomachs, not sharpen the appetite'; then a courgette soufflé seemed too smooth and floury; the dessert of parfait aux chocolat was also smooth-textured and lacked bitter edge. But Hilary Brown is a master of flavours, as was seen on an evening that started with tomato and mint soup, then proceeded through tricorns of smoked salmon mousseline on a pool of intense spinach and basil sauce, chicken with lentils and morels, and a soufflé glace of oranges with a marvellous caramel sauce: 'I rushed home to the recipe book to see if I could make it too.' From their base in south-west France the Browns provide a range of interesting and fairly priced wines. We are assured that policies are unchanged on the main list, in the course of revision. On one November night a customer found that too many of the wines were not available; an over-lengthy list can be difficult to keep in good order. House wine is £8.50.

CHEF: Hilary Brown   PROPRIETORS: David and Hilary Brown   OPEN: Mon, Tue, Thur and Sun L, and Fri and Sat D; 1, 8   CLOSED: 1 week June, Oct, 25 and 26 Dec, 1 and 2 Jan MEALS: Set L £16.75, Set Sun L £17.50, Set D £26   SERVICE: not inc   DETAILS: 30 seats. Private parties: 30 main room. Car park. Vegetarian meals with prior notice. Children welcome. No smoking during meals. Wheelchair access (1 step). No music

---

HADDINGTON Lothian   map 8

▲ Browns Hotel ⁵✱

| 1 West Road, Haddington EH41 3RD | COOKING 2 |
| HADDINGTON (0620) 822254 | COST £21–£32 |

Visitors are captivated by the cultured mood of this Georgian house full of plants and paintings. The design is colourful and dramatic without being hard on the eye; classical music fills the house and continues into the night. Colin Brown cooks to a short fixed-price menu based on good ingredients and classic sauces. One typically successful meal featured monkfish with lime and ginger en papillote, French onion soup, breast of pheasant with almonds and sauce Robert, and crêpes suzette followed by cafetière coffee and home-made chocolates. Some have found the quantities daunting and the cumulative effect of four courses rather overpowering, but most agree that the food is a 'sufficiency and as palate-teasing as haute cuisine should be'. Service is greatly appreciated. Seventy wines offer decent drinking at reasonable prices. House wines are from £7.40.

CHEF: Colin Brown   PROPRIETORS: Colin Brown and Alex McCallum   OPEN: all week, D only, and Sun L; 12.30 for 1, 7.30 for 8   MEALS: Set Sun L £15.50, Set D £22   SERVICE: not inc, card slips closed   CARDS: Access, Amex, Visa   DETAILS: 34 seats. Private parties: 34 main room. Car park. Vegetarian meals on request. Children's helpings. No smoking in dining-room. Wheelchair access (also WC). Music   ACCOMMODATION: 6 rooms, 5 with bath/shower. B&B £55.50 to £72. Deposit: £20. Children welcome. Baby facilities. Garden. TV. Phone. Doors close at midnight. Confirm by 6

HAWICK Borders   map 6

Old Forge ♥

Newmill-on-Teviot, nr Hawick TD9 0JU	
HAWICK (0450) 85298	COOKING 1
4m S of Hawick, on A7	COST £19–£24

There is something of the homespun here with the bare stone walls, relics of the one-time forge, and bits and bobs not out of place in a craft shop. Not so the cooking: home-made perhaps, but Margaret Irving indulges in handicraft from top to toe of her culinary range. Chutneys, jellies, bread, ice-creams, biscuits and all the trimmings are made by her; greenstuffs are grown by her. The menu moves through a most un-Borderlike repertoire of guacamole, Greek salad, rhubarb chutney with chicken liver pâté, spiced beef with raclette cheese and pickles, chicken with mango salsa, and sweetbreads with lemon and capers. Maybe it returns to its roots with whisky and honey ice-cream with marmalade, but Bill Irving's gentle service and his intelligent wine list make sure distinction from the general run of things is preserved. The choice of growers and sources is impeccable, the notes run on for a bit, but the prices are very fair. There is also no nonsense about concentrating only on France. House wine is £8.95 a litre. CELLARMAN'S CHOICE: Vouvray, Le Haut Lieu 1984, £11.95; St-Joseph 1989, Dom. Raymond Trollat, £16.50.

CHEF: Margaret Irving   PROPRIETORS: Bill and Margaret Irving   OPEN: Tue to Sat, D only; 7 to 9.30   CLOSED: first 2 weeks May, first 2 weeks Nov   MEALS: Set D £12.95 (Tue to Thur) to £15.95   SERVICE: net prices, card slips closed   CARDS: Access, Visa   DETAILS: 28 seats. Private parties: 30 main room. Car park. Vegetarian meals. Children's helpings. Wheelchair access. No music

---

INVERNESS Highland   map 8

▲ *Culloden House*

Inverness IV1 2NZ
INVERNESS (0463) 790461   COOKING 2
off A96, 3m E of Inverness   COST £23–£41

It's grand; it's stately; it's not exactly neighbourhood. Staff are well trained – too well for one couple who wished to linger but found tables being laid for breakfast as their dessert was served. Everyone agrees that the place is beautifully maintained and that the eighteenth-century mansion is impressive. The menu has none of the savagery of modern neo-peasant or fauvist cooking. Examples from their summer menu include a timbale of trout mousse wrapped with smoked salmon; a terrine, perhaps of duck liver and venison, perhaps of vegetable and chicken with a slice of goose liver; salmon wrapped in filo with truffle; scallops grilled with breadcrumbs on a bed (called a purée but definitely a bed) of leeks, courgettes and tomato; venison in pastry with an inner layer of spinach and mushrooms; lemon tart and lemon ice-cream, decorated of course with a strawberry; and chocolate marquise with a strawberry coulis. The cooking is competent, though errors in pastry-making, over-salting and over-sweetening have somewhat clouded the issue. The wine list is a decent one, with older vintages giving wine-buffs a chance. Concentration on the great names might label it expensive (margins are not low), but there is effort to provide affordable wines as well. It is possible to obtain a bottle of Croft 1963 vintage port for £47 including VAT. At Culloden House it costs £142.30; is £95.30 profit not rather a lot for this hotel to take? House wines are from £9.25.

CELLARMAN'S CHOICE: *Wines recommended by the restaurateur, normally more expensive than house wine.*

CHEF: Michael Simpson   PROPRIETORS: Ian and Marjory McKenzie   OPEN: all week;
12.30 to 2, 7 to 9   MEALS: alc L. Set D £27.50   SERVICE: not inc, card slips closed   CARDS:
Access, Amex, Diners, Visa   DETAILS: 50 seats. 3 tables outside. Private parties: 50 main
room, 25 private room. Car park. Vegetarian meals. Children's helpings. Jacket and tie. No
music   ACCOMMODATION: 24 rooms, all with bath/shower. B&B £99 to £175. Deposit: 1
night. No children under 10. Pets welcome. Afternoon teas. Garden. Sauna. Tennis.
Snooker. TV. Phone. Doors close at midnight. Confirm 28 days ahead. Fax: (0463) 792181

▲ Dunain Park ⚡✴

Inverness IV3 6JN	COOKING 1*
INVERNESS (0463) 230512	COST £28–£33

Ann Nicoll is a chatelaine whose mission to refurbish her Highland home has
lately yielded a comfortable but grander drawing-room: a fine place to sit,
admire the log fire and inspect a daily menu distinguished by clarity and a
short choice of three at each course. Satisfying soups such as turnip and pine-
kernels, parsnip, and curried carrot are permanent fixtures. Locally reared,
pasture-fed, slow-maturing Highland beef is a welcome and frequent feature.
Pheasant with oatmeal stuffing, bread sauce and bacon illustrates direct skill.
There is a good balance between traditional dishes and some quite punchy,
more modern sauces or ingredients. Wild mushrooms make a strong
appearance come the season; chutneys and flavour-heighteners are used to give
zip to things like skewered pigeon with bacon. Come the end of the meal, and
the sweets buffet beckons. The wine list is more than sound. It has good prices
and ranges across the world: Viña Ardanza 1983, João Pires Muscat or Tinto da
Anfora, Vieux Télégraphe Châteauneuf-du-Pape, or Ampeau's burgundies are
just some of the gems. House wines are £8.50.

CHEF: Ann Nicoll   PROPRIETORS: Ann and Edward Nicoll   OPEN: all week, D only; 7 to 9
CLOSED: 2 weeks Jan or Feb   MEALS: alc   SERVICE: not inc, card slips closed   CARDS:
Access, Amex, Diners, Visa   DETAILS: 36 seats. Private parties: 12 main room. Car park.
Children's helpings. Smart dress preferred. No smoking in dining-room. Wheelchair
access. No music   ACCOMMODATION: 14 rooms, all with bath/shower. Rooms for disabled.
B&B £55 to £130. Deposit: £50. Children welcome. Pets welcome (not in public rooms).
Afternoon teas. Garden. Swimming-pool. Sauna. TV. Phone. Doors close at midnight. Fax:
(0463) 224532 (The Which? Hotel Guide)

KENTALLEN Highland   map 8

▲ Ardsheal House ⚡ ✴

Kentallen PA38 4BX	COOKING 2
DUROR (063 174) 227	COST £24–£45

A long driveway leads you to the house, which stands white against the blue of
Loch Linnhe. A country-house atmosphere is very much fostered. On busy
summer nights the dining-room extends to a conservatory that is almost part of
the garden and a fine spot in which to dine at leisure. As the menu runs
through five, maybe six, courses, leisure you will have. On a night in June,
George Kelso's menu included warm salad of monkfish, bacon and mange-tout
with balsamic dressing, tomato, celery and apple soup, beef with grain

mustard sauce, and apricot pancakes with summer fruits sauce. These all proved to have faults of overcooking or lack of flavour, though the raspberry ice-cream with the pancakes was first-rate. But each of the alternate dishes on that same night was admirable: game parfait, cullen skink and prawns with saffron and cucumber sauce. 'It was as if there were two chefs working on each course' was the conclusion. Cheeses were not satisfactory, though breads, vegetables, canapés and petits fours proved that someone cared a lot. At these prices, however, one would hope for consistency. The wine list is admirable. There is care to offer good spread in the lower price range, and imagination has gone into the choice of bourgeois clarets. Bin-ends at the beginning of the year always make good reading. House wines are £9. CELLARMAN'S CHOICE: Menetou-Salon 1989, Pellé, £14; Valdepeñas, Gran Reserva, Pata Negra 1978, £11.50.

CHEF: George Kelso PROPRIETORS: Jane and Robert Taylor OPEN: all week; 12.30 to 2, 8.30 CLOSED: early Nov to Easter MEALS: Set L £17.50, Set D £32.50 SERVICE: not inc, card slips closed DETAILS: 40 seats. Private parties: 38 main room. Car park. Children's helpings. Smart dress preferred. No smoking in dining-room. Wheelchair access (also WC). Music ACCOMMODATION: 13 rooms, all with bath/shower. D,B&B £85 to £180. Deposit: variable. Children welcome. Baby facilities. Pets welcome. Afternoon teas. Garden. Tennis. Snooker. Phone. Doors close at midnight. Confirm by 6. Fax: (063 174) 342 (*The Which? Hotel Guide*)

KILLIECRANKIE Tayside   map 8

▲ *Killiecrankie Hotel* ⅗✳

Killiecrankie PH16 5LG   COOKING 2
PITLOCHRY (0796) 473220   COST £22–£35

'The setting is delightful, views are superb and the public rooms are light, comfortable and cheerful,' comments a reader. Unfortunately reports of a less cheerful demeanour among personnel have dimmed appreciation for some. The kitchen, mercifully, eludes fatigue. Salmon, smoked or grilled, receives tribute; convention and invention combine in a triumphant grilled Angus sirloin marinated in chilli oil; and there is good-quality game as in a dish of tender pieces of game pot-roasted on a bed of vegetables with redcurrant, orange juice and port as the flavouring. The dessert choice is now restricted to a tart and one other pudding. Bar lunches and suppers (about £18 for three courses and wine) are also available. The wine list is expanded and carefully constructed. House French is £9.50.

CHEF: Paul Booth PROPRIETORS: Colin and Carole Anderson OPEN: all week; 12.30 to 2, 7 to 8.30 CLOSED: Jan and Feb MEALS: bar meals. Set D £15.50 to £23 SERVICE: not inc, card slips closed CARDS: Access, Amex, Visa DETAILS: 34 seats. Car park. Vegetarian meals. Children's helpings. No infants in dining-room. No smoking in dining-room. Wheelchair access (also WC) ACCOMMODATION: 11 rooms, all with bath/shower. Rooms for disabled. D,B&B £61.50 to £134. Deposit: £25. Children welcome. Baby facilities. Pets welcome. Afternoon teas. Garden. TV. Phone. Doors close at midnight. Confirm by 6. Fax: (0796) 472451 (*The Which? Hotel Guide*)

SCOTLAND

KINBUCK Central   map 8

▲ *Cromlix House* ♈ ✳

Kinbuck FK15 9JT   COOKING 3
DUNBLANE (0786) 822125   COST £21–£41

Cromlix is not old, but if you ignore the lures set to capture the small
conference and corporate client, its values seem timeless: sport and the outside
life, honest service, lots of polished furniture, and a simple approach to eating
and drinking that respects quality nearly irrespective of cost. People enjoy the
aura of good living apparently effortlessly maintained. After a change of chef,
the place is once again on song. The menu is simple: a run through four courses,
with a single alternative offered at each. It does not go so far as to espouse the
cause of plain cooking, but nor is it over-fashionable. Mushroom consommé,
halibut with a salmon and truffle mousse, duck with orange and ginger
chutney, and coconut parfait with banana fritters are examples. The wine list
has good range and fine quality, well balanced with decent bottles around £12.
A glance at the bin-end selection might repay with economy and pleasure.
Wider, more adventurous buying would not be out of place. House wines are
£11. CELLARMAN'S CHOICE: Stoneleigh, Sauvignon Blanc 1990, £17.50;
Savigny-lès-Beaune premier cru 1986, Latour, £23.50.

CHEF: Ian Corkhill   PROPRIETORS: Edward and Victoria Eden   OPEN: all week; 12 to 2.30,
7 to 10   CLOSED: Feb   MEALS: Set L £15 to £22, Set D £32   SERVICE: net prices, card slips
closed   CARDS: Access, Amex, Diners, Visa   DETAILS: 60 seats. Private parties: 30 main
room, 12, 16 and 24 private rooms. Car park. Vegetarian meals. Children's helpings. No
smoking in dining-room. No music   ACCOMMODATION: 14 rooms, all with bath/shower.
B&B £68 to £210. Deposit: £100. Children welcome. Baby facilities. Pets welcome.
Afternoon teas. Garden. Tennis. Fishing. TV. Phone. Fax: (0786) 825450 (*The Which? Hotel
Guide*)

KINGUSSIE Highland   map 8

▲ *The Cross* ✳

25–27 High Street, Kingussie PH21 1HX   COOKING 3
KINGUSSIE (0540) 661762 and 661166   COST £32–£44

The news is that during the currency of this edition, the Hadleys are moving a
few hundred yards to a former tweed mill by the riverside. New buildings and
restoration will give them a larger restaurant (which may offer lunch), more
bedrooms and a better kitchen. This should not invalidate what we write here.
Ruth Hadley will still do the cooking, and Tony Hadley will continue to serve
the food and wine. 'It's almost a cabaret act,' writes one appreciative of his style
of service and customer care. More important, perhaps, is the fact that he knows
what he is talking about, particularly when it comes to the drink. The current
premises are small and surprising: 'It was a bit strange having a drink in a
shop window, but even on a cold winter's night, once inside you would never
have known the wild tempests were blowing.' Ruth Hadley has not changed
her approach: on a Saturday, seven courses with a choice of three alternatives
for the first course and the main dish are served; the rest of the week there is a
shorter meal of four courses (dropping the sorbet, fish course and separate

cheese stage) with choice all the way, except for the soup which comes second. Value is exceptional, especially when compared to many Highland country houses. Her repertoire is not of the widest. She has been heard to say that she sees no reason to respond to changes in fashion in south Britain, and seen here is a steady style of the early '80s: mousseline of pike with a cream prawn sauce, goats' cheese soufflé, marinated salmon, saddle of hare with a cèpe-flavoured game sauce, venison with port and redcurrant sauce, duck with blackcurrant sauce, salmon with sorrel cream sauce. The desserts are extremely good – filling but light, rich yet insubstantial. The wine list deserves the awards it gets. Of course, it's so cheap, it's worth a trip for that alone. The range is wide and includes not just France. The major blank is Italy, which Tony Hadley justifies by remarking that there were no takers for these wines. But this is a list that can be recommended without reservation. There are plenty of halves. House wines come as varying special selections.

CHEF: Ruth Hadley   PROPRIETORS: Tony and Ruth Hadley   OPEN: Tue to Sat, D only; 6.30 to 9.30   CLOSED: 3 weeks May, first 3 weeks Dec   MEALS: Set D £25 (Tue to Fri) to £32.50 (Sat)   SERVICE: not inc, card slips closed   DETAILS: 20 seats. Private parties: 18 main room. Vegetarian meals. No children under 12. No smoking in dining-room. Wheelchair access. No music   ACCOMMODATION: 3 rooms, all with bath/shower. B&B £65 to £130. Deposit: £25. No children under 12. Fax: (0540) 661080

KINLOCHMOIDART Highland   map 8

Kinacarra £ | NEW ENTRY |

Kinlochmoidart,
Lochailort PH38 4ND   COOKING 1*
SALEN (096 785) 238   COST £18–£30

'There is one building in Kinlochmoidart – the restaurant run by the MacLeans and the house attached. Now it is rose-clad and surrounded by a cottage garden, separated from Loch Moidart by an unfrequented road; once, it was a police station (during Kinlochmoidart's crime-wave?), then a school (until the baby-boom abated?).' Thus goes a report from the West Highlands. The MacLeans have clad their former school-cum-police station in pine and offer excellent food to all comers. Eat monster prawns from the loch, or moules marinière. Choose salmon in pastry with leeks and parsley, or baked chicken well spiked with spices. Finish enviably with apricot roulade or the lightest chilled strawberry soufflé. Frances MacLean is anxious to make flavours sing – she edges them with lemon (too much so in the mussels, to a tee in the roulade), or she ensures that 'spiced' means spiced. But the garlic is not overstated with the prawns, and the salmon was left to do its own thing. In other words, Frances MacLean is a cook with sense, producing with simplicity where necessary and never with any overload of fuss or bother. Angus MacLean is the right sort of host. Afternoon teas are available. House wine is £6.

CHEF: Frances MacLean   PROPRIETORS: Angus and Frances MacLean   OPEN: Tue to Sun (D only 1 Nov to 28 Feb); 12 to 2, 7 to 9   CLOSED: Mar   MEALS: alc   SERVICE: not inc   DETAILS: 24 seats. 1 table outside. Private parties: 30 main room. Car park. Vegetarian meals. Children's helpings. Wheelchair access. No music. Air-conditioned

LINLITHGOW Lothian

map 8

Champany Inn

Champany Corner, Linlithgow EH49 7LU
PHILPSTOUN (050 683) 4532 and 4388
2m NE of Linlithgow at junction of
A904 and A803

COOKING 3*
COST £28–£55

The inn is on a crossroads. The original inn is the Chop & Ale House – no reservations, great grills, and lower prices. The restaurant, all stone and solidity created with thorough-going flash by the Davidsons, has benefited from a revamped kitchen. The audience participation which is so much part of the 'Champany experience' has been extended from choosing your vegetables from a basket of raw produce, selecting your cut of meat for the grill or fingering your lobster in the tank, to watching the butcher do his stuff in full view. Champany is a steakhouse – with style, but a steakhouse. 'The most fantastic steaks we have ever had the pleasure of consuming,' states a happy returnee. The meat is properly selected, very well hung and then simply and accurately cooked. There are various sauces and variations on plain steak, but some wonder if these are desirable. The piquant sauce was so piquant for one reader 'as to be only suitable for people with heavy colds'. The menu is simplicity itself, revolving around the chargrill, with most people ordering beef or salmon. First courses of either clean shellfish or perhaps a soup, pâté or steak tartare are simple and good. There are also 'products of the smokehouse' – salmon or steak again – and the new menu, being introduced during 1992, offers more of that. Afterwards, move on to Stilton, then to a buffet of sweet things. The experience can cost. Vegetables are seriously dear, especially if you forget that the eight salads on the cold table come free in any event. Service is proficient, but not full-dress flunkeydom. 'Excessively encyclopaedic' was one reader's comment on the wine list; fine though the wines are, and despite the plaudits from all and sundry for 'outstanding list' and 'best cellar', the list perhaps takes too little account of the customer's time and possible knowledge. The own-label varietal wines clearly aid choice but user-unfriendliness extends to high prices on the main list. House wines are £9.25.

CHEFS: David Gibson and Clive Davidson   PROPRIETORS: Clive and Anne Davidson
OPEN: Mon to Sat, exc Sat L; 12.30 to 2, 7.15 to 10   CLOSED: 3 weeks from 24 Dec   MEALS:
alc. Set L £18.50. Minimum £14.50   SERVICE: 10%, card slips closed   CARDS: Access,
Amex, Diners, Visa   DETAILS: 50 seats. 13 tables outside. Private parties: 50 main room.
Car park. No children under 8. Smart dress preferred. Wheelchair access. No music. Fax:
(050 683) 4302

---

 denotes an outstanding wine cellar; ⏆ *denotes a good wine list, worth travelling for.*

Prices quoted in the Guide *are based on information supplied by restaurateurs. The prices quoted at the top of each entry represent a range, from the lowest meal price to the highest; the latter is inflated by 10 per cent to take account of likely price rises during the year of the* Guide.

MARKINCH Fife   map 8

▲ Balbirnie House

Balbirnie Park, Markinch KY7 6NE   COOKING 2
GLENROTHES (0592) 610066   COST £15–£46

In general, customers for this immaculate Greek-revival mansion come from
the boardrooms and open-plan offices of Silicon Valley in sufficient numbers to
fill the golf course, the beds and the acres of public rooms. Yet the individual is
not entirely forgotten. In the Gamekeeper's Inn you can have a light lunch;
there are a number of weekend deals; and lunch in the main dining-room is
competitively priced. As business hereabouts moves into the age of the chip, so
the cooking is not all pre-history. It is even possible to eat simply yet well
among the 'pillows of smoked salmon filled with crab and cottage cheese
parfait, with a pesto sauce', or 'breast of chicken with fresh asparagus and
lobster, served with a creamy white wine sauce with forest mushrooms'.
Service can be fairly approximate on a bad day. House wine is £10.25.

CHEF: George Mackay   PROPRIETORS: Balbirnie House Hotel Ltd   OPEN: all week; 12.30 to
2, 7 to 9.30   MEALS: alc. Set L £10.50 to £14, Set D £22 to £26.50   SERVICE: not inc, card
slips closed   CARDS: Access, Amex, Diners, Visa   DETAILS: 45 seats. Private parties: 60
main room, 16 and 60 private rooms. Car park. Vegetarian meals. Children's helpings.
Smart dress preferred. No cigars/pipes in dining-room. Wheelchair access (also WC).
Music   ACCOMMODATION: 30 rooms, all with bath/shower. Rooms for disabled. B&B £75
to £170. Children welcome. Baby facilities. Pets welcome. Afternoon teas. Garden. Golf.
Snooker. TV. Phone. Confirm by 6. Fax: (0592) 610529

MOFFAT Dumfries & Galloway   map 8

▲ Beechwood Country House Hotel ⭐

Moffat DG10 9RS   COOKING 1
MOFFAT (0683) 20210   COST £17–£26

The way to Beechwood is serpentine. Go to the north end of the high street,
look for the church and the school, and take the road between them. The hotel
is just outside the town, not far from Moffat Academy. Perhaps that is why the
house was once a school for 'young ladies'. Today, the more likely residents are
golfers or walkers, and Carl Shaw will keep them well nourished. He does not
shirk novelty. A spring menu contained steamed king prawns stuffed with
minced beef and served with a julienne of peppers, chicken with a mango
sauce, a vegetarian dish of grilled aubergine spiced with chilli and green
coriander, and lemon and coconut cake served with a rich lemon ice-cream.
Less complex things are not ignored: Carl's Yorkshire pudding, beef stew with
Guinness and cold rice-pudding. People find the welcome warm and the
dining-room ('glowing from peach table-covers and the silverware') a comfort.
Beechwood is not a grand hotel, but it is a pleasant one. The wine list
encompasses an acceptable general range at decent prices. House wines from
Justerini are £6.95 or £7.85.

CHEF: Carl Shaw PROPRIETORS: Lynda and Jeffrey Rogers OPEN: all week; 12 to 2, 7.30 to 9 CLOSED: 4 Jan to 8 Feb MEALS: Set L £11.50, Set D £17.50 SERVICE: not inc, card slips closed CARDS: Access, Amex, Visa DETAILS: 26 seats. 2 tables outside. Private parties: 26 main room. Car park. Vegetarian meals. Children welcome. Children's helpings. No smoking in dining-room. Wheelchair access (2 steps). Music ACCOMMODATION: 7 rooms, all with bath/shower. B&B £47 to £67. Children welcome. Baby facilities. Pets welcome. Afternoon teas. Garden. TV. Phone. Doors close at midnight. Fax: (0683) 20889 (*The Which? Hotel Guide*)

▲ *Well View*

Ballplay Road, Moffat DG10 9JU COOKING 2
MOFFAT (0683) 20184 COST £13–£27

'Sunday lunch is always a *menu surprise* of three courses and coffee. Yesterday, this consisted of a cheese and parsley soufflé, pork stuffed with apricots, cranberries, Japanese mushrooms and raisins, in a wild cranberry sauce, and plum and custard flan with vanilla sauce and home-made vanilla ice-cream. The soufflé was perfectly light, the pork tender and delicate, the flan an exact and most pleasing balance of tart and sweet. The vegetables with the main course were al dente, and it all came to £7 a head.' Janet Schuckardt's enterprising cooking is something of a surprise to people who think at first this is going to be just another little hotel in Dumfriesshire. Prices have risen a fraction from the quoted report for Sunday lunch early in 1992, and dinner is not quite so cheap. Janet Schuckardt sensibly keeps the choice short, but also manages real alternatives – for example, a slate of first courses that runs from crab soufflé, pigeon breast with a red wine and elderberry sauce, and a plate of sorbets with citrus fruit, to a salad of crottin de chèvre. There is an affection for fruits with meats and for exploiting the sweet-and-sour in savoury dishes. Menus give interesting wine suggestions, and the list itself shows much potential. Choice is broad, and although the Guigal 1982 Hermitage has attracted a £10 premium since 1992, the prices at the lower end remain fair. There are good petits châteaux and New World offerings are abundant. Growers' names are sometimes absent. House wine is £7.20. CELLARMAN'S CHOICE: Redwood Valley Estate, Chardonnay 1988, £19.20; Volnay, Caillerets 1987, £18.95.

CHEF: Janet Schuckardt PROPRIETORS: Janet and John Schuckardt OPEN: all week, exc Fri and Sat L; 12.30 to 1.30, 7 to 8.30 CLOSED: first week Jan, 1 week Nov MEALS: Set L £8 to £9, Set D £19 SERVICE: not inc, card slips closed CARDS: Access, Visa DETAILS: 24 seats. Private parties: 24 main room, 8 private room. Car park. Children's helpings. Smart dress preferred. No smoking in dining-room. Wheelchair access (2 steps; also WC). No music ACCOMMODATION: 6 rooms, all with bath/shower. B&B £30 to £76. Deposit: £10. Children welcome. Baby facilities. Pets welcome. Garden. TV. Doors close at 11.30. Confirm by 5.30

'Dark chocolate and rum mousse tasted sour and cheesey and at this point we complained and had the puddings deducted from our bill. The waiter expressed surprise because "the mousses were prepared on Saturday" – this was Tuesday.'
On eating in Warwickshire

MUIR OF ORD Highland   map 8

▲ *Dower House* ▮ ✳

Highfield, Muir of Ord IV6 7XN   COOKING 2*
MUIR OF ORD (0463) 870090   COST £37

The eighteenth-century house is not only a remarkable piece of eccentric
Scottish architecture, it also boasts wonderful grounds with ancient trees and
unusual plants. Robyn Aitchison loves the garden and takes much of its edible
harvest into his kitchen. Dinner is served in a rectangular room of majestic
proportions, with a white plasterwork ceiling, a grand piano and a splendid
white marble fireplace at one end. The concise four-course menu changes daily
and it highlights Robyn Aitchison's other consuming passion: fish. Dishes such
as salad of lobster with rocket and leeks, broad beans, skate wing sauté with an
assortment of chopped herbs and garlic, and darne of turbot coated in sesame
seeds with sorrel sauce have displayed confidence and accurate timing. Soups
are another highpoint, for example cream of lovage and 'outstandingly good'
sherry-coloured prawn consommé garnished with tendrils of seaweed and
fresh coriander. Meat-eaters might opt for loin of lamb with red pepper and
madeira sauce, or breast of duck with green peppercorn sauce. Desserts are
generally liked for their unusual combinations of ideas and flavours. Dainty
passion-fruit roulade with a sauce infused with sweet cicely (this is a kitchen
that knows its herbs), iced nougat with honey sauce, and praline ice-cream
with toffee-like sauce have been recommended. Breakfasts are rated as some of
the best in Scotland, according to a well-travelled reporter. Although not
cheap, the wine list shows needlepoint accuracy in searching out fine growers.
The New World barely gets a look in, but the French collection is carefully
balanced and thought through. House wines are £11.50. CELLARMAN'S
CHOICE: Haut-Médoc, Ch. Candale 1986, £19; Savigny-lès-Beaune, La
Dominode, Bruno Clair, £29.

CHEF: Robyn Aitchison PROPRIETORS: Robyn and Mena Aitchison OPEN: all week, D
only (L by arrangement); 7.30 for 8 MEALS: Set D £27.50 SERVICE: not inc, card slips
closed CARDS: Access, Amex, Visa DETAILS: 20 seats. 3 tables outside. Private parties: 20
main room. Car park. Vegetarian meals. Children's helpings. No smoking in dining-room.
Wheelchair access (also WC). No music ACCOMMODATION: 5 rooms, all with bath/
shower. Rooms for disabled. B&B £50 to £100. Deposit: 25%. Children welcome. Baby
facilities. Pets by arrangement. Garden. TV. Phone. Doors close at 11. Confirm by 4. Fax:
(0463) 870090

NEWTONMORE Highland   map 8

▲ *Ard-Na-Coille* ▮ ✳

Kingussie Road,
Newtonmore PH20 1AY   COOKING 3
NEWTONMORE (0540) 673214   COST £31

The 'austere and wood-panelled' dining-room strikes a note of sobriety in this
blue and white shooting-lodge smelling of honeysuckle and patrolled by a
friendly cat. Come here to get away from things – no television in the rooms –
but the stag's head gazing down on diners as venison is served for main course

may remind you of wider responsibilities. No-choice meals here are served to all guests simultaneously. Five courses are characterised by fresh materials treated directly – there may be a mousse or terrine at the start, but Barry Cottam eschews too much visible mutation of foods into 'dishes'. There are occasions when flavourings – the curry in the parsnip soup or the lime in the sauce with smoked trout, for example – win the battle with the base material, but most feel that Barry Cottam has achieved the right balance between art and simplicity, even if the appetite may be flagging by the end of the evening. A January meal consisted of smoked trout mousse wrapped with smoked trout, with a warm lemon dressing; courgette and basil soup; red deer with a port sauce; plain but accurate vegetables; a good set of cheese; and iced orange parfait with Grand Marnier and orange salad. A spring meal of scallops from the chargrill, leek and lime soup, pigeon on cabbage with port game sauce, and iced gâteau of chocolate rum and almonds with a vanilla sauce shows how the formula sometimes develops. The ancillaries are low-key: good bread and croissants, but no canapés or home-made petits fours. The same is true of the wine. Though the cellar is magnificent, service is muted and advice best sought from Barry Cottam before the meal. The prices here are remarkable, benefiting from fixed rather than percentage mark-ups. The range is classic when it comes to France – country wines are admitted only from the highest-profile new-wave makers – but there are some worthwhile selections from Italy, Spain and Australia. It would be otiose to list especially good makers; they all have their qualities and Barry Cottam will have explored them for you. Mature wines are there, particularly in claret and burgundy, even if the stocks of old Chablis have now gone. There is a short monthly selection of favourites if you can't face the long read. House selections start at £11.50. CELLARMAN'S CHOICE: Cloudy Bay, Sauvignon Blanc 1991, £15; Dom. de Trévallon 1987, £16.50.

CHEF: Barry Cottam   PROPRIETORS: Barry Cottam and Nancy Ferrier   OPEN: all week, D only; 7.45   CLOSED: mid-Nov and Dec   MEALS: Set D £25   SERVICE: not inc, card slips closed   DETAILS: 18 seats. Private parties: 18 main room. Car park. Children's helpings on request. No smoking in dining-room. No music   ACCOMMODATION: 7 rooms, all with bath/shower. D,B&B £55 to £130. Children welcome. Baby facilities. Pets welcome. Garden. Phone. Doors close at 11.30. Confirm by 4. Fax: (0540) 673453 (*The Which? Hotel Guide*)

NORTH BERWICK Lothian   map 8

Harding's ♥ ⚔

2 Station Road,
North Berwick EH39 4AU   COOKING 2
NORTH BERWICK (0620) 4737   COST £15–£33

Adjacent to the railway station, Harding's is a small, relaxed and informal restaurant. Walls are hung with kilims and furnishings are simple. A large hatch through to the kitchen gives a view of Christopher Harding preparing the food – 'soufflés sweatily beaten before you'. The daily-changing fixed-price dinner menu is short, drawn from a steady repertoire. There seems to have been a change of emphasis towards heartier portions and cruder presentation, while at the core the cooking remains sound and well-balanced. An inspection meal produced some sound food: quenelles of smoked salmon; beef fillet with strips of celeriac in a grain mustard and tarragon cream sauce; steamed turbot and monkfish fillet on steamed leeks with a lemon and dill sauce; hot pear and praline soufflé. Large portions of vegetables are carefully cooked, petits fours are good, but bread and butter and coffee could be better. Service is casual, occasionally too casual. A simpler lunch menu offers good value. Christopher Harding declares ex-pat loyalty with a list of antipodean wines that must exceed anything west of Perth (Australia). Quality is unstintingly fine, prices are fair, and with a range of half-bottles and decent house wines by the glass economy is attainable. The cursory glance at France looks less necessary by the year. The merits are interest and enthusiasm rather than balance. House wine is £7.20. CELLARMAN'S CHOICE: Victoria, Chardonnay 1989, Balgownie, £19.40; Victoria, Cabernet Sauvignon 1985, Dalwhinnie, £14.55.

CHEF/PROPRIETOR: Christopher Harding OPEN: Wed to Sat; 12.15 to 2, 7.30 to 9 MEALS: alc L. Set D £19.75 to £22.25 SERVICE: not inc DETAILS: 24 seats. Private parties: 24 main room. Car park. Children's helpings. No smoking. Wheelchair access (also WC). Music

---

OBAN Strathclyde   map 8

▲ *Knipoch Hotel* ▮

Oban PA34 4QT   COOKING 2*
KILNINVER (085 26) 251   COST £50

'Our room was really warm,' went one report. It needs to be, for hills and sea are not far distant, winds whip up ('we stopped our rattling window with a wedge of card') and a protective skin is a necessity. Inner warmth is provided by the cooking. The Craigs are self-sufficiency kings: roasting green coffee beans, smoking salmon (rather strongly), baking bread. They work to settled patterns, with a familiar repertoire that expands but slowly. 'A new dish this year,' one of the Craigs writes, 'is scallops with spring onions and green ginger.' 'Very fine' was one verdict. 'The ginger was subtle, the pan juices mixed with white wine were good enough for us to demand a spoon to finish them completely.' Dinner is five courses, set-price and no-choice, unless you really can't face some items, when plainer dishes can be substituted. A spring meal produced chicken consommé, sole wrapped round a salmon mousse with a white wine cream sauce, breast of duck with red wine and red cabbage, vignotte cheese (one named sort of cheese is offered on each menu), finishing with vanilla ice-cream in a sugar basket surrounded by mango and plum slices. Cooking tends to the simple, not to excess, and many are struck by its consistency. However, mistakes sometimes occur, made the more heinous by the price. The wine list affords hours of reading. As ever the range and the quality are as good as anywhere, reflected accurately by prices. Care in selection is evident regardless of grandeur. The enthusiast should arrive early for a prolonged read. There are nine good house wines from £7.90. CELLARMAN'S CHOICE: Aroona Valley, Chardonnay 1990, £9.90; Côtes du Rhône, La Haie aux Grives 1988, £9.90.

'''*My set meals are all à la carte.*''' On eating in London

CHEFS: Colin and Jenny Craig   PROPRIETORS: the Craig family   OPEN: all week, D only (L by arrangement); 7.30 to 9   CLOSED: mid-Nov to mid-Feb   MEALS: Set D £36   SERVICE: not inc, card slips closed   CARDS: Access, Amex, Diners, Visa   DETAILS: 46 seats. Private parties: 24 main room. Car park. Children's helpings. No music   ACCOMMODATION: 17 rooms, all with bath/shower. B&B £59 to £118. Children welcome. Baby facilities. Afternoon teas. Garden. TV. Phone. Doors close at 11. Confirm by 6. Fax: (085 26) 249 (*The Which? Hotel Guide*)

PEAT INN Fife   map 8

▲ *Peat Inn* 🍶

Peat Inn KY15 5LH
PEAT INN (033 484) 206
at junction of B940 and B941,   COOKING 4
6m SW of St Andrews   COST £24–£50

Peat Inn is a crossroads. Where once the village danced, the Wilsons have fashioned dining-rooms and kitchens; where once it drank, they have made a purple-carpeted reception and bar. If you were to say, 'What shall I convert into a luxury restaurant?' the inn would be the last to spring to mind. Suspend disbelief and France is summoned up: high-backed tapestry chairs, bare stone walls, an ineffably strange taste in décor that is not the world's but gains its converts. David Wilson went through a bad patch last year. Distress was more common than praise. The place has settled down again, though once a pinnacle is achieved there will always be marksmen eager to knock you off. There is a series of menus and meals, rising from lunch at under £20, through a set menu of the day, a six-course tasting menu (for a whole table only), to the à la carte. Broadly, the repertoire is as before: a lot of game and fish, definitely cooked with an eye to mainland Europe rather than Britain's island heritage, even if local materials do bulk large. There can be slight repetition here: 'Perhaps they specialise in "horizontal tastings" of small birds,' wrote one who felt she had had a surfeit after two days of eating. The tasting menu can move from seafood in a spiced butter sauce, through monkfish on potato and onion with a meat sauce, pigeon on a bed of pulses in a beef broth, to venison in a red wine sauce with port. This may be thought too close a progression, not helping appetite by jumps of tone and texture as well as of taste. Presentation is fussy, though tastes are not. Recommendations of dishes in the spring covered things as simple as salad of lobster with a citrus sauce to unexpected combinations like the scallops, monkfish and pork in a ragoût ('firm, yet yielding to the bite'). In a robust gratin of smoked haddock with chervil, the fish gained a pyrrhic victory over the cheese while it won hands down, and gloriously, when a piece of gleaming turbot was placed on a bed of leeks and wild mushrooms with a lightly reduced meat stock. 'Hearty elegance' was the term for fillet steak with ceps – great steak, on sweet and crunchy onion, with a galette of potato, some aubergine, broccoli and beans set around it, and a sauce so dark and intense, yet full of mushroom earthiness. The urge to multiply comes into its own with dessert. The highest praise has been reserved for a trio of caramel ice-cream, crème caramel, and caramelised apple tart with caramel sauce. A sorbet (pineapple and grenadine) will come with mango, three colours of grape, kumquat, passion-fruit, figs, lychee, strawberries and raspberries. Coffee is usually fine, but espresso would be better; petits fours get less support than do the slices of quiche at the outset, or the appetiser when you sit at table. Not everyone has yet been convinced of a return to form – the variations are surprising. One factor does seem to be the service. Though often charming, staff are not at the level of professionalism that Europeans expect, and there have been moments of grief. When running a hotel (for such the Peat Inn has to be called), it is not enough to expect people to find their own way in, to hunt up someone to help them, and so fuel insecurity. One area that continues to attract our unreserved enthusiasm is the clearly presented wine list. White burgundies and clarets are majestic, but selection is as sure from Spain and the antipodes. While there is much good drinking below £15, the higher reaches should not be spurned since price reflects quality fairly. Half-bottles are very pleasing. CELLARMAN'S CHOICE: Chablis 1989, Durup, £17; Penedès, Cabernet Sauvignon 1979, Jean Léon, £18.

CHEF: David Wilson   PROPRIETORS: David and Patricia Wilson   OPEN: Tue to Sat; 1 to 2.30, 7 to 9.30   CLOSED: 2 weeks Jan, 2 weeks Nov   MEALS: alc. Set L £17.50, Set D £28 to £38   SERVICE: net prices, card slips closed   CARDS: Access, Amex, Visa   DETAILS: 48 seats. Private parties: 24 main room, 12 private room. Car park. Children's helpings. No smoking during meals. Wheelchair access (also WC). No music   ACCOMMODATION: 8 rooms, all with bath/shower. Rooms for disabled. B&B £95 to £130. No children under 10. Garden. TV. Phone. Confirm by 4. Fax: (033 484) 530 (*The Which? Hotel Guide*)

PEEBLES Borders   map 8

▲ *Cringletie House* ¾✳

Eddleston, Peebles EH45 8PL
EDDLESTON (072 13) 233   COOKING 1
on A703, 2m N of Peebles   COST £17–£33

Telegraphic messages sometimes reach the *Guide*. Cringletie inspired this one: 'Excellent service, feel like one of the family, smiles all round, every wish anticipated, copious food beautifully cooked.' Aileen Maguire's cooking of such things as lamb's liver and onions and mustard, roast turkey stuffed with pine-kernels, smoked haddock with mushrooms and cream, and good roast beef has contented many. A menu of four or five choices per course, with a soup popped in the middle, is charged at a set price. The range will include things like salmon in an oatmeal crust, duck with a lychee sauce or pork with tomatoes, mushrooms and white wine. First courses mentioned have included jellied ham with parsley and peppercorns, an elderflower sorbet with melon, fresh pasta with crab and tomato, and a gratin of avocado and smoked haddock. Reports have been positive this year, including praise for the excellent breakfasts. The atmosphere of family service, enhanced by the turreted mansion, may calm the visitor, but professionalism is not forgotten when it comes to wines. The wine list is a broad range, at decent prices, of decent bottles; some are very good indeed. It has taken in a new clutch of clarets this year, but the representation from beyond France is very adequate. House Duboeuf is £10 a litre. CELLARMAN'S CHOICE: Krondorf Cabernet Sauvignon 1983, £13.50; Sanford Sauvignon Blanc 1988, £13.45.

CHEFS: Aileen Maguire and Sheila McKellar PROPRIETORS: Mr and Mrs Stanley Maguire OPEN: all week; 1 to 1.45, 7.30 to 8.30 CLOSED: Jan and Feb MEALS: alc L Mon to Sat. Set Sun L £13.50, Set D £22.50. Minimum £5.50 SERVICE: not inc, card slips closed CARDS: Access, Visa DETAILS: 56 seats. Private parties: 30 main room. Car park. Vegetarian meals. Children's helpings. No smoking in dining-room. No music ACCOMMODATION: 13 rooms, all with bath/shower. Lift. B&B £44 to £80. Children welcome. Baby facilities. Pets welcome. Afternoon teas. Garden. Tennis. TV. Phone. Doors close at 11. Confirm by 5. Fax: (072 13) 244 (*The Which? Hotel Guide*)

PERTH Tayside   map 8

Timothy's

24 St John Street, Perth PH1 5SP	COOKING 1
PERTH (0738) 26641	COST £13–£24

The Laings have been here since 1970. 'Like Tennyson's brook, Timothy's goes on for ever. We courted in Timothy's, celebrated our first daughter there, and visited it as often as our infrequent trips home would permit,' wrote a couple who have now returned to their home town and are 'revelling in getting to know it again'. The same hessian is on the walls (raffia mats too), and the random chairs and scrupulous cleanliness are unchanged. All this contributes to the self-confessed 'club-like' atmosphere, where most people are happy to be – the Laings are happy to serve them (knowing most of them anyway). The food is essentially open sandwiches, preceded by 'snitter' or appetisers, and flanked by larger dishes of lobster, salmon, ham or beef (all cold). Mayonnaise, prawns or chicken are vital elements to many of the fillings. Daily specials do occur, but not every day. Fondue bourguignonne is the major hot dish – with six sauces and green salads. The wine list is a careful one. House wine is £6.80; there are also aquavits.

CHEF: Caroline Laing PROPRIETORS: Caroline and Athole Laing OPEN: Tue to Sat; 12 to 2.30, 7 to 10 (post-theatre D by arrangement) CLOSED: 3 weeks summer MEALS: alc. Minimum £5.70 after 9.30pm SERVICE: not inc, card slips closed CARDS: Access, Visa DETAILS: 54 seats. Private parties: 20 main room. Vegetarian meals. Children's helpings. Wheelchair access. Music. Air-conditioned

---

PORT APPIN Strathclyde   map 8

▲ Airds Hotel ▮ ⁵✳

Port Appin PA38 4DF	COOKING 4
APPIN (063 173) 236	COST £51

The unassuming building has the scenery on its side: it sits right on Loch Linnhe, which adds piquancy of view to the emphatic flavours encountered on the plate. The external modesty may be thought false when the starched perfection of appointments within and the correctness of the service and attention are discovered. This is a very professionally run place, yet Eric Allen charms as well as convinces. Standards such as these need income to support them; hence the price is up there with the leaders, although the menu does not immediately strike the reader as demanding. Betty Allen's style is as deceptive as that of the building: it has little truck with over-elaboration and makes a virtue of seemliness. A choice of three or four dishes is offered at the first and main courses, and there is a soup in between; the dessert course offers more options. The simplicity is not backward-looking; new tendencies in kitchens here, in France and in Italy have been absorbed. Hence the appearance of dishes such as poached oysters with mango and lime butter, breast of pigeon with lentils and wild mushrooms, or a mousse of mussels with Muscadet sauce, and guinea-fowl stuffed with mushroom mousse on a sauce of soy, spring onion and honey. The chief quality people appreciate is that tastes are true: 'If it says mussels, then that's what you get.' Cooking is also usually accurate, and there are grace notes such as warm brioche with tomato and basil soup, onion marmalade and mint jelly with loin of lamb, or the walnut shortbread hearts served with a mango mousse. Quantities are well-judged so people who stay more than a night are not out-faced. At moments, the simplicity is regretted – for instance, with the vegetables – but all admit the usually great flavour. Cheese comes as a half-dozen slices already laid out on a plate, with grapes and oat biscuits. Two house wines from the recently improved house of Chapoutier indicate a wide-ranging and fair-minded approach to wine-buying. The burgundy cellar shows good maturity, but is more than matched by a page of very fine Italians. Price reflects quality closely, and although a quick glance may leave some aghast, closer inspection reveals canny selection and much good drinking well below £15. Also, there are good half-bottles. House wines are from £11.

CHEFS: Betty Allen and Graeme Allen   PROPRIETORS: Eric, Betty and Graeme Allen
OPEN: all week; 12.30 to 1.30 (snacks only), 8 for 8.30   CLOSED: 6 Jan to 6 Mar   MEALS:
Set D £35   SERVICE: not inc   DETAILS: 40 seats. Private parties: 40 main room, 8 private
room. Car park. Children's helpings. No children under 4. Smart dress preferred. No
smoking in dining-room. No music   ACCOMMODATION: 12 rooms, all with bath/shower.
B&B £83 to £178. Deposit: £100. No children under 5. Afternoon teas. Garden. TV. Phone.
Doors close at 11.30. Confirm by 4. Fax: (063 173) 535 (*The Which? Hotel Guide*)

PORTPATRICK Dumfries & Galloway   map 8

▲ *Knockinaam Lodge* ✣✳

Portpatrick DG9 9AD
PORTPATRICK (077 681) 471   COOKING 3*
off A77, S of Portpatrick   COST £26–£43

The house sits in its own cove, rocky headlands to each side, bare grass and gorse stretching up the hill behind. For counterpoint, plenty of swagged curtains, deep pelmets and panelled wainscot give comfort to the homebody. This is Scotland's version of a South Seas paradise: far horizons, soft sunlight, enveloping mist, the good old Gulf Stream keeping off the frost. Marcel Frichot comes from the Seychelles, so is expert in both forms of heaven. He is also a good host. Daniel Galmiche, a Frenchman, does the cooking. His origins are left in no doubt from the short nightly menu, but he practises a modern Gallic style, one that includes spices – cardamom with monkfish, for instance – as well as saucisson and lentils with *lieu jaune* (yellow pollack). Perhaps it is national habit that makes him 'slightly stingy with the vegetables', in the words of one repeat visitor. Technique, however, is à point, and invention keeps people who stay for more than a night happy with variety. 'The best meals we had in a two-week stay in the north,' reported one; and echoes have rebounded from the headlands. The style is pretty, but generally quantities are well judged. The wine list gives space, at a price, to Bordeaux, and the burgundies are represented strongly by the houses of Faiveley and Chanson. A foray into Australia (Knappstein), New Zealand (Nobilo) or even California (Sonoma-Cutrer) may give variety to the fairly conventional selection. House wines start at £9.25.

CHEF: Daniel Galmiche   PROPRIETORS: Marcel and Corinna Frichot   OPEN: all week; 12.30 to 2, 7.30 to 9   CLOSED: 4 Jan to 14 Mar   MEALS: Set L £19, Set D £30   SERVICE: not inc, card slips closed   CARDS: Access, Amex, Diners, Visa   DETAILS: 28 seats. Private parties: 40 main room. Car park. Children under 12 high teas only. Jacket and tie. No smoking in dining-room. Wheelchair access (1 step; also WC). Music   ACCOMMODATION: 10 rooms, all with bath/shower. B&B £65 to £130. Deposit: £50. Children welcome. Baby facilities. Pets welcome. Afternoon teas. Garden. Fishing. TV. Phone. Doors close at midnight. Confirm 7 days ahead. Fax: (077 681) 471 (The Which? Hotel Guide)

ST MARGARET'S HOPE Orkney   map 8

▲ The Creel £   NEW ENTRY

Front Road,
St Margaret's Hope KW17 2SL   COOKING 3
ST MARGARET'S HOPE (085 683) 311   COST £19–£37

Hit Orkney and choose: the Highland Park distillery, The Creel restaurant, a standing stone (or several). If the Stone Age is a mystery to you, then a restaurant as good as this will be a lifesaver. 'I was so enjoying studying the menu and making up my mind what to eat, that in a way it was a disappointment to be told that there was lobster tonight,' recounted one traveller. 'Of course, we had the lobster.' The point she makes is that Alan Craigie is a proper cook, not just a purveyor of matchless raw materials from inshore fishing, and it would be a shame to treat his restaurant as if it were simply a retailer of such materials. His style is not fancy: he knows where to stop, even when embarking on more complex dishes such as smoked lamb with melon, home-cured beef, monkfish with rhubarb butter sauce, or salmon with ginger and currants wrapped in pastry, served with a sorrel sauce. Thus scallops taste sweet and retain all their natural juice, mussels are plump and enhanced by rich broth of tomato and garlic, while smoked haddock soup is the business. Beef is from Orkney, and is generous and properly hung. You don't mess about with mainland supplies if you can get them from the islands and Alan Craigie makes every effort to rely on real vegetables and soft fruit. Try the beremeal bannocks – Orcadian barley bread. You will not lack for food here or gentle, pleasant service. 'I wish it weren't so far away,' ended one postcard, but then the charm might evaporate even if quality stayed the same. The wine list keeps life simple. House wines are £6.95.

Report forms are at the back of the book; write a letter if you prefer.

CHEF: Alan Craigie PROPRIETORS: Joyce and Alan Craigie OPEN: Tue to Sun D, Apr to Oct (Fri and Sat D only, Nov to Mar); 7 to 9.30 CLOSED: Jan MEALS: alc SERVICE: not inc, card slips closed CARDS: Access, Visa DETAILS: 38 seats. Private parties: 38 main room. Vegetarian meals. No children under 5. Wheelchair access (2 steps; also WC). Music ACCOMMODATION: 3 rooms, all with bath/shower. B&B £20 to £40. Deposit: £10. Garden. TV. Doors close at midnight. Confirm by 4

SCONE Tayside   map 8

▲ *Murrayshall Hotel*

Scone PH2 7PH   COOKING **3***
SCONE (0738) 51171   COST £22–£49

The views are very fine; the golf is much enjoyed; comfort abounds. Down at the Old Masters Restaurant (paintings, not retired golfers) Bruce Sangster cooks his heart out for the evening meal. Lunches in the Club House are not the same thing at all. There has been a consistent attempt to ennoble Scottish produce with techniques borrowed from classical cooking. Some solutions are particular; thus roe deer comes on a rösti, with cabbage and Chinese leaves in a whisky and pickled walnut sauce. Other solutions are more obvious, for instance a feuilleté of wild mushrooms and pigeon breast in brandy sauce. Bruce Sangster is not so blind to current fashion as to ignore Mediterranean manners applied to northern materials: a crab ravioli is served with a salmon mousse and olive oil, tomato and basil. His techniques are highly developed. He can bring off a spiced prawn soup glazed with a shellfish sabayon, as well as fillet of beef topped with a chicken and Stilton mousse. There is sometimes an overtone of nouvelle cuisine in the regular appearance of vinegars in the saucing and fruit-acid in the flavouring of savoury dishes, but he is well able to handle broader tastes as in a haddock chowder with lentils, potatoes and bacon. The value here is very fair. There are two fixed-price menus that mitigate the onslaught of the full *carte*, but they stint neither on materials nor elaboration. Desserts are often enjoyed, for presentation as well as taste: a filo moneybag of banana and pears, sticky toffee pudding and a hot caramel soufflé all come with two sauces; and one summer report found pleasure in the memory of an ad hoc combination of crème brûlée, chocolate truffle and an apple tart. Attention to detail, from the service to the ancillaries and incidentals, is close. Although the wine list proved less than accurate during the winter – perhaps as items were swept away and new ones brought in without notice – it does stand for a sound range of classic Franch material, with good reinforcements from Spain and California. These latter impart some class at economical rates. Halves are there aplenty. House wines are £10.50.

CHEF: Bruce Sangster PROPRIETORS: Macolsen Ltd OPEN: all week, D only, and Sun L; 12 to 2, 7 to 9.30 MEALS: alc. Set Sun L £12.75 to £15, Set D £20 to £35 SERVICE: not inc, card slips closed CARDS: Access, Amex, Diners, Visa DETAILS: 60 seats. Private parties: 20 main room, 70 private room. Car park. Vegetarian meals. Children welcome. Jacket and tie. Wheelchair access. Music ACCOMMODATION: 19 rooms, all with bath/shower. B&B £70 to £125. Deposit: 25%. No children under 10. Pets welcome. Afternoon teas. Garden. Tennis. Golf. TV. Phone. Fax: (0738) 52595 (*The Which? Hotel Guide*)

STEWARTON Strathclyde   map 8

▲ *Chapeltoun House* ♛ ✲

Stewarton KA3 3ED
STEWARTON (0560) 82696
2m from Stewarton, on B769   COOKING 2
towards Irvine   COST £22–£38

Sitting between Glasgow and the coast, this was a convenient spot for a
Glasgow merchant to build his country house in 1900. The house remains
substantially as it was then constructed: a handsome and austere exterior,
rooms a sometimes heavy Edwardian classical, though often lightened by paint
and drapes installed by the present owners. It is a comfortable place, not
without a certain formality, though 'service is good and the atmosphere
friendly'. Formality exists also in the cooking, which enjoys mousses, timbales
and chartreuses over simpler fare. A set-price menu at lunch and dinner offers
plenty of choice, and complexity is not compulsory: 'carrot and lovage soup, a
pair of quail stuffed with wild mushrooms and tarragon, followed by crème
brûlée' were admirable for one visitor, though he might have chosen a trout
and brill chartreuse, gratin of avocado and prawns, timbale of leek and
asparagus, terrine of guinea-fowl or roulade of chicken with a timbale of wild
rice. Desserts are laid out on a sideboard. The wine list is a model of clarity,
sound choice and fair spread, at often bargain prices. The range of clarets below
£30 is worth a look and there is a decent set of halves. You might drink
Canadian Chardonnay at £12.90, or house Bordeaux at £8.50 or £9.20.
CELLARMAN'S CHOICE: St-Emilion 1982, Ch. Corbin, £25.30; Notre Dame de
Landiras 1990, £10.60.

CHEF: Tom O'Donnell   PROPRIETORS: Colin and Graeme McKenzie   OPEN: all week; 12 to
2, 7 to 9.15   MEALS: Set L £16, Set D £23.50 to £26.50   SERVICE: not inc, card slips closed
CARDS: Access, Amex, Visa   DETAILS: 55 seats. Private parties: 35 main room, 20 and 55
private rooms. Car park. Vegetarian meals. No children under 12. Smart dress preferred. No
smoking in dining-room. Wheelchair access (3 steps; also WC). No music
ACCOMMODATION: 8 rooms, all with bath/shower. B&B £65 to £95. No children under 12.
Pets by arrangement. Afternoon teas. Garden. Fishing. TV. Phone. Doors close at midnight.
Confirm by 4. Fax: (0560) 85100 (*The Which? Hotel Guide*)

SWINTON Borders   map 8

▲ *Wheatsheaf Hotel,* *Four Seasons* ✲ £

Swinton TD11 3JJ   COOKING 2
SWINTON (089 086) 257   COST £14–£29

'We found the atmosphere welcoming, the service efficient, the ingredients
honest, prices fair and the place, deservedly, packed.' This conclusion of a
report on the Reids' small pub, hotel and restaurant explains succinctly the
attractions. Customers for the restaurant may choose from a long seasonal menu
or a quick-change *carte* of perhaps 10 dishes written on a blackboard in the bar.
Thus Alan Reid maintains the balance between planning (necessary for a very

busy bar trade) and immediacy in his cooking and buying. There are two dining-rooms, split between smokers and the supporters of pure air, of contrasting mood: one modern in a pine-ceilinged sun lounge, the other old and enclosed. The food, however, is of one purpose: good materials (for instance, the local smoked salmon and the beef) cooked with an eye to bold flavour and accurate seasoning. Thus marinated herrings as a first course come with a sweetish curried sauce, deep-fried Brie has a hot plum sauce, steak comes with 'wild' (oyster) mushrooms, chicken with Parma ham and cheese and a Marsala cream sauce. Fish, up from Eyemouth, is top-hole. 'The cooking is far from unenterprising, but does not suffer from excessive ambition' was another summary of the way Mr Reid does it. The wine list is sensibly priced and sensibly short, while taking in the world to give customers a fair choice of style. Very few bins cost more than £20. House wines are £6.50.

CHEF: Alan Reid PROPRIETORS: Alan and Julie Reid OPEN: Tue to Sun; 11.45 to 2, 6 to 10 CLOSED: 25 Dec, 1 Jan, 2 weeks Feb, 1 week Oct MEALS: alc SERVICE: not inc, card slips closed CARDS: Access, Visa DETAILS: 30 seats. Private parties: 30 main room, 28 private room. Vegetarian meals. Children's helpings. Smart dress preferred. No smoking in 1 dining-room. Wheelchair access (1 step; also WC). No music ACCOMMODATION: 4 rooms, 2 with bath/shower. B&B £25 to £55. Children welcome. Baby facilities. Pets welcome. Garden. TV. Doors close at midnight. Confirm by 6

TIRORAN Strathclyde   map 8

▲ *Tiroran House* ⑅✸

Tiroran, Isle of Mull PA69 6ES   COOKING 2*
TIRORAN (068 15) 232   COST £18–£39

You may take advantage of the loch view, set off by immaculate gardens, if you eat in the conservatory; or gaze inwardly in the panelled dining-room, accompanied by candlelight, table-tops aglow with polish, and a Chinese emperor's golden coat. This small hotel-restaurant takes residents only, unless there be chairs to spare and some prior warning. The Blockeys run it all house-party fashion, but not without system and routine: the dinner card is ready between 5.30 and 6pm; orders for first courses (there's a choice of three) are written by each guest on a sheet of paper before 6.45pm; dinner is served at 7.45pm; and if you want an aperitif, get down earlier, and Robin Blockey will take care of introductions to fellow guests. This is designed to get food to table in prime condition: 'Its timing was better than in many places where you all go through together, it was quite leisurely and Robin Blockey made us feel very much at home, yet without tedium or intrusion.' Cooking is extremely careful: an apple and mushroom soup with pastry croûtons, a Dunsyre blue tartlet, breast of duck with light juniper gravy, potatoes (parisienne), courgettes and green peas, then, from a laden dessert trolley, hot chocolate, ginger and meringue pudding and caramel ice-cream with caramel sauce followed by cheese. Coffee is from a communal pot in the lounge. This single account ignores the variety over the season: noisettes of lamb with a sorrel purée, wild salmon with sauce choron, chicken breast with port and a herb and ham stuffing, roast meats at the main course; interesting soups, smoked fish, perhaps tomatoes en cocotte with basil or a fluffy cheese omelette to begin;

good British puddings or a mousse affair to end. The wines are largely from Corney & Barrow and show the upper-crust connections of that firm – Leflaive, Ch. Latour à Pomerol, Simi, CVNE, Antinori, to name a few. Finish with a malt. House wines are £8.

CHEF: Sue Blockey   PROPRIETORS: Robin and Sue Blockey   OPEN: all week, D only (L residents only); 7.45   CLOSED: Oct to mid-May   MEALS: Set L £12.50, Set D £28.50   SERVICE: not inc   DETAILS: 20 seats. Private parties: 6 main room. Car park. No children under 10. Smart dress preferred. No smoking in dining-room. no music   ACCOMMODATION: 9 rooms, all with bath/shower. D,B&B £93 to £202. Deposit: £50. No children under 10. Pets by arrangement. Garden. Confirm by noon. Fax: (068 15) 232

TROON Strathclyde   map 8

▲ *Highgrove House*

Old Loans Road, Troon KA10 7HL	COOKING 1
TROON (0292) 312511	COST £22–£35

Bill Costley has worked in the grand hotels and competed with the chefs of Europe in salons culinaires. He knows his onions and cooks a soundly based classical menu in a comfortable house overlooking the Firth of Clyde. A meal of warm salad of wild mushrooms, duck and pine-kernels, curried parsnip and apple soup, medallions of beef Rossini-style, and banana gratin with kirsch showed a mix of old and new, generosity in quantity and competence in execution. The wine list has enough to choose from, though light in red burgundies and stronger in clarets. There are some strange alternate vintages even among first growths, and half-bottles are hardly thick on the ground. House wines are £8.75.

CHEF: William Costley   PROPRIETORS: William and Catherine Costley   OPEN: all week; 12 to 2.30, 7 to 9.30   MEALS: alc. Set brasserie menu 6 to 9.30 Sun to Fri £16.50   SERVICE: not inc   CARDS: Access, Amex, Visa   DETAILS: 80 seats. 8 tables outside. Private parties: 50 main room, 30 and 50 private rooms. Car park. Vegetarian meals. Children welcome. Smart dress preferred. Wheelchair access (also WC). Music   ACCOMMODATION: 9 rooms, all with bath/shower. B&B £49 to £67. Children welcome. Baby facilities. Afternoon teas. Garden. TV. Phone. Doors close at 1am. Confirm 2 days ahead

---

UIG Western Isles   map 8

▲ *Baille-Na-Cille* ⁵⋇

Timsgarry, Uig,	
Isle of Lewis PA86 9JD	
TIMSGARRY (085 175) 242	
B8011 to Uig, then right down	COOKING 1
track on shore	COST £24

'We are very, very, very informal,' writes Richard Gollin. In their converted manse, the mountains in the distance, white sands to the fore, the Gollins hold the ring between adults and children, feeding mothers their G&Ts while tinies eat high tea. Everyone gets round to eating in the end and Joanna Gollin cooks three courses, then there's cheese. Russian vegetable soup with pine-nut dumplings, duck stuffed with ham, walnuts, apricot and black pudding, and baked cheesecake with a strawberry sauce was one dinner; chicken liver pâté, trout with dill hollandaise, and rhubarb and hazelnut roulade was another. Vegetables are fresh, Joanna is an ace at baking bread, and variations to the menus for special circumstances are readily agreed. Wines come at two prices: house is £8.50, the rest are £12.50. A cheerful place.

CHEF: Joanna Gollin PROPRIETORS: Richard and Joanna Gollin OPEN: all week; 9.30 to 5 snacks, 7.30 CLOSED: 15 Oct to 1 Mar MEALS: daytime snacks. Set D £18 SERVICE: net prices, card slips closed CARDS: Access, Visa DETAILS: 30 seats. Private parties: 30 main room. Car park. Vegetarian meals. Children's helpings. No smoking in dining-room. No music ACCOMMODATION: 13 rooms, 9 with bath/shower. D,B&B £37 to £96. Deposit: £50. Children welcome. Baby facilities. Pets welcome. Afternoon teas. Garden. Fishing. Fax: (085 175) 241 (*The Which? Hotel Guide*)

ULLAPOOL Highland   map 8

▲ *Altnaharrie Inn* ♀ ⁵⁄✕

Ullapool IV26 2SS   COOKING 5
DUNDONNELL (085 483) 230   COST £56

Drive to Ullapool, park on the quay, phone Fred Brown, wait for the MV *Mother Goose*, cross the loch, watch out for the slippery steps – and you've arrived. Don't forget to pack the wellingtons. People make a thing of getting there, but Altnaharrie *is* isolated. It is also unique. At the inn, the clarity of vision and the well-pitched level of taste are immediately apparent from the decoration: comfortable, clean, ornament but a certain northern simplicity. Candles and torches by the bed cope with no volts from the generator after midnight. There is no smoking throughout. When they started, Fred Brown and Gunn Eriksen were meant to be owners, not executants. It was only the defection of their chosen managers that forced their hands to the pumps. Aren't we lucky? Gunn Eriksen is a natural cook, self-taught, responding to other people's practice, but answering too to her own artistic instincts and the demands of her locality. Hence sauces are properly made (professionalism), but ingredients have a fresh pitch (wild foods) and presentation of dishes is original. Dinner only is served at a set time. It will take several hours – 'three and a half hours of sheer bliss' – so fast eaters be warned. As Altnaharrie is a small operation, so the personal systems, such as ordering wine from the list in the lounge well in advance, listening to a recitation of the menu rather than reading it and the pace of the meal itself, are integral to the character. But you will want for nothing even if you do pour your own wine. The form of the meal is three savoury courses before cheese, then a choice of three desserts (or all of them); there is no choice at the beginning, however. Gunn Eriksen keeps a note of earlier visits by any returnees, to avoid repeating dishes. This does mean she will be cooking more than one menu on any day, which puts a different perspective on critics who say this is not a 'restaurant'. That said, the repertoire is well-practised. Given the complexity of some dishes, and their precision, this is no bad thing. In the summer an inspector ate asparagus in a pastry case with lemon sauce and mussels in a bitter cress sauce; ravioli of guinea-fowl with a vermouth sauce; roast turbot with a veal jus and a scallop sauce; kohlrabi and potatoes; cheese;

then Norwegian biscuit cups (*krumkaker*) filled with cloudberry ice-cream. The response, apart from real pleasure, was that a plainer dish would have been welcome at some point. Sauces are not heavy, but the cumulation tells. Leave that and consider the artistry of a piece of turbot turned to the shape of a conch, flanked by three scallops translucent as pearls, tiny rounds of black Sevruga and pink salmon caviare, tendrils of chanterelles and two sauces, each playing off the other. Sprigs of bitter ground elder were tucked beside the turbot. Taste matches the looks, just as layers of bitter chocolate dividing pears from vanilla ice-cream and sitting in a pool of eau-de-vie de poire William combined splendid architecture with keen need for the taste-buds to be cut by the clean spirit. Go to Altnaharrie, enjoy your fellow guests (it helps if you do) and eat. Often, outsiders cannot be taken in. Bedrooms full will mean all chairs taken. But telephone in case, and you might be able to eat here while sleeping elsewhere. In the main the wines are well chosen; allow time in the sitting-room because the list is long and remains rather idiosyncratically priced. The high mark-ups on burgundies may raise expectations, as one customer found with a Meursault that 'had not been worth the money'. Pitch the sights lower and there are many good bottles well below £20, and some very adequate half-bottles.

CHEF: Gunn Eriksen PROPRIETORS: Fred Brown and Gunn Eriksen OPEN: all week, D only; 8 CLOSED: mid-Nov to shortly before Easter MEALS: Set D £45 SERVICE: net prices DETAILS: 16 seats. Private parties: 16 main room. Car park. Vegetarian meals. No smoking. No music ACCOMMODATION: 8 rooms, all with bath/shower. D,B&B £100 to £250. Deposit: £75. Garden. Fishing. Confirm by 4 (*The Which? Hotel Guide*)

▲ *Morefield Motel* £

Ullapool IV26 2TH	COOKING 1
ULLAPOOL (0854) 612161	COST £9–£25

It takes its seafood seriously. The operation heaves with customers, in the bar (no bookings, but plenty of food and waitress service), or in the restaurant. In both, while elaboration may go up or down according to where you are, seafood and Aberdeen Angus beef are the major preoccupations: with justice, goes the universal comment. Do not expect great beauty or luxury, but try the lobsters straight out of the live tanks, the seafood platter, dressed crab or king prawns off the boats. House wine is from £7 a litre.

CHEFS: Steven Kenyon and Tracy Cockhill PROPRIETORS: David Smyrl and David Courtney Marsh OPEN: all week; 12 to 2, 6 to 9.30 CLOSED: restaurant Nov to Easter MEALS: alc. Set D £17.50 to £19.50 SERVICE: not inc, card slips closed CARDS: Access, Amex, Visa DETAILS: 106 seats. 6 tables outside. Private parties: 40 main room. Car park. Children's helpings. No-smoking area in lounge bar. Wheelchair access (also WC). Music ACCOMMODATION: 11 rooms, all with bath/shower. B&B £25 to £45. Deposit: 10%. Children welcome. Baby facilities. Afternoon teas. Garden. TV. Doors close at 11. Confirm by 5. Fax: (0854) 612870

⚡ *indicates that smoking is either banned altogether or that a dining-room is maintained for non-smokers. The symbol does not apply to restaurants that simply have no-smoking areas.*

▲ *Burrastow House* ⅚✳

Walls ZE2 9PB
WALLS (059 571) 307   COOKING 1
3m W of Walls   COST £14–£26

It is remote, but not so remote that Bo Simmons is not contemplating nearly doubling the size of the restaurant. Informality in decoration and mood underlies days and evenings spent at the house, and a certain zany quality gained from internal geography: 'A creaky dumb waiter rose and fell and the cook then hurried round through the side door to serve us.' Bo Simmons' cooking has not lost memories of mainland life in dishes such as leek and mushroom tart, aubergine and mozzarella kebabs, squid stuffed with pistachios and capers, or orange halva cake. Is Burrastow the most northerly site for Mediterranean flavours like gazpacho or ratatouille? Billecart-Salmon champagne, Luc Sorin's Irancy, Ch. Musar from the Lebanon or the Terres Blanches rosé from Les Baux are pleasing choices in a short but fair-priced wine list. House wines are £6.60.

CHEF/PROPRIETOR: Bo Simmons   OPEN: all week; 12.30 to 2.30, 7.30 to 9   CLOSED: Jan and Feb, mid-Oct to end Nov   MEALS: alc L. Set D £18.50   SERVICE: not inc   DETAILS: 20 seats. Private parties: 16 main room. Car park. Vegetarian meals. Children's helpings. No smoking in dining-room. Music   ACCOMMODATION: 3 rooms, 2 with bath/shower. D,B&B £61 to £112. Deposit: 10%. Children welcome. Baby facilities. Pets welcome. Afternoon teas. Garden. Fishing. Confirm by 4

Wales

Hive on the Quay £

Cadwgan Place,
Aberaeron SA46 0BU   COOKING 1
ABERAERON (0545) 570445   COST £10–£27

The Holgate family, who are in the honey business, run a summer café/
restaurant as well as a honey-bee museum on this spit of a wharf between two
harbours. An ice-cream menu and café service (there is a buffet at lunch-time)
run through the day, converting to a slightly more formal performance in the
evenings. Fish is the major ingredient: lobsters and crab, trout with sorrel,
mackerel stuffed with cockles, skate with peppercorns, or whelks for a first
course. They believe in organics here – in food and wine – and the intentions
are true. A rush of summer business may see corners cut in the service, but
value is fair. Children are properly treated and if fish is not being cooked, there
is probably something for vegetarians. House wines are £6.75.

CHEFS: Sarah Holgate and John Bromley   PROPRIETORS: Margaret and Sarah Holgate
OPEN: all week; 12 to 2, 6 to 9.30   CLOSED: end Sept to spring bank hol   MEALS: alc (self-
service L)   SERVICE: not inc L, 10% D, card slips closed   CARDS: Access, Visa   DETAILS:
55 seats. 2 tables outside. Vegetarian meals. Children's helpings. Wheelchair access. Music

▲ *Penhelig Arms Hotel* ▮

Aberdovey LL35 0LT   COOKING 2
ABERDOVEY (0654) 767215   COST £13–£25

After drinking Bailey's Bundarra Vineyards 1986 Shiraz from Victoria, one
correspondent was too overcome to finish her long report of a four-day stay
here that told of good wines, very sound food and excellent value at every meal.
The Hughes are good at hospitality. 'I think it's because Robert Hughes treats
everyone as special,' remarked someone who observed that he must cover
miles every day in his energetic supervision. There is almost a cult of
simplicity, but it avoids the boring. Silly excess is avoided in dishes such as a
coarse terrine with Cumberland sauce, melon and prawns with yoghurt and
ginger dressing, grilled breast of duck with port and ginger sauce, Conway
plaice with prawns and cheese, chocolate brandy truffle cake, and meringues
with bananas and chocolate sauce. Vegetables are more than plentiful, and

trimmings are sound. Sunday lunch is a particular bargain, and bar meals are getting better. Business is booming. The harbour setting is enticing, and what began as a very traditional pub with benches, and rooms with a modicum of comfort, is gradually being changed without being ruined. It is worth planning an early arrival for wine list reading, although most would be more than content with the page of house wines (from £7.50), including Isole e Olena Chianti at £13 and David Wynn's Chardonnay a bargain at £10.90. Experiment is called for when prices are so reasonable. Quality is fine across the board, but a special fondness is displayed for Italy. A wonderful list, and not overlong. CELLARMAN'S CHOICE: Graves, Ch. Couhins-Lurton 1987, £16.50; Provence, Ch. Réal Martin 1986, £12.

CHEF: Jane Howkins PROPRIETORS: Robert and Sally Hughes OPEN: all week; 12 to 2, 7 to 9 MEALS: alc L. Set Sun L £9.50, Set D £15.75 SERVICE: not inc, card slips closed CARDS: Access, Visa DETAILS: 42 seats. Private parties: 24 main room. Car park. Children's helpings. Music ACCOMMODATION: 11 rooms, all with bath/shower. B&B £36 to £78. Deposit: £30. Children welcome. Pets welcome. Afternoon teas. TV. Phone. Doors close at midnight. Confirm by 6. Fax: (0654) 767690 (*The Which? Hotel Guide*)

ABERSOCH Gwynedd   map 4

▲ *Porth Tocyn Hotel*

Abersoch LL53 7BU   COOKING 2
ABERSOCH (0758) 713303   COST £19–£32

'It may do two sittings of a Saturday dinner, but the output is ever consistent,' writes one North Walian who sees great virtue in that – so long as you know what you're in for. Another visitor was not so impressed. Consistency for her entailed a certain off-handedness; double sitting meant a table booked for 9pm was not available until 9.50pm. Twenty-five acres protect the hotel from the hurly-burly of yachtsmen and anoraks in Abersoch – Gwynedd's oldest marina – and allows the guest matchless views across Cardigan Bay to Snowdonia. In the right light, the West Indies has nothing on it. In the mist and the rain, it is best to retreat to the dining-room where the main activity is dinner, although breakfasts and light lunches (a large buffet on Sundays) get fair share of the effort. Dinner is a set-price daily menu of five courses, four choices at each principal stage. For those who feel five jumps makes too long a race, there is a shorter option. Cooking here is often described as 'Cordon Bleu', a name that has meant several things in its time. For sure, there is a tendency for first courses to be confections – mousses, bakes, gratins, pâtés or roulades – rather than the current fashion for heaps of ingredients savoured for themselves and enjoyed for the various counterpoints of flavour offered by the chef. However, main courses are usually meat/fish and sauce and avoid the excesses of stuffing and garnishing. The region's fish resources are allowed to shine. Desserts follow a regular pattern: English hot pudding, a tart or roulade, an ice-cream, sometimes a savoury. Fruit and cheese bring up the rear. Running the kitchens since 1948 they may have been, but the Fletcher-Brewers have not let time stand still. The wine list is soundly based. Without going overboard for length, the range is well judged and the prices are not exorbitant. There is a useful set of house selections, starting at £9.50. Nick Fletcher-Brewer has a sane approach to family parties – all ages are welcome, though 'we try to keep the under-5s away from dinner' – and to the service charge and tipping – 'a dead letter'.

CHEF: E.L. Fletcher-Brewer PROPRIETORS: the Fletcher-Brewer family OPEN: all week; 12.30 to 2, 7.30 to 9.30 MEALS: light L. Set Sun L £14, Set D £17.50 to £23 SERVICE: net prices, card slips closed CARD: Access DETAILS: 60 seats. 12 tables outside. Private parties: 60 main room. Car park. Children's helpings Sun L. No children under 7. Smart dress preferred. Wheelchair access (1 step; also WC). No music ACCOMMODATION: 17 rooms, all with bath/shower. Rooms for disabled. B&B £41.50 to £99. Deposit: £40. Children welcome. Baby facilities. Pets welcome. Afternoon teas. Garden. Swimming-pool. Tennis. TV. Phone. Doors close at midnight. Fax: (0758) 713538 (*The Which? Hotel Guide*)

▲ *Riverside Hotel*

| Abersoch LL53 7HW | COOKING 1 |
| ABERSOCH (075 881) 2419 and 2818 | COST £16–£30 |

'Splendid value,' averred one couple who stopped for lunch (served in the bar), were taken by the friendly welcome and munched (or sipped) chicken and vegetable soup, buttery croissants filled with bacon and cheese and then apricot, almond and black cherry tart on crisp pastry and a meringue ice-cream bombe with Drambuie and raspberries. This is very much a holiday hotel, undistinguished from the outside but better and more cheerful within. One report right at the end of the season did sound as if enthusiasm had flown with the swallows of happy seasiders, but most people are satisfied by robust cooking that tastes as advertised. Eat shellfish and fish, don't think you'll avoid the cream, and if you have tea by the river, watch out for hungry ducks. 'Coffee was a large pot, enough for thirds, and strong with it.' The short wine list has a useful supplement of 'better' things. House wines are £7.50.

CHEFS/PROPRIETORS: John and Wendy Bakewell OPEN: all week; 12 to 2, 7.30 to 9 CLOSED: Nov to Mar MEALS: bar meals. Set D £21 SERVICE: not inc, card slips closed CARDS: Access, Amex, Visa DETAILS: 34 seats. Private parties: 34 main room. Car park. Children welcome. Smart dress preferred. Music ACCOMMODATION: 12 rooms, all with bath/shower. B&B £40 to £80. Deposit: £40. Children welcome. Baby facilities. Afternoon teas. Garden. Swimming-pool. TV. Phone. Doors close at midnight. Confirm by 2. Fax: (075 881) 2671

BEAUMARIS Gwynedd   map 4

▲ *Ye Olde Bulls Head Inn* ♟

Castle Street, Beaumaris,	
Anglesey LL58 8AP	COOKING 2*
BEAUMARIS (0248) 810329	COST £16–£40

Charles Dickens' Uncommercial Traveller cogitates on food at 'the old-established Bull's Head' its 'ailing sweetbreads in white poultices, pale stewed bits of calf ineffectually relying for an adventitious interest on forcemeat balls'. This Bulls Head is not like that. It is old – dating from 1617, but with a plainer, later front; it still earns a living as an inn, serving food to all comers, whose reaction is a good deal more cheerful. Bar food gets some plaudits for items such as steak and kidney pie 'that was cooked with its pastry', pea, ham and barley broth, salmon with a sharpish mayonnaise, and apple crumble; and the restaurant is appreciated for fresh food (especially fish) cooked quite simply. Sea bream with garlic and parsley, Dover sole meunière, salmon and halibut with lobster sauce, and sea bass with lemon balm and orange were the specials one autumn day. There have been less successful meals, and sometimes the bar (which also offers snacks) does not rise above the general level of the district. Service is informed about the shopping and the recipes. Perhaps the team should improve the lemon tart, but keep plugging away with the crumbles, and the 'intense chocolate mousse in a pool of wonderful green mint cream sauce'. The wine list is not too long, but mighty intelligent. There are good growers, fair prices and a fine range. Altesino from Montalcino, Schinus Molle from Victoria, Vega Sicilia – the names trip off the tongue, but do not overawe. House Côtes de Castillon or Pinot Blanc from Alsace are £10.75.

CHEFS: Keith Rothwell and Anthony Murphy   PROPRIETORS: Rothwell and Robertson Ltd   OPEN: all week; 12 to 2.30, 7.30 to 9.30   MEALS: alc. Set Sun L £13.75. Bar meals SERVICE: not inc   CARDS: Access, Visa   DETAILS: 70 seats. Private parties: 70 main room, 40 private room. Car park. Children's helpings. No children under 7. No music ACCOMMODATION: 11 rooms, all with bath/shower. B&B £40 to £68. Children welcome. Baby facilities. TV. Phone. Doors close at midnight. Confirm by 6. Fax: (0248) 811294 (*The Which? Hotel Guide*)

BROAD HAVEN Dyfed   map 4

▲ *Druidstone Hotel* £

Broad Haven SA62 3NE   COOKING 1
BROAD HAVEN (0437) 781221   COST £14–£27

The Bells should get a long-service award for lasting two decades, maintaining the same instinct for hospitality, freedom and enjoyment as burned brightly at the end of the '60s. Quirkiness and informality can turn to sloppiness in the eyes of some, but if you don't like rules, try this. Jane Bell is back in the kitchen, with Rod helping on 'terrines, curries and other nourishing dishes'. She draws at present on the experience of cooking for hundreds at theatre workshops in the Polish countryside, so if you encounter goulash on the menu, that's the reason. You may also find big casseroles, hummus, Chinese prawn and sesame toasts, curries, fried chicken Kansas-style or falafel. The world is her culinary oyster. You can also eat in the bar. No bones are made about bulk or nourishment: beef and sage casserole followed by banana dumpling with cinnamon ice-cream and Jersey cream would feed any soul. 'Nothing, but nothing, is smart', but it is honest and children like it. Somehow the Bells allow professionalism to co-exist with all that informality. The wine list has under three dozen bottles, but they are wonderfully cheap and have been nicely chosen. There are hints of more in the cellar if you want to splash out. House wines are £5.50.

'To be greeted with the single word ''Drinkies?'' is not auspicious; to be pressed to take ice and lemon with one's kir was a warning we were foolish to ignore.'
On eating in Cumbria

CHEFS/PROPRIETORS: Rod and Jane Bell   OPEN: all week, exc Sun D; 12.30 to 2.30, 7.30 to 9.30   CLOSED: 4 Nov to 13 Dec, 6 Jan to 13 Feb (exc parties of 10 or more)   MEALS: alc   SERVICE: not inc, card slips closed   CARDS: Access, Visa   DETAILS: 36 seats. 8 tables outside. Private parties: 36 main room, 10 private room. Car park. Vegetarian meals. Children's helpings. Wheelchair access (also WC)   ACCOMMODATION: 9 rooms and 4 cottages. 2 cottages for disabled. Deposit: £20. Children welcome. Baby facilities. Pets welcome. Afternoon teas. Garden. Doors close at midnight (*The Which? Hotel Guide*)

CAPEL COCH Gwynedd   map 4

▲ *Tre-Ysgawen Hall*

Capel Coch, Llangefni,
Anglesey LL77 7UR
BANGOR (0248) 750750
on B5111, between Llangefni   COOKING **2***
and Amlwch   COST £21–£42

This late-Victorian hall is just the place for people who need to hold a wedding reception, and like killing pheasants or petting dogs. It also serves food. Some of the trappings are large-scale and impressive: a big staircased hall complete with grand piano (sometimes played, other times deserted for the hi-fi); a giant conservatory for dining in or holding receptions; acres of lounge; lots of four-posters. The scale of service can be impressive too: much chatting, much performance, even silver domes. The nature of the menu (middle-of-the-road country-house cuisine) is less enticing. After reading that you have ordered 'a supreme of pan-fried guinea-fowl served with the legs braised and stuffed with mushroom duxelles presented on a port sauce garnished with bacon lardons and baby button onions', you wonder if there is anything else to know about the dish. In fact it is decently cooked, the sauce is without fault, the guinea-fowl is bland (but that is often its nature), and on a side plate will arrive courgette and yellow squash, carrots, beans, broccoli and rösti potatoes. A fillet steak may be served with truffles and foie gras in micron-slim slices and the same vegetables. Cooking, again, is without error; the sauce has a meaty flavour with a sweet finish. Desserts can get elaborate: chocolate comes as a trio of soufflé, ice-cream and truffle cake; strawberry arrives as a mousse, ice-cream and the fruit from the bush. 'These had a sort of visual symmetry, a duo of trios.' Coffee and petits fours have been well up to the mark. The wine list carries Mateus Rosé, and a good fistful of fancy clarets. Otherwise, the range is very acceptable and not all the prices are impossible. House wines are £9.80.

CHEF: Steven Morris   PROPRIETORS: Mr and Mrs Ray Craighead   OPEN: all week; 12 to 2.30, 7 to 9.30   MEALS: alc. Set L £14, Set D £18   SERVICE: not inc   CARDS: Access, Amex, Visa   DETAILS: 84 seats. Private parties: 120 main room, 12 and 30 private rooms. Car park. Vegetarian meals. Children's helpings. Jacket and tie. Wheelchair access (also WC). Music   ACCOMMODATION: 20 rooms, all with bath/shower. Rooms for disabled. B&B £97 to £200. Deposit: 10%. Children welcome. Pets welcome. Afternoon teas. Garden. TV. Phone. Doors close at midnight. Confirm by noon. Fax: (0248) 750035 (*The Which? Hotel Guide*)

▲ *This symbol means accommodation is available.*

Armless Dragon

97 Wyeverne Road, Cathays,
Cardiff CF2 4BG   COOKING 2
CARDIFF (0222) 382357   COST £22–£34

Wales meets China and France. The Armless Dragon is in the seedy bed-sit
land of Cathays, the student quarter. This 'gives it a certain youthful vigour,
and plenty of young staff', who are invariably genial. The oriental jungle of the
window plants gives way to Quartier Latin tablecloths and posters. A semi-
permanent menu offering several ways with today's fish, a clutch of fillet
steaks, and a multi-cultural quartet of beginnings – laverballs, Thai-style
mushrooms, sesame prawn salad, or crab soup with lemon grass – is
augmented by a whiteboard of daily extras. There is mostly good fish: halibut,
sewin hollandaise, marlin or hake on one day; enjoyable cassoulet of duck with
spicy sausages; and seasonal dishes like prawn and samphire salad. Robust
cooking, just occasionally not too much of it, is supplemented by decent
vegetables, well-kept cheeses and straight desserts, and an espresso machine as
a bonus. The diner's interest is kept alive, and the spicing can be arresting.
There is not a lot of ceremony here, but it's not what the place is about. The
wines are as rapidly changing as the menu, the knowledge behind the buying
as lacking in convention as is the cooking. Prices are fair. House wine is £7.50.

CHEFS: David Richards and Debbie Coleman PROPRIETOR: David Richards OPEN: Tue to
Sat, exc Sat L; 12.30 to 2.15, 7.30 to 10.30 (11 Sat) CLOSED: Christmas to New Year
MEALS: alc SERVICE: not inc CARDS: Access, Amex, Visa DETAILS: 50 seats. Private
parties: 50 main room. Vegetarian meals. Children welcome. No cigars/pipes in dining-
room. Wheelchair access. Music

La Brasserie/Champers/Le Monde

60–61 St Mary Street, Cardiff CF1 1FE   COOKING 1
CARDIFF (0222) 372164/373363/387376   COST £14–£39

Three restaurants (and a banqueting suite) in three buildings can seat more
than 400 people. Therefore cooking, even with three kitchens, is fast and
furious; so is the service. The principles of direct methods – grilling, spit
roasting and chargrilling – have to operate, unless the enterprise converts to
soup kitchens. Everything does seem to work and Benigno Martinez can offer,
as he says, a valid alternative to 'mass-produced hotel food'. Champers is the
Spanish one, with excellent Riojas and a lot of grills with 'picante' sauces. La
Brasserie takes a French (and Welsh) line; fish and game are the brand leaders,
but these are closely followed by racks of Welsh lamb, prawns with samphire,
spit-roasted sucking pig and roast duck. Le Monde is the place to go for
seafood: salmon, sewin, soles, brill, hake, sea bass, and warm-water fish such
as mahi-mahi on the one hand, shellfish aplenty on the other. Expect no major
frills, but all is efficient. The island cooking-station in the newly expanded Le
Monde is visible sign of that. House wines are £6.95.

CHEFS: Franco Peligno (La Brasserie); Chris Kovkaras (Champers); Andrew Jones and Genaro Sandonato (Le Monde) PROPRIETOR: Benigno Martinez OPEN: Mon to Sat (and Sun D Champers); 12 to 2.30 (3 Le Monde), 7 to 12.15 MEALS: alc SERVICE: not inc, card slips closed CARDS: Access, Amex, Diners, Visa DETAILS: La Brasserie 75 seats, Champers 70 seats, Le Monde 180 seats. Private parties: 70, 75 and 120 main room, 40 private room. Vegetarian meals La Brasserie and Champers. Children welcome La Brasserie. No children under 4 Champers. No children under 10 Le Monde. Smart dress preferred La Brasserie and Le Monde. Music. Air-conditioned Le Monde. Fax: (0222) 668092

Le Cassoulet

5 Romilly Crescent, Canton,
Cardiff CF1 9NP   COOKING 2
CARDIFF (0222) 221905   COST £21–£47

The restaurant gets smarter. A extra front door has been added and stained-glass panels have appeared in the windows, although the staunchly French red, black and white interior – complete with a photograph of the Toulouse football team – is unchanged. Reports suggest that the cooking has moved up a gear, perhaps as a result of Paul Lane's presence in the kitchen. Lunch is a table d'hôte, dinner is a frequently changing *carte*. The cooking is as French provincial as the setting and reliably authentic, with robust, full-flavoured dishes typified by the eponymous cassoulet: an earthenware bowl filled with a hearty cocoction of haricot beans, cubes of pork fat, a big Toulouse sausage, a chunk of neck of pork, plus a duck leg sticking out of the breadcrumbed topping. Rillettes of chicken with a salad frisée dressed with walnut oil have been in the same rich vein. There are also delicate, modern touches in ravioli of lobster and crab on a slightly crunchy julienne of potato, and duck breast cooked pink and fanned round the plate with sweet-and-sour celery sauce. Cheese has been spoiled by being served too cold. Desserts have 'excelled', particularly a visually stunning tarte au citron served on a black glass plate, and intensely flavoured passion-fruit sorbet with orange segments and caramel and mango sauce. Service is unfailingly friendly and helpful. The French wine list has a strong regional bias, and there is a decent range of armagnacs. House wine is £6.95.

CHEF: Paul Lane PROPRIETORS: Gilbert and Claire Viader OPEN: Tue to Sat, exc Sat L; 12 to 2, 7 to 10 CLOSED: 1 week Christmas, 1 month summer MEALS: alc. Set L £16 SERVICE: not inc CARDS: Access, Amex, Visa DETAILS: 45 seats. Private parties: 45 main room. Children welcome. Wheelchair access (1 step). Music

Chikako's £   NEW ENTRY

10–11 Mill Lane, Cardiff CF1 1FL   COOKING 1
CARDIFF (0222) 665279   COST £18–£30

Chikako Cameron moved from Bath to open her new restaurant which is directly opposite the Holiday Inn. An unobtrusive door with a bell-push marks the entrance, but inside it is 'a different world'. A flight of steps leads down to a series of eating spaces on different levels, with white tiled floors and Japanese hangings on the plain light walls. A long curving bar counter with a huge hotplate running along it dominates the room. The menu offers an accessible choice of dishes, ranging from sashimi, teriyaki and tempura to cooked-at-table specialities such as teppanyaki and shabu-shabu. There are some creditable appetisers, including smoked salted tuna, silken tofu with bonito flakes and ginger, and ositashi (cooked spinach with sesame seeds). Among the sweets, pleasantly alcoholic plum wine sorbet and lemony Japanese cheesecake have been recommended. Ingredients are of excellent quality (many vegetables are organically grown by Chikako) and dishes are fresh and carefully prepared. There is a short wine list, as well as saké and Japanese beer. House French is £6.90.

CHEF/PROPRIETOR: Chikako Cameron OPEN: all week, D only (L by arrangement); 6 to 11 CLOSED: 25 Dec MEALS: Set L and D £11.80 to £19.50 SERVICE: 10%, card slips closed CARDS: Access, Visa DETAILS: 72 seats. Private parties: 50 main room, 20 private room. Vegetarian meals. Children's helpings. Music. Air-conditioned

Quayles

6–8 Romilly Crescent, Canton,
Cardiff CF1 9NR   COOKING 1
CARDIFF (0222) 341264   COST £20–£39

One view is that Quayles pitches itself well, by offering relatively low-priced, well-prepared food: 'It'll never aspire to greatness,' comments one reporter, 'and hopefully therein will lie its future success – a no-nonsense approach to cooking with just enough panache to lift it above the average.' While the consensus is in favour, the kitchen seems to lack consistency, and some readers have noted a rather slapdash attitude, which spills over into the décor and service. Irene Canning offers an assortment of eclectic dishes with brasserie overtones, and vegetarians have a full menu to themselves. Bresaola with fruit salad and pesto, grilled venison with port and grain mustard sauce, polenta with blue cheese sauce and Parmesan, and mushroom roast with tamari sauce show the range. The flavour of orange seems to be a current obsession: it appears as a sauce for baked salmon, as an accompaniment to nougat ice-cream and – in the form of candied peel – among the petits fours. Sunday brunch, special food and music evenings, plus visits from big-name chefs are features of the set-up. House Beaujolais is £8.75 a litre.

CHEFS: Irene Canning, Matthew Canning and John Khalid PROPRIETORS: Canning and Co (Cardiff) Ltd OPEN: all week, exc Sun D; 12 to 2.30, 7.30 to 10.30 CLOSED: 26 Dec, Easter Mon and bank hols MEALS: alc. Set L £11.95 SERVICE: not inc (10% for 10 or more), card slips closed CARDS: Access, Amex, Diners, Visa DETAILS: 48 seats. Private parties: 50 main room. Car park. Vegetarian meals. Children's helpings. No-smoking area. Wheelchair access (also WC). Music. Air-conditioned

All details are as accurate as possible at the time of going to press, but chefs and owners often change, and it is wise to check by telephone before making a special journey. Many readers have been disappointed when set-price bargain meals are no longer available. Ask when booking.

CHIRK Clwyd   map 4

▲ Starlings Castle

Bronygarth, nr Chirk SY10 7NU
OSWESTRY (0691) 72464   COOKING 3
5m NW of Oswestry   COST £24–£29

Pre-warned by last year's entry, one reader phoned for directions: 'Deep in the countryside, my mother was convinced we were lost but I did not waiver from the directions and we were not. It was a surprise to find anyone else there.' Another writes, 'It really is a long trek by car and a pretty spartan building should you find it, but the Pitts are delightful people and reward you for your travels.' 'Castle' is a flight of fancy; it is in reality a converted fortified farmhouse, now a restaurant-with-rooms. Antony Pitt changes his short menu daily. A strong preference for French provincial dishes – fish soup with rouille and croûtons, fromage de tête with sauce ravigote, and rib of beef 'marchand de vin' or with béarnaise sauce – is balanced by a modern touch – loin of pork stuffed with goats' cheese and olive paste, and breast of pigeon with spiced lentils and coriander – and by the odd indulgence such as paella à la Valenciana. For pudding, there are hot chocolate soufflé, peach and brandy ice-cream, and tarte au citron. Recommendations are many and praise for the food is unanimous, but visitors in colder months have remarked on a cool dining-room. The wine list, compiled with the help of Haughton Fine Wines, includes some organics and a small selection from the New World. House wines are from £6.75.

CHEF: Antony Pitt   PROPRIETORS: Antony and Jools Pitt   OPEN: all week, D only, and Sun L (other days L by arrangement); 12 to 2.30, 7 to 9.30 (10 Fri and Sat)   MEALS: alc. Set L and D £17 to £19   SERVICE: not inc   CARDS: Access, Visa   DETAILS: 30 seats. Private parties: 30 main room, 30 private room. Car park. Vegetarian meals. Children's helpings. No cigars/pipes in dining-room. Wheelchair access (also WC). Music   ACCOMMODATION: 8 rooms. B&B £20 to £40. Children welcome. Baby facilities. Pets welcome. Garden. TV. Doors close at midnight (*The Which? Hotel Guide*)

COLWYN BAY Clwyd   map 4

Café Niçoise £

124 Abergele Road, Colwyn Bay LL29 7PS   COOKING 2
COLWYN BAY (0492) 531555   COST £17–£33

On a dull November day it may be incredible to conceive any link between the Côte d'Azur and North Wales, but this is it. The mood inside is sunny enough and reports commend Carl Swift's output as abundant in flavour, particularly pan-fried monkfish with a warm lemon and herb vinaigrette, a casserole of seafood with pastis and dill, and magret duck on braised red cabbage with a fumet of ceps. Home-baked bread and 'exquisite' desserts are additional sources of pleasure. 'Service is intelligent and prompt but not rushed.' There is nothing niçoise about the wine list except that it is mostly French with a couple of pages of New World and Europe. Good to see Est! Est!! Est!!! di Montefiascone, and to note that mark-ups are not as savage as on the Côte d'Azur. House wines start at £6.55.

CHEF: Carl Swift   PROPRIETORS: Carl Swift and Lynne Curtis   OPEN: Mon to Sat, exc Mon L; 12 to 2, 7 to 10   MEALS: alc. Minimum £5.95 D   SERVICE: not inc, card slips closed CARDS: Access, Visa   DETAILS: 32 seats. Private parties: 30 main room. Vegetarian meals. No children under 3. Smart dress preferred. Music

---

DOLGELLAU Gwynedd   map 4

▲ *Dolmelynllyn Hall* 🍷 ⚡

Ganllwyd, Dolgellau LL40 2HP   COOKING 2
GANLLWYD (034 140) 273   COST £19–£30

'Three levels, three periods' gives some idea of the complexity of the history here, though for all the world the building looks like a Victorian number towering over the terraced garden. Inside 'the homely atmosphere that the Hall seems to promote is infinitely preferable to a clichéd interior-decorating job' – a plaudit for the Barkwiths, a father-daughter partnership. However, for some the delays in service that stretch a dinner almost to infinity make too much of homely style. The cooking is better than domestic. Sometimes the flavour combinations hark back to the halcyon days of the 1970s, as in dishes such as quail with smoked ham mousse, oyster mushrooms and a minted lime sauce (there is a general affection for fruit's acidity in savoury dishes), but some good things like braised beef with garlic and baby onions, duck with grapefruit and oregano, salmon and scallops in pastry with tarragon cream, or a vegetarian curry with creamed coconut, are up-to-the-minute as you could want. First courses like tomato ravioli with spinach and oyster mushrooms on a madeira sauce, twice-baked soufflés, or a beetroot and horseradish sauce with crab and fennel parcels, match the main dishes. The format is five courses at a set price, with choice at each stage: perhaps this is one reason for service being gently paced. The wine list is excellent. New countries and France are pillaged for good makers, many of them doing organics. Isole e Olena, Verdet, Newton and Marqués de Murrieta are just some to conjure with, and the prices allow you to play the field. For once, Bordeaux may offer the least interest. House wines are £8.25. CELLARMAN'S CHOICE: New Zealand, Neudorf, Chardonnay 1990, £15.50; Dolcetto d'Alba 1990, Vajra, £13.50.

CHEF: Joanna Barkwith   PROPRIETORS: Jonathan Barkwith and Joanna Barkwith   OPEN: all week, D only (L by arrangement); 7.30 to 9   CLOSED: Dec (exc D Thur to Sat) to end Feb   MEALS: Set L £13.50, Set D £21   SERVICE: not inc, card slips closed   CARDS: Access, Amex, Visa   DETAILS: 24 seats. Private parties: 44 main room, 40 private room. Car park. Vegetarian meals. No children under 8. Smart dress preferred. No smoking in dining-room. Wheelchair access (2 steps). No music   ACCOMMODATION: Mar to Nov only. 11 rooms, all with bath/shower. B&B £42.50 to £95. Deposit: £25. No children under 8. Pets welcome (no dogs in public rooms). Afternoon teas. Garden. Fishing. TV. Phone. Doors close at midnight. Confirm by 6

⚡ *indicates that smoking is either banned altogether or that a dining-room is maintained for non-smokers. The symbol does not apply to restaurants that simply have no-smoking areas.*

Dylanwad Da £

2 Smithfield Street,
Dolgellau LL40 1BS
DOLGELLAU (0341) 422870

COOKING 1
COST £16–£26

Though the Welsh language is firmly in evidence, it is lucky for the English visitors that the menu is written in their tongue. This is a much-loved bistro; reservations are therefore advised. Dylan Rowlands combines an acute sense of value for money with a willingness to roam the world for inspiration, use fresh foods and cook with flavour. Examples might be cabbage and haricot bean soup with a bit of bacon; chicken and apple turnover; a Greek-inspired spinach pie with Caerphilly cheese; lots of mustard in a sauce for breast of chicken; and lots of spice in Andalusian pork stew. Value – and quality – also extend to the wine list: hardly a bottle slips into double figures and all the right places have been selected for something that packs a punch on a budget. House wines are £7.40; choose between Plaimont's Côtes de Gascogne or Dom. de Raissac's Syrah from Languedoc.

CHEF/PROPRIETOR: Dylan Rowlands   OPEN: D only; all week Easter and Whitsun, July to Sept; Thur to Sat winter; 7 to 9.30   CLOSED: Feb   MEALS: alc   SERVICE: not inc   DETAILS: 30 seats. Private parties: 30 main room. Vegetarian meals. Children's helpings. Music

---

EGLWYSFACH Powys   map 4

▲ *Ynyshir Hall* £✳

Eglwysfach SY20 8TA
GLANDYFI (0654) 781209

COOKING 1
COST £22–£34

Ynyshir Hall is set in a natural amphitheatre, the microclimate brushed by the Gulf Stream, with acres of gardens insulating the long white-painted house. It is 'an island of peace', though the decoration is bold and forceful if peace-seekers are wont to doze. An example of the striking taste is the menu itself: Rob Reen is an artist and his work adorns this as well as many of the walls. The tendency noted last year for local materials to be highlighted on the set-price, six-choice monthly menus has continued, and there has been general agreement that David Dressler manages competently dishes such as a salad of avocado and smoked chicken; cabbage and bacon soup; a trio of local cheeses, deep fried, with a blackcurrant sauce; pheasant with red cabbage; duck with quince and orange blossom sauce; and trout in filo pastry with leeks. The methods used to treat the local materials are not local at all, or necessarily seasonal; they recall the cooking with a fruit-and-sweet touch of many country restaurants of the '80s. An excess of sweetness has also been noted in some desserts: for instance, a meringue filled with lemon curd and vodka, with a grapefruit mousse and orange sauce, or tropical fruits flamed in brandy. Quantities are generous – at least half-a-dozen vegetables may come with the main course – and value for money is perceived. 'A thoroughly good evening, but simplicity would be a virtue' was the remark of one Midland visitor. The Tanners' wine list is reliable and has something of everything. Prices are very fair. House wines start at £7.50.

CHEF: David Dressler PROPRIETORS: Joan and Rob Reen OPEN: all week; 12.30 to 1.30,
7 to 8.30 MEALS: Set L £15 to £18, Set D £20 to £23 SERVICE: not inc, card slips closed
CARDS: Access, Amex, Visa DETAILS: 30 seats. Private parties: 26 main room, 18 private
room. Car park. Vegetarian meals. No children under 9. No smoking in dining-room.
Music ACCOMMODATION: 9 rooms, all with bath/shower. 1 room for disabled. B&B £45 to
£120. Deposit: 20%. No children under 9. Pets by arrangement. Afternoon teas. Garden. TV.
Phone. Doors close at midnight. Confirm by 6. Fax: (0654) 781366 (*The Which? Hotel Guide*)

FISHGUARD Dyfed   map 4

Tate's Brasserie £   NEW ENTRY

Bay View House, Main Street,
Goodwick, Fishguard SA64 0BN   COOKING 2
FISHGUARD (0348) 874190   COST £12–£31

Miss the ferry for this: others do. The double-fronted Victorian house kicks off
with a 'cluttered but pleasantly informal' bar-cum-sitting area, then down
steep stairs to more tables and candlelight. It's an all-day operation (with a
flexible closing time), so Diana Richards offers a range of menus from snacks to
dinners proper. The common denominator is an adventurous approach that
encompasses 1960s-bistro moussaka and taramasalata (lumpy but tasting
lemon-fresh) as well as making the most of what can be found in Fishguard, be
that witch sole with sorrel sauce, sand dabs with cider and cream, Pen-clawdd
cockles with onions and laverbread, lamb with pesto, oxtail and olives, cod
niçoise or civet of hare. It sounds bold, and it is. It comes in big portions, it
comes cheap, and it comes properly cooked. 'The seafood pancake was both
light and substantial, oozing with intense cream, wine and fish sauce, stuffed
with ample supplies of shellfish.' Basque cherry tart and lemon posset are the
heavily endorsed stars of the pudding menu. Coffee is plentiful and strong. The
serious intent carries through to the wine list, which offers a range, classified
by grape and style, of well-chosen bottles from all over. Note the Houghton
Chardonnay and Verdelho, the Hardy's Nottage Hill Chardonnay and the
Recioto Amarone della Valpolicella. House wines are £6.75.

CHEF/PROPRIETOR: Diana Richards OPEN: all week, exc Tue (Tue D summer, winter by
arrangment); 12 (12.30 to 3 Sun) to 9 MEALS: alc D. Set L and bistro D £6.50 to £9.95 (inc
wine), Set D £11.25 to £12.75 SERVICE: not inc DETAILS: 34 seats. Private parties: 30
main room. Vegetarian meals. Children's helpings. Wheelchair access ground floor. Music

---

▲ *Three Main Street* ✸

3 Main Street, Fishguard SA65 9HG   COOKING 1
FISHGUARD (0348) 874275   COST £19–£33

'Cooked by an ex-college lecturer, served by an ex-social worker' – the
combination may seem made in heaven and the product is 'excellent, no
underdone vegetables, often rich without being sickly, well presented yet
served with a total lack of affectation', in the words of one happy family who
wished to differ from our comments of last year. The hotel used to be the Great
Western, a resort of many who passed through. Now, there is the restaurant, the

coffee-shop, and rooms. Marion Evans' daily menu shows affection for colour: beetroot and hazelnut salad, seafood provençale, spiced chicken with pimentos and almonds, almond and watercress tart with a red pepper purée, and aubergine baked with mozzarella, tomatoes and hazelnuts might appear to suggest that Fishguard was on the Mediterranean shore. But duck with red and white currants, Welsh lamb with wild garlic or scallops with shallots, parsley and cream will drag you back north. The kitchen's efforts are genuine, the hospitality is relaxed and gentle, and the coffee-shop is a useful spot for lunch. The wine list is short, with long notes, but the choice is up to the minute and not expensive. House wines are £8.95.

CHEFS: Marion Evans and Andrew Griffith   PROPRIETORS: Marion Evans and Inez Ford
OPEN: Tue to Sun, exc Sun D; 12 to 2.30, 7 to 9.30   MEALS: alc. Set Sun L £11.95   SERVICE: not inc   DETAILS: 24 seats. Private parties: 24 main room. Vegetarian meals. Children's helpings. No smoking in dining-room. Wheelchair access. No music   ACCOMMODATION: 3 rooms, all with bath/shower. B&B £30 to £50. Deposit: 25%. Children welcome. Afternoon teas. TV. Doors close at 12.30am. Confirm by 6 (*The Which? Hotel Guide*)

FORDEN Powys   map 4

▲ *Edderton Hall* £

Forden SY21 8RZ
FORDEN (093 876) 339 and 410   COOKING 1
off A490, 4m S of Welshpool   COST £18–£30

Warren Hawksley has been returned to Parliament, so we wait agog to hear how his hotel enterprise fares. One son (who also bakes the bread) has been recruited, but the Member is said to revert to his role as host when not at Westminster. The Georgian house has stunning views, 'and the only noise is from sheep and cows'. It has been furnished with Victoriana, giving it a lived-in atmosphere – 'a junk-shop feel', if you want to be uncharitable. The cooking is energetic, though service may not always be: 'We had the crown of lamb paraded round the dining-room, but it was then left unattended for 10 minutes before anyone thought to deal with it,' wrote one who was the first to leave after a Sunday lunch that ended at 4.30. On the monthly set-price *carte* some interesting angles are pursued. Duck comes with gooseberries and elderflower fritters; salmon is accompanied by laverbread and lemon and chive sauce; a first course of smoked chicken and mango has a coconut and chilli sauce; lamb comes with port, mint and raspberry. The results may be good, they are often fresh-tasting, but they may also misfire. There is now a 'bistro menu', offering more informal meals at lunch and dinner. The wine list is principally from Tanners, but strengthened by Warren Hawksley's expeditions to auction. A sound yet unexciting base may therefore benefit from extra clarets in particular. House wines are £7.75.

'The waiter (and he was French!) had no idea what cheeses he was serving – he offered the comment (I kid you not) that "this one's different from that one". Finally, we suggested names and he agreed!'   On eating in London

---

CHEF: Evelyn Hawksley PROPRIETORS: Evelyn and Warren Hawksley OPEN: all week;
12.30 to 2, 7.30 to 9.30 MEALS: alc bistro menu. Set Sun L £10.95, Set D £21. Minimum
£4.50 L, £6.50 D SERVICE: not inc, card slips closed CARDS: Access, Amex, Diners, Visa
DETAILS: 34 seats. Private parties: 25 main room, 65 private room. Car park. Children's
helpings. Smart dress preferred. Wheelchair access (1 step; also WC). Music
ACCOMMODATION: 8 rooms, all with bath/shower. B&B £27.50 to £90. Deposit: £20.
Children welcome. Pets welcome. Afternoon teas. Garden. TV. Phone. Doors close at
midnight. Confirm by 1. Fax: (093 876) 452

GLANWYDDEN Gwynedd   map 4

Queen's Head £

| Glanwydden LL31 9JP | COOKING 1 |
| LLANDUDNO (0492) 546570 | COST £15–£34 |

The pub stands in the centre of the village, just off Llanrhos Road which
connects the A470 and the A546. Conditions that exist in the bar are cramped,
but the food continues to bring in the crowds. Lunch and slightly more
ambitious evening menus are boosted by a strong list of chef's specials. Fish
shows up well: potted local seafood, dressed Conway crab, salmon and pasta
bake, and baked fillet of brill with brown shrimps and lemon butter are
typical. There is also a substantial choice of home-made sweets ranging from
spotted dick with custard to orange and Grand Marnier trifle. One favourably
reported lunch included apple and celery soup, smoked breast of goose with
kiwi fruit, and well-made lasagne – although the overall results were
described as 'patchy'. A short, carefully chosen wine list includes three house
wines from £7.95.

CHEFS: Robert Cureton and Neil McKenzie PROPRIETOR: Robert Cureton OPEN: all
week; 12 to 2.15, 6.30 (7 Sun) to 9 MEALS: alc SERVICE: not inc, card slips closed
CARDS: Access, Visa DETAILS: 120 seats. 12 tables outside. Private parties: 26 main room.
Car park. Vegetarian meals. No children under 7. Music

HARLECH Gwynedd   map 4

▲ Castle Cottage ⁵✕   NEW ENTRY

| Pen Llech, Harlech LL46 2YL | COOKING 1* |
| HARLECH (0766) 780479 | COST £15–£26 |

The street by the front door is the steepest motor road in Britain, and that's a
fact. The Robertses arrived here a year or two ago and admit to being 'happy
but broke'. This will account for one visitor saying: 'Décor is ancient, and so is
the furniture. Chairs vary but some are very uncomfortable.' Around you, there
are pigs – models, carvings, jokes, pictures – everywhere. The food is better,
and so is Jacqueline Roberts' hospitality. Warm Stilton and walnut tart with a
tomato sauce, ballottine of chicken with a pickle-like gooseberry chutney,
over-greened salads of scallops or of bacon and avocado, wonderful steak and
kidney and oyster pies, and some good lamb with parsnips are a few of the
things commented upon. Long-stayers in Harlech have observed some
variation in standards – in the aforementioned dishes as well as in the

vegetables. Sweet things can be big and enjoyable: for instance, a treacle tart, a blackcurrant fool or a pineapple strudel. Home-made Turkish delight sounds fine to gulp coffee with. The cheeseboard has not always been a good bet. The wines will not break the bank, but they are not worth a pilgrimage. House wines are £7.50.

CHEF: Glyn Roberts PROPRIETORS: Glyn and Jacqueline Roberts OPEN: all week, D only, and Sun L; 12.30 to 2.30, 7 to 9.30 MEALS: Set Sun L £10, Set D £14 to £16.50 SERVICE: not inc CARDS: Access, Visa DETAILS: 50 seats. Private parties: 50 main room. Vegetarian meals. Children's helpings. No smoking in dining-room. Music ACCOMMODATION: 6 rooms, 4 with bath/shower. B&B £19 to £41. Deposit: £10. Children welcome. Baby facilities. Dogs by arrangement. Doors close at midnight. Confirm by 6

▲ *Cemlyn* 🍾 ⁵✕

High Street, Harlech LL46 2YA	COOKING 3
HARLECH (0766) 780425	COST £25–£31

If you go up to the lounge on the first floor, the view of the castle built by Edward I to subdue the Welsh is better than that on a postcard. That subjugation was never going to work; witness the staff of the Cemlyn. Ken Goody, who retired from desks and things a decade ago to follow his preferences, had a bad year last year, reflected in our postbag. Spirits, however, have revived. Life looks better – or the inevitable is more accepted – and meals are more enjoyable. The dominant colour in the Cemlyn is brown, but not depressingly so. The place is over-run by frogs of every description save alive, and there are interesting pictures all over the walls. It feels right, and its individuality is in harmony with the cooking. Ken Goody cooks well and uses fine materials – not elaborately, but usually with good pitch. Thus a fillet of lamb was 'prime quality, tender, sweet and grassy, pink, succulent and in a lovely red wine sauce which was powerfully sweet and sharp at the same time, fiercely reduced but uncloying, with a fresh sprig of mint plus chopped mint in the sauce'. A counterpoint was provided by a small onion quiche. Mr Goody enjoys his sauces and accompaniments; they are proper jobs, not fussy ornaments. Thus a salmon fish-cake is not enough without plenty of strong aïoli; and smoked salmon comes as a large thick slice, with some prawns, avocado and cherry tomatoes and some more mayonnaise, this time herb. He also likes substance; one reporter advises two courses only – and at bargain cost. With first courses such as a baked egg with tongue, ham and mushrooms, or braised tongue with cream, mint and caper sauce, desserts along the lines of Mississippi mud pie or mint cheesecake are going to present problems. This hearty generosity, allied to good taste, is what people go to the Cemlyn for. Not all the details are at the level of the principles which inform the undertaking, but let's hope the spirits keep high, and business remains a joy, not a burden. The wines are worth a stop for their prices and their range. There are no poor makers. The Rhônes, Alsaces and Loires are favourite sections. House wines start at £7.50.

County round-ups listing additional restaurants that may be worth a visit are at the back of the Guide, after the Irish section. Reports on round-up entries are welcome.

CHEF/PROPRIETOR: Ken Goody OPEN: all week, D only (L by arrangement); 7 to 9.30
CLOSED: Nov to Easter MEALS: Set D £14.50 to £17.50 SERVICE: not inc CARDS: Access,
Visa DETAILS: 55 seats. 3 tables outside. Private parties: 40 main room, 10 private room.
Vegetarian meals. Children's helpings. No smoking in 1 dining-room. Wheelchair access
(also WC) ACCOMMODATION: 1 room, with bath/shower. B&B £30 to £40. No children
under 8. TV. Doors close at midnight. Confirm by 6

HAVERFORDWEST Dyfed   map 4

Jemima's ✳✸

Nash Grove, Freystrop,
Haverfordwest SA62 4HB
JOHNSTON (0437) 891109
on the Burton road   COOKING 2
S of Haverfordwest   COST £15–£31

'I continue in my eccentric style of using fresh, not frozen produce,' says Ann
Owston, 'and cooking by Calor Gas, not microwaves.' Her house on a hill some
way outside the town is marked only by a small nameplate, but it is the focus
for industrious cottage economy. In addition to running the restaurant, Ann has
begun opening on Friday and Saturday mornings to sell her range of home-
baked bread, cakes and preserves. Her menus are peppered with reminders of
fruitful enterprise: home-cured ham and gravlax, an impressive array of herbs
and garden vegetables, home-made ice-creams and sorbets. Loyalty is to local
produce but the repertoire is global: escabèche of mackerel and Szechuan
spiced prawns share the stage with shoulder of Welsh lamb with apricots, and
monkfish with vermouth, tomato and fennel. Many dishes have met with
approval: avocado, lettuce and rocket salad; leek and potato soup with walnut
bread; terrine of duck; casserole of kid; halibut with mussels; rabbit in Riesling
sauce. Sweets such as apple pie and rhubarb and almond tart generally come
with home-made ice-cream. The value for money is remarkable, especially at
lunch-time. The seasonally changing wine list has been chosen with care and
knowledge by Wendy Connelly, who now has a wine shop in Haverfordwest.
House Australian is £8.

CHEF: Ann Owston PROPRIETORS: Ann Owston, Wendy and April Connelly OPEN: Tue
to Sun, exc Sat L and Sun D; 12 to 2, 7 to 9 MEALS: alc. Set L £6 to £8.50, Set D £13.50
SERVICE: not inc, card slips closed CARDS: Access, Amex, Visa DETAILS: 20 seats. Private
parties: 26 main room. Car park. Children welcome. No smoking. No music

---

LLANBERIS Gwynedd   map 4

Y Bistro ✳✸

43–45 High Street,
Llanberis LL55 4EU   COOKING 1
LLANBERIS (0286) 871278   COST £23–£34

It's properly bilingual here and visitors from Lancashire were so taken by the
local colour that they insisted the male-voice choir be piped from the bar to the
dining-room (it was a recording, not a whole body of Welshmen). The visitors

had been at first surprised there was a bar at all, for the outside of the building takes on the apparent camouflage of a tea-room. Once you have settled with a green salad and crusty bread, the menu is *echt* bistro: chicken liver pâté, melon prawns and Marie Rose sauce, baked grapefruit, beef with garlic, port and mushrooms, salmon in pastry, then bread-and-butter pudding and brown sugar meringues with hazelnuts. Prices still constitute reasonable value and quantities are generous. People have approved the cured fish – salmon, herring, whitebait – the lamb with port and redcurrant, trout stuffed with spinach and oyster ('dry until they remembered the sauce') and the Welsh cheeses. The wine list is apposite for the location, though there won't be much joy if you only want a half-bottle. House wines are £7.50.

CHEF: Nerys Roberts   PROPRIETORS: Danny and Nerys Roberts   OPEN: Tue to Sat, D only; 7 to 9.30   CLOSED: Christmas week   MEALS: Set D £17.50 to £24   SERVICE: not inc, card slips closed   CARDS: Access, Visa   DETAILS: 48 seats. Private parties: 36 main room, 20 private room. Vegetarian meals. Children welcome. Smart dress preferred. No smoking in dining-room. Wheelchair access (2 steps). Music. Air-conditioned

---

LLANDEWI SKIRRID Gwent   map 4

Walnut Tree Inn ▮

Llandewi Skirrid NP7 8AW
ABERGAVENNY (0873) 852797   COOKING 4
on B4521, 2m NE of Abergavenny   COST £35–£57

A low, white house, the Inn has sprouted many bits and pieces over the years, but still hangs together as a unity. Cars form its front garden, but terraces and views compensate for these moving metal shrubs. The Inn began as a pub and the pub is still there, though few pop in for a pint. Pass the big flower arrangement and enter the cosy bar: small tables, a burning fire. Turn left for the bistro: a larger room, small tables, crowded. Continue to the restaurant: fractionally more comfortable, a large room decorated by Enzo Apicella. All the food is the same, no matter where you sit. There is little concession to flim-flam or trappings. Service is resolutely firm and cheerful, with plenty of character. It is usually also informed, even if a panaché of fish is described as white fish and turns up with salmon and shellfish. Wine service can be inept, especially if the standard of the list is borne in mind. What brings it all together is the food. Franco Taruschio has developed a large menu that explores Italian cooking in a way few have managed to emulate in Britain. It is not 'new-wave' mixtures of Mediterranean vegetables and pungent flavours, but rather real dishes, reflecting real life as lived in the Marches of Italy (and cooked in the Marches of Wales). To this is added a leavening of items that Franco has taken to his heart: Lady Llanover's recipe for salt duck (with gooseberries and a quince jelly), crispy crab pancakes, goujons of sole with a Thai dipping sauce, or escalope of salmon with rhubarb and ginger. The Walnut Tree is more than an Italian restaurant in a pub. 'How can a place whose menu we have explored over 27 years still provide new dishes that become favourites?', writes one who approves of things here. 'We ignored the fettucine, the smoked salmon and dill, the trenette con pesto and the crispy crab pancake and the calf's liver with roasted shallots, and the oxtail vaccinara and the brodetto and the plateau de fruits de mer – all those favourites – and took instead a salad of dried tomatoes, artichoke, Parmesan cheese and focaccia, a marvellous combination of feel and taste, sight and smell; and then an eighteenth-century recipe called Vincis Grassi Maceratese. What does it mean? Vincis Grassi was somebody's name and if this was his favourite dish, we understand why: a kind of lasagne with porcini mushrooms, Parma ham, rich velvety cheese and loads (I mean loads) of shavings of white truffles. Should we settle for that? Would a sweet spoil the meal? Elderflower sorbet was the perfect response.' That says enough to give some idea of the place. The Walnut Tree has a large and socially wide following built up over a number of years. Newcomers are shocked by the cost, which is high for the level of comfort. They are also sometimes outfaced by the food (you kick off anyway with some nibble such as spinach quiche, or triangles of filo with ricotta, or crisp potato skins with spring onion). Many of the first courses are large enough for a main course; many of the main courses (especially the brodetto and the seafood platter) are large enough for a meal. Careful choice will affect the bill and leave the eater a happier person. It would also leave room for one of the sweet things, which are often good. The wine list is wonderful. Sometimes the pressures of maintaining a list as long as this tell; readers report cellar-temperature reds, and wines arriving after the food is finished. Nevertheless, the wine list here, maintained by Reid Wines, is a check-list of classics, with Italy taking pride of place. Prices are fair with much below £12. House wine is £9.50.

CHEFS: Franco Taruschio and Nigel Ramsbottom   PROPRIETORS: Franco and Ann Taruschio   OPEN: Tue to Sat; 12 to 3.30, 7.15 to 10.30   CLOSED: 2 weeks Feb   MEALS: alc. Cover £1 dining-room   SERVICE: not inc   DETAILS: 80 seats. 5 tables outside. Private parties: 30 main room. Car park. Vegetarian meals. Children's helpings. Wheelchair access (also WC). No music. Air-conditioned

---

LLANDRILLO Clwyd   map 4

▲ *Tyddyn Llan*

Llandrillo LL21 0ST
LLANDRILLO (049 084) 264
on B4401, at end of   COOKING 2
Llandrillo village   COST £20–£34

Comings and goings through the year have left Bridget Kindred once more in charge of the kitchen. 'Itemised detail of what we ate is largely irrelevant – the four of us gave the menus a bashing over three days – as it was all excellent' is a sentiment often echoed. The house is 'elegant, attractive to the eye and understated', though not without decorative artifice, deep armchairs, lots of fabric, good log fires and now with the addition of a verandahed, high-roofed dining-room jutting out into surrounding lawns. Many come here for the landscape, the water, the walking and the sport. If Bridget Kindred controls, much of the execution is down to 'hands-on' chef Wendy Phillips. A set-price menu (with the possibility of soup or salad as a second, intermediate course) avoids the sillinesses of country-house cooking. Avocado is mixed with prawns and given a light curry mayonnaise; a hot fish terrine (light) comes with a sorrel sauce; goats' cheese is wrapped in filo, baked and served with a damson chutney; lambs' kidneys come with a mustard and sherry sauce; fish may be salmon, red mullet or perhaps a mélange, served with a julienne of vegetables and simple white wine sauce. Meats are more conventional: duck with orange, beef with horseradish (which actually did not appear on the day), pork with prune and apple compote. Vegetables are plentiful, but seem to rely more on market imports than the exactly seasonal. 'Puddings have a touch of the old English,' said one who was so bowled over by a baked lemon cream and a walnut and treacle tart that he had to wait until next time for the bread-and-butter pudding, the rhubarb crumble and pancakes with butterscotch that were also on offer one Sunday lunch. Peter Kindred's work at the front-of-house is relaxed but punctilious. The wines he offers are a good choice: note particularly the Spanish and the Italian selections at very fair prices. The number of half-bottles is greatly increased from last year and there are some attractive dessert wines to be had as well. Organic wines are dotted through many sections and the house wines begin at £8.

CHEF: Bridget Kindred   PROPRIETORS: Peter and Bridget Kindred   OPEN: all week, exc Mon L; 12.30 to 2, 7 to 9.30   MEALS: Set L £10 to £13, Set D £19.50 to £22   SERVICE: not inc, card slips closed   CARDS: Access, Visa   DETAILS: 60 seats. Private parties: 45 main room. Car park. Vegetarian meals. Children's helpings. Wheelchair access. Music ACCOMMODATION: 10 rooms, all with bath/shower. B&B £48 to £82. Deposit: 15%. Children welcome. Baby facilities. Pets welcome. Afternoon teas. Garden. Fishing. Phone. Doors close at midnight. Confirm by 6. Fax: (049 084) 264 (*The Which? Hotel Guide*)

LLANDUDNO Gwynedd   map 4

▲ *Bodysgallen Hall* ♟

Llandudno LL30 1RS
DEGANWY (0492) 584466
from A55 join A470 and follow
Llandudno signpost, hotel 1m   COOKING 2*
on right   COST £22–£50

The house is something special – it's owned by Historic House Hotels, experts at restoring and converting good buildings to commercial use. The Hall is ancient, atmospheric (a few say bits are dowdy, but it depends on your viewpoint) and enjoyed for the situation. Almost everyone finds the gardens exceptional. One couple thought them better than anything, having been condemned to a 70-minute wait before food was up and running. The Hall also seems to be full of old retainers who do not necessarily inspire the confidence imparted by experience: 'The waiter was out of breath, the effort of walking into the bar and bending over to put the dish on the table had evidently creased him,' one younger customer observed. The cooking here is country-house standard. Some of it is extremely competent: a puff pastry case with scrambled egg and oyster mushrooms was 'wonderfully light and fluffy, infused with as much flavour from oyster mushrooms as must be possible'; a fine piece of marinated venison was made even better by a very well-executed game sauce; even a lacklustre fillet of beef was worth eating for its madeira and truffle sauce. The trimmings may be over-the-top: a mid-way sorbet came with a great collection of tropical fruit – the diner must have thought dessert had arrived.

Ignore the fact that vegetables may not be so much lightly cooked as raw. Ignore the uninteresting and conventional sweet course – 'my mille-feuille was two feuilles' – and the patriotic but novelty conscious cheese selection. Some of the cooking is very professional. Whether £100 for two at dinner is a good bargain is a matter of judgement. The welcome was conspicuous by its absence on the night we sent two young inspectors. Lunches are much better value. Many people like it here, perhaps with a desire to enjoy life as it used to be lived. The wine list will bring them sharply close to reality. The list is wide-ranging, uses good sources, and has depth as well. But it is simply too dear. Any number of small private restaurants in the region, with just as good or better cooking, can do it cheaper. House wines start at £11.25.

CHEF: Miss Mair Lewis PROPRIETORS: Historic House Hotels OPEN: all week; 12.30 to 2, 7.30 to 9.30 MEALS: Set L £13.90 to £15.90, Set D £31 SERVICE: net prices, card slips closed CARDS: Access, Amex, Diners, Visa DETAILS: 40 seats. Private parties: 48 main room, 2 private room. Car park. No children under 8. Jacket and tie. No cigars/pipes in dining-room. Music ACCOMMODATION: 28 rooms, all with bath/shower. B&B £95 to £165. No children under 8. Pets welcome. Afternoon teas. Garden. Tennis. TV. Phone. Fax: (0492) 582519 (*The Which Hotel? Guide*)

Richard at Lanterns £

7 Church Walks,
Llandudno LL30 2HD
LLANDUDNO (0492) 877924

COOKING 1
COST £14–£29

Richard Hendey splits his efforts between two floors: restaurant above, bistro below. The cheaper bistro runs on the chargrill, with fish and daily extras plugged into the constants of steak, boneless chicken, lamb and duck. The chintzy restaurant goes for broke with two interlinking menus, one set-price, the other à la carte. The repertoire will not stop the ticking of conservative Welsh hearts when they read of peppered whisky steak, chicken stuffed with ham and cheese, served with leeks and wild mushrooms, or loin of pork with apple and a cider sauce. Sauces tend to be strong, helpings substantial. Enjoyment of the flavoursome comes across in first courses such as seafood in a 'raspberry-scented champagne sauce', mushrooms with garlic and Stilton cream, and guinea-fowl and pigeon terrine with a plum and orange sauce. There is a tremendous eagerness and conviction about Richard Hendey, and he gets full support from Sally Hendey. The wine list gives good value from a range fully adequate for the food. Take a look at the Spanish reds. House wines are £6.95.

CHEF/PROPRIETOR: Richard Hendey OPEN: Tue to Sun, D only, Mon D summer; 6.30 to 10 MEALS: alc. Set D £18.95 SERVICE: net prices, card slips closed CARDS: Access, Visa DETAILS: 24 seats. Private parties: 24 main room, 10 private room. Vegetarian meals. Children's helpings. Music

£ *indicates that it is possible to have a three-course meal, including coffee, a half-bottle of house wine and service, at any time the restaurant is open (i.e. at dinner as well as at lunch, unless a place is open only for dinner), for £20 or less per person.*

▲ *St Tudno Hotel* ⁵✳

North Parade, Llandudno LL30 2LP
LLANDUDNO (0492) 874411

COOKING 1
COST £17–£28

The hotel's white stucco Victorian façade faces the pier and promenade of this seaside town, but defies the tide of fashion. The Blands do not pander, but they have refurbished and modernised to a high standard. However, David Harding's attempts to steer kitchen output away from old standards such as grilled minute steaks and lamb with mint sauce and redcurrant jelly seem to be in difficulties. 'This year the lunch menu was unexciting and vegetables were served cold,' laments one reader. Another cites a crab salad 'with no sign of crab'. Despite lapses, modest invention and decent technique find favour in reports. Grilled fillet of lemon sole with a 'piquant sauce', banana fritter and mango chutney, and breast of chicken with coconut and sweet red pepper sauce demonstrate élan. And a fondness for fruit is carried to dessert stage. Slices from the Welsh cheeseboard have helped end dinner on a high note. There is also a coffee-lounge menu. The wine list, maintained by Haughton Fine Wines, has a good fine range and prices are fair, with many bottles below £12. Antipodeans are interesting, Italy is strong. House wines are from £8.75.

CHEF: David Harding   PROPRIETORS: Martin and Janette Bland   OPEN: all week; 12.30 to 2, 6.45 to 9.30 (9 Sun)   MEALS: Set L £12.50, Set D £23.50. Minimum £10   SERVICE: not inc, card slips closed   CARDS: Access, Amex, Visa   DETAILS: 60 seats. Private parties: 45 main room. Car park. Vegetarian meals. Smart dress preferred. No smoking in dining-room. Wheelchair access. No music. Air-conditioned   ACCOMMODATION: 21 rooms, all with bath/shower. 1 room for disabled. Lift. B&B £52.50 to £120. Deposit: £25. Children welcome. Baby facilities. Pets by arrangement. Afternoon teas. Swimming-pool. Air-conditioned. TV. Phone. Doors close at midnight. Fax: (0492) 860407

LLANGAMMARCH WELLS Powys

map 4

▲ *Lake Hotel* ⁵✳

Llangammarch Wells LD4 4BS
LLANGAMMARCH (059 12) 202

COOKING 2
COST £21–£37

Rhododendrons, parkland and a private lake on which to cast a fly are some of the outdoor amenities of an Edwardian country house that sports as much half-timbering as any in Weybridge or Esher. The Mifsuds have effected great transformations indoors: from a rather stark series of plain-coloured rooms to a riot of swags and chintzes. Richard Arnold's food enjoys a few swags too. Pigeon breast is served in a warm salad with baked avocado and chestnuts, and topped with a passion-fruit and walnut vinaigrette; salmon escalope is stuffed with crab and lobster mousse on a watercress cream sauce; winter desserts are heavy with red fruits. Devotees of this sort of elaboration find it pleasing; certain flavours – fruity acidity with meat and poultry, nuts of all sorts with everything, and some sweet spices like ginger – are consistent features, as are careful presentation, eager and committed service and a menu that offers three or four choices at each course for a single all-in price. The wine list (at 300 choices, too large for us to receive a copy) is catholic in its selection and ranges from the 'fabulously priced to the very reasonable'.

CHEF: Richard Arnold   PROPRIETORS: Jean-Pierre and Jan Mifsud   OPEN: all week D only, and Sun L (Mon to Sat L bookings only); 1 to 2.15, 7.30 to 9   CLOSED: Jan   MEALS: Set L £14.50, Set D £24.50   SERVICE: not inc   CARDS: Access, Amex, Visa   DETAILS: 38 seats. Private parties: 70 main room. Car park. Vegetarian meals. Children's helpings with prior notice. No children under 8. Jacket and tie. No smoking in dining-room. Wheelchair access (also WC)   ACCOMMODATION: 19 rooms, all with bath/shower. Rooms for disabled. B&B £65 to £90. Deposit: £30. Children welcome. Pets welcome. Afternoon teas. Garden. Tennis. Fishing. Snooker. TV. Phone. Fax: (059 12) 457 (*The Which? Hotel Guide*)

LLANGOLLEN Clwyd   map 4

▲ *Gales* ￼ £

| 18 Bridge Street, Llangollen LL20 8PF | COOKING 1 |
| WREXHAM (0978) 860089 | COST £12–£18 |

Endorsement of this wine bar continues for no-nonsense food and a happy welcome among much panelling and old church pews. There are good wines, too. A root vegetable soup with cream, tuna and macaroni stuffed to the gills with courgettes and mushrooms, substantial hotpots and various salads are items that get a mention, even if not every dart of taste hits the bull's-eye. The wine list is chiefly remarkable for its low, low prices. An enthusiast's supplement is offered for the interesting material. New World offerings are particularly strong, balancing a timid approach to burgundies. House wines are £6.60. CELLARMAN'S CHOICE: Mâcon, Pinot Chardonnay 1991, Sandler, £8.95; Gran Reserva 1982, Gran Marius, £10.95.

CHEFS: John Gosling and Jennifer Johnson   PROPRIETORS: Richard and Gillie Gale   OPEN: Mon to Sat; 12 to 2, 6 to 10   CLOSED: Christmas to New Year   MEALS: alc   SERVICE: not inc   CARDS: Access, Visa   DETAILS: 50 seats. 5 tables outside. Private parties: 8 and 12 private rooms. Car park. Vegetarian meals. Children welcome. Music   ACCOMMODATION: 8 rooms, all with bath/shower. B&B £29.50 to £48. Deposit: £20. Children welcome. Baby facilities. TV. Phone. Doors close at 11.30. Confirm by 6. Fax: (0978) 861313 (*The Which? Hotel Guide*)

LLANRWST Gwynedd   map 4

▲ *Meadowsweet Hotel* ￼ ￼

| Station Road, Llanrwst LL26 0DS | COOKING 2 |
| LLANRWST (0492) 640732 | COST £18–£28 |

The Evanses' privately run hotel is in a Victorian house overlooking fields just outside the town. John Evans' five-course dinner menus change monthly and guests are free to order any number or variety of courses. The kitchen makes good use of local and seasonal ingredients: Tamar salmon is served with honey and ginger sauce; fillet of Welsh lamb comes with ratatouille and garlic cream sauce (one reporter considered this 'outstanding'). Other recommended dishes have included mushrooms à la grecque, cauliflower soup ('substantially warm and welcoming as the April rain lashed against the windows'), guinea-fowl cooked in cider and cream, and chocolate mousse in orange sauce. There is also praise for the excellent selection of well-kept Welsh and French cheeses. Some people have found the cooking little more than average and reckoned that the place was 'resting on its laurels'. Service by local girls is not to everyone's taste: comments range from 'friendly and relaxed rather than ultra-professional' to 'appalling'. Breakfasts are rated as some of the best of their kind in Wales. The fair-priced wine list is a treasure-trove for seekers of the odd bottle, but also an intelligent assembly of good wines from the main producing countries. The Rhône, Alsace and the Loire are especially well covered; there are clarets too, and Italy, Spain and Australasia deserve close study. House wines are £9.25.

CHEF: John Evans   PROPRIETORS: John and Joy Evans   OPEN: all week, exc Mon to Sat L Nov to Easter; 12.15 to 1.30, 6.30 to 9.30   MEALS: alc. Set L £9.95 to £11.95, Set D £26 SERVICE: not inc, card slips closed   CARDS: Access, Visa   DETAILS: 36 seats. Private parties: 50 main room. Car park. Vegetarian meals. Children's helpings. Smart dress preferred. No smoking in dining-room. No music   ACCOMMODATION: 10 rooms, all with bath/shower. B&B £36 to £68. Deposit: £25. Children welcome. Baby facilities. Pets welcome. Afternoon teas. TV. Phone. Doors close at midnight. Confirm by 6

LLANSANFFRAID GLAN CONWY Gwynedd   map 4

▲ *Old Rectory* 🍷 ⁕

Llansanffraid Glan Conwy LL28 5LF	COOKING 3
LLANDUDNO (0492) 580611	COST £39

Spectacular views across the estuary to Conway Castle complement the Vaughans' lovingly restored Georgian rectory. Sophisticated in style, domestic in scale, the elegant restaurant holds but few people – telephone first, and be prepared for the steep driveway. Wendy Vaughan has reorganised her daily-changing dinner menu to offer a simpler two courses plus cheese, pudding and coffee, but with a choice still available only at the dessert stage. Her cooking matches up to the setting; the emphasis is on taste rather than volume and takes its cue from local ingredients: all beef and lamb is from the district. This year's postbag has yielded an abundant crop of recommendations, including oyster mushrooms and asparagus in puff pastry with madeira sauce; medallions of monkfish with mange-tout and red pepper sauce; poached breast of chicken wrapped in air-dried ham and spinach and stuffed with Welsh cheese on a bed of green lentils; chocolate and raspberry cheesecake; and lemon chiffon pie. Skill and finesse are apparent, with time well-spent on presentation. Those with an aversion to a communal dining-table – '"Bring back hanging and the birch" is not my chosen dinner conversation' – will be pleased to hear that they can request a separate table. The house has a no-smoking policy, but two new coach-house rooms offer a bolt-hole for resident addicts. An enlarged range of good half-bottles and Italian and Spanish wines has augmented the already carefully constructed and fairly priced wine list. Buying is intelligent, with encouraging evidence of the best being selected from a range of merchants. Alsace and Rhône are strong; but thankfully this is never a list which seeks to impress through size. A bottle is awarded this year. House wine is £11.90. CELLARMAN'S CHOICE: Pouilly Fumé, Dom. des Berthiers 1989, Dagueneau, £14.90; Haut-Médoc, Ch. Fourcas-Hosten 1982, £17.90.

CHEF: Wendy Vaughan PROPRIETORS: Michael and Wendy Vaughan OPEN: all week, D only; 7.30 for 8 CLOSED: 7 Dec to 1 Feb MEALS: Set D £26 SERVICE: not inc, card slips closed CARDS: Access, Visa DETAILS: 16 seats. Car park. Vegetarian meals. No children under 4. Jacket and tie. No smoking in dining-room and hotel. No music ACCOMMODATION: 6 rooms, all with bath/shower. B&B £69 to £89. No children under 7. Pets welcome (coach-house only). Afternoon teas. Garden. TV. Phone. Doors close at midnight. Fax: (0492) 584555 (*The Which? Hotel Guide*)

LLANWDDYN Powys

map 4

▲ *Lake Vyrnwy Hotel* ¾⊁

NEW ENTRY

Lake Vyrnwy, Llanwddyn SY10 0LY
LLANWDDYN (069 173) 692
on B4393, at SE end of Lake Vyrnwy

COOKING 1
COST £16–£31

The lake is not a lake, it's a reservoir, built in the 1880s to supply Liverpool. The great Gothic tower, that is central to any view from the conservatory extension to the dining-room, is a straining tower, filtering out any fish or detritus before the water enters the municipal mains. The house was built to take advantage of the new stretch of water, and afford a base for shooters over 24,000 acres of land. You do not lack for space here. Andrew Wood, who has been chef for the last four years, works in a restrained style that has gained support during his tenure. The style comes over very well with roast meats (three joints on Sundays), which are well bought, well hung and accurately cooked. It may not come over so impressively in some details like undifferentiated sauces. Residents speak highly of his ability to ring the changes on daily menus. Three first courses were hot chicken mousse with a truffled oil, fritters of prawns and avocado with a curry sauce, and fritters of Cheddar cheese; pot-roasted saddle of lamb with thin madeira sauce, quail with orange and redcurrants, and sole with a prawn mousse stuffing were three main dishes. Complexity, for example, in the cooking of vegetables (though home-grown), does not always pay off. Light syllabub has been excellent; designer bread-and-butter pudding shows a willingness to play it simple too. Much of the wine is supplied by Tanners of Shrewsbury, which guarantees quality. Prices are not unfair. There are some hefty clarets and useful Spanish and French country wines to beef up the bottom of the price range. Halves are not generously supplied. House wines are £8.25.

CHEF: Andrew Wood PROPRIETORS: Market Glen Ltd OPEN: all week; 12.30 to 1.45, 7.30 to 9.15 CLOSED: L Dec to Mar MEALS: Set L £10.45, Set Sun L £11.25, Set D £21.50 SERVICE: not inc, card slips closed CARDS: Access, Amex, Diners, Visa DETAILS: 80 seats. Private parties: 115 main room, 75 private room. Car park. Vegetarian meals. Children's helpings. Smart dress preferred. No smoking in conservatory. Wheelchair access. No music (exc Christmas Eve harpist) ACCOMMODATION: 30 rooms, all with bath/shower. B&B £55.50 to £112.50. Children welcome. Baby facilities. Dogs welcome (in bedroom only, kennels available). Afternoon teas. Garden. Tennis. Fishing. TV. Phone. Doors close at midnight. Confirm 5 days ahead. Fax: (069 173) 259 (*The Which? Hotel Guide*)

The Good Food Guide *is a registered trade mark of Consumers' Association Ltd.*

LLANWRDA Dyfed   map 4

Seguendo di Stagioni ♟ £

NEW ENTRY

Harford, nr Pumpsaint,
Llanwrda SA19 8DT   COOKING 1
PUMPSAINT (055 85) 671   COST £13–£27

Almost in the middle of nowhere, on the Lampeter Road (A482), is a
characterless building opposite a garage. Next door is the Pigs 'n' Piglets
transport café. The scenario may sound unpromising, but this place defies
prejudice and first impressions. The name means 'following the seasons' and
Aldo Steccanella delivers Italian cookery, taking his cue from local produce
and the markets. As one reporter remarked, 'Aldo has succeeded in injecting
some Lombardy warmth into this bleak part of Wales', without resorting to
false histrionics. The mood is infectiously cheerful, the cooking uncomplicated.
The menu rejects lasagne and spaghetti bolognese in favour of bruschetta with
fresh tomatoes; salad of cabbage, cheese and ham with balsamic vinegar
dressing; home-made ravioli with butter and sage sauce; and tenderloin of beef
with asparagus. Meat, from a butcher in Carmarthen, is excellent quality.
Tiramisù is a regularly praised sweet. From Tuesday to Thursday there is a
good-value 'pasta special' menu (and there are set meals for parties). The wine
list is a corker, bristling with reasonably priced bottles from classy Italian
growers. House wine from Tuscany is £6.95. CELLARMAN'S CHOICE: Soave
Classico, Pieropan 1989, £12.95; Chianti Classico, Isole e Olena 1987, £15.25.

CHEF: Aldo Steccanella   PROPRIETOR: Jennifer Taylor   OPEN: Tue to Sun; 12 to 3.30, 7 to
11.30   MEALS: alc. Set L and D £7.95   SERVICE: not inc, card slips closed   CARDS: Access,
Visa (3.5% surcharge)   DETAILS: 35 seats. 4 tables outside. Private parties: 35 main room.
Car park. Vegetarian meals. Children's helpings. No music

LLYSWEN Powys   map 4

▲ *Griffin Inn* ⁝✳ £

NEW ENTRY

Llyswen LD3 0UR   COOKING 1
LLYSWEN (0874) 754241   COST £16–£32

This ancient village inn with strong sporting connections has unspoilt bars and
better-than-usual food. Game in season is the real speciality and it generally
comes in casseroles ('rather raunchily presented') with rich and earthy sauces:
braised pigeon in cider, jugged hare, grouse with brandy – all good solid stuff.
If there is no game, then try fish. Monkfish with a curry sauce and fennel gets
high marks, but the laurels rest on River Wye salmon and trout, fresh or
smoked. For the rest, bar and restaurant rely on well-tried combinations:
Stilton, celery and port terrine, kidneys Turbigo, apple sauce with the roast
duck, mint with the lamb, onions with the steak. The cooking is 'good, tasty
country food'. Pudding, if you reach it, will not be small: treacle tart, fruit
meringues, cheesecakes and roulades give some idea of the parameters.
'Mouthwatering' was one reaction. House wine is £6.85 but there are others,
or draught Boddingtons.

CHEF: Eileen Havard PROPRIETORS: the Stockton family OPEN: all week (Sun D residents only); 12 to 2, 7 to 9 MEALS: alc SERVICE: not inc, card slips closed CARDS: Access, Amex, Diners, Visa DETAILS: 80 seats. 4 tables outside. Private parties: 35 main room, 12 private room. Car park. Vegetarian meals. Children's helpings. No smoking in dining-room. Wheelchair access (1 step). No music ACCOMMODATION: 8 rooms, 7 with bath/shower. B&B £28.50 to £50. Deposit: 20%. Children welcome. Baby facilities. Pets welcome. Fishing. Phone. Doors close at 12.30am. Confirm by 6. Fax: (0874) 754592

▲ *Llangoed Hall* 🍾 ⁵❋

Llyswen LD3 0YP
BRECON (0874) 754525   COOKING 3
on A470, 2m N of Llyswen   COST £22–£65

A house converted to a hotel by Sir Bernard Ashley, built in the first (or second) instance by Clough Williams-Ellis, is a natural for the 'country-house look' and this has it with a vengeance. The features worth remarking are the pictures assembled here by Sir Bernard (all Edwardian, some really interesting), the handsome dining-room that reproduces the Edwardian original and the Jacobean porch that Williams-Ellis allowed to survive from the first structure. Everyone strives for the country-house effect: the ideal of seamless service, as if you were master or mistress and the server was Jeeves, is often – but not invariably – achieved here, yet always avoids the snooty or unwilling. Mark Salter rules the kitchen. His manner, first given long outing at Cromlix House in Scotland (see entry, Kinbuck), is marked by some restraint (more of the English country house) yet is coupled with a certain elaboration of technique to lift it above the plain cooking once beloved of the gentry. He is therefore happy to top a fillet of beef with foie gras, serve a pea mousse with lobster or a leek timbale with veal fillet, though happier still to roast guinea-fowl, grill lamb cutlets, roast a chateaubriand or steam some brill with more straightforward accompaniments of potatoes in one form or another (new, saffron, dauphinois, sauté and rösti on a single menu). Some artfulness comes with earlier courses, where terrines are enjoyed, such as cauliflower with vegetable tempura and Stilton sauce, or chicken, wild mushroom and leek with a coriander sauce. Desserts are the English mixture: a hot sticky toffee, a hot soufflé (often praised), home-made ice-creams with fruit accompaniment, caramelised apple tart. The supporters to the meals have also been well reported, from home-made rolls to sweeties with the coffee. This is very sound cooking though perhaps suffering from self-imposed restraint. There is not quite so much restraint when it comes to cost. The wine list is an awe-inspiring range of classics balanced with mature Italians, magnificent Spanish – a 1978 Rioja Reserva 904 – and impeccable Californians. Rather stolid burgundies are more than compensated for by fine Rhônes and Mosels. CELLARMAN'S CHOICE: Crozes-Hermitage, Mule Blanche 1988, Jaboulet, £18.50; Haut-Médoc, Ch. Coufran 1983, £19.50.

Net prices *in the details at the end of an entry indicates that the prices given on a menu and on a bill are inclusive of VAT and service charge, and that this practice is clearly stated on menu and bill.*

CHEF: Mark Salter PROPRIETOR: Sir Bernard Ashley OPEN: all week; 12.15 to 2.15, 7.15 to 9.30 MEALS: alc. Set L £14.50 to £16.50, Set D £35.50 SERVICE: not inc, card slips closed CARDS: Access, Amex, Diners, Visa DETAILS: 48 seats. Private parties: 10 main room, 16 and 26 private rooms. Car park. Vegetarian meals. Children's helpings (early D only). No children under 8. Jacket and tie. No smoking in dining-room. Wheelchair access (2 steps; also female WC). Music ACCOMMODATION: 23 rooms, all with bath/shower. B&B £95 to £275. Deposit: £50. No children under 8. Baby facilities. Pets welcome (in kennels). Afternoon teas. Garden. Tennis. Fishing. Snooker. TV. Phone. Fax: (0874) 754545 (*The Which? Hotel Guide*)

MATHRY Dyfed   map 4

Ann FitzGerald's
Farmhouse Kitchen ♥

Mabws Fawr, Mathry SA62 5JB   COOKING 2
CROESGOCH (0348) 831347   COST £20–£38

Mind the potholes in the drive and discover 'past the screen of trees, not just the farmhouse, but a whole yard of barns and sheds slowly reverting to a sycamore jungle'. Thus came word from one explorer who drove past the caravan park on the Treffgarne Owen road just off the A487. But once you move indoors, that Larkin image is quickly lost: sophistication and comfort are found, and Ann FitzGerald herself is described as 'charming and immaculate'. 'We went round to enquire about a table and were followed in by a fisherman bearing a box of scallops,' recounted some American visitors. 'We ate them that night, cooked in a filo purse with cream, oregano and armagnac, then served with a lemon beurre blanc.' There is a long *carte* and a set-price menu with plenty of choice but, most appealing of all, you get lots of appetisers: 'Our party agreed that the best value would be had by eating the smoked pigeon breasts and various seafood offered as amuse-bouche, then skipping a first course' was one heretical announcement. The gesture indicates the generosity of the place and hints at the substance of the cooking. Sometimes the cream seduces at the appetite's expense. Dishes that have earned their stars this year include salmon with a dill and sparkling Alsace sauce, finished with cream and served with seaweed; king prawn tails with green pea soup; scallops and Japanese noodles; duck basted with orange and madeira, the sauce reinforced with cognac and white wine; guinea-fowl with grapes and cognac; great vegetables; and desserts, such as strawberries 'injected with crème de fraises, coated with a soufflé-like batter, deep-fried and served with a chilled strawberry coulis', that sink hardy souls with pleasure. The answer seems to be to starve beforehand. The wine list includes excellent choices from all round the world. The French spread is particularly careful and includes a good Madiran and Le Pigeoulet from the makers of Châteauneuf-du-Pape's Dom. du Vieux Télégraphe. The sight of Clos Fourtet 1983 at an affordable price is also welcome and the Italian wines, including Isole e Olena's Cepparello and Scarpia's Dolcetto Ripasso 1989, are equally impressive. House wines from Sicily cost £7.50.
CELLARMAN'S CHOICE: Côtes de Duras, Dom. de Malardeau 1990, £9; Argentina, Caves de Weinert Mendoza 1983, £12.

CHEFS: Lionel and Ann FitzGerald   PROPRIETOR: Ann FitzGerald   OPEN: all week; 12 to 2,
7 to 9   CLOSED: L Christmas to Easter   MEALS: alc. Set Sun L £14, Set D £21.50   SERVICE:
not inc   DETAILS: 40 seats. 4 tables outside. Private parties: 40 main room. Car park.
Vegetarian meals. Children's helpings. No children under 9. Wheelchair access. Music

---

NEWPORT Dyfed   map 4

▲ *Cnapan* ❦ ✻ £

East Street, Newport SA42 0WF   COOKING 1
NEWPORT (0239) 820575   COST £12–£28

Two generations of Lloyds run this popular, busy guesthouse that gets a flurry
of favourable reports for authentic, honest and inexpensive food. Influences
range beyond Europe in dishes like spiced chicken breast with peanut sauce
though materials are as local as local, down to the wild herbs used in the
marinade for lamb with olive oil, oregano, lemon and garlic with an onion and
apricot sauce. Chicken, ham and apricot terrine, pork with pineapple, Dijon
mustard and garlic, beef olives stuffed with minced lamb and mushrooms,
sticky apple pudding and chocolate truffle torte are other dishes that get three
cheers. There is a clear fruity bias to the cooking; also a certain love of garlic
and enthusiasm for vegetables – eight were served together, to one man's
delight. Lunch is light, except on Sunday. The wine list is a short but informed
choice from good growers. Prices are very fair indeed. House wines are £6.35.

CHEFS: Eluned Lloyd and Judi Cooper   PROPRIETORS: Eluned and John Lloyd, Judi and
Michael Cooper   OPEN: all week, exc Tue (Fri and Sat D and Sun L only, Nov to Mar); 12 to
2.30, 7 to 9   CLOSED: Feb   MEALS: alc D. Set Sun L £8.50. Light L menu   SERVICE: not inc,
card slips closed   CARDS: Access, Visa   DETAILS: 34 seats. 4 tables outside. Private parties:
36 main room. Car park. Vegetarian meals. Children's helpings. No smoking in dining-
room. Wheelchair access (also WC). Music   ACCOMMODATION: 5 rooms, all with bath/
shower. B&B £22 to £44. Deposit: £20. Children welcome. Baby facilities. TV. Phone. Doors
close at midnight. Confirm by 5 (*The Which? Hotel Guide*)

NORTHOP Clwyd   map 4

▲ *Soughton Hall*

Northop CH7 6AB
NORTHOP (035 286) 811   COOKING 2
off A5119, Northop to Mold   COST £23–£54

The house is a big one – once a bishop's palace – the avenue of limes is long,
there are good gardens, the air of grandeur is palpable, and guests are treated to
the attentions of the 'Resident Rodenhurst family', who undertook the
restoration and conversion in the 1980s. Many visitors are dazzled by all this; it
is a place of gesture rather than intimacy. The menu itself has gestures aplenty,
down to a sorbet after the first course ('strawberry tended to confuse the palate
between seafood pasta and rack of lamb'). Like the service by waitresses in
'elegant, pale-pink satin, backless frocks', the food is carefully dressed and
sounds elaborate. It does not help, however, if seafood pasta with basil butter
sauce has salmon and monkfish as its seafood, no basil but chervil, and a cream

rather than butter sauce. 'Best end of lamb on a port wine sauce with a redcurrant compote topped and glazed with a fresh mint sabayon' turned out in the event to be boneless lamb of decent flavour and 'cooked pink beautifully', with a sabayon more of leek than mint, and some 'bottled' redcurrants. Some of the touches are good: a salad of finely shredded vegetables in bird's-nest fashion proved an excellent accompaniment to steak; a chicken breast that had been marinated in lemon and honey made a delicious warm salad starter, even if advertised yoghurt and bacon seemed absent. A series of set-price menus is offered. The cheapest is not out of order, the most expensive is as dear as most in London. The cooking has to sprint to keep up. Wines are reasonably priced, and the range of the list is estimable. There are plenty of choices under £15 and the sources are reliable. House wine is £9.50. There is also a more informal restaurant (The Plassey, Eyton, near Wrexham, Tel: (0978) 780905), supervised by the Soughton team, that provides traditional English cooking in the form of bar lunches (from £1.95) and à la carte lunches and dinners from about £15 for three courses.

CHEF: Thomas Ludecke   PROPRIETORS: John and Rosemary Rodenhurst   OPEN: all week, D only, and Sun L (L Mon to Sat by arrangement); 12 to 2, 7 to 9.30 (10 Sat, 8 Sun)   MEALS: Set L £16.50 to £19.50, Set D £23.50 to £37.50   SERVICE: not inc, card slips closed   CARDS: Access, Amex, Visa   DETAILS: 50 seats. Private parties: 56 main room, 22 private room. Car park. Vegetarian meals. No children under 12. Jacket and tie. No cigars/pipes in dining-room. No music   ACCOMMODATION: 12 rooms, all with bath/shower. B&B £80 to £116. Deposit: 25%. No children under 12. Afternoon teas. Garden. Tennis. Snooker. TV. Phone. Fax: (035 286) 811 (*The Which? Hotel Guide*)

PENMAENPOOL Gwynedd   map 4

▲ *Penmaenuchaf Hall* 🛏✳   [NEW ENTRY]

Penmaenpool,
nr Dolgellau LL40 1YB
DOLGELLAU (0341) 422129   COOKING 2
on A493, 1½m W of Dolgellau   COST £21–£34

The Hall, standing in plenty of azalea-filled grounds above the Mawddach estuary has been newly converted to hotel use. It was a Victorian bolt-hole for a Bolton industrialist and comes complete with a good, original conservatory. When a reporter told of being greeted by a lady 'in cream and pink silk' one thought that it was the upholstery being described, for this is indeed cream in parts, and of luxury tantamount to silken. Nic Walton has come to cook here, matching the fabrics with a list of dishes that does not shy away from lobster and wild mushrooms, even if foie gras and truffles are beyond the bounds of the still-reasonable price. Some things read better than they taste, so a crab salad was on the dry side, the balance between meat and herb and cucumber sauce being wrong, and on the same evening mussels with a garlic and chive velouté should have been more eloquent of its flavourings. But duck that had been coated with a crust of greengages, then set on a 'cassoulet' of beans, though it seemed to ignore the origins and intentions of south-western France, was immensely successful, and a timbale of Dover sole round a light laverbread soufflé was exactly balanced by its saffron and lemon cream. The trouble taken to stuff tomatoes with fresh peas in cream was reckoned to be worth it. Nic Walton obviously knows his soufflés, so a hot one at the end is a good bet, just as pastry seems within his grasp. A good beginning, therefore, for which we need more reports to firm up the mark. The wine list is from Tanners and very acceptable, but do not expect much interest below £20, and halves are notional. House wines start at £9.85. Everything is keen as mustard at the moment; so would you be if you were in your first year.

CHEFS: Nic Walton and Blaine Reed   PROPRIETOR: Mark Watson   OPEN: all week; 12 to 2.15, 7 to 9.30   MEALS: Set L £12.50, Set D £19.95   SERVICE: not inc, card slips closed   CARDS: Access, Visa   DETAILS: 30 seats. Private parties: 25 main room, 100 private room. Car park. Vegetarian meals. Children's helpings. No smoking in dining-room. Wheelchair access (also WC). Music   ACCOMMODATION: 14 rooms, all with bath/shower. B&B £65 to £140. Deposit: £15. Children welcome. Baby facilities. Afternoon teas. Garden. Fishing. Snooker. TV. Phone. Doors close at 11.30. Confirm by 6. Fax: (0341) 422129

PONTFAEN Dyfed   map 4

▲ Tregynon Country Farmhouse Hotel ▮ ⅜ £

Gwaun Valley, Pontfaen SA65 9TU
NEWPORT (0239) 820531
B4313 towards Fishguard, first   COOKING 1
right, and right again for ½m   COST £19–£27

Old stone, history and landscape make a big appeal to first-timers at this farmhouse where special diets, wholefood, vegetarianism and good cooking are also pretty important. The fireplaces are enormous, the building blocks massive, and the atmosphere is rustic. The cooking is more up to date, ranging the world for leguminous inspiration in dishes such as falafel, dhal curry and chilladas, or indulging in a bit of self-sufficiency with farm-grown vegetables and home-smoked bacon. The vegetarian bias causes most first courses and soups to be free of meat or fish; the desire to cook for special diets makes the menu composition tailor-made to the intending diners. The style is substantial – plenty of vegetables with the main course, plenty of bread on the table – and freshness is a fetish. Though Tregynon is no distance from the sea, not much is heard of fish cookery. A winter visiting couple praised the care taken in every aspect of their visit: excellent steak with brandy and cream, tip-top vegetables, rather a restricted choice of pudding, but an abundance of coffee. They remarked a certain earnestness of atmosphere, but the place does deliver the goods. Those on special diets will testify how rare such places are. The wine list is excellent. The notes are very long and mighty instructive, the choice is interesting and catholic, and the prices are low. Peter Heard makes up for length (not more than 40 bins) by knowledge. A glass is awarded for balance and sheer reliability. House wines are £6.90. CELLARMAN'S CHOICE: Christian Brothers Chardonnay 1987, £12.75; Penfolds Bin 389 Cabernet Shiraz 1987, £15.75.

See inside the front cover for an explanation of the symbols used at the tops of entries.

CHEFS/PROPRIETORS: Peter and Jane Heard   OPEN: all week, D only; 7.30 to 8.45   MEALS: Set D £14 to £19   SERVICE: not inc, card slips closed   DETAILS: 28 seats. Private parties: 16 main room. Car park. Vegetarian meals. Children's teas. No smoking in dining-room. Music   ACCOMMODATION: 8 double rooms, all with bath/shower. Rooms for disabled. B&B £57 per room. Deposit: 25%. Children welcome. Baby facilities. Afternoon teas. Garden. TV. Phone. Fax: (0239) 820808 (*The Which? Hotel Guide*)

PORTHGAIN Dyfed   map 4

Harbour Lights

Porthgain SA62 5BW   COOKING **2**
CROESGOCH (0348) 831549   COST £18–£35

Everything is made on the premises at Anne Marie Davies' popular restaurant. What cannot be made, or grown by her father-in-law, is supplied by local fishermen or carefully bought – from prime organic meat to regional specialities. This adds up to a menu, available now for lunch as well as dinner, offering consistent food without frills. Freshness is the keynote, with a sensitive handling of flavour combinations. Of a seafood thermidor, one reader said, 'In every way worth the £3.50 extra on the set price, for the quality of the fish and the flavours.' Others have praised Porthgain crab with lime mayonnaise, grilled Dover sole with fresh herbs, escalope of salmon, and marinated breast of chicken filled with wild garlic and Llanboidy cheese. There is an abundance of first-class vegetables – prepared with as much attention as the main courses. Desserts range from apple and sultana pancakes to meringue with home-made ice-cream and red fruit sauce. Cheeses are local and served with home-made water biscuits. The wine list offers a decent range and is fairly priced. House wine is £7.50. If you are thinking of going out of season (November to February), ring first.

CHEFS: Anne Marie Davies and Bernadette Barker   PROPRIETOR: Anne Marie Davies
OPEN: Tue to Sat; 12 to 2, 7 to 9.30   CLOSED: Jan   MEALS: alc. Set D £19.50   SERVICE: not inc   CARDS: Access, Visa   DETAILS: 30 seats. 6 tables outside. Private parties: 25 main room. Car park. Vegetarian meals. Children's helpings. Wheelchair access. Music

---

PWLLHELI Gwynedd   map 4

▲ *Plas Bodegroes* 🍶 ⅚✳

Pwllheli LL53 5TH
PWLLHELI (0758) 612363 and 612510   COOKING **4**
on A497, 1m W of Pwllheli   COST £33

'Try not to run over the squirrels as you leave the road' and approach this pretty house in a glade just beyond Pwllheli. Beaches are a minute away, trees surround the gardens, quiet hangs over the rooftops, and all is well with the world. The new bedrooms give Plas Bodegroes economic flexibility and its guests much pleasure. The main event is dinner, served in rooms that show a certain interest in Venetian masquerade and are less 'country' than most in Wales. It really does work as a setting for the cooking: 'The surroundings, the drive, the lawns, the sophisticated and light dining-room, wow!' enthused one

587

happily benighted there. Christopher Chown's cooking is in tune with the relaxed assurance of the locale, just as Gunna à Trødni's service is a fine blend of the correct, the welcoming and the confident. There is a set price for dinner, stretching to five courses and coffee, but there is choice at each stage. This form is preferred so that equal weight may be given to the first three courses. There is no restricting fish to the second course or meat to the main. Christopher Chown is not in the peasant-food movement, yet his flavours are not lost through lack of courage or over-elaboration. New tastes are tried – kebab of lamb with coriander and garlic, or crab and avocado salad with pineapple vinaigrette – but the context is neo-classical cuisine. The crab in that salad was wrapped in smoked salmon; some toying with fruit in savoury dishes was repeated in the next course of lamb's liver with peaches and sage. The liver was excellently fresh, the fruit not too sweet and the use of sage judicious. Woodpigeon with foie gras worked with classical flavours, the materials again being of a standard that ensured acceptability. Vegetables are served on the plate. Desserts never let the side down: prune and port ice-cream sitting on a compote of autumn fruits, or a cinnamon biscuit of apples and rhubarb (or plums and apples) served with a complementing custard such as elderflower. Criticisms are rare. There are moments when juxtaposition is not felt to work, as in a dessert with chocolate, lime and mint which seemed to have one flavour too many; but the overall standards are consistently high, extending to the details such as amuse-gueules, bread and petits fours. Our enthusiasm for the wine list is reinforced with the arrival of yet more halves and further additions to the New World sections. The 'house selection' is one of the most informed and best value to be found; the main list is a joy, while the additional list of 'Fine Wines' alone would win friends and accolades. If we gave stars as well as bottles this list would be worth a constellation. House wines are £9. CELLARMAN'S CHOICE: Graves, Ch. Couhins-Lurton 1988, £17.50; Auxerrois 'Moenchreben' 1988, Rolly-Gassmann, £14.50.

CHEF: Christopher Chown PROPRIETORS: Christopher Chown and Gunna à Trødni
OPEN: Tue to Sun, D only (also bank hol Mons); 7 to 9   CLOSED: 1 Nov to 28 Feb   MEALS:
Set D £25   SERVICE: net prices, card slips closed   CARDS: Access, Visa   DETAILS: 45 seats.
Private parties: 60 main room, 18 private room. Car park. Children's helpings. No smoking
in dining-room. Wheelchair access (1 step; also WC). Music   ACCOMMODATION: 8 rooms,
all with bath/shower. B&B £25 to £90. Deposit: £50. Children welcome. Baby facilities.
Pets by arrangement. Garden. TV. Phone. Confirm by 4. Fax: (0758) 701247 (*The Which?
Hotel Guide*)

SWANSEA West Glamorgan   map 4

Annie's £

| 56 St Helen's Road, Swansea SA1 4BE | COOKING 1 |
| SWANSEA (0792) 655603 | COST £20–£26 |

Ann Gwilym's converted terraced house reminds some visitors of the '70s: all stripped pine and Sunday school-style chairs complete with racks for hymn books. The cooking, by contrast, is unashamedly French – along the lines of rillettes of pork; ragoût of seafood with wine, cream and saffron; and roast duck breast fanned on the plate with bacon, prunes and orange in a red wine and armagnac sauce. There is usually something for vegetarians. Apricot yoghurt with apricot compote is a well-reported sweet. Cheeses are Welsh, although one reporter described them as 'uninteresting'. The feeling is that the cooking is quite reasonable, but that it lacks excitement and challenge. Too often, the flavour notes of alcohol or spice, although written on the menu, simply do not arrive on the plate. Around 30 wines from Lay & Wheeler offer some pleasurable drinking at fair prices. House French is £7.40.

CHEFS: Ann Gwilym and Stephane Rivier   PROPRIETOR: Ann Gwilym   OPEN: Tue to Sat, D only (and Mon in summer); 7 to 9.30 (10.30 Fri and Sat)   MEALS: alc. Set D £14.80 SERVICE: net prices, card slips closed   CARDS: Access, Visa   DETAILS: 56 seats. Private parties: 34 main room, 22 private room. Vegetarian meals. Children's helpings on request. Music

La Braseria £

28 Wind Street, Swansea SA1 1DZ   COOKING 1
SWANSEA (0792) 469683   COST £15–£24

'Good-value, enjoyable establishment' just about sums it up. Two floors of 'the atmosphere of a Spanish bodega' is an alternative pitch. La Braseria operates along the same lines as Champers, Le Monde and La Brasserie in Cardiff (see entry under La Brasserie) with raw materials displayed in a refrigerated counter, chosen by the customer and cooked – mainly grilled. Fish is what most people eat, and it is fresh and good. Meat is fine too. There are no desserts. The wine list has some serious Spanish reds. House wine is £6.95.

CHEF: M. Tercero   PROPRIETORS: Iceimp Ltd   OPEN: Mon to Sat; 12 to 2.30, 7 to 12 MEALS: alc   SERVICE: not inc, card slips closed   CARDS: Access, Amex, Diners, Visa DETAILS: 180 seats. Children welcome. Smart dress preferred. Wheelchair access (1 step; also WC). Music

Happy Wok £

22A St Helen's Road,
Swansea SA1 4AP   COOKING 1
SWANSEA (0792) 466702   COST £9–£32

If this place is popular, it is not for the luxury of its surroundings. More likely, it is for the immediacy of the cooking and the bright flavours that many find here. The menu runs a stable and predictable course through sizzling dishes and Szechuan approach; squid, duck and Szechuan steaks are recommended. A certain unevenness common to many restaurants like this has been reported, but the consensus is more positive. The wine list, from The Celtic Vintner of Swansea, is not at all bad.

CHEF: K.W. Yuen   PROPRIETORS: I.M. Diu and K.W. Yuen   OPEN: Tue to Sun; 12 to 2.30, 6.30 to 11.30   CLOSED: 4 days Christmas   MEALS: alc. Set L £4.50 to £7.90, Set D £6 to £17. Minimum £7   SERVICE: not inc, card slips closed   CARDS: Access, Amex, Visa   DETAILS: 55 seats. Private parties: 60 main room. Children welcome. Smart dress preferred. Music. Air-conditioned

Keenans £

82 St Helen's Road,
Swansea SA1 4BQ   COOKING 2
SWANSEA (0792) 644111   COST £14–£30

The café-style front masks a warm and welcoming interior. Chris Keenan is
still in sole charge of the kitchen and dreaming up various ploys to cope with
the recession: 'Quantities down and prices up, I'd say' was the tart remark of a
lunch customer who had four courses and still felt peckish. There was no
(major) criticism of the cooking, though: a seafood salad (high on squid, low on
other things), a steak with well-balanced shallot sauce, duck with bilberry
sauce, Welsh cheese, then a 'small, rich and concentrated' chocolate mousse.
Others have agreed about the duck (cooked with honey) and endorsed rather
unconventional starters such as asparagus in a mille-feuille with red pimento
sauce and salmon risotto in filo pastry with a lemon sauce. A fruit pancake with
caramel cream was star of one show for dessert. Dishes come and go, with a
blackboard supplement to the main menu. Service waxes and wanes. Wines
seem sound. House wine is £6.95.

CHEF: Chris Keenan   PROPRIETORS: Chris and Lynda Keenan   OPEN: Tue to Sat, exc Sat L;
12.30 to 2, 7 to 11   CLOSED: 24 Dec to 2 Jan   MEALS: alc   SERVICE: not inc, card slips
closed   CARDS: Access, Amex, Visa   DETAILS: 26 seats. Private parties: 35 main room, 20
private room. Vegetarian meals. Children welcome. Wheelchair access (1 step). Music

Number One Wind Street £   NEW ENTRY

1 Wind Street, Swansea SA1 1DE   COOKING 2
SWANSEA (0792) 456996   COST £13–£31

Kate Taylor has made a successful transition from the Green Dragon Bistro to
smaller but more flexible premises round the corner – she can now open for
dinner. The staff moved too, headed by the ebullient Maggie Munday 'who
knows almost everyone in Swansea' and invests the place with a 'clubby'
atmosphere. Sometimes the service 'is not quite sure of the balance between
informality and indifference', but the kitchen does produce some good dishes.
The consensus is that Kate Taylor is cooking better than ever, with the
emphasis on local produce – laverbread, fish from the Swansea market, Welsh
cheeses – prepared in a French-inspired manner. Provençal fish soup,
galantine of duck with foie gras and truffles, and escalope of salmon beurre
blanc are typical dishes. More modern ideas also get a look in: hot oysters with
laverbread and Stilton (it works), well-cooked braised quails on not-so-
successful grilled polenta, noisettes of venison with wild mushrooms. Desserts
are not a strong point. The wine list is mainly French with a short foray into
Spain, and prices are very fair. House wine is £6.50.

CHEF: Kate Taylor   PROPRIETORS: Peter Gillen and Kate Taylor   OPEN: Mon to Sat L, Wed
to Sat D; 12 to 2.30, 7 to 9.30   CLOSED: bank hols   MEALS: alc. Set L £7.95 to £9.95
SERVICE: not inc   CARDS: Access, Amex, Visa   DETAILS: 40 seats. Private parties: 40 main
room. Vegetarian meals. Children welcome. Music. Air-conditioned

TALSARNAU Gwynedd   map 4

▲ *Maes-y-Neuadd* ⅝✳

Talsarnau LL47 6YA
HARLECH (0766) 780200   COOKING 2
off B4573, 1m S of Talsarnau   COST £17–£36

Maes-y-Neuadd is run with care and devotion by the Horsfall and Slatter
families. The Welsh granite and slate hotel harks back to the fourteenth century
but comforts are decidedly late-twentieth. In the past, the setting (a wooded
hillside) and the view (over the Snowdonia National Park) were thought to
have a decided edge over the food; but recent reports have indicated a welcome
change. 'Of course the atmosphere and the view help to raise one's spirits,'
writes a regular, but Andrew Taylor's set-price five-course dinner, with an
alternative first course and a couple of choices for the main, has begun to show
an exactness and surety of hand. The menu features local produce where
possible: steamed Teifi salmon in a pastry case of vegetable julienne and a
white butter sauce or roast saddle of Welsh veal with smoked chicken and herb
ravioli, for example. The Welsh cheeseboard is exemplary. One who went for
Sunday lunch was taken with a skilful terrine of quail and apricots with orange
and port jelly, tender beef in a well-rendered madeira sauce 'which was rich
without being in any way cloying' and good, straightforward vegetables.
Details display equal care: 'home-made bread rolls were excellent', coffee was
'fresh, strong cafetière' and canapés and petits fours have been good. The wine
list of 100-plus bottles takes in most of the world, even if the bulk is French.
House vin de pays is £7.60.

CHEF: Andrew Taylor   PROPRIETORS: Michael and June Slatter, Malcolm and Olive
Horsfall OPEN: all week; 12.15 to 1.45, 7.30 to 9.15   MEALS: Set L £12 to £14, Set D £20 to
£26   SERVICE: not inc, card slips closed   CARDS: Access, Amex, Diners, Visa   DETAILS: 46
seats. Private parties: 50 main room, 16 private room. Car park. Vegetarian meals.
Children's helpings. No children under 7 D. No smoking. Wheelchair access
ACCOMMODATION: 16 rooms, all with bath/shower. Rooms for disabled. D,B&B £69 to
£188. Deposit: £50. Children under 7 by arrangement. Baby facilities. Pets welcome.
Afternoon teas. Garden. TV. Phone. Doors close at midnight. Confirm by 5. Fax:
(0766) 780211 (*The Which? Hotel Guide*)

TALYLLYN Gwynedd   map 4

▲ *Minffordd Hotel* ⅝✳

Talyllyn LL36 9AJ
CORRIS (0654) 761665   COOKING 1
at junction of A487 and B4405   COST £22

The Pickles do not think of themselves as running a restaurant, 'more a dining-
room for residents and non-residents which has a family atmosphere, as one
would find in a country inn'. Substantial cooking holds in high esteem British
virtues and puddings (Sussex pond is a favourite). There are moments when
the substance becomes clumsy, but dinners are genuinely looked forward to.
'What! You're not staying on Sunday night?' commented one family to another.
'But you'll miss the roast beef. *And* the Yorkshire pudding.' A meal will offer

very simple first courses – soup, melon or maybe a terrine or pâté – then an alternative of fish or meat (often roast or baked), cheese then pudding and coffee (which could be a bit warmer). Puddings, such as Bakewell tart, crème caramel and chocolate roulade, are a strong point. Ill health has dogged Bernard Pickles this year; it is hoped the hotel sails on during his recovery. There's something for everyone on the short, extremely cheap wine list. House wines are £7.25.

CHEF: Jonathan Pickles   PROPRIETORS: Bernard and Jessica Pickles   OPEN: Tue to Sat, D only (all week residents); 7.30 to 8.30   CLOSED: Jan and Feb   MEALS: Set D £16
SERVICE: net prices, card slips closed   CARDS: Access, Diners, Visa   DETAILS: 28 seats. Private parties: 28 main room. Car park. Vegetarian meals. Children's helpings. No children under 3. Smart dress preferred. No smoking in dining-room. Wheelchair access ACCOMMODATION: 6 rooms, all with bath/shower. D,B&B £59 to £98. Deposit: 10%. No children under 3. Garden. Phone. Doors close at 8.30. Confirm by 6. Fax: (0654) 761517 (*The Which? Hotel Guide*)

THREE COCKS Powys   map 4

▲ *Three Cocks Hotel*

Three Cocks LD3 0SL
GLASBURY (0497) 847215
on A438 between Brecon   COOKING 2
and Hay-on-Wye   COST £23–£37

'For those who have eaten in Belgian restaurants, it is a trip down memory lane,' wrote a couple who had enjoyed the Winstones' abilities with lobster bisque, frogs' legs in garlic, salmon with basil and cream sauce plus a selection of eight vegetables, then finished with a goats' cheese served with honey and raspberry sauce, and a tarte au framboise. The menu from which they chose does not show great change from year to year – evidently the Winstones learned their lessons in Belgium (where once they had a restaurant) and have not wanted to graft on too many English variations (though a selection of eight vegetables is British enough). People enjoy the food, encouraged by the regular appearance of second helpings and pleased with the presentation. Other satisfactory dishes have included fricassee of lobster, kidneys with gin and juniper berries and turbot à la basquaise. The hotel building is impressive in its authentic garb of creepers, cobbles, mounting-blocks and all the tackle of an old inn. The central heating is also venerable, but the ultra-modern problems of traffic noise and disco music from across the road are less endearing. Lunch-time bar snacks are also available. A short French wine list and a useful list of Belgian beers keep thirst at bay. House Duboeuf is £8.40.

CHEF: M.E. Winstone   PROPRIETORS: Mr and Mrs Winstone   OPEN: Wed to Mon, exc Sun L; 12 to 1.30, 7 to 9   CLOSED: Dec, Jan and first 2 weeks Feb   MEALS: alc. Set L and D £22   SERVICE: net prices, card slips closed   CARDS: Access, Visa   DETAILS: 35 seats. Private parties: 35 main room. Car park. Children welcome. Smart dress preferred. Music ACCOMMODATION: 7 rooms, all with bath/shower. B&B £55. Children welcome. Baby facilities. Garden. Doors close at midnight. Confirm by 5 (*The Which? Hotel Guide*)

TREFRIW Gwynedd   map 4

Chandler's ✳ £

Trefriw LL27 0JH   COOKING 2
LLANRWST (0492) 640991   COST £20–£33

There is no standing on ceremony at this friendly, informal venue: 'If you're
wearing jeans,' commented the owner to one couple who enquired about
suitable dress (when booking), 'that's what I'll be wearing.' Some may find the
bench seats uncomfortable, but cushions can be provided. Adam Rattenbury's
short, eclectic menu offers some well-reported dishes such as baked Arbroath
smokies; hot goats' cheese salad; mustard-glazed roast rack of Welsh lamb; and
chicken with apples and walnuts in Stilton sauce. Supplies are keenly sought
out: fresh fish comes mostly from Liverpool, herbs, fruit and vegetables from
local gardens and markets. This ensures a regularly changing repertoire of
specials, ranging from red mullet with red wine sauce and onion marmalade,
and brill with samphire, to vegetarian options such as stuffed spinach pancakes
with tomato sauce. Main courses come with a tureen of spot-on vegetables.
Puddings such as passion-fruit and hazelnut roulade with home-made ice-
cream have been highly enjoyable. Adam Rattenbury says that 'the wine list
will remain haphazard as it enables me to change the wines if I find something
interesting'. What this means in practice is a rewarding short list strongest on
the New World, with very competitive prices and an excellent short choice of
halves. House French is £7.95.

CHEF: Adam Rattenbury   PROPRIETORS: Adam and Penny Rattenbury, and Tim Kirton
OPEN: Tue to Sat, D only; 7 to 10   MEALS: alc   SERVICE: not inc, card slips closed   CARDS:
Access, Visa   DETAILS: 36 seats. Private parties: 36 main room. Car park. Vegetarian meals.
Children welcome. No smoking. Music

WHITEBROOK Gwent   map 4

▲ *Crown at Whitebrook* ✳

Whitebrook NP5 4TX
MONMOUTH (0600) 860254
on narrow lane running between   COOKING 1*
A466 and B4293, 5m S of Monmouth   COST £19–£35

This is a rustic and remote refuge for visitors to the Wye Valley. Roger Bates is
an effusive host. There is much to choose from but reports have indicated some
uneven results. Behind the superfluous French titles the recipes are mainly
sound: breast of guinea-fowl with a wine and morel sauce; roast rack of Welsh
lamb topped with a kidney and with a madeira and stock sauce; and pork
tenderloin with a rosemary crust and stuffed with dates. Praise is heaped on the
diverse collection of Welsh and other British cheeses. A reader applauds the
baked Alaska as 'fun and the better for containing home-made ice-cream'. The
wine list is excellent for range and value: lots of halves, lots of countries, lots of
interest. House wines are £7.95.

CHEF: Sandra Bates   PROPRIETORS: Roger and Sandra Bates   OPEN: all week, exc Mon L
and Sun D (residents only); 12 to 2, 7 to 9.30   CLOSED: 2 to 3 weeks Jan, 2 weeks Aug
MEALS: Set L £14.75 to £25, Set D £25 to £28   SERVICE: not inc, card slips closed   CARDS:
Access, Amex, Diners, Visa   DETAILS: 30 seats. 6 tables outside. Private parties: 24 main
room, 10 and 24 private rooms. Car park. Vegetarian meals. Children's helpings. No-
smoking area. No cigars/pipes in dining-room. Wheelchair access (1 step)
ACCOMMODATION: 12 rooms, all with bath/shower. B&B £50 to £80. Children welcome.
Baby facilities. Pets welcome. Garden. TV. Phone. Fax: (0600) 860607 (*The Which? Hotel
Guide*)

WOLF'S CASTLE Dyfed

map 4

▲ *Stone Hall* £

Welsh Hook, Wolf's Castle SA62 5NS
LETTERSTON (0348) 840212
off A40, between Letterston
and Wolf's Castle

COOKING 2
COST £20–£29

The sounds of Piaf and Mireille Mathieu echo round the stone and slate
surfaces of this fourteenth-century manor house. Martine Watson may suffer
nostalgia while tending this outpost of France in west Wales, but no
melancholy affects her professionalism or hospitality. *La patrie* is all over the
menus: snails in white wine and shallots, scallops with cream and garlic, and
sirloin with a Roquefort sauce are instances that remind us that bourgeois
cooking can travel anywhere. Here it is enhanced by fine fish supplies, decent
pastry and sound technique, though no great sense of adventure. Service is not
noted for high speed. The wines are encouragingly cheap and no chauvinism is
shown. House wines are £8.40.

CHEF: Remi Faubel   PROPRIETORS: Alan and Martine Watson   OPEN: Tue to Sun, D only
(L by arrangement); 7 to 9.30   MEALS: alc. Set D from £15 to £16   SERVICE: not inc
CARDS: Access, Amex, Visa   DETAILS: 54 seats. Private parties: 45 main room, 20 private
room. Car park. Vegetarian meals. Children's helpings. No cigars/pipes in dining-room. No
music   ACCOMMODATION: 5 rooms, all with bath/shower. B&B £39 to £53. Deposit: £20.
Children welcome. Baby facilities. Afternoon teas. Garden. TV. Doors close at 11.45.
Confirm by 7. Fax: (0348) 840815

Isle of Man

BALLASALLA Isle of Man   map 4

La Rosette | NEW ENTRY |

Main Road, Ballasalla   COOKING 2
CASTLETOWN (0624) 822940   COST £20–£40

People liken the three tiny dining-rooms of La Rosette to a Pullman car. Cosy
they certainly are, and Rosa Phillips' personal greeting to regulars and visitors
alike make them all the cosier. Good and rich cream and alcohol sauces give
depth to Bob Phillips' cooking, which revolves around the twin poles of fillet
steak and shellfish. Prices are never low – vegetables are £4 for up to 10
different sorts, plus £2 for potatoes – but many feel the cooking is worth it,
even if the menu changes at a snail's pace. Recommended are the mixed hors
d'oeuvre, the generous pile of queenies with garlic, parsley and white wine,
the simple dressed crab, and the very fresh fish, such as brill finished with an
unassuming cream sauce. The wine list is serviceable. House wines are £9.50.

CHEFS/PROPRIETORS: Robert and Rosa Phillips   OPEN: Tue to Sat; 12 to 3, 7 to 10
MEALS: Set L £12.50, Set D £25   SERVICE: not inc, card slips closed   CARDS: Access, Visa
DETAILS: 40 seats. Private parties: 6 main room, 8, 10 and 16 private rooms. Vegetarian
meals. Children's helpings. Music

DOUGLAS Isle of Man   map 4

▲ *Boncompte's*

Admiral House,
Loch Promenade, Douglas   COOKING 2
DOUGLAS (0624) 29551   COST £17–£43

Jaime and Jill Boncompte maintain a steady following among the islanders
and the business community. People like the quality of service, the ever-ready
welcome and the elegance of this set of first-floor rooms in a hotel on the sea-
front. The repertoire is stable on the five-page menu; pineapple is still curried
for vegetarians and the approach is retro-cuisine. There is comfort in the flambé
work, the lobster thermidor, the kidneys Turbigo and the heavily laden cheese
and sweets trolleys. The wine list is adequate for the task, even if the
description of Sancerre as 'a wine growing in popularity, and a worthy
competitor for any white burgundy' might give subject for chat all through the
first bottle. It would help if the makers were given. House wines are £9.50.

CHEF: Michael Ashe PROPRIETORS: Jaime and Jill Boncompte OPEN: Mon to Sat, exc Sat L; 12.30 to 2, 7.30 to 10 CLOSED: 25 Dec MEALS: alc. Set L £10.50 SERVICE: not inc CARDS: Access, Diners, Visa DETAILS: 80 seats. Private parties: 80 main room. Car park. Children's helpings. Smart dress preferred. No cigars/pipes in dining-room. Wheelchair access (also WC). Music ACCOMMODATION: 12 rooms, all with bath/shower. Rooms for disabled. Lift. B&B £50 to £110. Children welcome. Baby facilities. Fishing. TV. Phone. Confirm 1 day ahead. Fax: (0624) 675021

LAXEY Isle of Man   map 4

Riverside Studio | NEW ENTRY |

Glen Gardens Pavilion, Laxey   COOKING 1
LAXEY (0624) 862121   COST £21–£39

Peter Ellenberger is a Swiss who cooks and plays the baritone saxophone. He used to run the Flying Artichoke, but as that became too small for his ambitions and his music he moved to Laxey Glen. This is a great Victorian pleasure garden where holidaymakers would wander, dance, and generally amuse themselves. The real thing here, apart from fondues, is the chargrill for the steaks or the lobsters. These are done just behind the bar, so there is plenty of time to tackle Peter Ellenberger about method, condition or taste. His approach is simple: no major sauces, though the morel sauce for beef is thought good, with not too much messing about. Finish with flamed banana or pancakes. This is an enjoyable place and a long night out if you want to listen to the jazz that is a regular feature. The wine list is short, but it includes a Bourgogne Blanc from Leflaive and a couple of Pinot Noirs from Corney & Barrow. House wines are £8.50.

CHEF/PROPRIETOR: Peter R. Ellenberger OPEN: all week, exc Sun D; 12 to 2, 7 to 10 MEALS: alc SERVICE: not inc CARDS: Access, Visa DETAILS: 70 seats. 8 tables outside. Private parties: 60 main room, 200 private room. Car park. Vegetarian meals. Children's helpings. Wheelchair access (also WC). Music

---

RAMSEY Isle of Man   map 4

Harbour Bistro £

5 East Street, Ramsey   COOKING 1
RAMSEY (0624) 814182   COST £18–£37

This is classic bistro: tiled table-tops, false ceiling, nets, candles in bottles, a glimpse of the harbour for a few, blackboard menus for daily specials, the whole kit. You go there for the oxtail soup – a long runner – the shellfish, the seafish, the fish pie and the deep-fried mushrooms in garlic butter. This is a happy place, back to its old form. The wine list will keep up the good mood, and won't bankrupt you either. House wine is £7.85 per litre.

CHEFS: Karl Meier and Karen Wong PROPRIETORS: Karl Meier, Karen Wong and Ken Devaney OPEN: all week, exc Sun D; 12 to 2.15, 6.30 to 10.30 CLOSED: 2 weeks Oct, 4 days Christmas MEALS: alc SERVICE: not inc CARDS: Access, Visa DETAILS: 46 seats. Private parties: 50 main room. Children's helpings. Wheelchair access (also WC). Music

Channel Islands

Apple Cottage £

La Brecque du Sud, Rozel Bay   COOKING 1
JERSEY (0534) 861002   COST £13–£37

Roses, beams, bare stone, wooden furniture, red frilly lampshades are
ingredients for this classic cottage recipe. The long menu includes chicken
Maryland and a number of other dishes that do not clash with the prevailing
ambience; but the real reason for visiting is the shellfish. 'Half a lobster and a
huge crab formed the basis of a seafood platter which was so large it defeated
us,' reported two satiated visitors from south Wales. There are unlimited local
oysters, scallops and mussels, or turbot, sea bass, red mullet or Jersey plaice for
lovers of sea fish. Business booms, so book ahead. The wine list has many
burgundies from Labouré-Roi, some strange years for clarets and may give best
value in its Italian and Spanish choices. House wines are £5.25.

CHEF: S.C. Pozzi PROPRIETORS: Mr and Mrs S.C. Pozzi OPEN: Tue to Sun, exc Sun D;
12 to 2.15, 7 to 9.30 CLOSED: Jan MEALS: alc. Set L £8.95 to £9.75 SERVICE: not inc,
card slips closed CARDS: Access, Visa DETAILS: 65 seats. 15 tables outside. Private
parties: 55 main room. Car park. Children's helpings. Smart dress preferred. No cigars/
pipes in dining-room. Wheelchair access (1 step; also WC). No music

Granite Corner

Rozel Harbour, Trinity   COOKING 3
JERSEY (0534) 863590   COST £17–£46

After a long trip round the island, one reporter came to this conclusion:
'Finally, someone knows how to cook and make guests happy in Jersey. This
was good eating as it should be – really pleasure-inducing.' The setting is a
converted cottage in the middle of sheltered Rozel Bay where the beach slopes
away gently towards the sea. Inside, it has an air of civilised peace. This is a
regime where kitchen and supplies operate hand in hand, although Jean-Luc
Robin is scrupulous about quality. He keeps contact and works closely with
local fishermen; a nearby organic farm produces fruit and vegetables; and
visitors have watched deliveries of bread coming in on trays fresh from the
bakery next door to the restaurant. It is 'very French, but with Jersey
ingredients,' observed one reporter, although there is a Périgord presence in
the potently rich confit of duck with potato galette and onion marmalade, and

fillet of beef with a slice of foie gras and truffle sauce. Otherwise, the repertoire is locally based, refined without being ostentatious: fresh Grouville Bay oysters with shallot and lemon vinaigrette, thick, intensely flavoured fish soup, 'wonderfully fresh' steamed sea bass with toasted hazelnuts and hazelnut vinaigrette, and breast of duck with sauté morels have all been excellent. Vegetables are miniatures. To finish, home-made Jersey honey ice-cream with raspberry sauce is a winner. Lunchtime visitors have been thoroughly won over by simpler offerings such as home-made pasta with spinach, cream of carrot soup, seafood pot au feu and spotted dick (translated on the menu as 'Richard Tacheté'). The wine list is a whistle-stop tour of most of the French regions, with affordable prices. House wine is £8.

CHEFS: Jean-Luc Robin and Tony Dorris PROPRIETORS: Jean-Luc and Louise Robin OPEN: all week, exc Mon L and Sun D; 12.30 to 1.30, 7.30 to 8.45 MEALS: alc. Set L £13 to £16 SERVICE: net prices, card slips closed CARDS: Access, Visa DETAILS: 25 seats. Private parties: 30 main room. Vegetarian meals with prior notice. Children's helpings L. Smart dress preferred. Wheelchair access (3 steps). Music. Fax: (0534) 864362

ST PETERS Guernsey   map 1

Café du Moulin | NEW ENTRY |

Rue du Quanteraine, St Peters   COOKING 1
GUERNSEY (0481) 65944   COST £17–£32

A solid stone watermill sunk in a quiet valley has been converted to float David and Gina Mann's ground-floor dining-room. The nautical mementoes confirm David Mann's contacts with the island's fishermen and divers. Scallops and lobster are delivered to the kitchen in enviably fresh condition. The crépinette of seafood is likely to combine the catch of the day: a farci of chopped king prawns, scallops and monkfish on a salmon fillet, wrapped in bacon, roasted and served with a lime hollandaise and saffron basmati rice. Sole is casseroled and in a filo basket with a light butter sauce. The straightforward approach is relieved by Asian influence: prawns may emerge tandoori-style and garnished with cucumber and mint raita, and fillets of beef are marinated with lemon grass, soy, chilli, ginger and garlic. Vegetables and fruit are island-produced. Desserts include lemon tart with caramel glaze and reporters cite a fine cheeseboard accompanied by home-made bread and oat biscuits. Service suffers from Guernsey's shortage of trained staff. The wine list is adequate and succinct. Prices are very reasonable. House wine is £6.25.

CHEF: David Mann PROPRIETORS: David and Gina Mann OPEN: Wed to Sun; 12.15 to 1.15, 7.15 to 9.15 CLOSED: 2 weeks Feb, 1 week June, 1 week Oct PRICES: alc. Set L £10.95 (£16) SERVICE: not inc CARDS: Access, Visa SEATS: 44. 11 tables outside. Private parties: 45 main room. Car park. Vegetarian meals. No children under 10. Smart dress preferred. No smoking while others are eating. Wheelchair access. Music

---

£ *indicates that it is possible to have a three-course meal, including coffee, a half-bottle of house wine and service, at any time the restaurant is open (i.e. at dinner as well as at lunch, unless a place is open only for dinner), for £20 or less per person.*

▲ *Longueville Manor* ⅝✶

St Saviour   COOKING **2***
JERSEY (0534) 25501   COST £21–£54

This grand retreat is admirably situated and managed with precision by the Lewises and the Duftys. Deportment in the restaurant matches Andrew Baird's enthusiasm. Unlike other Channel Island chefs, he takes maximum advantage of local seafood. Lobster might be with scallops and asparagus in a puff pastry pillow or cooked in a 'nage' of baby vegetables. Crab might arrive ravioli-covered on a shellfish cream or in a gâteau with mango and Jersey Royals. Every so often a 'stiff, old-fashioned demi-pension seaside hotel attitude' is reported – for example, the sauce accompanying a feuilleté of sweetbreads and baby leek was 'nondescript'. But modishness was reasserted in a fad for hazelnuts: a March dinner *carte* listed them in a salad with raisins and a warm artichoke mousseline, with endive and oven-baked goats' cheese and in another salad with asparagus and warm salmon. New hotel greenhouses have helped to improve vegetable choice. Desserts are fruit-based and include apple tart and strawberry shortbread. The cooking here of course maintains a standard, but it is one of competence rather than inspiration. Wines are predominantly French and of good pedigree. Prices look on the high side, but there are decent Alsaces and antipodeans well below £15. Good halves also help. House wine is £7.

CHEF: Andrew Baird   PROPRIETORS: the Lewis family and the Dufty family   OPEN: all week; 12.30 to 2, 7.30 to 9.30   MEALS: alc. Set L £17.50, Set D £27.50   SERVICE: net prices, card slips closed   CARDS: Access, Amex, Diners, Visa   DETAILS: 65 seats. 8 tables outside. Private parties: 75 main room, 20 private room. Car park. Vegetarian meals. Children restricted. Smart dress preferred. No smoking in 1 dining-room. Wheelchair access (also WC). No music. Air-conditioned   ACCOMMODATION: 32 rooms, all with bath/shower. Rooms for disabled. Lift. B&B £100 to £201. Deposit: £55. No children under 7. Pets welcome. Afternoon teas. Garden. Swimming-pool. Tennis. TV. Phone. Fax: (0534) 31613 (*The Which? Hotel Guide*)

Northern Ireland

BALLYNAHINCH Co Down   map 9

Woodlands

29 Spa Road, Ballynahinch BT24 8PT   COOKING 1
BALLYNAHINCH (0238) 562650   COST £28

The small eighteenth-century house surrounded by deep, quiet grounds
looking out over rolling countryside is a restaurant for three nights a week.
Roast meats are the centrepiece, with a piece of fish or a breast of pigeon as
alternatives, in a substantial meal cooked by Alison Sandford. Roast leg of
lamb or roast loin of pork, the one with a rowanberry and mint sauce, the other
with a bramble sauce, show the steady affirmation of British cooking. Smoked
haddock pancakes, grilled stuffed mushrooms or egg mayonnaise may start the
evening off. A very sound wine list deals with rock-solid names such as
Duboeuf, Drouhin and Michel. House wines are £8.75.

CHEF: Alison Sandford PROPRIETORS: Alison and David Sandford OPEN: Thur to Sat,
D only (private parties by arrangement at other times); 7.30 to 9.30 MEALS: Set D £21.50
SERVICE: net prices, card slips closed CARDS: Access, Visa DETAILS: 45 seats. Private
parties: 45 main room, 14 private room. Car park. Children welcome. No cigars/pipes in
dining-room. No music

BELFAST Co Antrim   map 9

Belfast Castle

Antrim Road, Belfast BT15 5GR   COOKING 1
BELFAST (0232) 370133 and 776925   COST £12–£30

Standing high above the city, this great Victorian pile, a fine escape from harsh
reality, was restored by the city fathers in the 1980s. Where once there echoed
the earnest conversation, or infantile shrieks, of the do-good Earls of
Shaftesbury, now are heard folk-nights on Friday in the Cellar Bistro, or the
measured tread of the 'rather catering-school' service in the series of rooms that
make up the more formal Ben Madigan restaurant on the ground and first
floors. Starters such as lamb carpaccio with roast cucumber and garlic cream, a
salad of spinach, field mushrooms and Parmesan shavings, followed by
blackened chicken on a spicy fruit salsa with pesto polenta, or confit of pork
with a dried pear chutney are all pointers to a renewal of the menu every bit as
thoroughgoing as the restoration of the mansion. This is cooking in the '90s
mode. Reports have spoken well of excellently flavoured meat (even though

butchery may be brutal) and simple sauces that depend on pan juices more than flour, water or cream. Roast sirloin with green peppercorns and best end of lamb with a rosemary and walnut stuffing have been enjoyed, though the finer details of presentation and finish were skimped. Vegetables are built into the service of the main dish. The impressive surroundings of giant staircase, chandeliers and overworked chimneypieces make this a natural for formal entertaining. Whether the food and service quite match the hardware is a moot point. The wine list is a fair range, at a fair price, but does not include any vintages. House wines start at £6.50.

CHEF: David Long PROPRIETOR: Carroll E. Falls OPEN: Ben Madigan restaurant Wed to Sat, D only, and Sun L; 12 to 3.30, 7.30 to 10. Bistro all week; 11am to 10.30 MEALS: alc. Set L £10 to £12.50, Set D £19.50 to £24 SERVICE: not inc CARDS: Access, Amex, Diners, Visa DETAILS: 50 seats. Private parties: 50 main room, 30, 50 and 150 private rooms. Car park. Vegetarian meals. Children welcome (exc restaurant D). Children's helpings (bistro). Smart dress preferred (restaurant). No-smoking area. Wheelchair access (also WC). Music. Air-conditioned (bistro). Fax: (0232) 370228

La Belle Epoque £

61–63 Dublin Road,
Belfast BT2 7RS   COOKING 2*
BELFAST (0232) 323244   COST £17–£28

The move away from the Europa Hotel may afford some respite from disturbance. The house has been thoroughly renovated to re-create the glories of art nouveau – mirrors, tiles, pictures of long ladies – but the enthusiasm of the service (if not the training) and the general bonhomie of the crowd of customers make for a bustling, not languid, atmosphere. While the made-dishes, such as a chicken roulade with green peppercorns, have not necessarily had wild raves, the meat cookery, for instance, a chargrilled fillet with white wine and mustard sauce, or juicy chunks of veal fillet with a curry sauce served with lightly cooked spaghetti, does seem accomplished. Good meat and proper sauces combine to satisfaction. This is aided and abetted by giant portions and excellent dauphinois potatoes, even if other vegetables may be less perfect. Desserts, like pear tart warm from the oven or a chocolate croustillant, restore any faded spirits. The place is now open for breakfast on weekdays. The wine list is sound enough and very fairly priced. House wines are £5.95.

CHEFS: Alan Rousse and Chris Fitzgerald PROPRIETORS: J. Delbart, Alan Rousse, Chris Fitzgerald and G. Sanchez OPEN: Mon to Sat, exc Sat L; noon to 11 (6 to 11 Sat) CLOSED: 25 and 26 Dec MEALS: alc. Set L £9.95 SERVICE: not inc CARDS: Access, Diners, Visa DETAILS: 70 seats. Private parties: 20 main room. Vegetarian meals. Children welcome. Wheelchair access (also WC). Music. Fax: (0232) 323244

Not inc *in the details at the end of an entry indicates that no service charge is made and any tipping is at the discretion of the customer.*

The text of entries is based on unsolicited reports sent in by readers, backed up by inspections conducted anonymously. The factual details under the text are from questionnaires the Guide sends to all restaurants that feature in the book.

Manor House £

43–47 Donegall Pass,
Belfast BT7 1DQ
BELFAST (0232) 238755

COOKING 1
COST £10–£35

This is Belfast's leading Cantonese restaurant. It runs long hours and the menu is long enough too, covering the well-trodden paths of British Cantonese cookery, which is executed satisfactorily. Shellfish is the best bet. House wines are £6.65.

CHEF: Joyce Wong PROPRIETOR: Joe Wong OPEN: all week; noon to 11.30 MEALS: alc. Set L £5.50, Set D £13.50 SERVICE: 10% CARDS: Access, Diners, Visa DETAILS: 120 seats. Private parties: 80 main room, 50 private room. Vegetarian meals. Children welcome. Wheelchair access. Music. Air-conditioned

Nick's Warehouse £

35–39 Hill Street, Belfast BT1 2LB
BELFAST (0232) 439690

COOKING 1
COST £20–£30

'My mother expressed great reservation about eating in a warehouse, but she was charmed into obliviousness by the waiter,' reported one visitor who was impressed by the professionalism and relaxed air of this place. Locals may object to the Guinness in cans, but the wines are impressive – fast-changing, and an enjoyable range. The restaurant part of the operation had been bombed into closure when one party visited, leaving the wine bar downstairs for food and sustenance. The chefs can cook: a bean soup was excellent, a chicken breast coated with sesame seed was also good, though a vegetarian lasagne seemed wrong with its cubed potatoes as well as the pasta, and overcooked courgettes and leeks. Salads are a good bet here, and so is the bread-and-butter pudding. The atmosphere is emphatically cheerful. House wines are from £6.50.

CHEFS: Nick Price and Simon Toye PROPRIETORS: Nick and Kathy Price OPEN: Mon to Fri; 12.30 to 2.30 (12 to 3 wine bar), 6 to 9 CLOSED: 25 and 26 Dec, 12 Jan MEALS: alc SERVICE: not inc (10% for 6 or more) CARDS: Access, Diners, Visa DETAILS: 50 seats. Private parties: 50 main room. Vegetarian meals. Children welcome. Wheelchair access (also WC). Air-conditioned

Roscoff ▼

Unit 7, Lesley House,
Shaftesbury Square, Belfast BT2 7DB
BELFAST (0232) 331532

COOKING 3*
COST £18–£43

Paul Rankin is the local Belfast boy made good. After travelling the world, then learning his craft at Le Gavroche (see entry, London), he returned to his home town and zoomed into the premier league. He is one of a small élite of chefs who can successfully deliver genuine restaurant food for the '90s, and, on current form, he can compete with the best on the mainland. His is a nautical dining-room, with waves as the recurring motif – on the sea-blue window mat, on the iron banister and on the room-dividers. There are seascapes on the bar walls; wavy sails hang from the ceiling. It feels sophisticated, urbane, cosmopolitan – a fitting backdrop for Rankin's pure, uncluttered ultra-modern cooking. He has the confidence to bring together different ideas and traditions, and the skill to carry them off. Overlapping slices of chargrilled salmon fillet are served with thinly sliced avocado and 'an intoxicating though alcohol-free' sun-dried tomato vinaigrette. Soya-marinated pork is paired with a creamy sauce of peppercorns and coriander; salt chilli turbot comes on a bed of wilted greens with tomato and basil. Among the sweets, lemon tart with a lemony-green kiwi coulis, and Drambuie ice-cream with pecan and caramel sauce deserve special mention. The ingredients are first-class; this is cooking where flavour comes before artifice. Four types of home-made bread and around a dozen impeccable cheeses have found favour. The well-organised and varied *carte* is supported by a short table d'hôte menu; both offer extraordinary value at this level – notably at lunch-time. Jeanne Rankin supervises the front-of-house, backed up by a cheerful band of young waiters. The wine list follows the philosophy of the place: it is wide-ranging, fairly priced and not over-long. Burgundies rely heavily on négociants rather than on the domaine-bottled, but are well chosen. Real effort is evident in the garnering of some of the better country wines and more modest bottles from the New World. House wines are from £8.95.

CHEF: Paul Rankin   PROPRIETORS: Paul and Jeanne Rankin   OPEN: Mon to Sat, exc Sat L; 12.15 to 2.15, 6.30 to 10.30   CLOSED: 12 and 13 July, Christmas   MEALS: alc. Set L £11.95, Set D £17.50   SERVICE: not inc (10% for 6 or more)   CARDS: Access, Amex, Diners, Visa DETAILS: 65 seats. Vegetarian meals. Children welcome. No-smoking area. Wheelchair access (also WC). Music

Strand £

12 Stranmillis Road,
Belfast BT9 5AA
BELFAST (0232) 682266

COOKING 1
COST £12–£23

Busy, bustling, not tremendously comfy, but the Strand is a regular place in which to refuel, converse and then move on. The menu is long, the specialities, such as Strand mushrooms deep-fried with garlic mayonnaise, or chilli con carne, are regulars, and the cost is not too great. You can have champ with your calf's liver; London is dying for champ, eat it here where it's at home. The wine list takes in Yugoslavia, Chile and Argentina, and French shippers Jadot, Moreau, Delas and Calvet are high in the list of suppliers. House wines are £5.95.

CHEF: M. McAuley   PROPRIETOR: Anne Turkington   OPEN: all week; noon to 11   MEALS: alc   SERVICE: not inc   CARDS: Access, Amex, Diners, Visa   DETAILS: 80 seats. Vegetarian meals. Children welcome. Music. Air-conditioned

---

'Faint Muzak completes the gaudy scene, which overall appears to have been decorated by someone with all the restrained taste of a deranged magpie.'   On inspecting in Surrey

'The "Lemony Tart" that followed had, I suspect, recently been liberated from a cardboard box.'   On eating in Cumbria

---

BELLANALECK Co Fermanagh   map 9

Sheelin £

Bellanaleck BT92 2BA   COOKING 1
FLORENCECOURT (036 582) 232   COST £11–£28

Although the Sheelin is largely a bakery, during the short season it serves
lunch, teas, high teas and suppers to visitors, and on Fridays and Saturdays
throughout the year the place is transformed into a restaurant offering a five-
course meal at a set price. The formula does not change: a first course, a stuffed
pancake, a sorbet, a main course of chicken, sole, beef or duck, plenty of mega-
sweets and then tea or coffee. Plenty is a leitmotif, duck is a favourite. The wine
list is seriously inexpensive. House wines are £5.25.

CHEF: Marion Cathcart PROPRIETOR: Arthur Cathcart OPEN: all week June to end Aug,
Sun L Apr to end Sept, Fri and Sat D all year; 12.30 to 2.30, 7 to 9.30 MEALS: alc D. Set L
£7.50 to £9.50, Set D £15 to £19 SERVICE: 10%, card slips closed CARDS: Access, Amex,
Visa DETAILS: 30 seats. Private parties: 24 main room. Car park. Vegetarian meals.
Children's helpings. Smart dress preferred. Music. Fax: (036 582) 8190

BUSHMILLS Co Antrim   map 9

▲ *Auberge de Seneirl* | NEW ENTRY |

28 Ballyclogh Road, Bushmills BT57 8UZ   COOKING 2
DERVOCK (026 57) 41536   COST £23–£30

Three miles from the Giant's Causeway is this old school, converted by the
French owners into an *auberge*. It has character: that of the original building,
carefully extended by M. Defres, and that stemming from the genuine
intentions of Mme Defres in the kitchen and the tactful service of her husband
front-of-house. 'No resorting to madeira sauce here' was the comment of one.
No, indeed: chocolate with duck breast, raspberry or blackberry with quail,
lime with pork, ginger with smoked duck, or pork with a West Indian spice
mix and bananas are all examples with harmonious results. They are supported
by soups with genuine flavour, substantial first courses such as savoury
pancakes filled with chicken, spinach, garlic and onion, or baked eggs with
plenty of wild mushrooms, herbs and cream. Come the end of the meal there is
no stopping the diplomat pudding or the banana and rum filled pancakes, or
ignoring the good ice-creams and sorbets, while remarking the quality of the
cheese (if not the cheese biscuits). Giants might eat here: not two, but four
quails for a main course. A special *dégustation* meal of eight or nine courses
(from £22.50) is available on the first Saturday of each month. The wine list is
ably handled by M. Defres, who tastes for everyone at a central table. It may be
characterised by sound sources, such as Duboeuf, Chanson and Drouhin, and
low prices; and it is entirely French. House wines start at £7.95.

---

*Restaurateurs justifiably resent no-shows. If you quote a credit card number when booking,
you may be liable for the restaurant's lost profit margin if you don't turn up. Always
phone to cancel.*

CHEF: Mme B.E. Defres   PROPRIETORS: J.L. and B.E. Defres   OPEN: Wed (Tue summer) to Sat, D only; 7 to 9.30   CLOSED: 2 weeks Christmas   MEALS: Set D £15.95 to £19.95   SERVICE: not inc   CARDS: Amex, Diners   DETAILS: 35 seats. Private parties: 25 main room, 10 private room. Car park. Children's helpings with prior notice. Wheelchair access. Music   ACCOMMODATION: 5 rooms, all with bath/shower. B&B £37 to £58. Deposit: £20. Children welcome. Baby facilities. Garden. Swimming-pool. Sauna. TV

COLERAINE Co Derry   map 9

▲ Macduff's £

112 Killeague Road, Blackhill,
Coleraine BT51 4HH   COOKING 1
AGHADOWEY (0265) 868433   COST £20–£30

A few giant steps back from the Causeway Coast, the Erwins have this old rectory – moss green in a verdant landscape – built by the bishop of Derry for the parish of Aghadowey, seven miles to the south of Coleraine. Comfort is the order of the day, and you may wake humming 'All things bright and beautiful' (written by the wife of a former rector) so well have you slept. Dining is taken care of in the cellar, and the menu is a sound example of steady output: Stilton puffs with sweet-and-sour sauce, salmon and prawn puffs with Indian dip, salmon steak or fillet steak, chicken tikka masala or quail with amandine sauce. The Indian and spicy line is the individual touch; for the rest, the cooking remains squarely conventional, but substantial and satisfying. The wine list is of similar character. House wines are £6.80.

CHEF: Margaret Erwin   PROPRIETORS: Joseph and Margaret Erwin   OPEN: Tue to Sat, D only; 7 to 9.30   MEALS: alc   SERVICE: not inc, card slips closed   DETAILS: 34 seats. Private parties: 34 main room, 16 private room. Car park. No children under 12. No music ACCOMMODATION: 5 rooms, all with bath/shower. B&B £30 to £55. Deposit: £10. No children under 12. Garden. Swimming-pool. TV. Doors close at 1am. Confirm by 6

LONDONDERRY Co Londonderry   map 9

▲ Beech Hill
Country House Hotel | NEW ENTRY |

32 Ardmore Road,
Londonderry BT47 3QP
LONDONDERRY (0504) 49279
off A6 Londonderry–Belfast
road at Faughan Bridge,   COOKING 2
opposite Ardmore Chapel   COST £13–£38

Not far from the city lie 32 acres of landscaped gardens, waterfalls and ponds. In their midst is this handsome Victorian house, recently converted to a hotel and restaurant. As one visitor put it, 'The welcome is unjaded'. Noel McMeel has worked with the best in the region, among them Paul Rankin and Ian McAndrew, and is cooking in full-blown style for the business community of Derry as well as tourists after the fish of the River Faughan. An inspection meal took in roast loin of rabbit with wild mushrooms served with a salad and some cloves of garlic dressed with nut oil, and a terrine of fish wrapped in leeks that was 'not at all bland' and benefited from freshness as well as judicious use of dill. A main course of chicken with tarragon cream sauce – the flesh left on the bone, the skin crisped under the grill – showed the worth of simple methods, while venison with a redcurrant jus was properly cooked and the venison properly bought. Cheeses come from the region, accompanied by slices of fruit from the world over. Pastry work is satisfactory, as are the bread rolls. This is a finished performance which should improve if the public maintains its appreciation. The wine list is light on vintage information, but is not dear and contains no surprises. House wines are from Moreau and cost £7.50.

CHEF: Noel McMeel   PROPRIETORS: Leo and Seamus Donnelly   OPEN: all week; 12 to 2.30, 6 to 9.45   MEALS: alc. Set L £8.50 to £10.95, Set D £15.95   SERVICE: not inc, card slips closed   CARDS: Access, Amex, Visa   DETAILS: 35 seats. Private parties: 80 main room, 12 and 22 private rooms. Car park. Vegetarian meals. Children's helpings. Wheelchair access (also WC). Music   ACCOMMODATION: 15 rooms, all with bath/shower. D,B&B £66.50 to £118. Children welcome. Baby facilities. Afternoon teas. Garden. Fishing. TV. Phone. Fax: (0504) 45366

PORTRUSH Co Antrim   map 9

Ramore £

The Harbour, Portrush BT56 8DQ   COOKING 2*
PORTRUSH (0265) 824313   COST £12–£32

A plain modern building overlooking the harbour and West Bay houses a wine bar on the ground floor (open lunch and dinner) and a restaurant above (dinner only). Two generations of the Caithness family keep order here, with son-in-law George McAlpin producing serious food in the restaurant and supervising the output of the wine bar. 'A haven for extended families' was the comment of one lunchtime visitor, who found the food magnificently generous yet somewhat approximate in execution. 'After I had battled for some while, I felt all kinds of tastes intermingling, warring against each other.' However, the possibility of ordering tagliatelle with salmon and curried cream sauce, or confit of duck with salad and chips, in this part of the world makes this a place of pilgrimage, and the welcome is warm. In some ways the restaurant dishes are less enterprising than those of the wine bar, although techniques are much tighter and results more satisfactory. Mushroom ravioli with a morel and vin jaune sauce, or cabbage-leaf parcels of chicken livers with lentils, bacon and an onion gravy, are light and true flavoured. George McAlpin's affiliations show in main courses such as breast of duck on a leaf of puff pastry with cabbage, confit and bacon, or fillet of pork with lemon beurre blanc and some pasta seasoned with crab meat and sun-dried tomatoes. Four sorts of potatoes are always available. The wine list goes straight for reliable, famous and authentic names: Drouhin or Michel in Burgundy and Mondavi or Ridge in California are instances of this. Prices are fair. House claret or white Rhône are £7.50

CHEF: George McAlpin   PROPRIETORS: John and Joy Caithness, and George and Jane McAlpin   OPEN: wine bar L and D Mon to Sat, restaurant D Tue to Sat; 12.30 to 2.30, 5.30 to 9.15 (restaurant 7 to 10)   CLOSED: last 2 weeks Jan   MEALS: alc   SERVICE: not inc   DETAILS: 55 seats. Private parties: 60 main room. Car park. Children welcome. Music

Republic of Ireland

The following entries are the result of our continued appeal for more reports in last year's *Guide*. Reporting still falls far short of the numbers and density achieved on the mainland of Britain, but we hope that this list will form a solid foundation for further expansion. We are grateful to those of you who have helped in this particular aspect, and would appeal to any who are intending a trip to the Republic this year that they bear us in mind. We would like to hear about your experiences.

It is quite clear that the Irish have a great gift for hospitality and, in many cases, an equal one for cooking, whether it be the simple conversion of matchless raw ingredients, more sophisticated modern cookery alive to current tendencies in Europe, or food in the tradition of the Anglo-Irish country house.

Prices quoted are in Irish punts. As we are still feeling our way, we have not given ratings for cooking as in the British Isles.

To telephone the Republic from mainland Britain, dial 010 353, followed by the area code and number we have listed dropping, however, the initial zero (0).

ADARE Co Limerick   map 9

▲ *Adare Manor*

Adare
LIMERICK (061) 396566   COST £22–£53

This is another of the very big houses that have gone into serious tourism. Ian McAndrew has left for England (see Flitwick Manor entry, Flitwick); his replacement, Colin Brown, offers modern international cooking – ravioli with oyster mushrooms and chervil, cod with potato purée and a sauce of chickpeas, courgette and yellow pimento, or breast of pheasant and rillettes of its leg with an armagnac sauce. The wine list is mega and classic. 'My suite was as big as a tennis court, the dining-room is very beautiful,' began one report that went on to add that the food is sound though not very expressive. House wine is £12.50.

CHEF: Colin Brown   PROPRIETORS: Mr and Mrs Tom Kane   OPEN: all week; 12.30 to 2.30, 7 to 10   MEALS: alc. Set L £14.95, Set D £26   SERVICE: 15% alc, net prices set meals, card slips closed   CARDS: Access, Amex, Diners, Visa   DETAILS: 70 seats. Private parties: 100 main room, 30, 60 and 150 private rooms. Car park. Vegetarian meals. Children's helpings. Jacket and tie. No-smoking area. Wheelchair access (also WC). Music   ACCOMMODATION: 64 rooms, all with bath/shower. Rooms for disabled. Lift. B&B £100 to £240. Deposit: 50%. Children welcome. Afternoon teas. Garden. Swimming-pool. Sauna. Fishing. TV. Phone. Confirm by 6. Fax: (061) 396124

AHAKISTA Co Cork	map 9

▲ *Shiro*

Ahakista
BANTRY (027) 67030   COST £44

Tucked away in the wilds, Kei and Werner Pilz run a Japanese dinner house. It seats very few people and there's not much point turning up without a booking, which is hard to come by. Dinner is authentic and very good indeed. In true oriental style, it runs along firm and unchanging lines. For the real thing, come to County Cork! Wine is from £9, saké is £10.

CHEF: Kei Pilz PROPRIETORS: Kei and Werner Pilz OPEN: all week, D only; 7 to 9
CLOSED: Jan to end Feb MEALS: Set D £32 SERVICE: net prices CARDS: Access, Amex, Diners, Visa (5% surcharge) DETAILS: 12 seats. Private parties: 12 main room, 8 private room. Car park. Vegetarian meals. No children under 12. Music ACCOMMODATION: 1 room with bath/shower. Pets welcome. Garden. Fishing. TV

BALLINA Co Mayo	map 9

▲ *Mount Falcon Castle*

Ballina
BALLINA (096) 21172   COST £27

The restaurant is mainly a dining-room for residents, and if the rooms are full, there's not a lot of room for extra visitors. In keeping with the character of the place, eating is a communal affair, around a single great table. Food is simple, wholesome and traditional. House wines are £8.50.

CHEF/PROPRIETOR: Constance Aldridge OPEN: all week, D only; 8 CLOSED: 3 days Christmas, Feb to Mar MEALS: Set D £17.50 SERVICE: 10%, card slips closed CARDS: Access, Amex, Diners, Visa DETAILS: 22 seats. Car park. Vegetarian meals. Children's helpings. No-smoking area by arrangement. No music ACCOMMODATION: 10 rooms, all with bath/shower. B&B £40 to £80. Deposit: 25%. Children welcome. Baby facilities. Pets welcome (not in bedrooms). Garden. Tennis. Fishing. Doors close at 2am. Confirm by midday. Fax: (096) 21172

BALLYDEHOB Co Cork	map 9

Annie's

Main Street, Ballydehob
BALLYDEHOB (028) 37292   COST £12–£32

'It could only work in Ireland, a café serving excellent food' was one reaction – capable of dispute on many counts, but about the good food there is no disagreement. The café-style of things gives way to greater elaboration come dinner-time and approval is gained for the beef and the fish, for instance, grilled black sole and monkfish with garlic butter. House wine is £10.50.

See the back of the Guide *for an index of restaurants listed.*

CHEFS/PROPRIETORS: Anne and Dano Ferguson   OPEN: Tue to Sat; 12.30 to 2.30, 6.30 to
9.30 (times may differ in winter)   CLOSED: first 3 weeks Oct, 25 and 26 Dec   MEALS: light
L. Set D £19.95   SERVICE: not inc   CARDS: Access, Visa   DETAILS: 24 seats. Children
welcome. No cigars/pipes in dining-room. Wheelchair access. Music

---

BALLYLICKEY Co Cork   map 9

▲ Sea View House Hotel

Ballylickey
BANTRY (027) 50073 and 50462   COST £17–£30

There are great views over Bantry Bay from this Victorian house where the
nightly dinner rings sufficient changes for visitors of more than a few nights
not to tire from repetition. The cooking has overtones of Cordon Bleu, and the
fish main courses (which outnumber meat) are excellent. House wine is £10.

CHEF/PROPRIETOR: Kathleen O'Sullivan   OPEN: all week, D only, and Sun L; 1 to 2, 7 to
9.30   CLOSED: 1 Nov to mid-Mar   MEALS: Set Sun L £10, Set D £19.50   SERVICE: 10%,
card slips closed   CARDS: Access, Amex, Visa   DETAILS: 45 seats. Private parties: 16 main
room. Car park. Vegetarian meals. Children's helpings. No cigars/pipes in dining-room.
Wheelchair access (also WC). No music   ACCOMMODATION: 17 rooms, all with bath/
shower. Rooms for disabled. B&B £35 to £90. Deposit: 1 night. Children welcome. Baby
facilities. Pets welcome (not in public rooms). Afternoon teas. Garden. TV. Phone. Doors
close at midnight. Confirm by 6. Fax: (027) 51555

BALLYVAUGHAN Co Clare   map 9

▲ Gregans Castle

Ballyvaughan
ENNIS (065) 77005   COST £19–£39

The landscape is impressive, and the hotel is comfortable. It runs for the season
only, but the cooking is serious, whether it's lunch served in the Corkscrew
Room or the main dinner menu, which makes more use of fish than meat (not
surprising considering how close the place is to Galway Bay). The style is not
Irish; in a few short years, aubergines, pimentoes, olive oil, grain mustard,
saffron and strange warm-weather herbs have swept through Irish larders.
Gregans Castle exemplifies this shift with style. House wines are from £11.

CHEFS: Peter Haden and Margaret Cronin   PROPRIETORS: Peter and Moira Haden
OPEN: all week; 12 to 3, 7 to 8.30   CLOSED: end Oct to end Mar   MEALS: alc L. Set D £25
SERVICE: 12.5%, card slips closed   CARDS: Access, Visa   DETAILS: 50 seats. Private parties:
80 main room. Car park. Vegetarian meals. Children's helpings. Smart dress preferred. No
cigars/pipes in dining-room. Wheelchair access (also WC). No music   ACCOMMODATION:
22 rooms, all with bath/shower. Rooms for disabled. B&B £68 to £150. Deposit: £40.
Children welcome. Baby facilities. Afternoon teas. Garden. Phone. Doors close at 11.30.
Fax: (065) 77111

'Thought I was eating alone at the bar, only to find a cockroach sitting next to me.'
On eating in London

BRAY Co Wicklow   map 9

Tree of Idleness

Seafront, Bray
DUBLIN (01) 2863498 and 2828183   COST £24–£46

It is sad to record the death of Akis Courtellas, but his widow Susan is keeping everything on the road and in the style to which people have become accustomed: a mixture of Greek cooking and international dishes such as lamb's liver with Dubonnet and orange, or fillet steak with truffle and red wine sauce. It is well-liked by locals and should be visited if nothing else for the wine list. It is a remarkable collection. House wine is £12.50.

CHEF: Ismail Basaran PROPRIETOR: Susan Courtellas OPEN: Tue to Sun, D only; 7.30 to 11 (10 Sun) CLOSED: Christmas, first 2 weeks Sept MEALS: alc. Set D from £15.50 to £19.50 SERVICE: 10%, card slips closed CARDS: Access, Diners, Visa DETAILS: 50 seats. Private parties: 18 main room. Vegetarian meals. Smart dress preferred. No pipes in dining-room. Wheelchair access. Music

CASHEL Co Tipperary   map 9

Chez Hans

Rockside, Cashel
CASHEL (062) 61177   COST £30–£44

This was once a chapel, as the religious paintings and no-holds-barred Victoriana may still recall. The cooking is very sound, very classic and very much enjoyed. Quality is never stinted, and the place feels happy as well as full. House wines are from £10.50.

CHEF/PROPRIETOR: Hans-Peter Matthiä OPEN: Tue to Sat, D only; 6.30 to 10 CLOSED: first 3 weeks Jan MEALS: alc SERVICE: not inc CARDS: Access, Visa DETAILS: 60 seats. Private parties: 60 main room. Car park. Vegetarian meals. Children's helpings. No-smoking area. Wheelchair access (also WC). Music

CASHEL Co Galway   map 9

▲ *Cashel House Hotel*

Cashel
CLIFDEN (095) 31001   COST £25–£46

The hotel is a holiday camp in itself: its own pony stud and riding facilities, bog treks, beach treks, very fine gardens, everything, in short, to keep the body amused. The food is sound country-house – a five-course meal with adequate choice (lobster a permanent resident) served in a glorious conservatory dining-room. It is also a good nineteenth-century structure with every comfort. House wine is £11.50.

▲ *This symbol means accommodation is available.*

CHEFS: Dermot McEvilly and Patrick Hernandez PROPRIETORS: Dermot and Kay McEvilly OPEN: all week; 12.30 to 2, 7.30 to 8.45 MEALS: alc. Set L £12 to £15, Set D £25 to £27.50 SERVICE: 12.5%, card slips closed CARDS: Access, Amex, Visa DETAILS: 70 seats. 4 tables outside. Car park. Vegetarian meals. Children's helpings. No children under 5. Jacket and tie. No-smoking area. Wheelchair access (also WC). No music ACCOMMODATION: 32 rooms, all with bath/shower. Rooms for disabled. B&B £46 to £120. Deposit: £100. No children under 5. Pets welcome. Afternoon teas. Garden. Tennis. Fishing. Golf. TV. Phone. Fax: (095) 31077

CLIFDEN Co Galway
map 9

O'Grady's £

Market Street, Clifden
CLIFDEN (095) 21450 and 21437
COST £15–£39

It helps if you have your own trawler; O'Grady's does. Although this is a self-proclaimed seafood restaurant, the menu would not lead you to think it: meat is allowed as much of an outing as fish. Scallops and mussels are first-rate, so are the soups – whether chowders or bouillabaisse. The skill, however, extends across the range, and people speak well of the happy welcome and hospitality; 'a confident and cheerful atmosphere' is how one person put it. House wines are from £9.

CHEF: P.J. Heffernan PROPRIETORS: Jack and Marion O'Grady, and Mike O'Grady OPEN: Mon to Sat; 12.30 to 2.30, 6.30 to 10 CLOSED: 16 to 30 Dec, 12 Jan to 12 Mar MEALS: alc. Set L £8.95 to £12.95, Set D £12.95 to £18.95. Minimum £9.95 SERVICE: not inc CARDS: Access, Visa DETAILS: 50 seats. Private parties: 10 main room, 8 private room. Vegetarian meals. Children restricted D. Smart dress preferred. No-smoking area. Music

---

CLONAKILTY Co Cork
map 9

Dunworley Cottage

Butlerstown, Clonakilty
BANDON (023) 40314
on coast between Clonakilty
and Bandon
COST £21–£35

Dunworley Cottage is remote – 'drive 500 miles due west, take 27 lefts and 8 rights through ill-posted side lanes, and you're there' was one person's specific instructions. It's also atmospheric and will convince the wavering chauffeur that all could be well. The accent is Scandinavian and the best things have a certain Nordic wildness – nettle soup, rhubarb tart, good black and white puddings, simple meats and relishes. The pig party is held every year and will be a lesson in whole-beast roasting. It may also rain. House wine is £9.75.

CHEF: Michael Olsson PROPRIETOR: Katherine Noren OPEN: Wed to Sun; 1 to 3, 6.30 to 9 CLOSED: 6 Jan to 17 Mar MEALS: alc SERVICE: not inc CARDS: Access, Amex, Diners, Visa DETAILS: 45 seats. Private parties: 20 main room, 15 and 20 private rooms. Vegetarian meals. Healthy eating options. Children's helpings. No-smoking area. Music

CONG Co Mayo   map 9

▲ Ashford Castle

Cong
CONG (092) 46003   COST £26–£64

The Castle is very large. One reader felt like the Duke of Omnium, wishing to escape from Gatherum and the frightening tribe of influentials invited there by Lady Glencora. Ashford has its stack of visitors, often in coaches, and this detracts somewhat from the charm and grandeur. 'The sing-along in the bar could be heard throughout the public rooms.' The cooking is expensive and acceptable. It is worth it just to feel the size. House wines are £15.

CHEF: Denis Lenihan   PROPRIETOR: Rory Murphy   OPEN: all week; 1 to 2.30, 7 to 9.45
MEALS: alc. Set L £15 to £19, Set D £32.50 to £45   SERVICE: 15%, card slips closed   CARDS:
Access, Amex, Diners, Visa   DETAILS: 40 seats. Private parties: 135 main room. Car park.
Vegetarian meals. Children's meals 6.30 to 7. No children under 7 D. Jacket and tie. No-smoking area. Wheelchair access. Music   ACCOMMODATION: 83 rooms, all with bath/shower. Rooms for disabled. Lift. B&B £140 to £292. Deposit: 50%. Children welcome.
Baby facilities. Afternoon teas. Garden. Tennis. Fishing. Golf. TV. Phone. Doors close at midnight

CORK Co Cork   map 9

▲ Arbutus Lodge

Middle Glanmire Road,
Montenotte, Cork
CORK (021) 501237   COST £19–£47

This is one of Ireland's essential staging posts. Even if it is grand, the personal touch is never absent. 'It was the Tall Ships weekend when we visited, yet Declan Ryan was happy to take us on a fascinating tour of his cellar,' wrote one family who urged that standards have never slipped here. They ate from the tasting menu: courgette flowers, mousseline of crab, sauce citronelle, fillet of brill with potato and garlic purée, sorbet, venison with Puy lentils, cheese, a trolley laden with desserts. There is a happy ability here to meld mainstream Europe with Irish tradition. The wine list is matchless. There are cheaper and faster meals available in the bar at lunch-times. House wines are from £11.75.

CHEFS: Michael Ryan and Harry McKeogh   PROPRIETORS: the Ryan family   OPEN: Mon to
Sat; 1 to 2 (12.30 to 3 bar lunches), 7 to 9.30   CLOSED: 24 to 29 Dec   MEALS: alc. Set L
£12.50, Set D £21. Bar menu   SERVICE: not inc   CARDS: Access, Amex, Diners, Visa
DETAILS: 60 seats. 8 tables outside (bar food). Private parties: 8 main room, 30 private room.
Car park. Vegetarian meals. Children's helpings. No cigars/pipes in dining-room.
Wheelchair access (3 steps; also WC). No music. Air-conditioned   ACCOMMODATION: 20
rooms, all with bath/shower. B&B £38.50 to £110. Deposit: £20. Children welcome. Baby
facilities. Garden. Tennis. Air-conditioned. TV. Phone. Fax: (021) 502893

Dining-rooms where live and recorded music are never played are signalled by No music
in the details at the end of an entry.

Clifford's

18 Dyke Parade, Mardyke, Cork
MARDYKE (021) 275333   COST £20–£40

The building was once Cork County Library but the Georgian house has been converted with tremendous style. There's no messing with fakery, just good pictures and fine furnishings. The cooking is pretty good too. Michael Clifford has a feel for flavour, an eye for bold presentation, an ear for current trends and a willingness to mobilise the best in Irish tradition as well as the best in local materials. The wine list is well thought out. House wines are from £13.50.

CHEF: Michael Clifford   PROPRIETORS: Michael and Deirdre Clifford   OPEN: Mon to Sat, exc L Mon and Sat; 12.30 to 2.30, 7.30 to 10.30   MEALS: Set L £12, Set D £25.50   SERVICE: not inc, card slips closed   CARDS: Access, Amex, Diners, Visa   DETAILS: 50 seats. Private parties: 50 main room, 35 private room. Vegetarian meals. Children's helpings. Smart dress preferred. No-smoking area. No music. Air-conditioned

Crawford Gallery

Municipal Art Gallery,
Emmet Place, Cork
CORK (021) 274415   COST £17–£31

The restaurant is an outpost of Ballymaloe House (see entry, Shanagarry), so benefits from the same lines of supply. Lunch is busy, so be prepared to queue. Dinner is offered on three nights a week when cooking shows natural treatment of good materials: lamb roasted with herbs and wild garlic, escalopes of baby beef with grain mustard sauce, or fresh fish from Ballycotton with brown bread and a salad are the sort of thing. There are also great smoked salmon, good soups, good coffee and friendly service. It closes firmly at 11pm when the security staff go home. House wine is £10.

CHEFS: Myrtle and Fern Allen, and Rosie Mcleod   PROPRIETORS: Myrtle and Fern Allen
OPEN: Mon to Sat L, Wed to Fri D; 10.30 to 5 (L 12 to 2.30), 6.30 to 9.30   CLOSED: 24 Dec for 2 weeks   MEALS: alc. Minimum £2.50 L   SERVICE: not inc   CARDS: Access, Visa
DETAILS: 70 seats. Private parties: 70 main room. Vegetarian meals. Children's helpings.
No-smoking area. Music. Fax: (021) 652021

DINGLE Co Kerry   map 9

▲ Doyle's

4 John Street, Dingle
TRALEE (066) 51174   COST £24–£37

You can stay here as well as eat the matchless fish. 'How nice to see the simplicity enhanced by the provision of linen napkins,' wrote one Oxford traveller who was impressed by the mussels in garlic butter, crab cocktail with good mayo and coffee as good as that at any French café. 'A not very inviting exterior leads into an Irish welcome and *wonderful* food' was the news from another. This is the place to stay at in Dingle, the place to eat lobster, and the place to try an excellent wine list. House wines are from £10.50.

CHEF: Stella Doyle   PROPRIETORS: John and Stella Doyle   OPEN: Mon to Sat, D only;
12.30 to 2.15, 6 to 9   CLOSED: mid-Nov to mid-Mar   MEALS: alc   SERVICE: 10%, card
slips closed   CARDS: Access, Diners, Visa   DETAILS: 45 seats. Private parties: 28 main
room. Children's helpings. No-smoking area. Wheelchair access (1 step; also WC). No
music   ACCOMMODATION: 8 rooms, all with bath/shower. 2 rooms for disabled. B&B £38
to £59. Deposit: 50%. Children welcome. Baby facilities with prior notice. TV. Phone.
Doors close at midnight. Fax: (066) 51816

Half Door

John Street, Dingle
TRALEE (066) 51600   COST £24–£36

This is next to the other fish restaurant in Dingle. Its intentions can hardly be
misunderstood from all the fishing paraphernalia that decorate it. Lobster from
the live tank again fills people's memories. 'Superb oysters and turbot; friendly
and brisk service. We returned within the week as we liked it so much and
were not disappointed.' House wines are £9.75.

CHEF: Denis O'Connor   PROPRIETORS: Denis and Teresa O'Connor   OPEN: all week, exc
Tue and Sun L Sept to June; 12.30 to 2.30, 6 to 10   CLOSED: Nov to 17 Mar   MEALS: alc
SERVICE: not inc   CARDS: Access, Diners, Visa   DETAILS: 52 seats. Private parties: 30 main
room. Vegetarian meals. Children's helpings. No-smoking area. Wheelchair access (also
WC). Music. Air-conditioned. Fax: (066) 51206

DOUGLAS Co Cork   map 9

▲ Lovetts

Churchyard Lane,
Well Road, Douglas
CORK (021) 294909 and 362204   COST £21–£44

The restaurant and bar occupy the ground floor of a handsome late-Georgian
house. The main interest of the kitchen is fresh fish. There are good reports of
game cooking, too. Sauces are light, and if the weather turns bad and the boats
stay at home, there may be little enough on offer. Don't worry, there's always
the smoked eel, the Galway oysters, the venison or the sirloin steak. House
wines are from £10.50.

CHEFS: Margaret Lovett and Greg Dawson   PROPRIETORS: Dermod and Margaret Lovett
OPEN: Mon to Sat; 12.30 to 2.15, 7 to 10   CLOSED: first 2 weeks Aug, 10 days Christmas
MEALS: alc. Set L £13.50 to £15.50, Set D £22 to £24   SERVICE: not inc, card slips closed
CARDS: Access, Amex, Diners, Visa   DETAILS: 35 seats. Private parties: 35 main room, 20
private room. Car park. Vegetarian meals. Healthy eating options. Children's helpings. No
cigars/pipes in dining-room. Wheelchair access (also WC). Music   ACCOMMODATION: 18
rooms, all with bath/shower. B&B £62. Deposit: £50. Children welcome. Baby facilities.
Garden. Phone. Fax: (021) 508568

Net prices *in the details at the end of an entry indicates that the prices given on a menu
and on a bill are inclusive of VAT and service charge, and that this practice is clearly stated
on menu and bill.*

Le Coq Hardi

35 Pembroke Road,
Ballsbridge, Dublin 4
DUBLIN (01) 689070 and 684130   COST £25–£72

Guests sometimes ask to be shown round the wine cellar next to the bar and
reception rooms of this grand, club-like restaurant in fine Georgian
accommodation. Who can blame them when the cellar boasts Mouton
Rothschild from 1870, Petrus 1959 and a host of gems? It may be a little more
difficult to find something really cheap. The cooking stalks the pathways of
classical haute cuisine, though John Howard is exploring some more robust
dishes such as black and white puddings, oxtail stews and 'even fish and
chips'. There is great skill in things like a fine consommé with a veal raviolo,
or a double escalope of salmon with watercress and Chablis sauce, though on
the day it was visited a lot of salt was in evidence in the flavours. Desserts come
on a trolley and are perhaps not as inventive as the cooking. House wines are
from £12.

CHEFS: John Howard and James O'Sullivan PROPRIETORS: John and Catherine Howard
OPEN: Mon to Sat, exc Sat L; 12.30 to 2.30, 7 to 11   CLOSED: 2 weeks Christmas, 2 weeks
Aug   MEALS: alc. Set L £16 to £19, Set D £30   SERVICE: 12.5%, card slips closed   CARDS:
Access, Amex, Diners, Visa   DETAILS: 50 seats. Private parties: 50 main room, 4, 10 and 20
private rooms. Car park. Children welcome. Jacket and tie. No-smoking area. Air-
conditioned. Fax: (01) 689887

Eastern Tandoori

34–35 South William Street, Dublin 2
DUBLIN (01) 710428 and 710506   COST £14–£40

There cannot be many Indian restaurants that can claim two sister branches in
Blackrock and Brussels. Perhaps it's the effect of the Common Market.
Anyway, this is considered a good place for a curry or something from the
tandoor if that is what you hanker for. House wine is £10.25. There is also a
branch at 1 New Street, Malahide, Co Dublin, Tel: (01) 8454155.

CHEFS: Henry Paul, Olli Ullah, Mohamed Ylinus Ali and Iqubal Ahmed   PROPRIETORS:
Mr and Mrs Feroze Khan OPEN: all week, exc Sun L; 12 to 2.30, 6 to 11.30   MEALS: alc.
Set L £6.95, Set D £14.50 to £17.95. Minimum £8.50 SERVICE: 12.5%, card slips closed
CARDS: Access, Amex, Diners, Visa   DETAILS: 74 seats. Vegetarian meals. Children's
helpings. No-smoking area. Wheelchair access (2 steps). Music. Air-conditioned.
Fax: (01) 779232

Card slips closed *in the details at the end of an entry indicates that the total on the slips
of credit cards is closed when handed over for signature.*

*The text of entries is based on unsolicited reports sent in by readers, backed up by
inspections conducted anonymously. The factual details under the text are from
questionnaires the* Guide *sends to all restaurants that feature in the book.*

Les Frères Jacques

| | NEW ENTRY |

74 Dame Street, Dublin 2
DUBLIN (01) 6794555   COST £21–£50

This is a French restaurant, make no mistake, opposite Dublin Castle. It cooks
excellent food such as cassolette of mussels and crab in fennel sauce; fine soups
such as sorrel and an oxtail consommé that was really oxtail, no essence flavour
to it; a fine vegetable terrine with a rosemary-scented fillet of lamb running
through the centre; and spring lamb with aubergine gratin. Light sauces are
infused with herbs, there is good pastry work, and coffee is strong. The prices
are those of a capital city, but the service is professional and the setting
pleasing. House wine is £9.50.

CHEFS: Eric Tydgadt and Tao Kennedy   PROPRIETORS: Jean-Jacques and Suzy Caillabet
OPEN: Mon to Sat, exc Sat L; 12.30 to 2.30, 7.30 to 10.30 (11 Fri and Sat)   CLOSED: 25 Dec to
2 Jan, Republic of Ireland bank hols   MEALS: alc. Set L £13, Set D £20   SERVICE: 12.5%
CARDS: Access, Amex, Visa   DETAILS: 65 seats. Private parties: 40 main room, 12 and 40
private rooms. Car park. Vegetarian meals. Children's helpings. No pipes in dining-room.
Music. Fax: (01) 6794725

Kapriol

45 Lower Camden Street,
Dublin 2
DUBLIN (01) 751235 and 2985496   COST £30–£52

A party visited three days after Christmas. Sr Peruzzi was recovering from
exhaustion induced by the frenzied festivities, but the staff gave as warm and
enthusiastic a welcome as if he were there. It seems to be that which provokes
returns, though the food is a variation on the trattoria theme (and dearly priced
at that). House wine is £10.40 per carafe.

CHEF: Egidia Peruzzi   PROPRIETORS: Giuseppe and Egidia Peruzzi   OPEN: Mon to Sat,
D only; 7.30 to 12   CLOSED: bank hols, 3 weeks Aug   MEALS: alc. Minimum £9   SERVICE:
12.5%   CARDS: Access, Amex, Diners, Visa   DETAILS: 30 seats. Private parties: 36 main
room. Vegetarian meals. Children's helpings. Smart dress preferred. Wheelchair access
(1 step). Music

Locks

1 Windsor Terrace,
Portobello, Dublin 8
DUBLIN (01) 543391 & 538352   COST £21–£49

The entrance is none too prepossessing, but once through the hall you are soon
charmed by waiters ('out of Joyce') and a fine atmosphere. The cooking was
acceptable on this year's visit, but not firing on all cylinders. There was 'a good
Irish stew and some decent vegetables', even if other parts of the meal had
some error. House wines are from £9.50.

See inside the front cover for an explanation of the symbols used at the tops of entries.

CHEF: Brian Buckley   PROPRIETOR: Claire Douglas   OPEN: Mon to Sat, exc Sat L; 12.30 to 2, 7.15 to 11   CLOSED: 1 week Christmas, bank hols   MEALS: alc. Set L £12.95, Set D £18.95   SERVICE: 12.5%   CARDS: Access, Amex, Diners, Visa   DETAILS: 50 seats. Private parties: 17 main room, 30 private room. Children's helpings. Wheelchair access. No music. Fax: (01) 538352

Patrick Guilbaud

46 James's Place, Dublin 2
DUBLIN (01) 764192   COST £25–£59

One English visitor who took his Irish cousins here remarked that it would be his number one target when next in Dublin, but without the family. This observation was made after he had seen the size of the 15 per cent service charge – enough to feed two or three people at another, cheaper, establishment. This is state-of-the-art French-influenced cookery, with materials brought from the homeland to match. Casserole of salmon with cumin and some oyster ravioli, salmon tartare with caviare cream, foie gras with peppered strawberries and spices, roast veal sweetbreads with deep-fried herbs, and lamb with aubergines and red pimento sauce are some of the offerings in the spring. The setting is very fine, with 'bizarre pyramidal columns, a view of the kitchen, lots of hanging baskets of trailing plants and good paintings'; the service is usually excellent; and the place is very full all the time. House wines are from £13.

CHEF: Guillaume Lebrun   PROPRIETOR: Patrick Guilbaud   OPEN: Tue to Sat; 12.30 to 2, 7.30 to 10.15   CLOSED: bank hols   MEALS: alc. Set L £15.50, Set D £25   SERVICE: 15% CARDS: Access, Amex, Diners, Visa   DETAILS: 85 seats. Private parties: 85 main room, 30 private room. Car park. Vegetarian meals. Children's helpings. Smart dress preferred. No-smoking area. Wheelchair access (1 step). Fax: (01) 601546

DUN LAOGHAIRE Co Dublin   map 9

Digby's

5 Windsor Terrace,
Dun Laoghaire
DUBLIN (01) 2804600 and 2809147   COST £17–£40

The maritime view must help fix the repertoire: it's strongest on fish (with game a second suit). Yet Paul Cathcart has not let the world float by without a few nods to fashion, and there is much southern style to his cooking. Wines are quite expensive. House wines are from £9.

CHEF: Paul Cathcart   PROPRIETORS: Paul and Jane Cathcart   OPEN: all week D, exc Tue, and Sun L; 12.30 to 3, 7 to 11   CLOSED: 24 to 27 Dec, Good Fri   MEALS: alc. Set L £10.50, Set D £16.50   SERVICE: 12.5%, card slips closed   CARDS: Access, Amex, Diners, Visa DETAILS: 50 seats. Private parties: 52 main room. Vegetarian meals with prior notice. Children's helpings. No-smoking area. Music. Air-conditioned

---

Restaurateurs justifiably resent no-shows. If you quote a credit card number when booking, you may be liable for the restaurant's lost profit margin if you don't turn up. Always phone to cancel.

Restaurant Na Mara

1 Harbour Road, Dun Laoghaire
DUBLIN (01) 2806767 and 2800509   COST £20–£44

The restaurant is owned by Irish Rail and set in the original railway terminal overlooking Dun Laoghaire harbour. Fish is the speciality, cooked classically for lovers of Newburg and thermidor, but with an eye to current fads with dishes such as turbot with a scallop mousse, ratatouille and red pimento sauce, or turbot and salmon wrapped in cabbage leaves and served with a saffron sauce. House wines are £10.

CHEF: Derek Dunne   PROPRIETORS: Irish Rail Co   OPEN: Mon to Sat; 12.30 to 2.30, 7 to 10.30   CLOSED: 1 week Christmas   MEALS: alc. Set L £12.75, Set D £22   SERVICE: 15%, card slips closed   CARDS: Access, Amex, Diners, Visa   DETAILS: 75 seats. Private parties: 45 main room, 30 private room. Vegetarian meals. Children welcome. Smart dress preferred. No-smoking area. Wheelchair access (2 steps). Music. Fax: (01) 2844649

DURRUS Co Cork   map 9

Blair's Cove House

Durrus
BANTRY (027) 61127   COST £26–£37

It's in a wonderful position and is a fine example of simple cooking done over the wood-fired grill on full view in the dining-room. There is a buffet replete with various cold items – crab, smoked salmon, oysters, tongue, brawn, marinated herrings and the like – and then it's on to a scan of the blackboard menu before choosing something from the grill or perhaps sweetbreads with brown butter, salmon with horseradish crust, steamed John Dory and sorrel sauce, or scallops with basil. Back to the buffet for sweets. House wines are from £10.

CHEF: Sabine de Mey   PROPRIETORS: Philippe and Sabine de Mey   OPEN: Tue to Sat, D only, Mon D July and Aug; 7.30 to 9.30   CLOSED: Nov to Feb   MEALS: Set D £17 to £23   SERVICE: 10%, card slips closed   CARDS: Access, Amex, Diners, Visa   DETAILS: 70 seats. 8 tables outside. Private parties: 35 main room. Car park. Vegetarian meals. Children's helpings. No-smoking area. Wheelchair access. Music

---

GOREY Co Wexford   map 9

▲ *Marlfield House*

Courtown Road, Gorey
GOREY (055) 21124   COST £24–£46

This is a very fine house and has equally fine gardens. You dine in a Victorian conservatory that may take the breath away. Bedrooms are glorious. All these are superlatives, and the cooking will not disappoint for its quality. The style is quite close to that of British country houses: not simple, the flavour-punch occasionally pulled, but giving the right impressions. The wine list (from £9.50 a bottle) is very impressive indeed.

CHEF: Rose Brannoch PROPRIETORS: Mary and Ray Bowe OPEN: all week; 12.30 to 2, 7.15 to 9.30 MEALS: Set L £17.50 to £19.50, Set D £28 to £31 SERVICE: 10%, card slips closed DETAILS: 60 seats. Private parties: 60 main room, 25 private room. Car park. Children welcome. Jacket and tie. No cigars/pipes in dining-room. Wheelchair access (also WC). No music ACCOMMODATION: 19 rooms, all with bath/shower. Rooms for disabled. B&B £65 to £367. Deposit: 1 night. Children welcome. Baby facilities. Afternoon teas. Garden. Sauna. Tennis. Fishing. TV. Phone. Doors close at midnight. Confirm by 5. Fax: (055) 21572

HOWTH Co Dublin map 9

King Sitric

East Pier, Harbour Road, Howth
DUBLIN (01) 325235 and 326729 COST £28–£48

Sip a drink and watch the yachts; eat fish here, or rack of lamb if you don't go for seafood. Lobster three ways is the speciality: one and a half fish per person, boiled, grilled and thermidor. It is even said that the restaurant has its own lobster boat, but the live tanks make sure that everything is in good condition. Shellfish platter and smoked salmon are also recommended. There is a good and classic wine cellar. House wines are £11.

CHEF: Aidan MacManus PROPRIETORS: Aidan and Joan MacManus OPEN: Mon to Sat, D only; 6.30 to 11 CLOSED: few days Christmas, Easter, bank hols MEALS: alc. Set D £22 SERVICE: not inc, card slips closed CARDS: Access, Amex, Diners, Visa DETAILS: 60 seats. Private parties: 48 main room, 24 private room. Vegetarian meals. Children's helpings. No-smoking area. Wheelchair access. Fax: (01) 392442

KANTURK Co Cork map 9

▲ Assolas Country House

Kanturk
KANTURK (029) 50015
signposted from N72, NE of Kanturk COST £38

This is a glorious, small late-seventeenth-century manor house, the river running to one side, with guest bedrooms both in the garden house and in the main building. The Bourke family have always lived here, and they run the hotel with as little fuss and fandango as possible. The cooking is natural and good, with no false artistry, but no ignoring of proprieties either. The wine list is excellent – not long, but with good makers. House wine is £13.

CHEF: Hazel Bourke PROPRIETORS: the Bourke family OPEN: all week, D only; 7 to 8.30 (8 Sun) CLOSED: 1 Nov to 14 Mar MEALS: Set D £26 SERVICE: net prices, card slips closed CARDS: Access, Diners, Visa DETAILS: 30 seats. Private parties: 8 main room, 18 private room. Car park. Vegetarian meals. No children under 10. Jacket and tie. No cigars/pipes in dining-room. Wheelchair access. No music ACCOMMODATION: 9 rooms, all with bath/shower. B&B £52 to £70. Deposit: 1 night. Garden. Tennis. Fishing. Phone. Doors close at 11.30. Confirm by 6. Fax: (029) 50795

KENMARE Co Kerry   map 9

▲ *Park Hotel*

Kenmare
KILLARNEY (064) 41200   COST £24–£66

This is a hotel in the grand manner, the vision of a single mind. There is a new chef this year, though he trained at the Park before spending years at work in Australia. The prices are higher than those of neighbouring rivals, but then the service is more cosseting, the surroundings more exactly what is needed for a languorous and pampered stay. What you get is grand cuisine of international pretension, excellently performed. House wines are £13.95.

CHEF: Brian Cleere PROPRIETOR: Francis Brennan OPEN: all week; 1 to 2, 7 to 9 CLOSED: mid-Nov to 23 Dec, 2 Jan to Easter MEALS: alc. Set L £16.50, Set D £35 SERVICE: net prices set meals, not inc alc CARDS: Access, Visa DETAILS: 90 seats. Private parties: 60 main room, 40 private room. Car park. Vegetarian meals. Healthy eating options. Children's helpings L. Jacket and tie. No cigars/pipes in dining-room. No-smoking area. Wheelchair access (also WC). Music ACCOMMODATION: 50 rooms, all with bath/shower. Rooms for disabled. Lift. B&B £117 to £240. Deposit: £200. Children welcome. Baby facilities. Afternoon teas. Garden. Tennis. Golf. Snooker. TV. Phone. Doors close at midnight. Confirm by 6. Fax: (064) 41402

KILKENNY Co Kilkenny   map 9

▲ *Lacken House*

Dublin Road, Kilkenny
KILKENNY (056) 61085   COST £28–£40

This is a great place to stay at, with fine breakfasts, a happy feel to everything and good cooking by Eugene McSweeney. There is a five-course dinner menu, or the eye may roam over a short speciality list priced individually. Crab gâteau, sauté of chicken livers with cognac, chicken stuffed with Cashel blue, and turbot with Dublin Bay prawns are some things mentioned in the spring. House wines are £12.

CHEF: Eugene McSweeney PROPRIETORS: Eugene and Breda McSweeney OPEN: Tue to Sat, D only; 7 to 10 CLOSED: Christmas MEALS: alc. Set D £22 to £30 SERVICE: net prices, card slips closed CARDS: Access, Amex, Diners, Visa DETAILS: 35 seats. Private parties: 40 main room, 10 private room. Car park. Vegetarian meals. Children's helpings. Smart dress preferred. No-smoking area. Music. Air-conditioned ACCOMMODATION: 8 rooms, all with bath/shower. B&B £31 to £49. Deposit: £10. Children welcome. Baby facilities. Garden. TV. Phone. Doors close at midnight. Confirm by 6. Fax: (056) 62435

The Good Food Guide *is a registered trade mark of Consumers' Association Ltd.*

£ *indicates that it is possible to have a three-course meal, including coffee, a half-bottle of house wine and service, at any time the restaurant is open (i.e. at dinner as well as at lunch, unless a place is open only for dinner), for £20 or less per person.*

KINSALE Co Cork   map 9

▲ *Blue Haven*

3 Pearse Street, Kinsale
CORK (021) 772209   COST £26–£38

This small hotel, pub and restaurant is plumb centre of Kinsale and hardly
lacks for customers. Fight your way to the bar and be assured of kindly service.
Wait for the shellfish to battle its way to your table and enjoy the wealth of
oysters or lobster. The house specials are brill and scallop bake and hot wood-
smoked mackerel coated with mustard and peppercorns. House wines are
£11.50.

CHEF: Brian O'Donoghue PROPRIETORS: Brian and Anne Cronin OPEN: all week; 12.30
to 3, 7 to 10.30 CLOSED: 25 Dec MEALS: alc SERVICE: 10%, card slips closed CARDS:
Access, Amex, Diners, Visa DETAILS: 70 seats. 7 tables outside. Private parties: 45 main
room, 22 private room. Vegetarian meals. Children's helpings. No-smoking area.
Wheelchair access (also WC). Music. Air-conditioned ACCOMMODATION: 10 rooms,
7 with bath/shower. Rooms for disabled. B&B £38 to £84. Deposit: £30. Children welcome.
Baby facilities. Afternoon teas. Garden. Air-conditioned. Fishing. TV. Phone. Doors close at
11.30. Confirm by 6. Fax: (021) 774268

LETTERFRACK Co Galway   map 9

▲ *Rosleague Manor* ⚡✳

Letterfrack
CLIFDEN (095) 41101   COST £12–£40

The manor house is equipped with everything that can be expected, down to
complete isolation and a view over a sheltered bay that seems like something
out of the West Indies when the sun shines hard. The cooking is country-house
format: a short menu and four courses for dinner with the emphasis on
materials over art, but not without plenty of skill. The tastes, as well as the
views of sunnier climes, are reflected in dishes such as beef with vegetable
tagliatelle and a red wine sauce, or monkfish with rosemary and garlic
ratatouille sauce. House wines are £10.50.

CHEF: Patrick Foyle PROPRIETORS: Anne and Patrick Foyle OPEN: all week; 1 to 2.30,
8 to 9.30 CLOSED: Nov to Easter MEALS: alc. Set L £6 to £10, Set D £22 to £25 SERVICE:
not inc, card slips closed CARDS: Access, Visa DETAILS: 70 seats. Private parties: 70 main
room. Car park. Vegetarian meals. Children's helpings. Smart dress preferred. No smoking
in dining-room. Wheelchair access (2 steps; also WC) ACCOMMODATION: 20 rooms, all
with bath/shower. Rooms for disabled. B&B £45 to £110. Deposit: £25. Children welcome.
Baby facilities. Pets welcome. Afternoon teas. Garden. Sauna. Tennis. Fishing. Snooker.
Phone. Doors close at midnight. Confirm by midday. Fax: (095) 41168

The 1994 Guide *will be published before Christmas 1993. Reports on meals are most
welcome at any time of the year, but are extremely valuable in the spring. Send them to*
The Good Food Guide, *FREEPOST, 2 Marylebone Road, London NW1 1YN. No stamp
is needed if posted in the UK.*

MALLOW Co Cork   map 9

▲ *Longueville House* ⁵✱

Mallow
MALLOW (022) 47156   COST £21–£50

The Georgian manor house overlooks the Blackwater and the ruins of
Dromineen Castle. It has a working farm and a vineyard. These are good starts
to a satisfactory meal, which may be served in the conservatory (also good), the
Presidents' Restaurant or the Library (if you happen to insist on smoking). It
may be grand and impressive, but everyone is relaxed enough to let lunch
parties linger until 6pm, and to look after children as if they were adults – and
serve them home-made apple juice. House wine is £11.

CHEF: William O'Callaghan   PROPRIETORS: the O'Callaghan family   OPEN: all week;
12.45 to 2, 7 to 9 (9.45 Sun)   CLOSED: 20 Dec to 1 Mar   MEALS: alc. Set L £13 to £15,
Set D £24 to £30   SERVICE: not inc, card slips closed   CARDS: Access, Amex, Diners, Visa
DETAILS: 50 seats. 8 tables outside. Private parties: 16 main room, 16 private room. Car
park. Vegetarian meals. Children's helpings. Jacket and tie. No smoking in dining-room.
No music   ACCOMMODATION: 16 rooms, all with bath/shower. B&B £50 to £150. Children
welcome. Baby facilities. Afternoon teas. Garden. Fishing. Snooker. TV. Phone. Doors close
at midnight. Confirm by 6. Fax: (022) 47459

MAYNOOTH Co Kildare   map 9

▲ *Moyglare Manor* ⁵✱

Moyglare, Maynooth
DUBLIN (01) 6286351
on N4, 2km W of Maynooth   COST £19–£42

It is a large and handsome house, with a repertoire that doesn't intend to test
conventional preferences, but is none the worse for that. The wine list may act
as a draw. Although not cheap, it has a remarkable range of clarets and Rhônes
among many other gems. House wines are from £11.50.

CHEF: Jim Cullinane   PROPRIETOR: Nora Devlin   OPEN: all week, exc Sat L; 12.30 to 2.30,
7 to 9.30 (11.30 Sat)   CLOSED: 24 to 26 Dec   MEALS: alc. Set L £9.95, Set D £18.50
SERVICE: 12.5%, card slips closed   CARDS: Access, Amex, Diners, Visa   DETAILS: 90 seats.
Private parties: 90 main room, 35 private room. Car park. Vegetarian meals. No children
under 12. Smart dress preferred. No smoking in dining-room. Wheelchair access (also WC).
Music   ACCOMMODATION: 17 rooms, all with bath/shower. Rooms for disabled. B&B £75
to £110. No children under 12. Afternoon teas. Garden. Tennis. TV. Phone. Doors close at
11.30. Confirm by 6. Fax: (01) 6285405

If a restaurant is new to the Guide *this year (did not appear as a main entry in the last
edition)* NEW ENTRY *appears opposite its name.*

⁵✱ *indicates that smoking is either banned altogether or that a dining-room is maintained
for non-smokers. The symbol does not apply to restaurants that simply have no-smoking
areas.*

MIDLETON Co Cork   map 9

Farm Gate

The Coolbawn, Midleton
MIDLETON (021) 632771   COST £12–£35

'This has gone from strength to strength in the past year and offers excellent
food at reasonable prices,' writes a local inspector. It only serves dinner on two
nights a week, but the name and the philosophy seem at one in getting
supplies as fresh as can be to the table on time. Duck is firmly recommended.
The rest of the week it is a delicatessen with a grand array of pastry and baked
goods for the dining-room behind. House wine is £9.50.

CHEF/PROPRIETOR: Máróg O'Brien   OPEN: Mon to Sat L, Fri and Sat D; 12 to 3.30, 7 to 9.45
CLOSED: 25 and 26 Dec, Good Fri   MEALS: alc. Set L £6, Set D £17   SERVICE: not inc
CARDS: Access, Visa   DETAILS: 60 seats. 6 tables outside. Private parties: 60 main room.
Vegetarian meals. Children's helpings. No-smoking area. Wheelchair access (also WC).
Music. Air-conditioned

MOYCULLEN Co Galway   map 9

Drimcong House

Moycullen
GALWAY (091) 85115 and 85585   COST £25–£44

Gerry Galvin is a very talented chef who works in his own way, not that of
Irish traditionalism, haute cuisine, or any other simple school. Great materials
are transformed in recipes that are never hackneyed. The wines are good, too.
House wine is £9.50.

CHEF: Gerry Galvin   PROPRIETORS: Gerry and Marie Galvin   OPEN: Tue to Sat, D only;
7 to 10.30   CLOSED: Christmas to Mar   MEALS: alc. Set D £17.95 to £30   SERVICE: 10%,
card slips closed   CARDS: Access, Amex, Diners, Visa   DETAILS: 50 seats. Private parties:
50 main room, 12 private room. Car park. Vegetarian meals. Children's helpings.
No-smoking area. Wheelchair access (3 steps; also WC). Music

NEWMARKET-ON-FERGUS Co Clare   map 9

▲ Dromoland Castle

Newmarket-on-Fergus
LIMERICK (061) 368144   COST £30–£68

This place is seriously large, seriously magnificent, seriously ostentatious, and
the cooking, wine list and whole panoply of service match it. The style is 100
per cent international, with a 'Taste of Ireland' set menu offered besides the
modern-mainstream *carte*, though squab stuffed with foie gras doesn't seem a
particularly Irish dish. The new conference centre is 'state of the art' stuff.
House wine is £14.

The Guide *always appreciates hearing about changes of chef or owner.*

CHEF: Jean-Baptiste Molinari   PROPRIETORS: Ashford Hotels Ltd   OPEN: all week; 12.30 to 2.30, 7 to 9.30   MEALS: alc. Set L £19, Set D £32   SERVICE: 15%   CARDS: Access, Amex, Diners, Visa   DETAILS: 90 seats. 4 tables outside. Private parties: 120 main room, 20 and 60 private rooms. Car park. Vegetarian meals. Children's helpings (evening tea for children under 8). Jacket and tie. No-smoking area. Wheelchair access. Music   ACCOMMODATION: 73 rooms, all with bath/shower. Rooms for disabled. B&B £105 to £385. Children welcome. Afternoon teas. Garden. Tennis. Fishing. Golf. Snooker. TV. Phone. Confirm by 6. Fax: (061) 363355

NEWPORT Co Mayo   map 9

▲ *Newport House* 🍴✳

Newport
NEWPORT (098) 41222   COST £12–£35

Fishing and bottles of wine may be thought the first priorities of most people who stay here. Both are good, both are sedulously cared for. The staff manage to colour the grand opulence of the place with their own brand of warmth and hospitality, making this a good place at which to stay. The mainstream-modern cooking contributes satisfactorily to the body's survival for the next day's casting of flies. During the winter, light lunches only are served. House wine is £10.

CHEF: John Gavin   PROPRIETORS: Kieran and Thelma Thompson   OPEN: all week; 12.30 to 2.30, 7.30 to 9.30   CLOSED: 30 Sept to 20 Mar (exc for light L)   MEALS: light L. Set D £26   SERVICE: net prices, card slips closed   CARDS: Access, Amex, Visa   DETAILS: 38 seats. Private parties: 28 main room. Car park. Vegetarian meals with prior notice. Children's helpings (before 7). No smoking in dining-room. Wheelchair access (1 step). No music   ACCOMMODATION: 19 rooms, all with bath/shower. 2 rooms for disabled. B&B £52 to £178. Deposit: £50. Children welcome. Baby facilities. Afternoon teas. Garden. Fishing. Snooker. Phone. Confirm by 6. Fax: (098) 41613

OUGHTERARD Co Galway   map 9

▲ *Currarevagh House* 🍴✳

Oughterard
GALWAY (091) 82312 and 82313
4m NW of Oughterard on Hill of
Doon Lakeshore road   COST £26

Lough Corrib is the draw, for the fishing. But the house is attraction enough: old-fashioned high country living. Dinner is good and simple: a joint is roast, served, then offered for seconds. It is framed both sides by a light starter and fish, then dessert and cheese. Tomato mousse, salmon with maître d'hôtel butter, haunch of venison, caramel oranges and cheese might be one meal. Baked Alaska is the Sunday evening special. 'The house promotes conversation among guests, but there is space for those who wish to avoid it,' writes one who enjoyed a gentle visit. House wines are from £7.90.

▲ *This symbol means accommodation is available.*

CHEF: June Hodgson   PROPRIETORS: Harry and June Hodgson   OPEN: all week, D only
(also snack L for residents); 8   CLOSED: Nov to Mar   MEALS: Set D £17.50   SERVICE:
10%   DETAILS: 30 seats. Private parties: 10 main room. Car park. Vegetarian meals.
Children welcome. Smart dress preferred. No smoking in dining-room. No music
ACCOMMODATION: 15 rooms, all with bath/shower. B&B £37 to £74. Deposit: £20. Children
under 12 by arrangement. Garden. Tennis. Fishing. Doors close at 12.30am. Confirm by
midday. Fax: (091) 82731

ROSSNOWLAGH Co Donegal
map 9

▲ Sand House Hotel

Rossnowlagh
DONEGAL (072) 51777
COST £15–£30

The hotel is open for the season only, right on the beach of Donegal Bay,
offering 'attractive home-cooking, based largely on local seafood, including
their own oyster beds and the produce of a large fishing port nearby'. The
'home-cooking' may extend to quenelles of brill or quail stuffed with apple
and walnuts. Visitors have enjoyed the wine list, particularly the bin-ends.
House wines are from £8.

CHEF: Liam Quinn   PROPRIETORS: Vin and Mary Britton, and Brian Britton   OPEN: all
week; 1 to 2.30, 7 to 8.30 (9 Sat)   CLOSED: Oct to Easter   MEALS: alc. Set L £10 to £12.50,
Set D £18.50 to £20   SERVICE: 10%, card slips closed   CARDS: Access, Amex, Diners,
Visa   DETAILS: 80 seats. Private parties: 60 main room, 12 and 30 private rooms. Car park.
Vegetarian meals. Children's helpings (children's D 6 to 7). No children under 7 D. Smart
dress preferred. No-smoking area. Wheelchair access (3 steps; also WC). No music
ACCOMMODATION: 40 rooms, all with bath/shower. B&B £30 to £90. Deposit: £40. Children
welcome. Baby facilities. Pets by arrangement. Afternoon teas. Garden. Tennis. Snooker.
Phone. Doors close at 11. Confirm by 3. Fax: (072) 52100

SHANAGARRY Co Cork
map 9

▲ Ballymaloe House ⚡✗

Shanagarry, Midleton
CORK (021) 652531
COST £24–£43

This grand country house – yet never too grand – goes on its unstoppable way.
The scale of the business is remarkable, but everyone keeps their smiles: 'They
are quite hard-pressed, the penalty – or reward – of their success and
reputation, but all is calm, jolly and good humoured, just like a family should
be.' The place is run with unerring taste – look at some of the pictures; and to
be able to produce excellent food into the bargain is icing on the cake. Many of
the raw materials are made here, and rightly so. The cooking is that halfway
house between super-family and professional restaurant: always careful,
attractive, yet not straying into serious complexity. 'We particularly enjoyed the
Friday night first course, listed simply as "Hors d'oeuvre", but a delight. Local
oysters, oursins, shrimps, three sorts of pâté, lots of other things. There used to
be half-lobsters, but there were at least good little lobster vol-au-vent.' Thus
reported one happy regular, who extolled the fish (particularly at breakfast),

the soups, the stuffed roast pork, the caramel ice-cream and the meringue roulade. A great place at which to stay. House wines are £13.

CHEFS: Paddy Cullinane and Myrtle Allen   PROPRIETORS: Ivan and Myrtle Allen   OPEN: all week; 1 to 2, 7 to 9.30   CLOSED: Dec 24 to 26   MEALS: Set L £15 to £16, Set D £29   SERVICE: not inc   CARDS: Access, Amex, Diners, Visa   DETAILS: 90 seats. Private parties: 35 main room, 10, 18 and 30 private rooms. Car park. Vegetarian meals. Children's helpings D. No-smoking rooms. Wheelchair access (also WC). Music   ACCOMMODATION: 30 rooms, 29 with bath/shower. Rooms for disabled. B&B £50 to £104. Deposit: £50. Children welcome. Baby facilities. Garden. Swimming-pool. Tennis. Phone. Fax: (021) 652021

WATERFORD Co Waterford   map 9

Dwyers £

8 Mary Street, Waterford
WATERFORD (051) 77478 and 71183   COST £18–£32

This used to be a police barracks – perhaps that is why you have to ring the bell to gain entry. It was visited by a reader during an electricity strike, yet for him the light was not undimmed and he extolled the virtues of Martin Dwyer's cooking, and the generosity when it came to portions – 'enough for four,' he recorded in wonder. The style is without flounce and with flavour, surely the right priorities. Brill stuffed with mushrooms and wrapped in filo, then baked and served with a mushroom and scallop sauce, monkfish with spinach, herbs and garlic, and black sole stuffed with prawns are examples of fish dishes. House wines are from £9.50.

CHEF/PROPRIETOR: Martin Dwyer   OPEN: all week, D only (L by arrangement); 6 to 10   CLOSED: 3 days Christmas, 2 weeks July   MEALS: alc. Set D £12   SERVICE: not inc, card slips closed   CARDS: Access, Amex, Diners, Visa   DETAILS: 42 seats. Private parties: 32 main room, 10 private room. Vegetarian meals. Children's helpings. No-smoking area. Wheelchair access (also WC). Music

---

WEXFORD Co Wexford   map 9

Granary | NEW ENTRY |

Westgate, Wexford
WEXFORD (053) 23935   COST £25–£47

As one person remarked, 'my pigeon breast came from a *very* happy bird'. This place does seem to be able to produce good cooking, and to present the cooking with humour and style. At least 10 scallops, big ones too, came in a pair of shells with a 'flotsam and jetsam' of vegetables and a 'sea' of sauce, plus puff pastry fishes' heads and tails to enliven the whole. It also tasted good. The large room, with tables round its perimeter in booths, is cheerful and characterful rather than suavely sophisticated, but excellent cooking is plentifully in evidence. House wine is £9.25.

Report forms are at the back of the book; write a letter if you prefer.

CHEFS: Mary Hatton and Vincent Whitmore PROPRIETORS: Paddy and Mary Hatton
OPEN: Mon to Sat, D only (Sun and post-opera D during Wexford Festival); 6 to 10
CLOSED: 3 days Christmas MEALS: alc. Set D £17.95 SERVICE: not inc CARDS: Access,
Amex, Diners, Visa DETAILS: 45 seats. Private parties: 15 main room, 30 private room.
Vegetarian meals. Children's helpings (6 to 7.30). No-smoking area. Wheelchair access.
Music

WICKLOW Co Wicklow   map 9

▲ *Old Rectory* ⁑✶

Wicklow
WICKLOW (0404) 67048   COST £30–£45

The anticipated completion of the conservatory dining-room has been
postponed until 1993, but this does not detract from the comfort of the guests or
the proficiency of the Saunders. Pyromaniacs may enjoy Paul Saunders'
collection of fire helmets; diners will relish Linda's nicely undoctrinaire
cooking – either from a set meal or from a short *carte*. She can even manage a
new edge to deep-fried cheese, using St Killian cheese and serving it with
braised cucumber and fennel rather than the usual horrific jams beloved of
amateur chefs. A vegetarian koulibiac with a red pepper sauce is also
recommended, as are Linda's soups, use of herbs and elaborate desserts (try
'fruitscape with butterfly' – 'an arrangement of fresh fruits with framboise
cream and a chocolate meringue butterfly'). The Saunders emphasise that their
establishment is small, not grand, a home, not an institution. House wines are
from £11.

CHEF: Linda Saunders PROPRIETORS: Paul and Linda Saunders OPEN: all week, D
only; 8 CLOSED: mid-Oct to Easter MEALS: alc. Set D £23 SERVICE: not inc, card slips
closed CARDS: Access, Amex, Diners, Visa DETAILS: 12 seats. Car park. Vegetarian
meals. Children's helpings. Smart dress preferred. No smoking in dining-room. Music
ACCOMMODATION: 5 rooms, all with bath/shower. B&B £58 to £84. Deposit: £20. Children
welcome. Baby facilities. Garden. TV. Phone. Doors close at 1am. Confirm by 6. Fax:
(0404) 69181

County round-ups

Each year we offer a revised selection of round-up entries. All the eating-places listed below have been recommended by readers but for one reason or another have not graduated to the main listings. They are not places that simply failed at inspection. We hope the list will be especially useful for anyone travelling around Britain. All reports on these places would be most welcome.

England

Avon

BATH *Circus* 34 Brock Street, (0225) 330208. Well-established and satisfactory small restaurant in the heart of architectural paradise.
Clarets Wine Bar 7A Kingsmead Square, (0225) 466688. Pleasing cooking includes imaginative starters, sauces and sweets. Decent wines.
Somerset House 35 Bathwick Hill, (0225) 466451/463471. Classical Regency B&B; traditional English food, no smoking.
Sukhothai 90A Walcot Street, (0225) 462463. Thai; seafood soup and grilled prawns with honey and tamarind sauce; subtle spicing.
HINTON CHARTERHOUSE *Homewood Park Hotel* (0225) 723731. Charming, friendly hotel. Fresh fish menu on Fridays recommended, otherwise lots of game.
OLDBURY-ON-SEVERN *Anchor Inn* Church Road, (0454) 413331. Rambling old inn on two levels. Imaginative, fresh bar food. Gets busy.

Bedfordshire

ASPLEY GUISE *Moore Place Hotel* The Square, (0908) 282000. Well-appointed Georgian house, traditional British cooking.
LEIGHTON BUZZARD *Swan Hotel* High Street, (0525) 372148. Chain-owned hotel popular with business people. Several menus, including full vegetarian.
WOBURN *Black Horse* 1 Bedford Street, (0525) 290210. Pub with pleasant garden; good for simple sandwiches and steaks.

Berkshire

COOKHAM *Alfonso's* 19–21 Station Hill Parade, (062 85) 25775. Popular, friendly Italian; home-cooking with daily specials.
Bel and the Dragon High Street, (062 85) 21263. Relaxing Tudor pub with garden; stay with the bar food.
ETON *Eton Wine Bar* 82–83 High Street, (0753) 854921. Lively, informal restaurant with conservatory; blackboard menu.
INKPEN *Swan Inn* Lower Inkpen, (048 84) 326. Traditional English pub for Singaporean cooking.
STREATLEY *Swan Diplomat* High Street, (0491) 873737. Hotel with riverside frontage; classic cooking, can be expensive.
TAPLOW *Cliveden* (062 86) 68561. Beautiful house, once home to the Astors; two expensive restaurants within.
WEST ILSLEY *Harrow* High Street, (063 528) 260. Prettily situated pub recently enlarged; imaginative bar food.

Buckinghamshire

BEACONSFIELD *China Diner* 7 The Highway, Station Road, (0494) 673345. Peking and Szechuan cooking that pulls in the customers. Booking recommended.
Leigh House 53 Wycombe End, (0494) 676348. Reliable Chinese with a relaxed atmosphere.
GREAT MISSENDEN *Rising Sun* Little Hampden, nr Great Missenden, (0494) 488393. Imaginative pub food and a regularly changing menu.
LONG CRENDON *Angel Inn* Bicester Road, (0844) 208268. Elizabethan pub;

adventurous, successful cooking in both bar and restaurant.

MEDMENHAM *Danesfield House* (0628) 891010. Incredibly opulent hotel with initially ambitious cooking. Has been put up for sale, thus future is in doubt.

MILTON KEYNES *Jaipur* Elder House, 502 Eldergate, (0908) 669796. Decent north Indian curries and tandooris in fancy pink surroundings.

SPEEN *Old Plow Inn* Flowers Bottom Lane, Flowers Bottom, (0494) 488300. Honest home-cooking off the beaten track.

Cambridgeshire

CAMBRIDGE *Browns* 23 Trumpington Street, (0223) 461655. Large, upbeat American-style brasserie; straight-forward, fun food, no booking.

King's Pantry 9A Kings Parade, (0223) 321551. Strictly vegetarian restaurant opposite King's College; good choice, some of it vegan.

Tai Cheun 12 St John's Street, (0223) 358281. Noteworthy Chinese; choose Peking duck, beef in black-bean sauce, king prawns.

FOWLMERE *Chequers Inn* High Street, (0763) 208369. Old, beamed pub with lovely garden and good food in both bar and restaurant.

LITTLEPORT *Fen House* 2 Lynn Road, (0353) 860645. Fens location for a monthly-changing menu; fish and game feature, good for Sunday lunch.

MADINGLEY *Three Horseshoes* High Street, (0954) 210221. Thatched pub with conservatory dining-room; bar meals include chargrilled poussin, game casserole and good chips.

MELBOURN *Pink Geranium* Station Road, (0763) 260215. Very popular, for elaborate cooking, but at a price. Limousines to whisk you away by arrangement.

Cheshire

BICKLEY MOSS *Cholmondeley Arms* Cholmondeley, nr Bickley Moss,

(0829) 720300. Superior pub; light snacks to full meals with pleasing puddings.

BOLLINGTON *Randalls* 22 High Street, Old Market Place, (0625) 575058. Honest food, fancily presented; try the lamb casserole with black pudding.

CHESTER *Franc's* 14A Cuppin Street, (0244) 317952. Formula French bistro that's fun; long menu with lots of choice and all the Gallic staples.

KNUTSFORD *Lymm Bistro* 16 Bridgewater Street, Lymm, nr Knutsford, (0925) 754852. Basic surroundings but an enthusiastic kitchen. Blackboard specials are the best bet.

MACCLESFIELD *Topo's* 15 Church Street, (0625) 422231. Is best for game in season. The right ideas exist here but execution may vary.

NESTON *Vineyards* 10 Parkgate Road, 051-336 2367. Main restaurant and lunchtime brasserie; ranges from inventive snacks to full dinners. Everything home-made, relatively imaginative ingredients. Not expensive.

TARPORLEY *Churtons* 55 High Street, (0829) 732483. Good cooking and rich sauces in smart country wine bar.

WILMSLOW *Stanneylands Hotel* Stanneylands Road, (0625) 525225. Red-brick house in grounds, patronised by Cheshire wealth; careful cooking, luxury ingredients.

Cornwall

CONSTANTINE *Trengilly Wartha Inn* (0326) 40332. Charming hotel run by husband and wife team; inventive soups and sauces.

FALMOUTH *Bistro de la Mer* 28 Arwenack Street, (0326) 316509. Good seafood served with chips and salad.

GWEEK *Mellanoweth* (032 622) 271. Old, comfortable Cornish inn; good roasts and spiced apple pie with clotted cream.

HELFORD *Shipwright's Arms* (032 623) 235. Peaceful estuary location; good bar meals, great for seafood.

TIDEFORD *Heskyn Mill* (0752) 851481. Converted watermill now offering fair cooking.

TREGONY *Kea House* 69 Fore Street, (087 253) 642. Self-consciously pink, pretty place; seafood, fish and meat, but puddings are best.

TRURO *Simons* Compton Castle, Back Quay, (0872) 70101. Evening restaurant on a paddle-steamer; pretty décor, light cooking; by day a flower/coffee-shop.

VERYAN *Nare Hotel* Carne Beach, (0872) 501279. Prime beach-side location with a penchant for flambéeing.

County Durham

BARNARD CASTLE *Fox and Hounds* Cotherstone, nr Barnard Castle, (0833) 50241. Pub in picturesque location; daily blackboard specials supplement a main menu.

Market Place Teashop 29 Horse Market, Market Place, (0833) 690110. Antiques, traditional tea-pots and good honest cooking; large portions, low prices.

BURNOPFIELD *Fairways* Hobson Municipal Golf Course, (0207) 70941. More than the usual nineteenth watering-hole; ambitious pub and restaurant meals, including a vegetarian choice.

DARLINGTON *Cottage Thai* 94–96 Parkgate, (0325) 361717. Thai restaurant still finding its feet but already popular. Long menu covers all aspects.

Imperial Express Café 2 Northumberland Street, (0325) 383297. Monochromatic décor and a mixture of Italian and Continental dishes at easily affordable prices.

Sardis 196 Northgate, (0325) 461222. Long-established trattoria; fresh pastas, strong espresso.

DURHAM *Almshouses* Palace Green, 091-386 1054. Cafeteria close to the cathedral; varied menu, all home-cooking.

And Albert 17 Hallgarth Street, 091-384 1919. Victoriana and a homely atmosphere; good-value bistro cooking.

ROMALDKIRK *Rose and Crown* (0833) 50213. Professionally run pub doing bar meals and a short restaurant menu. Fresh local produce includes fish and game; good selection of home-made puddings.

Cumbria

AMBLESIDE *Sheila's Cottage* The Slack, (053 94) 33079. Pretty cottage restaurant. Popular tourist-spot for afternoon tea.

Wateredge Hotel Borrans Road, (053 94) 32332. English cooking on the shores of Lake Windermere.

APPLEBY *Royal Oak* Bongate, (076 83) 51463. Old pub with a warm welcome; Lancashire shrimps, Cumberland sausage and big breakfasts.

BOWLAND BRIDGE *Masons Arms* Strawberry Bank, Cartmel Fell, Grange-over-Sands, (044 88) 486. A tiny bar but a wide range of beers; lovely pub, wholesome food.

BROUGHTON IN FURNESS *Beswicks* Langholm House, The Square, (0229) 716285. Charming Georgian house that's well-run; good home-cooking, friendly service.

CARLISLE *Crosby Lodge Hotel* Crosby-on-Eden, nr Carlisle, (022 873) 618/9. Family-run manor house boasting good bedrooms and honest cooking.

KESWICK *Maysons* 33 Lake Road, (0768) 774104. Self-service spot for good stews, brown rice and Lakeland ice-cream.

La Primavera Greta Bridge, High Hill, (076 87) 74621. English and Italian cooking close to the river; daily fish deliveries influence the menu.

MARYPORT *Retreat* Birkby, nr Maryport, (0900) 814056. Beat a retreat to Birkby for good, careful home-cooking.

MELMERBY *Shepherds Inn* (0768) 881217. Attractive old pub with well-kept ales and sound bar food; Cumberland sausage and black pudding a speciality.

WATERMILLOCK *Leeming House* (076 84) 86622. In landscaped gardens by Lake Ullswater; run by Forte; luxury ingredients.

Derbyshire

ASHFORD *Riverside Country House Hotel* Fennel Street, (062 981) 4275. Attractive Georgian house in gardens; imaginative dishes with fancy sauces.

BAKEWELL *Green Apple* Diamond Court, Water Street, (0629) 814404. Opening on to a private courtyard, this is hidden away. The short menu plunders many sources, mostly well enough.

BASLOW *Cavendish Hotel* (0246) 582311. Good views over the Chatsworth estate; choice of two restaurants, careful cooking.

BUXTON *Dandelion Days* 5 Bridge Street, (0298) 22843. Family-run vegetarian café above a health-food shop; wholesome choices, organic wines.

MELBOURNE *Bay Tree* 4 Potters Street, (0332) 863358. Good for Sunday lunch; roast lamb, calf's liver with black pudding, lemon and honey ice-cream.

Devon

ASHPRINGTON *Maltsters Arms* Bow Creek, Tuckenhay, nr Ashprington, (0803) 732350. Keith Floyd's enterprise is not your average boozer, but home to serious fish cooking and imaginative menu. Not cheap.

DARTMOUTH *Taylors* 8 The Quay, (0803) 832748. Fresh fish on the menu; friendly service.

DODDISCOMBSLEIGH *Nobody Inn* (0647) 52394. Unspoilt old pub; long and interesting wine and whisky list, wholesome cooking.

EXETER *Esmeraldas* Three Gables, Cathedral Yard, (0392) 214215. Tudor house enjoying cathedral views; terrific home-cooking, good ingredients, friendly service.

GITTISHAM *Combe House* (0404) 42756. Atmospheric Elizabethan manor in beautiful parkland, pursuing careful cooking with well-chosen wines.

KINGSTEIGNTON *Old Rydon Inn* Rydon Road, (0626) 54626. Pub with pretty conservatory and garden; adventurous bar food, real ales.

LUSTLEIGH *Primrose Cottage* (064 77) 365. Charming spot for traditional cream teas and substantial lunches.

PETER TAVY *Peter Tavy Inn* (0822) 810348. Snug pub that's very popular, perhaps for well-kept ales, certainly for wholesome cooking.

PLYMOUTH *Barretts* 27 Princess Street, (0752) 221177. All-day operation, near the theatre; good wines, very up and down cooking.

SALCOMBE *Spinnakers* Fore Street, (0548) 843408. Fresh fish simply cooked, overlooking the bay.

SHEEPWASH *Half Moon* (040 923) 232/ 376. Straightforward cooking in homely environs; roast turkey and all the trimmings.

Dorset

DORCHESTER *Yalbury Cottage* Lower Bockhampton, nr Dorchester, (0305) 262382. Restaurant-with-rooms under thatch; set menu, simple cooking.

MARSHWOOD *Shave Cross Inn* Shave Cross, Marshwood Vale, (0308) 68358. Thatched pub with timbered interior; reliable bar food.

OBORNE *Grange* (0935) 813463. Typical Italian; modest, pleasing results.

TARRANT MONKTON *Langton Arms* (025 889) 225. Good country location; ploughman's and boozy beef pie.

WEYMOUTH *Hamilton's* 5 Brunswick Terrace, (0305) 789544. Plain décor but plenty of decent blackboard choices; good sauces.

WIMBORNE *Les Bouviers* Merley, nr Wimborne, (0202) 889555. Attractive French, competent cooking; *carte* supplemented by daily *menu gourmand*.

East Sussex

ALFRISTON *Moonrakers* High Street, (0323) 870472. Popular, pretty spot cooking a short set-price menu; favourites include hot Sussex smokie and beef Wellington; interesting wines.

BATTLE *Powdermills* Powdermill Lane, (042 46) 5511. Opulent conversion to hotel and restaurant, but reports have been mixed.

BRIGHTON *La Caperon* 113 St Georges Road, Kemp Town, (0273) 680317. Civilised lunch spot complete with fish tank and classical Muzak; wholesome cooking, some organic vegetables, good sweets; cheap.

English's Oyster Bar 29–31 East Street, (0273) 27980. Fresh fish and shellfish on the edge of The Lanes; simple ideas presented well.

EASTBOURNE *Browns* 17 Carlisle Road, (0323) 28837. Relaxed restaurant close to the sea-front; straightforward cooking takes in fresh fish, caramelised duck with orange sauce, excellent vegetables.

Justin's 9 Compton Street, (0323) 22828. Friendly bistro with an imaginative menu.

FLETCHING *Griffin Inn* (0825) 722890. Olde-worlde pub with a good atmosphere but cooking can be variable. Above-average wine list.

HOVE *Le Classique* 37 Waterloo Street, (0273) 734140. Dependable neighbourhood French for reassuring cuisine bourgeois; comfortable ambience, care in the kitchen.

LEWES *Pailin* 20 Station Street, (0273) 473906. Sound Thai cooking from a short menu. Good salads of beef, squid or prawn, panang nue (dry beef curry) and the Pailin 'hotplate' of stir-fried items.

MAYFIELD *Rose & Crown* Fletching Street, (0435) 872200. Go for the bar food rather than the restaurant.

RYE *Monastery* 6 High Street, (0797) 223272. Italian-owned but Anglo-French food; may be quite useful.

TICEHURST *Bull* Three-legged Cross, (0580) 200586. Nice old building, good bar food and big helpings.

WEST FIRLE *Ram* (0273) 858222. Old pub in fine estate village; plain cooking, huge portions, real ales.

Essex

CASTLE HEDINGHAM *Old Moot House* 1 St James Street, (0787) 60342. Elizabethan building; traditional British fare that's worth a try.

Rumbles Castle St James Street, (0787) 61490. Convivial offshoot of Rumbles Cottage, Felsted (see main entry). Pleasing cooking with good incidentals.

CHELMSFORD *Kings Arms* Main Road, Broomfield, nr Chelmsford, (0245) 440258. Half-timbered sixteenth-century inn serving English food.

GOSFIELD *Green Man* (0787) 472746. Country-style cooking includes homemade pâté, English lamb and summer pudding.

HATFIELD PEVEREL *Scotts* Hatfield Cottage, The Street, (0245) 380161. Homely cottage restaurant with a monthly-changing menu.

ROCHFORD *Renoufs* Bradley Way, (0702) 544392. Long-established French with a strong local following; up-and-down cooking; may be useful.

ROXWELL *Farmhouse Feast* The Street, (0245) 248583. Rural location for sound home-cooking; good attention to detail.

SOUTHEND-ON-SEA *Alvaro's* 32–34 St Helen's Road, Westcliff-on-Sea, (0702) 335840. Portuguese cooking, with steaks also served. Selection of Portuguese wines and spirits complements.

Gloucestershire

BLOCKLEY *Crown Inn and Hotel* High Street, (0386) 700245. Comfortable accommodation, well-prepared food.

CHELTENHAM *Finns* 143 Bath Road, (0242) 232109. Modern bistro with conservatory extension; colourful food, plenty of fish, poor vegetables.

CHIPPING CAMPDEN *Greenstocks* The Square, (0386) 840330. Coffee-shop-cum-restaurant; home-made soup, spiced vegetable rissoles, salads.

NAILSWORTH *Stone Cottage* Old Market, (0453) 832808. Charming nooks and crannies interior; fancy ideas and over-elaborate treatment of materials confuses flavours. Stay with the simplest dishes.

TETBURY *Close Hotel* 8 Long Street, (0666) 502272. Fine ingredients but not always fine cooking within Cotswold stone.

TEWKESBURY *New World* 61 High Street, (0684) 292225. Vietnamese-run; long menu, decent sauces; try one of the 'Leave-it-to-us-feasts'.

WINCHCOMBE *Pilgrims Bistro* 6 North Street, (0242) 603544. B&B with a small bistro; home-cooking.

Greater London

HARROW *Percy's* 66–68 Station Road, North Harrow, 081-427 2021. Wine bar that's strictly no-smoking; light, healthy dishes are asterisked on the menu. Great vegetables; espresso coffee.

SOUTHALL *Omi's* 1 Beaconsfield Road, 081-571 4831. Indian; no-frills décor that's more café than restaurant, compensated for by fresh ingredients, mostly vegetarian food, some meat curries.

TWICKENHAM *Cézanne* 68 Richmond Road, 081-892 3526. Restaurant with a café style that seems unable to get it quite right, but can do when it tries.

Greater Manchester

ALTRINCHAM *Franc's* 2 Goose Green, 061-941 3154. French bistro style; good moules, crêpes, croque-monsieurs.

French 24 The Downs, 061-941 3355. Lively joint with a traditional brasserie menu; excellent desserts and value.

MANCHESTER *Bella Napoli* 6A Booth Street, 061-236 1537. Pleasant Italian that's good value and ideal for pre-theatre eating.

Café Primavera 48 Beech Road, Chorlton, 061-862 9934. Modern Mancunian cooking with Mediterranean overtones; its popularity can overstretch kitchen ability.

Chiang Rai 16 Princess Street, 061-237 9511. New Thai restaurant with an extensive vegetarian choice.

City Art Gallery Café Princess Street, 061-236 5244. Self-service spot for depleted picture-gazers; coffees and light lunches.

Luli 428 Cheetham Hill Road, 061-740 9001. Authentic African, drawing on Nigerian, Ghanaian and South African cuisines. Pepper goat soup, pounded yam, washed down with Nigerian lager or guava juice.

Penang Village 56 Faulkner Street, 061-236 2650. Manchester's only Malaysian restaurant; bamboo décor, decent satays, unusual desserts.

Royal Oak Hotel 729 Wilmslow Road, Didsbury, 061-445 3152. Pub famous for its huge choice of cheeses, eaten with chunks of bread.

Royal Orchid 36 Charlotte Street, 061-236 5183. Thai under same ownership as Siam Orchid (see main entry); acceptable cooking, good fish-cakes and satays.

Tung Fong 2 Worsley Road, Worsley, 061-794 5331. Suburban Chinese; smart surroundings and pan-regional cooking. A promising formula but uneven technique.

SALFORD *Punters Bistro* 194 Cromwell Road, 061-792 1490. Culinary frontier post with localised clientele; robust flavours, simple presentation, does get smoky. More reports, please.

Hampshire

ALDERHOLT *Moonacre* (0425) 653142. Fresh ingredients, particularly fish and game, cooked well; home-made walnut bread, roast lamb with quince jelly, lovely puddings.

BASINGSTOKE *Hee's* 23 Westminster House, Town Centre, (0256) 464410/ 460297. Useful Chinese, although service can get frenetic.

BEAULIEU *Montagu Arms* Palace Lane, (0590) 612324. Lovely location, ideal for Sunday lunch; good roasts and sorbets.

BROCKENHURST *Le Blaireau* Lyndhurst Road, (0590) 23032. Authentic French bistro in the New Forest with conservatory seating. Menus to suit all pockets and appetites.

EMSWORTH *36 on the Quay* The Quay, 47 South Street, (0243) 375592. Smart, upholstered surroundings and expensive, elaborate cooking. A new German, Roux-trained chef as we went to press prevented inclusion as a main entry. More reports, please.

EVERSLEY *New Mill* New Mill Road, (0734) 732277. Fine waterside location, mind the ford; great wine list; welcoming service; the cooking could be more defined and confident.

FORDINGBRIDGE *Hour Glass* Burgate, (0425) 652348. Fourteenth-century cottage with warm atmosphere and competent cooking; useful for the area.

GRATELEY *Plough Inn* (026 488) 221. Excellent fresh fish and mussels.

NEW ALRESFORD *Old School House* 60 West Street, (0962) 732134. Imaginative cooking includes speciality breads, sorbets and pleasing puddings.

WINCHESTER *Nine The Square* 9 Great Minster Street, The Square, (0962) 864004. A name change as we went to press; popular wine bar and restaurant with a range of menus; ambitious ideas that partly succeed, some fashionable ingredients; great views of the cathedral.

Hereford & Worcester

BROMSGROVE *Grafton Manor* Grafton Lane, (0527) 579007. Fine place to stay at, the cooking has its heart in the right place but sometimes skips a beat.

EVESHAM *Riverside* The Parks, Offenham Road, (0386) 446200. Hotel on a hill commanding valley views; pleasing cooking.

GLEWSTONE *Glewstone Court* (098 984) 367. Relaxed country house; good raw materials, variable execution.

MARTLEY *Talbot Hotel* Knightwick, nr Martley, (0886) 21235. Sound cooking and friendly service down by the River Teme.

ROSS-ON-WYE *Chase Hotel* Gloucester Road, (0989) 768330. Grand Georgian house in large garden, recently refurbished; careful cooking. More reports, please.

STOURPORT-ON-SEVERN *The Gables* Worcester Road, Great Witley, nr Stourport, (0299) 896944. Schoolhouse conversion cooking traditional English; also a tea-room and craft shop.

Severn Tandoori 11 Bridge Street, (029 93) 3090. North Indian cooking that's mixed, although spicing is good and service pleasant.

VOWCHURCH *Croft Country House* (0981) 550226. Comfortable guesthouse with a no-smoking policy; homely cooking includes fresh ingredients, creamy sauces and the recommended apple fudge pudding.

WEOBLEY *Jules Café* Portland Street, (0544) 318206. Laid-back to the point of nonchalance, the cooking is an imaginative mixed bag in conception and performance.

WHITNEY *Rhydspence Inn* (049 73) 262. Rural pub with lots on the menu; good langoustines, rack of lamb and home-made sweets.

Hertfordshire

BARNET *Wings* 6 Potters Road, 081-449 9890. Pekinese/Szechuan restaurant specialising in crab and lobster, crispy aromatic duck and crispy lamb.

BERKHAMSTED *Regal* 157–159 High Street, (0442) 865940. Pekinese/ Szechuan restaurant smartly decorated; mixed bag menu, mild flavours, seasonal specialities, high on flamboyant presentation.

COTTERED *Bull* (0763) 81243. Pleasant village pub with blackboard specials supplementing a more basic menu.

EAST BARNET *Le Papillon* 236 East Barnet Road, 081-440 7897. Average French; good moules, duck à l'orange, chocolate profiteroles.

HEMEL HEMPSTEAD *Gallery Coffee Shop* Old Town Hall Arts Centre, High Street, (0442) 232416. Much more than a mere coffee-shop, this café provides home-cooking, lunch and some dinners. Oriental fish curry, apple and almond tart.

Spinning Wheel 80 High Street, (0442) 64309. Jazzy bistro menu takes in wild mushroom ravioli and chargrilled cod with roasted peppers. Good value.

Humberside

BARTON-UPON-HUMBER *Elio's* 11 Market Place, (0652) 635147. Pleasant trattoria for good antipasti, Parma ham and fresh fish.

GRIMSBY *Danish Mission* 2 Cleethorpes Road, (0472) 342257. Christian mission feeding more than Scandinavian seamen. Self-service smorgasbord, coffee and sweets in a civilised atmosphere.

Granary 1st Floor, Haven Mill, Garth Lane, (0472) 346338. Grain-mill conversion cooking fish and other blackboard choices; useful for the area.

HORNSEA *When The Boat Comes In* 34 Cliff Road, (0964) 535173. Fresh fish, some steaks, good vegetables and home-made puddings. More reports, please.

SCUNTHORPE *Giovanni's* 44 Oswald Road, (0724) 281169. Good-value Italian that's best for fresh pasta.

Isles of Scilly

ST MARTIN'S *St Martin's Hotel* (0720) 22092. Luxurious yet low-key in an unspoilt setting; prime ingredients, presentation, intelligent service.

ST MARY'S *Tregarthens* (0720) 22540. Competent cooking and generous portions at this hotel; handy for the locale.

TRESCO *New Inn* (0720) 22844. Small pub with garden; simple bar lunches.

Isle of Wight

COWES *Sullivan's* The Parade, (0983) 297021. Small, pink restaurant. Fresh ingredients, including some fish and seafood, but sauces can be poor.

RYDE *Seaview Hotel and Restaurant* High Street, Seaview, (0983) 612711. Comfortable seaside hotel recently refurbished that's children-friendly. Both restaurant and bar food, locally caught fish and shellfish.

Kent

BARHAM *Old Coach House* Dover Road, (0227) 831218. Basic French roadside

restaurant-with-rooms; plain cooking, sometimes skimping on materials.

BIDDENDEN *Three Chimneys* (0580) 291472. Old pub that's a regular warren; well-kept real ales and wholesome bar meals, rich desserts.

CANTERBURY *Stowaways* Cogan House, 53 St Peter's Street, (0227) 764459. Ancient house with charming garden, hidden away; oyster bar, seafood restaurant, also does teas.

IVY HATCH *Plough* Coach Road, (0732) 810268. Assured bar food and more expensive conservatory dining-room.

TUNBRIDGE WELLS *Sankey's at the Gate* 39 Mount Ephraim, (0892) 511422. Unpretentious venue for fresh seafood and fish simply cooked; succeeds in part, though vegetables and coffee can be poor.

Lancashire

BLACKPOOL *Lagoonda* 37 Queen Street, (0253) 293837. Afro-Caribbean restaurant; good sauces, friendly service. More reports, please.

CRAWSHAW BOOTH *Valley Restaurant* 542 Burnley Road, (0706) 831728. Set menu with several choices; good home-cooking includes Normandy woodpigeon, hazelnut fish trio and double chicken pasta.

HASLINGDEN *Hazel Tree* 32 Manchester Road, (0706) 211530. Friendly place for English cooking with some Danish influences; more pronounced at weekday lunches and the once-weekly koltbord.

LANCASTER *Libra* 19 Brock Street, (0524) 61551. Wholesome vegetarian cooking setting high standards.

Sultan of Lancaster (0524) 61188. Beautifully converted evangelical chapel, now an Islamic restaurant, unlicensed.

LYTHAM ST ANNE'S *C'est la Vie* Dalmeny Hotel, 19–33 South Promenade, (0253) 712236. Useful seaside spot with a daily-changing set-price menu; quality ingredients imaginatively prepared.

MELLOR *Devonshire Arms* Longhurst Lane, 061-427 2563. Enterprising cooking of substantial and genuine food. Popular and friendly.

WHITEWELL *Inn at Whitewell* Forest of Bowland, (020 08) 222. Picturesque location for a popular pub; Cumberland sausage, home-made pies, wide range of wines.

Leicestershire

BOTTESFORD *La Petite Maison* 1 Market Street, (0949) 42375. Converted butcher's shop now cooking good things at fair prices.

EMPINGHAM *White Horse* Main Street, (078 086) 221/521. Refurbished stone pub; bar food makes use of local ham, cheeses and trout. Pleasing puddings.

LEICESTER *Bread and Roses* 70 High Street, (0533) 532448. Wholefood café with some Middle Eastern snacks; full menu now confined to evenings.
Sayonara 49 Belgrave Road, (0533) 665888. Vegetarian thali restaurant. More reports, please.
Water Margin 76–78 High Street, (0533) 516422. Chinese best for lunchtime dim-sum and one-plate meals; reasonable quality, though rather slow service.

LOUGHBOROUGH *Rafferty's* 11–12 Sparrow Hill, (0509) 231813. Attractive, old manor housing a brasserie-style operation. Salads, chargrilling, spicy sauces and rich desserts much in evidence.

REDMILE *Peacock Inn* Church Corner, (0949) 42554. Relaxed pub with frilly restaurant, also doing bar meals; good portions, pleasant service.

STRETTON *Ram Jam Inn* Great North Road, (0780) 410776. Haven for travellers on the A1; open all day for breakfasts, meals and snacks. Good ingredients on an interesting menu; excellent cappuccino.

UPPINGHAM *Lake Isle* 16 High Street East, (0572) 822951. Comfortable rooms; short set-price menu of fresh things that may occasionally be let down by sauces and uneven cooking. Excellent, all-encompassing wine list.

WALCOTE *Black Horse* Lutterworth Road, (0455) 552684. Traditional pub serving Thai food; short, accessible menu of curries, Thai mixed grill, stir-fries. Reasonable prices.

Lincolnshire

GEDNEY DYKE *Chequers* Main Street, (0406) 362666. Pub restaurant; decent menu includes a good banoffi pie.

HORNCASTLE *Mantles* 19 Lawrence Street, The Market Place, (0507) 526726. Fresh fish, seafood and superlative chips; eat in or take away. Licensed.

LINCOLN *Browns Pie Shop* 33 Steep Hill, (0522) 527330. Friendly place serving prime pies, also Lincolnshire sausage hotpot, East Coast seafood bake and pease pudding.

LOUTH *Ferns* 40 Northgate, (0507) 603209. Unprepossessing décor but a useful straightforward menu. Home-cooking, all-organic wine list.

NEWTON *Red Lion* (052 97) 256. Good beer, cold table, nicely served.

Merseyside

BIRKENHEAD *Pastime* 42 Hamilton Square, 051-647 8095. Basement restaurant; dull décor and contrived menu but competent enough cooking.

BOOTLE *Rui's* 13 Aintree Road, 051-922 1212. Almost entirely Italian menu, modest décor, useful for the area.

HESWALL *Crispins* 106 Telegraph Road, 051-342 8750. Continental dishes and a fair-priced set menu; sound cooking, good incidentals.

HOYLAKE *Lino's* 122 Market Street, 051-632 1408. A menu that's mostly French in influence; duck with chestnuts, almonds and brandy, chocolate marquise.

LIVERPOOL *Everyman Bistro* 9–11 Hope Street, 051-708 9545. Basic, licensed self-service cellar handy for theatre-goers; fresh salads, some vegetarian dishes and wonderful desserts.
Grande Bouffe 48A Castle Street, 051-236 3375. Busy bistro that continues to draw a lunchtime business crowd.

SOUTHPORT *Nostalgia* 215–217 Lord Street, (0704) 501294. Busy tea-rooms offering a wide range of beverages, light lunches and cakes; stay with the simpler confections.

Norfolk

FOULSHAM *Gamp* Claypit Lane, (036 284) 4114. Wholesome cooking decently priced; traditional Sunday lunch.

GREAT YARMOUTH *Waterside* Riverside, Cess Road, Martham, nr Great Yarmouth, (0493) 740881. Down a quiet river track; fresh fish simply done, from octopus to green-lipped mussels to lobster. Home-baked puddings.

LITTLE WALSINGHAM *Old Bakehouse* 33 High Street, (0328) 820454. Good B&B stop, popular restaurant with substantial old-fashioned cooking and limitless vegetables. Big portions.

NORWICH *Sam's* 58 Bethel Street, (0603) 627472. Diminutive restaurant with a short menu; able cooking and presentation; game terrine, brill with a langoustine coulis, fresh pasta.

Waffle House 39 St Giles, (0603) 612790. Fast and friendly, fresh ingredients, cheap.

STIFFKEY *Red Lion* (0328) 830552. Flint pub, real fire, blackboard menu; beef and ale pie, lamb's liver with bacon.

SWAFFHAM *Stratton's Hotel* Ash Close, (0760) 23845. Small, smart country-house hotel; sauces can overwhelm but ingredients are local, herbs from the garden.

UPPER SHERINGHAM *Red Lion Inn* The Street, (0263) 825408. Simple well-cooked food; split-pea and ham soup, crab salad, roast pork with crackling.

WEST RUNTON *Mirabelle* 7 Station Road, (0263) 837396. Straightforward cooking at affordable prices, takes in poached salmon on a lobster sauce and Norfolk duckling.

WYMONDHAM *Number Twenty Four* 24 Middleton Street, (0953) 607750. Restaurant and delicatessen; good ingredients, many local. Also does teas.

Northamptonshire

BYFIELD *Olinjkis* 49 Boddington Road, (0327) 60213. Curious Russian restaurant; some rich, Czarist dishes, some Balkan, and some concession to Western tastes.

CRICK *Edwards of Crick* The Wharf, (0788) 822517. Canalside coffee-house and restaurant with a choice of menus. Still cooking well.

FOTHERINGHAY *Falcon Inn* Main Street, (083 26) 254. Enlarged dining-room in an old pub; good cold table, finish with home-made syllabub or meringue.

KILSBY *Hunt House* High Street, (0788) 823282. Old hunting-lodge now turned over to cooking. Trout, steak and cream-laden sweets; vast collection of malt whiskies.

NORTHAMPTON *Ristorante Ca' d'Oro* 334 Wellingborough Road, (0604) 32660. Useful for decent pasta and espresso rather than the rest on the menu.

OUNDLE *Ship Inn* 18 West Street, (0832) 273918. Old-fashioned, filling bar food and well-kept ales.

STOKE BRUERNE *Bruerne's Lock* The Canalside, (0604) 863654. Young team running a canalside restaurant. English and Continental cooking, good atmosphere and attention to detail.

Northumberland

BERWICK-UPON-TWEED *Rob Roy* Dock Road, Tweedmouth, (0289) 306428. Fresh fish and excellent seafood.

CORBRIDGE *Corbridge Tandoori* 8 Market Place, (0434) 633676. Luxurious surroundings, first-rate service and all for the price of an ordinary curry house.

SEATON SLUICE *Waterford Arms* Collywell Bay Road, 091-237 0450. Basic food, of variable quality but big portions please some.

WARENFORD *Warenford Lodge* (0668) 213453. Old stone house with an open fire; excellent bar snacks include devilled crabmeat with toast, mussels in garlic and apricot crumble flan.

WARKWORTH *Jackdaw* 34 Castle Street, (0665) 711488. Café/restaurant for fresh fish and chocolate mousse pudding at fair prices.

Nottinghamshire

HUCKNALL *Longdale Rural Craft Centre* Longdale Lane, Ravenshead, (0623) 794858. Café in quiet countryside, catering well for vegetarians.

NETHER LANGWITH *Goff's* Langwith Mill House, Langwith Road, (0623) 744538. Delightful setting for consistent cooking; quality ingredients, good sauces, sticky toffee pudding.

NEWARK *Le Gourmet* Castle Gate House, 14 Castle Gate, (0636) 610141. Airy French bistro by the River Trent. Good-value set lunch; salad niçoise, chocolate mousse with coffee-bean sauce.

NOTTINGHAM *Jack Spratts* Heathcote Street, (0602) 410710. Modern décor and menu listing the likes of grilled sardines, spinach and feta strudel, couscous and cranberry chocolate trifle. More reports, please.

Ocean City 100–104 Derby Road, (0602) 475095. Chinese; Cantonese classics plus some innovations. Lunchtime dim-sum and one-plate meals.

Le Tetard 10 Pilcher Gate, (0602) 598253. Professionally run bistro high on presentation; competent cooking.

North Yorkshire

EAST WITTON *Blue Lion* (0969) 24273. Georgian house encasing pleasant pub; ambitious cooking features fresh game and fish. Prices match Yorkshire parsimony.

HARROGATE *La Bergerie* 11–13 Mount Parade, (0423) 500089. Stark restaurant in a quiet terrace. Some really good combinations needing better timing and execution. Successful desserts.

Bettys 1 Parliament Street, (0423) 502746. The original tea-rooms of this now illustrious chain; traditional teas and good savouries.

Lords 8 Montpelier Street, (0423) 508762. Busy wine bar with a cricketing theme; garlic mushrooms, brill, pork fillet in a pastry case.

HELMSLEY *Black Swan* Market Place, (0439) 70466. Comfortable accommodation – despite creaking floorboards – from Forte; competent enough cooking, good breakfasts.

NORTHALLERTON *Bettys* 188 High Street, (0609) 775154. Smaller branch of the famous tea-rooms; worth queueing for the cream teas and cakes.

RIPON *Old Deanery* Minster Road, (0765) 603518. Lovely atmosphere, pleasing cooking, home-baked bread, next to the cathedral.

SCORTON *St Cuthbert's Inn* Station Road, (0748) 811631. Small country pub with a long menu and daily specials; tasty sauces.

SKIPTON *Oats* Chapel Hill, (0756) 798118. Smart restaurant and hotel with an interesting menu; fresh egg tagliatelle, wild mushrooms in cream and garlic, red mullet.

THIRSK *Crab & Lobster* Dishforth Road, Asenby, nr Thirsk, (0845) 577286. Attractive old pub with an interesting selection of fish. Worth watching.

YORK *Bettys* 6–8 St Helen's Square, (0904) 659142. Cosmopolitan branch of the traditional tea-rooms. Sit in style for speciality teas, coffees and light meals, not forgetting cakes.

Partners 13A Ousegate, (0904) 627929. Good ingredients and realistic prices for a choice of menu with daily specials.

Oxfordshire

ABINGDON *Chez Joël* 17A Bridge Street, (0235) 521788. Small French bistro and restaurant covering a range of traditional dishes.

GREAT TEW *Falkland Arms* (060 883) 653. Atmospheric pub in a perfect spot; bar food takes in sandwiches, ploughman's and hot dishes of the day.

KINGHAM *Mill House Hotel & Restaurant* (0608) 658188. Homely, with quiet style; straightforward, pleasing cooking.

MARSH BALDON *Seven Stars* (086 738) 255. Village pub with farm origins offering an interesting menu.

OXFORD *Browns* 5–11 Woodstock Road, (0865) 511995. Long-standing Oxford favourite. Food is fun, hot salads are good, all portions huge. No bookings, and despite lots of tables expect to queue.

Le Petit Parisien 29 George Street, (0865) 726036. Go for the couscous and north African food. Fair value and some of it's good.

Thai Orchid 58A St Clements Street, (0865) 798044. Pleasant Thai with conservatory addition; mild flavours, good vegetarian menu.

SHIPTON-UNDER-WYCHWOOD *Lamb Inn* High Street, (0993) 830465. Traditional pub fare; choose fresh fish when available, otherwise roasts and treacle tart are mainstays.

SHRIVENHAM *Thatchers* 13 High Street, (0793) 783848. Small thatched cottage concentrating on traditional fare. Game, good sauces, tempting desserts.

STANDLAKE *Bell* 2 High Street, (0865) 300657. Refurbished pub with a blackboard menu; sound bar meals include home-made pies and fruit crumbles with custard.

WALLINGFORD *Trapp's Table* The Cellars, Lamb Arcade, (0491) 39606. Former wine vaults now given over to cooking; intimate atmosphere, good wines.

Shropshire

DITTON PRIORS *Howard Arms* (074 634) 200. Difficult to find but worth it for pleasant atmosphere and food.

EASTHOPE *Wenlock Edge Inn* Hilltop, (074 636) 403. Family-run pub much frequented by walkers; traditional fare with some good puddings, interesting wines.

HOPTON CASTLE *Park Cottage* (054 74) 351. Comfortable restaurant-with-rooms down the lane from the ruined castle keep. Sound country cooking, good incidentals, vegetables from the garden.

LUDLOW *Feathers at Ludlow* Bull Ring, (0584) 875261. Spotless hotel for sound cooking; roast duckling, Shropshire Figet pie, vegetarian choices.

MINSTERLEY *Stables* Drury Lane, Hope, nr Minsterley, (0743) 891344. Lovely pub enjoying long views; bar food with occasional barbecues.

OSWESTRY *Sebastian* 45 Willow Street, (0691) 655444. Useful spot for fresh fish, seafood, espresso coffee.

SHIFNAL *Odfellows* Star Hotel, 11 Market Place, (0952) 461517. Informal surroundings; traditional Sunday roast and other blackboard items.

TELFORD *Madeley Court Hotel* (0952) 680068. Medieval house retaining old charm; modern cooking features fish and game.

Somerset

MONKSILVER *Notley Arms* (0984) 56217. Quality bar food in the Quantocks catering for healthy appetites.

NORTH PERROTT *Manor Arms* (0460) 72901. Very popular pub; choice of bar or restaurant menu, fresh ingredients, careful presentation.

SOUTH PETHERTON *Royal Oak* Over Stratton, nr South Petherton, (0460) 40906. Friendly, oak-beamed pub; seafood pasta, home-made steak and kidney pie.

TAUNTON *Capriccio* 41 Bridge Street, (0823) 335711. Reliable Italian; excellent cold meats, fresh pasta, good sauces, espresso coffee.

Orchards Wrexon Farmhouse, Dipford Road, (0823) 275440. Well-preserved fifteenth-century farmhouse; sound English cooking and a good sweets trolley.

WELLINGTON *Hartleys* 41 High Street, (0823) 667646. Attractive, eighteenth-century house; enthusiastic cooking of mainly fish and seafood. Oriental influences are another strong point.

YEOVIL *La Chouette* 12 Bond Street, (0935) 20804. Small French-inspired restaurant, only open evenings; good ingredients reasonably cooked.

South Yorkshire

DONCASTER *Woods' Tea Rooms* 3A Wood Street, (0302) 327126. Classic North Country tea-room open for breakfast, lunch and teas. All is home-made, fine coffees, well-chosen wines.

SHEFFIELD *Parkes-La Bonne Bouche* 130 Pennistone Road North, (0742) 338388. Small bistro-type affair attracting a local following.

Just Cooking 16–18 Carver Street, (0742) 727869. Self-service place that's good for simple lunches; broccoli quiche, courgette lasagne, bread-and-butter pudding.

Staindrop Lodge Lane End, Chapeltown, (0742) 846727. Frequently changing menu, interesting vegetables, good sweets, in an old converted mansion.

TICKHILL *Forge* 1 Sunderland Street, (0302) 744122. Fancy combinations and Anglo-French food.

Staffordshire

BRANSTON *Old Vicarage* 2 Main Street, (0283) 33222. Well-run restaurant using good-quality materials to good effect.

LICHFIELD *Eastern Eye* 19B Bird Street, (0543) 254399. Reliable Indian serving decent thalis. Drink Kingfisher lager, don't mind the dingy lighting.

PENKRIDGE *William Harding's House* Mill Street, (0785) 712955. Small restaurant with some local support.

STONE *Granvilles* 3–5 Granville Square, (0785) 816658. Acceptable wine bar and restaurant with live music some nights.

Suffolk

BURY ST EDMUNDS *Angel Hotel* 3 Angel Hill, (0284) 753926. Old coaching-inn marrying traditional European dishes with more far-flung influences, from a German chef.

IPSWICH *Kwok's Rendezvous* 23 St Nicholas Street, (0473) 256833. Small but considered menu, fine wine list.

LAVENHAM *Angel* Market Place, (0787) 247388. Well-preserved pub; home-cured bream and Suffolk apple flan worth trying.

LONG MELFORD *Chimneys* Hall Street, (0787) 79806. Smart surroundings and Tudor beams; cooking can vary, but still pleases some.

Countrymen Black Lion, The Green, (0787) 79951/312356. Friendly hotel and fair cooking.

REDE *Plough* (028 489) 208. Thatched pub in a tranquil spot; Hungarian-style venison and strawberry royale are recommended.

SNAPE *Golden Key* Priory Road, (072 888) 510. In winter a large log fire, in summer chairs in the garden; relaxing pub for fine bar snacks and well-kept ales.

WALBERSWICK *Mary's* Manor House, (0502) 723243. Good for fresh fish but don't expect haute cuisine.

WOODBRIDGE *Wine Bar* 17 Thoroughfare, (0394) 382557. Good wines, potentially interesting food, idiosyncratic atmosphere.

Surrey

CROYDON *Willow* 88 Selsdon Park Road, Addington, nr Croydon, 081-657 4656. Chinese close to Croydon; crispy seaweed, aromatic crispy duck, sizzling dishes.

EWHURST *Windmill Inn* Pitch Hill, (0483) 277566. Expensive, smart pub serving good food, with wonderful views overlooking the South Downs.

FARNHAM *Krug's* 84 West Street, (0252) 723277. Austrian cooking takes in goulash, wiener schnitzel and good desserts, although service can be slow.

GUILDFORD *Rumwong* 16–18 London Road, (0483) 36092. Refined Thai restaurant employing fresh herbs and spices through an extensive menu.

RICHMOND *Cantina* 32 The Quadrant, 081-332 6262. More Mexican than most, some fair cooking and plenty of chillies.

SOUTH GODSTONE *Bonne Auberge* Tilburstow Hill Road, (0342) 893184. Modern French restaurant in attractive grounds. Popular dishes include scallops with ginger and orange and roast breast of duck.

WEYBRIDGE *Colony* 3 Balfour Road, (0932) 842766. Reliable Chinese in the suburbs; seaweed and salt and pepper prawns to chilli beef and steamed sole. *L'Ecluse* 10 Woodham Lane, New Haw, nr Weybridge, (0932) 858709. Basic décor, fair French cuisine, desserts the strongest point.

Tyne & Wear

NEWCASTLE UPON TYNE *Café Procope* 35 The Side, Quayside, 091-232 3848. Laid-back atmosphere and a homespun assortment of global village dishes. *Cooperage* 32 The Close, Quayside, 091-232 8286. Crooked, four-storey fourteenth-century house. Lots of character and genuine home-cooked pub food; kedgeree, black pudding with sausage, spicy chicken risotto. *Daraz* 4 Holly Avenue West, Jesmond, 091-281 8431. Popular local curry house; some interesting specials, fresh and vivid spicing. *Eastern Taste* 277 Stanhope Street, Fenham, 091-273 9406. Indian tandoori that's both reliable and cheap. Well-spiced food from two hardworking young brothers. *Ming Dynasty* 41 Stowell Street, 091-261 5787. Impressively revamped and the current front runner in Newcastle's Chinatown. Dim-sum and one-plate dishes through to large menu of old Cantonese and new-wave Peking, and Szechuan. More reports, please. *Rupali* 6 Bigg Market, 091-232 8629. Good-value, ebullient Indian restaurant; a long menu includes Singhalese, Malaysian, Nawabi and Akbari sections alongside more familiar dishes. *Tandoori Nights* 17 Grey Street, 091-221 0312. Smart décor and competent north Indian and Punjabi cooking. Reasonable prices and a choice of thalis. *Vujon* 29 Queen Street, 091-221 0601. Upmarket, fashionable face of Indian cooking in Newcastle. Eclectic, modern menu that sometimes succeeds; pricey.

Warwickshire

LEAMINGTON SPA *Balti Kitchen* Lesters Leisure Centre, Spencer Street, (0926) 311142. Incongruous site for a balti-house – in a leisure centre. Spotlessly clean, lively atmosphere, fantastic breads, food authentically served.

RUGBY *Occasions* 239 Lower Hillmorton Road, (0788) 547548. Small, friendly restaurant cooking fair English food.

RYTON-ON-DUNSMORE *Ryton Gardens Café* National Centre for Organic Gardening, Wolston Lane, (0203) 303517. Everything used is organic, some of it comes from the gardens; leek croustade, French onion tart, good cakes. Currently being expanded.

STRATFORD-UPON-AVON *Opposition* 13 Sheep Street, (0789) 269980. Unpretentious place useful for theatre-goers. Fresh things, simply cooked; friendly service.

WARWICK *Fanshawe's* 22 Market Place, (0926) 410590. Small restaurant with an enthusiastic menu. Some good raw materials, particularly fish, but sauces can sometimes let the side down.

West Midlands

BIRMINGHAM *Adil* 148–150 Stoney Lane, Sparkbrook, 021-449 0335. High-profile brand leader of the balti-houses. *Chung Ying Garden* 17 Thorp Street, 021-666 6622. Chinese that's back on form, although service can be slow. *Loon Fung* 37–41 Pershore Street, 021-622 7395/5056. Chinese that's best at lunch for an impressive range of dim-sum and one-plate rice and noodle dishes. Evenings, cooking is less assured. *Le Provençal* 1 Albany Road, Harborne, 021-426 2444. Fair French that's useful for the area. Cheap wines. *Punjab Paradise* 377 Ladypool Road, 021-449 4110. Civilised Indian balti-house; good mutton tikka, passable baltis.

STOURBRIDGE *French Connection* 1–3 Coventry Street, (0384) 390940. Reliable Gallic cooking and a frequently changing menu. Take-home dinner service from the delicatessen next door.

West Sussex

BURPHAM *George and Dragon* (0903) 883131. Charming pub down a very narrow lane. Good choice of menu, fine desserts including bannofi pie.
WEST HOATHLY *Cat Inn* North Lane, (0342) 810369. Old smugglers pub with an interesting menu, cooked with flair. Save room for mouthwatering desserts.
WORTHING *Paragon* 9–10 Brunswick Road, (0903) 233367. Unpretentious cooking that seems to please; fresh poached salmon, lime sorbet, sweets from the trolley.

West Yorkshire

BRADFORD *Bharat* 502 Great Horton Road, (0274) 521200. Popular tandoori restaurant with good breads and a middle-of-the-road menu.
Hansa's 44 Great Norton Road, (0274) 730433. Sister restaurant to Hansa's in Leeds; interesting starters, less fascinating mains, finish with spicy semolina with pistachios.
Royal Eastern Brighouse Road, (0274) 818766. Expensively furnished, with prices that match. Fresh ingredients, authentically treated.
GUISELEY *Harry Ramsden's* White Cross, (0943) 874641. Enjoy superior fish and chips, followed by trifle or ginger steamed pudding.
HUDDERSFIELD *Ramsden's Landing* Aspley Wharf, Wakefield Road, (0484) 544250. Big, bustling brasserie overlooking the canal. An eclectic menu, fresh ingredients, local cheeses.
ILKLEY *Bettys* 32–34 The Grove, (0943) 608029. One of the famous tea-shops, open till evening for omelettes, filled rolls, light meals and peerless cakes.
Rombalds West View, Wells Road, (0943) 603201. Small hotel on the edge of the moors. Simple bar snacks, buffet lunches, set dinners with elaborate trimmings.

LEEDS *Bryans* 9 Westwood Lane, Headingley, (0532) 785679. Superior fish and chips in Leeds suburbs. Eat in or take away.
Darbar 16–17 Kirkgate, (0532) 460381. Reliable tandoori offering great-value buffet lunch; lamb curry, pakoras and duck have all pleased.
Haley's Shire Oak Road, Headingley, (0532) 784446. Hotel and restaurant with period décor and a sense of occasion. Fancy ideas sometimes outshine results.
Salvo's 115 Otley Road, Headingley, (0532) 755017. Jolly Italian; good bruschetta, linguine and pizzas; not expensive.
SHELLEY *Three Acres Inn* Roydhouse, (0484) 602606. Family-run pub doing bar and restaurant meals; grilled goats' cheese salad, poached turbot, mille-feuille of salmon and king scallops.
SOWERBY BRIDGE *Java* Wharf Street, (0422) 831654. Indonesian restaurant with ethnic décor. Interesting food, try one of the set meals.
WENTBRIDGE *Wentbridge House* (0977) 620444. Despite sometimes rushed service, sound English cooking has been enjoyed.

Wiltshire

ALDBOURNE *Raffles* 1 The Green, (0672) 40700. Reliable cooking using quality materials, delicious poussin, good vegetables, reasonable prices.
BRADFORD-ON-AVON *Dandy Lion* 35 Market Street, (022 16) 3433. Pleasant pub with upstairs restaurant. Pink trout with tarragon mayonnaise, spicy lamb, brown bread ice-cream and raspberry tart with clotted cream.
BRINKWORTH *Three Crowns* (066 641) 366. Large blackboard menu, fresh fish, good seafood pie, plentiful vegetables. Conservatory addition creates space.
LACOCK *At the Sign of the Angel* Church Street, (0249) 730230. Fifteenth-century merchant's house in a National Trust village, with restaurant and accommodation. Roasts, Yorkshire

pudding, dark and white chocolate mousse.

MARLBOROUGH *Moran's* 2–3 London Road, (0672) 512405. Consistent cooking and a monthly-changing menu takes in home-made soups, fresh fish, flambéeing and rich sauces.

SALISBURY *Just Brahms* 68 Castle Street, (0722) 328402. Bistro with a choice of eating areas. Good home-cooking, imaginative sauces and desserts.

Scotland

ABERDEEN (Grampian) *Wild Boar* 19 Belmont Street, (0224) 624216. Popular, informal spot with regularly changing art exhibitions. Lunch includes salads, quiche, burgers and baguettes. Evenings are more ambitious, with vegetarian options.

ABERLOUR (Grampian) *Archiestown Hotel* By Aberlour, (034 06) 218. Comfortable hotel; fresh, local ingredients simply cooked; cold sea trout with dill mayonnaise, devilled chicken livers.

AYR (Strathclyde) *Fouter's Bistro* 2A Academy Street, (0292) 261391. Pleasing bistro fare, decent wines, finish with bread-and-butter pudding. .

BALLATER (Grampian) *Green Inn* 9 Victoria Road, (033 97) 55701. Unpretentious place cooking well; langoustine bisque, venison in bramble sauce, excellent desserts include chocolate marquise and sticky toffee pudding.

BRODICK (Strathclyde) *Creeler's* The Home Farm, Brodick, Isle of Arran, (0770) 2810. Small croft development housing plainly built restaurant and shop. Fresh fish and seafood cooked to order.

BRAE (Shetland) *Busta House* (080 622) 506. Baronial-style house that's been tastefully refurbished; fresh produce accurately cooked, including wide range of fish.

CARNAN (Western Isles) *Orasay Inn* Loch Carnan, South Uist, (087 04) 298.

Basic building on a beautiful, if bleak, island. Very fresh fish, good sauces, large helpings, friendly service.

DORNOCH (Highland) *Mallin House Hotel* Church Street, (0862) 810335. Plain post-war hotel that's useful for the area, cooking fresh fish and venison with rich sauces.

DUFFTOWN (Grampian) *Taste of Speyside* 10 Balvenie Street, (0340) 20860. First-class ingredients; carrot soup, smoked venison, home-made honey and whisky cheesecake, good coffee.

DULNAIN BRIDGE (Highland) *Auchendean Lodge Hotel* (047 985) 347. Edwardian hunting-lodge in a spectacular setting; evening meals cooked to order; Cullen skink, wild hare with rowan jelly, good cheeses, traditional breakfasts.

EDINBURGH (Lothian) *Chez Jules* 1 Craig's Close, 29 Cockburn Street, 031-225 7007. Pierre Levicky's latest; subterranean French with few frills, short menu, decent cooking, keen prices, fast service.

Cosmo Ristorante 58A North Castle Street, 031-226 6743. Dated businessmen's bolt-hole, but good seafood pasta and fish. Dull sweets, excellent wine list, espresso.

Cuisine d'Odile 13 Randolph Terrace, 031-225 5366. In the basement of the French Institute; imaginative and cheap dishes such as mushroom and lettuce soup, ragoût with rice, almond and pistachio tart. Only open weekday lunch.

Doric Tavern 15 Market Street, 031-225 1084. Sound, if unremarkable, bistro cooking; vegetable satay, seawolf stir-fry with black-bean sauce, pasta.

Dubh Prais 123B High Street, 031-557 5732. Small restaurant and an ambitious Scottish menu; lots of game and seafood, competently cooked.

Grain Store 30 Victoria Street, 031-225 7635. Inventive home-cooking in simple surroundings; warm duck liver salad, deep-fried chèvre salad, saddle of hare, marvellous puddings. More reports, please.

Indian Cavalry Club 3 Atholl Place, 031-228 3282. Upmarket Indian with smart décor and service. Inconsistent cooking but it mostly pleases; seafood banquet recommended.

Pukhet-Penang 176 Rose Street, 031-220 0059. Reliable Thai restaurant that's not expensive.

Spices 110 West Bow, 031-225 5028. Sister restaurant to Kalpna (see main entry, Edinburgh); tastefully decorated Indian, long, reasonably priced menu. More reports, please.

FORT WILLIAM (Highland) *Inverlochy Castle* Tor Lundy, (0397) 702177. A wonderful site, great luxury, but prices can be high.

GLASGOW (Strathclyde) *Ambala* Maxwell Road, 041-429 5620. Tiny Pakistani café with just four tables. Authentic cooking includes slow-cooked stews and tandoori roti. Take-aways also available.

Barbizon Brasserie 44 High Street, 041-552 2070. Gallery/café with a large bar. Eclectic offerings include salmon sausages, tagliatelle with courgette and lemon pine-nuts, trout in watercress sauce.

La Bavarde 19 New Kirk Road, Bearsden, 041-942 2202. Good value and an interesting repertoire; home-baked bread, pasta, pigeon pie.

Colonial India 25 High Street, 041-552 1923/6782. Good Karahi cooking, breads and vegetarian section. Not neccessarily cheap.

Namat Kadah 328 Maxwell Road, 041-429 0693. Small, basic restaurant cooking homely Pakistani dishes, high on flavour.

La Parmigiana 447 Great Western Road, Kelvinbridge, 041-334 0686. Small, popular Italian where everything's fresh; home-made pasta with ceps, wild pigeon, creamy sweets.

Scoff's Argyll Hotel, 969–973 Sauchiehall Street, 041-357 4711. Reasonably priced, robust meals; pheasant pâté, crab soup, roast duck, charlotte russe.

Two Fat Ladies 88 Dumbarton Road, 041-339 1944. Small, sparsely decorated restaurant looking on to the kitchen; mostly fish cooking – cod, halibut, sea trout, red snapper – with meat and vegetarian options.

HARRIS (Isle of Harris) *Ardvourlie Castle* Ard a Mhulaidh, nr Harris, (0859) 2307. Friendly, family-run lodge, home-cooking, fresh ingredients.

HELMSDALE (Highland) *Navidale House* (043 12) 258. Views of the Moray Firth, comfortable bedrooms, fresh fish and shellfish, good sauces and sweets.

ISLE ORNSAY (Highland) *Kinloch Lodge* Isle Ornsay, Isle of Skye, off A851 between Broadford and Armadale, (047 13) 214/333. Hotel and restaurant; great for nature study.

KELSO (Borders) *Sunlaws House Hotel* Heiton, nr Kelso, (0573) 5331. Country-house hotel with much history behind it; laudable ambitions partly realised, acceptable cooking but low on flair.

KILCHRENAN (Strathclyde) *Ardanaiseig Hotel* (086 63) 333. Lovely views overlooking Loch Awe; competent cooking includes toasted goats' cheese salad, smoked halibut, Scottish cheeses.

KILFINAN (Strathclyde) *Kilfinan Hotel* Tighnabruaich, nr Kilfinan, (070 082) 201. Old coaching-inn in remote location. Pleasing gravlax, Stilton baked in filo pastry, strawberry shortbread with bramble sauce.

MELROSE (Borders) *Marmion's Brasserie* Buccleuch Street, (0896 82) 2245. Lunch is the best bet for good home-cooking; casseroles, couscous, pasta. Charming service.

Melrose Station Restaurant Palma Place, (089 682) 2546. Old ticket hall now given over to self-service restaurant. Lunch options include quiche, salads and cakes. Dinner available Friday and Saturday.

NAIRN (Highland) *Longhouse* (0667) 55532. Simple yet successful cooking; local smoked salmon, roast lamb, burnt raspberry cream.

SPEAN BRIDGE (Highland) *Old Pines Guest House* Gairlochy Road, (039 781) 324. Open to non-residents though often booked up; short menu features fresh trout, wild venison, good desserts. Unlicensed, but bring your own.

STAFFIN (Highland) *Flodigarry Country House Hotel* Isle of Skye, (047 052) 203. Scottish home-cooking featuring fresh, local ingredients, decent sauces and sustaining breakfasts.

TARBERT (Strathclyde) *Anchorage* Harbour Street, (0880) 820881. Charming, informal spot specialising in fish and shellfish.

ULLAPOOL (Highland) *Ceilidh Place* 14 West Argyle Street, (0854) 612103. Unusual set-up – hotel and restaurant with bookshop and café – suiting all pockets. Good ingredients include local shellfish and fish. Vegetarian options.

Wales

ABERDOVEY (Gwynedd) *Old Coffee Shop* 13 New Street, (0654) 767652. Charming, well-known spot for wholesome lunches and peerless cakes; dark chocolate fudge cake and cherry and almond frangipane recommended.

BANGOR (Gwynedd) *Water's Edge* Gorad-y-Gyt, Gorad Road, (0248) 364672. Hard to find but worth it for beautiful waterside location with views of the Menai Straits. Service may be slow; good desserts.

BRECHFA (Dyfed) *Ty Mawr* (0267) 202332. Small, comfortable hotel that's well-run; pleasing cooking features cheese soufflé, noisettes of Welsh lamb with laverbread sauce, bread-and-butter pudding.

CARDIFF (South Glamorgan) *Bengal Brasserie* 147 Cowbridge Road, (0222) 226687. Reliable Indian restaurant.

Blas-ar-Cymru 48 Crwys Road, (0222) 382132. The name translates as 'taste of Wales', the restaurant tries hard to be authentic.

Bo Zan 78 Albany Road, Roath, (0222) 493617. Reliable neighbourhood Chinese, with a long, Szechuan menu; cooking is generally enjoyed.

Trillium 40 City Road, (0222) 463665. Careful cooking in an unprepossessing area; bouillabaisse, chicken with saffron and lime sauce, noteworthy desserts including sticky toffee pudding.

DINAS MAWDDWY (Gwynedd) *Old Station Coffee Shop* (0650) 531338. Self-service spot by the Meirion Woollen Mill; wholesome, unaffected cooking with much that's vegetarian. Good baking includes 'truly memorable' cheese scones.

FISHGUARD (Dyfed) *Farmhouse Kitchen* Glendower Square, Goodwick, nr Fishguard, (0348) 873282. A 'rustic parlour' serving all meals to hungry travellers.

HAWARDEN (Clwyd) *Imfeld* 68 The Highway, (0244) 534523. Swiss restaurant; fondue and raclette on Sunday evenings, more imaginative dishes the rest of the week. Lunch by appointment only.

LALESTON (Mid Glamorgan) *Great House* High Street, (0656) 657644. Attractive seventeenth-century house, friendly service, plenty of choice.

LETTERSTON (Dyfed) *Something's Cooking* The Square, (0348) 840621. Quality fish and chips and other things besides.

LLANDDOWROR (Dyfed) *Old Rectory* (0994) 230030. Not plush, but pleasing cooking and useful for the area. Such things as French onion soufflé soup, fillet of Welsh beef and crème brûlée.

LLANDUDNO (Gwynedd) *Number One Food and Wine Bar* 1 Old Road, (0492) 875424. Amiable, well-run wine bar; blackboard menu, good sauces; pasta sicilienne, prawn crêpes and fish dishes recommended. More reports, please.

LLANDYBIE (Dyfed) *Cobblers* 3 Church Street, (0269) 850540. Redecorated upstairs dining-room and ground-floor wine bar catering for all pockets. Interesting menus, fresh ingredients.

MOLD (Clwyd) *Chez Colette* 56 High Street, (0352) 759225. French-run bistro, good for simple dishes such as coq au vin and crêpes fourrées.

NEWCASTLE EMLYN (Dyfed) *Ffynone Arms* Newchapel, (0239) 841235. Village pub and restaurant; good home-cooking, real ales.

Glan Medini Betws Ifan, Beulah, (0239) 910197. Old country mansion offering bar meals and main dining-room fare. Fresh ingredients, good presentation, good ambience. Accommodation available.

NEWPORT (Dyfed) *Fronlas* Market Street, (0239) 820351. Interesting, useful café with chintzy, pretty décor. All fresh ingredients, good combinations, cheap.

NEWPORT (Gwent) *Celtic Manor* Coldra Woods, (0633) 413000. Expensive, over-ambitious menu; classical dishes may be let down by competing flavours and some uneven cooking.

PONTYPRIDD (Mid Glamorgan) *John & Maria's* 2–3 Strathan Square, (0443) 402977. Family-run, traditional Italian; spaghetti Pomodoro, grilled halibut and zabaglioni recommended. Excellent espresso.

PORTFIELD GATE (Dyfed) *Sutton Lodge* (0437) 768548. Set, no-choice menu that's over the top in detail but does deliver good results. Definite enthusiasm, although perhaps lacking direction.

PORTMEIRION (Gwynedd) *Hotel Portmeirion* (0766) 770228. Wonderful location, a great place to stay, wine list good, food very mixed, but not too dear.

PWLLHELI (Gwynedd) *Glynllifon Country House* Llanbedrog, (0758) 740147. Unusual idea; an Indian restaurant in house and grounds. Good cooking run on the buffet principle, ranging from mild to spicy. English and children's menus available.

REYNOLDSTON (West Glamorgan) *Fairyhill* (0792) 390139. Large house in a leafy acreage offering comfortable accommodation and competent cooking. Puddings particularly good.

ROSSETT (Clwyd) *Churton's* Machine House, Chester Road, (0244) 570163. Well-designed, two-level wine bar owned by long-established Cheshire wine merchants. Interesting bistro cooking, friendly service.

ST CLEARS (Dyfed) *Butchers Arms* High Street, (0994) 231069. Good bar snacks, also restaurant meals in pretty dining-room.

SWANSEA (West Glamorgan) *Roots* 2 Woodville Road, Mumbles, (0792) 366006. Vegetarian mood is described as 'buddhist' by some. Honest ingredients occasionally cooked with style, often without. Unlicensed.

TENBY (Dyfed) *Plantagenet* Quay Hill, Tudor Square, (0834) 842350. Old Tudor house, sympathetically furnished. Slow-changing menu supplemented by daily specials; imaginative home-cooking, vegetarian options.

WOLF'S CASTLE (Dyfed) *Wolfscastle Country Hotel* (043 787) 225. Good, relaxed ambience and pleasing cooking. More reports, please.

Isle of Man

BALLASALLA *Silverburn Lodge* (0624) 822343. Pleasing cooking; also does excellent bar meals.

DOUGLAS *Bowery* Peveril Square, (0624) 628082. Fun Tex-Mex food with appropriate décor and atmosphere; good service and value.

Brasserie Empress Hotel, Central Promenade, (0624) 661155. Atmospheric and stylish French that makes a good after-theatre spot. More reports, please.

Rafters Peter Louis Department Store, 9 Duke Street, (0624) 672344. Convenient shoppers' lunch venue; also open for breakfast and afternoon tea.

RAMSEY *Spice of Life* 8 Peel Street, (0624) 816534. Indian tandoori; careful spicing, good prawn puri, chicken korma and paratha bread.

Channel Islands

GOREY (Jersey) *Jersey Pottery Restaurant* (0534) 51119. Popular tourist spot for fresh seafood and pâtisserie at fair prices.

ROZEL (Jersey) *Château la Chaire* Rozel Bay, (0534) 63354. Elegant country-house hotel, fine cooking, friendly service. More reports, please.

ST PETER PORT (Guernsey) *Da Nello* 46 Pollet Street, (0481) 721552. Reliable and friendly Italian; fresh seafood, good vegetables and sweets.

Four Seasons Albert House, South Esplanade, (0481) 727444. Imaginative salads, local seafood, good desserts.

La Frégate Les Cotils, (0481) 724624. Hotel and restaurant enjoying panoramic views. French cooking; fresh ingredients handled well.

La Grande Mare Vazon Bay, (0481) 56809/56576. Comfortable surroundings for pleasing English cooking; mackerel pâté, plaice and desserts all good.

Le Nautique Quay Steps, (0481) 721714. Italian-run restaurant that's good for its fish.

San Lorenzo 42–44 Fountain Street, (0481) 722660. Consistently good Italian run with some flair.

Northern Ireland

HOLYWOOD (Co Down) *Bistro Iona* Church Road, (0232) 425655. Honest home-cooking; short, set-price menu; unlicensed, but bring your own.

MOY (Co Tyrone) *Grange Lodge* Grange Road, Dungannon, (086 87) 84212. Large Georgian house cooking good things; stuffed duck with plum and red wine sauce, timbales of turbot layered with salmon mousse and spinach.

NEWTOWNABBEY (Co Antrim) *Ginger Tree* 29 Ballyrobert Road, (0232) 848176. Northern Ireland's first Japanese restaurant. More reports, please.

Vintage Chart

SYMBOLS:

△ = immature

● = mature

▽ = drink up

□ = wines unlikely to be found in Britain, or undeclared vintages for port and champagne, which come from regions where only certain years are 'declared' or marketed as vintage wines.

★ = vintages not yet 'declared' or marketed (port, champagne)

All figures and symbols apply to the best wines of each vintage in each region.

Vintages have been rated on a 1 to 20 point scale (20 being the best).

	1	2	3	4	5	6	7	8	9	10	11
1991	15△	13△	13△	12△	14△	14△	11●	16●	15●	15△	13△
1990	17△	18△	14△	19△	19△	19△	19△	19●	19△	18△	18△
1989	19△	19△	17△	19△	17△	19△	20△	18●	18△	17△	18△
1988	18△	19△	16●	18△	18△	15●	16△	17●	19△	18△	17△
1987	14●	13●	15●	10△	13●	15●	8●	12●	12●	14●	11●
1986	19△	18△	14●	17△	14●	18●	16△	18●	16●	15△	16△
1985	18△	18△	18△	15△	19●	16●	18△	16●	17●	18△	19△
1984	13●	10●	12●	13●	11▽	12▽	8●	10▽	12▽	14●	13●
1983	18△	17△	18●	18△	14▽	17●	16△	14▽	18●	19△	17△
1982	19●	19●	16●	14●	13▽	15▽	13●	13▽	13▽	16●	15●
1981	16●	15●	15●	13●	11▽	8▽	16△	17●	16●	13●	12●
1980	11▽	10▽	11▽	12●	13▽	11▽	13●	12▽	8▽	14●	14●
1979	16●	18●	17●	14●	14▽	16▽	14●	14▽	10▽	15●	14●
1978	17●	17●	17●	12●	18●	17●	15●	18●	12▽	19●	18●
1977	9▽	9▽	7▽	6▽	7▽	10▽	5▽	8▽	7▽	8▽	7▽
1976	16▽	14▽	16▽	17●	14▽	14▽	18●	16▽	18●	18●	14▽
1975	16●	17●	17●	18●	4▽	6▽	16●	15▽	14▽	10▽	9▽
1974	12▽	10▽	9▽	8▽	11▽	10▽	8▽	11▽	10▽	9▽	11▽
1973	13▽	12▽	11▽	12▽	10▽	14▽	13▽	16▽	14▽	12▽	13▽
1972	8▽	8▽	6▽	9▽	12▽	10▽	8▽	6▽	5▽	14▽	15▽
1971	15●	16●	18●	16●	18●	17▽	16●	18●	19●	17●	17●
1970	18●	17●	16●	14●	13▽	13▽	16●	16▽	11▽	16●	18●
1969	11▽	9▽	8▽	13▽	16▽	17▽	18●	16▽	13▽	18●	17▽
1968	7▽	5▽	5▽	3▽	4▽	4▽	9▽	11▽	5▽	6▽	5▽
1967	12▽	12▽	11▽	17●	13▽	14▽	13▽	12▽	17▽	16●	18▽
1966	17▽	18●	16▽	14▽	16▽	17▽	15●	18●	16▽	17●	18▽
1965	3▽	3▽	3▽	6▽	2▽	3▽	6▽	7▽	4▽	8▽	6▽
1964	14▽	16▽	11▽	6▽	14▽	14▽	18●	14▽	15▽	17▽	16▽
1963	5▽	5▽	3▽	□	11▽	14▽	□	□	8▽	7▽	8▽
1962	14▽	15▽	16▽	17●	16▽	18▽	15●	14▽	14▽	17▽	16▽
1961	20●	20●	18▽	16▽	14▽	16▽	14●	16▽	18▽	20●	19●
1960	10▽	8▽	8▽	9▽	5▽	4▽	5▽	8▽	12▽	8▽	8▽

1 = Red Bordeaux: Médoc & Graves	11 = Southern Rhône
2 = Red Bordeaux: St-Emilion & Pomerol	12 = Midi
3 = Dry white Bordeaux	13 = Champagne
4 = Sweet white Bordeaux: Sauternes & Barsac	14 = Rioja
5 = Red burgundy	15 = Vintage port
6 = White burgundy	16 = Red Portuguese
7 = Loire (sweet)	17 = Barolo & Barbaresco
8 = Loire (dry)	18 = Tuscany
9 = Alsace	19 = Mosel–Saar–Ruwer
10 = Northern Rhône	20 = Rhinelands
	21 = Australia
	22 = New Zealand
	23 = California

12	13	14	15	16	17	18	19	20	21	22	23
16△	★	16●	★	16△	13△	14△	13●	14●	18△	17●	19△
19△	★	18△	★	17●	18△	20△	20△	20△	17△	15●	18△
18●	★	18△	□	17●	18△	13●	19△	18△	10●	19●	14●
19●	★	17●	□	11●	17△	19△	17●	17●	16●	14●	15●
14●	□	16●	17△	15●	14●	14●	6▽	7▽	18△	16●	12●
16●	15●	17●	□	9▽	15●	17△	11▽	13▽	19△	18●	14●
18●	19●	19●	19△	19●	20△	19●	15▽	15▽	17●	17●	19●
13●	□	13●	□	14▽	8▽	9▽	3▽	5▽	18●	15▽	13●
18●	14●	15●	18△	18●	13▽	15▽	16▽	14▽	14●	□	12▽
17▽	17●	16●	13●	15▽	19●	17●	7▽	8▽	19△	□	15●
17▽	16●	17●	□	10▽	13▽	14▽	8▽	10▽	13▽	□	14▽
15▽	10▽	16▽	16△	17●	11▽	13▽	3▽	4▽	18●	□	17●
15▽	17●	14▽	□	14▽	14▽	17●	11▽	12▽	16●	□	14▽
18▽	12▽	19●	□	15●	18●	16●	9▽	9▽	18●	□	16●
10▽	□	6▽	20△	16●	11▽	16▽	5▽	8▽	14▽	□	12▽
12▽	18●	13▽	□	12▽	14▽	13▽	19●	17●	17●	□	14▽
12▽	14▽	15▽	13▽	13▽	12▽	17▽	17●	18●	18●	□	14▽
□	9▽	14▽	□	10▽	16▽	14▽	3▽	4▽	11▽	□	18●
□	14▽	17▽	□	6▽	13▽	16▽	11▽	10▽	14▽	□	17●
□	□	7▽	□	12▽	10▽	9▽	6▽	7▽	13▽	□	15▽
□	17▽	9▽	□	9▽	18▽	18▽	20●	19●	20●	□	14▽
□	16▽	19●	18●	17▽	17▽	16▽	12▽	11▽	14▽	□	17●
□	14▽	12▽	□	9▽	14▽	14▽	16▽	13▽	□	□	16▽
□	□	10▽	□	9▽	13▽	17▽	□	□	14▽	□	19●
□	13▽	12▽	16●	14▽	16▽	18▽	17●	17●	15▽	□	14▽
□	16▽	15▽	18●	19●	15▽	16▽	16▽	16▽	19●	□	16▽
□	□	8▽	□	□	□	□	□	□	15▽	□	18▽
□	17▽	20●	□	□	19▽	18▽	17●	15▽	□	□	16▽
□	□	12▽	20●	16▽	□	□	12▽	12▽	17▽	□	16▽
□	15▽	13▽	□	□	13▽	16▽	14▽	16▽	18●	□	13▽
□	16▽	10▽	□	□	18▽	15▽	10▽	12▽	□	□	15▽
□	□	7▽	16●	17▽	10▽	12▽	6▽	5▽	□	□	14▽

House wines

Andrew Jefford

Most of us enjoyed a naive and modest childhood as diners-out. The memories are probably painfully clear. The waiter seemed authoritative and schoolmasterly, someone whom we should take great care not to upset; entering adulthood the menu was a genuine challenge to solvency, and ordering meant a tightrope walk between the pull of appetite and the pull of a single banknote; the ceremony itself was veiled in mysteries. I recall that when visiting a Chinese restaurant for the first time with my girlfriend, it was only the powerful smell of cheap cologne that prevented me from setting about what I thought was the first course of the set menu for two: a steaming white object, possibly soya-based, bearing a curious resemblance to a small face flannel.

And wine? Naturally, it would be a glass of the house red or white. There was considerable uncertainty as to whether it would taste nice or not; at least half of the time it did not, but of course there was nothing to be done about it. Wine was like that, wasn't it? And, after all, it *was* wine, real wine: it was drinking wine in a restaurant, rather than eating food, which made us feel so lordly and raffish and fine.

With the years come experience, familiarity and relative wealth. We learn to express coded displeasure at bad service, to read our way through the camouflage of menu euphemisms, and not to be distracted by the baroque niceties of old-school silver service, trolley rattling and cloche waving. Escaping the snares of house red, strange to say, seems harder.

Restaurateurs are more criticised for their wine lists than for any other aspect of the service they provide. Much of this criticism is unjust, based on the thoughtless and ill-founded assumption that the restaurant owners work hard to prepare food, while all they have to do is print a list in order to make a killing on the wine. This is simply not true. Building and maintaining a lively, richly textured wine list is a real, and rare, skill. Yet if customers are afraid to move on up the list, and if they stick to house wines with a heavy heart, then restaurateurs have only themselves to blame. As often as not, the house wine turns out to be the biggest rip-off on the wine list.

It's called something like Cuvée du Patron, and it's a French table wine, blended from tankerloads of cheap Midi wines, produced from sun-baked high-yielding vines at an industrial winery near Narbonne. Its blender rents an address in Nuits-St-Georges, which enables the restaurateur to describe it, implausibly, as 'burgundy' or 'burgundy-style'. Unlike any other wine on the list, its alcoholic strength is specified, suggesting that alcohol is the only reason why you should buy it – just as cost was the only reason why the restaurateur bought it. The wholesaler's deal means the *patron* got his *cuvée* at an ex-VAT price of around £23 per case – under £2 per bottle. He then sells it for £7.95 or £8.50. It's liquid cynicism.

As always happens when low quality and low price are coupled, the image plummets. House wines, consequently, are in danger of becoming pariahs. Out of 72 wine lists picked at random from *The Good Food Guide*'s 1993 files, 28 (40 per cent) no longer offer a house wine. Smart restaurants shudder at the very thought – it would be like including Coronation Chicken on the menu. Yet even when there are no designated 'house wines', these are what many customers still instinctively ask for – at which point they are guided gently, though sometimes unwillingly, towards half a dozen of the list's cheaper options.

House wines, you see, are a good idea. You've come in off the street, where the rain is beginning to turn to sleet; you're hungry, thirsty and tired. You can't be bothered to go through all that wine-list rigmarole, pretending that the names mean something to you, and you don't want to be palmed off with some dodgy claret at £20 by the wine waiter. The right house wine, served without fuss and with fresh bread and butter, will do more to restore your faith in life in general, and this restaurant in particular, than almost anything else anyone could bring you.

When a restaurateur works hard to find an inexpensive red and white wine to partner most things on the menu, with enough nascent complexity or country charm to drink well with or without food, and priced ungraspingly, then he or she is doing a great deal for the customers. Wine is a complicated subject, and ordering appropriately from a serious restaurant wine list requires both knowledge and confidence; moreover a good bottle of wine can, in some cases, very nearly double a restaurant bill. Ordering the house wine avoids crises of inadequacy and the sense of having overspent, neither of which will endear a restaurant to its customers.

The range of wines on offer for use in this way has never been better or larger. Buying an indifferent table wine when France is bulging with exciting vins de pays, and when Australia, New Zealand, California, South Africa and Chile are enthusiastically launching container after container of increasingly high-quality, inexpensive varietal wines across the oceans at us, is like buying fish fingers when you could have fresh turbot.

Indeed what becomes obvious when one looks through a selection of wine lists is that those restaurateurs who have set about the task with enthusiasm and imagination are so quickly impressed with what they have found that whittling the house selection down to two or three wines proves impossibly hard. Most settle for six or so. There's nothing wrong with a range of six house wines provided each is given a short tasting note; all six, preferably, should also be available by the glass. Gilbert's of London SW7 has a model list in this respect, and the wines chosen are admirably varied: the whites come from Sicily, Somerset and Chablis; the reds come from Rioja, the Jura and Chile. Prices vary from £8.90 (for the Sicilian white) to £15.60 (for the Chablis).

Bowlish House in Shepton Mallet stretches its range of house wines up to 10; again, all are given simple tasting notes, and the attractiveness of the offering is increased still further by presenting them all at £7.95 per bottle or £1.70 per glass. This should, I suggest, be a British model for 1993. The whites are listed 'from light and dry to full or medium sweet' while the reds range 'from light and dry to rich and oaky'. It's another good, wide-ranging selection, sourced from France, Chile, Australia, Italy, Spain and Germany, clearly laid out and well selected. I'd enjoy drinking my way through it on a succession of visits.

At the Penhelig Arms in Aberdovey, Robert Hughes' house wines number no fewer than 22. There are some crackers among them, including David Wynn's Chardonnay and Shiraz, Isole e Olena's Chianti Classico, Alain Brumont's Madiran Château Montus, half-bottles of Château Couhins-Lurton, Chardonnay from Martinborough and Hunter's Malborough Sauvignon Blanc: real wine-lovers' wines, full of exciting, untrammelled flavours. Prices are good, with most wines at under £10. But to call these 'house wines' is pushing the point a bit: it's really a selected wine list within a wine list. In other words, choosing from it requires knowledge and/or advice.

An ideal range of house wines, then, offers somewhere between two and ten choices, all annotated, so that customers can select for themselves based on a simple printed tasting note; all should carry the minimum mark-up that sound business practice would allow, ideally under 100 per cent; and all should be available by the glass as well as by the bottle. If every restaurant offered house wines in this way, then the institution would be a much-loved one, its name would not be mud, and drinking in restaurants would be a justly priced, reliable pleasure. There is no impediment to this; I believe every restaurant, right up to the heights of *The Good Food Guide*'s mark five, should offer a summary wine selection of this sort.

But what if you're a house-wine drinker and you find yourself confronted with a long, complicated, house-wine-less list? To conclude, let's explore some strategies for finding the house wines that the restaurateur doesn't want to own up to. The first thing to do is to forget all the classic French names for which you will always have to pay a premium; storm into the wine list, in other words, unblinded by prejudice. Look at prices to begin with: decide on the maximum you wish to pay, and only consider the wines below that price. You'll probably end up with a collection that includes, at best, two or three dry Loire wines, half a dozen wines from the south of France with one or two from the southern Rhône and Provence, possibly something from the fringes of Bordeaux, an English wine, half a dozen Spanish, Portuguese and Italian wines, maybe an Austrian wine, with another half-dozen drawn from Australia, New Zealand, California and, increasingly, South Africa.

Generalising ruthlessly, Australia and the south of France (particularly Corbières and Minervois) will offer the best value in full-bodied reds. Australia's will be softer, fruitier and fatter; France's tangier, herbier, more savoury. If you like lighter, very soft, well-aged reds, then Spain is a good bet; Portugal can be a complex, mid-weight substitute for France; Italy tends to be mid-weight to light, with very bright, high-toned flavours and quick acidity – perfect for pasta, of course. South African reds will give you lots of flavour, though it may be a little too punchy for comfort; while California goes all out for fruit: simple, sometimes sweetish, but with wide appeal.

The English white may be well worth a try if you like something light, dry and hedgerow-scented – though check it *is* dry before ordering. The Loire whites will give you more alcohol and backbone, while remaining very vital and dry (acidophobes may find them sharp). Austria and – in very adventurous establishments only – Czechoslovakia can make a reasonable substitute for Alsace's heady fruit, which may begin just above your price ceiling. New Zealand loads on the scent, again: green-grassy or vegetal, with positive, fresh-crushed-fruit flavours to match.

For bigger, possibly oaked whites, dig around those from the south of France and Australia. France is subtler and may be a better match for food, but if it is size and a bright sunshine-like embrace you want, no one is likely to beat Australia. Spain can provide oak cheaply, but fingers crossed that the fruit is there to match. Inexpensive whites from California and South Africa are on the simple side, but are generally pleasant, light and fruity; Italy's are neutral, and will go with everything – though you'll remember little about them afterwards.

The restaurant staff, of course, should be able to fill out the details, and confirm or repudiate the generalisations. Should be able to; some can; but many still greet queries on the wine list with a dreamy smile and glassy eye, and unless you phrase your question with a barrister's exactitude they are likely to tailor the answers to what they think you want to hear. The standard of wine waiting is rising in Britain, but painfully slowly.

As always, judge a restaurant as much by the wine it serves as the food it prepares. The Cuvée du Patron is no longer good enough: there is a teeming multitude of lively wine flavours out there, and every restaurateur should be up to netting enough of these to fill every corner of a list with light, fragrance and colour. There should be pre-selection for those who don't want to pass 10 minutes thinking about what to have, and there's nothing wrong with calling such a selection 'house wine'. Nothing wrong with drinking house wines, either – when they're good. If they aren't, say so. Only then will they be better next year.

Your rights in restaurants

This is the nasty bit of the *Guide*. No one wants to go out for a meal only to end up in court. No one wants to start a soufflé, then progress to a bout of fisticuffs with the waiting staff. That sort of behaviour ruins an appetite, and is certainly fatal to digestion. However, we should not be coy about money, or the goods and services that money buys. If those providing goods and services manifestly fail to deliver, we should expect reasonable recompense. It's not all one way. A restaurant has rights too. When you make a booking or you start to order food in a restaurant, you enter into a legally binding contract with the restaurant.

A restaurant is in the business of providing food to customers who consume it on the premises. It must therefore offer satisfactory food, safe practices of cooking and preparation, the equipment and hardware with which to eat it, and a place in which to eat it. The restaurant must also deliver things from the spot where they were prepared to the customer who is going to eat it. For food, read also wine and beverages. There is a lot of potential trouble in that short definition.

Satisfactory food means broadly that the dishes are as described on the menu and are prepared with reasonable skill and care. Food must be prepared in a way that does not endanger health and conforms to whatever standards are generally accepted. If a chef says that a bullet-hard potato is 'cooked', he may be expressing a new-wave theory about potatoes. It would be difficult to get him for endangering health, but you can easily claim the food has not been prepared properly.

Satisfactory equipment and furnishings for preparation and eating are rather easier to assess. This is not a matter of taste, more a question of potential injury. You can call on any number of experts to help determine whether these aspects of the restaurant's obligations conform to the law. If you can't abide eating in a blue room, and the owner has painted it cerulean – hard chips. That's just likes and dislikes.

Serving the food is integral to the restaurant's function. Bad service is often cause of complaint, perhaps dispute. While the restaurant should always provide reasonable service, it is never easy to determine when it passes from adequate to bad. This depends on the type of restaurant and the price you are asked to pay for the meal. If the service is not of a reasonable standard you are entitled to withold a charge for service.

But hold hard! You, the customer, have to conform to certain standards as well. A customer must behave reasonably, and may have to dress in an acceptable fashion (the rules for this are made up by the management); he or she must turn up to a reserved table at the time agreed; he or she must pay the bill if the meal and service are satisfactory. The restaurateur does have rights and these are often ignored by the public at large who think that restaurants are there to serve them 24 hours a day every day of the year: 'What, you don't open on bank holiday?' was an expostulation often encountered when the Editor of this guide used to run a restaurant. 'No,' he would answer, 'you're on holiday, so are we.' A restaurant can open and close when it chooses. A restaurant can refuse admission to whomever it wishes, unless it be on grounds of gender, colour or race. A restaurant can charge what it likes, provided it tells you first. And finally, a restaurant may cook what it chooses, so long as it has a menu displaying details in the correct places. If it wants to have a 'potato day' it can do an utterly tuberous menu.

All these rights can collide with wishes; all these obligations can turn to trouble if not performed. A superstructure of regulation has arisen to set out rights. Hence criminal laws such as the Consumer Protection Act 1987 (to prevent misleading price indications), the Trades Descriptions Act 1968 (to ensure that statements in menus and other promotional literature are accurate), the Food Act 1990 (covering hygiene in places where the public eats).

A chapter of accidents

Rodney and Samantha are celebrating their fifth wedding anniversary and decide the Pasty Diamond is the place at which to retie the knot. It has an entry in The Good Food Guide; *their friends speak highly of the food; everyone, it seems, has a good time there. Samantha says she will book a table for Wednesday night and rings up accordingly.*

A booking made is a contract between two parties. The intending customer must turn up at the time agreed. Any delay (for instance, because the car breaks down), should be notified to the restaurant. It is within its rights to refuse to re-arrange the time, and to re-let the table. If Rodney and Samantha don't turn up at all, then they are liable for the restaurant's loss of profit (not the entire cost) if the table cannot be re-let. It sometimes happens that people arrive at the Pasty Diamond and George the manager has no record of their booking. This can be very embarrassing. If George cannot give them a table and they really did make that booking, they can reasonably claim recompense for travel expenses, possibly even disturbance. If the transaction was not in writing, it can be difficult to prove your case. Many's the restaurateur who has people lying through their teeth that they made a booking; just as many's the customer who has found his or her reservation lost when in fact the place is a shambles that could never keep a diary straight. So keep a record of when you telephoned and to whom you spoke.

Actually, Rodney and Samantha make it on time and George's welcome is impeccable. Sitting on plump sofas with a glass of sherry each, they are handed the menu. Rodney's face falls. His friend Bill had assured him, '£30 a head'. But it is plain as a pikestaff that it's going to be more than that. 'Wonderful French food,' Samantha's workmate had told her. In fact, what she is reading is a menu full of Italian specialities.

The proper display of menus and charges is a pool of clarity in the fog surrounding 'trouble at table'. A restaurant must show a menu at or near its entrance. The prices must include VAT. Any extra costs must be displayed in as equally prominent type as the rest of the contents. Hence any cover charge, charge for bread and butter or additional levy for service must be clearly mentioned. A Code of Practice under the Consumer Protection Act 1987 suggests various ways of including 'extras' as inclusive prices with the food. The Code is very influential in the settlement of any dispute, but it is neither compulsory, nor has everyone heeded it. 'Discretionary' service charges, for instance, exist in many places even though the Code frowns on them. If the restaurant has conformed to regulations pertaining to display, there is nothing Rodney or Samantha can do about their misapprehensions. They can leave straight away but are breaking their contract. Otherwise, they are liable for what they should have found out about in the first place. Misleading price indications break the criminal law, but the law does not directly help aggrieved consumers.

Another problem is that Samantha is none too hungry. What she really fancies are two light first courses, not a substantial meat or fish main course. George the manager slides up to take the order and points out that the chef will not enjoy doing this. His attitude is 'I've bought all this food, now I'm going to sell it.' Actually, what he says is 'I fear there is a minimum charge, madam, you will have to order a main course.'

A minimum charge must be stated prominently on the menu. However, no customer is under any obligation to eat either prescribed dishes or in a prescribed order so long as he or she is willing to pay what is requested. Chef must curb any urge to say what the customer should eat. Similarly, if a customer asks for his or her meat well done, chef has to do it – unless something is declared on the menu along the lines of 'our meat is cooked medium or rare'.

That little problem over, George leaves the wine list to Samantha as he pops off to the kitchen. She chooses a Sancerre 1990. This comes from a maker other than the one who makes the wine she gets at the off-licence, for which she pays about £7. The Pasty Diamond has it on the list at £25. No sooner is the order taken than George leads Rodney and Samanatha to their table. He returns with the wine and offers it to Rodney for tasting – typical! Rodney passes it to Samantha, who gives it a good nose and careful tasting. It's off! George rushes round as if his tail's on fire, slurps some out of a glass and firmly disagrees.

The wine list is governed by the same rules as the menu. However, a restaurant need not display the whole list at its door, just a few representative entries. If the cellar is in chaos and 1989 is served instead of 1990, or the maker is different, then the customer is entitled to demand the correct vintage, or a replacement bottle (which doesn't mean it comes free). If you feel, as the customer, that £25 is much too much to pay, choose something cheaper. George can charge whatever he likes. Remember, however, that when you make these simplistic comparisons with supermarket prices the maker may make a considerable difference, so may the year, so may any variation between your benchmark and what is actually offered for sale. There is much difficulty about disputes over a wine's condition. How do you canvass opinion against George's denial? Do you approach other tables? You must hope to settle amicably. It is in George's interest to agree with you. The ultimate sanction would have to be to pay for the wine under protest, put it in your shopping bag and take it to an accepted expert: a vivid illustration of how uneasily legal disputes sit with the experience of dining out.

Our couple's dinner is fraught with disaster at every turn. Waits between courses are interminable, and the staff cannot even get the order right. When the waitress arrives with Samantha's monkfish and Rodney's medium-to-well-done entrecôte it turns out that George has told chef best end of lamb, not steak. Rodney sends the lamb back. The waitress doesn't know what to do. She leaves Samantha with her fish dish and rushes off to ask for a steak. By the time it appears, Samantha's fish and vegetables are cold. Starting to tremble every time she comes near the table, the waitress spills wine over Rodney's shirt. Already, the first courses have been fairly poor: the warm salad of calf's liver that Samantha had ordered was stone cold, and the liver like leather; she is convinced that Rodney's prawns were off-colour well before they were bathed in sauce.

Rodney is getting a case for 'bad service', even though it may not have been the waitress' fault, but due entirely to delays and confusions in the kitchen. However, it's still bad service in the eyes of the customer. The cold salad when the menu said 'warm' is a case of misrepresentation; the shoe-like liver is a matter of opinion, clear though it may seem to the hapless eater. If the prawns really do seem off, it is suicidal to eat them. This is the time to complain. Don't let things slide just because you wish to avoid a fuss. Actually, disregarding the trouble with the wine, Rodney and Samantha wanted to have a good time. Unfortunately, if you want to get your rights, you may have to sacrifice enjoyment. The wrong order is another self-evident fault that has to be rectified for the customer to be satisfied. However, the waitress went about it in the wrong way. People really do like to eat together. The only answer is to start the whole main course again. Spilling wine down Rodney's front will entitle him to be paid for dry cleaning or laundry, or even replacement. There was a fraudster last year who tried wishing fictitious dry-cleaning bills on to scores of restaurants. Some paid up, rather than argue the toss, even though he had never been near their doors.

It's pudding time and the couple order brown sugar meringues with bananas and cream. What turns up? Peaches instead of bananas. (Bananas were forgotten from the greengrocer's order.)
A restaurant may not vary the menu without warning. Mistakes can and do happen, but they need to be admitted before, not after, the dish arrives at table. Our man can't insist on bananas if there are none, but he could refuse the dish and try something else.

The consequences of real incompetence can sometimes be greater than restaurants realise. Rodney asks for the bill and notices that there is a 15 per cent service charge. He removes this from the total and suggests to George, the manager, that he should pay only a proportion of the bill. For George, this is the last straw. He reckons they have been fussing on purpose. He loses his temper and threatens to call the police. He also shows signs of becoming violent. So Rodney pays, but under protest. George won't take his cheque, and insists on cash.
A restaurant can refuse any form of payment by cheque or credit card. But Rodney is within his rights to deduct service, whether it be 'discretionary' or not, if he thinks the service has been truly bad. If service is included in the prices displayed on the menu, then he may deduct a proportion. He is also entitled to refuse payment for any dishes that are not what he ordered, or do not meet the description on the menu, or do not seem to be of a reasonable standard. However, if George cuts up rough, he may think it politic to leave the money. To protect any future action, he should make it clear that he is paying under protest – either write a note there and then, or write later (but not too late) and keep a copy. The police will not usually involve themselves in such disputes unless a breach of the peace is in question. If George thinks the whole affair was engineered, for some reason, he may be right to insist on payment. It is not easy to enforce this, but whatever happens, Rodney has to leave his name and address.

When the couple are about to leave, Samantha's coat can't be found.
A restaurant must take reasonable care of your belongings, yet most places have notices disclaiming liability. These are valid if your clothes are not left in a cloakroom and the notices are displayed prominently, but this doesn't get round negligence. If there is no

cloakroom, you need to ask staff to put your coat in a safe place, otherwise you may lose your right to compensation.

During the night, Rodney falls ill. It's those prawns.

Well, is it? Not every case of sickness after a meal in a restaurant is down to food poisoning. It may be drunkenness, unfamiliarity with rich cooking, coincidental illness. It is never easy to prove food poisoning, nor to point with confidence at the source. The only answer is to see a doctor, who will identify the symptoms and their possible cause. Then you need to call the Environmental Health Officer so that he or she may visit the restaurant and perhaps identify the source of danger – either in kitchen practice or in unsound foodstuffs. The ideal is that you should have samples of the foods consumed, but that is another development of the surreal premise that every meal in a restaurant is a case for lawyers, not a reason for enjoyment.

Rodney's and Samantha's anniversary celebration has been disastrous. What could they do about it? In the beginning, they need to complain. No anger necessary, merely a quiet word about what they were expecting. Restaurants prefer that complaints come on the spot, not in letters three weeks later. If it gets beyond this, then tinkering with the bill is one way to solve the problem – small comfort though this usually gives. All parties should work towards compromise from the word go. When Rodney rushes home vowing legal action, he would have to go to a solicitor, or get advice free from a Citizens Advice Bureau, Law Centre or Consumer Advice Centre. The Trading Standards departments or the Environmental Health Officers of the local council may be able to help him without his having recourse to legal advice. Or he could join *Which? Personal Service*, which gives help to individuals (write to Which? Personal Service, 2 Marylebone Road, London NW1 4DF for details).

Rodney could then, probably, write to the restaurant itself, stating his reasons for complaint and claiming a refund of his bill. If no satisfactory result is achieved, then a solicitor's letter could be the next step, or action under the small claims procedure in the county court (sheriff court in Scotland) – which can be undertaken without a solicitor. The financial limits to small claims cases (£1,000 in England, Wales and Northern Ireland; £750 in Scotland) are rarely going to be exceeded in a dispute with a restaurant.

General lists

London restaurants by cuisine

AFGHAN
Buzkash, SW15

ARAB & MID-EASTERN
Adams Café, W12
Al Bustan, SW1
Al Hamra, W1
Efes Kebab House, W1
Laurent, NW2
Maroush III, W1
Tageen, WC2

BURMESE
Mandalay, SE10

CHINESE
Cheng-du, NW1
Dorchester, Oriental, W1
Four Seasons, W2
Fung Shing, WC2
Green Cottage, NW3
Jade Garden, W1
Mandarin Kitchen, W2
Mayflower, W1
Mr Kong, WC2
New World, W1
Now & Zen, WC2
Panda Si Chuen, W1
Pearl, SW1
Poons (Leicester Street), WC2
Poons (Lisle Street), WC2
Royal China, SW15
Royal China, W2
Zen Central, W1

ENGLISH
Brady's, SW18
Connaught, W1
Dorchester, W1
English Garden, SW3
Faulkner's, E8
Grahame's Seafare, W1

Greenhouse, W1
Green's, SW1
Ivy, WC2
Quality Chop House, EC1
Savoy Grill, WC2
Upper Street Fish Shop, N1
Wiltons, SW1

FRENCH/BELGIAN
L'Arlequin, SW8
Les Associés, N8
Au Jardin des Gourmets, W1
L'Aventure, NW8
Belgo, NW1
Bibendum, SW3
Brasserie Faubourg, SW8
Le Cadre, N8
Café Normand, SW20
La Croisette, SW10
Emile's, SW6
L'Estaminet, WC2
Le Gavroche, W1
Gavvers, SW1
Inn on the Park,
   Four Seasons, W1
Lobster Pot, SE11
Lou Pescadou, SW5
Le Meridien Hotel,
   Oak Room, W1
Mon Petit Plaisir, W8
Mon Plaisir, WC2
Le P'tit Normand, SW18
St James's Court Hotel,
   Auberge de Provence,
   SW1
Les Saveurs, W1
Le Suquet, SW3
Tante Claire, SW3
La Truffe Noire, SE1

GREEK
Daphne, NW1
Kalamaras, W2

HUNGARIAN
Gay Hussar, W1

INDIAN
Bombay Brasserie, SW7
Gopal's of Soho, W1
Great Nepalese, NW1
Gurkha Brasserie, NW11
Malabar, W8
Ragam, W1
Salloos, SW1
Spice Merchant, W2

INDIAN VEGETARIAN
Diwana Bhel-Poori, NW1
Kastoori, SW17
Mandeer, W1
Rani, N3
Sabras, NW10
Sree Krishna, SW17
Surya, NW6

INDONESIAN/STRAITS
Melati, W1
Singapore Garden
   Restaurant, NW6

IRISH
Mulligans of Mayfair, W1

ITALIAN
L'Accento, W2
Alba, EC1
Al San Vincenzo, W2
L'Altro, W11
Bertorelli's, WC2
Casale Franco, N1
Cibo, W14
Eleven Park Walk, SW10

Florians, N8
The Halkin, SW1
L'Incontro, SW1
Neal Street Restaurant, WC2
Orso, WC2
Osteria Antica Bologna,
    SW11
Il Passetto, WC2
Pizzeria Castello, SE1
Pizzeria Condotti, W1
Riva, SW13
River Café, W6
San Martino, SW3
I Sardi, SW10

JAPANESE
Ikkyu, W1
Inaho, W2
Isohama, SW1
Kagura, WC2
Mitsukoshi, SW1

Miyama, W1
Nakano, SW3
Neshiko, N1
Suntory, SW1
Tatsuso, EC2
Wagamama, WC1
Wakaba, NW3
Yoisho, W1

KOREAN
Bu San, N7
Jin, W1

MAURITIAN
Chez Liline, N4
La Gaulette, W1

POLISH
Wódka, W8

SPANISH
Meson Don Felipe, SE1

SWEDISH
Anna's Place, N1

THAI
Bahn Thai, W1
Bedlington Café, W4
Blue Elephant, SW6
Chiang Mai, W1
Circle East, SE1
Sri Siam, W1
Thai Garden, E2
Thailand, SE14

London restaurants with tables outside

L'Accento, W2
Al Bustan, SW1
Al Hamra, W1
L'Altro, W11
Anna's Place, N1
L'Aventure, NW8
Blueprint Café, SE1
Bombay Brasserie, SW7
Brackenbury, W6
Brasserie du Marché aux
    Puces, W10
Buzkash, SW15
Le Cadre, N8
Café Fish, SW1
Café Normand, SW20

Casale Franco, N1
Chanterelle, SW7
Cheng-du, NW1
Chinon, W14
La Croisette, SW10
Daphne, NW1
dell'Ugo, W1
Eagle, EC1
Efes Kebab House, W1
Emile's, SW6
Est, W1
Florians, N8
Gilbert's, SW7
Joe's Café, SW3
Lou Pescadou, SW5

Maroush III, W1
Mijanou, SW1
Mon Petit Plaisir, W8
192, W11
Poissonnerie de
    l'Avenue, SW3
Le Pont de la Tour,
    SE1
Riva, SW13
River Café, W6
San Martino, SW3
I Sardi, SW10
Le Suquet, SW3
Tageen, WC2
La Truffe Noire, SE1

Restaurants with rooms (6 bedrooms or fewer)

England
Abingdon, Thame Lane
    House
Bakewell, Biph's
Barnstaple, Lynwood House
Barwick, Little Barwick
    House
Baslow, Fischer's at Baslow
    Hall
Birdlip, Kingshead House
Blandford Forum, La Belle
    Alliance

Bradfield Combust,
    Bradfield House
Bradford, Restaurant
    Nineteen
Bray, Waterside Inn
Brimfield, Poppies,
Bruton, Claire de Lune
Calstock, Danescombe
    Valley Hotel
Campsea Ash, Old Rectory
Cartmel, Uplands
Cleeve Hill, Redmond's

Clun, Old Post Office
Croyde, Whiteleaf at
    Croyde
Dartmouth, Billy Budd's
Dent, Stone Close
Diss, Salisbury House
Dorrington, Country
    Friends
Drewsteignton, Hunts
    Tor House
East Buckland, Lower Pitt
Erpingham, Ark

Eyton, Marsh
Glastonbury, No.3
Harwich, Pier at Harwich
Haworth, Weavers
Hayfield, Bridge End
Helford, Riverside
Holdenby, Lynton House
Kintbury, Dundas Arms
Kirkby Lonsdale, Lupton Tower
Lavenham, Great House
Leck, Cobwebs
Lower Brailes, Feldon House
Lympstone, River House
Manchester, Moss Nook
Mary Tavy, Stannary
Melksham, Toxique
Montacute, Milk House
Morston, Morston Hall
Oakhill, Oakhill House
Paulerspury, Vine House
Pool in Wharfedale, Pool Court
Poughill, Reeds
Poulton-le-Fylde, River House
Powerstock, Three Horseshoes
Redlynch, Langley Wood

Richmond, Howe Villa
Shepton Mallet, Bowlish House
Shipton Gorge, Innsacre
Spark Bridge, Bridgefield House
Staddlebridge, McCoy's
Staithes, Endeavour
Stoke-by-Nayland, Angel Inn
Storrington, Manleys
Thornton-Cleveleys, Victorian House
Torquay, Mulberry Room
Ulverston, Bay Horse Inn
Waterhouses, Old Beams
Whimple, Woodhayes
Wylam, Laburnum House
Yattendon, Royal Oak

Scotland

Canonbie, Riverside Inn
Dunvegan, Harlosh Hotel
Haddington, Browns Hotel
Kingussie, The Cross
Moffat, Well View
Muir of Ord, Dower House

St Margaret's Hope, The Creel
Swinton, Wheatsheaf Hotel, Four Seasons
Walls, Burrastow House

Wales

Fishguard, Three Main Street
Harlech, Castle Cottage
Harlech, Cemlyn
Llansanffraid Glan Conwy, Old Rectory
Newport (Dyfed), Cnapan
Talyllyn, Minffordd Hotel
Wolf's Castle, Stone Hall

Northern Ireland

Bushmills, Auberge de Seneirl
Coleraine, Macduff's

Republic of Ireland

Ahakista, Shiro
Wicklow, Old Rectory

Service charges

These restaurants state that they include the service charge as part of the net price shown on the menu and the bill. They also have stated that they close the total on the credit card slip before presenting it to the customer (save for those very few places, of course, that do not accept credit cards).

London

L'Arlequin, SW8
Capital Hotel, SW3
Clarke's, W8
Dorchester, W1
L'Estaminet, WC2
Gavvers, SW1
The Halkin, SW1
Inn on the Park, Four Seasons, W1
Leith's, W11
Lobster Pot, SE11
Mirabelle, W1
Nico Central, W1
Pied-à-Terre, W1
Rani, N3
Savoy, River Restaurant, WC2
Suntory, SW1

Turner's, SW3
Villandry Dining Room, W1

England

Abingdon, Thame Lane House
Aylesbury, Hartwell House
Bexhill, Lychgates
Bishop's Tachbrook, Mallory Court
Blandford Forum, La Belle Alliance
Bradfield Combust, Bradfield House
Bristol, Hunt's
Bristol, Markwicks
Calstock, Danescombe Valley Hotel

Chaddesley Corbett, Brockencote Hall
Chadlington, Manor
Chagford, Gidleigh Park
Chedington, Chedington Court
Claygate, Les Alouettes
Cleeve Hill, Redmond's
Cosham, Barnards
Croyde, Whiteleaf at Croyde
Dartmouth, Carved Angel
Dorking, Partners West Street
Evesham, Evesham Hotel, Cedar Restaurant
Eyton, Marsh
Hambleton, Hambleton Hall
Helford, Riverside
Holdenby, Lynton House

665

Horton, French Partridge
Langar, Langar Hall
Malvern Wells, Croque-en-
 Bouche
Mary Tavy, Stannary
Midhurst, Maxine's
Montacute, Milk House
New Milton, Chewton Glen
 Hotel, Marryat Room
Northleach, Wickens
Oakhill, Oakhill House
Painswick, Painswick Hotel
Roade, Roadhouse
 Restaurant
Rye, Landgate Bistro
St Leonards, Röser's
Ston Easton, Ston Easton
 Park
Sturminster Newton,
 Plumber Manor
Swanage, Galley
Thornbury, Thornbury
 Castle
Thundridge, Hanbury
 Manor
Torquay, Osborne Hotel,
 Langtry's
Tunbridge Wells, Cheevers

Tunbridge Wells,
 Thackeray's House
Ullswater, Sharrow Bay
Walton-on-Thames, Le
 Pêcheur at the Anglers
Whimple, Woodhayes
Wickham, Old House
Worcester, Brown's
York, Melton's
York, Middlethorpe Hall

Scotland
Aberdeen, Faraday's
Ballater, Craigendarroch
 Hotel, The Oaks
Dunkeld, Kinnaird
Edinburgh, Denzler's 121
Eriska, Isle of Eriska Hotel
Hawick, Old Forge
Kinbuck, Cromlix House
Peat Inn, Peat Inn
Uig, Baille-na-Cille
Ullapool, Altnaharrie
 Inn

Wales
Abersoch, Porth Tocyn
 Hotel

Llandudno, Bodysgallen
 Hall
Llandudno, Richard at
 Lanterns
Pwllheli, Plas Bodegroes
Swansea, Annie's
Talyllyn, Minffordd
 Hotel
Three Cocks, Three Cocks
 Hotel

Channel Islands
Rozel, Granite Corner
St Saviour, Longueville
 Manor

Northern Ireland
Ballynahinch, Woodlands

Republic of Ireland
Kanturk, Assolas Country
 House
Kilkenny, Lacken House
Newport, Newport House

Smoke-free eating

At these restaurants smoking is either banned altogether or one dining-room is maintained
for non-smokers. A restaurant is not listed if it simply has a no-smoking area. These
restaurants are marked in the *Guide* with a symbol –

London
Mijanou, SW1
Museum Street Café, WC1
San Martino, SW3
Thai Garden, E2
Villandry Dining Room, W1
Wagamama, WC1

England
Abingdon, Thame Lane
 House
Alnwick, John Blackmore's
Amberley, Amberley
 Castle, Queen's Room
Ambleside, Rothay Manor
Applethwaite, Underscar
 Manor
Ashbourne, Callow Hall
Aston Clinton, Bell
Barnstaple, Lynwood
 House
Baslow, Fischer's at Baslow
 Hall

Bath, Priory Hotel
Beaminster, Bridge House
Beckingham, Black Swan
Bilbrough, Bilbrough
 Manor
Blandford Forum, La Belle
 Alliance
Braithwaite, Ivy House
Bristol, Michael's
Brockenhurst, Le Poussin
Calstock, Danescombe
 Valley Hotel
Cartmel, Aynsome Manor
Cartmel, Uplands
Chadlington, Manor
Chester, Abbey Green
Cleeve Hill, Redmond's
Cockermouth, Quince &
 Medlar
Crudwell, Crudwell
 Court
Cuckfield, Ockenden
 Manor

Dedham, Fountain House
Dent, Stone Close
Diss, Salisbury House
East Grinstead, Gravetye
 Manor
Ely, Old Fire Engine House
Erpingham, Ark
Eyton, Marsh
Flitwick, Flitwick Manor
Gateshead, Eslington Villa
 Hotel
Gillingham, Stock Hill
 Country House Hotel
Glastonbury, No.3
Grasmere, Michael's Nook
Grasmere, White Moss
 House
Great Gonerby, Harry's
 Place
Great Milton, Le Manoir
 aux Quat'Saisons
Grimston, Congham Hall
Halford, Sykes House

Harvington, Mill at Harvington
Haslemere, Morels
Hawkshead, Tarn Hows Hotel
Hayfield, Bridge End
Herstmonceux, Sundial
Hetton, Angel Inn
Hexham, Black House
Hintlesham, Hintlesham Hall
Holdenby, Lynton House
Ipswich, Kinsella's
Ixworth, Theobalds
Jevington, Hungry Monk
Kendal, Moon
Keswick, Brundholme Country House Hotel
Keswick, Swinside Lodge
Kiln Pit Hill, Manor House Inn
Kingsbridge, Buckland-Tout-Saints Hotel, Queen Anne
King's Norton, Norton Place, Lombard Room
Kington, Penrhos Court
Kirkby Lonsdale, Lupton Tower
Langley Marsh, Langley House Hotel
Leck, Cobwebs
Ledbury, Hope End
Lewdown, Lewtrenchard Manor
Lichfield, Swinfen Hall Hotel
Lifton, Arundell Arms
Lower Beeding, Jeremy's at The Crabtree
Lower Beeding, South Lodge
Lymington, Provence
Malvern Wells, Croque-en-Bouche
Manningtree, Stour Bay Cafe
Mary Tavy, Stannary
Melmerby, Village Bakery
Montacute, Milk House
Newcastle upon Tyne, Fisherman's Lodge
North Huish, Brookdale House
Northleach, Wickens
Northwich, Nunsmere Hall
Norwich, Marco's
Oakhill, Oakhill House

Old Burghclere, Dew Pond
Oldbury, Jonathans
Oxford, Bath Place Hotel
Poughill, Reeds
Powburn, Breamish House
Powerstock, Three Horseshoes
Pulborough, Stane Street Hollow
Ramsbottom, Village Restaurant
Richmond, Howe Villa
Ridgeway, Old Vicarage
St Margaret's at Cliffe, Wallett's Court
Shaftesbury, La Fleur de Lys
Sheffield, Greenhead House
Shipton Gorge, Innsacre
Slaidburn, Parrock Head
South Molton, Whitechapel Manor
Southwold, Crown
Southwold, Swan Hotel
Spark Bridge, Bridgefield House
Standon, No.28
Stapleford, Stapleford Park
Ston Easton, Ston Easton Park
Stow-on-the-Wold, Wyck Hill House
Sutton Coldfield, New Hall
Sutton Courtenay, Fish at Sutton Courtenay
Tetbury, Calcot Manor
Thornbury, Thornbury Castle
Torquay, Osborne Hotel, Langtry's
Truro, Alverton Manor
Uckfield, Horsted Place
Ullswater, Sharrow Bay
Ulverston, Bay Horse Inn
Underbarrow, Tullythwaite House
Vowchurch, Poston Mill
Waterhouses, Old Beams
Watermillock, Rampsbeck Country House Hotel
Wells-next-the-Sea, Moorings
Willington, Stile
Windermere, Gilpin Lodge
Windermere, Miller Howe
Windermere, Miller Howe Café
Winkleigh, Pophams

Winteringham, Winteringham Fields
Witherslack, Old Vicarage
Worleston, Rookery Hall

Scotland

Aberfeldy, Atkins at Farleyer House
Achiltibuie, Summer Isles Hotel
Anstruther, Cellar
Arisaig, Arisaig House
Auchmithie, But'n'Ben
Ballater, Craigendarroch Hotel, The Oaks
Ballater, Tullich Lodge
Biggar, Shieldhill Hotel
Blairgowrie, Kinloch House Hotel
Canonbie, Riverside Inn
Cromarty, Thistles
Drumnadrochit, Polmaily House
Drybridge, Old Monastery
Dunkeld, Kinnaird
Dunvegan, Harlosh Hotel
Dunvegan, Three Chimneys
Edinburgh, Kalpna
Edinburgh, Martins
Edinburgh, Shore
Edinburgh, Vintners Rooms
Fort William, Crannog
Haddington, Browns Hotel
Inverness, Dunain Park
Kentallen, Ardsheal House
Killiecrankie, Killiecrankie Hotel
Kinbuck, Cromlix House
Kingussie, The Cross
Moffat, Beechwood Country House Hotel
Moffat, Well View
Muir of Ord, Dower House
Newtonmore, Ard-Na-Coille
North Berwick, Harding's
Peebles, Cringletie House
Port Appin, Airds Hotel
Portpatrick, Knockinaam Lodge
Stewarton, Chapletoun House
Swinton, Wheatsheaf Hotel, Four Seasons
Tiroran, Tiroran House
Uig, Baille-Na-Cille
Ullapool, Altnaharrie Inn
Walls, Burrastow House

Wales

Dolgellau, Dolmelynllyn
 Hall
Eglwysfach, Ynyshir Hall
Fishguard, Three Main
 Street
Harlech, Castle Cottage
Harlech, Cemlyn
Haverfordwest, Jemima's
Llanberis, Y Bistro
Llandudno, St Tudno Hotel
Llangammarch Wells, Lake
 Hotel
Llanrwst, Meadowsweet
 Hotel
Llansanffraid Glan Conwy,
 Old Rectory

Llanwddyn, Lake Vyrnwy
 Hotel
Llyswen, Griffin Inn
Llyswen, Llangoed Hall
Newport (Dyfed), Cnapan
Penmaenpool,
 Penmaenuchaf Hall
Pontfaen, Tregynon
 Country Farmhouse Hotel
Pwllheli, Plas Bodegroes
Talsarnau, Maes-y-Neuadd
Talyllyn, Minffordd Hotel
Trefriw, Chandler's
Whitebrook, Crown at
 Whitebrook

Channel Islands

St Saviour, Longueville
 Manor

Republic of Ireland

Letterfrack, Rosleague
 Manor
Mallow, Longueville House
Maynooth, Moyglare Manor
Newport, Newport House
Oughterard, Currarevagh
 House
Shanagarry, Ballymaloe
 House
Wicklow, Old Rectory

Cost-conscious eating

At these restaurants it should be possible to have a three-course meal, including coffee, a half-bottle of house wine and service, at *any* time the restaurant is open, for £20 or less per person. Meals may often cost much more than this, but, by choosing carefully, £20 should be achievable. These restaurants are marked in the Guide with a symbol – £.

London

L'Accento, W2
Adams Café, W12
Anna's Place, N1
Bedlington Café, W4
Belgo, NW1
Bertorelli's, WC2
Billboard Café, NW6
Bistrot 190, SW7
Brackenbury, W6
Brady's, SW18
Brasserie du Marché aux
 Puces, W10
Bu San, N7
Buzkash, SW15
Café Royal Brasserie, W1
Casale Franco, N1
Cheng-du, NW1
Circle East, SE1
Cork & Bottle, WC2
Daphne, NW1
dell'Ugo, W1
Diwana Bhel-Poori,
 NW1
Eagle, EC1
Efes Kebab House, W1
Emile's, SW6
Est, W1
Faulkner's, E8
Florians, N8
Four Seasons, W2
Fung Shing, WC2
Gopal's of Soho, W1

Grahame's Seafare, W1
Great Nepalese, NW1
Green Cottage, NW3
Gurkha Brasserie, NW11
Harveys Café, SW10
Ikkyu, W1
Inaho, W2
Jade Garden, W1
Jin, W1
Kalamaras, W2
Kastoori, SW17
Laurent, NW2
Lobster Pot, SE11
Malabar, W8
Mandarin Kitchen, W2
Mandeer, W1
Mayflower, W1
Melati, W1
Meson Don Felipe, SE1
Mr Kong, WC2
New World, W1
Osteria Antica Bologna,
 SW11
Panda Si Chuen, W1
Il Passetto, WC2
Pizzeria Castello, SE1
Pizzeria Condotti, W1
Poons (Leicester Street),
 WC2
Poons (Lisle Street), WC2
Quality Chop House, EC1
Ragam, W1
Rani, N3

Rotisserie, W12
Royal China, SW15
RSJ, SE1
Sabras, NW10
Singapore Garden
 Restaurant, NW6
Soho Soho, W1
Sree Krishna, SW17
Surya, NW6
Tageen, WC2
Thai Garden, E2
Thailand, SE14
Thistells, SE22
La Truffe Noire, SE1
Upper Street Fish Shop, N1
Wagamama, WC1
Yoisho, W1

England

Bakewell, Biph's
Bath, Tarts
Bath, Woods
Beaminster, Bridge House
Beckingham, Black Swan
Birmingham, Chung Ying
Birmingham, Days of the
 Raj
Birmingham, Henrys
Birmingham, Maharaja
Bollington, Mauro's
Brighton, Food for Friends
Bristol, Melbournes
Bristol, Rocinantes

Bruton, Claire de Lune
Burgh le Marsh, Windmill
Burnham Market, Fishes'
Bury St Edmunds, Mortimer's
Canterbury, George's Brasserie
Cheltenham, Mayflower
Cockermouth, Quince & Medlar
Colchester, Warehouse Brasserie
Consett, Pavilion
Croyde, Whiteleaf at Croyde
Croydon, 34 Surrey Street
Dartmouth, Billy Budd's
Dent, Stone Close
Easton on the Hill, Exeter Arms
Elton, Loch Fyne Oyster Bar
Epworth, Epworth Tap
Evesham, Evesham Hotel, Cedar Restaurant
Felsted, Rumbles Cottage
Folkestone, Paul's
Gateshead, Fumi
Gloucester, Yeung's
Grampound, Eastern Promise
Harrogate, Drum and Monkey
Harrow, Country Club
Haworth, Weavers
Horncastle, Magpies
Huddersfield, Paris II
Ipswich, Mortimer's on the Quay
Kendal, Duffins
Kendal, Moon
Kiln Pit Hill, Manor House Inn
Leeds, Brasserie Forty Four
Leeds, La Grillade
Leeds, Olive Tree
Leeds, Paris
Leeds, Sous le Nez en Ville
Leicester, Bobby's
Leicester, Man Ho
Leicester, Rise of the Raj
Lifton, Arundell Arms
Lincoln, Wig & Mitre
Long Melford, Scutchers Bistro
Longstock, Peat Spade Inn
Malvern Wells, Planters
Manchester, Granada Hotel, Armenian
Manchester, Koreana

Manchester, Kosmos Taverna
Manchester, Lime Tree
Manchester, Mr Kuks
Manchester, Pleasure
Manchester, Quan Ju De
Manchester, Sanam
Manchester, Siam Orchid
Manchester, Yang Sing
Manningtree, Stour Bay Cafe
Masham, Floodlite
Mawgan, Yard Bistro
Melmerby, Village Bakery
Midhurst, Angel Hotel
Midhurst, Maxine's
Nayland, Martha's Vineyard
Newcastle upon Tyne, Leela's
Norton, Hundred House Hotel
Norwich, St Benedicts Grill
Nottingham, Saagar
Nottingham, Sonny's
Orford, Butley-Orford Oysterage
Oxford, Al-Shami
Oxford, Cherwell Boathouse
Oxford, Gee's Brasserie
Oxford, Liaison
Oxford, Munchy Munchy
Pinner, La Giralda
Plumtree, Perkins Bar Bistro
Plymouth, Yang Cheng
Pool in Wharfedale, Pool Court
Porthoustock, Café Volnay
Powerstock, Three Horseshoes
Preston, Auctioneer
Rye, Landgate Bistro
Salisbury, Harper's
Slaidburn, Parrock Head
Southall, Madhu's Brilliant
Southwold, Crown
Staithes, Endeavour
Stoke-on-Trent, Ria
Stokesley, Chapters
Stratford-upon-Avon, Sir Toby's
Strete, Laughing Monk
Sudbury, Mabey's Brasserie
Tiverton, Lowman
Torquay, Mulberry Room
Vowchurch, Poston Mill
Wells, Ritcher's
Whitby, Magpie Café
Whitby, Trenchers

Whitstable, Whitstable Oyster Fishery Co
Willington, Stile
Windermere, Miller Howe Café
Winkleigh, Pophams
Worcester, Il Pescatore
York, Kites

Scotland

Auchmithie, But'n'Ben
Cairndow, Loch Fyne Oyster Bar
Canonbie, Riverside Inn
Cromarty, Thistles
Edinburgh, Chinese Home Cooking
Edinburgh, Kalpna
Edinburgh, Pierre Victoire
Edinburgh, Shore
Edinburgh, Waterfront Wine Bar
Glasgow, Café Gandolfi
Glasgow, October Café
Glasgow, Ubiquitous Chip
Kinlochmoidart, Kinacarra
St Margaret's Hope, The Creel
Swinton, Wheatsheaf Hotel, Four Seasons
Ullapool, Morefield Motel

Wales

Aberaeron, Hive on the Quay
Broad Haven, Druidstone Hotel
Cardiff, Chikako's
Colwyn Bay, Café Niçoise
Dolgellau, Dylanwad Da
Fishguard, Tate's Brasserie
Forden, Edderton Hall
Glanwydden, Queen's Head
Llandudno, Richard at Lanterns
Llangollen, Gales
Llanwrda, Seguendo di Stagioni
Llyswen, Griffin Inn
Newport (Dyfed), Cnapan
Pontfaen, Tregynon Country Farmhouse Hotel
Swansea, Annie's
Swansea, La Braseria
Swansea, Happy Wok
Swansea, Keenans
Swansea, Number One Wind Street

Trefriw, Chandler's
Wolf's Castle, Stone
  Hall

Isle of Man
Ramsey, Harbour Bistro

Channel Islands
Rozel, Apple Cottage

Northern Ireland
Belfast, La Belle Epoque
Belfast, Manor House
Belfast, Nick's
  Warehouse
Belfast, Strand
Bellanaleck, Sheelin
Coleraine, Macduff's
Portrush, Ramore

Republic of Ireland
Clifden, O'Grady's
Waterford, Dwyers

The Good Food Club 1992

Many thanks to all the following people who contributed to this year's *Guide* ...

Gail Abbot
Saad H. Abdalla
Sue Abell
Dr A.H. Abrahams
Dr Sidney Abrahams
Mrs M. Absolon
Ms Heather Acton
Arthur Adams
Keith Adams
Robert Adams
Ian Addison
P.G. Adlard
Dr J.B. Ainscough
John R. Aird
Wesley Aird
Ms Sue Aistrup
Dr A. Alaily
Mr and Mrs David Alcock
Hugh Aldersey-Williams
Mark Alexander
Minda and Stanley Alexander
Jane and Alisdair Alexander-Orr
J.C. Alflat
Ms L.S. Alford
Dr and Mrs A.A. Alibhai
Mrs Joy Allan
Mr and Mrs G. Allen
Dr J.P. Allen
Leon Allen
W.R. Allen
Mrs Allfrey-Pizer
Sir Anthony Alment
Graham Alston
John Alston
Lionel P. Altman
John Amis

Gary Anderson
M. Anderson
Mr R. Anderson
Miss J.D. Andrew
Derek Andrews
Gwen and Peter Andrews
Mrs Joyce B. Andrews
N.I. Andrews
Miss S.M. Andrews
Mr and Mrs Kurt Angelrath
Derek Angliss
R.M. Anklesaria
Don Anning
Peter Antolik
Mrs E.C. Appleby
T. Appleton
Mr and Mrs R.J. Apsimon
Fraulein Assunta Apuzzo
Mrs B. Archer
Mrs Cynthia Archer
G.L. Archer
J. Archer
George Archibald
David Arditti
Charles Arnold
Hugo Arnold
Mr D.A. Ash
Mrs H.G. Ashburn
John Ashby
Dr and Mrs R. Ashleigh
B. Astle-Bates
Mr Atkinson
Alison and Michael Atkinson
Rachel Atkinson
Mrs P.E. Attenborough
D. Attwood

M. Auclair
Mr and Mrs D.G. Austin
Mrs Heather Auton
Ms T. Avis and Mr D. Anciano
J.L. Awty
John and Sue Aylward
Mr and Mrs V. Bach
Mrs Mary Backhouse
Allan Baddeley
A.G. Badenoch
Caroline Bagley
Ben Baglio
G.I. Bailey
Richard Bailey
Mrs Sally Bailey
Ian C. Baillie
T.S. Baillie
A.J. Baines
R. Bairamian
A.A. Baker
Alan and Margot Baker
Ms Amanda Baker
Brad Baker
Mrs Julia Baker
K.I. Baker
Mr and Mrs I. Balaam
Mr and Mrs B. Baldwin
Tim Bales
Mrs Pat Ball
Mrs Sheila Ball
S.K. Ball
Mrs T.J. Ball
Mrs S. Ballinger
W. Ballmann
P.D. Balnave
Brian Bamford
C.J. Bancroft

Kate Banfield
Peter A. Banks
Ms Diana Bannister
H.F.H. Barclay
Jonathon Barclay
Mrs Carmel Bardsley
Lt Col K.A.S. Barker
David Barker
Ron Barker
Dr J.A. Barley
Tim Barlow
Anthony Barnes
Mrs B.M. Barnes
Miss C. Barnes
Mr C.A. Barnes
David Russell Barnes
P.M. Barnes
Dr R.D. Barnes
Ms Rebecca Barnetson
Mr R.G. Barnett
W.D. Barnett
Peter Barnsley
Mrs S.R. Barralet
Mrs P. Barratt
Mr and Mrs T. Barratt
Mrs Janet Barrett
Nigel Barrow
Mrs M.R. Barstow
Mr F.E. Bartholomew
Matthew Bartlett
A. du Bash
S.M. Batchelor
Ms S.E. Bates
Stanley Bates
P.J. Batley
David Batten
Dr John R. Batty
Louis Baum

Ms Sandra Baum
Mr R.T. Bayes
Conrad Bayliss
P.E. Bayliss
Ms Lara Bazeley
S. Beatty
Christopher Beaty
P.F. Beaumont
F.R. Beckett
Mr and Mrs Brian Bedwell
Dr Denise Bee
M. Bees
Mrs J. Beggs
Mr D.W. Bellingham
Michael J. Bellis
Kevin Bence
Mrs E. Benford
Peter Benner
Mr G.G. Bennett
Mrs Gladys Bennett
R.K. Bennett
Paul Benny
G.K. Bent
Mr M.F.M. Benton
Stephen Beresford
Cora Berg
Lady Berkeley
Mr and Mrs H.I. Berkeley
Mrs A. Bermingham
David Berry
Mr and Mrs E. Berry
M.J. Berry
P.E. Berry
Mrs S.C. Best
Mr W.J. Best
Ms J.Bewick
John Bewley
Mrs C.B. Bewsher
S.W. Bickford-Smith
K.B. Biddle
Mrs Pamela Billingham
A.D. Birch
E.R. Birch
Julian Bishop
Martin C. Black
Ms Susan Black
J.C. Blackburn
Capt C.C. Blackmore
Mr M. Blackstaff
Mr and Mrs S.D.J. Blackwell
Diana Blake
Timothy Blake
C. Blakeley

R.W. Blamey
Marilyn Blank
Mrs J.A. Blanks
Edward Blincoe
Mr and Mrs S. Bliss
Paul Bloomfield
Dr Kerry Bluglass
Dr S.M. Blunden
Mrs Norma Blythe
Heather M. Bogle
Hugh and Caroline Boileau
James R. Boles
Mrs F.M. Bomford
Mrs P.C. Bomford
Mia Bone
Barry Bonner
L. Bonner
Mr E. Bonnor-Maurice
Mrs Caroline Booth
Mr G.J. Booth
Mr and Mrs W.H. Booth
Ms Yvonne M. Booth
Mr C. Boothman
John W. Bosomworth
C.J. Bothwell
Anne Boucherat
Rev M.A. Bourdeaux
R.S. Bourne
Ms Anne Boustred
Richard Bowden
Mr A.J. Bowen
Dr Philip Bowen
Richard Bowen-Jones
Dr Bob Bowles
R.F. Bowman
Mrs Patricia Bowring
Major Roy Boxall
R. Boyse
Mr T.J. Bradbury
Michael Bradley
T. Bradley
Drs David and Elsa Bradshaw
R.G. Bradshaw
Mr M. Brady
J. Braham
Mr Bramall
P.M. Brash
Jennifer Brave
Nicholas Bray
G. Breakwell
Ms Kim Breckon
Dr and Mrs G. Bremner

Helen Bretherton
Edwin Brew
Dr D.M.C. Brewin
Mrs Jean Bridge
Mrs Jonica Bridge
Ms Sue Bridgwater
J.B. Brierley
Mr and Mrs D.J. Brine
Mr C.M. Brinton
Mrs E. Brise
Jennie Britten
Maurice Broady
Mr Brode
Kenneth Bromage
Roy Y. Bromell
Mr C.M. Brook
Douglas Brooks
Mrs G. Brooks
Tom Brooks
Mr and Mrs T.A. Broster
D.L. Brown
Michael Brown
Mr and Mrs Michael Brown
Mrs P.H. Brown
Mrs P.M. Brown
Rachel Brown
Rev Richard Brown
Dr Susan E. Brown
K.M. Brownson
David E.H. Bryan
Mr M. Bryan
Mr and Mrs Max Bryan
Mrs Rachel Bryan
Ian Bryant
John and Lynda Bryant
Donald Buachalla
Walter M. Buchanan
R.W. Buckle
Dr B. Bugg
G.A. Bull
Dave Bullen
Mrs Sylvia Bulley
Mrs Daphne Bullock
Lesley Bulman
Mr and Mrs J.E. Bulmer
S. Bulpitt
Mr D.J. Bunter
R.M. Burbeck
D.L. Burbidge
Mrs Daphne Burgess
Dr J.E. Burgess
A. Burnell
Mr R.D. Burnell

Maureen Burns
M.H. Burr
Mrs Mary Burrowes
Mr and Mrs Kenneth Burt
Mr W.B. Burt
Dr D. Burton
Mrs I. Butler
Jane Butler
Paul and Christine Butler
Ms Shazia Butt
Mrs R. Buxton
Robert Caldicott
P.G. Caldrey
Christopher Calthrop
Harry Calvert
J.A. Cameron
A.R.H. Cameron
Donald and Sylvia Cammack
A.T. Campbell
Col and Mrs D.J. Campbell
John Campbell
Michael Camps
Sue Candy
Dr and Mrs S.M. Cannicott
Andrew W.M. Canning
Ms Louise Capeling
Mr M.M. Capey
Lino Carbusiero
Peter M. Carey
Mr and Mrs Carlisle
Mrs E. Carman
Miss Y. Carpenter
Mrs J.J. Carr
Mrs Clare Carr-Archer
Dr John Carroll
John Carruthers
Mr N. Carter
Mr P.E. Carter
Philip Carter
R.V. Carter
Peter Cartledge
David Cartwright
R. Carty
Ann Carvalho
Mr H.J. Case
M. Case
Mrs Patricia Cassidy
A.G. Catchpole
Mrs P. Cate
R.E. Catlow
A.J.G. Cawsey
George C. Cernoch
Peter Chadwick

Mrs Liz Chambers
S. Chan
D.E. Chapman
A.V. Chappell
D.T. Chard
Mr and Mrs Chard
Mr S. Charles
Piers C. Robinson
Mr and Mrs S. Cheetham
Mrs E.J. Chesher
W.J. Chesneau
Mrs N.M. Cheung
Ms Jennifer Child
W.R.B. Chillingworth
G.H. Chipperfield
Mr and Mrs Andy Christie
Frederick Christmas
P.H. Chronnell
Norman Civval
Lesley Clare
Dr Justin Clark
Mrs P.A. Clark
Mrs P.M. Clark
Richard Clark
Mr and Mrs E. Clarke
Mrs P. Clarke
Mr and Mrs R.W. Clarke
V. Clarke
Dr and Mrs John R. Clayden
Mr S.J. Clayman
R.S. Clayton
Kenneth Cleveland
H.C. Clifford
Mr P.J. Clymer
C.D. Cockroft
Robert Cockcroft
E.G. Coe
F.N. Cogswell
Alan Cohen
Dr L. Cohen
Prof V. Cohen
Mrs S.J. Cole
Mr and Mrs G.G. Coleman
Janet Collett
Prof Leslie Collier
Ms Clare Collins
Dr and Mrs J.C. Collins
Rodney Collins
William H. Collins
S.D. Collinson
Peter Collis
M. Colton
R.T. Combe

Mr M. Comninos
Mr and Mrs J.R. Compton
Mr S. Conlin
P. Connelly
Sean Connolly
Gavin Convery
Mrs A. Cook
Geoffrey J. Cook
I.H. Cook
M. Cook
T.N. Cook
J.P.F. Cooke
Mrs J. Cookson
Ms Lisa Coombes
B.E. Coombs
Barry Coombs
Miss C. Cooper
D.B.M. Cooper
Ms Jackie Cooper
Peter F. Cooper
P.J. Cooper
Dr and Mrs J.C.W. Cope
Dr Peter Corbin
Mr J. Corbluth
Mr and Mrs Christopher Corin
M.G. Corkill
Mrs A. Corstorphine
Mr and Mrs Bernard Cosgrove
John Cotton
A. Cowan
H. Cowan
John Cowan
Ms Robina Cowan
Mr and Mrs A. Cowell
Teresa Cowherd
Mrs Gwyneth Cox
Philip Cox
Robert L. Cox
Peter Crabbe
W.M. Craig
Mr and Mrs Ian Crammond
Derek and Irene Cranston
Mr J.D. Cranston
Dr K.W.E. Craven
T.J. Craven
John Crawford
Paul Crawshaw
Mr J. Crewe
Mrs Paula Critchley
D. Crockett
Mr T.E. Crompton
Irene Cromwell

Ms Helen Crookston
Rodney Cross
Dr W.G. Cross
Barbara Crossley
Mr and Mrs M.R. Crowder
A.T. Crowther
T. Crowther
Dr D.A. Cruse
A.R.V. Culpeper Williams
John Cunliffe
Terence Curran
Steve Currid
Mr and Mrs S. Curtis
Mrs C.M. D'Arcy
Dr and Mrs S.R.D. Da Prato
Ronan Daffey
Mrs B.A. Dale
John G. Dale
M.J. Daly
Mr M. Dance
M. Daneshvar
Dr V.J. Daniel
John Dann
Peter Danny
Mrs P. Danvers
C.J. Darkens
Wg Cdr K. Dauncey
Mrs H.J. Davenport-Handley
David V. Davey
G.R. Davey
Mr and Mrs P. Davey
Dr T.J. David
Ms Kathryn Davidson
Mr W.H. Davidson
Barry Davies
Brian Davies
Mr and Mrs D.M. Davies
Handel Davies
Paul Davies
Roger Davies
Andrew Davis
Lawrence Davis
Lynn Davis
Mrs M.B. Davis
T.R. Davis
Elizabeth Davison
Dr G. Davison
J.M. Dawkins
Alan Day
John M. Day
Mr and Mrs D. Deacon

Nigel Deacon
Mrs Helen Dean
Mrs L. Deane
P.L. Degen
Conrad Dehn
Ms B. Deinhardt
D.B. Delany
Joan Dell
I.C. Dewey
V.H and B. Dewey
C.P. Dewhurst
Ms Fiona Dick
Dr D.O. Dickie
Mr and Mrs Neville Dickie
Dr J.H. Dickson
J. Diez
K.W. Diggle
Mr and Mrs Robert Dillon
Mr and Mrs A. Dinkin
John Dinsdale
Mrs J.A. Dixon
Mrs S.E. Dixon
George Dobbie
Mr R.L. Dobrek
Mr J. Dobson
M.L. Dodd
J.H.C. Dolby
Peta Dollar
Christopher Domine
Ms Jill Dourey
A.J. Dourleyn
Mr and Mrs G. Dove
John Drayson
Chris Driffill
Garth Drinkwater
Jeff Driver
Brian Drowley
Elizabeth Duff
Dr Carol M. Duffus
Mr C. Duggan
Mrs Jena Duke
Mrs P.A. Duncan
Mrs Anne Duncan
Mrs J. Dundas
Mrs B.E. Dunford
Mr and Mrs D.H. Dunger
Mr A. Dunn
David and Eileen Dunn
Denis Dunn
Mr M.H. Dunnett
Denis Durno
Ms Clare Durward
Claude Duval
Mrs Colette Dwelly
Paul Dwyer

Mrs H.W. Dycknall
Louise Dyson-
  Wingett
Mrs C.E. Earp
Colin Eastaugh
Mr and Mrs
  Eastham
Dr and Mrs J.C.
  Easton
Dr and Mrs L.M.
  Easton
E.P. Ebelen
Mr C.H. Eckert
Dr S. Eden
Neil Edkins
D.F. Edminson
Mr and Mrs David
  Edmonds
A. Edwards
Dr Brenda Edwards
Ms Kathryn
  Edwards
Mark Edwards
John Elder
Myra and Ray
  Elderfield
Mr R.S. Elegant
Steven V. Elief
Prof Walter Elkan
David Ellery
Mr R.V. Elliott
Ms Susan Elliott
A.N. Ellis
Mr D.R. Ellis
Mr and Mrs Gerry
  Ellis
Miss Katy Ellis
Martin Ellis
Philip Elson
Mr and Mrs I.
  Emanuel
George R.D.
  Emerson
Roger Emmott
Prof H.E. Emson
Prof and Mrs C.E.
  Engel
Eric Engledew
Robert Entwistle
Dr Diana
  Ernaelsteen
David Erskine
Mrs Evans
Mrs B. Evans
Mr and Mrs D.W.
  Evans
Mrs J.M. Evans
J.S. Evans
Lord Evans of
  Claughton
Ruth Evans
Mrs Veronica Evans

Mr and Mrs
  Edward Everest
Ms Edna Everitt
Mr E.G. Eyre
Ms Frances Fagan
Jed Falby
Mrs Jill H. Falconer
Mrs Elizabeth
  Fallaize
H.C. Fallek
Ms Fallows
Mr R.A. Farrand
Ms Ann Farrow
David Faulkner
Mr R. Fausset
Nick Fawcett
G.B. Fawcus
Jo Fearn
G.D. Fearnehough
Mrs I. Feesey
Brian Fellowes
Alan Fellows
Mr R.J. Fellows
A.J. Felmingham
Mr K.L. Fenner
Ms Christine
  Fenton
I.F.M. Ferguson
L. Ferrone
Mrs Helen E.
  Fielder
Mike Fieldsend
Peter D. Finch
Dr Paul Fincham
Mrs P.S. Fincher
Mr G.B. Findlay
Mrs C. Finnegan
Grace Fisher
Paul Fisher
Mr I.N. Fishman
E.A.L. Fitzwilliams
Ms Kay Flanagan
T.C. Flanagan
Amanda J. Flather
Mr A.T.R. Fletcher
Clare Fletcher
Mrs Susan Russell
  Flint
M.K. Florey
Mavis and Frank
  Florin
J.E. and I.A. Flower
Mrs E.W. Flynn
Mr M.R.D. Foot
Bronwen Forbes
J.C. Ford
Ms R. Ford
Stephen J. Ford
Anthony Forster
H.P.S. Forster
Mr and Mrs Roger
  Forward

Mrs W. Foster
Miss Nicola
  Foulston
J.A. Fowler
R.J.N. Fowler
A.E.L. Fox
Mr B. Foxall
Mrs A.W. Frame
Christopher and
  Lisa Francis-Lang
Mrs G. Franklin
Howard Franklin
Mr and Mrs Mike
  Franklin
H.C. Franks
Mr and Mrs C.
  Fraser
Duncan Fraser
Mrs Fiona Fraser
R.H. Fraval
John Freebairn
R. Freeman
M.R. Freeman
Anthony Froggatt
Prof Victoria A.
  Fromkin
Ms Elizabeth A.
  Frost
Jonathan Fry
Mr and Mrs D.
  Fryer
Mr and Mrs P.K.
  Fryer
Mrs M.J. Fuller
A.S. Fulton
Mr R. Furnell
Dr and Mrs R.
  Gadsby
John Gagg
V.G. Gale
J.C. Gallacher
Mr and Mrs M.
  Gallienne
J.R. Gallimore
Mrs E. Gard
Gp Capt T. Garden
Mrs M.P. Gardner
S. Garner
R. Garnsworthy
Amanda Garrett
Ms Jenny Garrett
C. Garside
L. Gassman
Kathleen M. Gates
Ms Tiggy Gatfield
Dr R.A.P. Gaubert
Stephenie Gavan
Mr and Mrs D.M.
  Gavin
Dr Ian Gavin
Donald M. Gay
Mrs Pauline Geake

David Gearing
H. Geddes
Mr and Mrs Charles
  J. Geiss
Julian Gent
E.J. George
Simon Gershon
Hunter M.
  Gholson
Michael Gibbon
Mr and Mrs Austin
  Gibbons
James F. Gibbons
Richard Gibson
Mr S.C. Gibson
D.R. Gifford
G.R. Gilbey
A.J. Gill
Ms Toni Gill
Mr M.E. Gilleland
Ms Susan Gillotti
Dr Alan Gilston
S. Girston
D. Gladwell
C.J. Glassock
Mrs B. Glover
Jon Glover
Mr and Mrs C.
  Godfrey
Don Godwin
Mr F. Golby
Mr and Mrs J.D.
  Gold
Ms Maria Goldberg
Joy and Raymond
  Goldman
Mr D.C. Goldrei
Diane Goldrei
B.J. Goldthorpe
A.T.T. Gompertz
Mr R.F. Gompertz
Tom Gondris
A.T. Goodchild
M. Goodchild
Norman Goodchild
D. Goodger
Linda Goodman
Mrs S. Goodson
Nigel Goodwin
D.V. Gordon
Mr and Mrs J.J.
  Gordon
Trevor Gordon
Mrs V.K. Gordon
J.N. Gordon-Lee
M. Gordon-Russell
Mrs E. Gordon-
  Smith
Bruce Gornick
D.B. Gorst
Dr J.R. Gosden
N.D. Goss

Mr and Mrs Brian Gotto
G.K. Gouldman
Mr R.J. Goundry
M. Gounsky
Hugh Graham
Ron Graham
Mrs Jane B. Grant
Mr and Mrs Keith Grant
Patrick Grant
Simon M. Gravett
D.W. Gray
Don Gray
Mr J.S. Gray
Peter Gray
Mrs Veronica Gray
Mr and Mrs S. Grayson
Mrs B.M. Green
Mrs G.D. Green
Hylton Green
J.A. Green
Mrs M. Green
Mrs R. Green
Nicolas Greenstone
Mr and Mrs K. Greenwood
Mr M. Greenwood
William N. Greenwood
Mr N. Greetham
Conal R. Gregory
Dr and Mrs A.R. Griew
Mrs S.A. Griffin
Dr D.J.O. Griffith
David J. Griffiths
Dr M.J. Griffiths
R. Griffiths
Christine A. Grimes
J.W. Grimes
Nigel Grimshaw
Mr N.M. Grimwood
Mrs I.L. Grint
Don Grisbrook
P. Gross
Mr R. Grover
A.D. Grumley-Grennan
D. and E. Gschell
Mr and Mrs B. Guard
Mr and Mrs R.K. Guelff
A.W.G. Guest
Candy Gummer
Mr J.H. Gunn
Mrs Gunnel Sygall
Alexander Gunning
Rosalind Gunning
Edward L.L. Gush

Pamela and Raymond Guy
Mrs P. Hackett
Richard Haes
Mr M.J. Haggett
Mrs T. Haile
Austin J. Haines
Mr R. Hainsworth and Ms C.Craig
Anthea Hall
C.J. Hall
Mrs Diana Hall
Godfrey Hall
Mr J.A. Hall
M. Hall
Mr and Mrs P.J. Hall
Mr R. Hall
Ms Ruth Halliday
Mrs G. Hallsworth
Tom Halsall
J.R.L. Hamilton
Mrs Meg Hamilton
Ms Claudia Hammett
F.A. Hammond
J.D. Hammond
M. Hancocks
Ms Penny Hand
Ms Mary Hanina
Sir Michael Hanley
B. Hannam
G.A. Hanscomb
P. Hansen
George Hanson and Peter Cork
Ms Jenny Hanson
Maurice Hanssen
Dr A.E. Hanwell
Edmund Happold
Mr K. Harding
Mr and Mrs J. Harding
Mr and Mrs S. Hardman
Simon Hardman-Mountford
R.H. Hardy
Joan Hare
R. Harland
Christopher Harlowe
Mr R. Harper
R.S. Harper
Michael Harrington
Mr and Mrs J. Harris
Malcolm Harris
Naomi Harris
Mr R. Harris
Raymond Harris

Mr and Mrs Blair Harrison
Bob Harrison
E.M. Harrison
W.D.M. Harrison
Mr C.P. Harrold
Mrs M. Hart
Miss W. Hart
J.V. Hartley
Donald Hartog
Mrs A. Hartrey
Mr and Mrs C. Harvey
Mrs J. Harvey
Mr and Mrs J. Harvey
Mrs M. Harvey
Dr Peter Harvey
Mr C. Harwood
Mr and Mrs Paul Harwood
Mrs S. Haward
Charles Hawes
John F. Hawkins
Gordon J. Hay
Mrs Glenys M. Hayers
Mr R. Hayes
Mr and Mrs A. Hayton
Mr S.P. Hayward
R.K. Haywood
Roger Heading
Miss Carol Heald
M. Healy
Mrs Rosemary Heath
K.T. Heather
Rev N.C. Heavisides
Mrs Dorothy Heber Percy
C. Heidelmeyer
A.D. Hein
J.H. Helliwell
D.P. Hemingway
Mr and Mrs M. Hemming
Mrs A.H. Henderson
John R. Henderson
R.H. Henderson
Dr W.A. Henderson
Mr Andrew S. Hendrie
Mrs Maureen Hennis
Mr N.F. Henshaw
Peter Hensher
Mr and Mrs M.G. Hensman
Gerhard Herbst

S.G. Heritage
Philip Herlihy
J. Hermans
Mrs M. Herniman
Craig Herron
Dr and Mrs Herxheimer
Dr M.A. Hession
Dr and Mrs Ivan Heong
Mr and Mrs B.F. Hewer
Ellin and John Hewes
Mrs J. Hewison
Mrs M.J. Hewitt
D.M. Heyderman
E.V. Hibbert
B.T. Hicks
David Hicks
Mr and Mrs Michael S. Hicks
Ms M.M. Hicks
Mr J.R. Higgins
Robert Higgins
Lt Col D.R. Hildick-Smith
J.E. Hilditch
J.M.M. Hill
Wendy Hillary
Mrs Colleen Hillier
Mr and Mrs D.W. Hills
J. Hincks
C.R. Hinde
Ronald and Maureen Hinde
Elizabeth Hjort
Mrs D. Hodgson
Malcolm C. Hodgson
Stephen G. Hodgson and Maria Falzon
Mrs Julie Hogbin
Neil Hogg
Robin Hoggard
David Holbrook
Derrick Holden
Mary B.T. Holden
Ms Sarah Holgate
Mr and Mrs Trevor Holley
Nick Hollis
Mr and Mrs Holmes
David Holmes
Mr and Mrs R. Holmes
Zoey M. Holmes
S.H. Honeyman
David and Valerie Hooley

Derek V. Hopes
R.C. Hopton
Mrs M. Horgan
Mrs H. Horn
Dr H.L. Horne
Sir John Hoskyns
Dr Keith Hotten
B.F.H. Houchin
Mr and Mrs W.D. Hough
T.P. Houghton
Peter Houlton-Jones
Mrs M.M. Housden
Mr and Mrs B. House
E.C. Housego
Mrs S.J. Howard
K.M. Howe
Geoffrey Howell
Mr and Mrs J. Howell
John I. Howells
R. Howgego
Mrs Carol Hoy
Prof W. Hryniszak
David G.T. Hudd
Nick Hudleston
A.M. Hudson
Joan and Peter Hudson
Mr and Mrs Hudson
Mr C. Hughes
Gwilym C. Hughes
Colin J. Hull
M.A. Humby
Sir Alan Hume
M.C. Hunt
Mrs M. Hunter
Muir Hunter
Mr C.J. Hurd
B.C. Hurley
Marvin Hurst
Mrs P.H. Hussey
Mr J. Hyams
Mr T.J. Hypher
B.L. Impey
Mrs Brenda Innes
F. Irons
Mr and Mrs M.J. Isaac
Dr S.D. Iversen
Dr Bruce Jackson
H.C. Jackson
Mr James McG. Jackson
Ms Joan G. Jackson
Ms Maggie Jackson
Eric Jaffé
Mrs C. James
David N. James
Mrs Sandra James

Lady James
Miss Valerie James
Mr J.R. Jameson
Mr B.G.W. Jamieson
Robert Jamieson
Mr and Mrs A.A. Janes
Moira Jarrett
J.M. Jarvis
Peter Jefferies
Drs Howard and Pat Jenkins
Richard M. Jenkins
T.S. Jenkins
J.C. Jennings
Mrs M.M.G. Jennings
Ms Mary Jennings
Michael J. Jervis
David Jervois
Peter Jessop
Dr Michael Jewess
B.M. Joce
Mrs E. Johnson
Ms E.S. Johnson
Gilbert Johnson
Mrs J.K. Johnson
L. Johnson
Dr M. Johnson
Peter Johnson
V.H. Johnson
Dr and Mrs Johnston
Duncan Johnston
Dr I.H.D. Johnston
S.H. Johnston
Edward Joll
Audrey Jones
Colin Jones
Mr and Mrs David L.E. Jones
Ian Jones
Mrs J. Jones
Mrs J.A.C. Jones
Dr J.B. Jones
Ms Karen Jones
Kay M. Jones
Melanie A. Jones
Dr Miranda Jones
Mr P. Jones
Peter Jones
S.D.A. Jones
Dr T.E.G. Jones
Timothy L. Jones
Peter Jordan
Charles Joseph
Nathan and Sarah Joseph
Dr David Joyce
J.M. Joyce

Mr and Mrs M. Joyce
Miss V. Joyce
M.R. Judd
A.K. Kameen
Mrs A. Katl
Dr Dina Kaufman
Dr Leon Kaufman
J.G. Kavanagh
Ashley J. Kean
W.B. Keates
Francis J. Keenan
Mrs Sheila Keene
Prof B. Keith-Lucas
Ann Kelley-Marshall
Peter and Maria Kellner
Miss J. Kelly
Mrs Kathleen Kelly
Mr and Mrs D.A. Kempner
Mr and Mrs D.J. Kennedy
Michael Kent
Neville Kenyon
Mr D. Kerr
Mrs L. Kerr
Ms Ann Kerswell
Mrs S.J. Kettell
Ashraf U. Khan
Dr Paul Khan
Sally Kibble
Ms Pauline A. Kilbride
J.H. Kilby
Mrs Maureen Killi
Rev A.B. King
Mr and Mrs Alan King
Mrs B.A. King
C.W. King
Derek King and Marion Turner
Jenny King
Capt R.E.H. King
Roger King
Stuart King
Elaine Kingett
Mrs Margaret Kinlay
Mr and Mrs W.A. Kinsman
Mr and Mrs Kirkman
Irwin Kishner
Dr Paul A. Kitchener
C.J. Knight
G.J. Knight-Adams
Mr A.J. Knights
Mrs A.K. Knox

Andrija Kojakovic
Alan Korobov
Youri Korsak-Koulagenko
Ms Judith Kramer
Richard Kunzer
D.S. Kyle
Dr D.W. Kyle
T.J. Lacey
Mr I. Laidlaw-Dickson
J.C. Lamb
Mrs A.L. Lambert
Gordon Lammie
Mr J. Lancaster
Anthony Land
Mr E. Landless
Mr and Mrs Lane
Robert Lane
S.B. Lane
Mrs P. Lang
Mr and Mrs John Langford
Mr A.T. Langton
Ray Lansley
Ms Anne Marie Larsen
Dr R.D. Last
Joel Latner
P.D.N. Laurie
Kenneth Lavanchy
Christopher Lawrence
John H. Lawrence
Susanne Lawrence
Steven Lawrence
Mr T.W. Lawrence
Fr David Lawrence-March
Neil Lawson-May
D.M. Lea
Dr Susan Lea
Dr A.D. Leading
Oliver Lebus
Shirley Le Coneur
Veronica Ledwith
A.J.N. Lee
Geoffrey Lee
Mrs R.M. Lees
Leslie M. Leeson
Cdr J.M. Lefeaux
V.J. Legg
M.B. Leggett
S.I. Leggett
M. Leijs
R.C. Leslie
M.R. Lett
Ms Caitlin Levene
Mr L. Leventhal
Ms E. Lever
Mr A.S. Levitt
B.K. and R.S. Levy

Philip Levy
Warren Levy
David Lewis
Mr and Mrs E. Lewis
Mrs J.M. Lewis
Mrs Maggie Lewis
P.A. Lewis
Richard Lewis
Mrs A. Lewis-Smith
Mr and Mrs L.S. Licht
Mr M.A. Lightfoot
Ms L. Lim
G.M. Lindey
Ms Zena Linfield
Prof D.V. Lindley
Mrs K. Lindop
Mrs I. Lindsay
Sheila A. Lindsay
L. Lindsey
Mr and Mrs R.V.R. Link
David Linnell
D.R. and A.J. Linnell
Miss E.A. Linton
R. Linton
Stephen Litherland
E.W.R. Little
Jeremy C.A. Little
Mrs Alice M. Livie
Andrew Lobberkog
Mrs Lockwood
Ms Victoria Logue
Miss S.C. Lomas
Mr and Mrs R.W. Lomer
David Long
Mrs J. Long
Peter Long
Robert J. Lorrimer
Ian Louden
Mrs V. Low
Peter and Jenny Lowater
Richard Lown
P.S. Luckin
Dr John Lunn
John Lunn
Stephen Lusty
Mr H. Denison Lying
Jan Lyons
Torrens Lyster
Michael Mabbs
Mrs H.M.F. Macandrews
J.S. Macfarlane
R.B. MacGeachy

Mr and Mrs D.B. Mack
Dr M. Mack
Rupert Mackeson
C.H.N. Mackey
A.H. Mackie
Ms Miranda Mackintosh
David P.H. Maclennan
Allan Macleod
Mrs J. Macleod
Ms Karen MacLeod
Ms Morag MacMillan
Mr S.R. Maconochie
Jim MacWilliam
A.F. Maddocks
Kiki Magireli
Mark P. Maguire
P.J. Mahaffey
J. Main
Peter Mair
Mrs Verity Majumdar
Robbie Malloy
Bernard Mander
Ms Deborah Manley
Mr and Mrs D.C. Mann
Dr and Mrs D.M. Mann
Mrs Mann
Rev Robin Mann
Paul Manners
Laurence Manning
Mrs C.J. Mansell
Mrs Susan Mansfield
Mr K.W. Mapp
Ms Char March
Ms Suna Mardin
L.L. Margarson
J.P. Marland
Leonard Marlow
Michael Marlow
Mrs T.A. Marriner
Ms Veronica Marris
Rosemary Marsh
Mrs Susan Marshall
R.O. Marshall
Mr and Mrs T.F. Marshall
W.D. Marslen-Wilson
Ms E. Martin
Dr Jane Martin
Janet Martin
Mrs Joan Martin

Mr and Mrs L. Martin
Mr M.J. Martin
Robert Martin
Tony and Heather Martin
Mrs R.N. Martineau
Mrs A. Mason
Mrs Ruth Mason
Dr Stephen Mason
Mrs Yvonne Mason
Christopher Mason-Watts
Mr and Mrs Derek Massey
Graham and Wiescka Masterton
Andrew Mate
K.G. Mather
Paul Mather
Mr and Mrs H.B. Mathewson
Mr and Mrs Peter Matthews
Ms S.A.R. Matthews
Patrick Matthiesen
Mrs Alison Mauley
Mrs Sheila Mawer
Tom Maxwell
Ian May
Mr and Mrs D.G. McAdam
James McBryde
Brian McCabe
R.B.G. McCall
Mr and Mrs David McCalman
Dr Graham McCann
Mr and Mrs G.A. McConnell
John McCracken
Miss S. McCrodden
Mrs A.C. McCulloch
Mr and Mrs I. McCutcheon
Ms J.A. McCutcheon
Paul McDonald
Kate McDowall
Miss M. McEvary
Mr C.J. McFeeters
Colin and Lilian McGhee
Dr Ian McGill
Jackie McKenna
Peter McLeod
A.McLoughlin
B.S. McMillan
R.N.H. McMillan

Robert McNaught
Mrs M.S. McPhee
A.J. McQuillin
Sir Patrick Meaney
M.R. Medcalf
Dr A. Mehta
Mrs H. Mheta
Ms Joanna Melhuish
Dr Joseph Melling
Ms S. Melling
Ms Diane Mercer
Mr L.C.J. Mercer
Major J.B. Merritt
E. Merry and Miss J. Galt
Ms Anita Metcalfe
C.W. Metcalfe
Hilary Meth
Mr E.F.P. Metters
Barry Metzger
Ms Patricia Michelson
Mrs V.A. Middlebrook
Mrs Linda Middleton
Robin Middleton
R.T. Middleton
C. Migliore
Rev Mill
Mrs E.M. Milbourn
Mrs C.H. Miles
J. Miller
John B. Miller
Dr and Mrs U. Miller
Miss Ann Milligan
Mr J.R. Milligan
Paul Millington
Mr O.S. Mills
Mrs F. Millward
K. Millych
Mary and Rodney Milne-Day
Mr A.J. Milton
Dr J. Mindell
Daniel Mitchell
Ian Mitchell
Mr I.W. Mitchell
K.F. Mitchell
Mr and Mrs R.E. Mitchell
Sir William and Lady Mitchell
G. Mitcheson
David Mizon
M. Mogano
A. Moliver
Ralph Molland
Dr J. Mollon
C.J. Monk

Janet Monk
Dr Carolyn A.
  Monks
Edward Monro
Roger Monro
John Montgomery
Miss E. Moody
N. Moody
Eric Moonman
Nigel Moor
Mr and Mrs M.
  Moorcock
Mr M. Moore
Michael J. Moran
Mrs Elizabeth
  Morcom
Mr and Mrs
  Moreton
David R. Moreton
Ms Sarah E.
  Moreton
Mr D. Morgan
J. Morgan
Mr and Mrs L.P.
  Morgan
Martin Morgan
P.A. Morgan
Veronica Morgan
Bob and Linda
  Morley
Mr F. Morrell
Aubrey Morris
Mrs Barbara Morris
Mrs Carole Morris
Colin Morris
Mr and Mrs F.
  Morris
Mrs Joan Morris
Mr and Mrs Morris-
  Kirby
Mr J. Morrison
Mr and Mrs
  Morrison
Dr S.J.A. Mort
John Morton
P. Moscrop-Young
Mr Moss
Joe and Richard
  Moss-Norbury
E.W.T. Mosselmans
Dr and Mrs A.C.
  Mottershead
Mr and Mrs W.A.
  Moxon
Richard F. Moy
Ian G. Mucklejohn
David Mudd
Mr and Mrs P.
  Mumford
Peter Munnoch
David Murdoch
Dr I. Murphy

Mrs G.M. Murray
Mrs M.L. Murray
  Smith
Ali Musa
Carol Myson
Dr M. Myszor
M. de Navarro
M.H.W. Neal
T. Neate
C. Netting
Julia Neuberger
Michael Neve
Graham Neville
Philip Newfield
Martin Newlan
Brian Newman
G.A. Newman
Miss Jane Newman
Mr and Mrs A.B.
  Newman-Young
Dr William H.
  Newnham
John Newson
Mr Nicholas
D.R. Nicholas
David Nicholls
Tom Nicholls
Mrs Judith
  Nicolson
Dr John Nocton
Ms Katrina Noel
Mrs Y.T. Norikoshi
Geoff Normile and
  Linda Avery
Ann Norris
Mr J.G. Norris
G. and P. Northcott
Peter W. Northey
Graham Norwood
A.D. Nunn
Miss M.L. Nunn
G.H. Nuttall
Katie O'Brien
M. O'Connor
Ms Marian O'Dea
W.B. O'Neill
C.B. O'Regan
B.A. O'Sullivan
M.D. Oakley
Mr Oddey
John Oddey
Nicholas Offen
R.A.L. Ogston
H.N. Olden
Fred Oldfield
Dr B. Olding
Martin H. Oldridge
J.N. Oldroyd
Mrs A.M. Oliphant
G. Oliver
Mrs Mary Oliver
Steve Ongeri

M.G. Opie
S.J. Orford
Mrs E. Orme
Mrs A. Orton
Jonathan Osborne
Mr and Mrs R.E.
  Osborne
A.M. and S. Otiv
B.T. Overall
A.J. Owen
Mr and Mrs D.C.
  Owen
Lt Col D.L.H. Owen
C.J. Padfield
Nadia Pallatt
Mrs K. Palmer
Mr R. Paris
Dr Richard Parish
Mrs W.M. Parish
Martin Park
Andrew Parker
J.M. Parker
Ms Valerie Parker
J. Parker-Jervis
Peter Parkes
J.D. Parkinson
K. Parry
Dr C. Parsons
T.G. Parsons
Miss E. Passon
M.H.O. Paterson
Mrs D.S. Paterson-
  Fox
James Patrick
Mr F.D. de Paula
S. Pavlovich
Mrs E.H. Payne
Mrs H.L. Payne
Mr and Mrs L.
  Payne
P. Payton-Smart
H. Peach
Mr H.R. Pearce
Simon B. Pearce
Mr and Mrs Pearson
C.J. Pearson
D.S. Pearson
R.H. Pearson
P. Peers
M.A. Pelham
Mrs P.A. Pellett
Adrian J.G.
  Pellman
Tim Pemberton
Miss S. Pembroke
A. Pendlebury
Michael T. Penny
Adrian Penrose
A.D.J. and H.E.K.
  Perkins
D.R. Perryman
Helen Peston

Eric B. Petch
D.N. Peters
F. Peterson
L. Petts
John Pharoah
Anne Phellas
Mrs A. Phillips
Mr B.J.F. Phillips
Ms C. Phillips
Mr C. Phillips
Claire Phillips
Mrs G. Phillips
Mrs Lorraine
  Phillips
Mr T.M. Phillips
Ms V. Phillips
Alicia Gregg
  Phillips
Mrs I.L. Phillipson
Mr and Mrs B.
  Phipps
Mrs S.R. Pickering
A.M. Pickup
Mr and Mrs G.
  Pickup
Dr A.D. Picton
Paolo Piergiovanni
Mrs E.M. Pigott
T.R.M. Pigott
Mr and Mrs R.C.M.
  Pilgrim
Joan S. Pirrie
Michael Pitel
Hugh Pitt
R.N. Pittman
Mrs J. Plante Cleall
Mrs Lois J. Plascott
Michele Platman
Mr A. Platts
Catherine Plummer
G. Poole
Mrs John Pope
P.S.M. Pope
Richard Popham
Ms Matilda Popper
Andrew Porter
Mrs J. Portlock
Mr D. Potter
Mr and Mrs A.
  Powell
I.R. Powell
Miss J. Powell
Michael Power
Mrs P.J. Powis
Wendy Poynton
Miss Rio Pratten
Adam Preece
D.B. Prell
Mrs R. Pressberg
Frank Prial
F.C. Price
J.K. Price

Roger Price
Mr W. Prime
J.F. Pritchard
J. Procter
Mrs N.M. Profit
J.A.B. Pugh
Pippa Purcell
Chris Purchase
Stephen J. Purse
Howard Pursey
Mrs M.J. Pye
Michael
　Quenington
Ms Deborah Quilter
J.J. Quinn
J.P. Quinn
Mr H. Rabinowitz
Dr and Mrs. Frank
　Rackow
Ms Ingrid Radford
Mrs J.C. Radice
Ms Jackie Rae
John Rae
Ms Amanda Raif
Mr A. Rampton
Dr and Mrs
　Rampton
J. Randall
Mrs Y. Randall
Dr A.M. Rankin
William Rankin
Mrs Caroline
　Raphael
J. Rathbone
Marc Rawcliffe
Michael Rawling
Ms Tamsin Rawlins
Mrs J.M. Raymond
Mrs Mary Rayner
Peter Rea
Christopher
　McCartney Read
Paul Reding
Christopher
　Redman
Miss P.H. Read
Pamela M. Read
Dr J. Reed
Kirsty Reid
Mike and Reina
　Reinstein
Dr and Mrs W.
　Reith
Mr A.L. Rennie
C. Renwick
Angela Reynolds
Mr P.L. Reynolds
Prof C.T. Rhodes
Ms Sian Rhys
M. Bernard Ribault
Brian Rice
G.G. Rice-Smith

Mrs H. Richards
J.M. Richards
Mr C.J. Richardson
P.D.I. Richardson
Tony Rickaby
J.K. Rickard
M.E. Ricketts
M.J. Ridgway
Mr and Mrs D.G.
　Ridgwell
Lloyd C. Ridgwell
Ms S. Risdon
Alison Ritchie
Dr B. Ritson
William Robb
Alan G. Roberts
Mrs Angela Roberts
J.C. Roberts
Ms Mimi Roberts
Dr A.J. Robertson
B.C. Robertson
Sheelagh Robertson
Mrs C. Robinson
D.R. Robinson
Derek Robinson
Ian Robinson
Ivor Robinson
Libby and Jonathan
　Robinson
Mrs P.N. Robinson
David A. Robson
Mrs H.J. Robson
Mr J. Rochelle
John Rodgers
A. Rogers
Anthony Rogers
Brian Rogers
Sir Frank Rogers
T.G.P. Rogers
John Rogerson
Ms S.E. Roles
Anthony Rooley
Mrs B.S. Rose
Daniel Rose
G.A. Rose
Mr and Mrs Jeffery
　Rose
Philippa Rose
Prof Richard Rose
Mr Rosier
Connie Ross
D.W. Ross
Mr and Mrs Harold
　Ross
Ms O.E. Ross
Robert Ross
Mrs Virginia Routh
R.H. Rowan
Mr B.C. Rowe
Michael Rowland
Dr Angela
　Rowlands

David and Diana
　Rowlands
Jill Rowley
Mr and Mrs C.J.
　Rowsell
Angela M. Royle
Peter Rozee
Hilary Rubenstein
Mr G. Ruff
Mr R.J.Ruffell
A.J. Rugg
J.A. Rumble
John Rumsey
Mrs Sarah Rush
C.M. Rushforth
Sue Rusholme
Alexander B.
　Russell
Mr D. Russell
Prof J.K. Russell
Mr and Mrs R.E.P.
　Russell
Timothy M.S.
　Russell
Dr H.N. Rutt
F G. Rutter
Mr J.S. Rutter
A. Ryder
R.S. Ryder
P. Sachs
Ron Salmon
Keith Salway
Fiona Sample
Colin W. Sanders
P. Sanders
Mrs L. Sandler
Dr R.J. Sandry
Dr E. Saphier
Anthony Sargent
C.J.P. Saunders
Peter Saunders
Mrs C. Sausman
Helen Savage
John W. Savery
Canon Michael
　Saward
Lt Col E.H.
　Sawbridge
G. Sawyer
George Sayer
Ms Sally Saysell
B. Scaife
Mr P.J. Scherer
Prof P.J. Scheuer
Tony Schneider
Dr M. Schneider-
　Marz
Michael Schofield
Mr I.C. Scholes
Alexander
　Schouvaloff
John Schroder

Dr M. Schroder
Miss J. Schroeder
Dr Joseph Schwartz
Mr R. Schwarz
A. Scott
Prof J.S. Scott
Lady Scott
M. Scott
M.K. Scott
Mrs Priscilla Scott
Mrs P.H. Scott
Stella Scott
C.G.P. Scott-
　Malden
Kenneth H. Scoular
Tony Scull
Philip Seaman
Dan Sears
J.R.E. Sedgwick
Peter Seglow
Ms Lucy Selby
Mrs J. Seller
G. Sellors
E. Selsdon
W.D.C. Semple
Colin Senior
Ms A. Sennett
K. Seston
E.H. Setwright
Mrs C.A. Sevitt
Henry and Maria
　Shaftoe
Mr and Mrs
　Shamash
A. Sharp
Dr C.W. Sharp
John T.L. Sharpe
D. Shaw
Derek Shaw
Miss Fiona J.M.
　Shaw
H. Shaw
Jean and David
　Shaw
Ms Karen Shaw
Mr and Mrs Martin
　Shaw
J.H. Sheffner
Mrs E.R. Shelver
Mrs M. Shenton
R.S.H. Shepard
Mrs K. Sherr
N.C. Sherston
Sir Robert
　Sherston-Baker
F.H. Sherwood
S. Sherwood
David Shillitoe
Bernard F.
　Shinkman
Gordon J. Shirra-
　Gibb

Dr Wharton Shober
F.D. Short
Mr and Mrs G. Short
Sir Evelyn Shuckburgh
Alan Sibbald
Dr and Mrs T.E. Sicks
Ms Emma J. Siggs
D.R.W. Silk
Brian Silverstone
George H.B. Sim
Mr B. Simmons
Mrs Diana M. Simpkins
Andrew Simpson
Mrs C.F.D. Simpson
Mrs O. Simpson
W.A. Sims
Ms Anne Sinclair
Mr and Mrs B. Sinclair
Mr R. Sinclair-Taylor
Dr S. Skevington
William Skyvington
Mr D.A. Slade
Mrs K. Slay
J.H. Sleeman
W.L. Sleigh
Ms Maureen Sleight
Mrs E. Smart
N.S.L. Smart
A.E. Smith
Mrs A.J. Smith
C.G. Smith
Craig Smith
Mr D.C. Smith
Ms F.M.K. Smith
F.N. Smith
Ivo Smith
Mrs Jan Smith
John Smith
John R. Smith
Julian A.V. Smith
Kenneth E. Smith
L.A. Smith
Miss M.A. Smith
Pamela Smith
P.M. Smith
P.R. Smith
Robert J.A. Smith
Mrs Rosemary Smith
S. Smith
Mrs S. Smith
Mrs Shirley Smith
T.A. Smith

W.F. Smith
W.M. Smith
Richard Smith Wright
Mrs J.C. Smye
D.J. Solomon
Mrs Irene Solomon
Dr B. Solomons
Mrs A. Southall
Mrs W.S. Soutter
L.M. Spalton
Mrs G.E. Sparrow
Mr and Mrs Philip Spearey
Mr and Mrs Peter Spence
Martha Smith Spencer
Drs R. and J. Spencer-Jones
Adrian Spicer
Stephen Spicer
Mr T. Spickett
Ms Coralie Spiegelberg
Nicholas Spruyt
Clive P. Stadler
Miss A. Standish
K.B. Standring
Paul Stanford
Frank Stanger
Mr T.J.G. Stannus
Mr A. Stanton
Ms Sarah Starr
John Stead
Mrs Rosalyn Steele Jones
Mrs G.M. Stein
Mr F.M. Steiner
Dr J. Steinert
Mrs D.M. Stemp
Mrs M.J. Stephens
A.M. Stephenson
Richard Stevens
Bruce Stevenson
Dr and Mrs J. Stewart
Capt and Mrs J.S. Stewart
Ms Margaret Stewart
R.C. Stewart
William S. Stewart
Mrs C. Burton Stewart
R.H.C. Stiff
Dr Caroline Stock
Mrs Jill Stockton
A.C. Stoker
Hugh Stokes
Mr and Mrs A.L. Stone

C.M.R. Stoneham
Gerry Stonhill
J.C. Stott
Mr and Mrs J. Strafford
J.W. Straw
R. Stringer
Trudy Stringer
Charles Stuart
R.F. Stupples
Mrs C. Styles
Michael Sugden
Mr R.M. Summers
Ms A.M. Sutcliffe
A.J. Sutherland
A.M. Sutton
Liliane Sutton
J.C.F. Swan
Mrs Moyra Swan
James E. Swindells
Alan W. Symes
Dr David N. Symon
Mrs Elizabeth Syrett
Ms Elizabeth M. Tagat
J.A. Talbot
G.D. Tan
D.E.T. Tanfield
Mr and Mrs Ian Tanner
N.M. Tapley
Mr J.A. Tarrant
Mr D.W. Tate
Mr and Mrs M.B. Tate
Dr P.H. Tattersall
Mr and Mrs G. Tayar
Mrs J.A. Taylar
Mrs M.F. Tayler
Mr A. Taylor
Mrs A.M.B. Taylor
Derek Taylor
Mrs E.K. Taylor
George Taylor
Ms Jean Taylor
Russ Taylor
S.D. Taylor
Mr and Mrs Steven Taylor
T.W. Taylor
P. Teather
Pat and Jeremy Temple
K.J. Tetley
T.C. Thackray
Alan Thomas
Fred Thomas
Dr H.J.W. Thomas
R.E. Thomas

Richard and Carol Thomas
Stella-Maria Thomas
David Thompson
Ms Jaqueline Thompson
John Thompson
Miles M. Thompson
N. Thompson
R. Thompson
Mrs Sheila Thomson
Miss Debby Thorn
Mr D. Thornton
G.N. Thornton
Howard Thrift
Michael Thrusfield
Margaret Tillyard
Julian Tobin
Waldemar Tobolewski
Dr The Hon J.M. Todd-Mann
L.R. Tollemache
C. and D. Tomlinson
Michael Tomlinson
Mrs Susan Tompkins
J.M. Toogood
Jennifer Tora and Nick Anvill
Philip C. Tordoff
A. Towler
Dr M. Townend
A.T. Townley
Mrs J. Trafford
Dr P.D. Tremlett
Mrs S. Trench
Paul Trevisan
Dr Michael R. Trimble
Chris and Karen Trinder
Mrs J. Trodd
Victoria Trombetta
Nick Tsatsas
J.A. Tully
J.R. Tunnadine
Mrs Janet M. Tunstall
Charles Turner
Mr D.A. Turner
David Turner and Ms J. Collier
Mr and Mrs G. Turner
P.E. Turner
R.K. Turner
R.L. Turner
Stuart Turner

Mr J.S. Turpin
Mr and Mrs R.D. Turvil
Mrs Curzon Tussaud
Mrs Elizabeth Tweddle
Eric Twigg
Alan Tye
Ms Debbie Tyler
D.R. Tyler
Mr I. Tysh
Ms Monika Uhe-Woldt
Adrian Underwood
Mrs R.J. Upchurch
Mr P.G. Urben
Mr I.M.W. Ure
Mrs S. Usher
Patricia Valentine
Mr J. Varley
Mr and Mrs Varley
M. Vaughan
R.W. Vaughan-Williams
Bill Venables
Graham Venables
Dr M.G.M. Venables
M.B. Venning
A.C. Verdie
A.W. Vernon-Harcourt
Mrs Melanie Vicary
Lidunka Vocadlo
Dr M.H.G. Waddington
Peter Wade
D.G. Wadsworth
Mr J.I. Wailes
Mr P.H. Wainman
Mrs J. Wainwright
J.R. Walford
Tom and Angela Walford
Dr A. Walker
Christopher Walker
Mrs Diana Walker
Mr F.M.F. Walker
Hazel Walker
Miss H.P. Walker
Mrs V. Walker-Dendle
Andrew Wall
M. Wall
Drs D. and A. Wallace
Mr E.J. Waller
Mr and Mrs W. Waller
D.J. Wallington
A.P.R. Walls

Mrs G.M. Walls
John Walsh
Mrs P.R. Walters
Mrs Margaret Warburton
Mr and Mrs David Ward
Mrs Jane C. Ward
K.G. Ward
Mrs Jane C Ward
Mrs Susan Ward
Mr and Mrs Wardell
Mr A.J. Wardrop
Ms Christine M. Wares
Alan Wark
Mrs D.S. Warland
Mr and Mrs Warren
G.M. Warrington
Mr R.A. Wartnaby
Mr and Mrs Alban Warwick
Toshio Watanabe
L. Waters and P. Vanderweele
Dr Paul E. Waters
Mrs Anne Watkins
M.B. Watmore
A.J.M. Watson
Andrew R. Watson
H.D. Watson
Stephen Watson
Mr and Mrs E.K. Watts
Dr and Mrs J. L. Wearn
Christopher Webb
A. and C. Webber
J.G. Webley
L.J. Webster
Mr and Mrs J.C.S. Weeks
M.S. Weightman
Mrs S. Weijand
Robin Walsh
Ms Barbara Wensworth
M.J. West
J.F.M. West
Dr and Mrs M. West
John and Anne Westcott
J.M. Weston
Dr John Weston
Sarah Weston
G. Weston-Smith
Robert Wharton
Mrs M. Whelan
Ben Whitaker
Ginger J. Whitaker
Dr D.R. Whitbread

Mrs Janet Whitcut
Alan White
Drusilla and Colin White
E. Clifford White
James White
Mrs J.M. White
W.E. White
Ms Jill Whitehead
Maurice Whitehouse
Howard Whiteley
Mr and Mrs Whitlock
Paul Whittaker
Neville T. Whittle
John Whyte
Mr G.W. Wicken
Miss L. Wickes
P.E. Wiffen
Lord Wigoder
R.N. Wilby
Mr K. Wilcox
Dr Ernest Wilde
R.C. Wiles
J. Wiley
Michael Wilkes
John B. Wilkin
G.R. Wilkins
Dr M.P. Wilkins
Peter Wilkins
Lloyd Wilkinson
Ms Shiella Wilkinson
J.A. Wilks
Prof Yorick Wilks
John Willard
Mrs A.A. Williams
B. Williams
David Williams
Mr and Mrs J. Williams
Ms J. Williams
John Williams
Jonathan Williams
J.R. Williams
K.E. Williams
Neil Williams
P.R. Williams
Mr Peter J. Williams
W.A. Williams
Mr W.G. Williams
Mr and Mrs A. Williamson
D. Williamson
J.R. Williamson
Mark and Heather Williamson
N.M. Williamson
Stephen Williamson

Mr and Mrs M.J. Williets
Mr G.D. Wills
Mrs Jean Willson
Gregory Wilsdon
Anthony Wilshaw
George Wilson
H. Wilson
James A. Wilson
Janet Wilson
Rev J.L. Wilson
Ms Joan Wilson
M.F. Wilson
Nicholas J. Wilson
Prof P.N. Wilson
R.R. Wilson
Miss S. Wilson
Mrs S. Wilson
J. Wiltshire
R.D. Windsor
Mr A. Winfrow
Anthony Wingate
Mr G. Withers
John Withers
Mr and Mrs T. Withers
D.E. Witts
Kelvin Wong
A.R. Wood
Christopher Wood
Hugh Wood
Keith P. Wood
K.W.J. Wood
J. Woodall
Mr and Mrs T. G. Woodburn
Dr F. Peter Woodford
Mr and Mrs Michael Woodroffe
Mrs R. Woodward
Clive P. Woodwards
Barbara M. Wooldridge
R.C. Woolgrove
Alan Worsdale
Paul Worsley
Nicholas Wraight
A.S. Wray
Alan Wright
Andrew Wright
Mrs C. Wright
Gail Wright
Geraldine Wright
H.M. Wright
Mr G.L. Wright
Jeremy Wright
Paul Wright
Ms S.J. Wright
Dr Stephen Wright

681

Mr and Mrs
  Stephen Wright
Jacqueline Wyatt
Mrs Jill L.
  Wyatt
Richard Wyatt
R.A. Wyld

Mr and Mrs M.
  Wyndham
Mrs S. Wyndham
Mrs S.J. Wynn
T. Wynn-Harries
Steven Yapp
Dr D.P. Yates

Dr and Mrs G.N.
  Yates
Simon York
Mrs C.S. Yorke
C.S. Youd
Patrick Young
Philip Young

Mr and Mrs R.F.
  Young
Simon J. Young
Mrs K. Younger
Nicholas van
  Zanten
Ann Zwemmer

Alphabetical list of main entries

Seafood Restaurant, Great Yarmouth, Norfolk

Seafood Restaurant, Padstow, Cornwall

Sea View House Hotel, Ballylickey, Co Cork

Seguendo di Stagioni, Llanwrda, Dyfed

La Sémillante, London W1

September Brasserie, Blackpool, Lancashire

Shamiana, Edinburgh, Lothian

Sharrow Bay, Ullswater, Cumbria

Sheelin, Bellanaleck, Co Fermanagh

Shieldhill Hotel, Biggar, Strathclyde

Shifting Sands, Brighton, East Sussex

Shiro, Ahakista, Co Cork

The Shoes, High Ongar, Essex

Shore, Edinburgh, Lothian

Siam Orchid, Manchester, Greater Manchester

Silver Darling, Aberdeen, Grampian

Silver Plough, Pitton, Wiltshire

Simply Nico, London SW1

Singapore Garden Restaurant, London NW6

Singing Chef, Ipswich, Suffolk

Sir Charles Napier Inn, Chinnor, Oxfordshire

Sir Edward Elgar, Swallow Hotel, Birmingham, West Midlands

Sir Toby's, Stratford-upon-Avon, Warwickshire

Sloans, Birmingham, West Midlands

Snows on the Green, London W6

Soho Soho, London W1

Sonny's, London SW13

Sonny's, Nottingham, Nottinghamshire

Sophisticats, Bournemouth, Dorset

Soufflé, Maidstone, Kent

Soughton Hall, Northop, Clwyd

Sous le Nez en Ville, Leeds, West Yorkshire

South Lodge, Lower Beeding, West Sussex

Spencers, Emsworth, Hampshire

Spice Merchant, London W2

Spindlewood Hotel, Wadhurst, East Sussex

Sportsman's Arms, Wath-in-Nidderdale, North Yorkshire

The Square, London SW1

Sree Krishna, London SW17

Sri Siam, London W1

Stane Street Hollow, Pulborough, West Sussex

Stannary, Mary Tavy, Devon

Stapleford Park, Stapleford, Leicestershire

Starlings Castle, Chirk, Clwyd

The Starr, Great Dunmow, Essex

Stephen Bull, London W1

Stephen Bull's Bistro and Bar, London EC1

Stile, Willington, Co Durham

Stock Hill Country House Hotel, Gillingham, Dorset

Ston Easton Park, Ston Easton, Somerset

Stone Close, Dent, Cumbria

Stone Hall, Wolf's Castle, Dyfed

Stonor Arms, Stonor, Oxfordshire

Stour Bay Cafe, Manningtree, Essex

Strand, Belfast, Co Antrim

Sully's, Canterbury, Kent

Summer Isles Hotel, Achiltibuie, Highland

Summer Lodge, Evershot, Dorset

Sundial, Herstmonceux, East Sussex

Suntory, London SW1

Le Suquet, London SW3

Surinder's, London W2

Surya, London NW6

Swallow Hotel, Sir Edward Elgar, Birmingham, West Midlands

Swan Hotel, Southwold, Suffolk

Swinfen Hall Hotel, Lichfield, Staffordshire

Swinside Lodge, Keswick, Cumbria

Sykes House, Halford, Warwickshire

Table, Torquay, Devon

Tageen, London WC2

Le Talbooth, Dedham, Essex

Tante Claire, London SW3

Tarn Hows Hotel, Hawkshead, Cumbria

Tarts, Bath, Avon

Tate's Brasserie, Fishguard, Dyfed

Tatsuso, London EC2

Thackeray's House, Tunbridge Wells, Kent

Thai Garden, London E2

Thailand, London SE14

Thame Lane House, Abingdon, Oxfordshire

That Café, Manchester, Greater Manchester

Theobalds, Ixworth, Suffolk

34 Surrey Street, Croydon, Surrey

Thistells, London SE22

Thistles, Cromarty, Highland

Thompsons, Chichester, West Sussex

Thornbury Castle, Thornbury, Avon

Three Chimneys, Dunvegan, Isle of Skye

Three Cocks Hotel, Three Cocks, Powys

Three Horseshoes, Powerstock, Dorset

Three Lions, Stuckton, Hampshire

Three Main Street, Fishguard, Dyfed

Timothy's, Perth, Tayside

Tiroran House, Tiroran, Isle of Mull

Toxique, Melksham, Wiltshire

Tree of Idleness, Bray, Co Wicklow

Tregynon Country Farmhouse Hotel, Pontfaen, Dyfed

Trenchers, Whitby, North Yorkshire

Tre-Ysgawen Hall, Capel Coch, Gwynedd

La Truffe Noire, London SE1

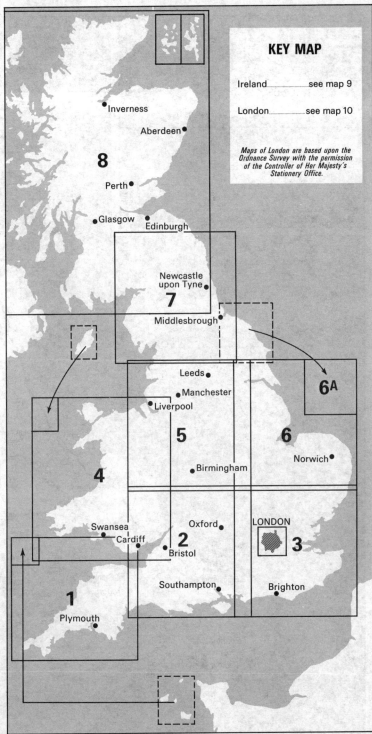

KEY MAP

Ireland .... see map 9

London .... see map 10

Maps of London are based upon the Ordnance Survey with the permission of the Controller of Her Majesty's Stationery Office.

Inverness

Aberdeen

8

Perth

Glasgow

Edinburgh

Newcastle upon Tyne

7

Middlesbrough

Leeds

Manchester

Liverpool

5

6ᴬ

6

Norwich

Birmingham

4

Swansea

Cardiff

Oxford

LONDON

2

3

Bristol

Southampton

Brighton

1

Plymouth

Base Map Copyright © Bartholomew 1992

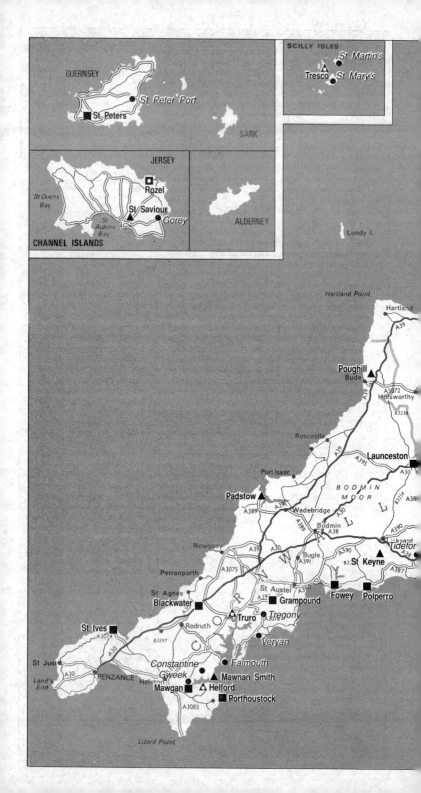

1

DEVON and CORNWALL

CHANNEL ISLANDS

Legend:
- ■ Restaurant
- ▲ Restaurant with accommodation
- ● Round-up entry
- △ ▱ Combined restaurant and round-up entries

0 Miles   10   20

BRISTOL CHANNEL

Lynton
Ilfracombe
MINEHEAD
Watchet
Croyde
EXMOOR
Williton
Braunton
Monksilver
East Buckland
Langley Marsh
Barnstaple
Wellington
Bideford
South Molton
Great Torrington
Bampton
Chulmleigh
eepwash
Winkleigh
Tiverton
Hatherleigh
Cullompton
DEVON
Broadhembury
Okehampton
Drewsteignton
Honiton
Whimple
Gittisham
Lewdown
Chagford
Exeter
ifton
Doddiscombsleigh
Lympstone
Mary Tavy
Lustleigh
Bovey Tracey
Budleigh Salterton
Peter Tavy
Exmouth
Dawlish
vistock
Kingsteignton
Calstock
Newton Abbot
Buckfastleigh
Crown Hill
Torquay
North Huish
Ashprington
Plymouth
Totnes
Brixham
oint
Kingswear
Dartmouth
Strete
Kingsbridge
Salcombe
Start Point

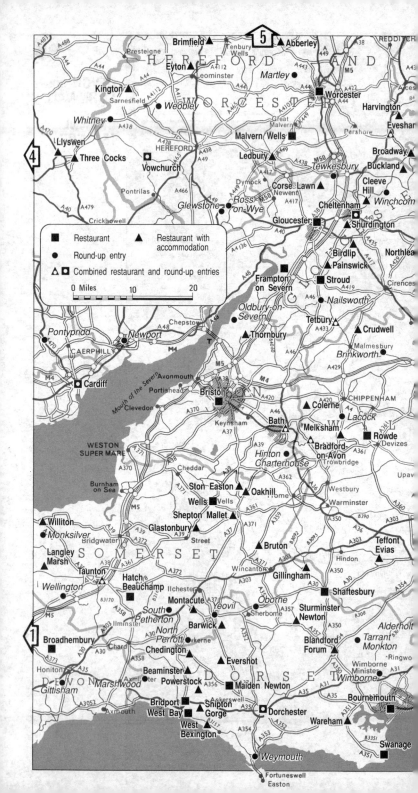

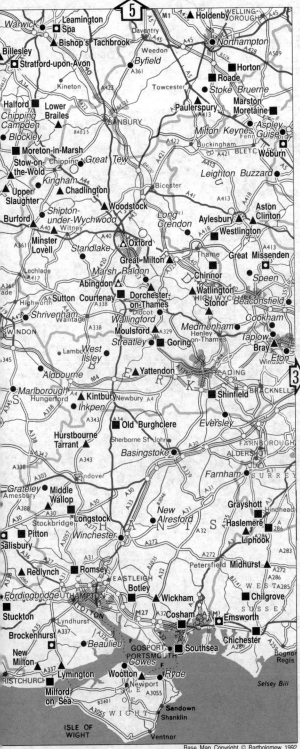

Warwick
Leamington Spa
Bishop's Tachbrook
Billesley
Stratford-upon-Avon
Daventry
M1
Holdenby
WELLINGBOROUGH
M45
A45
Byfield
Northampton
Horton
Kineton
Towcester
Roade
Stoke Bruerne
Halford
Chipping Campden
Lower Brailes
Paulerspury
Marston Moretaine
Blockley
Milton Keynes
Aspley Guise
Moreton-in-Marsh
Buckingham
Woburn
Stow-on-the-Wold
Chipping
Great Tew
Leighton Buzzard
Upper Slaughter
Kingham
Chadlington
Bicester
Burford
Shipton-under-Wychwood
Woodstock
Aston Clinton
Minster Lovell
Witney
Long Crendon
Aylesbury
Westlington
Standlake
Oxford
Great Missenden
Lechlade
Marsh Baldon
Great Milton
Chinnor
Speen
Abingdon
Watlington
Shrivenham
Sutton Courtenay
Dorchester-on-Thames
Stonor
Beaconsfield
Highworth
Wantage
Didcot
HIGH WYCOMBE
Wallingford
Medmenham
Cookham
SWINDON
Moulsford
Henley-on-Thames
Taplow
Lambourn
West Ilsley
Streatley
Goring
Bray
Eton
Aldbourne
Yattendon
READING
Windsor
Marlborough
Hungerford
Kintbury
Newbury
Shinfield
BRACKNELL
Inkpen
Old Burghclere
Eversley
FARNBOROUGH
Hurstbourne Tarrant
Sherborne St John
ALDERSHOT
Andover
Basingstoke
Farnham
SURREY
Grateley
Amesbury
Middle Wallop
New Alresford
Grayshott
Hindhead
Stockbridge
Longstock
Haslemere
Pitton
Winchester
Liphook
Salisbury
HANTS
Redlynch
Romsey
Petersfield
Midhurst
WEST
Fordingbridge
SOUTHAMPTON
Botley
Wickham
Chilgrove
Stuckton
TOTTON
Cosham
Emsworth
SUSSEX
Brockenhurst
Lyndhurst
Beaulieu
GOSPORT
Southsea
Chichester
New Milton
PORTSMOUTH
Cowes
Ryde
Bognor Regis
Lymington
Wootton
Newport
Selsey Bill
Milford on Sea
RYDE
ISLE OF WIGHT
Sandown
Shanklin
CHRISTCHURCH
ISLE OF WIGHT
Ventnor

Base Map Copyright © Bartholomew 1992

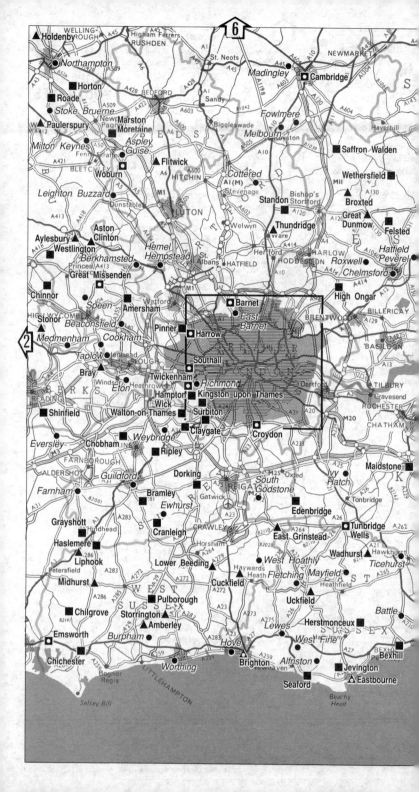

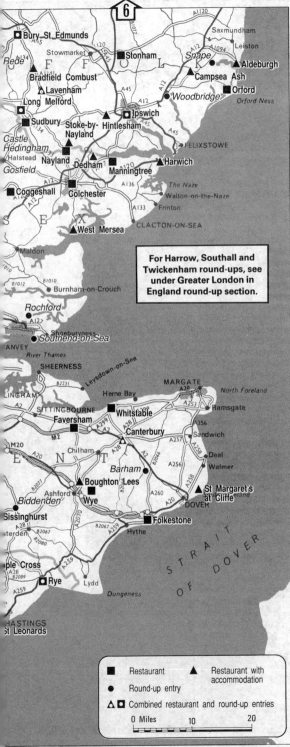

For Harrow, Southall and
Twickenham round-ups, see
under Greater London in
England round-up section.

Restaurant ▲ Restaurant with
accommodation
● Round-up entry
△ ◻ Combined restaurant and round-up entries

0 Miles   10   20

Base Map Copyright © Bartholomew 1992

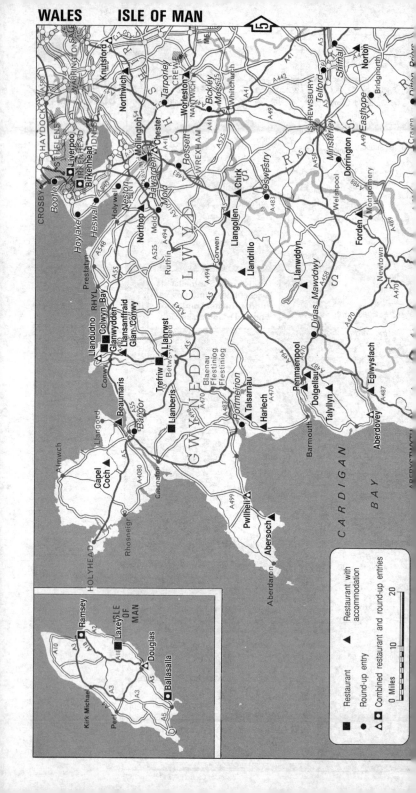

WALES   ISLE OF MAN

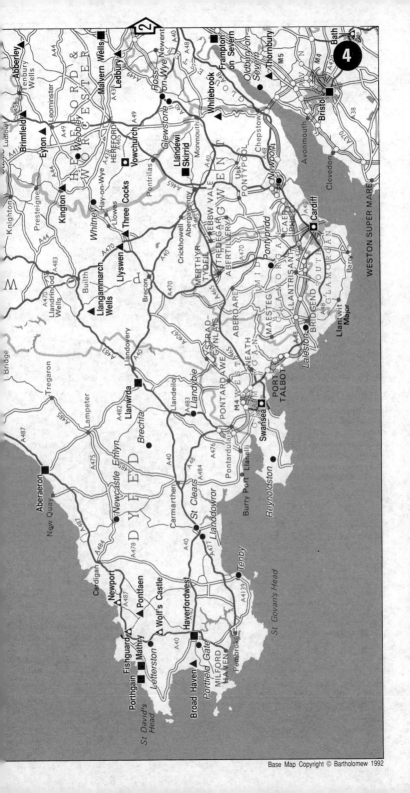

Base Map Copyright © Bartholomew 1992

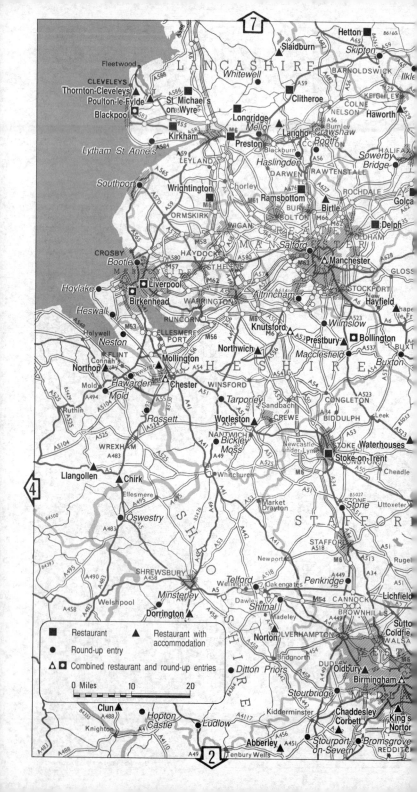

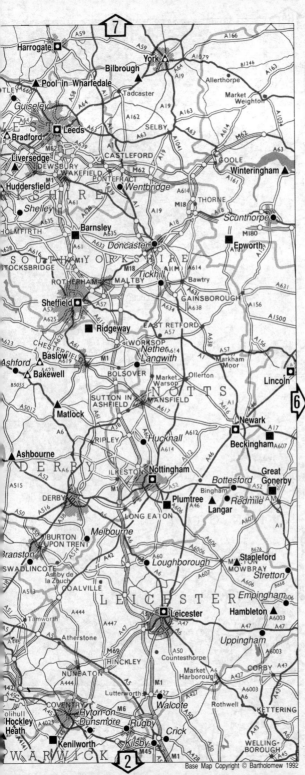

Base Map Copyright © Bartholomew 1992

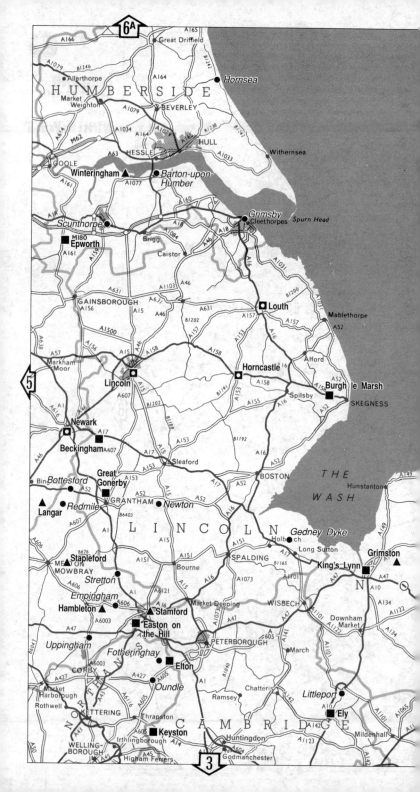

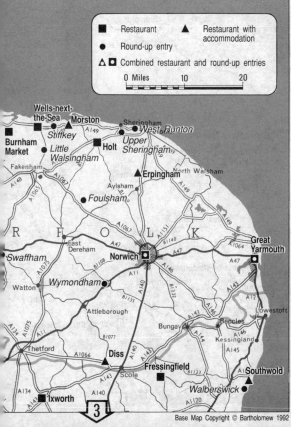

Restaurant ▲ Restaurant with accommodation

● Round-up entry

△ ◘ Combined restaurant and round-up entries

0 Miles   10   20

Base Map Copyright © Bartholomew 1992

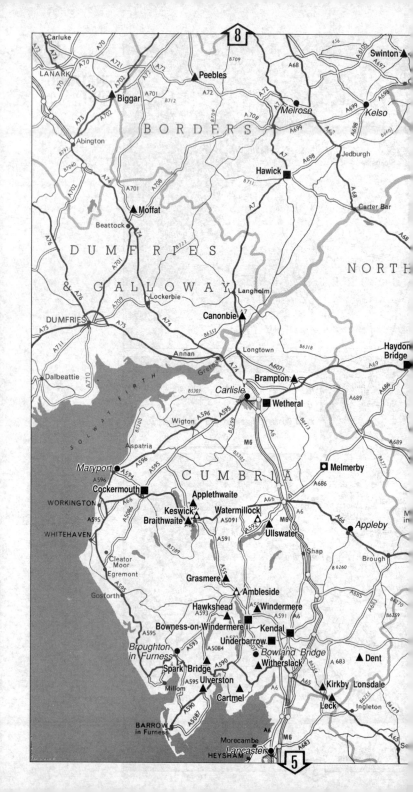

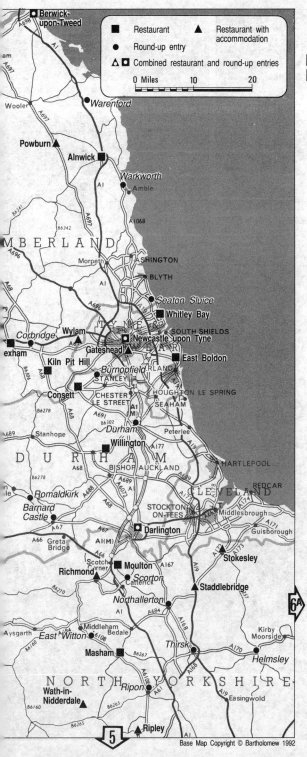

Restaurant

▲ Restaurant with accommodation

● Round-up entry

△ ◻ Combined restaurant and round-up entries

0 Miles   10   20

Berwick-upon-Tweed

Warenford

Wooler

Powburn

Alnwick

Warkworth

Amble

MBERLAND

Morpeth

ASHINGTON

BLYTH

Seaton Sluice

Whitley Bay

SOUTH SHIELDS

Corbridge

Wylam

TYNE

Newcastle upon Tyne

exham

Gateshead

East Boldon

Kiln Pit Hill

Burnopfield

STANLEY

Consett

CHESTER LE STREET

HOUGHTON LE SPRING

SEAHAM

Stanhope

Durham

Peterlee

Willington

DURHAM

BISHOP AUCKLAND

HARTLEPOOL

Romaldkirk

CLEVELAND

REDCAR

Barnard Castle

STOCKTON ON-TEES

Greta Bridge

Middlesbrough

Guisborough

Darlington

Scotch Corner

Moulton

Stokesley

Richmond

Scorton

Catterick

Staddlebridge

Northallerton

Aysgarth

East Witton

Middleham

Bedale

Kirby Moorside

Masham

Thirsk

Helmsley

NORTH YORKSHIRE

Wath-in-Nidderdale

Ripon

Easingwold

Ripley

5

6A

Base Map Copyright © Bartholomew 1992

SCOTLAND

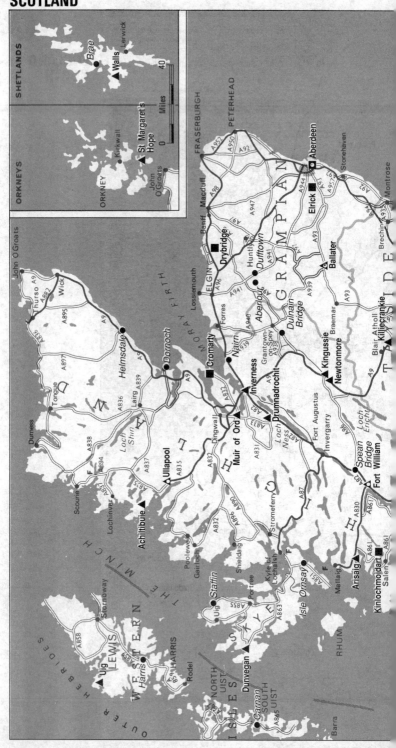

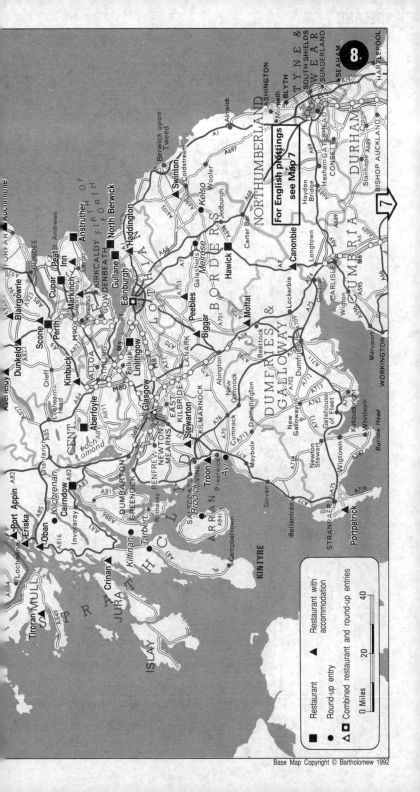

IRELAND

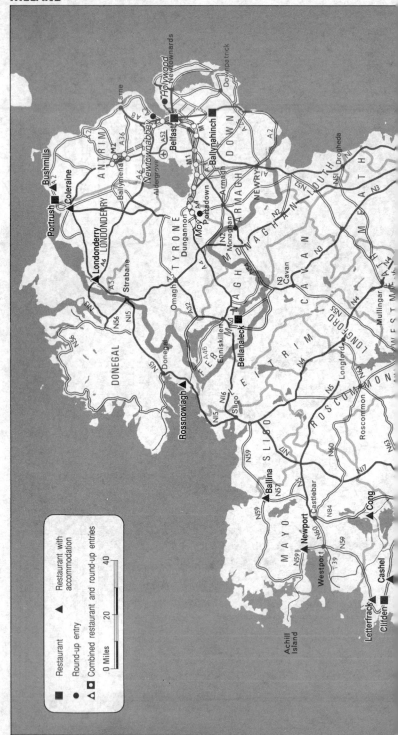

Dun Laoghaire
Bray
Wicklow
N11
Arklow
WICKLOW
Gorey
N11
Wexford
Maynooth
M7
Naas
KILDARE
N9
N80
CARLOW
Enniscorthy
N25
N30
Tullamore
N80
Curragh
Port-Laoise
Carlow
6N
New Ross
N9
Waterford
Dunmore East
OFFALY
N52
LEIX
N7
N10
Kilkenny
N8
KILKENNY
N25
WATERFORD
N62
Roscrea
Birr
N52
Clonmel
N7
Nenagh
Cashel
N24
N72
N9
TIPPERARY
Shanagarry
Midleton
N8
N25
N2
GALWAY
Ballyvaughan
N18
N6
CLARE
Newmarket-on-Fergus
N18
Ennis
N68
Shannon Airport
N7
Limerick
Adare
N21
N20
Cobh
Kinsale
N73
N72
CORK
Kilkee
N69
LIMERICK
N20
Mallow
8N
Cork
Douglas
Kanturk
N72
N20
Clonakilty
N2
Dingle
Tralee
KERRY
Killorglin
N70
Killarney
N21
N22
N72
Kenmare
Ballylickey
Bantry
Durrus
Ballydehob
N70
N71
Ahakista

Base Map Copyright © Bartholomew 1992

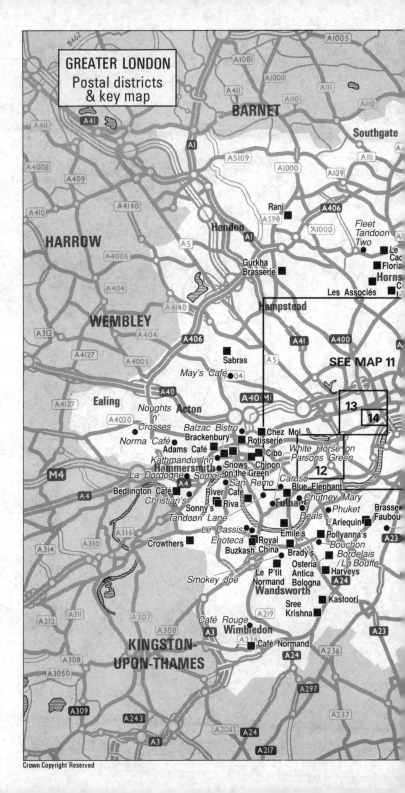

GREATER LONDON
Postal districts
& key map

BARNET

Southgate

HARROW

Hendon

Rani

Fleet
Tandoori
Two

Le
Cac
Floria

Horns
C
L

Gurkha
Brasserie

Les Associés

WEMBLEY

Hampstead

SEE MAP 11

Sabras

May's Café

Ealing   Acton

13

14

Noughts
n'
Crosses

Balzac Bistro
Brackenbury

Chez Moi

Norma Café

Rotisserie

Adams Café

Cibo

Kathmandu Inn

Snows
on the Green

White Horse on
Parsons Green

Hammersmith

Chinon

La Dordogne

Caruso

12

Sumos

San Remo

Blue Elephant

Bedlington Café

River Café

Chutney Mary

Christian's

Riva

Phuket

Brasser
Faubou

Sonny's

Fulham

Deals

L'Arlequin

Tandoori Lane

Le Cassis

Emile's

Pollyanna's

Bouchon
Bordelais
/ La Bouffe

Crowthers

Enoteca

Royal
China

Brady's

Buzkash

Osteria
Antica
Bologna

Harveys

Smokey Joe

Le P'tit
Normand

Wandsworth

Kastoori

Sree
Krishna

Café Rouge

Wimbledon

KINGSTON-
UPON-THAMES

Café Normand

Crown Copyright Reserved

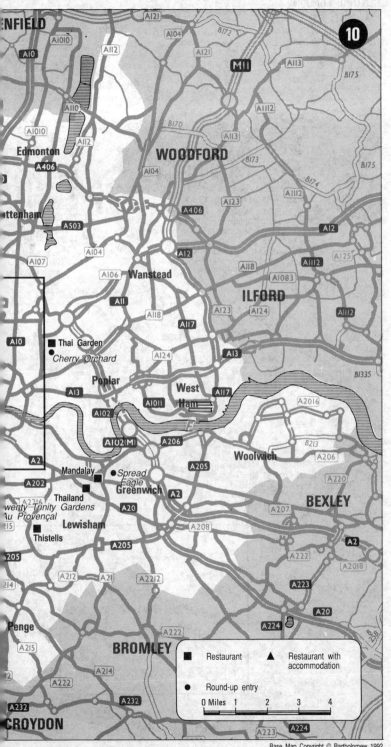

CENTRAL LONDON

Child's Hill
Quincy's
Laurent
Hampstead Heath
Carapace
Fortune Green
Surya
Kenny's
Gospel Oak
GORDON HO. RD.
B518
FLEET
POND
Café des Arts
Café Flo
HAMPSTEAD
Belgo
Primat
Wakaba
Green Cottage
Czech Club
Billboard Café
Swiss Cottage
Lemonia
Camden Brasserie
Odette's
Daphne
Singapore Garden Restaurant
Primrose Hill
Cheng-du
PA
Greek Valley
L'Aventure
WELLINGTON RD.
Regents Park
Diwana
Bhel-Pu
Haan
Kilburn
Maida Vale Avenue
Ben's Thai
Raoul's
Martin's
Canal Brasserie
MARYLEBON
Le Muscadet
Brasserie du Marché aux Puces
Galicia
PADDINGTON
Satay House
Los Remos
OXFORD STRE
Limited
Ac
SEE MAP 13
L'Altro
Books for
Cooks
Surinder's
L'Accento
Al San Vincenzo
192
First Floor
Four Seasons
Maroush III
Inaho
Leith's
Kalamáras
Mayfair
Royal China
Rasa Sayang
Spice Merchant
Mandarin Kitchen
Julie's
Malabar
Geales
Kensington Place
Hyde Park
Lily's
Clarke's
Kensington Gardens
La Pomme d'Amour
Boyd's
Halcyon Hotel
Mon Petit Plaisir
KNIGHTSBRIDGE
WEST
KENSINGTON
St James's Court Ho
Auberge de Provence
Belvedere
L'Escargot Doré
SEE MAP 12
Isohama
Sim
Nic
Navigator
PIMLICO
Lou Pescadou
Pomegrana
GROSVENC
CHELSEA
Argyll
Pimlic
La Croisette
La Famiglia
Harveys Café
Wilds
Sardi
La Reserve
Busabong Too

Crown Copyright Reserved

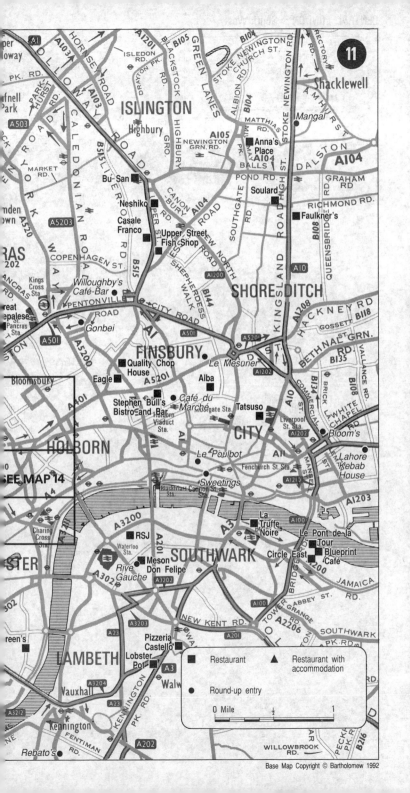

11

Shacklewell

ISLINGTON

Highbury

Mangal

Anna's Place

Bu-San

Soulard

Neshiko

Faulkner's

Casale Franco

Upper Street Fish Shop

SHOREDITCH

Willoughby's Café-Bar

Kings Cross Sta.

Great Nepalese

Pancras Sta.

Gonbei

Le Mesurier

FINSBURY

Quality Chop House

Alba

Eagle

Café du Marché

Tatsuso

Bloomsbury

Stephen Bull's Bistro and Bar

Liverpool St. Sta.

Bloom's

HOLBORN

Le Poulbot

All

Lahore Kebab House

SEE MAP 14

Fenchurch St. Sta.

Sweetings

Charing Cross Sta.

La Truffe Noire

RSJ

Le Pont de la Tour

Waterloo Sta.

Blueprint Café

Meson Don Felipe

SOUTHWARK

Circle East

Rive Gauche

JAMAICA RD.

green's

Pizzeria Castello

Lobster Pot

LAMBETH

Walw

■ Restaurant	▲ Restaurant with accommodation
● Round-up entry	

Vauxhall

0 Mile   ½   1

Kennington

Rebato's

WILLOWBROOK RD.

Base Map Copyright © Bartholomew 1992

CENTRAL LONDON : South-West

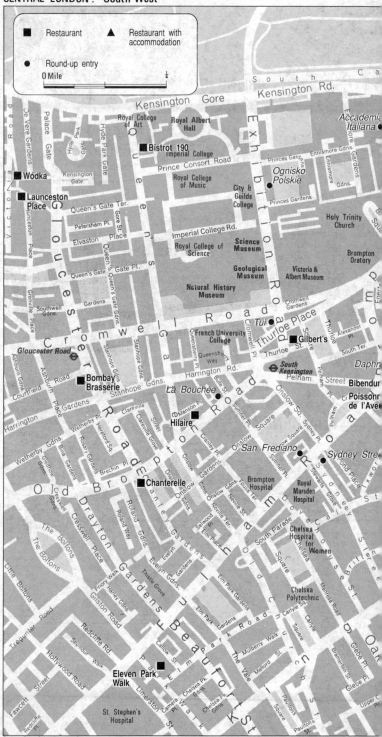

Restaurant

Restaurant with accommodation

Round-up entry

0 Mile   ¼

Kensington Gore   Kensington Rd.

South   Ca

De Vere Gardens

Palace Gate

Hyde Park Gate

Kensington Gate

Royal College of Art

Royal Albert Hall

Bistrot 190
Imperial College

Prince Consort Road

Royal College of Music

City & Guilds College

Exhibition Road

Ognisko Polskie

Princes Gardens

Ennismore Gdns.

Ennismore Gardens

Gdns.

Accademia Italiana

Wódka

Launceston Place

Queen's Gate Ter.   Gore St.

Petersham Pl.

Elvaston   Place

Queen's Gate Pl.

Gloucester   Road

Kensington Gate

Imperial College Rd.

Royal College of Science

Science Museum

Geological Museum

Victoria & Albert Museum

Holy Trinity Church

Brompton Oratory

Queen's Gate   Queen's Gate Gardens

Natural History Museum

Southwell Gdns.

Cromwell   Road

Cromwell Gdns.

Tui

Thurloe Place

Thurloe

Alexander Pl.

Grenville Place

Greville Place

French University College

Queensberry Pl.

Cromwell Pl.

Thurloe   St.

South Ter.

Gilbert's

Daphn

Gloucester Road

Stanhope Gdns.

Stanhope Pl.

Queensberry Way

Harrington Rd.

South Kensington

Pelham

Street   Bibendur

Ashburn Gdns.

Ashburn Place

Courtfield   Road

Bombay Brasserie

Stanhope Gdns.

La Bouchée

Onslow Sq.

Sydney Pl.

Pelham

Poissonr de l'Ave

Harrington   Gardens

Wetherby Pl.

Clareville   Grove

Hereford Sq.

Rosary Gardens

Marson Pl.

Hilaire

Cranley Pl.

Sumner Pl.

Onslow Square

Sydney St

Wetherby Gdns.

Bina Gardens

Gledhow Gardens

Rosary Gardens

Brechin Pl.

Clareville Street

Roland Gdns.

Onslow   Gardens

San Frediano

Sydney Stre

Old   Brompton   Road

Chanterelle

Stanley   Gardens

Roland Gdns.

Onslow Gdns.

Selwood Pl.

Neville St.

Foulis Ter.

Brompton Hospital

Sumner Pl.

Sydney Place

Sydney Grove

Stewarts Grove

Sixworth

Royal Marsden Hospital

The Boltons

Cresswell Place

Cresswell Gdns.

Roland Way

Evelyn Gdns.

Thistle Grove

Selwood Pl.

Elm Place

South Parade

Elm Park Gardens

Chelsea Hospital for Women

Sydney Square

Ixworth St

The Boltons

Priory Walk

Harley Gdns.

Elm Park Gardens

Chelsea Polytechnic

Marlborough Road

Little Boltons

Gilston Road

Redcliffe Rd.

Evelyn Gardens

Carlyle Square

Carlyle

Treherne Road

Seymour Walk

Fawcett   Street

Redcliffe   Pl.

Hollywood Road

Callow St.

Eleven Park Walk

St. Stephen's Hospital

Limerston   St.

Camera Pl.

Chelsea Pk. Gdns.

Chelsea Pk. Gdns.

Park Walk

Mulberry Walk

Mallord St.

Beaufort   St.

The Vale

Paultons   Square

Glebe Pl.

Bramerton St.

Glebe Pl.

Upper

Oa

Paultons

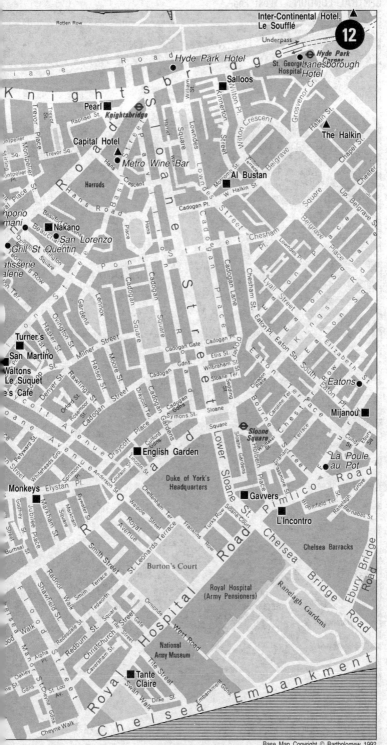

CENTRAL LONDON: West End

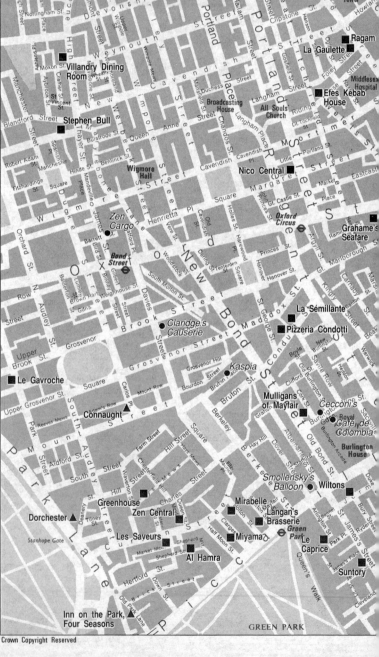

Crown Copyright Reserved

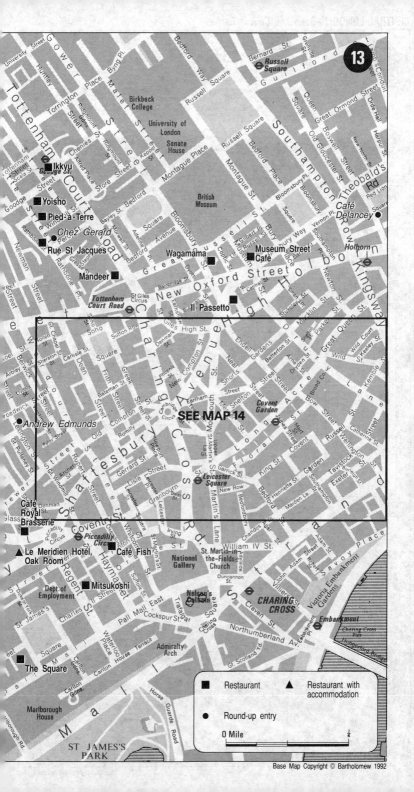

13

University Street
Huntley Street
Gower Street
Torrington Place
Byng Pl.
Malet Street
Gordon St.
Bedford Way
Russell Square
Bernard St.
Russell Square
Guilford St.
Glenville St.
St. Conduit

Tottenham Street
Scala St.
Goodge St.
Chenies St.
Alfred Place
Store Street
Keppel Street
Montague Place
Birkbeck College
University of London
Senate House
Russell Square
Bedford Way
Montague St.
Bedford Place
Southampton Row
Queen Square
Great Ormond Street
Orde Hall
Harbur St.
Theobald's Rd
Red Lion Square

■ **Ikkyu**

■ **Yoisho**
■ **Pied-a-Terre**
Percy Street
● *Chez Gerard*
■ **Rue St Jacques**
Charlotte Street
Rathbone St.
Rathbone Pl.
Goodge Pl.

■ **Mandeer**
Newman Street
Eastcastle Street

Bayley St.
Bedford Square
Adeline Pl.
Gt. Russell St.
British Museum
Bloomsbury Street
Bloomsbury Square
Bury St.
Gilbert Pl.
Russell St.
Bloomsbury Way
Southampton Pl.
Vernon Pl.
Bloomsbury Sq.
Café Delancey ●
Holborn

■ **Wagamama**
Museum Street Café ■
Museum Street
Coptic St.
W. Central St.
Newton St.
High Holborn
Kingsway

Bainbridge St.
Tottenham Court Road ⊖
St Giles Circus
New Oxford Street
Bucknall St.
West Central
Dyott St.
Smart's Pl.
Stukeley St.
Great Queen Street

■ **Il Passetto**

SEE MAP 14

Soho Square
Sutton Row
St Giles High St.
Denmark St.
Charing Cross Road
Endell Street
Betterton Street
Drury Lane
Wild Court
St. Kesley St.
Wild
Great Queen St.

● *Andrew Edmunds*

Shaftesbury Avenue
Charing Cross Rd.
Floral Street
Covent Garden
Covent Garden ⊖
Long Acre
Bow Street
Russell St.
Catherine St.
Tavistock St.
Wellington St.
Exeter St.
Southampton St.

Café Royal Brasserie

Gerrard Street
Lisle Street
Cranbourn St.
● *Leicester Square*
Leicester Square ⊖
New Row
St Martin's Lane
Garrick St.
King St.
Bedford St.
Henrietta St.
Maiden La.
Chandos Pl.

Coventry St.
Piccadilly Circus ⊖
● *Piccadilly Circus*
Haymarket
■ **Café Fish**

▲ **Le Meridien Hotel, Oak Room**

Regent Street
Dept. of Employment
■ **Mitsukoshi**

National Gallery
St. Martin-in-the-Fields Church
William IV St.
John Adam Street
Adam Street
Savoy Place
Villiers St.
Duncannon St.

Nelson's Column
Trafalgar Square
Charing Cross
CHARING CROSS ⊖
Craven St.
Northumberland Av.
Victoria Embankment Gardens
Embankment ⊖
Embankment
Charing Cross Pier
Hungerford Bridge

Charles St.
Pall Mall East
Cockspur Street
Suffolk St.

■ **The Square**
St James's Square
Pall Mall
Waterloo Pl.
Carlton House Terrace
Admiralty Arch
Gt. Scotland Yd.

Marlborough House
Carlton Gons.
Horse Guards Road
ST JAMES'S PARK
The Mall

■ Restaurant	▲ Restaurant with accommodation
● Round-up entry	

0 Mile   ¼

Base Map Copyright © Bartholomew 1992

14

Keeley St.

Kemble St.

Wild Court

Wild Street

Queen Street

Parker Street

Kingsway

Drury Lane

Great Queen Street

Christopher's

Joe Allen

Piccolo Mondo

Catherine St.

Wellington Street

Orso

Exeter St.

Burleigh St.

Savoy

Tavistock St.

Magno's

Bow Street

Bertorelli's

Russell Street

Covent Garden

Southampton St.

Henrietta St.

Rules

Dryden St.

Arne St.

Betterton Street

Endell Street

Neal Street

Neal Street Restaurant

Neal's Yard

Shorts

Street

Langley St.

James Street

Floral Street

Bedford St.

King Street

L'Estaminet

Garrick St.

New Row

Bedford St.

Bedfordbury

Mon Plaisir

Monmouth St.

Mercer Street

Shelton Street

Earlham Street

Tower St.

Slingsby Pl.

Tageen

Upper St. Martin's La.

St. Martin's Lane

St. Martin's Lane

Now & Zen

Arts Theatre Café

Newport St.

Beotys

Kagura

Ivy

West St.

Litchfield St.

C h a r i n g   C r o s s   R d

Cork & Bottle

Cranbourn St.

Cambridge Circus

Phoenix St.

Poons

M² Kong

Leicester Pl.

Fung Shing

Leicester Sq.

Swiss Centre

Gay Hussar

Au Jardin des Gourmets

Greek St.

Sri Siam

Soho Brasserie

Kettners

New World

China China

Gerrard Street

Mayflower

Wong Kei

Manzi's

Poons

Jade Garden

Lisle Street

Leicester Square

dell'Ugo

Soho Soho

Bahn Thai

Frith Street

Old Compton St.

Romilly St.

Jin

Soho Square

Est

Chiang Mai

Gopal's of Soho

Alastair Little

Dean Street

Panda Si Chuen

Rupert Street

Chuen Cheng Ku

Shaftesbury Avenue

Mildred's

L'Hippocampe

Aroma

Gt. Chapel St.

Hollen St.

Soho St.

Carlisle

St.

Wardour Street

Berwick Street

Melati

Gt. Windmill St.

Denman St.

Brewer Street

Legend

▲ Restaurant with accommodation

■ Restaurant

● Round-up entry

0 yards   110   220

Report forms

The following pages may be cut out and used to make reports to the *Guide* about meals that you eat out. Previous messages throughout this book will have alerted you to the importance we place on your reactions, assessments and accounts of restaurants that form entries in the *Guide*, that you feel should be new entries, or even those that you think unworthy of inclusion.

The majority of reports we receive in our office are constructive and positive. The image of the disgruntled consumer, always whingeing and carping, is a false one. Do not hold back on criticism, and just because all you have is praise, do not think the report is of any less use.

We are not asking you to write the last volume of a world history, so brevity is no dishonour. Just because you have forgotten certain details, lost the bill or mislaid your fountain pen is no excuse for not writing. A letter is enough. Our address is FREEPOST, so you do not have to use a stamp. Your summary judgement may be enough to alert us to the existence of a new gem in the countryside, or to look into problems or trouble nearer to home.

A final exhortation: please use these forms. This is *your* guide, your *vade-mecum*. If you had fun, wouldn't you like to let others know? If someone else had fun, wouldn't *you* like to know where?

Report Form

To the Editor *The Good Food Guide*
FREEPOST, 2 Marylebone Road, London NW1 1YN

From my personal experience the following establishment
should/should not be included in the *Guide*.

Telephone_____

I had lunch/dinner/stayed there on _____ 19____

I would rate this establishment _____ out of five.

please continue overleaf

My meal for ____ people cost £ _____ *attach bill where possible*

☐ Please tick if you would like more report forms

I am not connected in any way with management or proprietors.
Name and address (BLOCK CAPITALS)

_____

_____

Signed _____

Report Form

To the Editor *The Good Food Guide*
FREEPOST, 2 Marylebone Road, London NW1 1YN

From my personal experience the following establishment
should/should not be included in the *Guide*.

_____

_____

Telephone_____

I had lunch/dinner/stayed there on _____ 19____

I would rate this establishment _____ out of five.

please continue overleaf

My meal for _____ people cost £ _____ *attach bill where possible*

☐ Please tick if you would like more report forms

I am not connected in any way with management or proprietors.
Name and address (BLOCK CAPITALS)

_____

_____

Signed _____

To the Editor *The Good Food Guide*
FREEPOST, 2 Marylebone Road, London NW1 1YN

From my personal experience the following establishment
should/should not be included in the *Guide*.

_____

_____

Telephone_____

I had lunch/dinner/stayed there on _____ 19____

I would rate this establishment _____ out of five.

please continue overleaf

My meal for ____ people cost £ _____ *attach bill where possible*

☐ Please tick if you would like more report forms

I am not connected in any way with management or proprietors.
Name and address (BLOCK CAPITALS)

_____

_____

Signed _____

Report Form

To the Editor *The Good Food Guide*
FREEPOST, 2 Marylebone Road, London NW1 1YN

From my personal experience the following establishment
should/should not be included in the *Guide*.

Telephone_____

I had lunch/dinner/stayed there on _____ 19____

I would rate this establishment _____ out of five.

please continue overleaf

My meal for _____ people cost £ _____ *attach bill where possible*

☐ Please tick if you would like more report forms

I am not connected in any way with management or proprietors.
Name and address (BLOCK CAPITALS)

Signed _____

To the Editor *The Good Food Guide*
FREEPOST, 2 Marylebone Road, London NW1 1YN

From my personal experience the following establishment
should/should not be included in the *Guide*.

_____

_____

Telephone_____

I had lunch/dinner/stayed there on _____ 19___

I would rate this establishment _____ out of five.

please continue overleaf

My meal for _____ people cost £ _____ *attach bill where possible*

☐ Please tick if you would like more report forms

I am not connected in any way with management or proprietors.
Name and address (BLOCK CAPITALS)

_____

_____

Signed _____

To the Editor *The Good Food Guide*
FREEPOST, 2 Marylebone Road, London NW1 1YN

From my personal experience the following establishment
should/should not be included in the *Guide*.

_____

_____

Telephone_____

I had lunch/dinner/stayed there on _____ 19____

I would rate this establishment _____ out of five.

please continue overleaf

My meal for ____ people cost £ _____ *attach bill where possible*

☐ Please tick if you would like more report forms

I am not connected in any way with management or proprietors.
Name and address (BLOCK CAPITALS)

_____

_____

Signed _____

FREE

TRY OUR MAGAZINES
FREE
FOR 3 MONTHS

FREE (vertical, left and right margins)

Which? magazines are available only on subscription – you won't find them in newsagents or on bookstalls. So, to give you a chance to find out what our magazines are like – without paying anything – we'd like you to try them FREE for 3 months. There are 4 magazines to choose from, each giving you information and advice that's completely independent and unbiased.

Which? helps you make the right decisions when buying goods and services for yourself, your family and your home. **Gardening from Which?**, packed with facts and colourful design ideas, gives you advice based on scientific research, tests, surveys and consultations with top horticultural experts. **Which? way to Health** helps you and your family stay healthy, with advice on fitness, diet, detecting health problems at an early stage, the NHS and alternative therapies. **Which? Wine Monthly** gives you results of tastings, recommended wines and information on stockists who offer wine of particularly good value.

To find out how to get your free magazines, simply complete and detach (or copy) the form below and send it to Consumers' Association, Dept DM01, PO Box 44, Hertford X, SG14 1SH, today!

▼ DETACH HERE ▼

- ✂

To: Consumers' Association, Dept DM01, PO Box 44,
      Hertford X, SG14 1SH

Please send me details of how I can claim a 3-month free trial subscription to:

☐ Which?   ☐ Gardening from Which?

☐ Which? way to Health   ☐ Which? Wine Monthly

Please tick appropriate box(es)

Name: _____

Address: _____

_____

_____ Postcode: _____